ANNUAL REVIEW OF
NUTRITION

EDITORIAL COMMITTEE (1993)

Responsible for the organization of Volume 13
(Editorial Committee, 1991)

International Correspondents

ANNUAL REVIEW OF NUTRITION

VOLUME 13, 1993

ROBERT E. OLSON, *Editor*

State University of New York, Stony Brook

DENNIS M. BIER, *Associate Editor*

Washington University

DONALD B. McCORMICK, *Associate Editor*

Emory University

ANNUAL REVIEWS INC.   4139 EL CAMINO WAY   P.O. BOX 10139   PALO ALTO, CALIFORNIA 94303-0897

PREFACE

The nutrition community is having an identity crisis. Both those who work in the field of nutrition and those who observe us appear to be confused about our goals and responsibilities. Who are nutrition scientists and who are nutritionists and what do they do? Can they be distinguished from one another by background, education, and professional training? The simple answer is that nutrition scientists are scientists from many biological disciplines who investigate scientific problems in nutrition. Nutritionists, on the other hand, are practitioners from diverse backgrounds (medicine, dietetics, nursing, public health) who apply nutrition science to clinical and public health problems. The distinction becomes blurred for some individuals who engage in both research and practice.

Nutrition scientists, like all scientists, should be devoted to the discovery of new knowledge, whereas nutrition practitioners should combat malnutrition wherever it is found. This dichotomy is not unlike the one that distinguishes medical scientists from medical practitioners. At present, new stresses and strains are appearing in the relationship between scientists and practitioners no matter in what field they work, particularly now as both groups face diminishing financial and political support.

In the prefatory chapter in this volume (13) of the *Annual Review of Nutrition,* Alan Berg, a public health practitioner with the World Bank, criticizes nutrition scientists for not providing graduate students with the practical tools and skills needed to effectively apply nutrition concepts to the problems of malnutrition in the Third World. Berg states that a "marriage of research and operations is required . . . what we need are *nutrition engineers.*" He suggests that academic nutrition departments (which like the MIT department are disappearing at an appalling rate) should divert more resources and trainees to applied nutrition. His essay, while admirable in concept, underscores tensions that already exist between nutrition scientists and nutrition practitioners and provides no clear prescription except to indicate that a new institutional setting is needed. It is my opinion that an institutional setting is available for just the sort of training that Berg envisions, namely university-based schools of public health, many of which have unwisely abandoned programs in nutrition during the past two decades.

v

The problem of nutrition science vs its application was considered earlier in this series by Austin & Overholt in their chapter on "Building the Bridge Between Science and Politics" (*Annual Review of Nutrition, 1988, 8:1–20*). They urged students of nutrition to learn more about the political process in order to cope with the world's nutritional problems. Berg and Austin & Overholt have made strong points about the tactics required to correct malnutrition on our planet, but their advice remains largely in the realm of the theoretical because of obstacles in translating their recommendations into practice.

The reason for this predicament is the diminishing state of nutrition as a biological science. At present, fewer students are applying to fewer departments which have reduced resources. Advances in nutrition knowledge, as represented by our reviews, are coming increasingly from different departments in the biological and medical sciences and not from departments of nutrition. It is not essential for advances in nutrition science to come from members of a nutrition department, but the fact is that nutrition as a field has become so dispersed that it is hardly recognizable.

Many practitioners of nutrition, furthermore, are undertrained and overworked. Nutrition education in medical schools is sadly neglected since only 21 of 124 medical schools in North America offer required courses in clinical nutrition. The electives offered by other schools provide only a kiss and a promise. The same can be said of the paramedical schools that provide nutrition education. The practitioners of nutrition, furthermore, are overwhelmed by propaganda from food companies, health food organizations, and proponents of "alternative (unconventional) medicine" that continue to confuse and mislead the public. One of the casualties in this interplay between nutrition practitioners and nutrition politicans is the definition of an essential nutrient.

Although there is evidence that some vitamins may ameliorate some of the chronic degenerative diseases when used as drugs over long periods of time, there is no evidence that they are functioning in their usual preventive mode. Even the Food and Nutrition Board (FNB) of the National Academy of Science/National Research Council, which is composed mainly of nutrition scientists, is considering altering the Recommended Dietary Allowances (RDAs) to increase the allowance of certain vitamins because of their possible long-term effects in reducing the risk of cancer and heart disease.

Nutrients are required to prevent deficiency diseases at levels of 0.5 to 1.5 × the RDA, which are defined as "levels of intake of essential nutrients that on the basis of scientific knowledge are judged by the FNB to be adequate to meet the known nutrient needs of *practically all healthy persons.*" The RDAs do not apply to persons with illnesses such as malabsorption, hypermetabolism, and genetic disorders affecting the disposition of nutrients that alter nutritional requirements. Likewise they should not be recommended to combat the susceptibility of some individuals to the chronic degenerative diseases. Vitamins and other nutrients recommended at levels of 5 × the RDA or more should be considered drugs that are not needed by "practically all healthy persons."[1]

Even the use of a supplement of 400–4000 μg (1–10 × RDA) of folic acid in pregnancy to prevent neural tube defects is not needed by "practically all healthy persons." In fact there is no relationship between the folate status of an individual woman and her risk of neural tube defects. The same is true for the use of antioxidant vitamins to retard aging, vitamin A for acne, nicotinic acid for hyperlipidemia, and 1,25-dihydroxycholecalciferol for osteoporosis. The prescription for these agents should be in the hands of physicians, not public health agencies or the health food lobby.

Besides the prefatory chapter by Berg, Volume 13 of the *Annual Review of Nutrition* contains a wide range of reviews dealing with basic nutrition, clinical nutrition, and public health nutrition. This year 60% of the reviews are devoted to fundamental studies of the metabolism, regulation, and function of nutrients. More is being learned about the genetics of nutritional events. The genetics of obesity, the molecular biology of nitrogen fixation and glucokinase, and the genetic engineering of plants are considered in four reviews. Eight reviews deal with the metabolism and regulation of lipids including short-chain fatty acids and carotenoids, lipoprotein receptors, flavin coenzymes, amino acid transport, tetrahydrobiopterin-dependent systems, and pyruvate dehydrogenase.

Three reviews focus on minerals (aluminum, iron, and selenium), and a very interesting essay asks whether oxygen is an essential nutrient. The toxicology of fungi in food is also considered. The clinical reviews address the nutritional management of glycogen storage disease, the effects of somatotropins on lactation, the effect of polyunsaturated fatty acids on blood pressure, and the nutritional management of osteoporosis and cystic fibrosis. Finally, there is a review on the clinical physiology of taste and smell.

I thank my associate editors, Dennis M. Bier and Donald B. McCormick, for reviewing manuscripts, all members of the Editorial Committee for their help in assembling the list of topics and authors, and the authors who contributed the excellent reviews that appear in Volume 13. Production editor Joan Cohen in Palo Alto, California, deserves our thanks for her diligence in producing this volume.

Robert E. Olson
Editor

[1]Council on Scientific Affairs of the AMA, 1987. Vitamin preparations as dietary supplements and as therapeutic agents *J. Am. Med. Assoc.* 257:1929–36.

Annual Review of Nutrition
Volume 13, 1993

CONTENTS

SLIDING TOWARD NUTRITION MALPRACTICE: TIME TO RECONSIDER
AND REDEPLOY, *Alan Berg*   1

BIOSYNTHESIS AND FUNCTION OF ENZYMES WITH COVALENTLY
BOUND FLAVIN, *K. F. Decker*   17

ALUMINUM METABOLISM, *J. L. Greger*   43

REGULATION OF SELENOPROTEINS, *Raymond F. Burk and Kristina
E. Hill*   65

NUTRITIONAL MANAGEMENT OF GLYCOGEN STORAGE DISEASE, *P. H.
Parker, M. Ballew, and H. L. Greene*   83

NUTRITIONAL MANAGEMENT OF CYSTIC FIBROSIS, *P. B. Pencharz
and P. R. Durie*   111

RECENT ADVANCES IN MAMMALIAN AMINO ACID TRANSPORT,
Michael S. Kilberg, Bruce R. Stevens, and Donald A. Novak   137

FUNGAL TOXINS IN FOODS: RECENT CONCERNS, *Ronald T. Riley,
William P. Norred, and Charles W. Bacon*   167

IMPACT OF PLANT GENETIC ENGINEERING ON FOODS AND NUTRITION,
Luca Comai   191

BIOLOGICAL EFFECTS OF SHORT-CHAIN FATTY ACIDS IN
NONRUMINANT MAMMALS, *Maurice Bugaut and Marc Bentéjac*   217

EFFECTS OF POLYUNSATURATED FATS ON BLOOD PRESSURE, *James
M. Iacono and Rita M. Dougherty*   243

NEW TETRAHYDROBIOPTERIN-DEPENDENT SYSTEMS, *Seymour
Kaufman*   261

NUTRITIONAL FACTORS IN OSTEOPOROSIS, *Robert P. Heaney*   287

BIOLOGICAL NITROGEN FIXATION, *Robert H. Burris and Gary P.
Roberts*   317

GENETICS OF OBESITY, *Claude Bouchard and Louis Pérusse*   337

REGULATION OF PLASMA LDL-CHOLESTEROL LEVELS BY DIETARY
CHOLESTEROL AND FATTY ACIDS, *D. K. Spady, L. A. Woollett,
and J. M. Dietschy*   355

Is Oxygen an Essential Nutrient?, *Robert E. Forster and Ronald W. Estabrook* 383

Clinical Physiology of Taste and Smell, *Susan S. Schiffman and Carol A. Gatlin* 405

Effects of Exogenous Bovine Somatotropin on Lactation, *Dale E. Bauman and Richard G. Vernon* 437

Mammalian Glucokinase, *Richard L. Printz, Mark A. Magnuson, and Daryl K. Granner* 463

Regulation of the Pyruvate Dehydrogenase Multienzyme Complex, *R. H. Behal, D. B. Buxton, J. G. Robertson, and M. S. Olson* 497

Iron Deficiency and Cognitive Function, *Ernesto Pollitt* 521

Lipid Modulation of Cell Function, *Alfred H. Merrill, Jr. and Joseph J. Schroeder* 539

Actions of Carotenoids in Biological Systems, *Norman I. Krinsky* 561

Indexes

Subject Index 589
Cumulative Index of Contributing Authors, Volumes 9–13 615
Cumulative Index of Chapter Titles, Volumes 9–13 617

SOME RELATED ARTICLES IN OTHER *ANNUAL REVIEWS*

From the *Annual Review of Biochemistry,* Volume 62 (1993)

Oxidation of Free Amino Acids and Amino Acid Residues in Proteins by Radiolysis and by Metal-Catalyzed Reactions, *E. R. Stadtman*

From the *Annual Review of Medicine,* Volume 44 (1993)

Serum Transferrin Receptor, *J. D. Cook, B. S. Skikne, and R. D. Baynes*
The Molecular Biology of Cystic Fibrosis, *Thomas J. Sferra and Francis S. Collins*
Atherosclerosis Regression, Plaque Disruption, and Cardiovascular Events: A Rationale for Lipid Lowering in Coronary Artery Disease, *B. Greg Brown, Xue-Qiao Zhao, Dianne E. Sacco, and John J. Albers*

From the *Annual Review of Physiology,* Volume 55 (1993)

The Molecular Basis of GI Transport, *David C. Dawson*
The Cystic Fibrosis Transmembrane Conductance Regulator, *J. R. Riorden*
Toxigenic Diarrheas, Congenital Diarrheas and Cystic Fibrosis: Disorders of Intestinal Ion Transport, *M. Field, C. E. Semrad*

From the *Annual Review of Public Health,* Volume 14 (1993)

Diet, Hormones, and Cancer, *David P. Rose*
Why is Low Blood Cholesterol Associated with Risk of Nonatherosclerotic Disease Death?, *David R. Jacobs, Jr.*

ANNUAL REVIEWS INC. is a nonprofit scientific publisher established to promote the advancement of the sciences. Beginning in 1932 with the *Annual Review of Biochemistry*, the Company has pursued as its principal function the publication of high quality, reasonably priced *Annual Review* volumes. The volumes are organized by Editors and Editorial Committees who invite qualified authors to contribute critical articles reviewing significant developments within each major discipline. The Editor-in-Chief invites those interested in serving as future Editorial Committee members to communicate directly with him. Annual Reviews Inc. is administered by a Board of Directors, whose members serve without compensation.

For the convenience of readers, a detachable order form/envelope is bound into the back of this volume.

Alan Berg

Annu. Rev. Nutr. 1993. 13:1–15

SLIDING TOWARD NUTRITION MALPRACTICE:
Time to Reconsider and Redeploy[1]

Alan Berg

Population, Health and Nutrition Department, The World Bank, Washington, DC 20433

KEY WORDS: nutrition engineers, nutrition malpractice, applied nutrition research, nutrition policy (international), nutrition programs (international)

CONTENTS

The Perceived Obstacles 3
The Research Chain 5
Training for Operations 6
The Constraints to Applied Research 8
The Nutrition Market 8
The Prescription 11
New Institutional Setting Needed 13

In the past several years the receptivity of the international development community toward pursuing the goal of improved nutrition has changed markedly. Today much of that community takes seriously the need for better nutrition. Nutrition initiatives are now widely understood not only as a consumption good that promotes human welfare but as an investment that directly influences productivity of the labor force and school force, and as a key factor in development. Major nutrition initiatives are now supported by development economists, who no longer have to be convinced about their usefulness. Increasingly, they acknowledge that something has to be done

---

[1]This article is a distillation of the annual Martin J. Forman Memorial Lecture, given in Washington, DC, on June 24, 1991, and has also appeared in *Am. J. Clin. Nutr.* 1993. 57:3–7. Reprinted with permission from *Am. J. Clin. Nutr.*

1

0199-9885/93/0715-0001$02.00

about malnutrition. No longer, for example, can they make structural adjustments in the economy without concern for their effects on nutrition.

This is particularly significant for the disadvantaged countries of the world, where the arithmetic of nutrition has barely changed in recent decades. Malnutrition is still staggering, and in some places, particularly sub-Saharan Africa, it is getting worse (2).

We of the international nutrition community, I am embarrassed to say, have made a disappointingly small dent in improving that condition. Many of us have spent decades working to solve nutrition problems in developing countries. In the past twenty years $1.6 billion in US government-sponsored research alone has been directed to these problems.

Of course, progress in the nutrition status of some populations has been made, but most of the improvement has occurred not so much because of our nutrition community, but largely because of rising incomes in parts of Asia. True, some direct nutrition programs also have been successful in Iringa in Tanzania, Chile, Thailand, and Tamil Nadu in India. But in relatively few other actions has the nutrition community had a major role in bringing about improved nutrition of sizable populations. We have a great deal to show in scientific and technological advances, but very little to show in terms of combatting malnutrition in the world.

With the aid of vitamin A technology, for example, we now have the ability to prevent the deaths of as many as 2.5 million children each year (6). We are, of course, nowhere close to achieving that goal. Another micronutrient—iodine—provides an even starker case. Ever since Dr. V. Ramalingaswami's classic study of salt fortification in the Kangra Valley of North India more than a quarter of a century ago, we have known what needed to be done (5, 7). Yet today, still more than 200 million people have goiter, probably several times that number have subclinical iodine deficiency, and we now know that even mild and moderate iodine deficiency affects cognitive capacities.

From work that we had the opportunity to help initiate, we know that salt also can be fortified with iron to fight the one billion cases of iron-deficiency anemia in developing countries. Moreover, for some years, the idea of fortifying salt with a combination of iron and iodine, making possible a major reduction of two important public health problems with one shake, has been discussed. But where are the people trying to make it happen?

Is it not something of a scandal that we have done so little in applying our scientific knowledge? At the 1991 meeting of the United Nation's Sub-Committee on Nutrition, which encompasses the major UN and bilateral assistance agencies involved in nutrition, it was noted that our performance on micronutrients should be regarded as a collective embarrassment. We understand precisely the etiology and the consequences of, say, iodine deficiency;

we know who suffers from it and where they are; we know exactly what needs to be done, and we have in hand very low-cost technologies to do it. Still, there are upwards of 200 million iodine-deficient people in the developing countries. Such a performance can only be called *nutrition malpractice*.

The Perceived Obstacles

What is the reason for our failure to make larger dents in malnutrition? Asking more than thirty leading international nutritionists that question, I commonly hear three arguments. First, there are insufficient resources for large-scale operations. Second, the political commitment in developing countries themselves is inadequate. And third, not enough money is available to support nutrition research programs of academic institutions. I would contend, however, that the above do not explain why the nutrition community's contribution has been so limited.

For some time now, more money has been available to support nutrition operations than there are good projects to support. For example, in the three fiscal years ending June 1991, World Bank-assisted nutrition operations involved about $1 billion in investments, slightly over half of that financed by the Bank and most of the rest by the benefitting countries themselves. Projections for the next three fiscal years are nearly double that. These figures do not reflect contributions to nutrition efforts often now included in structural adjustment operations. They are impossible to quantify, but their magnitude can be judged by the more than sevenfold increase—from $102 million in 1989 to $761 million in 1991—in Venezuela's targeted food and nutrition programs.

Expenditure on UNICEF nutrition programs has more than tripled in the past twenty years, from an annual average of $9 million in the 1970s to $24 million in 1987 and $29 million in 1990. This grossly understates the real figures because of the major reorientation to nutrition in much of UNICEF's other work. Nutrition serves as an organizing principle for a substantial part of UNICEF's program in the 1990s. Interest in nutrition is also growing in several bilateral assistance programs. The German aid agency, for instance, now screens all relevant projects for their nutrition effects, and Canada is providing new multimillion dollar support for micronutrient programs. Other countries' resources for nutrition have also begun to increase as a result of the 1990 Children's Summit. There are exceptions but, overall, resources and attention for nutrition—even in an era of tight resources and compassion fatigue—are clearly on an upsurge. We in nutrition no longer are trying to walk up the down escalator.

The funding agencies are increasingly committed, but is there political commitment in the developing countries themselves? If we define political commitment to mean commitment to spend money and give speeches in favor of feedling large numbers of people, the answer in many countries clearly is yes. True, what is sometimes promoted in the name of better nutrition makes little real contribution to improved nutrition: untargeted food subsidies in many countries are the best example of this. But even if we limit our definition to those governments with a genuine interest in the malnutrition problem, and who seek to undertake actions for reasons beyond pure political popularity, there is a good deal of commitment. A number of governments want to start large new programs.

Of course, the nature and degree of political commitment to overcome malnutrition varies with forms of governance and the other problems facing a country at any given time. Clearly, political will is inadequate in some places. But those international agency staff who deal regularly with planning ministries and finance ministries not uncommonly are surprised by how much interest in nutrition exists in a developing country. Often they find that a country's needs are not so much for more political commitment as for good program design and management, including a better understanding of how to get the fruits of existing technologies into the hands and stomachs of those who need them.

A different type of perceived constraint is the lack of outside funding for nutrition research. "University starving," sometimes suggesting almost a divine right to receive research funds from public institutions, is a recurrent theme among academic nutritionists. Although universities clearly are in need of more money, arguably the level of funding is not the only issue. In the 1970s, the US Agency for International Development (AID) offered generous funds under its so-called 211(d) grant program, which sought to strengthen university capacity to contribute to international development efforts. In nutrition, one after another of those grants led to disappointment. In several cases, universities used the money to do things they were going to do anyway, rather than adding the policy and programmatic dimensions to nutrition as they had agreed. How would we grade those results? With some exceptions, the record is poor for the academic community as a whole, especially in applied work.

The fault does not lie with the academic community alone. Our operational nutrition community is also responsible for much of the malpractice: for opportunities lost, efforts misdirected, local needs and preferences ignored. And even more so is the failure of operational and academic communities to learn to work together.

Assuming, then, that at least in some countries the obstacle is not a lack of operational resources or political commitment and is not simply due to inadequate funding available for universities, why then has the nutrition community not made more of a dent in malnutrition? Could the answer lie in how we go about trying to solve the problem?

The Research Chain

We confront two main problems. We have been emphasizing the wrong research issues and we have been negligent in preparing people to work operationally in nutrition. A chain of questions must be addressed to bring about large-scale improvements in nutrition. Those questions begin, on the malnutrition side, with *why* and move through *who* and *where*, *what*, and *how* to the nutrition-improvement side of the chain.

Consider the example of vitamin A deficiency. Under the *why* category falls research into why a deficiency occurs and why bother with it: its biomedical pathways, its socioeconomic determinants, and its consequences. Next is work to determine *who* is vulnerable to vitamin A deficiency and *where* they are. The *what* category involves research on the size and frequency of dosage to prevent vitamin A deficiency and the mechanisms to deliver it. The *how* category deals with the organization and management of vitamin A delivery, how the families of the intended recipients perceive the problem and the proposed intervention effort, how a delivery program can be responsive to families' perceptions, the effects of public information efforts, program evaluations, and so on.

What is the relative importance of each of these research categories? Work in connection with the *World Food and Nutrition Study,* which was undertaken in the mid-1970s for the National Academy of Sciences, found that of funds obligated by US government agencies for international nutrition research, some 67% was directed to the *why* question, about 20% to *who and where* (mostly survey work), about 11% to the question of what to do about it, and less than 2% to *how* to do it (4). Although it is impossible to specify that distribution today, budgets of several involved agencies suggest hardly any change over the years, even though the state of nutrition knowledge has changed dramatically.

We know enormously more now than we did one or two decades ago about the causes and consequences of malnutrition. We know so much about who and where the vulnerable groups are that it is reasonable to question whether we are getting adequate return on investment in more nutrition status surveys, at least as they have traditionally been undertaken—sometimes measuring simply for the sake of measuring. We also know what to do about nutrition problems in many circumstances. A number of techniques and technologies with the potential for sizable impact have been developed and are part of today's nutrition arsenal.

Yet almost no one seems to be trying to address the key question of how to reach the payoff. Although research needs have changed markedly, we continue to do what we know how to do. Remarkably little intellectual attention has been given to the *how* end of the chain. A chasm separates all we have learned through basic research from the actions needed to cause something basic to happen. So much knowledge build up. So little benefit.

Unless we give a lot more atttention to *how* and somewhat more to *what to do* (the latter particularly to address the rural problem in the Sahel and other impoverished rural areas of sub-Saharan Africa), the value of other research is close to nil. In an economic sense, the return to nutrition research, say, in terms of lives saved, for work now on the *why* and *who* side of the chain is low, whereas the potential benefits at the opposite end of the chain are very high. With warehouses filled with potentially useful research papers on *why*, more research value would seem to lie in determining *how,* for example, a particular fortified food could be pushed through knots in the distribution system, how it is perceived by the people who are supposed to eat it, how it is allocated within a family, and what it will take to make a program effective. Why are we not concentrating on this kind of research?

Training for Operations

The second major problem in international nutrition is the lack of appropriately trained and experienced people to design and manage large-scale nutrition policies, programs, and projects. Today there is more money available for nutrition than there are good projects. In the World Bank, if twenty more solid proposals that met specificity and other standards were to emerge, I am confident that at least eighteen would be financed, and I hear the same from other agencies. The climate is favorable. But who has the capacity to prepare those proposals? And, once projects are financed, who has the capacity to manage them?

For years, nutritionists have challenged the broader development community to take nutrition seriously. Now it has, and we are not able to provide the people to meet the demand. The World Bank over the last year has added half a dozen new nutrition staff members and this number is likely to grow. Much of the work until now has been done by persons with no nutrition background. They know planning and management, but not much about nutrition. We need people who know both. Currently, UNICEF is recruiting some forty new nutrition-oriented staff members. The Inter-American Development Bank is recruiting in nutrition for the first time. Both within the Bank and outside, demand exists for people trained or experienced for operational jobs or consultancies in nutrition. But identifying qualified people to do this work is difficult. We can find people to do one more survey or once again formulate a more nutritious weaning food. But what if we want better understanding of the nuts and bolts of a program and its cultural setting so that we can figure out how to make it work better? The population field has such people. The population curriculum at Johns Hopkins University provides courses in Policies and Programs, Family Planning Administration, Evaluation, Family Planning Communication, and Economics of Population and Its Planning. Why are Johns Hopkins as well as the Universities of Michigan and North Carolina preparing students to do practical, hands-on work in population programs but not in nutrition?

Most graduate students in nutrition are equipped to teach and do fairly narrow research. Rarely do doctoral dissertations focus on broad-based applied research: In the early 1970s, only 5% bore titles in international applied nutrition, and the percentage had fallen close to zero by 1990. Among the dozen-or-so programs at leading US universities that fifteen years ago were training students for international nutrition, including some applied work, two of the strongest programs have either disappeared (Massachusetts Institute of Technology, MIT) or virtually disappeared (Harvard) from the list. In seven other universities, the program size has withered, in several cases substantially. Only two universities have increased their commitment in this area.

Reports I have received indicate that enrollment in international nutrition is down, enrollment in nutrition generally is down, and the number of applicants for nutrition programs is down even more. Cornell in 1990 had 140 applications for nutrition training, compared to annual requests a decade ago that numbered in the 300s. Tufts accepted two out of five applicants in 1985; it accepted two out of three in 1990. Even though the level of student enrollment levels in some universities is being maintained, the pool from which to select those students is shrinking.

It is not inconceivable that one explanation for the decline in student interest is the relevance of the programs. Not too many years ago, when I was a member of a small panel reviewing a prestigious Ivy League university's nutrition department, I was struck by the lack of fit between the interests and expectations of the students I encountered and the interests and the work of the faculty. Although the descriptions in the course catalog appeared relevant, the teaching commonly reflected narrow interests of individual professors. A number of the foreign nutrition students we interviewed suggested that the university should be sued for false advertising.

Here is a laudable statement of goals from the current course bulletin of a major East Coast university: "The major objective . . . is the development of logical approaches for the prevention of malnutrition in less developed countries . . ., faculty from a variety of disciplinary backgrounds . . . work collaboratively on divisional teaching, research, and service activities." But the catalog lists only one obviously applied nutrition course offered by the department each year. The course catalogs of six other prominent universities reveal similar situations.

Of course some universities give more attention to applied concerns, and within universities some faculty are more sensitive to these needs. But, overall, the problem of relevance is real. By and large, institutions of higher learning, both in industrialized and developing countries, have not equipped their students for the broad role of designing and managing nutrition efforts. How different might be the state of nutrition in the world had they done so.

The Constraints to Applied Research

What is the reason for this unfortunate situation of misdirected research and a lack of appropriately trained people? There probably are several explanations. The academic nutrition community has not addressed the important question of how to implement the benefits of nutrition research either in its research programs or in its training. This is partly because the reward system of academia leads in other directions.

The lack of interest in applied research partly stems from the way research is defined. The director of one of the largest university nutrition programs, who reflects the view of many, described research as a process that produces knowledge that is universally applicable. This rules out sizable portions of the needs in international nutrition. The knowledge produced by answers to the *how* question often is culture- or site-specific: it applies to one program at one place at one time. (This is not to say, of course, that applied research cannot sometimes produce approaches or principles with broad applicability.)

It is also often hard to measure things precisely when dealing with the *how* question, particularly since a good part of the nutrition problem is poverty, alienation, disorientation, and inability to cope. Because the search for answers moves into the economic, political, social, and administrative realms, writing a good academic paper is difficult. The pressure in the academic world to publish has become a widespread infectious disease that already has spread to academia in developing countries, so that applied work there too carries less weight.

The Nutrition Market

Research is surely driven by research grants. For what kind of research is money available these days? Although total resources for nutrition research have not fallen, the largest portion in the US today focuses on the domestic market and the nutrition needs of well-off consumer. Unlike 20 years ago, much more money is spent on studying ways to reduce excess fat in the diets of affluent adult males than on ways to add fat to the diets of children who do not have enough to supply the energy they need. Furthermore, the percentage of articles in the *American Journal of Clinical Nutrition* that are devoted to problems in developing countries is less than half of what it was in the 1970s. That is all the more reason why most of those financial resources that still are available to solve international nutrition problems need to be dedicated to answering the questions of *what* and *how*.

It is no accident that some international nutritionists, instead of shifting from basic to applied research, are moving into domestic research, in response to where the money is. Certainly, work on the relationship of nutrition to cancer and heart disease is important, but research needs in international applied nutrition are being neglected because domestic concerns are so much better funded.

We in operating agencies probably are being unfair or unrealistic in our expectations. Because of the very considerable contributions that those in the universities have made to nutrition, particularly in the early years, we look to them for leadership. It was the academic nutrition community, after all, that generated the initial interest that brought the problem of malnutrition to world attention, and over the years it has tried to better understand the nature of the problem and its consequences. Its members developed and organized the nutrition institutes around the world and prompted the formation of the Protein Advisory Group, which evolved into the United Nations Sub-Committee on Nutrition. They have made important contributions in a hundred other ways. So it is natural that we turn to them.

With their main orientation toward biomedical research, though, nutrition policies and programs are seen as appendages of research, rather than the reverse. Nor do they generally have the disposition or inclination to deal with constraints that are addressed by policy- and project-oriented research. It would not be fair—and clearly not realistic—to expect all those working on nutrition in universities suddenly to address *how* problems. But, at least, the climate can be made more hospitable to that small band of academics who want to address applied problems, and to efforts made to expand that band.

Nor is neglect of applied research limited to the academic community. Those of us working in policy and operations also seldom make a systematic effort to see how and what difference a policy or a technique or a product makes. Practitioners generally give remarkably little attention to project evaluations, for instance. One recent analysis of 104 mostly government child-feeding programs in Latin America found that only 10 included any kind of evaluation, and of these evaluations only three were judged to be adequate (3). One reason for the lack of objective standards is humanitarian. Many people believe that they are doing God's work and that it cannot fail to pay off; common sense tells you that if hungry children are given food, they will be better off. The second reason is bureaucratic. A manager who is paid to deliver food, and whose performance is judged by how much food he distributes, is going to concentrate on moving the food.

The two obstacles are very different but have an identical impact on whether things get done right. The harassed missionary trying to feed hungry children is not going to choose to spend a peso of his limited funds on evaluation. And the harassed bureaucrat, who never has enough money and is trying to hold his staff together on low pay, runs the risk of an evaluation's discovery that what was assumed to be a reasonable effort is, in fact, not so—an outcome that is more likely to make him look bad than good.

There are people who defend food coupons to the death and people who think they are the work of the devil; but after coupons are distributed, hardly anyone ever checks on what happens. The same is true of milk distribution and flour distribution. We hear over and over again that if a family is given a kilo of food and told that it is for the two-year-old child, the two-year-old may not get more than 200 or 300 grams of it. But nobody knows what determines whether the child gets 50 or 100 or 500 grams. So we simply make assumptions about dilution and plan rations on that basis. But we do not have a clue whether such assumptions are right. Yet whether the child actually gets half of the ration or a tenth may make the difference between life and death.

But then consider why the Iringa (Tanzania) and Tamil Nadu (India) projects have been successful in markedly reducing malnutrition: operations research, including evaluations, was conducted at each step. Over the first six years in Tamil Nadu, the government undertook or sponsored through local universities and research groups 37 discrete pieces of applied research. Many findings led to changes. For example, studies examined the causes of relapse into malnutrition of previously recovered children in an attempt to determine if there were predictable patterns. Other studies sought to learn why children were absent from growth-monitoring sessions. A study of the effectiveness of various growth cards led to use of the bubble chart (1). And a study of how long it took worm loads to reach debilitating levels in children had important cost-benefit implications, since the cost of deworming twice a year was half that for deworming four times a year. At the outset of the project the Tamil Nadu government set up a separate fund for the studies, and 2.1% of this $81 million nutrition project was earmarked for monitoring and evaluations.

Clearly, a marriage of research and operations is required. Understanding nutrition behavior in a given setting, through a systematic search, *is* important knowledge. And if such a search is not academically acceptable, then academic norms of acceptability need reexamination. According to E. J. R. Heyward, for many years Deputy Executive Director of UNICEF, "the results of the nutrition profession are disappointing because, although the science has made good progress, the context for its application has been neglected. Improving the state of nutrition means changing peoples' behavior. Who studies their perceptions and their constraints—not in the abstract but in the context of launching a new nutrition program?"

Often, what is most needed are pilot and demonstration activities, with strong evaluation components; quasi-experimental programs; behavioral re-

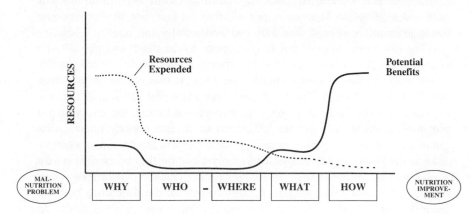

Figure 1   Relationship between potential benefits and resources expended on nutrition research in the past 25 years.

search studies of the social marketing type, including not just the behavior of clients of services, but the behavior of the deliverers of those services as well; and participatory research that helps communities identify their own solutions. Whatever we call it, we need to have a better understanding of how things work and the reasons they do not work.

I do not mean to suggest that all the necessary research answers on the *why* and *who* side of the nutrition chain are in hand, but the research agenda is out of balance and its results skewed so that the potential benefits do not justify the current expenditure patterns.

Figure 1 illustrates how the relationship has changed between potential benefits and resources expended on research questions over the past 25 years. We in the nutrition community will ultimately be measured by our return on investment. It is time for some serious stock-taking.

The Prescription

In the area of training, universities should be asking what kinds of policies and programs are necessary to alleviate malnutrition and what knowledge and skills are necessary to make that happen. Have current training programs equipped people to build careers in nutrition service? What will it take to provide nutritionists with the skills needed to design and manage and evaluate nutrition programs? Is the faculty capable, through its experience, of teaching such practical skills? Hard decisions need to be made on how to use new university staff resources, and even harder decisions on how to reallocate existing resources. What I am proposing is not just a stock taking but a redeployment.

What we need are students trained in economics, administration, logistics, planning and budgeting, and the dozen other necessary skills in addition to nutrition science. We need people who are at home in both the scientific and bureaucratic worlds, people who can do nuts-and-bolts work in getting projects going in new sets of circumstances month after month. In short, what we need are *nutrition engineers*. Webster defines an engineer as "a person who carries through an enterprise and brings about a result." Unlike many other fields, nutrition does not have the equivalent of engineers—it has the equivalent of physicists, but not of engineers. We need engineers badly. We need to stop inventing and reinventing wheels, and to start putting wheels on the wagons we have.

Nutrition programs designed without an understanding of the relative importance of real income, belief patterns, and infection in the causation of malnutrition, or of the more structural, less proximate determinants of malnutrition, are likely to be poorly designed programs. Those responsible for the design of nutrition programs would be as negligent in ignoring such factors as would a structural engineer in ignoring such factors as wind velocity and ground swells.

How could academic programs be changed to produce nutrition engineers? Several avenues have been suggested, from revamping university nutrition departments by encouraging financial support for innovative programs committed to *how* concepts, to encouraging the development of a nutrition stream in management and public policy schools.

A preferred option would be to resuscitate the concept of an integrated program, such as that tried by MIT 20 years ago. Nutrition normally cuts across university departments, including food science, biochemistry, political science, agriculture, and medicine. The MIT program tried to bring cohesion to this work by looking at the totality of the problem. It used case studies in the style of Harvard's Business School. It addressed implementation and management issues. It followed projects from beginning to end. It emphasized evaluation.

For a while the MIT program encompassed both doctorates in nutrition planning and short courses for mid-career practitioners. Former students of that program are now in important nutrition positions around the world—in UNICEF, the International Food Policy Research Institute, UNESCO, the World Bank—as well as working as principal nutritionists for a number of governments. For a while it did work, but because it was viewed as partly nonacademic, the program was at odds with the university culture and reward system, and eventually faded away.

Maybe it was an idea before its time. If so, maybe now is the time to recapture it and develop institutes dedicated to applied work and the training of nutrition engineers. Not that the MIT program should be copied exactly, but the concept and experience could be used to build something new and appropriate for today's needs. For a foundation looking for an entry point into international nutrition, a center or institute that addresses this neglected area of work, critical for much else that has been done to have a substantial impact, would be an attractive option for funding.

Any university that wished to pursue this direction would need to follow several basic tenets: (*i*) Place greater emphasis on applied subjects for research and training, including nondegree as well as degree programs, and teach the techniques of location-specific empirical analysis, illustrated with examples of real research. (*ii*) Incorporate research and training and the analysis and evaluation of operations in a feedback loop. (*iii*) Stimulate more interaction with local nutrition managers and local institutions, and between universities and programs in the field. Some things cannot be learned in the classroom, so training must take place in the field.

Whatever is done, the academic nutrition community will have to question some basic values if it is to contribute more. Perhaps the number of articles contributed to professional journals is not so important after all. Perhaps we need to forget about the third and fourth decimal points on old issues and examine the whole numbers on new issues that matter. Perhaps requirements for faculty positions have to be reconsidered. To train nutrition engineers will mean attracting faculty members who themselves are program designers and managers and who have spent much of their careers in developing countries, people who often do not have conventional academic qualifications. I do not suggest that standards be compromised, but that their order of priority be changed. For these new programs the primary standard should be how much difference the program will make in overcoming malnutrition.

New Institutional Setting Needed

In the area of research, the academic culture is less likely to change. Even with programs that emphasize applied training, universities are unlikely to address many practical needs. Operating agencies should not try to turn universities into instruments to satisfy their own nutrition research requirements, for universities legitimately have a different role and objectives. So instead of converting universities into something they are not, perhaps the nutrition community should give attention to creating another kind of institution.

The experience of the US Agency for International Development in population programs may be instructive. In the mid-1970s, it gave universities considerable sums to study population growth, but those studies were leading to little change. Then AID changed course and made more resources available to mount pilot and demonstration activities in family planning (including evaluation components) on a scale large enough to be illustrative if scaled up to a national level. To get what it wanted, AID entered into agreements with the Population Council and other private contractors. The payoff was substantial; governments in Bangladesh, Egypt, Kenya, Taiwan, and Thailand, for example, looked at the results obtained in those small quasi-government settings and used those programs as the basis for what are now national programs.

The Population Council is a kind of halfway house between university and consulting firm: it is problem driven, unlike the university, and unlike the consulting firm which is essentially client-driven. The Council exists specifically to find ways to solve a problem, in this case the population problem. And it is flexible enough and has an agenda broad enough to permit attempts at understanding many dimensions of the problem. In addition to an operational interest, it has a research interest (mostly operations research). It is very much involved in the field testing of ideas. Endowed by foundations with an independent international board and its own funds, it can set its own agenda.

Improving the capacity *within* developing countries to produce nutrition engineers and to develop demonstration projects should be the primary objective of, respectively, a university-based institute and a nutrition equivalent of the Population Council. A major goal of all that is done in the international nutrition effort should be to strengthen those who will be the mainstay in running nutrition programs and to develop or expand the capacity of local research and training institutions to incorporate a policy and programmatic orientation.

*   *   *   *

What the nutrition community has learned in a few places like Iringa and Tamil Nadu is opening up some large-scale operational opportunities. International funding agencies are spending increased amounts of money: in some cases on activities where we know we are on the right track; in other cases where perhaps we are doing it right but inefficiently for lack of better *how* answers and better-equipped people; and, finally in those cases where we probably are making mistakes but should at least be learning in the process.

What is needed now is the leadership and institutional underpinnings required to move in new directions. A first step toward achieving this goal will be to corral intellectual energies and try to recapture the excitement of earlier years—to convince the nutrition community that applied work on the *how* end of the chain is not only beneficial but also intellectually satisfying. What could be more satisfying than addressing the most important constraints that prevent us from making a serious dent in malnutrition?

Literature Cited

1. Griffiths, M. 1987. The bubble chart. *Mothers Child. Bull. Infant Feed. Maternal Nutr.* 6(1):7
2. Horwitz, A. 1991. *Second Annual Martin J. Forman Memorial Lecture.* New York: Helen Keller Int.
3. Musgrove, P. 1991. *Feeding Latin America's Children: An Analytical Survey of Food Programs. Latin American and the Caribbean Regional Studies Rep. 11, November.* Washington, DC: The World Bank
4. National Research Council Commission on International Relations. 1977. Nutrition. In *World Food and Nutrition Study: Supporting Papers,* Vol. 4. Washington, DC: Natl. Acad. Sci.
5. Ramalingaswami, V. 1991. *First Annual Martin J. Forman Memorial Lecture.* New York: Helen Keller Int.
6. Sommer, A. 1991. *Third Annual Martin J. Forman Memorial Lecture.* New York: Helen Keller Int.
7. Sooch, S. S., Ramalingaswami, V. 1969. Preliminary report on an experiment in the Kangra Valley for the prevention of Himalayan endemic goiter with iodized salt. *Bull. WHO* 32(3): 229–45.

Annu. Rev. Nutr. 1993. 13:17–41

BIOSYNTHESIS AND FUNCTION OF ENZYMES WITH COVALENTLY BOUND FLAVIN

K. F. Decker

Institute of Biochemistry, Albert-Ludwigs University, Freiburg im Breisgau, Germany

KEY WORDS: apoenzyme, flavinylation, covalent flavoproteins, FAD, riboflavin, site-directed mutagenesis

CONTENTS

COVALENT COFACTOR-APOENZYME ATTACHMENT 18
   General Features of Coenzyme Attachment 18
   Discovery and Occurrence of Covalently Bound Coenzymes in Flavoproteins . . . 18
BIOSYNTHESIS OF THE COVALENT FLAVIN-PROTEIN BOND 21
   Synthesis of the Histidyl(N3)-8α-Flavin Linkage 21
   Specific Features of Covalent Flavoproteins 25
PRESENTLY KNOWN FLAVOPROTEINS WITH COVALENTLY BOUND
      FLAVIN COFACTORS (FAD OR FMN) 29
   Flavoproteins with a Histidyl(N1)-8α-Flavin Linkage 29
   Flavoproteins with a Histidyl(N3)-8α-Flavin Linkage 32
   Flavoproteins with Flavin Bound to a Cysteinyl Residue 37
   Flavoprotein with a Tyrosyl(O)-8α-Flavin Linkage 38

Proteins with the flavin coenzyme covalently linked to an amino acid side-chain (henceforth called covalent flavoproteins) have interested flavinologists for the last 25 years. The subject has been reviewed in some detail recently (12, 14). This review emphasizes the mechanism of synthesis of the covalent bond, but a brief outline of the occurrence and functions of the presently known covalent flavoproteins is also given.

17

0199-9885/93/0715-0017$02.00

COVALENT COFACTOR-APOENZYME ATTACHMENT

General Features of Coenzyme Attachment

Most enzymes require cofactors for their activity. Cations are the most common; they are usually involved in the stabilization of transition states. Coenzymes, which are of organic nature, generally occur in a freely dissociable form, but some are known as covalently bound cofactors only (Table 1). Several cofactors, however, occur both in free and covalently attached form. The flavoproteins belong to the latter group.

Discovery and Occurrence of Covalently Bound Coenzymes in Flavoproteins

Covalent attachment of flavin coenzyme and apoprotein was first observed in 1955 by Singer and associates, who were studying succinate dehydrogenase of beef heart mitochondria (55). Until this time, it was thought that all the flavoproteins contained their cofactor, FMN or FAD, only noncovalently attached to the polypeptide structure; in many instances the reversible removal of the coenzyme was experimentally demonstrated.

Table 1   Free and bound forms of coenzymes[a]

Vitamins	Coenzymes	Covalently bound in	Noncovalently attached to
Biocytin	Biotin	Acetyl-CoA carboxylase	—
—	α-Lipoic acid	Dihydrolipoyl transacetylase	—
Retinol	13-*cis*-Retinal	Rhodopsin	—
Pantothenic acid	4-P-Pantetheine	Acyl carrier protein	—
	Coenzyme A	—	Pyruvate dehydrogenase
—	Heme	Cytochrome *c*	Cytochrome *b*
Pyridoxine	Pyridoxal-P	Phosphorylase	Alanine aminotransferase
Riboflavin	FAD	Succinate dehydrogenase	D-Amino acid oxidase
	FMN	Trimethylamine dehydrogenase	NADH-Q reductase

[a] Coenzymes derived from the following vitamins were always found in noncovalent attachment: cobalamin, folic acid, niacin, phylloquinone and thiamin.

After the discovery of the first covalent flavoprotein, it was soon recognized that more than one type of bond can be formed between flavin and apoprotein (Figure 1): Histidyl residues can be attached through N-atom 1 or 3 to the 8α-methyl group of the isoalloxazine ring forming a secondary amine bond; cysteinyl groups of a polypeptide chain may form a thioether linkage with either the 8α-methyl group or with carbon atom 6 of the xylene ring of the flavin molecule; a fifth binding type is represented by the tyrosyl(O)-8α-flavin bond. The physicochemical properties of the differently bound flavin derivatives and the methods used to identify the bond type have been presented recently in great detail (17).

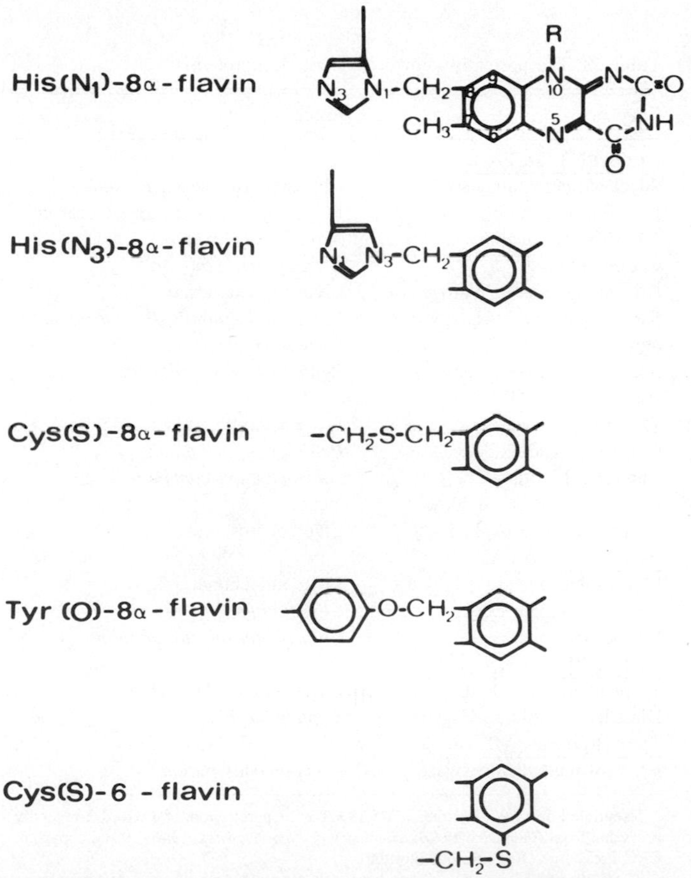

Figure 1 Aminoacyl-flavin bonds observed in flavoproteins. Reprinted from *BioFactors* 3:71 (1991) with permission of Oxford University Press and from *Chemistry and Biochemistry of Flavoenzymes* 2:347 (1991), copyright CRC Press, Inc. Boca Raton, Florida.

During the past 35 years, some 20 flavoproteins (Table 2) have been identified as covalent flavoproteins. This list does not reveal an obvious relation between bond type and either the mechanism of the catalyzed reaction or the source of the enzyme. The His(N3)-8α-FAD linkage appears to be the most abundant in nature. The simultaneous existence, often within the same organism, of covalently and noncovalently linked flavoproteins raises the question of the significance of covalency. Presently, the covalent flavoenzymes appear to be the minority. Inspection of Table 2, however, reveals that many covalent flavoproteins are engaged in the dissimilation of organic material. The potential of many bacterial species to degrade oxidatively a wide variety of natural and manmade organic compounds is almost without limit. One

Table 2 The presently known covalent flavoproteins[a]

Enzyme	Source
Histidyl(N3)-8α-FAD	
Succinate dehydrogenase	Mitochondria, yeast, *B. subtilis*
Fumarate reductase	*W. succinogenes*, *E. coli* (anaerobic)
6-Hydroxy-D-nicotine oxidase	*Arthrobacter oxidans*[b]
Choline oxidase	*Arthrobacter globiformis*
Dimethylglycine dehydrogenase	Liver mitochondria
Sarcosine dehydrogenase	Liver mitochondria, *Pseudomonas*
Sarcosine oxidase	*Corynebacterium* sp. U-96
D-Gluconolactone oxidase	*Penicillium cyaneofulvum*
Histidyl(N1)-8α-FAD	
Thiamin dehydrogenase	Soil bacterium (ATCC 25589)
Cyclopiazonate oxidocyclase	*Penicillium cyclopium*
Cholesterol oxidase	*Schizophyllum commune*
L-Galactonolactone oxidase	Yeast
L-Gulonolactone oxidase	Liver microsomes
Cysteinyl(S)-8α-FAD	
Monoamine oxidase	Liver mitochondria
Flavocytochrome c_{552}	*Chromatium*
Flavocytochrome c_{553}	*Chlorobium thiosulfatophilum*
Cysteinyl(S)-6-FMN	
Trimethylamine dehydrogenase	Bacterium sp. W_3A_41
Dimethylamine dehydrogenase	*Hyphomicrobium X*
Tyrosyl(O)-8α-FAD	
p-Cresol methylhydroxylase	*Pseudomonas putida*

[a] Reprinted from *BioFactors* 3:70 (1991) with permission of Oxford University Press and from *Chemistry and Biochemistry of Flavoenzymes* 2:346 (1991), copyright CRC Press, Inc. Boca Raton, Florida.

[b] Recently, *Arthrobacter oxidans* has been renamed *Arthrobacter nicotinovorans* (Kodama, Y., Yamamoto, H., Amano, N., Amachi, T. 1992. Reclassification of two strains of *Arthrobacter oxydans* and proposal of *Arthrobacter nicotinovorans* sp. nov. *Int. J. System. Bacteriol.* 42:234–39).

might expect, therefore, to find in oxidative catabolisms additional covalent flavoproteins. In cells of higher organisms, particularly in mammalian species, the number of covalent flavoproteins is limited. Four covalent flavoproteins were distinguished in rat liver mitochondria (1, 53): succinate dehydrogenase, monoamine oxidase, sarcosine dehydrogenase, and dimethylglycine dehydrogenase. Another covalent flavoprotein, L-gulonolactone oxidase, was discovered in liver microsomes (32).

BIOSYNTHESIS OF THE COVALENT FLAVIN-PROTEIN BOND

Covalent bond formation requires the expenditure of free enthalpy; in the case of biotinylation it is provided by ATP. Mechanisms involving ATP can also be formulated for covalent flavoprotein formation; they would necessitate either the activation of the coenzyme, e.g. by hydroxylation of the 8α-CH_3 group followed by (pyro)phosphorylation, or the formation of a highly reactive N-derivative of the imidazole moiety of the receiving amino acid, e.g. phosphohistidyl-apoprotein. These mechanisms would certainly require enzymatic catalysis. However, activation processes not involving ATP (or similar kinds of metabolic energy) or even enzymes can be envisaged (11, 21, 60).

Insight into the details of the synthesis of the covalent apoenzyme-flavin bond has been gained recently for the histidyl(N3)-8α-FAD linkage in 6-hydroxy-D-nicotine oxidase. This flavoprotein is involved in the oxidative degradation of D-nicotine in the soil bacterium *Arthrobacter oxidans* (13). Several of the question raised above can now be answered for that particular enzyme. Whether or not the same principle of synthesis is valid for other enzymes of the same type or even for other covalent cofactor-apoprotein linkages is still unknown.

Synthesis of the Histidyl(N3)-8α-Flavin Linkage

COVALENT ATTACHMENT IN VITRO   Covalent FAD attachment to the growing peptide chain of the apoenzyme in an extract of *A. oxidans* was demonstrated in 1980 (25). Substantial progress was made when the gene of 6-hydroxy-D-nicotine oxidase was identified on a plasmid (pAO1) (7), cloned, and sequenced. It could be expressed in a cell-free coupled transcription/translation system from *Escherichia coli* (3). The synthesis of a flavin-free apoprotein was achieved in UV-irradiated *E. coli* extracts by immunoprecipitation and by SDS gel electrophoresis (2). Addition of FAD to this system led to the formation of the enzymatically active protein with covalently bound cofactor. A highly purified apo-6-hydroxy-D-nicotine oxidase was obtained either from cell-free extracts of diphenyl iodonium (DPI)-treated *E. coli* cells carrying the

6-hydroxy-D-nicotine oxidase gene or through the formation of a fusion protein with β-galactosidase (15).

The apoprotein of 6-hydroxy-D-nicotine oxidase could be flavinylated and converted into the enzymatically active form in the presence of an ATP-regenerating system and FAD (8-demethyl-FAD could not replace FAD) without further additions, thereby suggesting at first the participation of an ATP-dependent enzymatic process.

Eventually it was observed that the ATP-regenerating system can be replaced by phosphoenolpyruvate alone and even by other phosphorylated three-carbon compounds such as glycerol 3-phosphate, glyceraldehyde 3-phosphate, or glycerate 3-phosphate (4). The K_m value for FAD in this reaction is 3 μM; that for phosphoenolpyruvate is about 1 mM. The latter value is in the range reported for the phosphotransferase system of bacterial carbohydrate metabolism (52). Similar concentrations of C_3-compounds are found in cell lysates.

The effector molecules do not participate in the reaction; neither [14]C- nor ^{32}P-phosphoenolpyruvate are bound to the protein or cleaved during the flavinylation. The high efficiency of glycerol 3-phosphate also excludes an energy-providing function. Evidently, these phosphate esters serve as allosteric modulators of the protein. The presence of 45% glycerol allows a conformation of the apoprotein that facilitates the access of FAD to its binding site and the spontaneous covalent attachment. Still, glycerol 3-phosphate increases the rate of holoenzyme formation even in the presence of glycerol. The same observation was made in the presence of 20% saccharose (5).

The flavinylation of the apo-6-hydroxy-D-nicotine oxidase in vitro does not require an additional enzyme; the most highly purified preparations of the apoprotein are flavinylated and converted to the active enzyme at the same rate as the apoenzyme of crude extracts.

Two flavin derivatives, 8-Cl-FAD and 5-deaza-FAD, were tested as possible substitutes for FAD. In 8-Cl-FAD the –CH$_3$ group is replaced by a reactive, electronegative group (5). 5-Deaza-FAD cannot adopt the quinomethide form of FAD that has been proposed as intermediate in the mechanism of FAD binding (Figure 2). Neither derivative is able to bind covalently to the apoenzyme or to restore the enzymatic activity of apo-6-hydroxy-D-nicotine oxidases. The strong influence of the methylene bridge between the isoalloxazine and the histidine rings on the enzymatic activity is remarkable.

SITE-DIRECTED MUTAGENESIS   Knowledge of the primary structure of 6-hydroxy-D-nicotine oxidase made it possible to elucidate the specificity and importance of individual amino acids for covalent binding of the coenzyme as well as for the catalytic process. Replacement of His$_{71}$ by uncharged residues such as alanine or hydroxyamino acids (serine, tyrosine) allowed neither binding nor enzymatic activity (43). Cysteine acts as covalent acceptor of the 8-methyl group of flavin in a number of flavoproteins (Table 2). Substituting His_{71} in 6-hydroxy-D-nicotine oxidase with cysteine did not lead to covalent FAD binding under a variety of conditions; however, a substantial amount of enzyme activity was obtained with the mutated apoenzyme in the presence of FAD and substrate. This surprising finding suggests that covalent attachment per se is not a necessary prerequisite of activity; rather, the correct topology at the active center is important and can be best accomplished in some enzymes by covalent fixation of the cofactor.

One can also expect that the environment of the active center, i.e. amino acid residues near the binding or catalytic site of the enzyme, influences the enzymatic activity. As an example, the role of Arg_{67} was studied in some detail (41). Replacement of Arg with Ala abolished covalent FAD attachment. Covalent flavinylation of apo-6-hydroxy-D-nicotine oxidase was reestablished by Lys in position 67. However, incorporation of FAD into the Lys_{67}-polypeptide was dependent to a much higher degree on the presence of the allosteric effector glycerol 3-phosphate than the incorporation into the wild-type protein. This finding underlines the importance of a certain conformational state of the apoenzyme for the covalent binding of the cofactor.

SH-group blockers were found to be potent inhibitors of holoenzyme formation from apoenzyme and FAD. The inhibitory effect of dithiodinitrobenzoic (DTNB) on the flavinylation reaction could be prevented by mercaptoethanol. Interestingly, iodacetamide, a compound that reacts with the thiolate ion, had no effect on holoenzyme formation at concentrations up to 1 mM. The conformation of the 6-hydroxy-D-nicotine oxidase is not stabilized by a disulfide bridge. Apparently, the inhibitory effect of SH-blockers on holoenzyme formation and enzyme activity is not so much an effect on the conformation of the enzyme but rather one that involves an interaction with an SH group in the reaction centers essential for FAD binding and enzymatic activity.

MECHANISM OF COVALENT FLAVIN ATTACHMENT The proposed nonenzymatic mechanism of holo-6-hydroxy-D-nicotine oxidase synthesis (Figure 2) requires a particularly high conformational specificity of the binding region. The incoming flavin cofactor could then be arranged and held for a finite time in a position that would put the 8α-C in exact and close proximity to the binding atom of the proper amino acid residue; furthermore, a base would have to be in a position to facilitate proton abstraction. The endergonic condensation reaction would be thermodynamically compensated by the reoxidation of the intermediately formed $FADH_2$. Thus, this mechanism requires an oxidant capable of taking electrons from the reduced flavin. In contrast to the process involving a (mono-oxygenase-type) hydroxylation, however, oxygen is not

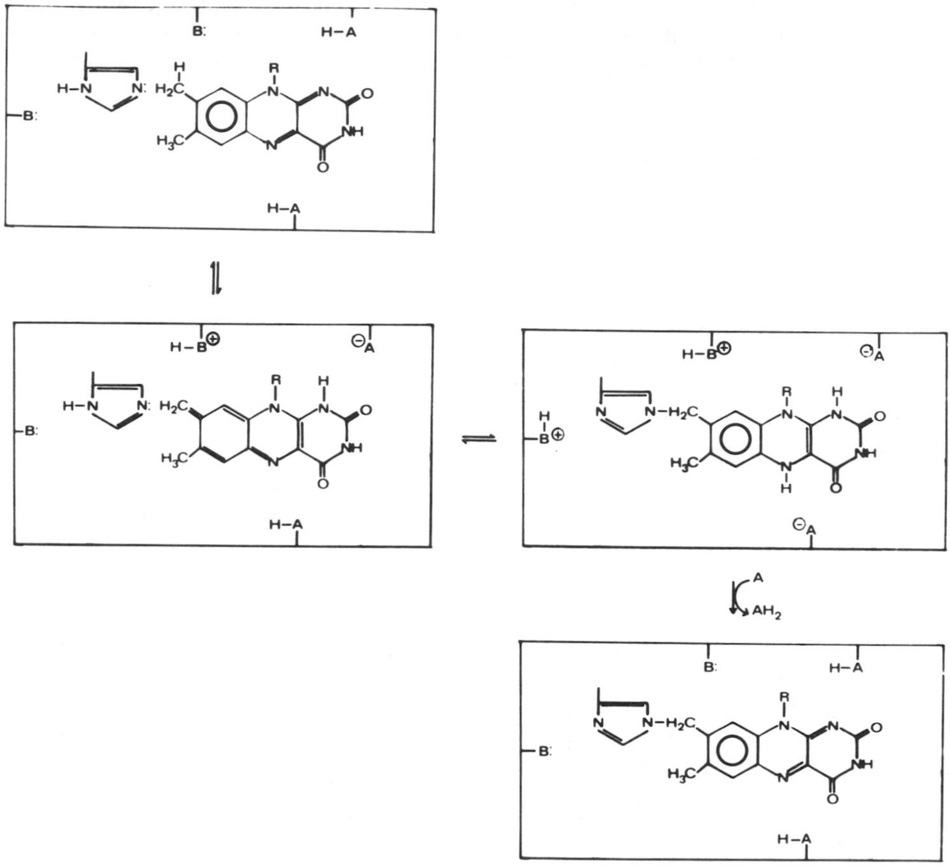

Figure 2   Mechanism of covalent flavinylation of a N3-histidyl residue.

necessarily required. This mechanistic difference can be used to elucidate the coupling reaction.

Reoxidation of the reduced adduct of FAD and the apoenzyme was proposed as the thermodynamic driving force in the establishment of a stable covalent flavoprotein (11). This mechanism (Figure 2) implies that covalent incorporation of FAD into the apoenzyme can take place in the absence of oxygen, provided that an electron acceptor is present to dehydrogenate the fully reduced flavin. Recent experiments (5) indicate that holoenzyme formation takes place in the absence of molecular oxygen, but a requirement of an external electron acceptor could not be demonstrated. Thus, the details of the mechanism,

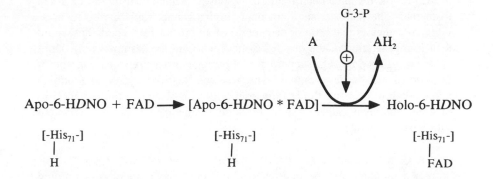

Figure 3   Autocatalytic holoenzyme formation: The flavinylation of 6-hydroxy-D-nicotine oxidase.

including the possibility of an internal electron acceptor, remain to be elucidated.

The covalent flavinylation represents a synthetic chemical reaction that requires the presence of a protein and a cofactor and displays high specificity for both components (Figure 3). The "enzymatic" character of the reaction is further stressed by the absolute requirement for an allosteric effector with certain structural features.

The cell-free flavinylation of the flavoprotein subunit of succinate dehydrogenase and fumarate reductase overexpressed in *E. coli* also seem to need allosteric effectors; in this case it is a dicarboxylic acid, e.g. citrate, isocitrate, succinate or fumarate (4), again indicating a certain degree of specificity of the effector molecule. The "enzymatic" process of flavinylation differs from any other enzymatic reaction in that the "enzyme" is also the substrate and the catalytic cycle operates only once!

Specific Features of Covalent Flavoproteins

CLEAVAGE OF THE COVALENT BOND   The mechanism of biological cleavage of the aminoacyl-flavin bond is yet to be discovered. The turnover of all natural products requires that every molecule that is biosynthesized must also be degraded at a similar rate. Therefore, every type of bond encountered in covalent flavoproteins has to be cleaved by a biological process—not necessarily, however, in the same organism. Both 8α-S-cysteinyl- and

N-histidyl-flavins have been found to be partly metabolized in and excreted from rats. The fact that such covalent flavins cannot replace riboflavin as vitamins indicates that little or no rupture of an 8α-linkage occurs that would lead to regeneration of the original 8-methyl within the mammal (8a). Until now, no instance has been reported of a biological reaction breaking one of the known protein-flavin bonds. The 7α- and 8α-hydroxyflavins found in mammalian tissues and fluids (50) resemble a first stage in the metabolism of free riboflavin rather than a product of the cleavage of a covalent flavin-protein adduct.

IS COVALENT FLAVIN ATTACHMENT NECESSARY OR ADVANTAGEOUS?   Although a rationale for the existence of covalent flavin-apoprotein binding cannot be presented yet, the possibility of an advantage of covalency in special circumstances should not be dismissed out of hand. Further investigations are needed to consider the energy profiles of the transition states and the redox potentials of reactions catalyzed by covalent flavoproteins as compared to flavoenzymes bearing noncovalently attached cofactors. Particular attention should be given to the metabolic stabilities of the different types of flavoproteins. It will be interesting to learn more about the proteolytic inactivation and the turnover of covalent vs noncovalent flavoproteins in various cell types. Covalent bonding might also be a means of cofactor economy, particularly in cells where the supply of riboflavin is likely to become a limiting metabolic factor.

At present it is difficult to assign specific qualities to the covalent versus the noncovalent flavoproteins and to correlate the binding mode with the functions of the enzymes. Neither the observed differences in the fluorescence properties nor those found in NMR studies of histidyl-flavins allow such assignments. Structurally, the presently known amino acid sequences adjacent to the binding group do not reveal a common denominator. Possibly, there exist certain common features of the tertiary structure that characterize the FAD-binding domains of some covalent flavoproteins but are not evident from the short stretches of available amino acid sequences.

Similar considerations apply to the transition states in flavin catalysis. The firm attachment of the aromatic ring to the polypeptide backbone is likely to influence the mobility of the molecular structure of the coenzyme. Such an effect would be expected to reveal itself in several physical properties of the enzymes, most conspicuously in the redox potentials of the flavin/semiquinone and semiquinone/dihydroflavin couples. Measurements (16, 20, 54) of some histidyl(N)- and cysteinyl(S)-flavins as well as of the free forms (riboflavin and FAD) indicate that 8α-substituted flavins have a more positive (ca 25 mV) redox potential than the free flavins. A significant difference between the various binding types does not exist. In view of the wide range of redox potentials of flavoproteins, it is difficult to attribute functional significance to the differences between covalently and noncovalently bound flavins, especially as the measurements were taken not on flavoproteins of comparable function but on model compounds.

The primary structure of 6-hydroxy-D-nicotine oxidase as derived from the genomic DNA lacks the characteristic nucleotide-binding region, -x-x-Gly-z-Gly-z-z-Gly-x- (where x stands for a hydrophobic amino acid such as Leu or Val and z for an unspecified amino acid). This motif has been identified in flavoproteins both with (e.g. succinate dehydrogenase) and without (e.g. 6-hydroxyl-L-nicotine oxidase) covalent flavin attachment. It is thought to be instrumental in the initial attachment of the coenzyme.

Recently, a cDNA for the dimethylglycine dehydrogenase from rat liver mitochondria has been isolated and sequenced (39). Upstream of the flavinylated histidine residue, the deduced amino acid sequence exhibits a motif resembling the dinucleotide-binding site characteristic of the flavoprotein subunit of succinate dehydrogenase and fumarate reductase. The same combination of a site for covalent binding of FAD and the dinucleotide-binding domain is also found in monoamine oxidase of the outer mitochondrial membrane (51). These features suggest a primary interaction of FAD with the dinucleotide-binding domain. The ensuing folding of the polypeptide chain might bring a reactive amino acid side-chain in close proximity to the isoalloxazine ring and thus determine the chance of covalent flavinylation.

Is covalent flavin binding to the apoenzyme correlated to the type of the catalyzed reaction? An unequivocal answer to that question cannot yet be given; in two instances only, succinate dehydrogenase and choline oxidase, is it obvious at present that the enzyme from many sources contains covalent FAD and apparently always of the same binding type; the similarity of the bond type even crosses the prokaryote/eukaryote border. It may be that flavoproteins catalyzing a given reaction have the same kind of coenzyme attachment irrespective of the species. This relationship, however, could reflect a genetic inheritance as well as a requirement of the reaction mechanism.

The 6-hydroxynicotine oxidases from *Arthrobacter oxidans* that catalyze the same type of reaction in the same organism but on the enantiomeric (D- and L-)substrates only are genetically unrelated and use free and covalently bound FAD, respectively. Thus, the catalyzed reaction per se cannot be a decisive factor in the choice of coenzyme binding. It is questionable in that case whether the stereospecificity of the reaction requires a specific type of cofactor binding. The apoenzyme of 6-hydroxy-D-nicotine oxidase is catalytically inactive and cannot regain substantial enzymatic activity by the sole addition of (free) FAD. A succinate dehydrogenase-deficient mutant of *Bacillus subtilis* characterized by the lack of covalently bound FAD in the flavoprotein subunit (26) is still able to integrate the latter into the membrane-associated enzyme (27); enzymatic activity of this mutated succinate dehydrogenase could not be restored by addition of (free) FAD. Nevertheless, an intrinsic correlation between covalent FAD attachment and certain functions, e.g. stereospecificity or assembly of integrated structures, cannot be deduced from these findings.

One aspect of covalency is the potential difference in metabolic stability between covalent and noncovalent flavoproteins. The apoenzyme of 6-hydroxy-D-nicotine oxidase is much more susceptible to proteolytic degradation than the holoenzyme (6). The faster destruction of the apoproteins can be seen as part of an ordered intracellular turnover.

Thus, the question whether covalent attachment of the cofactor in a holoenzyme has prevailed throughout the evolutionary screening process because of biological significance or whether it is a chance event of neutral selective value (11) is still unresolved. However, the fact that at least in two instances a requirement exists for a rather specific allosteric effector would argue against the latter assumption.

NUTRITIONAL ASPECTS   The well-known features of riboflavin deficiency need not be elaborated here; but we must ask whether covalent attachment requires specific levels or ways of vitamin availability. This discussion is seriously hampered by the fact that most data on covalent flavoproteins and on the relation between their synthesis and the cofactor supply come from studies with prokaryotic organisms and with eukaryotes that are able to synthesize riboflavin de novo. One has to be very careful in transposing such data to the vitamin-requiring human or animal.

The riboflavin-requiring mutant strain of *A. oxidans* (24) provided some clues regarding the vitamin dependence of the syntheses of covalent and noncovalent flavoproteins. While the synthetic capacity for the latter was fully engaged at an extracellular riboflavin concentration of 2 μM, the maximal production of the covalent flavoprotein, 6-hydroxy-D-nicotine oxidase, required a concentration of 8 μM. The decisive value, of course, is that of the intracellular precursor pool, free FAD. In the mutant bacteria, this pool increased proportionally up to an extracellular riboflavin concentration of 12 μM. At 15 μM it was 6 times the FAD level found at 2 μM; concomitantly, the activity of 6-hydroxy-D-nicotine oxidase increased 5.3-fold (29). The half-maximal rate of enzyme synthesis required 5 μM free FAD while the average half-saturation of the noncovalent flavoproteins was attained at < 1 μM. At full saturation of covalent flavoprotein synthesis, the intracellular concentration of free FAD was 43 μM, the total FAD content 66 nmol per gram wet weight (30). In comparison, the FAD content of rat liver is about 35 nmol per gram wet weight corresponding to a cytosolic concentration of ca 50 μM. Apparently, the riboflavin supply of a well-fed rat is very near the saturation level of covalent flavoprotein synthesis but quite in excess of the level necessary for the production of noncovalent flavoproteins—if these syntheses proceed under conditions comparable to those in the mutant bacteria. In this case, reduced availability of the vitamin may primarily affect the synthesis of covalent flavoproteins both for lack of sufficient cofactor and as a result of an increased rate of apoenzyme proteolysis (see above).

Table 2 clearly shows that important reactions of the energy-providing pathway (succinate dehydrogenase), the regulation of hormone and neurotransmitter levels (monoamine oxidase, enzymes of choline degradation), and the homeostasis of the phospholipid spectrum of membranes (dimethylglycine and sarcosine dehydrogenases) are afflicted by impaired activity of covalent flavoproteins. Ongoing studies of the mechanism of synthesis of the latter enzymes (R. Brandsch, personal communication) may soon provide us with data about the effects of riboflavin and cofactor availability on covalent flavoprotein function in mammals.

PRESENTLY KNOWN FLAVOPROTEINS WITH COVALENTLY BOUND FLAVIN COFACTORS (FAD OR FMN)

Flavoproteins with a Histidyl(N1)-8α-Flavin Linkage

THIAMIN OXIDASE   The bacterial enzyme (23, 46) consists of a single peptide chain of $M_r = 50,000$ containing one mole of covalently bound FAD. It catalyzes the sequential dehydrogenations of the alcoholic form to the carboxylate form, yielding under anaerobic conditions 1 mol of fully reduced $FADH_2$ after addition of 0.5 mol thiamin; oxygen is reduced to H_2O_2 (Equation 1).

1.

Thus it is an oxidase with redox potentials of the two couples (oxi-dized/semiquinone and semiquinone/reduced form of FAD) of $+ 80$ and $+ 30$ mV at pH 7.2, respectively. The type of covalent binding between FAD and the apo-thiamin oxidase was established (18, 31) as His(N1)-8α-FAD using amino acid analysis as well as spectrophotometric, fluorescence, NMR, and EPR measurements.

Oxythiamin and pyrithiamin that are sometimes used as "antivitamins" react with thiamin oxidase, the former as substrate, the latter as irreversible inhibitor (23, 46). The coenzyme form of thiamin, thiamin diphosphate, is neither a substrate nor an inhibitor of the enzyme.

CYCLOPIAZONATE OXIDOCYCLASE   An enzyme from *Penicillium cyclopium* has been obtained in homogeneous form that catalyzes the dehydrogenation and cyclization of β-cyclopiazonate to α-cyclopiazonate (Equation 2).

2.

The enzyme contains FAD covalently attached via its 8α-methyl group to the N1 of a histidyl residue (19) as shown by NMR measurements, spectroscopy and fluorescence quenching ($pK_a = 5.2$), as well as by its ability to be reduced by borohydride and to form 8-formyl-riboflavin upon storage.

CHOLESTEROL OXIDASE *Schizophyllum commune*, a soil organism, is the source of cholesterol oxidase that converts free cholesterol into cholest-4-en-3-one with the concomitant production of H_2O_2 (Equation 3); coupled with peroxidase and a chromogenic substrate, this reaction is widely used for the determination of cholesterol in biological samples.

3.

Cholesterol oxidase is an auto-oxidizable, monomeric protein of $M_r = 53,000$ containing one mole of covalently bound FAD (22). The covalent linkage between the peptide and the FAD was identified as His(N1)-8α-riboflavin by its absorption spectrum and the typical pH-dependent fluorescence quenching ($pK_a = 5.8$; 5.05 after acid hydrolysis to the aminoacyl-flavin) of His(N1)-8α-riboflavin derivatives.

L-GALACTONOLACTONE OXIDASE   The last steps of L-ascorbic acid synthesis in yeast cells are the formation of 2-keto-L-galactono-γ-lactone from L-galactonolactone followed by isomerization to L-ascorbate (Equation 4).

4.

The cofactor FAD is covalently bound in L-galactonolactone oxidase to the apoenzyme by a histidyl(N1)-8α-flavin linkage (33).

L-GULONO-γ-LACTONE OXIDASE   This enzyme catalyzes the last enzymatic step in the biosynthesis of L-ascorbic acid in some animal tissues. It converts L-gulonolactone to 2-keto-gulono-γ-lactone and thence by isomerization to L-ascorbate (Equation 5).

$$
\begin{array}{c}
\text{CH}_2\text{OH} \\
| \\
\text{HOCH} \quad O \\
\end{array}
\;=\!O \;+\; O_2 \;\longrightarrow\;
\begin{array}{c}
\text{CH}_2\text{OH} \\
| \\
\text{HOCH} \quad O \\
\end{array}
\;=\!O \;+\; H_2O_2
$$

5.

The lack of L-gulonolactone oxidase in humans, primates, and guinea pigs renders these species dependent on an external supply of L-ascorbate (vitamin C). The structure of the oxidase is highly conserved throughout the animal kingdom as demonstrated by immunological methods (47). L-Gulonolactone oxidase from rat liver possesses a M_r of 50,605 as shown by sequence analysis of a cDNA (37). The covalent flavin of this enzyme was identified as His(N1)-8α-riboflavin by the methodology used to analyze the cofactor of thiamin dehydrogenase.

Flavoproteins with a Histidyl(N3)-8α-Flavin Linkage

SUCCINATE DEHYDROGENASE AND FUMARATE REDUCTASE   The flavoprotein most widely distributed among aerobic organisms is succinate dehydrogenase (SDH). The corresponding enzyme of the anaerobic world is fumarate reductase (FR). Both enzymes share not only the same chemical reaction (Equation 6) (though physiologically operating in opposite directions) and the binding type of the apoenzyme but also a common genetic ancestry.

$$
^-\text{OOC-CH}_2\text{-CH}_2\text{-COO}^- \;\underset{\substack{\text{FR} \\ \text{FAD} \quad \text{FADH}_2}}{\overset{\substack{\text{FAD} \quad \text{FADH}_2 \\ \text{SDH}}}{\rightleftharpoons}}\; ^-\text{OOC-CH=CH-CH}_2\text{-COO}^-
$$

6.

Succinate dehydrogenase of eukaryotic organisms is a multienzyme complex located on the matrix side of the inner mitochondrial membrane. It forms complex 2 of the respiratory chain. The electrons of its FADH$_2$ are transferred directly to ubiquinone. Aerobically grown bacteria make use of a similar succinate dehydrogenase complex present in the cytoplasmic membrane.

The basic structure of the complexes of succinate dehydrogenase and of fumarate reductase has been highly conserved during evolution. They all consist of two hydrophilic subunits forming the catalytic part of the complex that is anchored to the mitochondrial and cytoplasmic membranes, respectively, by one or two hydrophobic polypeptides (28). The larger (about 70 kDa) of the hydrophilic subunits (Sdh A and Fr A, respectively) carry both covalently bound FAD and iron-sulfur clusters as cofactors. The same type of cofactor binding is present in the mitochondrial succinate dehydrogenase of beef heart (55), in *Saccharomyces cerevisiae* (48), and in succinate dehydrogenase and fumarate reductase of bacterial origin (34).

In anaerobic phosphorylation-coupled electron transport, fumarate reductase catalyzes the reverse reaction (Equation 6), the hydrogenation of fumarate to succinate. This constitutes the terminal step in some fermentations, e.g. in *Wollinella succinogenes* (40).

By site-directed mutagenesis of the *E. coli frd* operon, the FAD-carrying histidine$_{44}$ of fumarate reductase was replaced by Cys, Ser, Tyr, and Arg (1a). FAD was bound firmly but noncovalently in these fumarate reductase mutants. They retained significant fumarate reductase activity when assayed by reduction of benzyl viologen but were unable to oxidize succinate (1). Apparently, covalent FAD binding to the enzyme is required for the oxidation of succinate ($E_m = +30$ mV) but not for fumarate reduction by menaquinol ($E_m = -74$ mV), the physiological electron donor.

6-HYDROXY-D-NICOTINE OXIDASE   6-Hydroxy-D-nicotine oxidase, a flavoprotein of *Arthrobacter oxidans* with FAD covalently attached through a His(N3)-8α-riboflavin bond (45), acts specifically on the D-isomer of 6-hydroxy(nor)nicotine. This enzyme is instrumental in the catabolism of D-nicotine and D-nornicotine (Figure 4); while D-nicotine has not yet been detected in natural sources, D-nornicotine has been found in tobacco plants.

6-Hydroxy-D-nicotine oxidase catalyzes the stoichiometric conversion of 6-hydroxy-D-nicotine to 6-hydroxy-N-methylmyosmine and the hydrolysis of the latter to [6-hydroxypyridyl(3)](N-methylaminopropyl)-ketone ("ketone") with the simultaneous reduction of molecular oxygen to H_2O_2. The enzyme consists of a single peptide chain of $M_r = 47,077$, as derived from the gene structure, including 1 mol of covalently bound FAD (8). Some of its properties are listed in comparison with those of 6-hydroxy-L-nicotine oxidase in Table 3.

The elucidation of the synthesis of 6-hydroxy-D-nicotine oxidase and its regulation were greatly facilitated by the use of a riboflavin-requiring (rf) mutant of *A. oxidans* (24). Quantitative riboflavin incorporation experiments and the appearance of 6-hydroxy-D-nicotine-oxidase-specific mRNA in the

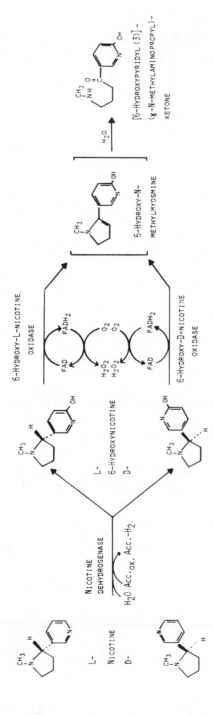

Figure 4 Initial steps in the bacterial degradation of nicotine.

Table 3 Properties of 6-hydroxy-D-nicotine oxidase (HDNO) and 6-hydroxy-L-nicotine oxidase (HLNO)[a]

Property	HDNO	HLNO
Relative mol mass (M_r)	49,077	106,600
Polypeptide chains/mol	1	2
FAD (mol/mol enzyme)	1	2
Binding of FAD	Covalent	Noncovalent
N-terminal amino acids	V-S-S-K-L-	-M-Y-D-A-I
C-terminal amino acids	N-L-Q-S-A	-A-H-I-S-L
Turnover number	1,320 (pH 9.2)	4,160 (pH 7.5)
(mol/min/mol, 30°C)		
K_m (K_i) (mM)		
6-hydroxy-D-nicotine	0.05	(0.1)
6-hydroxy-L-nicotine	(1.5)	0.02
λ_{max} vis (nm)	355, 450, 475(S)	370, 443, 463(S)
Reactivity towards		
oxygen	Yes	Yes
1 e-acceptors	No	No
2 e-acceptors	Yes	No
Intermediate flavin		
radical		
with $S_2O_3^{2-}$	Anionic (red)	
with hν + EDTA		Anionic (red)

[a] Reprinted from *BioFactors* 3:73 (1991) with permission of Oxford University Press and from *Chemistry and Biochemistry of Flavoenzymes* 2:351 (1991), copyright CRC Press, Inc. Boca Raton, Florida

stationary phase of growth (42) indicate that about 50% of the total covalently bound flavin resides in 6-hydroxy-D-nicotine oxidase, while the other half belongs to constitutive proteins including succinate dehydrogenase.

CHOLINE OXIDASE   The metabolic degradation of choline has been observed in animal as well as in microbial cells. Two major pathways emerged from these studies: the first one operates mainly in animal cells and employs two separate enzymes, choline dehydrogenase forming betaine aldehyde and betaine dehydrogenase converting the aldehyde to betaine. Choline dehydrogenase from rat liver might also contain a modified flavin as the prosthetic group; its structure has yet to be identified. The second route requires only one enzyme for both processes: choline oxidase converts choline to betaine with the reduction of oxygen to hydrogen peroxide (Equation 7).

$$(CH_3)_3N^+\text{-}CH_2\text{-}CH_2OH + 2 O_2 + H_2O \longrightarrow$$
$$(CH_3)_3N^+\text{-}CH_2\text{-}COO^- + H^+ + 2 H_2O_2 \qquad 7.$$

This oxidase activity is present in several microorganisms. The coenzyme of choline oxidase is FAD covalently bound to N3 of a histidyl residue by its 8α-C (49).

DIMETHYLGLYCINE DEHYDROGENASE AND SARCOSINE DEHYDROGENASE Betaine can be further metabolized to dimethylglycine, sarcosine (monomethylglycine), and glycine. In animal tissues this reaction sequence is catalyzed by dehydrogenase-type flavoproteins. In bacteria, oxidases seem to convert sarcosine to glycine. The overall process consists in the stepwise oxidative removal of both methyl groups of dimethylgycine (Equations 8 and 9):

$$(CH_3)_2N\text{-}CH_2\text{-}COOH + A_{ox} + THF \longrightarrow$$
$$CH_3NH\text{-}CH_2\text{-}COOH + A_{red} + 5,10\text{-methylene THF} \qquad 8.$$

$$CH_3NH\text{-}CH_2\text{-}COOH + A_{ox} + THF \longrightarrow$$
$$H_2N\text{-}CH_2\text{-}COOH + A_{red} + 5,10\text{-methylene THF.} \qquad 9.$$

Tetrahydrofolate (THF) is the cofactor noncovalently bound to the dehydrogenases that accepts the methyl groups at the oxidation level of formaldehyde as 5,10-methylenetetrahydrofolate.

The animal dehydrogenases involved in the conversion of dimethylglycine to glycine are present exclusively in liver mitochondria (9); they are structurally related but clearly distinguishable entities.

The sarcosine oxidases isolated from bacterial sources contain 1 mol each of noncovalently and covalently [histidyl(N3)-8α-] bound FAD per mole of enzyme. The two types of FAD cofactors may serve different functions in enzymatic catalysis. It appears that the noncovalent FAD participates in the dehydrogenase function and transfers its electrons to the covalent flavin. The covalent $FADH_2$ then reduces oxygen to hydrogen peroxide, thus acting as an oxidase flavin (38). The sarcosine oxidase of *Corynebacterium sp. P-1* is also unusual because its subunit composition contains four dissimilar subunits (38).

D-GLUCONOLACTONE OXIDASE (DEHYDROGENASE)   Analogous to the synthesis of L-ascorbic acid is the production by *Penicillium cyaneo-fulvum* of D-erythorbic (D-araboascorbic) acid (Equation 10); while the former pathway involves the oxidation of L-gulono-γ-lactone in animals or galactono-γ-lactone in plants, the latter requires the action of D-glucono-γ-lactone oxidase.

Oxygen is the most efficient electron acceptor. Hydrogen peroxide is formed in stoichiometric amounts during erythorbic acid production (58); the enzyme appears to be an oxidase rather than a dehydrogenase.

10.

Flavoproteins with Flavin Bound to a Cysteinyl Residue

This group of covalent flavoproteins includes two different binding types: polypeptides bound through cysteinyl residues to the 8α position of the flavin and those where the thioether linkage is between a cysteinyl sulfur and the carbon atom 6 of the isoalloxazine ring.

MONOAMINE OXIDASE   The most intensively studied representative of the Cys-S-8α type is monoamine oxidase (MAO) (59). The enzyme is widely distributed in animal tissues where it resides in mitochondria. It is instrumental in the inactivation of various neurotransmitters, hormones, and drugs. The oxidation of the amine results in the formation of the corresponding aldehyde and hydrogen peroxide (Equation 11)

$$R\text{-}CH_2\text{-}NH_2 + O_2 + H_2O \longrightarrow R\text{-}CHO + NH_3 + H_2O_2. \qquad 11.$$

This enzyme of $M_r = 52,000$ contains one mole of covalent FAD as the prosthetic group. Phenylhydrazine and some amines with an acetylenic structure, e.g. pargyline, are able to attach covalently to the flavin of MAO. These "suicide inhibitors" lead to an irreversible inactivation of the enzyme.

FLAVOCYTOCHROMES C   Some bacterial species, e.g. *Chromatium* and *Chlorobium*, contain flavocytochromes c in which both the heme and the flavin component are covalently attached to different subunits of the enzyme (10). Heme and flavin exist in a 2:1 ratio. In both the purple and the green phototrophic sulfur bacteria, the FAD is bound by a thioether bridge between its 8α-carbon and a cysteinyl residue of the respective subunit (35, 36). These flavocytochromes c apparently act as electron acceptors in the oxidation of sulfide to elemental sulfur. Another flavocytochrome c catalyzing the hydroxylation of *p*-cresol in *Pseudomonas* has a differently bound flavin and is discussed below.

TRIMETHYLAMINE DEHYDROGENASE   Trimethylamine dehydrogenase is unique among the flavoproteins with covalent cofactor attachment: the flavin component is FMN rather than FAD, and the bond between the apoenzyme and the coenzyme is a thioether involving cysteine and the 6-position of the isoalloxazine ring of FMN (57). The evidence for this type of linkage came mainly from NMR spectroscopy, sulfur chemistry, lack of the fluorescence typical for 8α-substituted flavins, and the reactions with thiol reagents such as iodoacetamide.

Trimethylamine dehydrogenase is induced in a variety of obligate and facultative methylotrophic bacteria growing on trimethylamine as sole carbon source. The enzyme is a dimer of two identical subunits of M_r 83,000 each; it contains one iron-sulfur cluster of the 4 Fe-4 S^{2+} type and one covalent flavin per subunit. The enzyme catalyzes the oxidative demethylation of trimethylamine yielding dimethylamine and formaldehyde; in the cell, the electrons are transferred to a FAD-containing electron transfer protein. Using an artificial electron acceptor the reaction (Equation 12) is

$$(CH_3)_3N + H_2O + A_{ox} \longrightarrow (CH_3)_2NH + CH_2O + A_{red}. \qquad 12.$$

The enzyme does not oxidize monoamines; however, the "suicide inhibitors" of monoamine oxidase are also effective inhibitors of trimethylamine dehydrogenase.

DIMETHYLAMINE DEHYDROGENASE   Dimethylamine dehydrogenase converts the product of the trimethylamine dehydrogenase reaction, dimethylamine, to methylamine, formaldehyde, and hydrogen peroxide in an analogous fashion (Equation 12). The spectral and structural properties of the enzyme are similar to those of trimethylamine dehydrogenase although they are different proteins. The dimer (M_r 138,000) contains a similar iron-sulfur cluster and 6-S-cysteinyl-FMN as the flavin prosthetic group (56).

Flavoprotein with a Tyrosyl(O)-8α-Flavin Linkage

p-CRESOL METHYLHYDROXYLASE   Pseudomonas putida and some other members of this family initiate the anaerobic degradation of p-cresol by dehydrogenation/hydration of its methyl group followed by the reversible dehydrogenation of the intermediate p-hydroxybenzaldehyde to p-hydroxybenzyl alcohol (Equation 13).

$$HO-\!\!\!\left\langle\bigcirc\right\rangle\!\!\!-CH_3 + A_{ox} + H_2O \longrightarrow HO-\!\!\!\left\langle\bigcirc\right\rangle\!\!\!-CH_2OH + A_{red}$$

$$13.$$

$$HO-\!\!\!\left\langle\bigcirc\right\rangle\!\!\!-CH_2OH + A_{ox} \longrightarrow HO-\!\!\!\left\langle\bigcirc\right\rangle\!\!\!-CHO + A_{red}$$

A constitutive isozyme and an inducible isozyme of *p*-cresol methylhydroxylase, both with similar enzymologic properties, have been observed on a plasmid of the pseudomonad [see (10)]. The enzyme consists of two flavin- and two heme-carrying subunits. *p*-Cresol methylhydroxylase is the sole flavoprotein known so far to have the prosthetic group FAD attached through the 8α-carbon of the isoalloxazine ring to the phenolic O- of a tyrosyl residue of the respective subunit (44).

ACKNOWLEDGMENTS

The work of the author and his associates was supported by grants from the *Deutsche Forschungsgemeinschaft,* Bonn, and *Fonds der Chemischen Industrie,* Frankfurt-M, Germany.

Literature Cited

1. Addison, R., McCormick, D. B. 1978. Biogenesis of flavoprotein and cytochrome components in hepatic mitochondria from riboflavin-deficient rats. *Biochem. Biophys. Res. Commun.* 81:133–38.

1a. Blaut, M., Whittaker, K., Valdovinos, A., Ackrell, B. A. C., Gunsalus, R., et al 1989. Fumarate reductase mutants of *Escherichia coli* that lack covalently bound flavin. *J. Biol. Chem.* 264: 13599–13604

2. Brandsch, R., Bichler, V. 1986. Studies *in vitro* on the flavinylation of 6-hydroxy-D-nicotine oxidase. *Eur. J. Biochem.* 160:285–89

3. Brandsch, R., Bichler, V. 1987. Covalent flavinylation of 6-hydroxy-D-nicotine oxidase involves an energy-requiring process. *FEBS Lett.* 224:121–24

4. Brandsch, R., Bichler, V. 1989. Covalent cofactor binding to flavoenzymes requires specific effectors. *Eur. J. Biochem.* 182:125–28

5. Brandsch, R., Bichler, V. 1991. Autoflavinylation of apo6-hydroxy-D-nicotine oxidase. *J. Biol. Chem.* 266: 19056–62

6. Brandsch, R., Bichler, V., Krauss, B. 1989. Binding of FAD to 6-hydroxy-D-nicotine oxidase apoenzyme prevents degradation of the holoenzyme. *Biochem. J.* 258:187–92

7. Brandsch, R., Decker, K. 1984. Isolation and partial characterization of plasmid DNA from *Arthrobacter oxidans. Arch. Microbiol.* 138:15–17

8. Brandsch, R., Hinkkanen, A., Mauch, L., Nagursky, H., Decker, K. 1987. 6-Hydroxy-D-nicotine oxidase of *Arthrobacter oxidans*; gene structure of the flavoenzyme and its relationship to 6-hydroxy-L-nicotine oxidase. *Eur. J. Biochem.* 167:315–20

8a. Chia, C. P., Addison, R., McCormick, D. B. 1978. Absorption, metabolism, and excretion of 8α-(amino acid)riboflavins in the rat. *J. Nutr.* 108:373–81

9. Cook, R. J., Misono, K. S., Wagner, C. 1980. Identification of the covalently bound flavin of dimethylglycine dehydrogenase and sarcosine dehydrogenase from rat liver mitochondria. *J. Biol. Chem.* 259:12475–80

10. Cusanovich, M. A., Meyer, T. E., Bartsch, R. G. 1991. Flavocytochrome c. In *Chemistry and Biochemistry of Flavoenzymes*, ed. F. Müller, 2:377–93. Boca Raton: CRC Press. 506 pp.

11. Decker, K. 1982. Biosynthesis of covalent flavoproteins. In *Flavins and Flavoproteins*, ed. V. Massey, C. H. Williams, pp. 465–72. New York/Amsterdam/Oxford: Elsevier North-Holland. 890 pp.

12. Decker, K. 1991. Covalent flavoproteins. See Ref. 10, pp. 343–75

13. Decker, K., Bleeg, H. 1965. Induction and purification of sterespecific nicotine oxidizing enzymes from *Arthrobacter oxidans. Biochim. Biophys. Acta* 105: 315–24

14. Decker, K., Brandsch, R. 1991. Flavoproteins with a covalent histidyl(N3)-8α-riboflavin linkage. *BioFactors* 3: 69–81.

15. Decker, K., Nagursky, H., Bichler,

V., Mauch, L., Brandsch, R. 1991. Covalent flavinylation of apo-6-hydroxy-D-nicotine oxidase. In *Flavins and Flavoproteins,* ed. B. Curti, S. Ronchi, G. Zanetti, pp. 101–4. Berlin: de Gruyter. 445 pp.

16. Edmondson, D. E., De Francesco, R. 1987. 8α-Imidazolylflavins: Application of their redox and spectral properties to flavoenzyme systems. In *Flavins and Flavoproteins,* ed. D. E. Edmondson, D. B. McCormick, pp. 653–62. Berlin/New York: de Gruyter. 775 pp.

17. Edmondson, D. E., De Francesco, R. 1991. Structure, synthesis, and physical properties of covalently bound flavins and 6- and 8-hydroxyflavins. In *Chemistry and Biochemistry of Flavoenzymes,* ed. F. Müller, 1:73–103. Boca Raton: CRC Press. 436 pp.

18. Edmondson, D. E., Kenney, W. C. 1976. Identification and properties of 8a-{N(1)-histidyl}-riboflavin: The flavin component of thiamine dehydrogenase and β-cyclopiazonate oxidocyclase. Biochem. Biophys. Res. Commun. 68: 242–48

19. Edmondson, D. E., Kenney, W. C., Singer, T. P. 1976. Structural elucidation and properties of 8α-(N^1-histidyl)riboflavin: The flavin component of thiamine dehydrogenase and β-cyclopiazonate oxidocyclase. *Biochemistry* 15:2937–45

20. Edmondson, D. E., Singer, T. P. 1973. Oxidation-reduction properties of the 8α-substituted flavins. *J. Biol. Chem.* 248:8144–49

21. Frost, J. W., Rastetter, W. H. 1980. Biomimetic 8α functionalization of riboflavin. *J. Am. Chem. Soc.* 102:7157–59

22. Fukayama, M., Miyake, Y. 1979. The purification and properties of cholesterol oxidase from *Schizophyllum commune.* In *Flavins and Flavoproteins,* ed. K. Yagi, T. Yamano, pp. 289–95. Tokyo: Japan Sci. Soc. Press. 740 pp.

23. Gomez-Moreno, C., Choy, M., Edmondson, D. E. 1979. Purification and properties of the bacterial flavoprotein: thiamine dehydrogenase. *J. Biol. Chem.* 254:7630–35

24. Hamm, H.-H., Decker, K. 1978. Regulation of flavoprotein synthesis studied *in vivo* in a riboflavin-requiring mutant of *Arthrobacter oxidans.* Arch. Microbiol. 119:65–70

25. Hamm, H.-H., Decker, K. 1980. Cell-free synthesis of a flavoprotein containing the 8α-(N^3-histidyl)-riboflavin linkage. *Eur. J. Biochem.* 194:391–95

26. Hederstedt, L. 1983. Succinate dehydrogenase mutants of *Bacillus subtilis* lacking covalently bound flavin in the flavoprotein subunit. *Eur. J. Biochem.* 132:589–93

27. Hederstedt, L. 1987. Covalent binding of FAD to *Bacillus subtilis* succinate dehydrogenase. See Ref. 16, pp. 729–35

28. Hederstedt, L., Rutberg, L. 1981. Succinate dehydrogenase—a comparative review. *Microbiol. Rev.* 45:542–55

29. Hinkkanen, A., Decker, K. 1982. The intracellular FAD pools of *Arthrobacter oxidans* and their correlation to 6-hydroxy-D-nicotine oxidase synthesis. See Ref. 11, pp. 478–82

30. Hinkkanen, A., Decker, K. 1983. Luminometric determination of FAD in subpicomole quantities. *Analyt. Biochem.* 132:202–8

31. Kenney, W. C., Edmondson, D. E., Seng, R. L. 1976. Identification of the covalently bound flavin of thiamin dehydrogenase. *J. Biol. Chem.* 251: 5386–90

32. Kenney, W. C., Edmondson, D. E., Singer, T. P., Nakagawa, H., Asano, A., et al. 1978. Identification of the covalently bound flavin of L-gulono-gamma-lactone oxidase. *Biochem. Biophys. Res. Commun.* 71: 1194–1200

33. Kenney, W. C., Edmondson, D. E., Singer, T. P., Nishikimi, M., Noguchi, E., Yagi, K. 1979. Identification of the covalently bound flavin of L-galactonolactone oxidase from yeast. *FEBS Lett.* 97:40–42

34. Kenney, W. C., Kröger, A. 1977. The covalently bound flavin in *Vibrio succinogenes* succinate dehydrogenase. *FEBS Lett.* 73:239–43

35. Kenney, W. C., McIntire, W., Yamanaka, T. 1977. Structure of the covalently bound flavin of *Chlorobium* cytochrome c$_{553}$. *Biochim. Biophys. Acta* 483:467–74

36. Kenney, W. C., Singer, T. P. 1977. Evidence for a thioether linkage between the flavin and polypeptide chain of *Chromatium* cytochrome c$_{552}$. *J. Biol. Chem.* 252:4767–72

37. Koshizaka, T., Nishikimi, M., Ozawa, T., Yagi, K. 1988. Isolation and sequence analysis of a complementary DNA encoding rat liver L-gulono-γ-lactone oxidase, a key enzyme for L-ascorbic acid biosynthesis. *J. Biol. Chem.* 263:1619–21

38. Kvalnes-Krick, K., Jorns, M. S. 1986. Bacterial sarcosine oxidase: Comparison of two multisubunit enzymes con-

taining both covalent and noncovalent flavin. *Biochemistry* 25:6061–69
39. Lang. H., Polster, M., Brandsch, R. 1991. Rat liver dimethylglycine dehydrogenase. Flavinylation of the enzyme in hepatocytes in primary culture and characterization of a cDNA clone. *Eur. J. Biochem.* 198:793–99
40. Lauterbach, F., Körtner, C., Albracht, S. P. J., Unden, G., Kröger, A. 1990. The fumarate reductase operon of *Wollinella succinogenes. Arch Microbiol.* 154:386–93
41. Mauch, L., Bichler, V., Brandsch, R. 1990. Lysine can replace arginine 67 in the mediation of covalent attachment of FAD to histidine 71 of 6-hydroxy-D-nicotine oxidase. *J. Biol. Chem.* 265:12761–62
42. Mauch, L., Krauss, B., Brandsch, R. 1989. Growth stage-dependent expression of 6-hydroxy-D-nicotine oxidase of the nicotine regulon of *Arthrobacter oxidans. Arch. Microbiol.* 152:95–99
43. Mauch, L., Krauss, B., Brandsch, R. 1989. Site-directed mutagenesis of the FAD-binding histidine in 6-hydroxy-D-nicotine oxidase. *FEBS Lett.* 257:86–88
44. McIntire, W., Edmondson, D. E., Hopper, D. J., Singer, T. P. 1981. 8α-(O-tyrosyl)flavin adenine dinucleotide, the prosthetic group of bacterial *p*-cresol methylhydroxylase. *Biochemistry* 20:3068–75
45. Möhler, H., Brühmüller, M., Decker, K. 1972. Covalently bound flavin in D-6-hydroxynicotine oxidase. Identification of the 8α-(N₃-histidyl)-riboflavin-linkage between FAD and the apoenzyme. *Eur. J. Biochem.* 29:152–55
46. Neal, R. S. 1970. Bacterial metabolism of thiamine. III. Metabolism of thiamine to 3-(2'-methyl-4'-amino-5'-pyrimidylmethyl)-4-methyl-thiazole-5-acetic acid (thiamine acetic acid) by a flavoprotein isolated from a soil microorganism. *J. Biol. Chem.* 245:2599–2604
47. Nishikimi, M., Yamauchi, N., Kiuchi, K., Yagi, K. 1981. Homology of L-gulonolactone oxidase of species belonging to *Mammalia, Aves, Amphibia. Experientia* 37:479–80
48. Oestreicher, G., Grossman, S., Goldenberg, J., Kearney, E. B., Edmondson, D. E., et al. 1980. Succinate dehydrogenase from baker's yeast: Comparative biochemistry and biosyn-

thetic variants containing covalently bound flavin analogues. *Comp. Biochem. Physiol.* B 67:395–402
49. Ohishi, N., Yagi, K. 1979. Covalently bound flavin as prosthetic group of choline oxidase. *Biochem. Biophys. Res. Commun.* 86:1084–88
50. Ohkawa, H., Ohishi, N., Yagi, K. 1983. New metabolites of riboflavin appear in human urine. *J. Biol. Chem.* 258:5623–28
51. Powell, J. F., Hsu, Y.-P. P., Weyler, W., Chen, S., Salach, J., et al. 1989. The primary structure of bovine monoamine oxidase type A. *Biochem. J.* 259:407–13
52. Saier, M., Schmidt, M., Lin, P. 1980. Phosphoryl exchange reaction catalyzed by enzyme I of the bacterial phosphoenolpyruvate:sugar phosphotransferase system. *J. Biol. Chem.* 255:8579–84
53. Sato, M., Ohishi, N., Nishikimi, M., Yagi, K. 1977. Proteins with covalently bound flavin in rat liver mitochondria. *Biochem. Biophys. Res. Commun.* 78:868–73
54. Singer, T. P., Edmondson, D. E. 1974. 8α-Substituted flavins of biological importance. *FEBS Lett.* 42:1–14
55. Singer, T. P., Kearney, E. B., Massey, V. 1955. Observations on the flavin moiety of succinic dehydrogenase. *Arch. Biochem. Biophys.* 60:255–57
56. Steenkamp, D. J. 1979. Structure of the covalently bound coenzyme of trimethylamine dehydrogenase. *Biochem. Biophys. Res. Commun.* 88:244–50
57. Steenkamp, D. J., McIntire, W., Kenney, W. C. 1978. Structure of the covalently bound coenzyme of trimethylamine dehydrogenase. Evidence for a 6-substituted flavin. *J. Biol. Chem.* 253:2818–24
58. Takahashi, T., Yamashita, H., Kato, E., Mitsumoto, M., Murakawa, S. 1976. Purification and some properties of D-glucono-γ-lactone dehydrogenase. D-Erythorbic acid producing enzyme of *Penicillium cyaneo-fulvum. Agric. Biol. Chem.* 40:121–23
59. Walker, W. H., Kearney, E. B., Seng, R. L., Singer, T. P. 1971. The covalently bound flavin of hepatic monoamine oxidase. *Eur. J. Biochem.* 24:328–31
60. Walsh, C. 1980. Flavin coenzymes: At the crossroads of biological redox chemistry. *Acc. Chem. Res.* 13:148–55

Annu. Rev. Nutr. 1993. 13:43–63

ALUMINUM METABOLISM

J. L. Greger

Department of Nutritional Sciences, University of Wisconsin,
Madison, Wisconsin 53706

KEY WORDS: food additives, citrate, kidney function, age, renal osteodystrophy

CONTENTS

ORAL EXPOSURE TO ALUMINUM 43
   Diet and Water as Sources of Aluminum 43
   Pharmaceutical Products as Sources of Aluminum 46
METABOLISM OF ALUMINUM 46
   Absorption of Aluminum 46
   Aluminum Distribution and Excretion 52
IS ALUMINUM ESSENTIAL? 56
TOXIC EFFECTS OF ALUMINUM 57

ORAL EXPOSURE TO ALUMINUM

Diet and Water as Sources of Aluminum

The aluminum in the food supply comes from natural sources, water used in food preparation, food additives, and contamination by aluminum utensils and containers. Considering the average amounts of aluminum added by these sources and typical food patterns, Greger (55) estimated that most Americans consume 2–25 mg aluminum daily from food and water. Pennington & Jones (116) reported that the daily menu for 25- to 30-year-old males in the Total Diet Study by the Food & Drug Administration (FDA) contained 13.77 mg aluminum. Ellen et al (35), using duplicate portion techniques, reported that Dutch adults consume 0.60 to 33.3 mg aluminum per day.

Some aluminum is present naturally in most foods (Table 1) (52, 60, 116, 128, 136). Soil adhering to vegetables may be the source of some aluminum in certain fruits and vegetables. The aluminum content of soil is variable, but on average is estimated to be 7.1% (76). Even so, few foods, except "aluminum accumulators" such as herbs and tea leaves, naturally contain more than 5 µg

43

Table 1 Estimated aluminum concentrations of selected foods

Foods	Aluminum concentration (μg/g)	Foods	Aluminum concentration (μg/g)
Animal products		Vegetables, fruits, and legumes	
Most meats cooked	0.2–1.2[a]	Common fruits (apples, bananas, oranges, peaches)	0.05–0.4[b,e]
Cheese, cheddar	0.2[b]	Common vegetables (cabbage, cauliflower, corn,	0.01–0.2[a,b]
Cheese, processed	297[c]	cucumbers, tomatoes)	
Milk, whole	0.06[b]	Asparagus	4.4[d]
		Beans, green cooked	3.4[a]
Grains		Lettuce	0.6[d]
Biscuits, baking powder, refrigerated	16.3[b]	Peanut butter	5.8[b]
Bran, wheat	12.8[d]	Peas, green, cooked	3.4[a]
Bread, white	3.0[e]	Potatoes, unpeeled, baked	2.4[a]
Bread, whole wheat	5.4[e]	Spinach, cooked	25.2[d]
Corn chips	1.2[b]	Strawberries, fresh	2.2[b]
Cornbread, homemade	400[b]	Other	
Rice, cooked	1.7[a]	Baking powder	2300[e]
		Beer, canned	0.7[b]
Herbs and spices		Cocoa	45[d]
Basil	3082[e]	Cola, canned	0.1[b]
Celery seed	465[e]	Cream substitute, powdered	139[b]
Cinnamon	82[e]	Pickles with Al additives	39.2[c]
Oregano	600[e]	Salt with additives	164[c]
Pepper, black	143[e]	Tea, steeped	4.3[c]
Thyme	750[e]		

[a]Greger et al (60).
[b]Pennington & Jones (116).
[c]Greger (52).
[d]Schlettwein-Gsell & Mommsen-Straub (128).
[e]Sorenson et al (136).

Al/g food. The aluminum content of these "aluminum accumulators" can vary greatly with plant varieties and soil conditions, including pH (34, 71). For example, Eden (34) estimated that tea leaves contain 1000 μg Al/g, but some contain as much as 17,000 μg Al/g.

In general, the amount of aluminum naturally present in the diets of Americans is small (1–10 mg per day) (52). This reflects the limited use of most herbs and the insolubility of aluminum in tea leaves.

WATER   Generally, water is not a major source of aluminum. The amount of aluminum in surface and groundwater is variable; 0.012 to 2.25 mg Al per liter have been reported in North American rivers (76). When the pH of water is 5, the amount of soluble aluminum in water tends to increase.

Aluminum-containing flocculants are used to clarify municipal water supplies. Miller et al (108) estimated that there was a 40–50% chance that aluminum coagulants increased the aluminum concentration of finished water above that naturally present in water. However, the median level (0.017 mg per liter) of aluminum in the finished water samples studied was very low (range 0.014–2.67 mg per liter). Thus, individuals consuming two liters of water daily would ingest less than 0.04 mg aluminum in water.

FOOD ADDITIVES   Food additives are a major source of dietary aluminum in the United States, although aluminum-containing additives are present in only a limited number of foods (52, 115). In 1982 approximately four million pounds of aluminum were used in food additives in the United States (17).

The data compiled by the Committee on the GRAS List Survey-Phase III (18) indicated that individual usage of these aluminum-containing food additives varied greatly. About 5% of adults in the United States consumed more than 95 mg aluminum in food additives daily; 50% consumed 24 mg or less aluminum daily in food additives. The most commonly used aluminum-containing food additives are acidic sodium aluminum phosphate (leavening agent in baked goods); the basic form of sodium aluminum phosphate (emulsifying agent in processed cheese); aluminum sulphates (acidifying agents); bentonite (materials-handling aid); aluminum lakes of various food dyes and colors; and aluminum silicates (anti-caking agents) (52, 115).

Calculations based on industrial production figures may slightly overestimate aluminum intake from food additives (17, 18, 52). But estimates based on standardized menus such as those used in the Total Diet Study (116) tend to underestimate the usage of additives.

PACKAGING AND UTENSILS   Several physicians have suggested that aluminum cooking utensils were a major source of aluminum in food (89, 143). Investigators have found that many foods accumulated statistically significant amounts of aluminum when cooked or stored in aluminum pans, trays or foil as compared to similar batches of food processed in stainless steel containers. However, most foods accumulated less than 2 μg Al/g food during preparation and storage (60).

Low pH, long cooking periods, and the use of brand new pans or pressure cookers have all been found to result in greater aluminum accumulation by foods (60, 74, 113). Organic acids, including citric acid, fluoride, and copper in foods may also increase the solubilization of aluminum from pans and foil slightly (5, 35, 40, 125). However, it is doubtful that the use of aluminum utensils adds more than 2 mg aluminum to the diet of Americans daily.

INFANT FORMULAE   Recently a number of investigators have become concerned about the aluminum content of infant formulae (85, 105, 130). The aluminum content of human or cow's milk is negligible (0.05 μg/ml) (85). Dabeka & McKenzie (21) reported that ready-to-use milk-based and soy-based formulae contained 0.01–0.36 and 0.40–6.4 μg Al/g, respectively. Thus 1–3-month-old infants consuming certain soy-based formulae could take in as much as 2.1 mg Al daily, whereas infants fed human or cow's milk would consume only 3 μg Al daily. A major source of the aluminum would be contamination in added calcium salts.

Pharmaceutical Products as Sources of Aluminum

The typical quantities of aluminum consumed in foods and beverages amount to less than 1% of the quantities that can be consumed in pharmaceutical products (90, 91). Lione (91) estimated that 126–728 mg and 840–5000 mg were possible daily doses of aluminum in buffered analgesics and antacids, respectively.

Calcium supplements, especially those based on oyster shells, have been reported to contain 0.2–0.6% aluminum (9). These products would be a minor source of pharmaceutical aluminum (12 mg per day).

Of special concern are parenterally delivered pharmaceuticals, because the protective barrier of the gut is bypassed. Several substances administered intravenously, including albumin (1,822 μg Al/g), calcium salts (5,056 μg Al/g), and phosphate salts (5,977–16,598 μg Al/g) have been reported to contain significant quantities of aluminum (129).

METABOLISM OF ALUMINUM

Absorption of Aluminum

Aluminum absorption has been very difficult to quantify. One reason is that no suitable radioisotopes of aluminum are available. Most aluminum isotopes (^{23}Al, ^{24}Al, ^{25}Al, ^{28}Al, ^{29}Al, and ^{30}Al) have half-lives of less than 10 minutes

(10). The only aluminum isotope with a biologically usable half-life is ^{26}Al (7.2 × 10^5 years), but it is too scarce and expensive to use in sufficient quantities for radiochemical detection (24).

A second reason is that collection and analysis of fecal samples do not provide data sensitive enough to monitor mineral, including aluminum, absorption when absorption is less than 1% (2, 53). When human subjects were fed pharmacological doses of aluminum (~1–3 g per day), fecal losses of aluminum were generally found to be less than aluminum intake (12, 15, 51, 121). The sensitivity of these measurements could be questioned because subjects in these balance studies appeared to absorb 100–600 mg Al per day but excreted at most only an additional 0.5 mg Al per day in urine. At that rate of excretion, aluminum levels in tissues would rapidly exceed any ever observed in autopsy tissues (2). Moreover, when subjects were fed 5–125 mg Al per day, aluminum losses in feces approximated dietary intake (12, 51, 57, 131, 141).

In response to this methodological quandary, Ganrot (49) suggested that urinary aluminum excretion could be assumed to equal aluminum absoprtion. Accordingly, he estimated that subjects in an earlier study (77) ingesting 2.2 g aluminum hydroxide absorbed 0.01% of the supplemental aluminum. On that basis, subjects ingesting a diet containing 5 mg aluminum daily absorbed 0.78% of the dietary aluminum and absorbed 0.094% of 120 mg of supplemental aluminum added to the diet as aluminum lactate (57).

However, the assumption that all absorbed aluminum is excreted in urine appears to be faulty because animals and humans accumulate aluminum in tissues with continued exposure (6, 47, 58, 59, 61, 68, 112, 113, 132, 133, 146). Moreover, it might be expected that the relative percentage of absorbed aluminum that is retained (not excreted in urine) could vary with kidney function, age, disease states, and/or perhaps other dietary factors.

Thus, Greger & Powers (62) hypothesized that an alternate way to estimate relative aluminum absorption was to compare tissue accumulation of aluminum in relation to dose in animals fed aluminum and in animals matched for age and weight and injected with aluminum. Using this methodology, they estimated that weanling Sprague Dawley rats fed 1–3 g Al as aluminum hydroxide per kilogram diet absorbed 0.011–0.036% of dietary aluminum. Percent apparent absorption of aluminum was less when higher concentrations of aluminum were fed.

Estimates of absorption based on urinary excretion of aluminum in the same rats tended to be slightly lower and ranged from 0.006 to 0.013% (62). Moreover, the relative effects of dietary treatments appeared to differ when aluminum absorption was estimated by the two different methods. Rats fed 3 g Al/kg diet excreted a higher percentage of oral aluminum intake than rats fed 1 g Al/kg diet.

Finally, Day et al (24) measured absorption of ^{26}Al in one adult human subject. The individual was fed 100 ng ^{26}Al with less than 1 μg of natural aluminum ^{27}Al in a sodium citrate solution. The ratios of ^{26}Al/^{27}Al in blood were measured in blood after 6, 12, and 18 hr. The investigators estimated that 1% of the tiny dose of aluminum was absorbed by this fasted subject.

In general, all these whole animal techniques indicate that aluminum absorption is very low (1%) and that the percent absorbed is sensitive to aluminum intake. Aluminum absorption was 10- to 100-fold greater when human or other animals were fed small amounts of aluminum (i.e. 5 mg per day for humans) rather than pharmaceutical doses of aluminum (i.e. 1–3 g per day for humans and 1–3 g/kg diet for rats).

MECHANISMS   Although much has been published on intestinal absorption of aluminum, no clear, unified explanation has emerged. It is believed that intestinal absorption of aluminum includes both paracellular passage routes along enterocytes and through tight junctions by passive processes and transcelluar passage routes through the enterocyte, involving passive, facilitated, and active transport processes (147).

A number of investigators using in situ rat jejunal preparations (119), everted gut sacs (39), perfused duodenum (1, 16), and jejunal gut slices (118) have demonstrated that at least part of gut absorption of aluminum is due to active processes that are inhibited by dinitrophenol, sodium cyanide, vanadate, and/or the absence of glucose or sodium in the perfusate. Adler & Berlyne (1) using in vivo isolated duodenal segments estimated that about 23% of aluminum uptake was due to nonsaturable process and the rest was due to saturable (active) processes when aluminum was perfused as $AlCl_3$ at pH2.

At least part of the active absorption of aluminum may be due to processes shared with active absorption of calcium. Mayor et al (102, 103) found that parathyroid administration enhanced aluminum uptake by rats, but Ittel et al (75) noted that parathyroidectomy did not alter aluminum absorption in either normal or uremic animals. Adler & Berlyne (1) demonstrated that saturable absorption of aluminum was significantly less in vitamin D deficient rats than in normal rats.

Cochran et al (16) tried to assess the importance of calcium channels on aluminum absorption. They observed small but significant decreases in duodenal uptake of aluminum when verapamil, a calcium-channel blocking agent, was administered. Because the doses were high, the investigators only hypothesized that calcium channels might be an entry site for aluminum.

Interpretation of all of this work and comparisons among studies are difficult because the experimental conditions varied greatly. The relative importance of each absorptive process is dependent on the section of the intestine that is involved, concentrations of aluminum in gut and in blood, pH of the gut, speciation of aluminum, and other dietary factors (96, 114, 147).

Speciation of aluminum in water is complex and changes dramatically with pH (Figure 1) (95). For example, the concentration of free aluminum (Al^{+3}) in aluminum hydroxide solution is one thousand times greater at pH 4.2 than at pH 7.4 (2). Thus, it is not surprising that intestinal absorption of aluminum in in situ perfusion systems of the rat small intestine was found to be greater at pH4 than at pH7 (148). Similarly, it is logical to assume that aluminum absorption is apt to be greater in the proximal duodenum than in distal segments of the intestine because the lower pH of the proximal duodenum would result in more soluble aluminum. However, Beynon & Cassidy (7) could not demonstrate that patients with achlorhydria absorbed aluminum less efficiently than normal subjects.

DIETARY FACTORS AFFECTING ALUMINUM ABSORPTION   The latter study demonstrates that although pH of the gut mileau is important in predicting the speciation and solubility of aluminum, the efficiency of aluminum absorption is also dependent on a variety of other factors. Two important dietary factors affecting absorption of aluminum are citrate and inorganic anions.

CITRIC ACID   Several groups of clinicians observed increased aluminum absorption (as judged by serum and urine aluminum concentrations) among

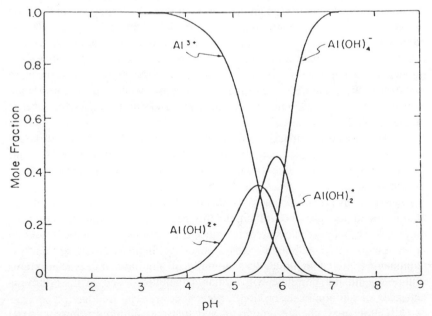

Figure 1   Distribution of soluble, mononuclear aluminum ion species in aqueous solution. At any pH the individual mole fraction sum to unity. Reprinted with permission from *Clinical Chemistry* (1986) 32(10):1798. Copyright American Association for Clinical Chemistry, Inc.

patients treated with both citrate-containing pharmaceuticals, such as Shohl's solution, and aluminum-containing pharmaceuticals (4, 80, 81, 111). Similarly, normal subjects were found to have higher serum aluminum concentrations when aluminum hydroxide was ingested with lemon juice (a source of citric acid) rather than water (134).

This led to real concern by physicians about the effect of citrate on aluminum toxicity (2, 69). But few investigators have reported the effect of chronic oral exposure to citrate on aluminum retention.

The practical significance of citrate on aluminum absorption varies in these studies. Slanina et al (132, 133) demonstrated elevated brain, blood and bone aluminum concentrations in rats treated daily by gavage with an aluminum citrate solution rather than aluminum hydroxide. Fulton and associates (46, 47) showed that the addition of citrate to drinking water containing aluminum hydroxide elevated bone and plasma aluminum concentrations in rabbits but increased only intestinal aluminum concentrations in rats.

Ecelbarger & Greger (31) found that ingestion of citrate (5–31 mmol added citrate per kilogram diet) increased aluminum retention in bones of rats fed 1 g Al/kg diet for ~28 days. Greger & Powers (62) noted that rats fed citrate (2.5 mol added citrate per kilogram diet) with aluminum excreted more aluminum in urine and had elevated tibia aluminum concentrations.

In general, animals chronically fed aluminum and citrate in diets (31, 62) retained more aluminum than animals given citrate with aluminum in drinking water (46, 47) but less aluminum than animals dosed with only citrate and aluminum by gavage (132, 133). The presence of other substances in the gut, as occurs when aluminum and citrate are added to feed and water, may have moderated the effect of citrate on aluminum absorption. Many of these substances (i.e. fluoride, phosphates, calcium) would not be important constituents in the gut lumen when aluminum and citrate were administered by gavage to fasted animals.

Citrate probably enhances aluminum absorption by several different mechanisms. (a) Citrate increases the solubility of aluminum in the gut. Martin (95) has shown that aluminum occurs as a neutral soluble complex in the presence of citrate at pH 2.5–5.5, a pH range in which aluminum is normally insoluble. Froment et al (44) demonstrated that solubility of aluminum in the presence of citrate did not totally explain the effect of citrate when they administered by gavage a variety of aluminum citrate mixtures to rats. Although citrate generally increased the amount of aluminum excreted in urine, the solubility of aluminum in these mixtures (38–91%) did not correlate with urinary aluminum (used in this study as an index of aluminum absorption).

(b) Citrate may chelate aluminum and transport aluminum into mucosal cells. Van der Voet et al (150) noted that dinitrophenol, an inhibitor of active transport, decreased citrate enhanced aluminum absorption. If citrate-aluminum complexes are absorbed, it is logical to expect that aluminum absorption might be increased as the amount of citrate was increased. But Ecelbarger & Greger (31) observed that although the presence of citrate (5 to 31 mmol/kg diet) increased aluminum retention by rats, the response was not linear as the molar ratio of aluminum to citrate decreased from 1:3.7 to 1:1.2.

(c) Citrate has been demonstrated to open epithelial tight junctions in cultured cells, presumably by chelating calcium (98). Froment et al (45) demonstrated that aluminum citrate but not aluminum chloride increased the presence of ruthenium red, a low molecular weight surface marker, in the intercellular spaces of isolated intestinal loop preparations and induced prolonged significant reductions in transmural resistance.

Although the interaction of citrate and aluminum is practically important, the uniqueness of the interaction has been overstated. Domingo et al (27) observed that the addition of a variety of organic acids besides citric acid (including lactic acid, oxalic acid, and tartaric acid) to the drinking water of rats resulted in greater retention of aluminum in tissues. Moreover, citric acid has been found to increase the absorption of other minerals including calcium (66), lead (50), and zinc (73).

INORGANIC ANIONS   A number of investigators have demonstrated that large oral doses of aluminum depress phosphorus absorption in humans (15, 26, 56, 93, 137), laboratory animals (112, 113), and livestock (122, 146). In fact, aluminum salts are used to treat hyperphosphatemia in renal patients because aluminum greatly reduces phosphorus absorption by forming insoluble complexes with phosphates in the gut (127).

Similarly, ingestion of large quantities of aluminum reduces fluoride absorption and retention in humans (56, 138) and livestock (64, 124). Accordingly, increasing phosphorus or fluoride intake should reduce aluminum absorption, *provided* that the molar quantities of phosphate or fluoride in the gut are significant in comparison to the molar quantities of aluminum. Typically that would not occur in regard to fluoride.

Potentially, silicates could also affect aluminum absorption (8). Exley et al (37) demonstrated that the addition of silicon to water reduced symptoms of aluminum toxicity in salmon fry. Birchall (8) hypothesized that silicon reduced the systemic absorption of aluminum by the salmon because above pH 6.6 silicates replace phosphates as primary complexors of aluminum in solution.

A few investigators have compared the biological effects of various aluminum salts. Although these investigators did not actually measure aluminum absorption, the studies provide insights on the interactions of anions with aluminum in the gut.

Storer & Nelson (140) observed that large oral doses of aluminum phosphate were less toxic to chicks than equal doses of aluminum as chloride, sulfate, nitrate, and acetate salts. Similarly, Kaehny et al (77) found that subjects had a greater rise in serum and urine aluminum when they were given 2.2 g aluminum daily as aluminum hydroxide, aluminum carbonate, or dihydroxy-aluminum aminoacetate rather than as aluminum phosphate. Yokel & McNamara (156) found that the increases in serum aluminum concentrations in rabbits after being fed similar doses of aluminum as aluminum borate, hydroxide, chloride, glycinate, sucralfate, and acetate were statistically similar but were significantly smaller than those increases in serum aluminum concentrations observed after doses of aluminum citrate or nitrate.

Greger et al (58) observed when moderate amounts of aluminum (200–300 mg Al/kg diet) were incorporated into diets of rats that aluminum accumulation in tissues was fairly similar whether the rats were fed aluminum hydroxide, aluminum phosphate, aluminum palmitate, or aluminum lactate. This suggests that the form of aluminum fed was less important when moderate quantities of aluminum were incorporated into diets rather than given in isolation because the speciation of aluminum in the gut was dependent on the total gut milieu (25).

Aluminum Distribution and Excretion

Ganrot (49) estimated that the total aluminum load for healthy individuals was 30 to 50 mg with about 50% present in skeleton and 25% in lungs. Skalsky & Carchman (131) in contrast suggested that the total body aluminum load is 0.3 g. Limited data suggest that, except for the lungs, bone generally has the highest concentrations of aluminum (5–10 mg Al/kg wet weight) (49, 145).

Generally, the concentrations of aluminum in soft tissues are much lower than in bone (i.e. 1 mg Al/kg wet weight) (49). Concentrations of aluminum in serum are even lower than in other tissues. Estimates of 1–5 μg Al/per liter are typical for samples drawn from fasted normal subjects when modern methods are used and contamination from anticoagulants and glassware is prevented (49, 86, 126).

ACCUMULATION OF ALUMINUM IN TISSUES WITH EXPOSURE AND AGING
Aluminum has been observed to accumulate in most tissues when large doses of aluminum were injected intentionally or were given through contaminated dialysis fluids (6, 20, 42, 154–157). Generally, aluminum accumulation was greater in spleen, liver, bone, and kidneys than in brain, other nervous tissues, muscle, heart, or lung. The sequence in which elevated aluminum concentrations appeared in tissues, and the actual accumulation of aluminum, varied with the aluminum salts administered (156). The species studied and the injection routine (i.e. intravenous, intraperitoneal, or subcutaneous and

repeated doses or single dose) appeared to affect tissue aluminum deposition. Greger & Powers (62) found that aluminum concentrations in tibias ($r = 0.941$), liver ($r = 0.727$), kidneys ($r = 0.977$), and sera ($r = 0.863$) were strongly correlated (p 0.0001) to injected (i.p.) aluminum loads when loads were varied from 0.01 to 94.5 μmol.

Oral ingestion of aluminum has most often been found to elevate bone, liver, and serum aluminum concentrations and to a lesser extent to elevate kidney aluminum concentrations (28, 48, 58, 59, 61, 62, 132, 133, 146). Brain aluminum concentrations have been measured less frequently and have often been found not to respond to dietary aluminum exposure. Greger & Powers (62) observed that tissue aluminum concentrations (tibia, $r = 0.742$; liver, $r = 0.731$; kidney, $r = 0.265$; sera, $r = 0.678$) were less tightly correlated with oral aluminum loads than with injected aluminum loads; rats were fed aluminum 0.01–3g Al/kg diet for 30 days.

In general, bone and liver aluminum concentrations are most often used as indices of aluminum exposure studies. Aluminum concentrations in these tissues are sensitive to oral and parenteral aluminum exposure and contamination is less of a problem than with serum.

Several groups of researchers believe that aluminum accumulates in the neurofibrillary tangles of individuals with Alzheimer's disease and amyotrophic lateral sclerosis with Parkinson's dementia in Guam (48, 117). Other investigators have been unable to demonstrate increased aluminum concentrations in brains of individuals with Alzheimer's disease but have demonstrated that brain aluminum concentrations increased with age (94, 104). Limited data indicate that aluminum accumulates in other tissues with age in humans (49), mice (100), *Drosophila* (101), and rats (32, 33).

Aluminum accumulation with age may reflect several factors. Even moderate reductions in kidney function in rats, as occurs with aging, have been correlated to increased aluminum accumulation in bone (32, 33). Although gut absorbtion of Ga-67 (an isotope sometimes used as a marker for aluminum) was low in rats of all ages, absorption was significantly greater in 18-month old rats than mature 5- or 8-month old rats (32).

The observed increases in aluminum concentrations with age in rodents have not been as large as predicted (32, 33, 100). This may reflect changes with age in tissue turnover or the exchangeability of aluminum in body pools. For example, a dose of desferrioxamine mobilized more than twice as much aluminum from tissues of 23-month old rats than from tissues of 8-month old rats, even though tissue aluminum concentrations of the 23-month old rats were generally only 30–50% greater than those of 8-month old rats (32).

PLASMA PROTEIN BINDING OF ALUMINUM   Estimates of the percentage of aluminum in serum that is protein bound and nonfilterable in ultrafiltration studies range from 0 to 98% (151). The percentage of plasma aluminum that is ultrafilterable has been found to be inversly related to plasma aluminum concentrations in normal human subjects and patients with chronic renal failure (120), in normal rabbits (156), and in rats (11, 92). Although much of this decrease in ultrafilterability was the result of increased protein binding of aluminum, the insolubility of aluminum at very high concentrations was also increased (92). Ultrafilterability of aluminum compounds, such as $AlCl_3$ and Al lactate, was also found to be greater at pH 5 and 9 than at pH 7 because of increased solubility (151).

The nonfilterable aluminum in plasma is bound to plasma proteins, predominantly transferrin and albumin, and to low molecular weight compounds, predominantly citrate (38, 97, 142). The relative importance of these factors as chelators of aluminum is debatable. The stability constants for transferrin binding to Al^{+3} (log K_1 = 12.9, log K_2 = 12.3) are many fold lower than for binding to Ga^{+3} (log K_1 = 20.3, log K_2 = 19.3) or Fe^{+3} (log K_1 = 22.7, log K_2 = 22.1) (97). But the binding of aluminum to albumin is even weaker than to transferrin. However, the large excess of albumin to transferrin in plasma and the ability of human serum albumin to bind about three aluminum ions per molecule are important (38). Accordingly, Fatemi et al (38) estimated that 60% of the aluminum in human plasma (at pH 7.4, with a concentration of 5 μM aluminum) would be bound to transferrin, 34% to albumin, and the remainder to citrate.

A variety of factors would affect the relative importance of these chelaters. Fatemi et al (38) estimated that the percentage of aluminum bound to transferrin would be reduced to 50% if the concentration of plasma aluminum was increased to 7.6 μM aluminum. The percentage of aluminum bound to transferrin would also be reduced by small shifts in pH from pH 7.4. The presence of other ions particularly of iron, calcium and magnesium, could be important because aluminum would have to compete with these ions for binding sites on transferrin, albumin, and citrate (65, 97). Moreover, the route of aluminum administration may affect the binding of aluminum in plasma. Orally administered manganese is distributed in body tissues as if it was bound to albumin (23), but manganese in serum is primarily bound to transferrin during the first four hours after dosing (22).

TRANSFERRIN AFFECTS ALUMINUM ACCUMULATION   Although very little aluminum is generally found in the brain, transferrin provides a physiologic route of entry. Roskams & Connor (123) demonstrated that transferrin interacted with transferrin receptors similarly whether the transferrin was complexed with aluminum or iron. Morris et al (110) demonstrated that the distribution of aluminum in the brain cells of renal dialysis patients corresponded to the density of transferrin receptors in the brain. Finally, Fleming & Joshi (41) reported that rats fed aluminum accumulated almost threefold more aluminum in the ferritin of their brains than did control rats.

Anemia is a common symptom of aluminum intoxication (29). Competition between iron and aluminum in the gut has been hypothesized (54). However, van der Voet & de Wolff (149) observed that the presence of Fe III in in situ perfusion systems did not affect the luminal disappearance or intestinal absorption of aluminum. The work of Cannata and associates (13, 14) suggests that the mechanism by which iron intake may affect aluminum absorption is mediated by transferrin and relates to nutritional status of iron, not iron intake per se. Cannata et al (13) observed that rats overloaded with iron by injections with iron dextran had lower concentrations of aluminum in serum and brain than did control rats, whereas rats depleted of iron by phlebotomy had higher concentrations of aluminum in serum and brain than did control rats. Similarly, serum aluminum concentrations of hemodialysis patients with high ferritin levels increased less after a dose of aluminum than those of patients with low or normal serum ferritin levels (14).

URINARY EXCRETION OF ALUMINUM   As already noted, humans typically excrete little aluminum in urine, usually less than 100 μg per day (49). This primarily reflects the fact that little aluminum is absorbed. Thus when the protection of the gut was removed (as occurred when patients were infused with parenteral solutions contaminated with aluminum), subjects excreted 0.7 to 3.8 mg aluminum daily (83).

The accumulation of aluminum in tissues that occurs when humans and animals have high concentrations of aluminum in their sera reflects the inability of the kidneys to rapidly excrete aluminum. Lote et al (92) observed that the fractional excretion of aluminum in urine by rats infused with insulin and 0, 25, or 800 μg aluminum was 12, 24, and 53%, respectively, in 4 hr. Several investigators have attributed this inefficiency in urinary excretion of aluminum to tubular reabsorbtion of filtered aluminum (11, 63). It is more likely that the inefficiency reflects the high plasma binding of aluminum, which prevents rapid filtration of plasma aluminum (92, 151). In any case, the elevation of plasma aluminum concentrations for several hours, theoretically at least, allows more transfer of aluminum to tissues.

EXCRETION IN BILE VS URINE   The very small amounts of aluminum in urine have caused a number of researchers to search for an alternate route of aluminum excretion. Several groups in the 1920s and 1930s observed that dogs injected with aluminum excreted aluminum in the bile as well as in urine (36, 107, 144).

More recently, Gupta et al (63) found that rats excreted 60% of an intravenous dose of aluminum chloride in urine and 40% in feces. Yokel &

McNamara (157) found that rabbits infused for six hr with aluminum lactate had significant elevation in biliary excretion 4 hr, but not 12 hr, after completion of the infusion. Smeyers-Verbeke et al (135) noted that rats loaded with aluminum intraperitoneally continued to have elevated concentrations of aluminum in bile and urine for 200 days after the loading period.

However, the two most definitive studies indicate that bile is a fairly minor route of aluminum excretion, at least when aluminum is administered parenterally (84, 87). Kovalchik et al (87) found that dogs with their ureters ligated excreted more aluminum in their bile after dialysis with fluids that contained about 2.3 mg aluminum than did intact dogs. But biliary excretion of aluminum accounted for less than 0.1% of the total load of aluminum in both groups of dogs. Moreover, intact dogs excreted 27% of the aluminum load in urine. Similarly, Klein et al (84) found that rats infused with 5 mg aluminum/kg per day for 7 or 14 days excreted only 3 to 7% as much aluminum in bile as in urine.

In contrast, Williams et al (152) observed that patients ingesting aluminum containing antacids had greater concentrations of aluminum in their bile than in their urine 48 hr after the dose. It may be that excretion patterns of orally and parenterally administered aluminum differ as do excretion patterns of orally and parenterally administered manganese (23). The differences in volumes of urine and bile excretion, which were not reported (152), could also affect interpretation of data.

The aluminum salt administered may also affect bilary excretion of aluminum. Allain et al (3) found sixfold higher levels of aluminum in bile when rats were injected with aluminoxamine (the aluminum chelate of deferoxamine) than when they were injected with equal doses of aluminum as $Al(NO_3)_3$.

IS ALUMINUM ESSENTIAL?

Aluminum is the third most abundant element in the earth's crust. Horecker et al (72) in 1939 suggested that aluminum promoted the reaction between cytochrome C and succinic dehydrogenase in vitro. More recently, the activation of the purified guanine nucleotide binding the regulatory component of adenyl cyclase by fluoride was shown to require the presence of Al^{+3} (78, 139). The significance of these observations in vivo is not known. In fact, no conclusive evidence suggests that aluminum is essential for growth, reproduction, or survival of humans or animals (49, 145).

Kleber & Putt (82) reviewed articles in which the relationships between oral exposure to aluminum and the incidence of dental caries was considered. They concluded that aluminum was a cariostatic agent both by itself and in combination with fluoride.

TOXIC EFFECTS OF ALUMINUM

Aluminum is not a nutrient but it should be of interest to nutritionists for two main reasons. (*a*) Many of the toxic effects of aluminum are due to its interactions with nutrients, such as phosphorus, calcium, fluoride, magnesium, iron, and vitamin D (54). (*b*) It is well established that aluminum toxicity has been induced not only by infusion of aluminum-contaminated dialysate fluids and parenteral nutrition solutions but also by ingestion of aluminum-containing pharmaceutical products. A number of researchers also believe that high concentrations of aluminum in drinking water (30, 99) and even in food (43, 48, 117) resulted in toxic effects among sensitive individuals.

Thousands of papers and a number of reviews have been published on the toxic effects of aluminum (49, 53, 67, 88), especially as related to dialysis dementia and osteodystrophy and to Alzheimer's disease and amyotrophic lateral sclerosis with Parkinson's dementia in Guam (19, 70, 79, 106, 109, 153). Despite these massive efforts, the mechanism by which aluminum induces toxic effects and even the relationship of aluminum to a number of neurological and skeletal disorders remains debatable. This at least partially reflects our limited understanding of the metabolism of aluminum.

ACKNOWLEDGMENTS

Support was provided by College of Agricultural and Life Sciences Project 2623 and National Institutes of Health grant DK41116.

Literature Cited

1. Adler, A. J., Berlyne, G. M. 1985. Duodenal aluminum absorption in the rat: Effect of vitamin D. *Am. J. Physiol.* 249:G209–13
2. Alfrey, A. C. 1988. Physiology of aluminum in man. See Ref. 50a, pp. 101–24
3. Allain, P., Leblondel, G., Mauras, Y. 1988. Effect of aluminum and deferoxamine on biliary iron elimination in the rat. *Proc. Soc. Exp. Biol. Med.* 188:471–73
4. Bakir, A. A., Hryhorczuk, D. O., Ahmed, S., Hessl, S. M., Levy, P. S., et al. 1989. Hyperaluminemia in renal failure: the influence of age and citrate intake. *Clin. Nephrol.* 31:40–44.
5. Baxter, M., Burrell, J. A., Massey, R. C. 1988. The effects of fluoride on the leaching of aluminum saucepans during cooking. *Food Addit. Contam.* 5:651–56
6. Berlyne, G. M., Ari, J. B., Knopf,

E., Yagil, R., Weinberger, G., et al. 1972. Aluminum toxicity in rats. *Lancet* 1:564–68
7. Beynon, H., Cassidy, M. J. D. 1990. Gastrointestinal absorption of aluminum. *Nephron* 55:235–36
8. Birchall, J. D. 1992. The interrelationship between silicon and aluminum in the biological effects of aluminum. In *Aluminum Biology and Medicine, Ciba Found. Symp. 169*, pp. 50–61. Chichester: Wiley
9. Bourgoin, B. P. 1992. Alumino-silicate content in calcium supplements derived from various carbonate deposits. *Bull. Environ. Contam. Toxicol.* 48:803–8
10. Bureau of Radiological Health and Training Institute. 1970. *Radiological Health Handbook,* pp. 237–38. Rockville, Md: US Dept. Health, Educ. Welfare
11. Burnatowska-Hledin, M. A., Mayor, G. H., Lau, K. 1985. Renal handling

of aluminum in the rat: clearance and micropuncture studies. *Am. J. Physiol.* 249:F192–97

12. Cam, J. M., Luck, V. A., Eastwood, J. B., deWardener, H. E. 1976. The effect of aluminum hydroxide orally on calcium, phosphorus and aluminum metabolism in normal subjects. *Clin. Sci. Mol. Med.* 52:407–14

13. Cannata, J. B., Fernàndez-Soto, I., Fernàndez, M. J., Fernàndez-Martin, J., McGregor, S. J., et al. 1991. Role of iron metabolism in absorption and cellular uptake of aluminum. *Kidney Int.* 39:799–803.

14. Cannata, J. B., Suarez, C. S., Cuesta, V., Roza, R. R., Allende, M. T., et al. 1984. Gastrointestinal aluminum absorption: Is it modulated by the iron-absorptive mechanism? *Proc. Eur. Dialysis Transplant. Assoc.* 21: 354–59

15. Clarkson, E. M., Luck, V. A., Hynson, W. V., Bailey, R. R., Eastwood, J. B., et al. 1972. The effect of aluminum hydroxide on calcium, phosphorus and aluminum balances, the serum parathyroid hormone concentration and the aluminum content of bone in patients with chronic renal failure. *Clin. Sci.* 43:519–31

16. Cochran, M., Goddard, G., Ludwigson, N. 1990. Aluminum absorption by rat duodenum: further evidence of energy-dependent uptake. *Toxicol. Lett.* 51:287–94

17. Committee on Food Additives Survey Data. 1984. *Poundage Update of Food Chemicals 1982, PB 84-16214.* Washington, DC: Natl. Acad. Press

18. Committee on the GRAS List Survey-Phase III. 1979. *The 1977 Survey of Industry on the Use of Food Additives.* Washington, DC: Natl. Acad. Sci.

19. Committee on Nutrition. 1986. Aluminum toxicity in infants and children. *Pediatrics* 78:1150–54

20. Constantini, S., Giordana, R., Ioppola, A., Mantovani, A., Ballanti, P., et al. 1989. Distribution of aluminum following intraperitoneal injection of aluminum lactate in the rat. *Pharmacol. Toxicol.* 64:47–50

21. Dabeka, R. W., McKenzie, A. D. 1990. Aluminum levels in Canadian infant formulae and estimation of aluminum intakes from formulae by infants 0–3 months old. *Food Addit. Contam.* 7:275–82

22. Davidson, L., Lönnerdal, B., Sandström, B., Kunz, C., Keen, C. L. 1989. Identification of transferrin as the major plasma carrier protein for manganese introduced orally or intravenously or after in vitro addition to the rat. *J. Nutr.* 119:1461–64

23. Davis, C. D., Zech, L., Greger, J. 1993. Manganese metabolism in rats: An improved methodology for assessing gut endogenous losses. *Proc. Soc. Exp. Biol. Med.* 202:103–8

24. Day, J. P., Barker, J., Evans, L. J. A., Perks, J., Seabright, P. J., et al. 1991. Aluminum absorption studied by ^{26}Al tracer. *Lancet* 337:1345

25. Dayde, S., Filella, M., Berthon, G. 1990. Aluminum speciation studies in biological fluids, part 3. Quantitative investigation of aluminum-phosphate complexes and assignment of their potential significance in vivo. *J. Inorg. Biochem.* 38:241–59

26. Dent, C. E., Winter, C. 1974. Osteomalacia due to phosphate depletion from excessive aluminum hydroxide ingestion. *Br. Med. J.* 1:551–52

27. Domingo, J. L., Gomez, M., Llobet, J. M., Corbella, J. 1991. Influence of some dietary constituents on aluminum absorption and retention in rats. *Kidney Int.* 39:598–601

28. Donald, J. M., Golob, M. S., Gershwin, M. E., Koen, C. H. 1989. Neurobehavioral effects in offspring of mice given excess aluminum in diet during gestation and lactation. *Neurotoxicol./Teratol.* 11:345–51

29. Drüeke, T. B., Lacour, B., Touam, M., Jucquel, J. P., Plaehot, J. J., et al. 1986. Effect of aluminum on hematopoiesis. *Kidney Int.* 29:S45–S48

30. Eastwood, J. B., Levin, G. E., Pazianas, M., Taylor, A. P., Denton, J., Freemont, A. J. 1990. Aluminum deposition in bone after contamination of drinking water supply. *Lancet* 336: 462–64

31. Ecelbarger, C. A., Greger, J. L. 1991. Dietary citrate and kidney function affect aluminum, zinc and iron utilization in rats. *J. Nutr.* 121:1755–62

32. Ecelbarger, C. A., Greger, J. L. 1991. Aluminum and Ga-67 metabolism in aging animals. *FASEB J.* 5:7408 (Abstr)

33. Ecelbarger, C. A., MacNeil, G., Greger, J. L. 1992. Effect of reduced kidney function and tissue turnover on aluminum accumulation and distribution in aging rats. *FASEB J.* 6:4136 (Abstr.)

34. Eden, T. 1976. *Tea*, pp. 8–15. London: Longman

35. Ellen, G., Egmond, E., Van Loon, J. W., Sahertian, E. T., Tolsma, K. 1990. Dietary intakes of some essential and nonessential trace elements, nitrate, nitrite and N-nitrosamines, by Dutch

adults: estimated via a 24-hour duplicate portion study. *Food Addit. Contam.* 7:207–21

36. Everleeth, D. F., Meyers, V. C. 1936. Studies on aluminum. II. Storage of intravenously injected aluminum in the dog. *J. Biol. Chem.* 113:467–71

37. Exley, C., Chappell, J. S., Birchall, J. D. 1991. A mechanism for acute aluminum toxicity in fish. *J. Theor. Biol.* 151:417–28

38. Fatemi, S. J. A., Kadir, F. H. A., Moore, G. R. 1991. Aluminum transport in blood serum. *Biochem. J.* 280: 527–32

39. Feinroth, M., Feinroth, M. V., Berlyne, G. M. 1982. Aluminum absorption in the rat everted gut sac. *Mineral Electrolyte Metab.* 8:29–35

40. Flaten, T. P., Odegard, M. 1989. Dietary aluminum and Alzheimer's disease—a reply. *Food Chem. Toxicol.* 27:496–98

41. Fleming, J., Joshi, G. 1987. Ferritin: Isolation of aluminum-ferritin complex from brain. *Proc. Natl. Acad. Sci. USA* 84:7866–70

42. Flendrig, J. A., Krvis, H., Dos, H. A. 1976. Aluminum and dialysis dementia. *Lancet* 1:1235

43. Freundlich, M., Abitbol, C., Zillervelo, G., Strauss, J., Faugere, M. C., et al. 1985. Infant formula as a cause of aluminum toxicity in neonatal uraemia. *Lancet* 2:527–29

44. Froment, D. H., Buddington, B., Miller, N. L., Alfrey, A. C. 1989. Effect of solubility on the gastrointestinal absorption of aluminum from various aluminum compounds in the rat. *J. Lab. Clin. Med.* 114:237–42

45. Froment, D. P., Molitoris, B. A., Buddington, B., Miller, N., Alfrey, A. C. 1989. Site and mechanism of enhanced gastrointestinal absorption of aluminum by citrate. *Kidney Int.* 36: 978–84

46. Fulton, B., Jaw, S., Jeffery, E. H. 1989. Bioavailability of aluminum from drinking water. *Fundam. Appl. Toxicol.* 12:144–50

47. Fulton, B., Jeffery, E. H. 1990. Absorption and retention of aluminum from drinking water. I. Effect of citrate and ascorbic acids on aluminum tissue levels in rabbits. *Fundam. Appl. Toxicol.* 14:788–96

48. Gajdusek, D. C. 1985. Hypothesis: Interference with anoxal transport of neurofilament as a common pathogenetic mechanism in certain diseases of the central nervous system. *N. Engl. J. Med.* 312:714–18

49. Ganrot, P. O. 1986. Metabolism and possible health effects of aluminum. *Environ. Health Perspect.* 65:363–441

50. Garber, B. T., Wei, E. 1974. Influence of dietary factors on the gastrointestinal absorption of lead. *Toxicol. Appl. Pharmacol.* 27:685–91

50a. Gitelman, H. J., ed. 1988. *Aluminum and Health: A Critical Review.* New York: Marcel Dekker

51. Gorsky, J. E., Dietz, A. A., Spencer, H., Osis, D. 1979. Metabolic balance of aluminum studied in six men. *Clin. Chem.* 25:1739–43

52. Greger, J. L. 1985. Aluminum content of the American diet. *Food Technol.* 9(5):73, 74, 76, 78–80

53. Greger, J. L. 1987. Aluminum and tin. *World Rev. Nutr. Diet.* 54:255–85

54. Greger, J. L. 1988. Aluminum in the diet and mineral metabolism. In *Metal Ions in Biological Systems,* ed. H. Sigel, 24:199–215. New York: Marcel Dekker

55. Greger, J. L. 1992. Dietary and other sources of aluminum intake. See Ref. 8, pp. 26–35

56. Greger, J. L., Baier, M. J. 1983. Effect of dietary aluminum on mineral metabolism of adult males. *Am. J. Clin. Nutr.* 38:411–19

57. Greger, J. L., Baier, M. J. 1983. Excretion and retention of low or moderate levels of aluminum by human subjects. *Food Chem. Toxicol.* 21:473–77

58. Greger, J. L., Bula, E. N., Gum, E. T. 1985. Mineral metabolism of rats fed moderate levels of various aluminum compounds for short periods of time. *J. Nutr.* 115:1708–16

59. Greger, J. L., Donnaubauer, S. E. 1986. Retention of aluminum in the tissues of rats after the discontinuation of oral exposure to aluminum. *Food Chem. Toxicol.* 24:1331–34

60. Greger, J. L., Goetz, W., Sullivan, D. 1985. Aluminum levels in foods cooked and stored in aluminum pans, trays and foil. *J. Food Prot.* 48:772–77

61. Greger, J. L., Gum, E. T., Bula, E. N. 1986. Mineral metabolism of rats fed various levels of aluminum hydroxide. *Biol. Trace Element Res.* 9:67–77

62. Greger, J. L., Powers, C. F. 1992. Assessment of exposure to parenteral and oral aluminum with and without citrate using a desferrioxamine test in rats. *Toxicology.* 76:119–32

63. Gupta, S. K., Waters, D. H., Gwilt, P. 1987. Absorption and disposition of aluminum in the rat. *J. Pharm. Sci.* 75:586–89

64. Hahn, P. H. B., Guenter, W. 1986. Effect of dietary fluoride and aluminum on laying hen performance and fluoride concentration in blood, soft tissue, bone and egg. *Poultry Sci.* 65: 1343–49

65. Harris, W. R., Sheldon, J. 1990. Equilibrium constants for the binding of aluminum to human serum transferrin. *Inorg. Chem.* 29:119–24

66. Harvey, J. A., Zobitz, M. M., Pak, C. Y. C. 1988. Dose dependency of calcium absorption: a comparison of calcium carbonate and calcium citrate. *J. Bone Miner. Res.* 3:253–58

67. Haug, A. 1984. Molecular aspects of aluminum toxicity. *CRC Crit. Rev. Plant Sci.* 1:345–73

68. Herzog, P., Schmitt, K. F., Grendahl, T., van der Linden, J. Jr., Holtermuller, K. H. 1982. Evaluation of serum and urine electrolyte changes during therapy with magnesium-aluminum containing antacid: results of a prospective study. In *Antacids in the Eighties,* ed. F. Halter, pp. 123–35. Munchen: Urban & Schwarzenberg

69. Hewitt, C. D., Poole, C. L., Westervelt, F. B., Savory, J., Willis, M. R. 1988. Risks of simultaneous therapy with oral aluminum and citrate compounds. *Lancet* 2:849

70. Hewitt, C. D., Savory, J., Wills, M. R. 1990. Aspects of aluminum toxicity. *Clin. Lab. Med.* 10:403–22

71. Hopkins, H., Eisen, J. 1959. Mineral elements in fresh vegetables from different geographic areas. *Agric. Food Chem.* 7:633–38

72. Horecker, B. L., Stotz, E., Hogness, T. R. 1939. The promoting effect of aluminum, chromium and the rare earths in the succinic dehydrogenase-cytochrome system. *J. Biol. Chem.* 128:251–56

73. Hurley, L. S., Lönnerdal, B. 1982. Zinc binding in human milk: citrate versus picolinate. *Nutr. Rev.* 40:65–71

74. Inoue, T., Ishiwata, H., Yoshihara, K. 1988. Aluminum levels in food-simulating solvents and cooked in aluminum pans. *J. Agric. Food Chem.* 36:599–601

75. Ittel, T. H., Buddington, B., Miller, N. L., Alfrey, A. C. 1987. Enhanced gastrointestinal absorption of aluminum in uremic rats. *Kidney Int.* 32:821–26

76. Jones, K. C., Bennett, B. G. 1986. Exposure of man to environmental aluminum—an exposure commitment assessment. *Sci. Total Environ.* 52:65–82

77. Kaehny, W. D., Hegg, A. P., Alfrey, A. C. 1977. Gastrointestinal absorption of aluminum from aluminum-containing antacids. *N. Engl. J. Med.* 196:1389–90

78. Kahn, R. A. 1991. Fluroide is not an activator of the smaller (20–25 kDa) GTP-binding proteins. *J. Biol. Chem.* 266:15595–597.

79. King, S. W., Savory, J., Wills, M. R. 1981. The clinical biochemistry of aluminum. *CRC Crit. Rev. Clin. Lab. Sci.* 14:1–20

80. Kirschbaum, B. B., Schoolwerth, A. C. 1989. Acute aluminum toxicity associated with oral citrate and aluminum-containing antacids. *Am. J. Med. Sci.* 197:9–11

81. Kirschbaum, B. B., Schoolwerth, A. C. 1989. Hyperaluminemia associated with oral citrate and aluminum by dioxide. *Hum. Toxicol.* 8:45–47

82. Kleber, C. J., Putt, M. S. 1984. Aluminum and dental caries: A review of the literature. *Clin. Prev. Dent.* 6:14–25

83. Klein, G. L., Alfrey, A. C., Miller, N. L., Sherrard, D. J., Hazlet, T. K., et al. 1982. Aluminum loading during total parenteral nutrition. *Am. J. Clin. Nutr.* 35:1425–29

84. Klein, G. L., Heyman, M. B., Lee, T. C., Miller, N. L., Marathe, G., et al. 1988. Aluminum-associated hepatobiliary dysfunction in rats: Relationships to dosage and duration of exposure. *Pediatr. Res.* 23:275–78

85. Koo, W. W. K., Kaplan, L. A., Krug-Wispe, S. K. 1988. Aluminum contamination of infant formulas. *J. Parenter. Enteral Nutr.* 12:170–73

86. Kostyniak, P. J. 1983. An electrothermal atomic absorption method for aluminum analysis in plasma: Identification of source contamination in blood sampling procedures. *J. Anal. Toxicol.* 7:20–23

87. Kovalchik, M. T., Kaehny, W. P., Hegg, A. P., Jackson, J. T., Alfrey, A. C. 1978. Aluminum kinetics during hemodialysis. *J. Lab. Clin. Med.* 92:712–20

88. Krueger, G. L., Morris, T. K., Suskind, R. R., Widner, E. M. 1984. The health effects of aluminum compounds in mammals. *CRC Crit. Rev. Toxicol.* 13:1–24

89. Levick, S. E. 1980. Dementia from aluminum pots. *N. Engl. J. Med.* 303: 164

90. Lione, A. 1983. The prophylactic reduction of aluminum intake. *Food Chem. Toxicol.* 21:103–9

91. Lione, A. 1985. Aluminum intake from non-prescription drugs and sucralfate. *Gen. Pharmacol.* 16:223–28

92. Lote, C. J., Wood, J. A., Saunders, H. C. 1992. Renal filtration, reabsorption and excretion of aluminum in the rat. *Clin. Sci.* 82:13–18

93. Lotz, M., Zisman, E., Bartter, F. C. 1968. Evidence for a phosphorus-depletion syndrome in man. *N. Engl. J. Med.* 278:409–15

94. Markesbery, W. R., Ehmann, W. D., Alauddin, M., Hossain, T. I. M. 1984. Brain trace element concentrations in aging. *Neurobiol. Aging* 5:19–28

95. Martin, R. B. 1986. The chemistry of aluminum as related to biology and medicine. *Clin. Chem.* 32:1797–1805

96. Martin, R. B. 1992. Aluminum speciation in biology. See Ref. 8, pp. 5–25

97. Martin, R. B., Savory, J., Brown, S., Bertholf, R. L., Wills, M. R. 1987. Transferrin binding of Al^{+3} and Fe^{+3}. *Clin. Chem.* 33:405–7

98. Martinez-Palomi, A., Meza, I., Beaty, G., Cereijido, M. 1980. Experimental modulation of occluding junctions in a cultured transporting epitheliom. *J. Cell Biol.* 87:736–45

99. Martyn, C. N., Osmond, C., Edwardson, J. A., Barker, D. J. P., Harris, T. C., et al. 1989. Geographical relation between Alzheimer's disease and aluminum in drinking water. *Lancet* 1:59–62

100. Massie, H. R., Aiello, V. R., Tuttle, R. S. 1988. Aluminum in the organs and diet of ageing C57BL/6J mice. *Mech. Ageing Dev.* 45:145–56

101. Massie, H. R., Williams, T. R., Aiello, V. R. 1985. Excess dietary aluminum increases *Drosophila's* rate of aging. *Gerontology* 31:309–14

102. Mayor, G. H., Keiser, J. A., Makdoni, D., Ku, P. 1977. Aluminum absorption and distribution: Effect of parathyroid hormone. *Science* 197:1187–89

103. Mayor, G. H., Sprague, S. M., Hourani, M. R., Sanchez, T. V. 1980. Parathyroid hormone-mediated aluminum deposition and egress in the rat. *Kidney Int.* 17:40–44

104. McDermott, J. R., Smith, I., Iqbal, K., Wisniewski, H. M. 1979. Brain aluminum in aging and Alzheimer disease. *Neurology* 29:809–14

105. McGraw, M. E., Bishop, N., Jameson, R., Robinson, M. J., O'Hara, M., et al. 1986. Aluminum content of milk formulae and intravenous fluids used in infants. *Lancet* 1:157

106. McLachlan, D. R., Fraser, P. E., Dalton, A. J. 1992. Aluminum and the pathogenesis of Alzheimer's disease; a summary of evidence. See Ref. 8, pp. 87–108

107. Meyers, V. C., Morrison, D. B. 1928. The influence of the administration of aluminum upon the aluminum content of the tissues of the dog. *J. Biol. Chem.* 78:615–24

108. Miller, R. G., Kopfler, F. C., Kelty, K. C., Stober, J. A., Ulmer, N. S. 1984. The occurrence of aluminum in drinking water. *J. Am. Water Assoc.* 76:84–91

109. Monteagudo, F. S. E., Cassidy, M. J. D., Folb, P. I. 1989. Recent developments in aluminum toxicology. *Med. Toxicol.* 4:1–16

110. Morris, C. M., Candy, J. M., Oakley, A. E., Taylor, G. A., Mountfort, S., et al. 1989. Comparison of the regional distribution of transferrin receptors and aluminum in the forebrain of chronic renal dialysis patients. *J. Neurol. Sci.* 94:295–306

111. Nordal, K. P., Dahl, E., Sorbus, K., Berg, K. J., Thomassen, Y., et al. 1988. Gastrointestinal absorption and urinary excretion of aluminum in patients with predialysis chronic renal failure. *Pharmacol. Toxicol.* 63:351–54

112. Ondreička, R., Kortus, J., Ginter, E., Kortus, J. 1966. Chronic toxicity of aluminum in rats and mice and its effects on phosphorus metabolism. *Br. J. Ind. Med.* 23:305–12

113. Ondreička, R., Kortus, J., Ginter, E. 1971. Aluminum, its absorption, distribution and effects on phosphorus metabolism. In *Intestinal Absorption of Metal Ions, Trace Elements and Radionuclides*, ed. S. C. Skonyna, D. Waldron-Edward, pp. 293–305. Oxford: Permagon

114. Partridge, N. A., Regnier, F. E., White, J. L., Hem, S. L. 1989. Influence of dietary constituents on intestinal absorption of aluminum. *Kidney Int.* 35:1413–17

115. Pennington, J. A. T. 1987. Aluminum content of foods and diets. *Food Addit. Contam.* 5:161–232

116. Pennington, J. A. T., Jones, J. W. 1988. Dietary intake of aluminum. See Ref. 50a, pp. 67–100

117. Perl, D. P. 1985. Relationship of aluminum to Alzheimer's disease. *Environ. Health Perspect.* 63:149–53

118. Provan, S. D., Yokel, R. A. 1988. Influence of calcium on aluminum accumulation by the rat jejunal slice. *Res. Commun. Chem. Pathol. Pharmacol.* 59:79–92

119. Provan, S. P., Yokel, R. A. 1988. Aluminum uptake by the in situ rat

gut preparation. *J. Pharmacol. Expl. Ther.* 245:928–31

120. Rahman, H., Skillen, A. W., Channon, S. M., Ward, M. K., Kerr, D. N. S. 1985. Methods for studying the binding of aluminum by serum protein. *Clin. Chem.* 31:1969–73

121. Recker, R. R., Blotcky, A. J., Leffler, J. A., Rack, E. P. 1977. Evidence for aluminum absorption from the gastrointestinal tract and bone deposition by aluminum carbonate ingestion with normal renal function. *J. Lab. Clin. Med.* 90:810–15

122. Rosa, I. V., Henry, P. R., Ammerman, C. B. 1982. Interrelationships of dietary phosphorus, aluminum and iron on performance and tissue mineral composition in lambs. *J. Anim. Sci.* 55:1231–40

123. Roskams, A. J., Connor, J. R. 1990. Aluminum access to the brain: A role for transferrin and its receptor. *Proc. Natl. Acad. Sci. USA* 87:9024–27

124. Said, A. N., Slagsvold, P., Bergh, H., Laksesvela, B. 1977. High fluorine water to wether sheep maintained in pens: Aluminum chloride as a possible alleviator of fluorosis. *Nord. Vet. Med.* 29:172–80

125. Savory, J., Nicholson, J. R., Wills, M. R. 1987 Is aluminium leaching enhanced by fluoride? *Nature* 327:107–8

126. Savory, J., Wells, M. R. 1988. Analytical techniques for the analysis of aluminum. See Ref. 50a, pp. 1–24

127. Schaefer, K., vonHerrath, D., Erley, C. M. M. 1988. Treatment of uremic hyperphosphatemia—Is there still a need for aluminum salts? *Am. J. Nephrol.* 8:173–78

128. Schlettwein-Gsell, D., Mommsen-Straub, S. 1973. Spurenelemente in Lebensmitteln. XII. Aluminium. *Int. Z. Vitamin Ernaehrungsforsch.* 43:251–63

129. Sedman, A. B., Klein, G. L., Merritt, R. J., Miller, N. L., Weber, K. O., et al. 1985. Evidence of aluminum loading in infants receiving intravenous therapy. *N. Engl. J. Med.* 312:1337–43

130. Simmer, K., Fudge, a., Teubner, J., James, S. L. 1990. Aluminum concentrations in infant formulae. *J. Pediatr. Child Health* 26:9–11

131. Skalsky, H. L., Carchman, R. A. 1983. Pharmokinetics of aluminum: A review. *J. Am. Coll. Toxicol.* 2:405–23

132. Slanina, P., Falkeborn, Y. 1984. Aluminum concentrations in the brain and bone of rats fed citric acid, aluminum citrate or aluminum hydroxide. *Food Chem. Toxicol.* 33:391–97

133. Slanina, P., Frech, W., Berhardson, A., Cedergren, A., Mattsson, P. 1985. Influence of dietary factors on aluminum absorption and retention in the brain and bone of rats. *Acta Pharmacol. Toxicol.* 56:331–36

134. Slanina, P., Frech, W., Ekstrom, L. G., Loof, L., Slorach, S., Cedergren, A. 1986. Dietary citrate enhances absorption of aluminum in antacids. *Clin. Chem.* 32:539–41

135. Smeyers-Verbeke, J., Verbeelen, D., Massart, D. L. 1983. Investigation of the accumulation and excretion of Al in rats. In *Trace Element Analytical Chemistry in Medicine and Biology*, ed. P. Brätter, P. Schramel, 2:333–40. New York: de Gruyter

136. Sorenson, J. R. J., Campbell, I. R., Tepper, L. B., Longg, R. D. 1974. Aluminum in the environment and human health. *Environ. Health Perspect.* 8:3–95

137. Spencer, H., Kramer, L., Norris, C., Osis, P. 1982. Effect of small doses of aluminum-containing antacids on calcium and phosphorus metabolism. *Am. J. Clin. Nutr.* 36:32–40

138. Spencer, H., Kramer, L., Norris, C., Wiatrowski, E. 1981. Effect of aluminum hydroxide on plasma fluoride and fluoride excretion during a high fluoride intake in men. *Toxicol. Appl. Pharmacol.* 56:140–44

139. Sternweis, P. C., Gilman, A. G. 1982. Aluminum: A requirement for acitivation of the regulatory component of adenyl cyclase by fluoride. *Proc. Natl. Acad. Sci. USA* 79:4888–91

140. Storer, N. L., Nelson, T. S. 1968. The effect of various aluminum compounds on chick performance. *Poultry Sci.* 47:244–47

141. Tipton, I. H., Stewart, P. L., Martin, P. G. 1966. Trace elements in diets and excreta. *Health Phys.* 12:1683–89

142. Trapp, G. A. 1983. Plasma aluminum is bound to transferrin. *Life Sci.* 33:311–16

143. Trapp, G. A., Cannon, J. B. 1981. Aluminum pots as a source of dietary aluminum. *N. Engl. J. Med.* 304:172

144. Underhill, F. P., Peterman, R. I., Steel, S. L. 1929. Studies in the metabolism of aluminum. IV. The fate of intravenously injected aluminum. *Am. J. Physiol.* 90:52–61

145. Underwood, E. J. 1977. Aluminum. In *Trace Elements in Human and Animal Nutrition*, pp. 430–33. New York: Academic. 4th ed.

146. Valdivia, R., Ammerman, C. B., Henry, P. R., Feaster, J. P., Wilcox,

C. J. 1982. Effect of dietary aluminum and phosphorus on performance, phosphorus utilization and tissue mineral composition in sheep. *J. Anim. Sci.* 55:402–10

147. Van der Voet, G. B. 1992. Intestinal absorption of aluminum. See Ref. 8, pp. 109–17

148. Van der Voet, G. B., de Wolff, F. A. 1986. Intestinal absorption of aluminum in rats: Effect of intraluminal pH and aluminum concentration. *J. Appl. Toxicol.* 6:37–41

149. Van der Voet, G. B., de Wolff, F. A. 1987. The effect of di- and trivalent iron on the intestinal absorption of aluminum in rats. *Toxicol. Appl. Pharmacol.* 90:190–97

150. Van der Voet, G. B., van Ginkel, M. D., de Wolff, F. A. 1989. Intestinal absorption of aluminum in rats: Stimulation by citric acid and inhibition by dinitrophenol. *Toxicol. Appl. Pharmacol.* 99:90–97

151. Wilhelm, M., Jäger, D. E., Ohnesorge, F. K. 1990. Aluminum toxicokinetics. *Pharmacol. Toxicol.* 66:4–9

152. Williams, J. W., Vera, S. R., Peters, T. G., Luther, R. W., Bhattacharya, S., et al. 1986. Biliary excretion of aluminum in aluminum osteodystrophy with liver disease. *Ann. Intern. Med.* 104:782–85

153. Wisniewski, H. M., Wen, G. Y. 1992. Aluminum and Alzheimer's disease. See Ref. 8, pp. 142–54

154. Yokel, R. A. 1983. Persistent aluminum accumulation after prolonged systemic aluminum exposure. *Biol. Trace Element Res.* 5:467–74

155. Yokel, R. A. 1987. Toxicity of aluminum exposure to the neonatal and immature rabbit. *Fundam. Appl. Toxicol.* 9:795–806

156. Yokel, R. A., McNamara, P. J. 1988. Influence of renal impairment chemical form and serum protein binding in intravenous and oral aluminum kinetics in the rabbit. *Toxicol. Appl. Pharmacol.* 95:32–43

157. Yokel, R. A., McNamara, P. J. 1989. Elevated aluminum persists in serum and tissues of rabbits after a six-hour infusion. *Toxicol. Appl. Pharmacol.* 99:133–38

Annu. Rev. Nutr. 1993. 13:65–81

REGULATION OF SELENOPROTEINS

Raymond F. Burk and Kristina E. Hill

Division of Gastroenterology, Department of Medicine and Center in Molecular Toxicology, Vanderbilt University School of Medicine, Nashville, Tennessee 37232

KEY WORDS: selenium metabolism, selenium function, oxidant defenses

CONTENTS

INTRODUCTION 65
FORMS OF SELENIUM IN PROTEIN 66
   Selenocysteine 66
   Selenomethionine 66
   Selenotrisulfides 66
   Selenium-Heavy Metal Complexes 67
   Other Forms 67
IMPORTANCE OF SELENOPROTEINS 67
   Cellular Glutathione Peroxidase (cGSH-Px) 67
   Extracellular Glutathione Peroxidase (eGSH-Px) 68
   Phospholipid Hydroperoxide Glutathione Peroxidase (phGSH-Px) 68
   Type I Iodothyronine 5'-Deiodinase (5'DI) 69
   Selenoprotein P (Se-P) 69
EVIDENCE THAT SELENOPROTEINS ARE REGULATED 69
MECHANISMS OF SELENOPROTEIN SYNTHESIS 70
SELENOPROTEIN SYNTHESIS IN SELENIUM DEFICIENCY 74
   Posttranslational Effects 74
   Levels of mRNA 75
   Supply of Selenium 76
OTHER FACTORS INFLUENCING SELENOPROTEIN LEVELS 76
CONCLUSIONS 77
SUMMARY 77

INTRODUCTION

Nearly all the selenium in animal tissues is associated with protein. Several protein-bound forms have been identified, but only one, selenocysteine encoded by a UGA in mRNA, has been shown to be specific for the element and to be regulated physiologically. Proteins containing this form of selenium are referred to as selenoproteins in this review. Other types of protein binding

65

0199-9885/93/0715-0065$02.00

of selenium are recognized, but they lack specificity and are frequently related to the chemical similarities between selenium and sulfur. The less specific terms "selenium-containing protein" and "selenium-binding protein" are suggested to refer to them.

This review focuses on selenoprotein synthesis and its regulation. Related reviews have appeared in recent years (14, 17, 58, 59, 61).

FORMS OF SELENIUM IN PROTEIN

Selenocysteine

All proteins that have been shown to incorporate selenium stoichiometrically contain it in the form of selenocysteine. This form was first identified in 1976 in protein A of the glycine reductase complex of *Clostridium sticklandii* (25). Since then it has been found in several other proteins, and a specific mechanism for its synthesis and incorporation has been characterized (see below). Proteins containing selenocysteine are selenium dependent. That is, they are present in diminished concentration when selenium supply is restricted. This review focuses on proteins containing selenium as selenocysteine and refers to them as selenoproteins.

Selenomethionine

Plants and bacteria synthesize selenium-containing amino acids, including selenomethionine. Most evidence suggests that animals do not distinguish this amino acid from methionine. Thus it appears to be incorporated into protein in place of methionine and to have no selenium-related function. Incorporation of selenium administered as selenomethionine into animal proteins is directly correlated with selenomethionine intake and inversely correlated with methionine intake (69). Under appropriate conditions, most of the selenium in animal tissues can be in this form. This selenium is released and utilized in specific selenium pathways when selenomethionine is catabolized.

Selenomethionine can be metabolized to selenocysteine by the transsulfuration pathway. However, the resultant selenocysteine is catabolized by selenocysteine β-lyase (27) and does not serve as a form of selenocysteine for specific incorporation into proteins. There is evidence that selenocysteine can be incorporated into protein in place of cysteine by some bacteria (60). Such incorporation should be prevented by selenocysteine β-lyase activity in cells containing this enzyme.

Selenotrisulfides

The reaction of selenite with thiol compounds leads to the formation of selenotrisulfides such as selenodiglutathione (33). Selenotrisulfide formation in a protein was induced by adding selenite to reduced pancreatic ribonuclease (34). This nonspecific incorporation of selenium appears to be largely an in vitro phenomenon and is not likely to be of physiological importance.

Selenium-Heavy Metal Complexes

There is evidence that selenium occurs in proteins in complexes with heavy metals, especially mercury (18). Binding to selenium may reduce the toxicity of the heavy metals, but this also reduces the bioavailability of the selenium.

Other Forms

Recently a group investigating anticarcinogenic properties of selenium has shown that injected selenium associates with several proteins in rodent tissues that do not contain the element as selenocysteine (5). Selenium deficiency does not cause a decrease in the concentrations of these proteins, and the form and stoichiometry of selenium in them is not known. Thus, it is uncertain whether selenium association with these proteins has biological significance.

IMPORTANCE OF SELENOPROTEINS

Under physiological conditions selenium has several metabolic fates. A major one in a quantitative sense is incorporation into selenoproteins. A five-month equilibration study, in which selenite labeled with ^{75}Se was administered in the drinking water to rats fed a selenium-deficient diet, revealed that over 80% of the ^{75}Se in the rat was present as selenocysteine in protein (38). Two other fates of the element are known. Methylated forms of selenium are synthesized for excretion (15), and selenium has been shown to be incorporated into certain tRNAs in cultured cells (23). The physiological significance of these tRNAs has not been established.

Selenoproteins with known enzymatic activity are redox enzymes and contain selenocysteine in their active sites. Replacing selenium with sulfur causes a sharp decline in activity (4, 11, 52). Thus, effective function of these enzymes depends on their selenium.

Studies utilizing polyacrylamide gel electrophoresis of tissue extracts from rats which were administered ^{75}Se point to the presence of 10 to 15 high-abundance selenoproteins (7). Based on this figure, and the inference from the number of genes present in the genome that ten nonabundant proteins are present for every abundant one, it seems reasonable to speculate that as many as 100 selenoproteins exist in animals. Five selenoproteins have been characterized to the extent of cloning their cDNA and determining their sequences.

Cellular Glutathione Peroxidase (cGSH-Px)

This enzyme was discovered 36 years ago (48) and was noted to be dependent on selenium 20 years ago (53). It represented the only known biochemical role of selenium for many years and has been used extensively to assess selenium nutritional status. cGSH-Px is found in virtually all cells, but its specific activity varies greatly between species and tissues. In the rat, cGSH-Px contains more selenium than any other selenoprotein (38). Approximately 25% of rat total body selenium is present in liver cGSH-Px (9).

The active enzyme comprises four identical 22-kDa subunits. Each subunit contains one selenocysteine residue. Glutathione is required as the reducing substrate. Hydrogen peroxide and free organic hydroperoxides, including free fatty acid hydroperoxides, can be reduced by cGSH-Px. Fatty acid hydroperoxides esterified in phospholipids cannot serve as substrates (36).

cGSH-Px is thought to regulate intracellular hydroperoxide concentrations. Its importance has been questioned, however, because deficiency of selenium resulting in a fall in cGSH-Px activity to less than 1% of control in liver has no obvious effect on the health of the rat. Moreover, direct evidence that it affects levels of hydrogen peroxide or other free hydroperoxides under physiological conditions has not been presented. Because cGSH-Px contains a large fraction of the total body selenium and its loss appears to be well tolerated, researchers have proposed that it represents a reserve of selenium that can be mobilized for other uses (19, 61, 70). A family of cGSH-Px proteins appears to exist because related cDNAs have been cloned and sequenced (1, 28). This observation indicates that a great deal remains to be learned about cGSH-Px function.

Extracellular Glutathione Peroxidase (eGSH-Px)

Plasma glutathione peroxidase was recognized as a different enzyme from cGSH-Px in 1986 (63). Since then, its presence has been demonstrated in milk, and it has been referred to as eGSH-Px. Its activity in plasma is a convenient index of selenium nutritional status.

eGSH-Px shares some sequence identity with cGSH-Px but is clearly a separate gene product (62). It consists of four identical 23-kDa subunits, each of which contains one selenocysteine. Recent work indicates that it is synthesized in the kidney and in the lung (24).

The function of eGSH-Px is not known. The fact that its reducing substrate, glutathione, is present at very low concentrations in extracellular fluids has led to suggestions that the enzyme might have a function other than as a glutathione peroxidase.

Phospholipid Hydroperoxide Glutathione Peroxidase (phGSH-Px)

This third glutathione peroxidase has been characterized in recent years (57). It is a monomer of 20 kDa and is similar to one subunit of the other two glutathione peroxidases. It contains one selenocysteine. Thiol compounds other than glutathione can serve as its reducing substrate. It is capable of reducing fatty acid hydroperoxides esterified to phospholipids (66).

phGSH-Px is found in several tissues but has a distribution different from that of cGSH-Px. Relatively little is present in rat liver while it is quite abundant in the testis (54). It has been suggested that this enzyme plays a role in eicosanoid metabolism (67) and that it protects against lipid peroxidation (65).

Type I Iodothyronine 5'-deiodinase (5'DI)

Thyroid function depends on the conversion of thyroxine to triiodothyronine. Several deiodinase enzymes can perform this conversion and one of them is a selenoprotein (2, 8, 11). The enzyme is a homodimer and each 27-kDa subunit contains one selenocysteine (11). The enzyme is present in the endoplasmic reticulum of liver and kidney (13).

The function of 5'DI is to deiodinate thyroxine, thus producing triiodothyronine. A reducing substrate is required which, in vivo, is probably glutathione. In selenium deficiency, thyroxine levels in plasma rise as a consequence of the decrease in 5'DI activity (6). Triiodothyronine levels are depressed slightly by selenium deficiency (6), but selenium-deficient animals remain euthyroid (16).

Selenoprotein P (Se-P)

The existence of a plasma selenoprotein other than eGSH-Px has been known for over 15 years, but the purification and characterization of Se-P has been accomplished only in the last five years. In the rat, Se-P contains 65% of the plasma selenium (50).

A cDNA for Se-P has been cloned and sequenced (41). There are ten TGAs (UGAs in mRNA) in the open reading frame (ORF), indicating that the protein contains ten selenocysteine residues in its primary structure. It is the only selenoprotein characterized so far that contains more than one selenocysteine per polypeptide chain. The protein is a glycosylated single polypeptide chain of 41 kDa (50).

The function of Se-P is not known. Its appearance in plasma correlates with protection against free radical injury of the liver by diquat (20, 21). Thus, it may be a free radical scavanger. Another hypothesis is that it transports selenium from the liver to other tissues. However, Se-P mRNA has been detected in several tissues, thus indicating that it is synthesized in sites other than the liver (40). Also the half-life of its selenium is not affected by the selenium status of the animal (20). These observations make a transport role unlikely.

EVIDENCE THAT SELENOPROTEINS ARE REGULATED

Selenium availability regulates selenoproteins. Although it is likely that there are other modifiers that are specific for individual proteins, deficiency of selenium causes a fall in the concentration of all selenoproteins that have been

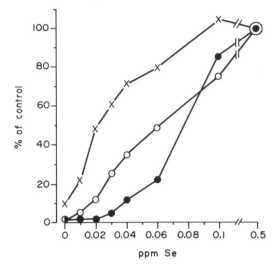

Figure 1   Effect of dietary selenium supplementation on selenoproteins in the rat. cGSH-Px in liver (•), eGSH-Px in plasma (o), and Se-P in plasma (x) were measured in animals fed varying levels of selenium in the diet for 8 weeks. Values are means of 6 animals. See Reference 70 for experimental details. The dietary requirement of the rat for selenium is 0.1 ppm. The control group was fed a diet supplemented with 0.5 ppm selenium (0.5 mg selenium per kg). As selenium was introduced into the diet, Se-P increased first and was followed by eGSH-Px. Liver cGSH-Px was the last to increase in response to dietary selenium.

studied. This finding suggests that synthesis of selenoproteins is decreased by selenium deficiency.

Figure 1 compares the effect of dietary selenium level on cGSH-Px in liver, eGSH-Px, and Se-P. All three measures of these selenoproteins are sharply decreased when no selenium is added to the deficient diet. As small amounts of selenium are provided, Se-P and then eGSH-Px increase before liver cGSH-Px begins to rise. This demonstrates that selenoproteins are regulated by the supply of selenium and that regulation of individual proteins occurs at different levels of the element. Evidence also indicates that 5′DI is better preserved than cGSH-Px in selenium deficiency (3).

MECHANISMS OF SELENOPROTEIN SYNTHESIS

The synthesis of selenocysteine and the incorporation of it into protein are components of a complex process. Studies by Böck and coworkers utilizing *E. coli* mutants have characterized the process in prokaryotes (14). Figure 2 shows the major steps. A UGA codon in the open reading frame of the mRNA corresponds to selenocysteine in the protein. Four unique gene products are

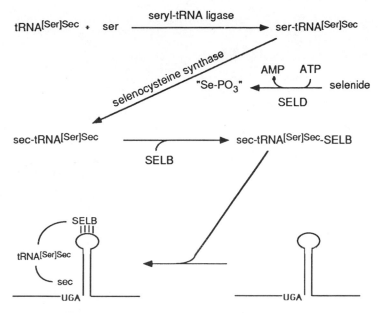

Figure 2   Synthesis of selenocysteine and incorporation of it into selenoproteins by prokaryotes. tRNA[Ser]Sec contains the anticodon for UGA. Unique structural features of tRNA[Ser]Sec allow it to bind to selenocysteine synthase (formerly known as SELA) after charging with serine (31). Selenocysteine synthase, a pyridoxyl 5-phosphate enzyme, catalyzes the replacement of the side-chain oxygen in serine by selenium, yielding selenocysteine (29). A selenophosphate compound is required for this reaction (68). It is produced from selenide and ATP by an enzyme known as SELD (29, 44). The sec-tRNA[Ser]Sec is released from selenocysteine synthase and is bound by a unique elongation factor, SELB. SELB has a 43-kDa region similar to EF-Tu, the elongation factor that serves for all other amino acid-tRNAs (32). The additional 25 kDa of SELB allows it to recognize the sec-tRNA[Ser]Sec (30) and presumably to bind to the stem-loop structure of the selenoprotein mRNA. This sec-tRNA[Ser]Sec-SELB complex attached to the stem loop facilitates incorporation of selenocysteine into the protein. It might function by bringing the sec-tRNA[Ser]Sec into the vicinity of the UGA codon. Additionally, it might block access of release factor 2 to the A site on the ribosome where it acts to terminate translation.

required: In addition to tRNA[Ser]Sec which carries the anticodon for UGA, two enzymes, selenocysteine synthase and SELD, and an elongation factor, SELB, are needed. A stem-loop structure with a specific sequence on the loop is required in the mRNA immediately downstream from the UGA. This structure is necessary for the UGA to specify selenocysteine incorporation instead of termination. It binds the elongation factor-tRNA[Ser]Sec-selenocysteine complex and facilitates its interaction with the UGA (39). Thus, the location of the stem loop in proximity with the UGA is necessary for this mechanism.

Much less is known about the process in eukaryotic systems (Figure 3). A

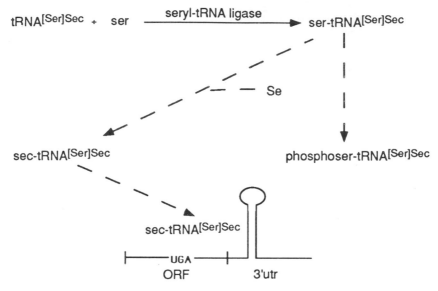

Figure 3 Synthesis of selenocysteine and incorporation of it into selenoproteins by eukaryotes. The compounds named in the figure have been identified in animal cells. The *solid line* indicates a characterized reaction. Eukaryotes contain tRNA$^{[Ser]Sec}$, which is charged with serine (46). *Broken lines* indicate pathways for which evidence has been presented but which have not been characterized in detail. tRNA$^{[Ser]Sec}$ has been isolated in three amino acid-acylated forms—with serine, phosphoserine, and selenocysteine attached (46). Details of the conversion of serine to selenocysteine in eukaryotes have not been firmly established, but a recent report (49) presents evidence for the existence of enzymes analogous to selenocysteine synthase and SELD in prokaryotes. Phosphoser-tRNA$^{[Ser]Sec}$ did not appear to be a precursor of sec-tRNA$^{[Ser]Sec}$, and its formation was speculated to compete with the selenocysteine synthase reaction (49). As yet, no elongation factor has been identified but, by analogy with the prokaryotic system, one is likely to be involved in the association of sec-tRNA$^{[Ser]Sec}$ with the mRNA. A UGA in the ORF of the selenoprotein mRNA corresponds to selenocysteine in the protein. Essential stem-loop structures are present in the 3'utr instead of in the ORF as in prokaryotes. The interaction of the three elements known to be essential for insertion of selenocysteine into protein (sec-tRNA$^{[Ser]Sec}$, the stem loop, and UGA) has not been characterized. Thus, only partial characterization of the eukaryotic system has been achieved. However, facts that have been established indicate that it differs from the prokaryotic mechanism in at least one major way—the location of the stem-loop structure in mRNA, which is essential to the decoding of UGA as selenocysteine.

unique tRNA$^{[Ser]Sec}$ has been described and, like the bacterial tRNA$^{[Ser]Sec}$, it has the anticodon for UGA. Two forms of this tRNA exist, and both differ in sequence from that predicted by the genomic DNA sequence (26). This finding indicates that the forms of tRNA$^{[Ser]Sec}$ isolated from the cell are both edited versions of the original transcript. tRNA$^{[Ser]Sec}$ is charged with serine in a manner similar to the bacterial tRNA. tRNA$^{[Ser]Sec}$ has been recovered in three forms—with serine, phosphorylated serine, or selenocysteine attached (46). The mechanism of conversion of the serine to selenocysteine has not been characterized in detail. There has been speculation that the phosphorylated compound is an intermediate, but recent evidence suggests that a selenocysteine synthase converts ser-tRNA$^{[Ser]Sec}$ directly to sec-tRNA$^{[Ser]Sec}$ (49).

mRNA context plays a role in eukaryotic, as well as in prokaryotic, systems. Essential stem-loop structures have been described in eukaryotic selenoprotein mRNAs. Berry and coworkers studied requirements for expression of transfected 5'DI in cultured animal cell lines and determined that a segment of the 3' untranslated region (3'utr) of about 200 bases was necessary for readthrough of the message with incorporation of selenocysteine at the UGA codon (10). They named this segment a selenocysteine-insertion sequence (SECIS) motif (Figure 4A). None of the 3'utr was needed for readthrough when the UGA was mutated to a codon for cysteine. A stem-loop structure was found in the 200-base 3'utr segment by computer analysis. Analysis of the 3'utr of cGSH-Px mRNA revealed a similar stem loop. These structures contained only a small amount of sequence identity, but the segment from cGSH-Px could nevertheless replace that from 5'DI in supporting expression of 5'DI in the cultured cell lines (10). Thus eukaryotic systems utilize stem loops in mRNA to specify UGA coding for selenocysteine. A major difference from prokaryotic systems is that the stem loops in eukaryotes are not adjacent to the UGA but are separated from it by hundreds of bases.

Recently the mRNA of Se-P has been analyzed for stem loops (40). Two were predicted (Figure 4B) and both contained elements of the SECIS motif, proposed by Berry et al (10), in the form of some common sequence in unpaired regions. Se-P mRNA contains ten UGAs in the open reading frame, so there is no strict stoichiometry of stem loops to UGAs. This raises the possibility that the stem loops in eukaryotic mRNAs function differently from those in bacterial mRNAs. It would seem unlikely that two stem loops are enough to bind complexes containing tRNA$^{[Ser]Sec}$-selenocysteine and deliver them to the ribosome rapidly enough to serve the ten UGAs in Se-P mRNA. Another function the stem loops might subserve is to prevent the release factor from interacting with the ribosome at the UGA codons and terminating translation. This would suppress the termination function of UGA and allow the UGAs to specify selenocysteine incorporation. Expression of Se-P has not yet been achieved. Once it has, these possibilities can be examined.

Figure 3 shows the elements of selenocysteine synthesis and incorporation that are known in eukaryotic systems. Major gaps in this scheme still remain, but at least one important difference between it and the prokaryotic scheme (Figure 2) is evident. That is the location of the essential stem loop in the mRNA. This difference is sufficient to account for the failure of attempts to express eukaryotic selenoprotein messages in prokaryotic systems (51). In fact,

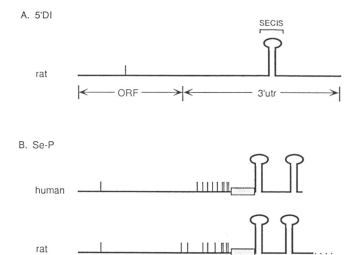

Figure 4 Features of the mRNAs of 5′DI (*A*) and Se-P (*B*). The mRNAs are shown as a *line* with the ORF and the 3′utr indicated by the *arrows* below. The positions of UGA codons, corresponding to selenocysteine residues in protein, are marked by *vertical lines* arising from the ORF. 5′DI contains one (11) and Se-P contains ten (41). The SECIS motif is indicated in the 3′utr of the 5′DI (10). It contains a stem-loop structure necessary for readthrough of the UGA as selenocysteine (see text). Comparison of rat and human Se-P mRNAs reveals two conserved stem loops, which appear to be SECIS motifs (40). In addition, the first 261 bases of the 3′utr (shown as a *shaded box*) are highly conserved. The function of this segment is unknown.

it is even possible that different eukaryotic systems might be incompatible with one another. A better understanding of the process of selenocysteine synthesis and incorporation into protein by eukaryotes will be required before all potential sites of regulation of selenoprotein synthesis can be identified.

SELENOPROTEIN SYNTHESIS IN SELENIUM DEFICIENCY

Posttranslational Effects

cGSH-Px has been studied in selenium deficiency more than any other selenoprotein. A fall in the activity of the enzyme uniformly accompanies the development of deficiency. An early hypothesis of selenoprotein synthesis proposed posttranslational modification of a serine or a cysteine in the primary structure of the protein. Replacement of serine oxygen or cysteine sulfur by selenium posttranslationally was supposed to yield selenocysteine in the primary structure of the protein. In selenium deficiency, the precursor protein would have been expected to accumulate. Several studies sought such a precursor protein by comparing cGSH-Px activity with protein levels measured using antibodies. No evidence of an inactive precursor protein was found (45, 71). Even though the posttranslational modification hypothesis is now known to be incorrect, these experiments provided useful information. They indicate that no protein recognizable by the polyclonal antibody preparation accumulates in selenium deficiency. This includes the polypeptide terminating at the UGA codon for selenocysteine. Thus, these experiments suggest that regulation of cGSH-Px synthesis by selenium deficiency occurs at the level of translation initiation or before.

Limited information is available on turnover of selenoproteins in selenium deficiency. The half-life in rat plasma of ^{75}Se administered intravenously as eGSH-Px was approximately 12 h and the half-life of ^{75}Se administered as Se-P was 3–4 h. Neither was affected by selenium deficiency (20). Thus, there is no evidence that selenium deficiency affects turnover of selenoproteins.

Levels of mRNA

The synthesis rates of many proteins are regulated by changes in the concentration of their mRNAs. The effect of selenium deficiency on cGSH-Px mRNA has been examined. Most groups have noted a fall in this mRNA in rodent liver as a consequence of selenium deficiency (42, 55, 64, 72), although one group did not (47). Transcription rate can determine mRNA levels, so nuclear run-on studies were performed to assess the effect of selenium deficiency on the synthesis of cGSH-Px mRNA. No effect was found (47, 64), even when mRNA levels were very low. This implies that regulation of mRNA by selenium status resides at a posttranscriptional site.

No studies that examine mRNA degradation or activation in selenium deficiency have been reported. Such processes are likely to underlie the mRNA regulation related to selenium status. Comparison of 3′ utr of human and rat Se-P mRNAs reveals two segments of highly conserved sequence (Figure 4B). Part of the first segment and all of the second one consist of predicted stem-loop structures thought to facilitate decoding of the UGAs. However, no function is known for the portion of the first conserved segment between the open reading frame and the stem-loop structure. Possibly this segment is involved in regulation of the mRNA.

Regulation of mRNAs of individual selenoproteins could serve as a means of using limited amounts of selenium in the most efficient manner. Thus selenoproteins of greatest importance to survival of the organism could be preserved by decreasing mRNA (and thus synthesis) of less essential selenoproteins. Evidence of such a differential regulation of selenoprotein mRNAs has been presented (42). Rats were fed a selenium-deficient diet for 14.5 weeks and liver mRNA levels were compared with levels in control livers. cGSH-Px mRNA levels were 3% of control while those of Se-P were 19% of control. This finding provides an explanation for the observation that selenium supplied to selenium-deficient rats led to a rapid rise in Se-P concentration but that cGSH-Px activity appearance was delayed (20). These results strongly suggest that the synthesis of individual selenoproteins can be controlled by regulation of mRNA level.

Supply of Selenium

Regulation of mRNA is not the only mechanism by which selenium status affects selenoprotein synthesis. Cultured cells deprived of selenium exhibit a fall in cGSH-Px activity without a concomitant fall in its mRNA (22). In the study discussed above in which mRNAs of cGSH-Px and Se-P fell to 3% and 19% of control, respectively, cGSH-Px activity was 0.8% of control and Se-P concentration was 4.3% of control (42). Thus, there was an additional effect beyond that of mRNA decrease, and it was approximately the same for both selenoproteins. This suggests that supply of selenium in the form needed for incorporation into protein can limit selenoprotein synthesis.

Figures 2 and 3 illustrate that the supply of selenium to the ribosome is a complex process and involves many gene products that might be affected by selenium status. Studies in bacteria involving expression of selenoproteins indicate that individual gene products can limit selenoprotein synthesis under these conditions (56). A preliminary report indicates that selenium status affects the editing of the tRNA$^{[Ser]Sec}$ in animal tissues (37). The function of these two forms of the tRNA$^{[Ser]Sec}$ is not known, but possibly each form favors a different mRNA population and thus changes in the forms would regulate selenoprotein synthesis. That is speculation and will require study. Other steps in the scheme for eukaryotes will have to be characterized and studied in selenium deficiency. At present, results indicate that the selenium supply affects selenoprotein synthesis. No direct evidence indicates that this effect varies from one selenoprotein to another, but so little is known about this process in eukaryotes that further work will be needed before a conclusion can be reached.

OTHER FACTORS INFLUENCING SELENOPROTEIN LEVELS

Selenoprotein expression varies by species and by tissue. The activity of cGSH-Px is very low in guinea pig liver and kidney in comparison to the activity in the same rat tissues, but the activity in red cells is comparable in the two species. A recent report studied cGSH-Px mRNA levels and transcription rates in guinea pig tissues (43). mRNA levels and transcription rates were very low in liver and kidney, thus accounting for the low enzyme activity. Values were higher in reticulocytes and erythroblast-enriched bone marrow. Thus, tissue differences in this enzyme would appear to be determined by transcriptional regulation.

Clinical circumstances other than selenium deficiency can influence the activities of cGSH-Px (35) and 5'DI (12). Little is known about the mechanisms of these effects and whether selenium is involved.

CONCLUSIONS

1. The synthesis of selenoproteins is a complex process that has been characterized in detail in prokaryotic systems. Several steps of the process have not been characterized in eukaryotic systems, and a full understanding of its regulation in them will be possible only after the process has been completely characterized.
2. Levels of selenoproteins fall in selenium deficiency as a result of decreased synthesis.
3. The supply of selenium appears to have a general effect on synthesis of selenoproteins. When selenium supply is limiting, synthesis of all selenoproteins is depressed.
4. Selenoproteins are also regulated individually through changes in their mRNA levels. This allows maintenance of some selenoproteins at the expense of others when selenium supply is limiting.
5. Expression of selenoproteins varies between species and tissues. Limited evidence suggests that transcriptional regulation accounts for this variation of expression.

SUMMARY

Selenium exerts its biological activity largely through selenoproteins, which contain the element in the form of selenocysteine. Five selenoproteins have been characterized in animal tissues and there is evidence that a number of others exist. Selenoprotein synthesis is a complex process that has been well characterized in prokaryotic systems but incompletely characterized in eukaryotic systems.

Selenium deficiency causes a decrease in selenoproteins, but the decrease is not uniform and some selenoproteins are maintained better than others. The selenoprotein most sensitive to selenium deficiency is liver cGSH-Px. It contains a significant fraction of the selenium in the body, and decreased synthesis of it under deficiency conditions might serve to increase the selenium available for synthesis of selenoproteins that are more important to the survival of the animal than is cGSH-Px.

The regulation of individual selenoproteins in selenium deficiency appears to be at the mRNA level. Factors that affect mRNA levels have not been completely characterized, but the fall in cGSH-Px mRNA in rat liver is not accompanied by decreased transcription, which suggests that it is regulated through changes in degradation.

ACKNOWLEDGMENTS

The authors' research is supported by NIH Grants ES 02497, ES 06093, HL 36371, and ES 00267.

Literature Cited

1. Akasaka, M., Mizoguchi, J., Takahashi K. 1990. A human cDNA sequence for a novel glutathione peroxidase-related protein. *Nucleic Acids Res.* 18: 4619

2. Arthur, J. R., Nicol, F., Beckett, G. J. 1990. Hepatic iodothyronine 5'-deiodinase. *Biochem. J.* 272:537–40

3. Arthur, J. R., Nicol, F., Hutchinson, A. R., Beckett, G. J. 1990. The effects of selenium depletion and repletion on the metabolism of thyroid hormones in the rat. *J. Inorg. Chem.* 39:101–8

4. Axley, M. J., Böck, A., Stadtman, T. C. 1991. Catalytic properties of an *Escherichia coli* formate dehydrogenase mutant in which sulfur replaces selenium. *Proc. Natl. Acad. Sci. USA* 88:8450–54

5. Bansal, M. P., Ip, C., Medina, D. 1991. Levels and ^{75}Se-labeling of specific proteins as a consequence of dietary selenium concentration in mice and rats. *Proc. Soc. Exp. Biol. Med.* 196:147–54

6. Beckett, G. J., Beddows, S. E., Morrice, P. C., Nicol, F., Arthur, J. R. 1987. Inhibition of hepatic deiodination of thyroxine is caused by selenium deficiency in rats. *Biochem. J.* 248: 443–47

7. Behne, D., Hilmert, H., Scheid, S., Gessner, H., Elger, W. 1988. Evidence for specific selenium target tissues and new biologically important selenoproteins. *Biochim. Biophys. Acta* 966:12–21

8. Behne, D., Kyriakopoulos, A., Meinhold, H., Köhrle, J. 1990. Identification of type I iodothyronine 5'-deiodinase as a selenoenzyme. *Biochem. Biophys. Res. Commun.* 173: 1143–49

9. Behne, D., Wolters, W. 1983. Distribution of selenium and glutathione peroxidase in the rat. *J. Nutr.* 113:456–61

10. Berry, M. J., Banu, L., Chen, Y., Mandel, S. J. Kieffer, J. D. et al. 1991. Recognition of UGA as a selenocysteine codon in Type I deiodinase requires sequences in the 3' untranslated region. *Nature* 353:273–76

11. Berry, M. J., Banu, L., Larsen, P. R. 1991. Type I iodothyronine deiodinase is a selenocysteine-containing enzyme. *Nature* 349:438–40

12. Berry, M. J., Kates, A.-L., Larsen, P. R. 1990. Thyroid hormone regulates type I deiodinase messenger RNA in rat liver. *Mol. Endocrinol.* 4:743–48

13. Berry, M. J., Larsen, P. R. 1992. The role of selenium in thyroid hormone action. *Endocrine Rev.* 13:207–19

14. Böck, A., Forchhammer, K., Heider, J., Baron, C. 1991. Selenoprotein synthesis: an expansion of the genetic code. *Trends Biochem. Sci.* 16:463–67

15. Bopp, B. A., Sonders, R. C., Kesterson, J. W. 1982. Metabolic fate of selected selenium compounds in laboratory animals and man. *Drug Metab. Rev.* 13:271–318

16. Burk, R. F. 1983. Biological activity of selenium. *Annu. Rev. Nutr.* 3:53–70

17. Burk, R. F. 1991. Molecular biology of selenium with implications for its metabolism. *FASEB J.* 5:2274–79

18. Burk, R. F., Foster, K. A., Greenfield,

P. M. Kiker, K. W. 1974. Binding of simultaneously administered inorganic selenium and mercury to a rat plasma protein. *Proc. Soc. Exp. Biol. Med.* 145:782–85

19. Burk, R. F., Gregory, P. E. 1982. Some characteristics of ^{75}Se-P, a selenoprotein found in rat liver and plasma, and comparison of it with selenoglutathione peroxidase. *Arch. Biochem. Biophys.* 213:73–80

20. Burk, R. F., Hill, K. E., Read, R., Bellew, T. 1991. Response of rat selenoprotein P to selenium administration and fate of its selenium. *Am. J. Physiol.* 261:E26–30

21. Burk, R. F., Lawrence, R. A., Lane, J. M. 1980. Liver necrosis and lipid peroxidation in the rat as the result of paraquat and diquat administration. *J. Clin. Invest.* 65:1024–31

22. Chada, S., Whitney, C., Newburger, P. E. 1989. Post-transcriptional regulation of glutathione peroxidase gene expression by selenium in the HL-60 human myeloid cell line. *Blood* 74:2535–41

23. Ching, W.-M. 1984. Occurrence of selenium-containing tRNA's in mouse leukemia cells. *Proc. Natl. Acad. Sci. USA* 81:3010–13

24. Chu, F.-F., Esworthy, R. S., Doroshow, J. H., Doran, K., Liu, X.-F. 1992. Expression of plasma glutathione peroxidase in human liver in addition to kidney, heart, lung, and breast in humans and rodents. *Blood* 79:3233–38

25. Cone, J. E., Martín Del Río, R., Davis, J. N., Stadtman, T. C. 1976. Chemical characterization of the selenoprotein component of clostridial glycine reductase: Identification of selenocysteine as the organoselenium moiety. *Proc. Natl. Acad. Sci. USA* 73:2659–63

26. Diamond, A. M., Montero-Puerner, Y., Lee, B. J., Hatfield, D. 1990. Selenocysteine inserting tRNAs are likely generated by tRNA editing. *Nucleic Acids Res.* 18:6727

27. Esaki, N., Nakamura, T., Tanaka, H., Suzuki, T., Morino, Y., Soda, K. 1981. Enzymatic synthesis of selenocysteine in rat liver. *Biochemistry* 20:4492–4500

28. Esworthy, R. S., Chu, F.-F., Paxton, R. J., Akman, S., Doroshow, J. H. 1991. Characterization and partial amino acid sequence of human plasma glutathione peroxidase. *Arch. Biochem. Biophys.* 286:330–36

29. Forchhammer, K., Böck, A. 1991. Selenocysteine synthase from *Es-*

cherichia coli. Analysis of the reaction sequence. *J. Biol. Chem.* 266:6324–28

30. Forchhammer, K., Boesmiller, K., Böck, A. 1991. The function of selenocysteine synthase and SELB in the synthesis and incorporation of selenocysteine. *Biochimie* 73:1481–86

31. Forchhammer, K., Leinfelder, W., Boesmiller, K., Veprek, B., Böck, A. 1991. Selenocysteine synthase from *Escherichia coli.* Nucleotide sequence of the gene (*sel*A) and purification of the protein. *J. Biol. Chem.* 266:6318–23

32. Forchhammer, K., Rücknagel, K.-P., Böck. A. 1990. Purification and biochemical characterization of SELB, a translation factor involved in selenoprotein synthesis. *J. Biol. Chem.* 265:9346–50

33. Ganther, H. E. 1968. Selenotrisulfides. Formation by the reaction of thiols with selenious acid. *Biochemistry* 7:2898–2905

34. Ganther, H. E., Corcoran, C. 1969. Selenotrisulfides. II. Cross-linking of reduced pancreatic ribonuclease with selenium. *Biochemistry* 8:2557–63

35. Ganther, H. E., Hafeman, D. G., Lawrence, R. A., Serfass, R. E., Hoekstra, W. G. 1976. Selenium and glutathione peroxidase in health and disease—A review. In *Trace Elements in Human Health and Disease,* ed. A. S. Prasad, 2:165–218. New York/San Francisco/London: Academic

36. Grossman, A., Wendel, A. 1983. Nonreactivity of the selenoenzyme glutathione peroxidase with enzymatically hydroperoxidized phospholipids. 135:549–52

37. Hatfield, D., Lee, B. J., Hampton, L., Diamond, A. M. 1991. Selenium induces changes in the selenocysteine tRNA[[Ser]Sec] population in mammalian cells. *Nucleic Acids Res.* 19:939–43

38. Hawkes, W. C., Wilhelmsen, E. C., Tappel, A. L. 1985. Abundance and tissue distribution of selenocysteine-containing proteins in the rat. *J. Inorg. Biochem.* 23:77–92

39. Heider, J., Baron, C., Böck, A. 1992. Coding from a distance: dissection of the mRNA determinants required for the incorporation of selenocysteine into protein. *EMBO J.* 11:3759–66

40. Hill, K. E., Lloyd, R. S., Burk, R. F. 1992. Conserved nucleotide sequences in the open reading frame and 3'-untranslated region of selenoprotein P mRNA. *Proc. Natl. Acad. Sci. USA.* 90:537–41

41. Hill, K. E., Lloyd, R. S., Yang, J.-G., Read, R., Burk, R. F. 1991. The

cDNA for rat selenoprotein P contains 10 TGA codons in the open reading frame. *J. Biol. Chem.* 266:10050–53

42. Hill, K. E., Lyons, P. R., Burk, R. F. 1992. Differential regulation of rat liver selenoprotein mRNAs in selenium deficiency. 185:260–63

43. Himeno, S., Takekawa, A., Toyoda, H., Imura, N. 1992. Tissue-specific expression of glutathione peroxidase gene in guinea pigs. *Biochim. Biophys. Acta.* In press

44. Kim, I. Y., Veres, Z., Stadtman, T. 1992. *Escherichia coli* mutant SELD enzymes. *J. Biol. Chem.* 267:19650–54

45. Knight, S. A. B., Sunde, R. A. 1987. The effect of progressive selenium deficiency on anti-glutathione peroxidase antibody reactive protein in rat liver. 117:732–38

46. Lee, B. J., Worland, P. J., Davis, J. N., Stadtman, T. C., Hatfield, D. L. 1989. Identification of selenocysteyl-tRNA^Ser in mammalian cells that recognizes the nonsense codon, UGA. *J. Biol. Chem.* 264:9724–27

47. Li, N., Reddy, P. S., Thyagaraju, K., Reddy, A. P., Hsu, B. L. et al. 1990. Elevation of rat liver mRNA for selenium-dependent glutathione peroxidase by selenium deficiency. *J. Biol. Chem.* 265:108–13

48. Mills, G. C. 1957. Hemoglobin catabolism. I. Glutathione peroxidase, an erythrocyte enzyme which protects hemoglobin from oxidative breakdown. 229:189–97

49. Mizutani, T., Kurata, H., Yamada, K., Totsuka, T. 1992. Some properties of murine selenocysteine synthase. *Biochem. J.* 284:827–34

50. Read, R., Bellew, T., Yang, J.-G., Hill, K. E., Palmer, I. S., Burk, R. F. 1990. Selenium and amino acid composition of selenoprotein P, the major selenoprotein in rat serum. 265:17899-17905

51. Rocher, C., Faucheu, C., Hervé, F. Bénicourt, C., Lalanne, J.-L. 1991. Cloning of murine SeGPX cDNA and synthesis of mutated GPX proteins in *Escherichia coli*. *Gene* 98:193–200

52. Rocher, C., Lalanne, J.-L., Chaudiere, J. 1992. Purification and properties of a recombinant sulfur analog of murine selenium-glutathione peroxidase. *Eur. J. Biochem.* 205:955–60

53. Rotruck, J. T., Pope, A. L., Ganther, H. E., Swanson, A. B., Hafeman, D., Hoekstra, W. G. 1973. Selenium: Bio-chemical role as a component of glutathione peroxidase. *Science* 179: 588–90

54. Roveri, A., Casasco, A., Maiorino, M., Dalan, P., Calligaro, A., Ursini, F. 1992. Phospholipid hydroperoxide glutathione peroxidase of rat testis. *J. Biol. Chem.* 267:6142–46

55. Saedi, M. W., Smith, C. G., Frampton, J., Chambers, I., Harrison, P. R., Sunde, R. A. 1988. Effect of selenium status on mRNA levels for glutathione peroxidase in rat liver. *Biochem. Biophys. Res. Commun.* 153:855–61

56. Sawers, G., Heider, J., Zehelein, E., Böck, A. 1991. Expression and operon structure of the *sel* genes of *Escherichia coli* and identification of a third selenium-containing formate dehydrogenase isoenzyme. *J. Bacteriol.* 173: 4983–93

57. Schuckelt, R., Brigelius-Flohé, R., Maiorino, M., Roveri, A., Reumkens, J., et al. 1991. Phospholipid hydroperoxide glutathione peroxidase is a selenoenzyme distinct from the classical glutathione peroxidase as evident from cDNA and amino acid sequencing. *Free Radical Res. Commun.* 14:343–61

58. Stadtman, T. C. 1990. Selenium biochemistry. *Annu. Rev. Biochem.* 59: 111–27

59. Stadtman, T. C. 1991. Biosynthesis and function of selenocysteine-containing enzymes. *J. Biol. Chem.* 266: 16257–60

60. Stadtman, T. C., Davis, J. N., Zehelein, E., Böck, A. 1989. Biochemical and genetic analysis of *Salmonella typhimurium* and *Escherichia coli* mutants defective in specific incorporation of selenium into formate dehydrogenase and tRNAs. *BioFactors* 2:35–44

61. Sunde, R. A. 1990. Molecular biology of selenoproteins. *Annu. Rev. Nutr.* 10:451–74

62. Takahashi, K., Akasaka, M., Yamamoto, Y., Kobayashi, C., Mizoguchi, J., Koyama, J. 1990. Primary structure of human plasma glutathione peroxidase deduced from cDNA sequences. *J. Biochem.* 108: 145–48

63. Takahashi, K., Cohen, H. J. 1986. Selenium-dependent glutathione peroxidase protein and activity: Immunological investigations on cellular and plasma enzymes. *Blood* 68:640–45

64. Toyoda, H., Himeno, S., Imura, N. 1990. Regulation of glutathione perox-

idase mRNA level by dietary selenium manipulation. *Biochim. Biophys. Acta* 1049:213–15

65. Ursini, F., Bindoli, A. 1987. The role of selenium peroxidases in the protection against oxidative damage of membranes. *Chem. Phys. Lipids* 44:255–76

66. Ursini, F., Maiorino, M., Gregolin, C. 1985. The selenoenzyme phospholipid hydroperoxide glutathione peroxidase. *Biochim. Biophys. Acta* 839: 62–70

67. Ursini, F., Pelosi, G., Tomassi, G., Benassi, A., Di Felice, M., Barsacchi, R. 1987. Effect of dietary fats on hydroperoxide-induced chemiluminescence emission and eicosanoid release in the rat heart. *Biochim. Biophys. Acta* 919:93–96

68. Veres, Z., Tsai, L., Scholz, T. D., Politino, M., Balaban, R. S., Stadtman, T. C. 1992. Synthesis of 5-methylaminomethyl-2-selenouridine in tRNAs: ^{31}P NMR studies show the labile selenium donor synthesized by the *sel*D gene product contains selenium bonded to phosphorus. *Proc. Natl. Acad. Sci. USA* 89:2975–79

69. Waschulewski, I. H., Sunde, R. A. 1988. Effect of dietary methionine on utilization of tissue selenium from dietary selenomethionine for glutathione peroxidase in the rat. *J. Nutr.* 118:367–74

70. Yang, J.-G., Hill, K. E., Burk, R. F. 1989. Dietary selenium intake controls rat plasma selenoprotein P concentration. 119:1010–12

71. Yoshida, M., Iwami, K., Yasumoto, K. 1982. Purification and immunochemical analysis of rat liver glutathione peroxidase. *Agric. Biol. Chem.* 46:41–46

72. Yoshimura, S., Takekoshi, S., Watanabe, K., Fujii-Kuriyama, Y. 1988. Determination of nucleotide sequence of cDNA coding rat glutathione peroxidase and diminished expression of the mRNA in selenium-deficient rat liver. *Biochem. Biophys. Res. Commun.* 154:1024–28

Annu. Rev. Nutr. 1993. 13:83–109
Copyright © 1993 by Annual Reviews Inc. All rights reserved

NUTRITIONAL MANAGEMENT OF GLYCOGEN STORAGE DISEASE

P. H. Parker

Department of Pediatrics, University of Mississippi, Jackson, Mississippi 39216

M. Ballew

Department of Pediatrics, Vanderbilt University, Nashville, Tennessee 37232

H. L. Greene

Meade Johnson Research Center, Evansville, Indiana 47721

KEY WORDS: dietary therapy glycogenosis, glycogenoses therapeutics

CONTENTS

INTRODUCTION 84
TYPE I GLYCOGEN STORAGE DISEASE 86
   Blood Glucose Changes 87
   Lactic Acid Changes 88
   Hyperlipidemia 89
   Hyperuricemia 90
   Hypophosphatemia 92
   Platelet Dysfunction 93
   Growth Impairment 94
   Hepatic Adenoma and Carcinoma 94
   Renal Involvement 94
NUTRITIONAL MANAGEMENT OF GSD-I 95
   Nocturnal Nutrient Infusion 95
   Daytime Feedings 97
   Patient Education 98
   Prognosis 101
TYPE II GLYCOGEN STORAGE DISEASE 101
TYPE III GLYCOGEN STORAGE DISEASE 102
TYPE IV GLYCOGEN STORAGE DISEASE 104
TYPE V GLYCOGEN STORAGE DISEASE 104
GLYCOGEN STORAGE DISEASES VI–X 106

0199-9885/93/0715-0083$02.00

INTRODUCTION

In 1929, the initial clinical and pathologic recognition of glycogen storage disease (GSD) affecting the liver and kidney was made by von Gierke (85). Three years later, a second type of glycogen storage disease involving not only the liver and kidney but most other organs as well was described by Pompe (69). In 1952, Cori & Cori found a deficiency of glucose-6-phosphatase activity in patients with von Gierke's disease (15). Since then the glycogenoses have been classified by the type of enzymatic defects and the primary organs involved. Abnormalities involving most every step of glycogen

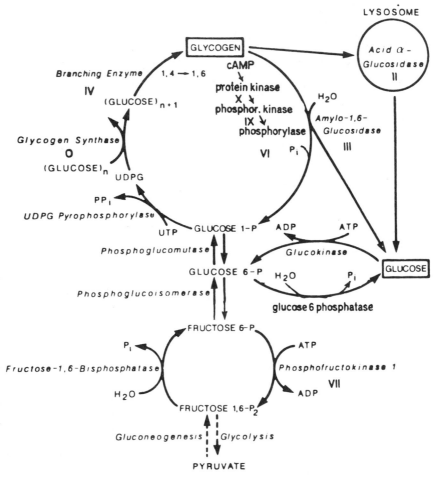

Figure 1 Diagram of the pathway of liver glycogen metabolism and its enzymic defects in various types of glucose storage disease.

Table 1 Classification of glycogen storage diseases (GSD)s

Type	Enzyme affected	Primary organ involved	Manifestations
O	Glycogen synthetase	Liver	Hypoglycemia, hyperketonemia. FTT[a] early death
Ia	Glucose-6-phosphatase	Liver	Enlarged liver and kidney, growth failure, fasting hypoglycemia, acidosis, lipemia, thrombocyte dysfunction
Ib	Microsomal membrane G-6-P transporter	Liver, PMN leucocytes	As in Ia; in addition, recurrent neutropenia, bacterial infections
Ic	Microsomal membrane PP$_i$ transporter	Liver	As in Ia
II	Lysosomal acid α-glucosidase (acid maltase)	All lysosome-containing organs	Infantile form: early-onset progressive muscle hypotonia, cardiac failure, death before 2 years; juvenile form: later-onset myopathy with variable cardiac involvement; adult form: limb-girdle muscular dystrophy-like features
III	Amylo-1,6-glucosidase (debrancher enzyme)	Liver, skeletal muscle, heart	Fasting hypoglycemia; hepatomegaly in infancy in some myopathic features; rarely, clinical cardiac features
IV	Amylo-1,4-1,6-trans-glucosidase (brancher enzyme)	Liver	Hepatosplenomegaly, cirrhosis
V	Muscle phosphorylase	Skeletal muscle	Exercise-induced muscular pain cramps and progressive weakness, sometimes with myoglobinuria
VI	Liver phosphorylase	Liver	Hepatomegaly, mild hypoglycemia, good prognosis
VII	Phosphofructokinase	Muscle, RBC	As in V; in addition, enzymopathic hemolysis
IXa	Phosphorylase b kinase	Liver	As in VI.
IXb	Phosphorylase b kinase	Liver, muscle (?), leucocytes	Hepatomegaly, sex-linked inheritance
IXc	Phosphorylase b kinase	Liver, muscle, blood cells	Hepatomegaly, autosomal inheritance
X	Cyclic AMP dependent kinase	Liver, muscle	Hepatomegaly

[a] FTT, failure to thrive; PMN, polymorphonuclear leucocytes.

synthesis and degradation have been described and are illustrated in Figure 1. A classification system of GSDs—the nomenclature of various types, enzyme or protein deficiency, organ involvement, and a summary of the main clinical features—is provided in Table 1. In spite of differences in the specific enzyme defects, most of the syndromes are not readily distinguishable on clinical grounds alone, and tissue analyses for glycogen content and enzymatic activity are necessary to confirm the diagnoses (41, 46).

In recent years, a better understanding of the pathophysiology of the GSDs has led to more effective therapy and an improvement in the quality of life and prognosis in these patients. However, increasing longevity has been accompanied by new problems that require further investigation and new therapeutic approaches. Because the greatest advances have been made in treatment of type I glycogen storage disease (GSD-I), we review this disorder and its management in detail. Special emphasis is placed on both the pathophysiologic mechanisms present in GSD-I and their response to nutritional therapy. In addition, specific practical dietary management of GSD-I is discussed. Finally we briefly review other types of GSD that may benefit from dietary therapies.

TYPE I GLYCOGEN STORAGE DISEASE

Type I glycogen storage disease (GSD-I) is due to a deficiency in the activity of glucose-6-phosphatase in the liver, kidney, and small intestine. This form of glycogenosis is transmitted in an autosomal recessive manner and accounts for about one fourth of all cases diagnosed (27, 36).

Type I GSD has been divided into at least five subtypes (IA, IASP, IB, IC, ID). This system of classification is based on the finding that for some patients in vitro activity of glucose-6-phosphatase is nearly normal, whereas in vivo activity is absent. Our understanding of the glucose-6-phosphatase enzyme system has expanded considerably and has been recently reviewed by Burchell & Waddell (9). The recognition of various types may help explain the wide variations in severity between patients and the presence of unusual features such as neutropenia in type IB. Since the different types have similar metabolic changes and a similar response to treatment, a general discussion of type IA (designated GSD-I) is presented.

Most enzymatic defects in the GSDs involve either the degradation of glycogen to glucose-6-phosphate or, rarely, the synthesis of glycogen from glucose-6-phosphate. In patients with GSD-I, the absence of activity of the gluconeogenic enzyme, glucose-6-phosphatase, results in an inability to release normal amounts of glucose from glucose-6-phosphate. The absence of enzymatic activity at such a crucial metabolic "crossroads" results in

Type I glycogen storage disease

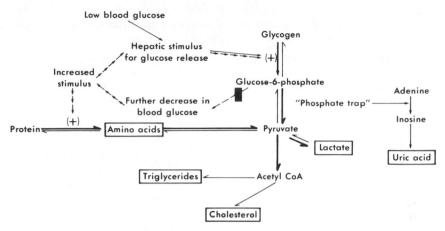

Figure 2 Biochemical basis for the primary laboratory findings in patients with glucose-6-phosphatase deficiency (*indicated by the solid rectangle*). The increased production of glucose-6-phosphate that results from continuous stimulation of glycogen breakdown apparently increases glycolysis, which in turn results in a net increase (*indicated by dark arrows*) in the production of lactate, triglyceride, cholesterol, and uric acid. Both glycogenolysis and gluconeogenesis are involved in the overproduction of substrate.

many of the biochemical and clinical features of GSD-I that are unique among the glycogen storage diseases. For example, lactic acidosis, hyperlipidemia, hyperuricemia, platelet dysfunction, and hepatic adenomas accompany GSD-I but are not seen with the other glycogenoses. The study of mechanisms whereby deficiency of glucose-6-phosphatase activity results in such striking aberrations in carbohydrate, lipid, and purine metabolism has been instrumental in the development of effective forms of therapy for this disorder (Figure 2).

Blood Glucose Changes

The most consistent and life-threatening feature of GSD-I is the hypoglycemia that occurs after relatively short periods of fasting. A decrease in blood glucose to less than 70 mg/dl almost always occurs after a 2- to 4-hr fast, and it is not uncommon to observe 6- to 8-hr fasting levels of 5 to 10 mg/dl. In normal individuals, blood glucose levels are maintained within a relatively narrow range by agents such as glucagon, which release glucose from glycogen, or by gluconeogenesis (13). In GSD-I both glycogenolysis and gluconeogenesis occur normally in response to hypoglycemia; however, because of an absence of glucose-6-phosphatase, glucose is not released from glucose-6-phosphate and blood glucose levels continue to decline. These patients have an appropriate hormonal (glucagon and insulin) response to changes in blood glucose concentrations (41, 79). In the absence of exogenous glucose, the blood glucose continues to decline and further hormonal stimulus occurs, resulting in far-reaching effects on various metabolic pathways.

Patients with untreated GSD-I do not always manifest the characteristic clinical features of hypoglycemia and may function completely normally with levels of blood glucose below 20 mg/dl. This adaptation to hypoglycemia has been attributed to high levels of lactate, which can serve as an alternate fuel for brain metabolism (17, 34). When patients are metabolically and hormonally stabilized with adequate therapy, their clinical response to hypoglycemia is the same as seen in normal individuals (27, 64).

As glucose-6-phosphatase provides the final common pathway for glucose production from both glycogenolysis and gluconeogenesis, one would expect a block at this step to result in a major reduction in endogenous glucose production. In 1969, Havel et al reported that two adults with GSD-I showed near-normal basal rates of glucose production (34). This observation has been verified in patients of all ages by several investigators (53, 70, 81). Although the source of this endogenous glucose production is currently unknown, these studies have important therapeutic implications. (*i*) Patients with GSD-I can release glucose into the circulation at close to normal basal rates but cannot increase glucose release during fasting, in response to exercise, or following a pharmacologic dose of glucagon. Thus, their maximal rate of glucose production is fixed and substantially below that present in normal individuals. (*ii*) Maximal glucose production rates are variable between patients and related to the individual patient's tendency for fasting-induced hypoglycemia and the severity of the clinical illness. (*iii*) Endogenous production of glucose is not inhibited unless an exogenous source of glucose is provided at a rate of 8 mg/kg per minute, an amount that maintains blood glucose levels at about 90 mg/dl.

Lactic Acid Changes

Under normal circumstances, most circulating lactate is generated by muscle glycolysis during exercise and is efficiently metabolized by the liver (13). In patients with GSD-I most of the circulating lactate is generated by hepatic glycolysis (75). In the latter case, apparently hepatic stimulation to release glucose from glycogen is combined with inefficient gluconeogenesis. The excessive glucose-6-phosphate formed during glycogenolysis cannot be hydrolyzed to free glucose because of the lack of glucose-6-phosphatase activity and is diverted through the glycolytic pathway. The result is increased lactate formation.

Hyperlipidemia

Elevation of plasma lipids is a consistent and striking abnormality: Triglyceride levels reach 6000 mg/dl and cholesterol levels 400–600 mg/dl (19, 27, 49). Free fatty acid levels are also usually elevated. Xanthomas typically appear over extensor surfaces usually around puberty, but they may also develop in childhood.

As with lacticemia, elevated triglyceride and cholesterol levels appear to be a consequence of increased rates of glycogenolysis and glycolysis. In GSD-I excessive hepatic glycolysis increases hepatic nicotinamide-adenine dinucleotide (NADH), nicotinamide-adenine dinucleotide phosphate (NADPH), and acetyl coenzyme A (CoA), three compounds important in fatty acid and cholesterol synthesis (75). The increases in glycerol-3-phosphate and acetyl CoA generated by the glycolytic pathway, together with elevated levels of reduced cofactors, could sustain an increased rate of triglyceride and cholesterol synthesis (20, 65). In addition to this apparent increased rate of lipid synthesis, hypoglycemia stimulates lipolysis from peripheral lipid stores. This further augments hyperlipidemia and hepatic steatosis by increasing circulating free fatty acids (19, 20, 44, 65).

The institution of a strict dietary regimen to maintain near-normal blood glucose levels results in a marked reduction in serum lipids. However, most patients with GSD-I have had persistent hypertriglyceridemia, even after years of treatment (28, 58). While this phenomenon appears to result primarily from increased lipid synthesis, other patients have shown decreased levels of postheparin lipoprotein lipase and lipid clearance in GSD-I (20, 34).

A detailed analysis of plasma lipids in 12 patients with GSD-I was recently published (30). All patients had triglyceride levels between 1440 and 6120 mg/dl before treatment. After treatment to maintain blood glucose levels of 75–85 mg/dl, triglyceride levels were between 189 +/–31 and 510 +/– 60 mg/dl in 11 patients. One patient, whose triglyceride levels remained elevated despite dietary treatment, was given several treatment strategies that have been useful in the management of hyperlipidemia. Clofibrate, niacin, and fish oil resulted in a temporary decline in triglyceride levels. However, lovastatin, a 3-hydroxy-3-methylglutaryl CoA reductase inhibitor, resulted in a substantial increase in triglyceride levels, although the serum cholesterol decreased significantly. The mechanism of these changes in response to lovastatin has not been studied but might be explained by the possible diversion of acetyl CoA from cholesterol synthesis to fatty acid and triglyceride synthesis.

Combined treatment with clofibrate and niacin provided a more sustained reduction in triglyceride levels; however, the tendency to become resistant to pharmacologic intervention, together with possible complication from these agents, may prevent their long-term use.

In addition to the hyperlipidemia in patients with GSD-I, Levy et al suggested that the low-fat diet used in treatment may promote an essential fatty acid (EFA) deficiency that could contribute to impaired growth (57). No other clinical signs of EFA deficiency were noted in these patients. To evaluate the possibility of EFA deficiency, the plasma fatty acid composition and urinary prostaglandin excretion was evaluated in six patients with GSD-I (30). Increased percentages of 16:0 and $16:_{w7}$ and decreased percentages of $18:2_{w6}$ and $20:4_{w6}$ were found. These changes are generally characteristic of EFA deficiency. However, although the $20:3_{w6}/20:4_{w6}$ ratio was increased, there was no increase in $20:3_{w9}$, the characteristic fatty acid present in EFA deficiency, in either these patients or those of Levy. The most likely explanation for the changes in plasma fatty acids in GSD-I is the increased rate of hepatic lipogenesis. Havel et al demonstrated a high rate of synthesis and release of free acids in triacylglycerols, predominantly of 16:0 and $16:1_{w9}$, which could stimulate triglyceride and lipoprotein production by the liver (34). Indeed, the increased levels of 16:0 and $16:1_{w9}$ observed in these patients are consistent with the suggested increase in hepatic fatty acid synthesis in GSD-I. An absence of EFA deficiency is further supported by the normal excretion of prostaglandin E-M (PGE-M) in these patients (21).

Hyperuricemia

Although blood levels of uric acid and the tendency to develop nephropathy and gouty arthritis vary in different patients, those surviving to puberty often have gouty complications (18, 39). The hyperuricemia was originally attributed to the increased levels of blood lactate and lipids, which competitively inhibit urate excretion at a renal level (18, 42). However, the high level of urate excretion together with the increased rate of incorporation of C^{14}-L-glycine into plasma and urinary urate indicates that an increased rate of purine synthesis de novo is probably more important than a decrease in urate excretion in the genesis of hyperuricemia (50, 54). At least two mechanisms can influence the rate of purine synthesis: (i) alteration of the precursor concentration and (ii) alteration of the end product, or purine concentration (31, 71). Supporting the former mechanism is the observation that two substrates, phosphoribosylpyrophosphate (PRPP) and glutamine, are necessary for the first committed reaction of purine synthesis. This reaction transfers the amine from L-glutamine to PRPP to form 5-phosphoribosyl-1-amine and is apparently the rate-limiting step for the entire sequence of purine synthesis (Figure 3). Blood levels of glutamate and glutamine obtained from hyperuricemic patients

Figure 3   Purine synthesis as a result of increased precursor concentrations.

with GSD-I are three- to eightfold higher than are values obtained after urate is normalized by glucose infusion (29). The high levels of glucose-6-phosphate produced during periods of hypoglycemia and excessive glycogenolysis may increase hexose monophate shunt activity and increase synthesis of ribose-5-phosphate, the second important substrate in purine synthesis (18, 40). This suggests that an apparent increased availability of purine precursors, glutamine, and ribose-5-phosphate may cause a secondary increase in PRPP and thus increase the rate of purine synthesis. Studies using human leukocytes indicate, however, that an increase in availability of glutamine and ribose-5-phosphate does not necessarily increase the generation of PRPP (7). If this is true in the liver, then low concentration of intracellular purine may be more important in increasing the rate of purine synthesis in patients with GSD-I.

In support of the second mechanism of hyperuricemia, low levels of purine ribonucleotides would favor an increase in the rate of purine biosynthesis by releasing glutamine pyrophosphate-ribose-phosphate amidotransferase from end-product inhibition (37). Although hepatic nucleotide levels during hypoglycemic episodes have not been measured directly, indirect evidence suggests that hypoglycemia can reduce adenyl ribonucleotide concentrations in GSD-I (26). Such a reduction in ATP has been shown to favor the rapid degradation of adenyl or guanyl ribonucleotides to inosine, xanthine, and uric acid (73). These reactions are also promoted by low levels of intracellular phosphate, which apparently occur through "phosphate trapping" of the phosphorylated intermediates of the Emden-Meyerhoff pathway (22, 73). These observations suggest that the increase in uric acid production is due to recurrent episodes of hypoglycemia, which result in compensatory glucagon release (Figure 4). Glucagon stimulates glycogen degradation to glucose-6-phosphate, and an absence of phosphatase activity results in a phosphate-trapping effect and lowering of ATP levels, which in turn promotes degradation of preformed purines to uric acid. Finally, the decrease in purine concentration promotes a high rate of purine biosynthesis.

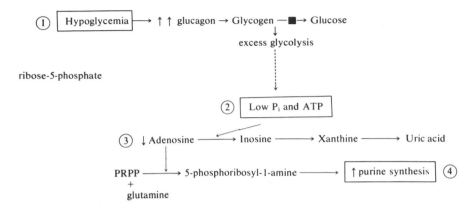

Figure 4   Purine synthesis as a result of increased purine degradation.

Hypophosphatemia

Low levels of circulating phosphate are not an invariable finding but are often present during periods of hypoglycemia and acidosis. This phenomenon is thought to be created by the phosphate trap resulting from glucose-6-phosphatase deficiency. Because of their inability to release inorganic phosphate, liver cells must take up phosphorus from the plasma with a consequent decline in circulating phosphate levels (22) (Figure 5). In addition, a relative metabolic block at the aldolase step of glycolysis would be expected because of the progressive increase in NADH formed during the initial phase of the reaction cascade from glucose-6-phosphate to pyruvate. This metabolic block would

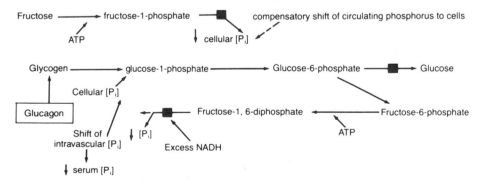

Figure 5   Serum phosphate changes in GSD-I.

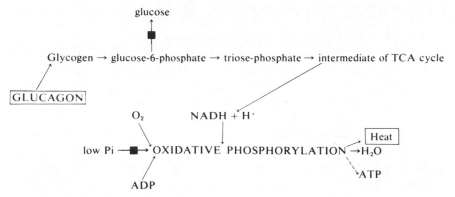

Figure 6   Uncoupling of oxidative phosphorylation in GSD-I.

promote even more phosphate-trapping with a further shift of circulating phosphate to the intracellular pool. As the phosphate is lost from the metabolic intermediates, a compensatory return of phosphate back into the circulation would be expected. Hypophosphatemia may also explain the recurrent episodes of fever occasionally seen in patients with GSD-I during episodes of severe hypoglycemia and acidosis. The febrile response may represent an uncoupling of oxidative phosphorylation secondary to a lack of intracellular Pi. For example, following exogenous glucagon administration to stimulate hypoglycemia, some patients became febrile with severe lactic acidosis and hypophosphatemia (22). It has been suggested that the burst of glycolysis produced by glucagon resulted in a high level of reduced cofactors, which normally produce high-energy phosphates. Owing to limited levels of intracellular phosphate, oxidative phosphorylation would be expected to result in heat production rather than chemical energy in the form of ATP (Figure 6).

Platelet Dysfunction

Frequent nosebleeds and a hemorrhagic tendency during surgical procedures have been observed in patients with GSD-I. In the majority of these patients a prolonged bleeding time, abnormal platelet aggregation, reduced platelet adhesiveness, and an impaired ability of platelets to release ADP in response to collagen or epinepherine were demonstrated (1, 14, 23). These defects in platelet function may be secondary to systemic metabolic abnormalities such as hypoglycemia, hyperlipidemia, and hyeruricemia. Czapek et al have shown that the platelet dysfunction in GSD-I can be corrected by improving the metabolic state of the patients with parenteral or nasogastric therapy (16). Thus, while the specific mechanism causing the abnormal platelet function is not clearly defined it is correctable by maintenance of a blood glucose concentration within the normal range (70–100 mg/dl).

Growth Impairment

Children with GSD-I are of short stature but without disproportionate head size or extremity length. Bones may be osteoporotic, and some patients have delayed bone age. The mechanisms leading to these changes are not clear. Thyroid hormone and growth hormone levels are normal or increased (29, 41). Measurement of caloric-protein intake in GSD-I indicates adequate caloric consumption. Chronic lactic acidosis and reversal of the insulin-glucagon ratio have been proposed as factors in preventing normal growth. Recently, Yudkoff et al studied whole-body protein synthesis in four patients with GSD-I (88). A depletion of their amino acid pool, presumably due to excessive protein catabolism associated with decreased protein synthesis, was found. This process was reversed when glucose was administered at 150% of the expected normal glucose production rate. This catabolic state, which exists in the presence of insufficient glucose administration, may contribute to the poor growth in these patients.

Hepatic Adenoma and Carcinoma

The majority of patients with GSD-I who are more than 20 years old have adenomatous nodules in their liver. These adenomas usually develop during the second decade of life, but may occur in younger patients. A number of patients have had a malignant degeneration of these adenomas to hepatocellular carcinoma, most often after 30 years of age (43, 59, 68, 74). The mechanism causing these adenomas or their malignant change is unknown. Strict adherence to dietary therapy may reduce the tendency for adenoma formation, but in the authors' experience all patients eventually develop adenomas (66). This suggests that chronic stimulation of the liver by hepatotrophic agents (glucagon and others), which increase blood glucose level, may be important in the genesis of the adenomas.

Renal Involvement

The kidneys are enlarged in GSD-I and have no glucose-6-phosphatase activity. The elevated serum level of uric acid in GSD-I has been associated with the development of uric acid nephropathy (12, 18, 54). This complication has decreased considerably with improved dietary therapy, which results in decreased blood uric acid levels, and occasional allopurinol administration. Recently, cases of chronic renal disease with a progressive glomerulosclerosis have been described in older patients with GSD-I (10). The renal disease in these patients may progress to renal failure and death. Although the cause of the lesion is unclear, apparently the incidence is lowered by good metabolic control, since none of the authors' nine patients, ages 25 to 34, show renal abnormalities.

NUTRITIONAL MANAGEMENT OF GSD-I

The objective of dietary therapy in GSD-I is to provide a constant source of carbohydrate sufficient to maintain blood glucose levels between approximately 70 and 100 mg/dl. Preventing fluctuations of greater magnitude minimizes organic acidemia, hyperlipidemia, hyperuricemia and maximizes achievement of full growth potential. In fact, virtually all clinical manifestations of the disorder can be reversed through appropriate nutritional management. This objective may be achieved through a combination of a nocturnal nutrient infusion and frequent daytime feedings of a high starch diet in which raw cornstarch is used to provide a steady, "time-release" source of glucose.

Traditionally, the Recommended Dietary Allowances (RDA) have been used as a guideline to estimate the initial energy requirements. While no data indicate that energy requirements for individuals with GSD-I differ from the norm, this approach may be inappropriate for predicting the needs of individuals, particularly when disease imposes the potential for altered nutrient utilization. Initially, infants and children with GSD-I are often below the fiftieth percentile for age on National Center for Health Statistics growth charts; however, they are often above average weight for height. Thus, alterations in body composition limit the applicability of standard equations for predicting energy requirements in this disorder.

Ideally, the calorie content of the GSD-I diet should be determined through actual measurement of 24-hr energy expenditure. Unfortunately, metabolic chambers are usually available only in research settings. However, portable metabolic carts that determine energy requirements through measurement of O_2 consumption and CO_2 production have become increasingly available in the past ten years and may prove useful in the management of this group of patients.

The 1989 RDA are used to establish protein requirements for the individual with GSD-I. These age-specific standards are used as a guideline to ensure that minimum daily protein requirements are met.

Nocturnal Nutrient Infusion

Once energy requirements are established, this component of nutritional therapy is planned. Nutritionally complete elemental formulas in which glucose polymers are the predominant energy source are ideal for this purpose. The formula provides 30–40% of total energy needs. Infusion rate is calculated based on hepatic glucose production rate, which, in the authors' experience, ranges from 4 to 6 mg/kg per minute during sleep. This usually requires an 8- to 10-hr infusion period beginning within 3 hr of the last daytime feeding and ending 30 minutes after the first meal the following morning to avoid precipitous declines in blood glucose levels. The need for consistent delivery of glucose mandates the use of pump-assisted infusion, and it is essential that the enteral feeding pump be equipped with an alarm system in the event that tube occlusion, power failure, or other problems interrupt the infusion during the night (19). Calculation of a nocturnal nutrient infusion is shown in Table 2.

Various commercial elemental formulas have been used successfully and include Criticare HN®, Tolerex®, Vital HN®, and Vivonex TEN®. Other elemental formulas of lower osmolality for improved gastrointestinal tolerance are now available. Unfortunately, the high fat content of these formulas limits their applicability in GSD, since fat does not contribute to blood glucose maintenance. Pregestimil® and Prosobee®, two infant formulas that contain glucose oligosaccharides as the sole carbohydrate source, are used in children less than one year of age (19).

Table 2 Calculation of a GSD-I diet

Patient: 4-year old female

Weight: 16 kg (50th percentile); height: 37½ inches (5th percentile); average weight for height: 14 kg
Predicted energy needs: 1260 kcal/day
Proteins needs: 15–18 gm/day
Nocturnal nutrient infusion

Criticare HN: 1.06 kcal/cc; 220 gm CHO/L; 38 gm pro/L
   1260 kcal × 25% = 318 kcal
   Volume required: 300 cc
   Infusion rate: 30 cc/hr × 10 hr (6.9 mg glucose/kg/min)
Daytime feedings

Remaining energy needs: 942 kcal
Carbohydrate: 942 × 65% = 612 kcal (153)
Protein: 942 × 15% = 141 kcal (35 gm)
Fat: 942 × 20% = 188 kcal (21 gm)

ADA exchanges	Carbohydrate	Protein	Fat
10 starch/bread	150	30	10
2 meat (lean)	—	14	6
1 fat	—	—	5
Total (gm)	150	44	21
kcal/gm	×4	×4	×9
Total (kcal)	600	176	189
Actual nutrient distribution	62%	18%	20%

Nocturnal nutrient infusions should be instituted in a closely monitored setting where serial measurements of blood glucose, lactic acid, uric acid, and triglycerides taken at 3- to 4-hr intervals can be used to evaluate efficacy of therapy. Infants and small children may experience improved gastrointestinal tolerance if formula is prepared at 20-kcal/oz concentration, However, if higher caloric density (i.e. 30 to 40 kcal/oz) is tolerated, urinary frequency during the infusion may be diminished. A number of investigators have successfully utilized uncooked cornstarch to avoid nocturnal infusions in patients at all ages, including infants (11, 87). In the authors' experience, growth rates were less with the raw starch regimen than with nocturnal infusions. Thus, while cornstarch feedings may be beneficial in some patients, careful monitoring of blood glucose levels is essential to ensure that treatment is optimal for individual patients. Once growth potential is achieved and glucose requirements decrease, cornstarch feedings may be used in place of the nocturnal nutrient infusion in most patients.

Daytime Feedings

The remainder of the calculated energy requirements is provided in small, high starch meals administered every 3 hr or as frequently as needed to maintain desired blood glucose levels between approximately 70 and 100 mg/dl.

Carbohydrate, supplied primarily in the form of starch, should provide 60–70% of the calories in daytime meals. Establishing carbohydrate content of daytime feedings at 8 to 9 mg/kg per minute has proven successful in achieving adequate metabolic control (19).

Raw cornstarch, which provides a gradual and sustained increase in blood glucose, may be administered with or between meals to achieve carbohydrate intake goals. Quantities equivalent to 1.75–2.5 gm cornstarch/kg (1 tablespoon = 10 gm cornstarch) given every 4 hr, or any amount needed to achieve desired metabolic response, may be mixed in relatively small quantities of water or sugar-free noncarbonated beverages. Rice cereal may be used as an alternative in infants who do not tolerate cornstarch feedings. Experiments using glucose and glucose polymers (Polycose® and Moducal®) have produced less favorable results. Both are rapidly absorbed, resulting in significant elevation of blood glucose. Subsequently, a rapid decline due to substantial insulin output occurs when blood glucose concentration exceeds 90 mg/dl.

Grain products and starchy vegetables should be the predominant sources of carbohydrate in daytime feedings, as the sugars contained in these foods are broken down entirely to glucose (33). Vegetables used in limited quantities are considered "free" choices. Additional benefits may be realized by including foods with high dietary fiber content. In the late 1970s, Jenkins et al demonstrated that dietary fiber reduced postprandial blood glucose in patients with diabetes mellitus (51). These findings have been confirmed by others, and a comprehensive review of this subject was published by Anderson et al in 1987 (3). Soluble dietary fibers such as pectin and guar gum have been shown to have the most favorable effect on blood glucose response. The mechanism of action is thought to be related to their ability to delay glucose absorption in the proximal small intestine. In GSD-I, this delay theoretically minimizes peaks in blood glucose concentration and the subsequent rapid lowering of blood sugar because of reactive insulin release.

While the ingestion of fructose and galactose does not exert a toxic effect in GSD-I, the metabolic defect associated with this disorder prevents their conversion to glucose. Thus, foods containing fructose or galactose contribute less to the prevention of hypoglycemia than do grains and starches. Also, liberal intake of these sugars predisposes to inadequate starch intake. Therefore, fruits, juices, table sugar, and dairy products are limited but not omitted from the diet.

Dietary protein should provide 10–20% of total energy intake in daytime meals. Overall intake of protein from meat, poultry, fish, and eggs should meet the 1989 RDA based on age of the individual. Commercial enteral formulas used in the nocturnal nutrient infusion also contribute to the high quality protein content of the diet.

Fat should provide no more than 20–25% of calories in daytime feedings. Although this nutrient contributes little to elevations of cholesterol and triglycerides seen in GSD-I, it has no measurable effect in preventing hypoglycemia. Unrestricted use of fat can be detrimental if it replaces starch in the diet or contributes to excessive caloric intake resulting in obesity.

Long-term restriction of foods containing fructose and galactose results in inadequate intake of calcium and vitamin C. A portion of the deficits will be supplied by the formula used for nocturnal feeding. Supplementation with an appropriate multivitamin preparation and with calcium to meet the RDA for age group is recommended.

Patient Education

Education of the patient and caregivers should be initiated as soon as the diagnosis of GSD-I is confirmed. As with any modified diet, thorough understanding of the rationale for dietary modifications will enhance compliance. Clearly conveying priorities concerning dietary management facilitates appropriate choices by the patient and caregivers when the diet cannot be followed to perfection. For example, adhering to the meal schedule and intake of high starch foods is much more important in day-to-day treatment than the need to completely avoid foods containing fructose and galactose. The dietitian can help alleviate unnecessary anxiety if this information is clearly conveyed at the beginning of the teaching session.

Detailed guidelines on the management of home enteral nutritional support have been published elsewhere (19, 24). Instruction manuals and educational pamphlets are also readily available from formula and equipment manufacturers to facilitate training in this aspect of nutritional therapy. Instructions should include technique for tube placement and removal since most patients with GSD-I prefer to be completely free from the apparatus during the day.

Food exchange lists for the GSD-I diet were made available in 1984 (19). However, the most recent edition of the "Exchange Lists for Meal Planning" published by the American Diabetes Association and the American Dietetic Association in 1986 is an appropriate tool for teaching principles of meal planning. Information regarding the cornstarch equivalent of a bread/starch food choice (2 tablespoons cornstarch = 1 exchange) should be added to the exchange lists. Foods containing increased amounts of fiber as well as those of low fat content are highlighted to encourage frequent inclusion in the diet. Restriction of fructose and galactose can be accomplished simply by limiting choices from the fruit list, the milk list, and "Food for Occasional Use." Sample menus are shown in Table 3.

Finally, patients and caregivers should be educated on recognition and management of hypoglycemia. Symptoms of mild hypoglycemia include sweating, shakiness, irritability, and hunger and usually occur following a missed meal, an unusual amount of physical activity or during gastrointestinal illness. The condition may progress rapidly to unconsciousness if steps are not taken to raise blood glucose.

Early signs of hypoglycemia are best treated with administration of raw cornstarch (15–30 gm or 1.5 to 3 tablespoons) or cooked wheat starch (two to four crackers or 1/2 to 1 slice of bread). Overly concerned parents or children have been known to administer glucose or polysaccharides (corn syrup, Polycose, or Moducal) so frequently that rapid shifts in blood glucose between hypo- and hyperglycemia have occurred. However, in the event of severe hypoglycemia, these preparations may be necessary to achieve a more rapid increase in blood sugar. In such an instance, one teaspoon of powdered or two teaspoons of liquid glucose polymer per 30 pounds of body weight is usually sufficient to raise blood glucose by 30–40 mg/dl. If necessary, corn syrup containing no added sucrose (two teaspoons per 30 pounds) may be given. If neither is available, sweetened carbonated beverages or fruit juice may be given, but these have less effect on blood sugar since fructose cannot be converted to glucose in GSD-I.

Patients should be reevaluated initially after six months and annually thereafter, preferably in the hospital setting. During the first two days of hospitalization, diet and tube feedings should be administered exactly as reported to have been given at home. Effects on blood glucose are monitored and therapy is altered accordingly. Adjustments in nutrient intake to meet

Table 3 Meal pattern and menu for 4-year-old with GSD-I

Meal pattern	Day 1	Day 2	Day 3
7:30 A.M.			
2 starch/bread	2 slices whole grain	1 cup oatmeal, cooked	1 fat-free waffle
⅓ fat	toast	1 tsp diet margarine	2 tbsp artif. sweet syrup
Free choices	1 tsp diet margarine	Brown sugar substitute	8 oz ½% milk[a]
	2 tsp artif. sweet jelly	1 oz apple juice[a]	
	4 oz orange juice[a]		
10:00 A.M.			
2 starch/bread	12 oz cornstarch be-	12 oz cornstarch be-	12 oz cornstarch be-
Free choices	verage[b]	verage[b]	verage[b]
12:30 P.M.			
2 starch/bread	6 saltine crackers	15 baked tortilla chips	¼ of 10 inch cheese
1 meat	10 ¾ oz can chunky	Tuna salad sandwich: 2	pizza[c]
⅓ fat	soup	slices low calories,	1 cup lettuce salad
Free choices	Diet soft drink	high fiber bread	2 tbsp low calorie ranch
		¼ cup tuna packed in	dressing
		water	Diet soft drink
		1 tsp reduced calorie	
		mayonnaise	
		Celery, chopped	
		8 oz ½% milk[a]	
3:00 P.M.			
2 starch/bread	3 cups popcorn, with	¾ oz pretzels	18 reduced fat cheese
Free choices	butter-flavored season-	6 oz cornstarch be-	crackers
	ing	verage[b]	6 oz cornstarch be-
	6 oz cornstarch be-		verage[b]
	verage[b]		
6:00 P.M.			
2 starch/bread	½ cup lima beans	1 medium corn on cob	⅔ cup rice, cooked
1 meat	cooked	1 hamburger bun, small	1 chicken drumstick,
⅓ fat	1 dinner roll, plain	1 oz lean hamburger	baked
Free choices	1 oz pork tenderloin,	patty	½ cup steamed broccoli
	grilled	1 tsp reduced calorie	Butter Buds®
	2 tsp brown gravy	mayo	½ cup sliced peaches[a]
	½ cup carrots steamed	Mustard	Water
	Butter Buds	1 tbsp catsup	
	8 oz ½% milk[a]	Butter Buds	
		1 cup artif. sweet.	
		gelatin	
		2 tbsp whipped topping	
		Diet soft drink	

[a]Limited amounts of dairy products, fruits and juices are included to increase nutritional value of the diet and to enhance acceptance.
[b]Cornstarch beverage contains 2 tbsp raw cornstarch per 6 oz water or artificially sweetened fruit drink.
[c]Contains entire daily fat allowance.

changing requirements for growth with age and activity should also be made at this time.

A lifetime need for dietary modifications and specialized nutritional therapy imposes psychological demands on the patient, especially during adolescence. The dietitian should strive to accommodate food preferences and lifestyle as much as possible to enhance compliance without sacrificing metabolic control, particularly during stressful times. The Association for Glycogen Storage Disease is an excellent source of additional information and support for patients and family members affected by this disease.

Prognosis

While long-term follow-up of the results of aggressive dietary therapy is not complete, a ten-year follow-up indicates that these patients have many fewer problems than they had prior to treatment. As long as blood glucose is consistently maintained between 70 and 100 mg/dl, most children appear to lead fairly normal, healthy lives, with normal growth and development. In general, patients tolerate fasting better after completing adolescence. One of our adult patients can now fast for over eight hours without developing significant hypoglycemia (25).

As more patients are moving into adult life, close evaluation for the development of hepatic adenomas, complications because of hyperlipidemia, and renal disease is essential. We strongly feel that the occurrence of many of these problems may be related to intermittent, suboptimal control of an adequate glucose level, and we cannot overemphasize the need for close follow-up of these patients.

TYPE II GLYCOGEN STORAGE DISEASE

Type II glycogen storage disease (GSD-II) is a lysosomal storage disorder that is due to a deficiency of acid α-glucosidase (35, 69). The disease is inherited in a autosomal recessive manner and is clinically heterogeneous. Three types have been recognized, infantile, juvenile, and adult, based on the age of onset and the severity of symptoms. In the infantile form, symptoms become manifest during the first months of life, with weakness, hypotonia, respiratory difficulties, and cardiac failure usually resulting in death by one to two years of age despite all therapeutic interventions. In the late onset juvenile and adult types, skeletal muscle weakness is usually the only clinical symptom, with resultant respiratory failure being the major cause of death (35, 36, 72).

The severity of symptoms in GSD-II correlates closely with the level of residual α-glucosidase activity and the extent of lysosomal storage of glycogen (36, 61, 72). This storage is due to an inability to degrade lysosomal glycogen to glucose in the absence of α-glucosidase. In the infantile form, the muscle weakness has been attributed to a disruption of muscle fibers by this excessive lysosomal accumulation of glycogen (32, 45, 77). In the juvenile and adult types, the pathogenesis of the weakness is less clear because morphological changes may be minimal (61, 77). An additional factor, increased net muscle catabolism, may play a role in the development of the myopathy in these patients. In GSD-II both a high rate of muscle turnover and increased use of muscle proteins as a source of energy have been documented (82). These findings have prompted the adoption of high protein diets in treating this disorder. A number of studies have shown that diets providing 30–47% of total calories as protein resulted in significant improvement in muscle strength in juvenile or adult type GSD-II (48, 60, 77, 82).

A group of five adults with acid glucosidase deficiency were treated with a diet containing 16–22% protein for six months (83). A decrease in protein degradation was noted, but no improvement in strength occurred. Possibly, a higher protein intake for longer periods may have had a clinical effect.

High protein diets result in increased levels of branched-chain amino acids (BCAA) (77). These BCAA are the principal amino acids involved in muscle protein synthesis and utilization. Mobarhan et al supplemented a normal diet with an enteral formula containing high levels of BCAA (Travesorb Hepatic®) in an adult with GSD-II (62). Approximately 36% of the patient's total daily caloric intake of 2700 kcal was supplied by the enteral formula. This diet resulted in a significant increase in muscle strength, comparable to that seen with high-protein diets. In addition, higher postprandial concentrations of BCAA were found after the enteral feedings when compared to a high protein meal. As large quantities of food rich in BCAA (fruits, vegetables, meats, dairy products) must be ingested to be beneficial (and maintain adequate total protein intake), the use of an enteral supplement would appear logical. In addition, the use of a liquid supplement is particularly useful in the extremely weak or ventilator-dependent patient. Other enteral formulas containing high levels of BCAA include Hepatic Aid II®, Vivonex TEN®, Stresskin®, and Transverse-Aid HBC®.

TYPE III GLYCOGEN STORAGE DISEASE

Type III glycogen storage disease (GSD-III) is an autosomal recessive disorder that is due to a deficiency of debranching enzyme (amylo-1,6-glucosidase) activity in a number of cells including liver, muscle, leukocyte, erythrocyte, and fibroblast (36, 47). The purified enzyme consists of a single polypeptide chain with two separate catalytic activities: an α-1,4-glucan transferase and an α-glucosidase. A striking enzymic variability is found among patients regarding overall debrancher activity in various tissues and the activities of the transfer and hydrolytic enzymes. On this basis, GSD-III patients have been divided into eight subtypes (a–h). An absence of enzyme activity in both liver and muscle (GSD-IIIa) accounts for over 75% of the cases (63).

Clinically, GSD-III has many similarities to GSD-I with both conditions manifesting hypoglycemia, hepatomegaly, and growth retardation in early life (22, 36). The clinical course in GSD-III is generally much milder than that of GSD-I, and severe hypoglycemia is not a problem except with prolonged fasting. Serum levels of transaminases are consistently moderately elevated (300 to 600 IU; normal 40 IU), although some patients show elevations of 900–2000 IU, thus indicating varying degrees of hepatocellular damage (22). Patients with GSD-III usually have evidence of hepatic fibrosis but do not necessarily progress to cirrhosis and liver failure. Hug has found several patients with combined defects in phosphorylase and phosphorylase kinase. These patients are generally more severely affected and tend to develop cirrhosis (46). The actual frequency of cirrhosis in GSD-III will obviously require both accurate determination of specific enzyme deficiencies and long-term follow-up.

Lipid levels in serum are variably elevated and to some extent seem to be related to the individual tendency toward fasting hypoglycemia. Uric acid levels are generally normal, but rare patients (usually those with muscle involvement) reportedly have slight elevations. Serum levels of creatinine kinase are elevated in virtually all patients with muscle involvement even prior to or in the absence of clinical weakness.

In addition to hepatic involvement, a number of patients with GSD-III have muscle weakness and some patients may develop a progressive myopathy (36, 63). Low serum levels of branched-chain amino acids have been found in GSD-III and have been considered indicators of increased muscle protein turnover. Excessive gluconeogenesis, as evidenced by low levels of glucogenic enzymes such as alanine, may impose a drain on muscle amino acids and be partly responsible for the muscle wasting reported in isolated cases (64). Glycogen may also accumulate in the heart, and moderate cardiomegaly with nonspecific electrocardiographic and echocardiographic changes may occur (36). However, significant cardiac problems are rare.

The development of hypoglycemia after prolonged fasting may occur in GSD-III patients with liver involvement during infancy and early childhood. This problem may be managed with continuous nocturnal infusions and frequent daytime feedings, as in GSD-I. Treatment of older patients with GSD-III remains investigative and should be restricted to those who have obvious muscle involvement, progressive fibrotic changes in the liver, or both. Current investigative trials combine the technique of nocturnal feeding with known responses to protein and amino acids.

In GSD-III (with muscle involvement) increased dietary protein may be beneficial not only by providing amino acids as substrate for gluconeogenesis but also for muscle protein synthesis and, possibly, as an alternate fuel for muscle metabolism (64). Slonim and co-workers treated a patient with a high protein diet (25% of total calories) during the day and continuous nasogastric infusions of a high protein formula at night with a resultant improvement in growth and muscle strength (77). More recently, in a patient with only hepatic involvement, Borowitz & Greene found that growth, transaminase levels, and blood glucose values were more positively influenced by a high starch diet with a standard protein intake (6). These studies are encouraging, but more extensive follow-up evaluation over a longer period of time is needed. In addition, the necessity of an accurate diagnosis in regard to specific organ involvement is obviously essential for planning therapy and assessing response.

TYPE IV GLYCOGEN STORAGE DISEASE

Type IV glycogen storage disease (GSD-IV), a rare form of glycogenosis, is due to a deficiency of branching enzyme activity (α-1,4-glucan-6-glycosyl transferase) in the liver as well as in cultured skin fibroblasts and other tissues including the brain, heart, and skeletal muscle (2, 8, 36). A deficiency of this enzyme results in the formation and accumulation of an insoluble and irritating form of glycogen, with longer outer and inner chains and few branch points. The lack of solubility of the abnormal glycogen has been thought to induce a foreign body reaction that results in cellular damage and death (36, 47).

These infants appear normal at birth with an insidious onset of symptoms during the first year of life. The disorder is usually diagnosed because of hepatosplenomegaly, abdominal distention, hypotonia, nonspecific gastrointestinal symptoms, and failure to thrive. Patients who live beyond infancy develop cirrhosis, and death is usually due to chronic hepatic failure by three to four years of age (22, 36).

In these infants, other than supportive nutritional management for terminal cirrhosis, no specific treatment appears to be beneficial. Liver transplantation is currently the recommended form of treatment for these patients. The results of liver transplantation in seven patients with GSD-IV have recently been published and are quite encouraging (76).

TYPE V GLYCOGEN STORAGE DISEASE

Type V glycogen storage disease (GSD-V), a rare form of glycogenosis is due to a deficiency in the activity of myophosphorylase in skeletal muscle (67). As a result of this deficiency, muscle glycogenolysis is impeded, and the utilization of glycogen as an immediate source of fuel is lost. Patients with GSD-V have exercise-induced muscle cramping and weakness usually beginning in childhood with progression to myopathy during adult life in some patients (36).

In normal individuals, resting or minimally active muscle derives the majority of its energy from the oxidation of fatty acids. If muscular contraction is intense or prolonged, the oxygen supply becomes insufficient for the aerobic oxidation of these fatty acids. When this occurs, glucose units are promptly released from muscle glycogen by the phosphorylase enzyme and fed into the glycolytic pathway. The transition from an aerobic to anaerobic metabolism is detectable by the elevation of serum lactate (36, 67).

An absence of myophosphorylase activity results in an inability to release glucose from skeletal muscle glycogen stores. The energy normally produced by anaerobic glycolysis is thus unavailable to these patients during periods of increased muscle activity, with resultant muscle cramping and weakness during exercise. This disruption in energy supply results in alteration of muscle membrane, which is reflected by the presence of muscle enzymes (creatinine kinase) and myoglobin in the blood. Myoglobin is also present in the urine, and renal failure may occur in up to seven percent of patients (37). The lack of a rise in blood lactate during ischemic work in GSD-V is a useful clinical manifestation of impaired anaerobic muscle metabolism. This finding is not unique to GSD-V but is found in deficiencies of any of the glycolytic enzymes. Likewise, excessive degradation of the adenine nucleotide pool with resultant elevation in blood ammonia and uric acid may occur in GSD-V and other myopathic enzyme deficiency states (36, 80). The actual determination of enzyme activity is therefore essential to distinguish between these disorders.

Therapy for GSD-V consists of (i) Avoidance of strenuous exercise and (ii) dietary attempts to fuel skeletal muscle anaerobic metabolism. Exercise limitation is often impractical and undesirable in young, otherwise healthy individuals. In addition, over 20% of these patients will develop a myopathy in later life despite exercise avoidance (36, 78). Dietary supplementation with glucose or fat in an attempt to substitute for glycogen consumption as an energy source has been unsuccessful (56, 78, 84). The use of high protein diets has yielded conflicting results in GSD-V and is briefly reviewed.

In normal subjects glucose (glycogen) and fatty acids are the main fuel during muscle activity while amino acids contribute minimally to energy production. However, exercise is associated with increased protein degradation and decreased protein synthesis (5). In addition, normal subjects lose alanine from muscle during exercise, whereas patients with GSD-V have a net uptake of alanine by muscle (86). This suggests that amino acids might play a role in energy production in this disorder. Slonim & Goans demonstrated a marked uptake of leucine and isoleucine by muscle in a patient with GSD-V. Administration of a high protein diet (25–30% of total caloric intake) resulted in improved endurance but not muscle strength (78). It was postulated that a metabolic adaptation allows patients with GSD-V to utilize amino acids as a direct source of muscle energy. The use of the BCAA as an alternate muscle fuel would be expected to decrease the availability of these substances for muscle protein synthesis, leading to net muscle catabolism and progressive muscle weakness and wasting. High protein diets and/or supplementation with BCAA might provide additional fuel and substrate for muscle protein synthesis in these patients.

A recent study using magnetic resonance spectroscopy demonstrated improved strength and endurance after 6 weeks of a high protein diet (29% of total caloric intake) in a patient with GSD-V (52). Interestingly, an intravenous infusion of amino acids did not improve muscle kinetics. This finding suggests that intracellular protein degradation is the main source of amino acids for energy production in these patients.

A number of other investigators have found no significant improvement in muscle function after either high protein diets or supplementation with BCAA (4, 38, 55). These conflicting results emphasize the need for larger cooperative studies so that the effects of heterogenity and/or other sources of variation can be observed by the same investigators and analyzed with statistical rigor.

GLYCOGEN STORAGE DISEASES VI-X

The remaining glycogen storage diseases (GSD-VI-X) are summarized in Table 1. In most of these disorders specific dietary therapy is not required. Possible exceptions are the types with muscle involvement (GSD's VII, IXb, and IXc). Based on experience with the other muscle glycogenoses, a trial with a high protein diet may be of some benefit.

Literature Cited

1. Ambruso, D. R., McCabe, E. R. B., Anderson, D., Beaudet, M. D., Ballas, L. M., et al. 1985. Infectious and bleeding complications in patients with glycogenosis Ib. *Am. J. Dis. Child.* 139:691–97
2. Anderson, D. H. 1952. Studies on glycogen disease with report of a case in which glycogen was abnormal. In *Carbohydrate Metabolism,* ed. V. A. Ajjar, pp. 28–42. Baltimore: Johns Hopkins Press
3. Anderson, J. W., Gustafon, N. J., Bryant, C. A., Tiotyen-Clark, J. 1987. Dietary fiber and diabetes: A comprehensive review and practical application *J. Am. Diet. Assoc.* 87: 1190–97
4. Argov, Z., Bank, W. J., Maris, J., Chance, B. 1987. Muscle energy metabolism in McArdle's syndrome by in vivo phosphorus magnetic resonance spectroscopy. *Neurology* 37:1720–24
5. Bier, D. M., Young, V. R. 1983. Exercise and blood pressure: nutritional

considerations. *Ann. Int. Med.* 98:864–69
6. Borowitz, S. M., Greene, H. L. 1987. Cornstarch therapy in a patient with type III glycogen storage disease. *J. Pediatr. Gastroenterol. Nutr.* 6:631–34
7. Brosh, S., Boer, P., Jupfer, J., deVries, A., Sperling, O. 1976. De nove synthesis of purine nucleotides in human peripheral blood leukocytes: excessive activity of the pathway and hypoxanthine quanine phosphoribosyl transferase deficiency. *J. Clin. Invest.* 58: 289–300
8. Brown, B. I., Brow, D. 1966. Lack of an α-1,4-glucan: α-1,4-glucon-6-glycosyl transferase in a case of type IV glycogenosis. *Proc. Natl. Acad. Sci. USA* 56:725–29
9. Burchell, A., Waddell, I. D. 1991. The molecular basis of the hepatic microsomal glucose-6-phosphatase system. *Biochim. Biophys. Acta* 1092:129–37

10. Chen, Y. T., Coleman, R. A., Scheinman, J. I., Kolbeck, P. C., Sidbury, J. B. 1988. Renal disease in type I glycogen storage disease. *N. Engl. J. Med.* 318:7–11

11. Chen, Y. T., Cornblath, M., Sidbury, J. B. 1984. Cornstarch therapy in type I glycogen-storage disease. *N. Engl. J. Med.* 310:171–75

12. Cohen, J. L., Vinik, A., Falker, J., Fox, I. H. 1985. Hyperuricemia in glycogen storage disease type I. Contributions by hypoglycemia and hyperglucagonemia to increased urate production. *J. Clin. Invest.* 75:251–57

13. Coleman, J. E. 1974. Metabolic interrelationships between carbohydrate, lipids, and proteins. In *Diseases of Metabolism*, ed. P. K. Bondy, L. E. Rosenberg, pp. 107–220. Philadelphia: Saunders.

14. Corby, D. G., Putnam, C. W., Greene, H. L. 1974. Impaired platelet function in glucose-6-phosphatase deficiency. *J. Pediatr.* 85:71–76

15. Cori, G. T., Cori, D. F. 1952. Glucose-6-phosphatase of the liver in glycogen storage disease. *J. Biol. Chem.* 199:661–70

16. Czapek, E. E., Deykin, D., Salzman, E. W. 1973. Platelet dysfunction in glycogen storage disease type I. *Blood* 41:235–47

17. Fernandes, J., Berger, R., Smit, G. P. A. 1984. Lactate as a cerebral metabolic fuel for glucose-6-phosphatase deficient children. *Pediatr. Res.* 18:335–39

18. Fine, R. N., Strauss, J., Donnell, G. N. 1966. Hyperuricemia in glycogen storage disease type I. *Am. J. Dis. Child.* 112:572–76

19. Folk, C. C., Greene, H. L. 1984. Dietary Management of Type I glycogen storage disease. *J. Am. Diet. Assoc.* 84:3, 293–301

20. Forget, P. P., Fernandes, J., Begemann, P. H. 1974. Triglyceride clearing in glycogen storage disease. *Pediatr. Res.* 8:114–19

21. Friedman, Z. V. I., Seyberth, H., Lamberth, E. L., Oates, J. 1978. Decreased prostagladin E turnover in infants with essential fatty acid deficiency. *Pediatr. Res.* 12:711–14

22. Ghishan, F. K., Greene, H. L. 1990. Inborn errors of metabolism that lead to permanent liver injury. In *Hepatology A Textbook of Liver Disease*, ed. D. Zakim. T. D. Boyer, pp. 1300–48. Philadelphia: Saunders. 2nd ed.

23. Gilchrist, G. S., Fine, R. N., Donnell, G. N. 1968. The hemostatic defect in glycogen storage disease type I. *Acta Paediatr. Scand.* 57:205–8

24. Greene, H. L., Helinek, G. L., Folk, C. C., Courtney, M. E., Thompson, S., et al. 1981. Nasogastric tube feeding at home: A method of adjunctive nutritional support of malnourished patients. *Am. J. Clin. Nutr.* 34:1131

25. Greene, H. L., Parker, P. H., Slonim, A. E., Burr, I. M. 1981. Resolution of the need for continuous nocturnal feeding in a patient with severe type I glycogen storage disease. *J. Pediatr.* 99:602

26. Greene, M. L., Seegmiller, J. E. 1969. Elevated erythrocyte phosphoribosylphrophosphate in x-linked uric aciduria: importance of PRPP concentration in regulation of human purine biosynthesis. *J. Clin. Invest.* 48:32a

27. Greene, H. L., Slonim, A. E., Burr, I. M. 1979. Type I glycogen storage disease: a metabolic basis for advances in treatment. *Adv. Pediatr.* 26:63–92

28. Greene, H. L., Slonim, A. E., Burr, I. M., Moran, J. R. 1980. Type I glycogen storage disease: five years of management with nocturnal intragastric feeding. *J. Pediatr.* 96:590–95

29. Greene, H. L., Slonim, A. E., O'Neill, J. A., Burr, I. M. 1976. Continuous nocturnal intragastric feeding for the management of type I glycogen storage disease. *N. Engl. J. Med.* 294:423

30. Greene, H. L., Swift, L. L., Knapp, H. R. 1991. Hyperlipidemia and fatty acid composition in patients treated for type IA glycogen storage disease. *J. Pediatr.* 119:398–403

31. Greene, H. L., Wilson, F. A., Hefferan, P., Terry, A. B., Moran, J. R., et al. 1978. ATP depletion, a possible role in the pathogenesis of hyperuricemia in glycogen storage disease type I. *J. Clin. Invest.* 62:321–28

32. Griffin, J. L. 1984. Infantile acid maltase deficiency. I. Muscle fiber destruction after lysosomal rupture. *Virchows Arch. B* 45:123–35

33. Hardinge, M. G., Swarner, J. B., Crooks, H. 1965. Carbohydrates in foods. *J. Am. Diet. Assoc.* 46:197–214

34. Havel, R. J., Balasse, E. O., Williams, H. E., Kane, J. P., Segel, N. 1969. Splanchnic metabolism in von Gierke's disease (glycogenosis type I). *Trans. Assoc. Am. Physicians* 82:305–23

35. Hers, H. G. 1963. α -Glucosidase deficiency in generalized glycogen-storage disease (Pompe's disease). *Biochem. J.* 86:11–16

36. Hers, H. G., Van Hoof, F., Barsy, T. 1989. Glycogen storage diseases.

In *The Metabolic Basis of Inherited Disease,* ed. C. R. Scriver, A. L. Beaudet, W. S. Sly, D. Valle, pp. 425–52. New York: McGraw-Hill. 6th ed.

37. Holmes, E. W., McDonald, J. A., McCord, J. M., Wyngaarden, J. B., Kelly, W. N. 1973. Human glutamine phosphoribosyl-pyrophosphate amidotransferase: kinetic and regulatory properties. *J. Biol. Chem.* 248:143–50

38. Hopewell, R., Yeater, R., Ullrich, I. 1989. The effect of three test meals on exercise tolerance of an individual with McArdle's disease. *J. Am. Coll. Nutr.* 7:485–89

39. Howell, R. R. 1965. The interrelationship of glycogen storage disease and gout. *Arthritis Rheum.* 8:780–86

40. Howell, R. R. 1968. Hyperuricemia in childhood. *Fed. Proc.* 27:1078–89

41. Howell, R. R. 1978. The glycogen storage diseases. In *The Metabolic Basis of Inherited Disease,* ed. J. B. Stanbury, J. B. Wyngaarden, D. S. Fredrickson, pp. 137–59. New York: McGraw-Hill. 4th ed.

42. Howell, R. R., Ashton, D. M., Wyngaarden, J. B. 1962. Glucose-6-phosphatase deficiency glycogen storage disease. Studies on the interrelationships of carbohydrate, lipid, and purine abnormalities. *Pediatrics* 29:553–62

43. Howell, R. R., Stevenson, R. E., Ben-Menachem, Y., Phyliky, R. L., Berry, D. H. 1976. Hepatic adenomata with type-1 glycogen storage disease. *J. Am. Med. Assoc.* 236:1481–84

44. Huelsmann, W. C., Eijkenboom, W. H. M., Koster, J. F., Fernandes, J. 1970. Glucose-6-phosphatase deficiency and hyperlipidemia. *Clin. Chim. Acta* 3:775–82

45. Hudgson, P., Fulthorpe, J. J. 1975. The pathology of type II skeletal muscle glycogenosis. *J. Pathol.* 116:139–47

46. Hug, G. 1976. Glycogen storage disease. *Birth Defects* 12:145–75

47. Illingworth, B., Cori, G. T. 1952. Structure of glycogens and amylopectins. III. Normal and abnormal glycogen. *J. Biol. Chem.* 199:653–60

48. Issacs, H., Savage, N., Badenhorst, M., Whistler, T. 1986. Acid maltase deficiency: a case study and review of the pathophysiological changes and proposed therapeutic measures. *J. Neurol. Neurosurg. Psychiatry* 49:1011–18

49. Jakovcic, S., Khachadurian, A. K., Hsia, D. Y. Y. 1966. The hyperlidemia in glycogen storage disease. *J. Lab. Clin. Med.* 68:769–79

50. Jakovcic, S., Sorensen, L. B. 1967. Studies of uric acid metabolism in glycogen storage disease associated with gouty arthritis. *Arthritis Rheum.* 10:129–34

51. Jenkins, D. J. A., Wolever, T. M. S., Nineham, R., Bacon, S., Smith, R., Hockaday, T. D. 1979. Dietary fiber and diabetic therapy: a progressive effect with time. *Adv. Exp. Med. Biol.* 119:275–79

52. Jensen, K. E., Jakobsen, J., Thomsen, C., Henriksen, O. 1990. Improved energy kinetics following high protein diet on McArdle's Syndrome. A31P magnetic resonance spectroscopy study. *Acta Neurol. Scand.* 81:499–503

53. Kalhan, S. C., Gilfillan, C., Tsering, K., Savin, S. M. 1982. Glucose production in type I glycogen storage disease. *J. Pediatr.* 101:159

54. Kelley, W. N., Rosenbloom, F. M., Seegmiller, J. E., Howell, R. R. 1968. Excessive production of uric acid in type I glycogen storage disease. *J. Pediatr.* 72:488–96

55. Kushner, R. F., Berman, S. A. 1990. Are high protein diets effective in McArdle's disease? *Arch. Neurol.* 47:383–84

56. Layzer, R. B. 1985. McArdles disease in the 1980's. *N. Engl. J. Med.* 6:370–71

57. Levy, E., Letarte, J., Lepage, G., Thibault, L., Roy, C. C. 1987. Plasma and lipoprotein fatty acid composition in glycogen storage disease type I. *Lipids* 22:381–85

58. Levy, E., Thibault, L. A., Roy, C. C., Bendayan, M., Lepage, G., et al. 1988. Circulating lipids and lipoproteins in glycogen storage disease type I with nocturnal intragastric feedings. *J. Lipid. Res.* 29:215–26

59. Limmer, J., Fleig, W. E., Leupold, D., Bittner, R., Ditschuneit, H., et al. 1988. Hepatocellular carcinoma in type I glycogen storage disease. *Hepatology* 8:531–37

60. Margolis, M. L., Hill, A. R. 1986. Acid maltase deficiency in an adult. *Annu. Rev. Respir. Dis.* 134:328–31

61. Mehler, M., DiMauro, S. 1977. Residual acid maltase activity in late onset acid maltase deficiency. *Neurology* 27:178–84

62. Mobarhan, S., Pintozzi, R. L., Damle, P., Friedman, H. 1990. Treatment of acid maltase deficiency with a diet high in branched chain amino acids. *J. Parent. Enterol. Nutr.* 14:210–12

63. Moses, S. 1990. Muscle glycogenosis. *J. Inherit. Metab. Dis.* 13:452–65

64. Moses, S. W. 1990. Pathophysiology

and dietary treatment of the glycogen storage diseases. *J. Pediatr. Gastroenterol. Nutr.* 11:155–74

65. Ockerman, P. A. 1965. Glucose, glycerol, and free fatty acids in glycogen storage disease type I blood levels in the fasting and nonfasting state: effect of glucose and adrenalin administration. *Clin. Chim. Acta* 12:370–78

66. Parker, P., Burr, I., Slonim, A. E., Ghishan, F. K., Greene, H. L. 1981. Regression of hepatic adenoma in type Ia glycogen storage disease with dietary therapy. *Gastroenterology* 81:534–36

67. Pearson, C. M., Rimer, D. G., Mommaerts, W. F. H. M. 1961. A metabolic myopathy due to absence of muscle phosphorylase. *Am. J. Med.* 30:602–10

68. Poe, R., Snover, D. C. 1988. Adenomas in glycogen storage disease type I. *Am. J. Surg. Pathol.* 12:477

69. Pompe, J. C. 1932. Over idopatische hypertophie van het hart. *Ned. Tijdschr. Geneeskd.* 76:304–14

70. Powell, R. C., Wentworth, S. M., Brandt, I. K. 1981. Endogenous glucose production in type I glycogen storage disease. *Metabolism* 30:433–50

71. Ravio, K. O., Seegmiller, J. E. 1973. Role of glutamine in purine synthesis and in quanine nucleotide formation in normal fibroblasts and in fibroblasts deficient in hypoxanthine phosphoribosyl transferase activity. *Biochim. Biophys. Acta* 299:282–92

72. Reuser, A. J. J., Kroos, M., Willemsen, R., Swallow, D., Tager, J. M., et al. 1987. Clinical diversity in glycogenosis type II: biosynthesis and in situ localization of acid d-glucosidase in mutant fibroblasts. *J. Clin. Invest.* 79:1689–99

73. Roe, T. F., Kogut, M. D. 1977. The pathogenesis of hyperuricemia in glycogen storage disease, type I. *Pediatr. Res.* 11:664–69

74. Roe, T. F., Kogut, M. D., Buckingham, B. A. 1979. Hepatic tumors in glycogen-storage disease type I. *Pediatr. Res.* 13:931–35

75. Sadeghi-Nejad, A., Presente, E., Binkiewiez, A., Senior, B. 1974. Studies in type I glycogenosis of the liver: the genesis and disposition of lactate. *J. Pediatr.* 85:49–55

76. Selley, R., Starzl, T. E., Yunis, E., Brown, B. I., Kendall, R. S., et al. 1991. Liver transplantation for type IV glycogen storage disease. *N. Engl. J. Med.* 324:32–42

77. Slonim, A. E., Coleman, R. A., McElligot, M. A., Najjar, J., Hirschhorn, I. 1983. Improvement of muscle function by high-protein therapy. *Neurology* 33:34–38

78. Slonim, A. E., Goans, P. J. 1985. Myopathy in McArdle's syndrome: improvement with a high protein diet. *N. Engl. J. Med.* 312:355–59

79. Slonim, A. E., Lacy, W. W., Terry, A. B., Greene, H. L., Burr, I. M. 1979. Nocturnal intragastric therapy in type I glycogen storage disease: effect on hormonal and amino acid metabolism. *Metabolism* 28:707–15

80. Sutton, J. R., Toews, C. J., Ward, G. R., Fox, R. H. 1980. Purine metabolism during strenuous exercise in man. *Metabolism* 29:254–60

81. Tsallkion, E., Simmons, P., Gerich, J. E., Howard, C., Haymond, M. W. 1984. Glucose production and utilization in children with glycogen storage disease type I. *Am. J. Physiol.* 247: E513–19

82. Umpleby, A. M., Trend, P. St. J., Chubb, D., Conaglen, J. V., Williams, C. D., et al. 1989. The effect of high protein diet on leucine and alanine turnover in acid maltase deficiency. *J. Neurol. Neurosurg. Psychiatry* 52:954–61

83. Umpleby, A. M., Wiles, C. M., Trend, P. StJ., Scobie, I. N., Macleod, A. F., et al. 1987. Protein turnover in acid maltase deficiency before and after treatment with a high protein diet. *J. Neurol Neurosurg. Psychiatry* 50:587–92

84. Viskokper, R. J., Wolf, E., Chaco, J., Katz, R., Chowers, I. 1975. McArdle's syndrome: the reaction to a fat rich diet. *Am. J. Med. Sci.* 269:217–21

85. von Gierke, E. 1929. Hepatonephromagalia glykogenia (Glykogenspeicherkrankheiten Leber und Niepen). *Biete. Pathol. Anat.* 82:497–508

86. Wahren, J., Felig, P., Havel, R. J., Jorfeldt, L., Pernow, B., et al. 1973. Amino acid metabolism in McArdle's syndrome. *N. Engl. J. Med.* 288:744–77

87. Wolfsdorf, J. I., Plotkin, R. A., Crigler, J. F. 1990. Continuous glucose for treatment of patients with type I glycogen-storage disease: comparison of the effects of dextrose and uncooked cornstarch on biochemical variables. *Am. J. Clin. Nutr.* 52:1043–50

88. Yudkoff, M., Nissim, I., Stanley, C., Baker, L., Segal, S. 1984. Glycogen storage disease: effect of glucose infusion on [15N]glycine kinetics and nitrogen metabolism. *J. Pediatr. Gastroenterol. Nutr.* 3:81–88

Annu. Rev. Nutr. 1993. 13:111–36

NUTRITIONAL MANAGEMENT
OF CYSTIC FIBROSIS

P. B. Pencharz

Division of Clinical Nutrition, Department of Paediatrics, and the Research
Institute, The Hospital for Sick Children, Toronto, Ontario and the Departments of
Paediatrics and Nutritional Sciences, University of Toronto, Toronto, Ontario,
Canada

P. R. Durie

Division of Gastroenterology, Department of Paediatrics, and the Research
Institute, The Hospital for Sick Children, Toronto, Ontario and the Department of
Paediatrics, University of Toronto, Toronto, Ontario, Canada

KEY WORDS: Growth, malnutrition, energy needs

CONTENTS

GENERAL FEATURES OF CYSTIC FIBROSIS 112
OVERVIEW OF NUTRITIONAL PROBLEMS IN CYSTIC FIBROSIS 114
PATHOGENESIS OF ENERGY IMBALANCE 116
    Energy Losses 116
    Energy Intake 118
    Energy Expenditure and Metabolism 119
    Pathogenesis of an Energy Deficit 122
DEFICITS OF ESSENTIAL NUTRIENTS 123
    Water-Soluble Vitamins 123
    Fat-Soluble Vitamins 123
    Trace Metal Deficiencies 124
    Essential Fatty Acid Deficiency 124
NUTRITIONAL EVALUATION AND THERAPY 125
    Clinical 125
    Biochemical 126
    Age-Related Nutritional Guidelines 127
NUTRITIONAL INTERVENTION 129
    Short-Term Studies 129
    Long-Term Studies 130
CONCLUSION 132

111

0199-9885/93/0715-0111$02.00

GENERAL FEATURES OF CYSTIC FIBROSIS

Cystic fibrosis (CF) is an inherited disorder that affects children and young adults. It is inherited as an autosomal recessive trait; heterozygotes with one normal CF allele and one mutant allele are entirely asymptomatic and are considered to be carriers. A child born to two carriers has a one in four chance of being affected with CF by acquiring a mutation from each parent (7). Disease frequency varies considerably among ethnic groups; it is highest among people of northern European origin, where approximately one in 2,500 newborns is affected. It is hardly ever seen in people of mongoloid or negroid origin.

The predominant clinical feature of CF is respiratory tract involvement, where obstruction of airways by sticky mucus gives rise to infection, especially with *pseudomonas* species. Most patients experience gastrointestinal difficulties; 85% show pancreatic insufficiency due to obstruction in small pancreatic ducts, which in turn gives rise to pancreatic fibrosis and atrophy (27). In the newborn period, over 10% of affected patients present with bowel obstruction due to meconium ileus (37). Up to 5% of patients develop overt liver disease, frequently in adolescence or adulthood. Infertility in males is virtually universal (59). Undernutrition is a significant cause of morbidity in affected children, adolescents, and young adults (32, 39, 57, 67). This review addresses the pathogenesis of the various factors that contribute to an energy deficit and describes approaches to nutritional evaluation and therapy.

In 1989, following concerted efforts of a number of investigators throughout the world, the CF gene was identified by Lap-Chee Tsui and Jack Riordan of the University of Toronto in collaboration with Francis Collins of the University of Michigan (36, 53, 55). The CF gene comprises 27 exons spanning 230 kb of DNA. The gene product, named the cystic fibrosis transmembrane conductance regulator (CFTR), is a protein of 1,480 amino acids. The predominant mutation, which accounts for approximately 70% of all the CFTR genes worldwide, is a three base pair deletion in exon 10 of the candidate gene, which results in the loss of a single amino acid, phenylalanine, at codon 508 (Δ508). The remaining 30% appear to be rather heterogeneous. More than 170 mutations have already been described; some of them appear to be relatively infrequent, others are clearly private mutations.

It is not surprising to note that expression of the CF gene is largely restricted to epithelial cells (70). The highest mRNA levels have been found in the pancreas, salivary glands, sweat glands, intestine, and the reproductive tract, but in all affected tissue mRNA is transcribed at relatively low levels. Studies of CFTR expression in the human lung have indicated very low expression in the respiratory epithelium and higher expression within submucosal glands.

The predicted amino acids sequence of CFTR showed striking homology to a family of proteins involved in active transport of cell membranes (44). This super family has several features in common, notably the presence of transmembrane domains and nucleotide-binding folds. CFTR also contains a unique domain that has been called the R (regulatory) domain. The function of CFTR has been the subject of intense scientific investigation. Data from electrophysiological studies and DNA transfection studies, together with reconstituting experiments in which purified CFTR is reinserted into lipid bilayers, now provide fairly conclusive evidence that CFTR itself can function as a cAMP-regulated chloride channel. The CFTR protein may carry out other important functions as well (3, 70). For example, intracellular organelles may be defectively acidified in patients with CF; this abnormality may in turn affect vital intracellular functions, including intracellular processing of proteins.

In 1989 Dr. Tsui initiated the coordination of an international effort, the Genetic Analysis Consortium. Pooling the research efforts of geneticists around the world provided an opportunity to identify further gene mutations and to determine the population frequencies of each possible CF gene mutation. The prevalence of Δ508 appears to vary considerably in different patient populations, the highest percentage occurring in northeast Europe and the lowest in southern Mediterranean countries and in the Middle East (18). For example, the predominant mutation Δ508 accounts for about 85% of the mutations in Denmark but for only 30% in Israel. Worldwide, the combination of all mutations discovered to date accounts for about 84% of all the CF chromosomes analyzed. Other mutations may be found with a high frequency in specific populations; for example, in Ashkenazic Jews, the mutation W1282X has a prevalence of 60%.

As information about the variety of CF mutations has accumulated, we have gained considerable insight into the genotype-phenotype relationships. From the clinical and nutritional point of view, mutations can be grouped into those that cause pancreatic insufficiency (PI) and those that cause pancreatic sufficiency (PS) (27). The term pancreatic sufficiency is an operational one, describing patients who almost always have pancreatic disease but retain sufficient pancreatic function to permit normal digestion and absorption of nutrients. Pancreatic-sufficient patients, who constitute approximately 15% of the population, have much milder disease expression. It is characterized by diagnosis at a later age (presumably due to milder symptoms), more slowly progressive lung disease, better growth, and a far superior survival rate than found in patients with pancreatic insufficiency. We have proposed that mutations in the CFTR gene can be divided into two classes, severe and mild, according to the status of pancreatic function (38). Our data show that patients with two severe mutations will develop pancreatic insufficiency, while those with one or two mild alleles have pancreatic sufficiency. Exceptions to this rule are few. It is interesting that when mild mutations are examined at the molecular level, they all appear to be missense, single amino acid substitutions, whereas severe mutations are generally manifest as more severe defects at the gene level (40). To date, all other mutations classed as single amino acid deletions, stop/splice junction and frame shift mutations have been severe with regard to pancreatic function status.

OVERVIEW OF NUTRITIONAL PROBLEMS IN CYSTIC FIBROSIS

Chronic undernutrition with significant weight retardation and linear growth failure has long been recognized as a general problem among most CF patient populations. Some researchers thought that it was an inherent consequence of the disease, while others argued that it resulted from physiologic adaptation to advanced pulmonary disease. Some early studies of CF patients, however, showed a good correlation between the degree of malnutrition and the severity of pulmonary disease, which in turn adversely affected the survival rate (39, 67). It has been suggested that these two factors are causally associated, but it is not clear whether prevention of malnutrition and growth failure would slow the progression of lung disease and improve survival. The past decade has seen renewed interest in evaluating the multiple interdependent variables that give rise to chronic malnutrition and growth failure. In most CF centers around the world, nutritional support is now viewed as an integral part of the multidisciplinary care of patients with cystic fibrosis, and aggressive programs have been instituted to prevent malnutrition.

Growth retardation in CF patients is now viewed as the result of an unfavorable energy balance rather than as a factor inherent in the disease. Over ten years ago, in contrast to results of studies elsewhere, reports from Toronto indicated that most patients attending the CF clinic at The Hospital for Sick Children closely conformed to the normal distribution of growth in the general population (15, 32, 57). Cross-sectional data from the Toronto clinic showed a normal distribution of height percentiles in males and females (15). In females, however, particularly after adolescence, weight distribution was skewed toward the lower centiles, but weight retardation was far less evident than in reports from other centers. In a comparative study of two CF clinic populations of similar size and age distribution (Toronto and Boston), Corey et al (16) found a marked difference in median age of survival: 21 years in Boston versus 30 in Toronto (Table 1). Furthermore, after 10 years of age there was a dramatic separation in survival curves between the two centers. Pulmonary function was no different in the two clinic populations. Males and females attending the Toronto clinic, however, were taller than those in the Boston clinic, and males in Toronto were heavier. With the exception of nutritional management of their patients, the general approach to patient care,

Table 1 Characteristics of CF clinic populations in Boston and
Toronto (1982)[a]

	Boston	Toronto
Number of patients	499	534
male/female (%)	57/43	58/42
Age: Mean ± SD (years)	15.9 ± 9.6	15.2 ± 8.3
Range (years)	0–45	0–43
Median survival (50%) in years	21	30

[a] Adapted from Corey et al (16).

particularly pulmonary care, was similar in the two clinics. It was suggested that the higher survival rate in the Toronto CF population could be attributed to superior nutritional status.

An examination of dietary practices in the two clinics revealed a striking difference in philosophy. The approach in Boston (63), which closely resembled that in most centers, was to prescribe a low-fat, carbohydrate-rich diet. It was reasoned that reduction in dietary fat would improve bowel symptoms and reduce stool bulk. Recognizing the problem of maldigestion and poor absorption of long-chain triglycerides, many centers advocated use of artificial diets with protein hydrolysates and substitution of long-chain fat with medium-chain triglycerides (MCT) (1). However, other reports showed no long-term benefits to growth when protein hydrolysates and MCT were used as supplements or substitutes (30). The effect was to provide CF patients with a restrictive, unpalatable diet and to exclude them from the many energy-rich foods that comprise some of the more tasty choices in a "normal" Western diet. Fortunately, these supplements are now rarely advocated for reasons of cost, poor compliance, and unpalatability. Chronic malnutrition from reduced energy intake appears to have been an unfortunate yet deliberate iatrogenic effect in most CF programs throughout the world.

Since the early 1970s, the Toronto group advocated a calorically enriched diet by encouraging rather than restricting dietary fat and recommending additional enzyme supplements to enhance digestion (17, 49). Because fat is the most energy-rich, economical, and appetizing energy source, patients were encouraged to eat larger portions than their peers, to add fat in the form of butter or untrimmed meat, and to eat high-calorie snacks between meals and before bed. Fat malabsorption occurred, but with additional pancreatic enzyme supplements, net absorbed energy improved and better growth resulted. In recent years it is gratifying to see that most CF caregivers have adopted a similar philosophy for the nutritional care of their patients. Coincidentally, it is generally accepted that the primary objective of nutritional management is to achieve normal nutrition and growth for children of all ages. This view is reflected in the following statement from a Consensus Conference, organized by the United States Cystic Fibrosis Foundation, on Nutritional Assessment and Management in Cystic Fibrosis: "There is no reason to accept nutritional failure and/or impaired growth in any individual with CF" (51).

PATHOGENESIS OF ENERGY IMBALANCE

A variety of complex, related, and unrelated factors may give rise to energy imbalance in patients with cystic fibrosis. The net effect on growth potential varies considerably from patient to patient, according to marked differences in disease expression and with disease progression. In simple terms, an energy deficit results from an imbalance between energy needs and intake (Table 2) and is determined by three factors: energy losses, energy expenditure, and energy intake.

Energy Losses

Fecal nutrient losses from maldigestion/malabsorption are known to contribute to energy imbalance. Only 1 to 2% of residual pancreatic capacity for secreting digestive enzymes is required to prevent maldigestion (29), and yet in the majority of CF patients (approximately 85%) evidence of pancreatic failure is present at diagnosis. In those who exhibit maldigestion, very good correlations exist between residual pancreatic function (colipase secretion) and the severity of fat malabsorption (Figure 1). Patients with documented steatorrhea, therefore, have variable but very limited residual pancreatic function. This observation partially explains why some patients with pancreatic insufficiency digest nutrients better than others when given pancreatic enzyme supplements with meals. Despite improvements in the enzymatic potency and intestinal delivery of ingested pancreatic enzyme supplements,

Table 2 Energy imbalance in cystic fibrosis

Increased needs	Reduced intake
Increased intestinal losses	Reduced intake
Pancreatic insufficiency	Iatrogenic fat restriction
Bile salt metabolism	Anorexia
Hepatobiliary disease	Feeding disorders
Regurgitation from reflux	Depression
	Esophagitis
Increased urinary losses	
Diabetes mellitus	
Increased energy expenditure	
Pulmonary disease	
Primary defect?	

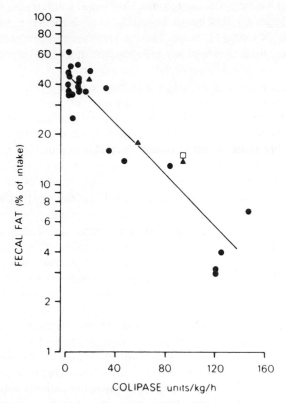

Figure 1 Comparison of fecal fat excretion (percent of fat intake) with pancreatic colipase secretion in 28 patients with steatorrhea due to pancreatic insufficiency. *Closed circles*: patients with cystic fibrosis. *Closed triangles*: patients with Shwachman syndrome. *Open square*: patient with congenital pancreatic hypoplasia. $r = -0.92$, p 0.001. From Gaskin et al (29).

many patients continue to have severe steatorrhea and azotorrhea, even when they receive adequate amounts of enzyme supplements.

In the absence of adequate pancreatic bicarbonate secretion (28), gastric acid entering the duodenum may lower intestinal pH until well into the jejunum. The acid-resistant coating of the newer enzyme preparations may not dissolve in the proximal intestine. Pancreatic lipase is readily denatured below pH 2, and even if not denatured, enzymatic activity is considerably reduced at a low pH. Bile acids are readily precipitated in an acid milieu (77), and duodenal bile acid concentration may fall below the critical micellar concentration, thereby exacerbating fat maldigestion. Precipitated bile salts also appear to be lost from the enterohepatic circulation in greater quantities, thus reducing the total bile salt pool and altering the glycocholate:taurocholate ratio. Bile salt losses are exacerbated by the binding of salts to unabsorbed protein or neutral lipid. Oral taurine supplements have been reported to benefit some patients (5). Viscid, thick intestinal mucus, with altered physical properties, may have a deleterious effect on the thickness of the intestinal unstirred layer, further limiting nutrient absorption.

Two other factors, more prevalent in adolescents and adult patients with CF, may contribute to energy losses. Diabetes mellitus, if not adequately controlled, may increase caloric losses due to glycosuria. Advanced liver disease with multifocal biliary cirrhosis may result in inadequate bile salt secretion, which in turn results in severe fat malabsorption.

Energy Intake

Actual energy intakes in healthy patients with cystic fibrosis have been poorly documented. Nevertheless, it has been widely accepted that energy intake should exceed normal requirements, and crude estimates have suggested that patients may require 120–150% of the Recommended Daily Allowance (RDA) for age and sex (57). When we accurately evaluated nutrient intakes of a group of healthy adolescents, we were surprised to learn that energy intakes were close to the normal range for age, body weight, and sex (4). Patients with normal growth percentiles for height and weight did show higher energy intakes than those with growth retardation. Other CF centers, which have developed more liberal attitudes to dietary fat intake, have noted a corresponding improvement in energy intake and growth (19, 46). However, in most reports nutrient intakes were found to be close to the normal range.

Patients with cystic fibrosis are especially prone to complications that might limit oral intake. Esophagitis induced by acid reflux is quite common in patients with advanced pulmonary disease and is frequently associated with pain, anorexia, and vomiting following bouts of coughing (24, 58). The distal intestinal obstruction syndrome (meconium ileus equivalent), an unusual form of subacute obstruction within the distal ileum and proximal colon (56), is seen in some adolescents and adults with pancreatic failure; it frequently causes recurrent, crampy abdominal pain that is often aggravated by eating. Other abdominal symptoms, including extrahepatic biliary obstruction, cholangitis, advanced liver disease, and severe constipation, are less likely to be associated with a prolonged reduction in dietary intake.

Respiratory problems usually cause restricted oral intake due to anorexia, resulting in acute weight loss. With improvement in respiratory symptoms, patients with mild pulmonary disease usually show rapid catch-up in weight. However, in the terminal stages of pulmonary disease, chronic anorexia is a consistent feature. Further, patients with a severe chronic disease are prone to bouts of clinical depression, which in the adolescent or adult may lead to severe anorexia.

Over the past few years we have seen a number of younger children (infancy to 8 years of age) with behavioral feeding difficulties; their absorption and energy expenditure are within the normal range. Their treatment has proven difficult. In some, behavior management with oral supplements has been successful, but in others we have had to resort to the use of supplemental feeding with gastrostomy tubes to achieve satisfactory nutritional results. This nutrition support modality has reduced parental anxiety and facilitated the implementation of behavior modification feeding programs.

Energy Expenditure and Metabolism

In recent years, a number of studies have focused on examining the rates of energy expenditure in patients with cystic fibrosis. In 1984, Pencharz et al (48) evaluated the relationship between heart rate and energy expenditure, using an exercise cycle with graded workloads. Simultaneous measurements of oxygen consumption and carbon dioxide production were taken using a closed-circuit indirect calorimeter and heart-rate telemetry. The subjects were malnourished and had moderate to advanced pulmonary disease. The patients were receiving nutritional rehabilitation by continuous nasogastric tube feeding with a semielemental diet. Absorbed energy intake was calculated by subtracting stool energy content from the energy content of the feed. The energy needs of the patients were shown to be 25–80% higher than those of healthy persons of the same age, sex, and size. It was hypothesized that energy expenditure increased because of the increased work of breathing in patients with advanced lung disease. Consequently, a patient with advanced lung disease might not be able to ingest sufficient calories to meet energy needs, resulting in energy imbalance and weight loss. In a subsequent study, resting energy expenditure (REE) was measured by continuous computerized open-circuit indirect calorimetry in 71 patients (8.9 to 35.5 years) who were not suffering from an acute respiratory infection (74). Nutritional status and pulmonary function were studied simultaneously. Resting energy expenditure was found to be above normal (range 95% to 153%) of predicted values for age, sex, and weight and was negatively correlated with pulmonary function and nutritional status (percentage of body fat). In addition, in agreement with the observations of others (39), pulmonary function was positively correlated with nutritional status. These findings have since been confirmed by Buchdahl et al (9), who demonstrated that patients with cystic fibrosis had a resting energy expenditure of 9% above body weight and 7% above lean body mass, respectively, in comparison with healthy controls.

These two studies hinted at the possibility that the CF gene might have a direct effect on basal metabolism. Feigal & Shapiro (23) had earlier reported that mitochondria from cultured fibroblasts from CF homozygotes and heterozygotes had increased O_2 consumption associated with calcium transport. Rates in the homozygote were two times as high and in the heterozygote 1.5 times as high as those in controls. In a subsequent study of CF nasal epithelium, oxygen consumption exceeded that of control tissue by two to three times (68). Shepherd et al (62) investigated total daily energy expenditure using the doubly labelled water method in clinically well, appropriately nourished CF infants without clinical evidence of lung disease, and data were compared with studies in healthy infants. This methodology permits measurement of total energy expenditure in unrestricted subjects. CF infants had rates of energy expenditure 25% higher than values obtained in healthy infants matched for age and body weight. We were concerned about some methodologic difficulties that were brought to the attention of the investigative group (50). Over the next two years, when additional subjects were evaluated, the differences between the infants with CF and the controls disappeared. When the gene responsible for CF was identified (55), it was suggested that the gene product might be directly involved in the regulation of ion transport across membranes (53), since CFTR shared structural similarity with several other transport systems with transmembrane regions and ATP-binding domains. Recent studies strongly suggest that CFTR is a cAMP-regulated chloride channel and provide further evidence that the genetic defect might have a direct effect on basal metabolism. Following this line of investigation, O'Rawe et al (44) reported preliminary results supporting the hypothesis that the genetic defect may have such an effect. Resting energy expenditure was increased by 25% in subjects homozygous for the most common CF mutation (ΔF508) and by 10% in those with ΔF508 on one chromosome and an undefined CF gene mutation on the other. However, their study did not control for lung function or nutritional status. This is important, because we had shown that lung function has a significant effect on REE (74). Further, we have also shown that undernutrition results in a decreased REE (71). We recently published the results of a study in which we controlled for these two confounding variables (26). Little if any increase in REE was seen in healthy, normally nourished CF males with good lung function. Furthermore, we were unable to demonstrate any difference in REE in patient groups with different genotypes. Thus, if there is a primary genetic cause for increased REE in patients with CF, its effects must be minimal. Conversely, lung function is a major determinant of an increase in REE. Once forced expiratory volume in one second (FEV$_1$) fell below 75% of predicted, the subject's REE rose in a curvilinear (quadratic) fashion (Figure 2). Thus, it appears that deteriorating lung function is the major factor associated with an increase in REE. Recently O'Rawe et al (45) published a full report of their study, in which they controlled for nutritional status but not for lung function. The FEV$_1$ data for their homozygous group (ΔF508/ΔF508) was 48–64% of predicted (mean 56%) and for their heterozygous group (ΔF508/other) was 52–74% of predicted (mean 63). It is therefore not surprising, if the pulmonary function data shown in Figure 2 are considered, that the REE values in each group were increased to 121 and 109% of predicted, respectively. The authors did attempt to correct for the effects of lung function, using analysis of covariance; however, their data are open to the alternate explanation, namely, that the increased REE is secondary to reduced lung function.

Protein synthesis is thought to be responsible for up to 25% of REE (69). We therefore measured REE and whole-body protein synthesis in normal controls, in undernourished patients with CF, and in patients with anorexia nervosa matched to the CF patients by nutritional status (72). There were no differences in protein synthesis between the three groups. However, the patients with anorexia nervosa had reduced REE while the CF patients had increased REE compared with controls. Further, we measured protein synthesis and REE in CF patients during renourishment with nocturnal supplemental feedings. REE rose significantly with refeeding but no changes were seen in protein synthesis (71). The increase in REE with refeeding is evidence that the CF patient does adapt to a negative energy balance in the same manner as patients with self-imposed food restriction (75). Following refeeding, the patients with anorexia nervosa increased their REE in a similar pattern to the undernourished patients with CF (71, 75). Thus at least two factors appear to affect REE in the undernourished CF patient with impaired lung function. The first is a normal response to a negative energy balance, and the second appears to be related to the severity of lung function. The precise causes of

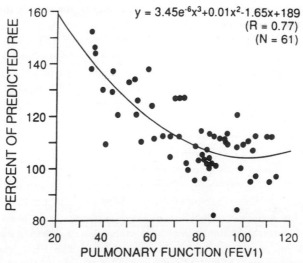

$$y = 3.45e^{-6}x^3 + 0.01x^2 - 1.65x + 189$$
$$(R = 0.77)$$
$$(N = 61)$$

Figure 2 Resting energy expenditure (percent of predicted) versus pulmonary function in normally nourished males with cystic fibrosis. From Fried et al (26).

increased REE in CF patients with moderate to severe lung disease remain to be elucidated. However, the evidence is compelling that alterations in protein metabolism are not responsible (71, 72).

Resting energy expenditure can also be increased by drugs used in the management of CF lung disease. Prior to chest physiotherapy, for example, many patients use inhaled bronchodilators, usually symphomemetic amines. One of these, the β-agonist salbutamol, has been shown to be absorbed through the respiratory tree and to result in a significant increase in REE (approximately 10%) over a period of three hours (73).

In practical terms, energy requirements should be determined by assessing total daily energy expenditure (TDEE). A significant increase in TDEE probably would result in a negative energy balance, which if left untreated would lead to undernutrition. It is interesting that patients with moderate lung impairment adapt to an increased REE by reducing their activity levels, thereby maintaining TDEE at levels comparable to controls (66).

Pathogenesis of an Energy Deficit

We have proposed a model to explain the cause of the energy deficit in CF patients (Figure 3), which helps to define the web of interdependent variables giving rise to chronic malnutrition and growth failure in these patients. It must be reemphasized, however, that most patients with cystic fibrosis can maintain normal growth velocity and nutritional status by voluntary intake of calories, particularly when lung function remains relatively unimpaired (16). Expressed another way, most patients are capable of compensating for the various factors that may contribute to an energy deficit. We and others have speculated that

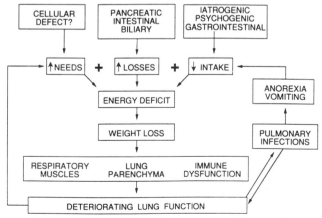

Figure 3 Interdependent factors that may give rise to progressive energy deficit and weight loss as lung function deteriorates. From Durie & Pencharz (21).

malnutrition and decline in pulmonary function are closely interrelated, but a cause-effect relationship remains to be proven. As lung disease worsens, most commonly in older adolescents and young adults, several factors come into play that might predispose the patient to an energy deficit. The frequency and severity of pulmonary infections may increase, inducing anorexia. Chest infections often give rise to vomiting, which may further reduce intake. These factors, in combination with the increase in REE that accompanies advancing lung disease, may lead to an energy deficit. Weight loss will result, initially producing a significant loss of adipose tissue but with time a loss of lean tissue along with muscle wasting. Respiratory muscle wasting would adversely affect respiratory motion and prevent effectuve coughing, thereby further contributing to the deterioration of lung function. Malnutrition is known to adversely affect lung elasticity and a variety of aspects of immune function (11). Taken together, these factors would appear to contribute to progressive deterioration of lung function. In essence, a vicious cycle is established, leading inevitably to end-stage pulmonary failure and death.

DEFICITS OF ESSENTIAL NUTRIENTS

Deficits of essential micronutrients can occur as a result of primary malnutrition or secondary features of the disease, such as pancreatic failure (12, 14). By way of example, CF patients with pancreatic insufficiency frequently malabsorb fat-soluble vitamins, and thus risk developing signs and symptoms of nutritional deficiency.

Water-Soluble Vitamins

With the exception of vitamin B_{12}, water-soluble vitamins are well absorbed, and there is no evidence of clinically significant deficiencies in well-nourished patients. In pancreatic-insufficient patients, vitamin B_{12} absorption can be normalized with adequate pancreatic enzyme replacement therapy. Vitamin B_{12} administration is not necessary, apart from patients with meconium ileus who have undergone extensive ileal resection and show biochemical evidence of B_{12} deficiency.

Fat-Soluble Vitamins

Deficiencies of vitamins A, D, E, and K have been demonstrated at diagnosis (12, 14, 64). Fat-soluble vitamin supplements are a necessary part of the nutritional care of CF patients with pancreatic insufficiency or severe liver disease. Vitamins A and E are of the greatest concern, particularly in patients with severe malabsorption or liver disease. Vitamin D deficiency is more of a concern with inadequate sunlight exposure (52) or with advanced cholestatic liver disease. Current recommendations for supplementation with fat-soluble vitamins were provided in the proceedings of a recent consensus conference on nutrition assessment and management (51).

Trace Metal Deficiencies

No obvious defect of trace metal absorption or metabolism has been observed in cystic fibrosis. Plasma zinc levels, for example, appear to be low only in patients with moderate to severe malnutrition, and the levels correlate directly with plasma proteins, retinol-binding protein, and vitamin A (65). Plasma levels of copper and ceruloplasmin may be elevated in patients with cystic fibrosis, but usually in proportion to the severity of pulmonary disease, because ceruloplasmin is an acute-phase reactant (65). No reliable evidence supports the concept that selenium is of any clinical significance (10). Symptomatic hypomagnesemia, with evidence of a positive Trousseau sign, tremulousness, muscle cramps, and weakness, may develop in patients receiving aminoglycosides (31) and is reported to be a secondary complication in patients treated for distal intestinal obstruction syndrome with repeated oral doses of N-acetylcysteine.

Iron-deficiency anemia with low serum ferritin is frequently seen in patients with advanced pulmonary disease (12), but may also be seen in the stable patient (2). In patients with pulmonary insufficiency, polycythemia seems to occur less commonly than in other pulmonary disorders of comparable severity, suggesting that these patients have a relative anemia. However, hemoglobin values do respond to nutritional repletion of the undernourished patient (42). The precise mechanism of iron-deficiency anemia is poorly understood, since there is no evidence of a defect of iron absorption or metabolism. In fact, some reports demonstrated increased iron absorption in children with CF not receiving pancreatic extracts, but these studies may have been carried out in children with depleted iron stores (33).

Essential Fatty Acid Deficiency

In infancy, particularly before diagnosis, clinical features of essential fatty acid deficiency (EFAD) can occur with desquamating skin lesions, increased susceptibility to infection, poor wound healing, thrombocytopenia, and growth retardation. In older patients who are adequately treated, clinical evidence of EFAD is extremely rare. Most patients with pancreatic insufficiency, nevertheless, have biochemical abnormalities of blood and tissue lipids (22). Changes include decreased linoleic and increased palmitoleic, oleic, and eicosatrienoic acids. It has been suggested that these biochemical abnormalities reflect an underlying defect of fatty acid metabolism (54), while others have argued that the low plasma and tissue levels are due to increased metabolic usage in undernourished patients (35). In a survey of 32 patients, we found that low plasma essential fatty acid levels were confined to patients with less than 5% of pancreatic function (25). Furthermore, Parsons et al (47) concluded that suboptimal caloric intake and undernutrition are important determinants in the development of EFAD. EFAD levels in tissues were restored by providing malnourished CF patients with caloric supplements via nasogastric tube feeding.

NUTRITIONAL EVALUATION AND THERAPY

Clinical

Nutritional support should be an integral part of the care of CF patients and requires close clinical evaluation, monitoring of growth rates, and appropriate dietary counseling. At diagnosis, height and weight (percentiles) should be carefully measured, and anthropometric measurements taken (skin folds, mid-arm circumference). During routine follow-up visits, growth should be carefully monitored, and where necessary, dietary counselling provided. When patients receive an adequate diet, normal growth can be expected until impeded by advanced respiratory disease. Patients who fail to grow at a normal rate deserve careful evaluation, particularly young children with little pulmonary disease.

Close involvement of a qualified, experienced dietitian is invaluable. Both energy intake and compliance with pancreatic enzyme supplements should be carefully evaluated; in addition, the adequacy of stool fat absorption (72-hr fecal fat) should be determined and fat and energy intake documented during administration of regular pancreatic enzyme supplements. The dose of enzymes may need to be adjusted with or without the judicious use of agents to inhibit or neutralize gastric acid secretion.

Patients with mild pulmonary disease will often lose weight following an acute respiratory infection but generally catch up after recovery. Those suffering from recurrent abdominal pain due to distal intestinal obstruction syndrome often reduce caloric intake to control their symptoms. In these cases, aggressive treatment may be necessary, and in our experience, is best achieved by intestinal lavage with a balanced electrolyte solution containing polyethylene glycol (13). Similarly, signs of esophageal reflux and esophagitis (24, 58) must be sought and aggressive treatment instituted because severe symptoms will reduce caloric intake. Generally, patients with hepatic disease will grow normally, except in rare instances of severe cholestasis or hepatic decompensation.

The diet must be calorically adequate for individual needs and should be as normal for age and peer group as possible. Actual energy requirements of patients with cystic fibrosis are extremely variable, for the reasons described earlier. Dietary intake may be affected by a patient's level of self-esteem and general feeling of well-being. It is therefore essential that patients who have nutritional difficulties receive psychological support, especially in adolescence and adulthood. Exercise programs aimed at improving physical capacity are considered important. Improved muscle mass may lead to a sense of accomplishment and stimulate an interest in providing nutritional support for physical goals.

As a general rule, protein intakes of children with CF are more than adequate (4), but nitrogen balance may be particularly sensitive to insufficient total energy intake. Provided the latter is adequate, we recommend that protein intake equal the recommended daily allowance for age, sex, and weight. The use of fat as a source of energy, previously discussed in some detail, provides an excellent supply of palatable, energy-rich calories. The limited reserves of essential fatty acids in CF patients and the vulnerability of malnourished patients to essential fatty acid deficiency require specific attention. Although there is no evidence to suggest that biochemical essential fatty acid deficiency has any major clinical impact, we do recommend a diet that contains adequate quantities of linoleic acid to maintain normal or close to normal fatty acid profiles. There is no known defect in the transport of monosaccharides, and some investigators have even suggested enhanced glucose absorption. Complex carbohydrates are quite well tolerated and are good sources of energy. Supplemented doses of fat-soluble vitamins are indicated in patients with pancreatic insufficiency or severe hepatic-biliary disease; generally, two to three times normal intake is recommended.

Biochemical

Biochemical evaluation at diagnosis requires a careful assessment of pancreatic and nutritional status. To determine pancreatic status and the need for pancreatic enzymes, we recommend quantitative evaluation of fecal fat losses while accurately measuring fat intake. Alternatively, recent modifications to the oral bentiromide test (N-benzyl-tyrosyl-aminobenzoic acid) provide a less costly and time-consuming method of evaluating pancreatic function (76). Poor substitutes include documentation of fat on stool microscopy, stool trypsin or chymotrypsin activity, serum carotene, and vitamin A and E levels. Many of these tests are useful, however, for monitoring response to treatment on return visits. Serum levels of immunoreactive trypsinogen may be reduced in the patient with pancreatic insufficiency, but only after the age of 7–8 years (20). The most accurate method of assessing pancreatic function is the direct pancreatic stimulation test (29), but this invasive, difficult test should be reserved for evaluating patients with pancreatic sufficiency, in order to better define reserve exocrine function.

Routine laboratory studies of nutritional status in patients with CF were recently reviewed and a consensus report has been published (51). It was recommended that a complete blood count, plasma retinol, and alpha-tocopherol be performed at diagnosis and yearly as a part of routine care. If low levels of retinol and/or alpha-tocopherol are detected, the patient needs a more complete evaluation of fat absorption and liver function, and an increase in the dose of vitamins A and E. If there is evidence of iron deficiency in routine hematologic studies, then iron status must be measured more accurately, i.e. serum iron, transferrin, and ferritin.

Electrolytes, acid-base status, and serum albumin should be measured at diagnosis. Subsequently, serum albumin is indicated only if there is weight loss, growth failure, or clinical deterioration. Electrolytes and acid-base measurements are indicated with prolonged fever or in the summer heat, particularly in breast-fed infants. Infants may well need a salt supplement on hot summer days. Shorter half-life proteins like transferrin, retinol-binding protein, and pre-albumin are unnecessary, since they offer no advantage over serum albumin combined with anthropometry.

Age-Related Nutritional Guidelines

Standard guidelines for the nutritional evaluation and support of patients with cystic fibrosis must be modified according to individual needs, the age of the patient, and specific complications of the disease.

We now approach these patients diagnostically from the perspective of energy balance. Key factors are energy intake, absorption, and expenditure. Intake is determined from diet records, usually over 3 to 5 days. Absorption is measured by 3-day stool collection combined with a 3-day food record; hence the coefficient of fat absorption can be calculated. Energy expenditure is measured using open-circuit indirect calorimetry (74). We recognize that most centers will not have access to indirect calorimetry; therefore, on the basis of our experience, we have suggested a way of estimating the REE of a patient with CF based on normal standards, lung function, age, and gender (51). Estimated REE enables the calculation of daily energy needs. The reader is referred to the recent consensus report for further details (51).

INFANCY TO TWO YEARS   The majority of patients with CF are diagnosed in infancy because of meconium ileus or a nutritional disturbance. The time of diagnosis is a crucial period for instituting therapeutic interventions, dietary counselling, and nutrition education. Furthermore, this is a phase of rapid growth and high energy needs.

Newly diagnosed infants may be profoundly anorexic and indifferent to food. Those presenting with hypoalbuminemia, edema, and anemia of infancy require careful attention. In addition, during the neonatal period active nutritional management is imperative after surgery for meconium ileus. A short course of intravenous nutrition and/or enteral tube feeding may be the only way to ensure adequate nutrition in the first few weeks of care. In general, patients improve rapidly with adequate attention to caloric requirements, vitamin needs, and pancreatic enzyme supplementation; routine oral feeding with a standard age-appropriate formula becomes possible very quickly. In some instances a formula with a higher caloric density may be needed. In many infants with CF, normal growth can be sustained on human milk, provided adequate attention is paid to their caloric needs and sodium requirements. Protein hydrolysates, medium-chain triglycerides, and polysaccharide supplements are rarely required. Infants who cannot maintain adequate growth with high-calorie standard nutrients hardly ever do better when given these supplements unless they are artificially delivered by enteric tubes.

TWO TO FIVE YEARS   At this age, children develop some independent feeding habits, expressed through clear food preferences. Daily intake varies considerably. Since feeding habits are developing at this age, it is important to maintain close attention to energy balance and nutrient needs, using an organized system of guidance and dietary counselling.

SIX TO TWELVE YEARS   Children in this age group are expected to develop a greater sense of personal responsibility for their treatment and daily activities. This, in turn, may cause difficulties with drug compliance (pancreatic enzymes and vitamins); in addition, peer pressure may have an impact on their choice of nutrients.

ADOLESCENT YEARS   The period of adolescence is associated with an increase in energy requirements due to accelerated growth, pubertal development and, in many instances, a high level of physical activity. Poor growth and delayed development of puberty can create considerable emotional stress. Peer pressure may cause patients to deny their disease. Although the reasons have not been clearly defined, females with CF appear to be at the greatest risk of undernutrition and growth failure. During adolescence, patients with more advanced pulmonary disease are at greatest risk of suffering from the ill effects of energy imbalance.

ADULTHOOD   If close attention is paid to energy needs and food intake, it is possible to maintain adequate energy balance for optimal growth to adulthood in most patients, especially when lung function is not severely impaired. A minority of affected adults, especially females, will suffer weight loss in association with advanced pulmonary disease. These patients have an energy imbalance since they seem unable to maintain adequate energy intake by voluntary means.

NUTRITIONAL INTERVENTION

A variety of approaches to artificial nutritional supplementation has been taken in patients who fail to respond to routine nutritional management. The hope is that restoration of nutritional status may result in easier control of chest infections, ameliorate the rate of decline in respiratory function, and extend survival. High-energy liquid dietary supplements are advocated, and although they are convenient to use and may be successful in the short term, no reliable information is available regarding long-term efficacy. It is our impression that many of these energy rich-supplements are at best substitutes for normal dietary habits and do not result in long-term improvement in nutritional status. Patients with growth failure or weight loss, particularly those with deteriorating pulmonary function, therefore may be considered candidates for more invasive, artificial forms of supplementary nutrition. We have critically reviewed the current literature on the subject.

Short-Term Studies

A variety of short-term parenteral and enteral feeding techniques has been used with malnourished CF patients. Shepherd et al (60) evaluated malnourished CF patients (mean age, 5.43 years) 6 months before and 6 months after a 3-week period of parenteral nutrition. During the pre-treatment period, while receiving "conventional" dietary management, the patients showed inadequate growth velocity, but 6 months after the short period of intravenous nutrition they appeared to exhibit continuing catch-up growth, fewer pulmonary infections, and a significant improvement in clinical score.

Other studies have failed to show lasting improvement following short-term nutritional support. The improved nutritional status in the patients in Shepherd's study could be explained by aggressive pulmonary management while the patients were hospitalized. In addition, the very young age of their patients suggests that closer attention to voluntary nutrition may well have prevented the problem at the outset. Mansell et al (43), who evaluated older malnourished CF patients (aged 10–17 years), also demonstrated improvement in nutritional status following a 1-month period of supplemental parenteral nutrition when patients were provided 120% of their energy needs. Immediately following supplementation, body weight, triceps skinfold thickness, and mid-arm muscle circumference increased significantly. Maximum inspiratory airway pressure also increased, suggesting improvement in respiratory muscle strength, but none of the indices of lung function improved. One month after parenteral nutrition, however, the patients were once again malnourished, falling back to levels similar to those seen before treatment. In a study from Montreal (6), supplemental feeding by nasogastric tube was instituted while patients were in hospital and was continued at home for 4 weeks. Patients showed considerable weight gain, attributable to increased caloric intake, but the nutritional changes were transient and not accompanied by long-term improvement in growth. In a study from our center, Pencharz et al (48) evaluated body composition, nutritional status, and energy needs of six undernourished adolescents and adults with cystic fibrosis. Lean body mass was preserved but there was significant wasting of adipose tissue. Following a brief period of nasogastric feeding with a semi-elemental diet, the effects of refeeding on body composition were reassessed. After refeeding, body weight, body fat, and total body potassium increased significantly, but fat-free body mass and total body nitrogen did not change. None of the subjects was able to continue for longer than 2 to 3 months because of nasal irritation and coughing up the tube. Thus, nutritional benefits derived from brief periods of supplemental nutrition are short-lived and do not produce long-term improvement in growth or function. The failure of brief periods of supplemental feeding to effect long-term benefit is not surprising if the pathogenesis of the energy imbalance is considered (Figure 3), since the underlying causative factors are not reversed.

Long-Term Studies

Since the effects of brief periods of energy supplementation on chronically malnourished CF patients were transient, long-term approaches were clearly necessary to achieve and maintain normal nutrition in patients unable to meet their own energy needs. In addition, it was thought that reversal of malnutrition might have a favorable influence on the course of pulmonary disease and consequently on survival.

As shown in Table 3, three major studies have addressed the problem by using forms of nocturnal enteral supplements (8, 41, 61). In a study from Toronto (41), patients were given nocturnal supplemental feeding of a semi-elemental formula by gastrostomy tube for an average period of 1 year. The adolescent and adult patients were suffering from moderate to severe lung disease and all were markedly wasted or stunted. Gastrostomy tubes were placed endoscopically under local anesthesia. A contemporary group of patients with CF (matched for age, sex, nutritional status, and pulmonary function) drawn from the clinic's computerized data bank werte pair-matched to the study group. In a second Canadian study (8), 10 malnourished CF patients (mean age, 13.6 years) with moderate to severe lung disease were provided with nocturnal supplemental feeding of an intact formula by a needle jejunostomy tube for periods of 10 to 36 months. Pancreatic enzyme supplements were added to the formula. In the third study, from Australia, Shepherd et al (61) evaluated 10 undernourished CF patients (mean age, 8.9 years) who were unable to maintain normal growth by oral means. They were followed during a 1-year course of nutritional supplement with a balanced-

Table 3 Long-term enteral feeding of malnourished patients with cystic fibrosis[a]

Variable	Toronto	Ottawa	Brisbane
Study Design			
Patients (male/female)	14 (5/9)	10 (5/5)	10 (5/5)
Age: Mean (years)	12.9	13.6	8.9
Range (years)	5–22	6–21	3–13
Enteral route	Gastrostomy	Jejunostomy	Nasogastric/Gastrostomy
Supplement type	Semielemental	Intact	Semielemental
Duration (years)	1.1	1.6	1.0
Controls	Concurrent	Retrospective	Prospective
Patient characteristics			
Weight as % of height	82 ± 10	80 ± 9	No data[b]
FEV_1 (%)[c]	47 ± 15	No data	66 ± 16
FVC (%)[d]	53 ± 13	64 ± 18	84 ± 12

[a] Adapted from Durie & Pencharz (21).
[b] Expressed as Z-score.
[c] FEV_1 = forced expiratory volume in one second.
[d] FVC = forced vital capacity.

peptide or a semi-elemental formula given overnight by nasogastric or gastrostomy feeding. These patients were compared concurrently with patients receiving conventional nutritional therapy, and matched for height, sex, and pulmonary function. In all three studies, normal activity and regular meals were permitted during daytime hours.

In each study, long-term enteral supplemental feeding resulted in a significant improvement in catch-up growth and positive changes in body composition (Table 4). There appeared to be beneficial effects on pulmonary

Table 4 Effects of long-term enteral feeding in malnourished patients with cystic fibrosis[a]

Variable	Toronto	Ottawa	Brisbane
Nutritional status			
Δ Weight (kg)	↑	↑	↑
Δ Height (cm)	↑	↑	↑
Δ Weight as % of Height (%)	↑	↑	↑
Total body potassium (g)	↑	No data	No data
Body fat (%)	↑	No data	No data
Mid-arm muscle circumference	No data	↑	No date
Protein synthesis	No data	No data	↑
Respiratory function			
Patients	Unchanged	Unchanged[b]	Improved
Controls	Deteriorated	Deteriorated[b]	Deteriorated

[a] Adapted from Durie & Pencharz (21).
[b] Compared with year before intervention.

Table 5   Approach to nutritional treatment of patients with cystic fibrosis

Encourage good feeding habits early
In patients with growth failure, assess:
   energy intake
   absorptive function
   for gastrointestinal complications that would reduce intake
   energy expenditure
   psychological/family dysfunction
Provide voluntary supplements and/or modify enzyme therapy
Consider invasive methods of nutritional supplementation before severe undernutrition occurs
Avoid invasive methods in patients with end-stage pulmonary failure, as these will only prolong
   the agony of dying

function, but the effect on survival remains unanswered. In the two Canadian studies (8, 41), nutritional supplements appeared to slow the rate of deterioration of pulmonary function. In Shepherd's study (61), respiratory function deteriorated in the control group but appeared to improve in the patient group; however, the patients were considerably younger than those in the two Canadian studies.

Following our initial publication of long-term gastrostomy supplemental feeding (41), we established a multidisciplinary approach to the evaluation and care of the failing patient (Table 5). This approach uses the services of dietitians, nutrition support nurses, social workers, and physicians. Patients identified as having an energy problem are seen first by the dietitian. If diet counselling and/or voluntary supplements are not effective, the patient is referred for assessment for long-term gastrostomy feeding. It involves both a family and social evaluation and a medical/nutritional assessment. Once all the factors for and against nutritional intervention are considered by the multidisciplinary team, the patient and family are brought into the decision-making process. Currently only 24 of the 550 patients attending our CF clinic are receiving supplementary gastrostomy feeds. Very few patients have been able to discontinue gastrostomy feeding, since their energy needs remain elevated. In the past 12 months we have moved from percutaneous, endoscopically-placed gastrostomy tubes to placement by an interventionist radiologist under diagnostic imaging control (34). This procedure is well tolerated, and patients are discharged about 3 days after gastrostomy insertion.

CONCLUSION

If close attention is paid to the individual patient's energy needs and nutritional status, undernutrition can be prevented or promptly treated. In the vast majority of patients, normal growth and nutrition can be achieved with the rational use of a normal, high-energy diet. However, in a small group of patients, advanced lung disease causes a rise in energy expenditure, and energy imbalance may result. At this stage, long-term, invasive methods of nutritional support should be considered. In patients with more advanced lung disease who are candidates for a lung transplant, prior maintenance of nutritional status is an important prognostic factor. Aggressive nutritional therapy, however, is likely to be unsuccessful during the terminal stages when the patient is suffering from end-stage cardiopulmonary failure (42).

ACKNOWLEDGMENTS

Much of the work from our laboratories referred to in this manuscript has been made possible through the generous support of the Canadian Cystic Fibrosis Foundation. This chapter was prepared with the assistance of Medical Publications, The Hospital for Sick Children, Toronto, Ontario.

Literature Cited

1. Allan, J. D., Mason, A., Moss, A. D. 1973. Nutritional supplementation in treatment of cystic fibrosis of the pancreas. *Am. J. Dis. Child.* 126:22–26

2. Ater, J. L., Herbst, J. J., Landaw, S. A., O'Brien, R. T. 1983. Relative anemia and iron deficiency in cystic fibrosis. *Pediatrics* 71:810–14

3. Bear, C. E., Li, C. H., Kartner, N., Bridges, R. J., Jensen, T. J., et al. 1992. Purification and functional reconstitution of the cystic fibrosis transmembrane conductance regulator (CFTR). *Cell* 68:809–18

4. Bell, L., Linton, W., Corey, M. L., Durie, P., Forstner, G. G. 1981. Nutrient intakes of adolescents with cystic fibrosis. *J. Can. Diet. Assoc.* 42(1):62–71

5. Belli, D. C., Levy, E., Darling, P., Leroy, C., Lepage, G., et al. 1987. Taurine improves the absorption of a fat meal in patients with cystic fibrosis. *Pediatrics* 80:517–23

6. Bertrand, J. M., Morin, C. L., Lasalle, R., Patrick, J., Coates, A. L. 1984. Short-term clinical, nutritional, and functional effects of continuous elemental enteral alimentation in patients with cystic fibrosis. *J. Pediatr.* 104:41–46

7. Boat, T. F., Welsh, M. J., Beaudet, A. L. 1989. In *The Metabolic Basis of Inherited Disease,* ed. C. R. Scriver, A. L. Beaudet, W. S. Sly, D. Valle,

2:2649–80. New York: McGraw-Hill. 6th ed

8. Boland, M. P., Stoski, D. S., MacDonald, N. E., Soucy, P., Patrick, J. 1986. Chronic jejunostomy feeding with a non-elemental formula in undernourished patients with cystic fibrosis. *Lancet* 1:232–34

9. Buchdahl, R. M., Cox, M., Fulleylove, C., Marchant, J. L., Tomkins, A. M., et al. 1988. Increased resting energy expenditure in cystic fibrosis. *J. Appl. Physiol.* 64:1810–16

10. Castillo, R., Landon, C., Eckhardt, K., Morris, V., Levander, D., et al. 1981. Selenium and vitamin E status in cystic fibrosis. *J. Pediatr.* 99:583–85

11. Chandra, R. K., Newberne, P. M. 1977. *Nutrition, Immunity and Infection: Mechanisms of Interaction.* New York: Plenum

12. Chase, P. M., Long, M. A., Lavin, M. H. 1979. Cystic fibrosis and malnutrition. *J. Pediatr.* 95:337–47

13. Cleghorn, G. J., Stringer, D. A., Forstner, G. G., Durie, P. R. 1986. Treatment of distal intestinal obstruction syndrome in cystic fibrosis with a balanced intestinal lavage solution. *Lancet* 1:8–11

14. Congden, P. J., Bruce, G., Rothburn, M. M., Clarke, P. C. N., Littlewood, J. M., et al. 1981. Vitamin status in treated patients with cystic fibrosis. *Arch. Dis. Child.* 56:708–14

15. Corey, M. 1980. Longitudinal studies

in cystic fibrosis. In *Perspectives in Cystic Fibrosis. Proc. 8th Int. Congr. Cystic Fibrosis*, ed. J. M. Sturgess, pp. 264–55. Toronto: Can. Cystic Fibrosis Found.

16. Corey, M., McLaughlin, F. J., Williams, M., Levison, H. 1988. A comparison of survival, growth, and pulmonary function in patients with cystic fibrosis in Boston and Toronto. *J. Clin. Epidemiol.* 41:583–91

17. Crozier, D. N. 1974. Cystic fibrosis. A not-so-fatal disease. *Pediatr. Clin. North Am.* 21:935–50

18. The Cystic Fibrosis Genetic Analysis Consortium. 1990. Worldwide survey of the ΔF508 mutation—Report from the Cystic Fibrosis Genetic Analysis Consortium. *Am. J. Hum. Genet.* 47: 354–59

19. Daniels, L., Davidson, G. P., Martin, A. J. 1987. Comparison of macronutrient intake of healthy controls and children with cystic fibrosis on low fat or nonrestricted fat diets. *J. Pediatr. Gastroenterol. Nutr.* 6:381–86

20. Durie, P. R., Forstner, G. G., Gaskin, K. J., Moore, D. J., Gleghorn, G. J., et al. 1986. Age-related alterations of immunoreactive pancreatic cationic trypsinogen in sera from cystic fibrosis patients with and without pancreatic insufficiency. *Pediatr. Res.* 20:209–13

21. Durie, P. R., Pencharz, P. B. 1989. A rational approach to the nutritional care of patients with cystic fibrosis. *J. R. Soc. Med.* 82(Suppl. 16):11–20

22. Farrell, P. M., Mischler, E. H., Engle, M. J., Brown, D. J., Lau, S-M. 1985. Fatty acid abnormalities in cystic fibrosis. *Pediatr. Res.* 19:104–9

23. Feigal, R. J., Shapiro, B. L. 1979. Mitochondrial calcium uptake and oxygen consumption in cystic fibrosis. *Nature* 278:276–77

24. Feigelson, J., Girault, F., Pecau, Y. 1987. Gastro-oesophageal reflux and esophagitis in cystic fibrosis. *Acta Paediatr. Scand.* 76:989–90

25. Forstner, G., Durie, P., Corey, M. 1988. Cystic fibrosis, progress in gastroenterology and nutrition. *Int. Cystic Fibrosis Congr., 10th, Sydney, Australia. Excerpta Med., Asia Pac. Congr., Ser. 74*, pp. 154–60

26. Fried, M. D., Durie, P. R., Tsui, L-C., Corey, M., Levison, H., et al. 1991. The cystic fibrosis gene and resting energy expenditure. *J. Pediatr.* 119:913–16

27. Gaskin, K., Gurwitz, D., Durie, P., Corey, M., Livison, H., et al. 1982. Improved respiratory prognosis in patients with cystic fibrosis with normal fat absorption. *J. Pediatr.* 100:857–62

28. Gaskin, K. J., Durie, P. R., Corey, M., Wei, P., Forstner, G. G. 1982. Evidence for a primary defect of pancreatic HCO$_3$- secretion in cystic fibrosis. *Pediatr. Res.* 16:554–57

29. Gaskin, K. J., Durie, P. R., Lee, L., Hill, R., Forstner, G. G. 1984. Colipase and lipase secretion in childhood-onset pancreatic insufficiency. Delineation of patients with steatorrhea secondary to relative colipase deficiency. *Gastroenterology* 86:1–7

30. Gracey, M., Burke, V., Anderson, C. M. 1969. Assessment of medium-chain triglyceride feeding in infants with cystic fibrosis. *Arch. Dis. Child.* 44:401–3

31. Green, C. G., Doershuk, C. F., Stern, R. C. 1985. Symptomatic hypomagnesemia in cystic fibrosis. *J. Pediatr.* 107:425–28

32. Gurwitz, D., Corey, M., Francis, P. W. J., Crozier, D., Levison, H. 1979. Perspectives in cystic fibrosis. *Pediatr. Clin. North Am.* 26:603–15

33. Heinrich, H. C., Bender-Götze, C., Gabbe, E. E., Bartels, H., Oppitz, K. H. 1977. Absorption of inorganic iron- (59Fe2+) in relation to iron stores in pancreatic exocrine insufficiency due to cystic fibrosis. *Klin. Wochenschr.* 55:587–93

34. Ho, C-S., Gray, R. R., Goldfinger, M., Rosen, I. E., McPherson, R. 1985. Percutaneous gastrostomy for enteral feeding. *Radiology* 156:349–51

35. Hubbard, V. S., Dunn, G. D. 1980. Fatty acid composition of erythrocyte phospholipids from patients with cystic fibrosis. *Clin. Chim. Acta* 102: 115–18

36. Kerem, B.-S., Rommens, J. M., Buchanan, J. A., Markiewicz, D., Cox, T. K., et al. 1989. Identification of the cystic fibrosis gene: genetic analysis. *Science* 245:1073–80

37. Kerem, E., Corey, M., Kerem, B., Durie, P., Tsui, L-C., et al. 1989. Clinical and genetic comparisons of patients with cystic fibrosis, with or without meconium ileus. *J. Pediatr.* 114:767–73

38. Kerem, E., Corey, M., Kerem, B.-S., Rommens, J., Markiewicz, D., et al. 1990. The relation between genotype and phenotype in cystic fibrosis—analysis of the most common mutation (delta F508). *N. Engl. J. Med.* 323: 1517–22

39. Kraemer, R., Rüdeberg, A., Hadoroon, B., Rossi, E. 1978. Relative underweight in cystic fibrosis and its prog-

nostic value. *Acta Paediatr. Scand.* 67:33–37

40. Kristidis, P., Bozon, D., Corey, M., Markiewicz, D., Rommens, J., et al. 1992. Genetic determination of exocrine pancreatic function in cystic fibrosis. *Am. J. Hum. Genet.* 50:1178–84

41. Levy, L. D., Durie, P. R., Pencharz, P. B., Corey, M. L. 1985. Effects of long-term nutritional rehabilitation on body composition and clinical status in malnourished children and adolescents with cystic fibrosis. *J. Pediatr.* 107:225–30

42. Levy, L., Durie, P., Pencharz, P., Corey, M. 1986. Prognostic factors associated with patient survival during nutritional rehabilitation in malnourished children and adolescents with cystic fibrosis. *J. Pediatr. Gastroenterol Nutr.* 5:97–102

43. Mansell, A. L., Anderson, J. C., Muttart, C. R., Ores, C. N., Loeff, D. S., et al. 1984. Short-term pulmonary effects of total parenteral nutrition in children with cystic fibrosis. *J. Pediatr.* 104:700–5

44. O'Rawe, A., Dodge, J. A., Redmond, A. O. B., McIntosh, I., Brock, D. J. H. 1990. Gene/energy interaction in cystic fibrosis. *Lancet* 335:552–53

45. O'Rawe, A., McIntosh, I., Dodge, J. A., Brock, D. J., Redmond, A. O., et al. 1992. Increased energy expenditure in cystic fibrosis is associated with specific mutations. *Clin. Sci.* 82:71–76

46. Parsons, H. G., Beaudry, P., Dumas, A., Pencharz, P. B. 1983. Energy needs and growth in children with cystic fibrosis. *J. Pediatr. Gastroenterol. Nutr.* 2:44–49

47. Parsons, H. G., O'Loughlin, E. V., Forbes, D., Cooper, D., Gall, D. G. 1988. Supplemental calories improve essential fatty acid deficiency in cystic fibrosis patients. *Pediatr. Res.* 24:353–56

48. Pencharz, P., Hill, R., Archibald, E., Levy, L., Newth, C. 1984. Energy needs and nutritional rehabilitation in undernourished adolescents and young adult patients with cystic fibrosis. *J. Pediatr. Gastroenterol. Nutr.* 3(Suppl. 1):S147–53

49. Pencharz, P. B. 1983. Energy intakes and low-fat diets in children with cystic fibrosis. (Editorial). *J. Pediatr. Gastroenterol. Nutr.* 2:400–2

50. Pencharz, P. B., Berall, G., Vaisman, N., Corey, M., Canny, G. 1988. Energy expenditure in children with cystic fibrosis. *Lancet* 2:513–14

51. Ramsey, B. W., Farrell, P. M., Pencharz. P., and the Consensus Committee. 1992. Nutritional assessment and management in cystic fibrosis: A consensus report. *Am. J. Clin. Nutr.* 55:108–16

52. Reiter, E. O., Brugman, S. M., Pike, J. W., Pitt, M., Dokoh, S., et al. 1985. Vitamin D metabolites in adolescents and young adults with cystic fibrosis: Effects of sun and season. *J. Pediatr.* 106:21–26

53. Riordan, J. R., Rommens, J. M., Kerem, B-S., Alon, N., Rozmahel, R., et al. 1989. Identification of the cystic fibrosis gene: Cloning and characterization of complementary DNA. *Science* 245:1066–73

54. Rogiers, V., Dab, I., Crokaert, R., Vis, H. L. 1980. Long chain non-esterified fatty acid pattern in plasma of cystic fibrosis patients and their parents. *Pediatr. Res.* 14:1088–91

55. Rommens, J. M., Iannuzzi, M. C., Kerem, B-S., Drumm, M. L., Melmer, G., et al. 1989. Identification of the cystic fibrosis gene: Chromosome walking and jumping. *Science* 245:1059–65

56. Rosenstein, B. J., Langbaum, T. S. 1983. Incidence of distal intestinal obstruction syndrome in cystic fibrosis. *J. Pediatr. Gastroenterol. Nutr.* 2:299–301

57. Roy, C. C., Darling, P., Weber, A. M. 1984. A rational approach to meeting macro- and micronutrient needs in cystic fibrosis. *J. Pediatr. Gastroenterol. Nutr.* 3(Suppl. 1):S154–62

58. Scott, R. B., O'Laughlin, E. V., Gall, D. G. 1985. Gastroesophageal reflux in patients with cystic fibrosis. *J. Pediatr.* 106:223–27

59. Scott-Jupp, R., Lana, M., Tanner, M. S. 1991. Prevalence of liver disease in cystic fibrosis. *Arch. Dis. Child.* 66:698–701

60. Shepherd, R., Cooksley, W. G. E., Domville Cooke, W. D. 1980. Improved growth and clinical, nutritional, and respiratory changes in response to nutritional therapy in cystic fibrosis. *J. Pediatr.* 97:351–57

61. Shepherd, R. W., Holt, T. L., Thomas, B. J., Kay, J., Isles, A., et al. 1986. Nutritional rehabilitation in cystic fibrosis: Controlled studies of effects on nutritional growth retardation, body protein turnover, and course of pulmonary disease. *J. Pediatr.* 109:788–94

62. Shepherd, R. W., Holt, T. L., Vasques-Velasquez, L., Coward, W. A., Prentice, A., et al. 1988. Increased

energy expenditure in young children with cystic fibrosis. *Lancet* 1:1300–3

63. Shwachman, H. 1960. Therapy of cystic fibrosis of the pancreas. *Pediatrics* 25:155–63

64. Sokol, R. J., Reardon, M. C., Accurso, F. J., Stall, C., Narkewicz, M., et al. 1989. Fat-soluble-vitamin status during the first year of life in infants with cystic fibrosis identified by screening of newborns. *Am. J. Clin. Nutr.* 50: 1064–71

65. Solomons, N. W., Wagonfeld, J. B., Rieger, C., Jacob, R. A., Bolt, M., et al. 1981. Some biochemical indices of nutrition in treated cystic fibrosis patients. *Am. J. Clin. Nutr.* 34:462–74

66. Spicher, V., Roulet, M., Schutz, Y. 1991. Assessment of total energy expenditure in free-living patients with cystic fibrosis. *J. Pediatr.* 118:865–72

67. Sproul, A., Huang, N. 1964. Growth patterns in children with cystic fibrosis. *J. Pediatr.* 65:664–76

68. Stutts, M. J., Knowles, M. R., Gatzy, J. T., Boucher, R. C. 1986. Oxygen consumption and ouabain binding sites in cystic fibrosis nasal epithelium. *Pediatr. Res.* 20:1316–20

69. Summers, M., McBride, B. W., Milligan, L. P. 1988. Components of basal energy expenditure. In *Aspects of Digestive Physiology in Ruminants: Proc. of a Satellite Symp. of the 30th Int. Cong. of the Int. Union of Physiol. Sci.,* ed. A. Dobson, M. Dobson, pp. 257–85. Ithaca, NY: Cornell Univ. Press

70. Tizzano, E. F., Buchwald, M. 1992. Cystic fibrosis: beyond the gene to therapy. *J. Pediatr.* 120:337–49

71. Vaisman, N., Clarke, R., Pencharz, P. B. 1991. Nutritional rehabilitation increases resting energy expenditure without affecting protein turnover in patients with cystic fibrosis. *J. Pediatr. Gastroenterol. Nutr.* 13:383–90

72. Vaisman, N., Clarke, R., Rossi, M., Goldberg, E., Zello, G. A., et al. 1992. Protein turnover and resting energy expenditure in patients with undernutrition and chronic lung disease. *Am. J. Clin. Nutr.* 55:63–69

73. Vaisman, N., Levy, L. D., Pencharz, P. B., Tan, Y. K., Soldin, S. J., et al. 1987. Effect of salbutamol on resting energy expenditure in patients with cystic fibrosis. *J. Pediatr.* 111:137–39

74. Vaisman, N., Pencharz, P. B., Corey, M., Canny, G. J., Hahn, E. 1987. Energy expenditure of patients with cystic fibrosis. *J. Pediatr.* 111:496–500

75. Vaisman, N., Rossi, M., Corey, M., Clarke, R., Goldberg, E., et al. 1991. Effect of refeeding on the energy metabolism of adolescent girls who have anorexia nervosa. *Eur. J. Clin. Nutr.* 45:527–37

76. Weizman, Z., Forstner, G. G., Gaskin, K. J., Kopelman, H., Wong, S., et al. 1985. Bentiromide test for assessing pancreatic dysfunction using analysis of para-aminobenzoic acid in plasma and urine. Studies in cystic fibrosis and Shwachman's syndrome. *Gastroenterology* 89:596–604

77. Zentler-Munro, P. L., Fine, D. R., Batten, J. C., Northfield, T. C. 1985. Effect of cimetidine on enzyme inactivation, bile acid precipitation, and lipid solubilisation in pancreatic steatorrhea due to cystic fibrosis. *Gut* 26:892–901

Annu. Rev. Nutr. 1993. 13:137–65

RECENT ADVANCES IN MAMMALIAN AMINO ACID TRANSPORT

Michael S. Kilberg,[1] *Bruce R. Stevens,*[2] *and Donald A. Novak*[3]

Departments of Biochemistry and Molecular Biology,[1] Physiology,[2] and Pediatrics,[3] University of Florida College of Medicine, Gainesville, Florida 32610

KEY WORDS: biological transport, amino acid metabolism, liver, intestine, brain

CONTENTS

AMINO ACID TRANSPORT SYSTEMS 137
   Facilitated Transporters 138
   Secondary Active Transporters 143
   Transporters of the Brain 147
IMPACT OF TRANSPORT ON METABOLISM 149
   Hepatic Zonal Heterogeneity 149
   Adaptive Regulation in Intestinal Brush Border 150
CELL PROLIFERATION AND TRANSPORT 152
   Growth Factors, Cytokines, and Transformation 152
   Cell Cycle and Regeneration 155
AMINO ACID DELIVERY TO THE FETUS 155
   Substrate Flux in Whole Animals 155
   Impact on Fetal Development 157
SUMMARY 157

AMINO ACID TRANSPORT SYSTEMS

Characterization of mammalian amino acid transport systems began with the pioneering work of Christensen and his coworkers in the early 1950s (37). Many of the features of Systems y^+, A, ASC, and L originally described in the Ehrlich cell also hold for these systems in other cell types as well, but a number of activities, such as Systems Gly, N, and those specific for imino or anionic amino acids, are not expressed by the Ehrlich cell. In hindsight, the relative simplicity of amino acid transport by the Ehrlich cell may have facilitated the original description of the systems, but now it might be

0199-9885/93/0715-0137$02.00

considered atypical in comparison to other mammalian cells. Most mammalian cells express a common "core" set of amino acid transport activities, but all also exhibit wide variations in the total number, type, and activity of these transport systems. As a result each cell type is unique with regard to the processes available for amino acid accumulation, and has undoubtedly adapted for its particular physiological role and metabolic needs.

A number of reviews have covered, through the early 1980s, some of the more common amino acid transport systems that exist in many cell types and have described individual transport activities and the associated regulation (26–30, 52, 128, 157). The present report focuses primarily on the more recent advances of the last decade. Progress has been made in identifying transporter proteins and cloning the corresponding cDNAs. As expected, this newly acquired information has reaffirmed some of the principles derived from whole cell studies, but it has also introduced unexpected and exciting new insights.

Facilitated Transporters

SYSTEM L   One of the first amino acid transport systems described for mammalian cells was a Na^+-independent system termed System L (113). Until recently, most investigators have somewhat arbitrarily assigned all saturable, Na^+-independent uptake to this activity, especially in those cases where the analog 2-aminobicyclo-(2,2,1)-heptane-2-carboxylic acid (BCH) was used because of its System L specificity in the Ehrlich cell (32). However, it is now clear that several distinct systems may contribute to the saturable Na^+-independent transport in any given cell type. Regulation by substrate availability of the System L activity in CHO cells has been studied by Oxender and his colleagues and reviewed elsewhere (39). They have demonstrated that System L activity is increased when leucyl-tRNA becomes limiting either by reduction of leucine content in the medium or by inactivation of leucyl-tRNA synthetase in a temperature-sensitive mutant cell line.

What was initially thought to be a single System L activity in isolated hepatocytes (107) was later shown to exhibit heterogeneity (68, 167). In hepatocyte primary cultures, the kinetics of leucine, histidine, or BCH saturable uptake in the absence of Na^+ are biphasic. Component I (L_1) is a high affinity, low capacity agency with estimated K_m values of less than 200 µM, whereas component II (L_2) is a low affinity, high capacity system with K_m values of 2–5 mM. System L_2 activity is relatively high in freshly isolated cells and declines during the first 24 hr of culture, while uptake by System L_1 is barely detectable immediately after cell isolation, but increases from two- to fivefold after an initial lag period of 12–24 hr. Although the factors controlling these changes are unknown, it is known that the increase in System L_1 requires de novo synthesis of both RNA and protein (167).

System L activity is decreased in B-lymphocytes from patients who have chronic lymphocytic leukemia (CLL) (135). Other amino acid transport activities are normal, despite a 80–90% reduction in System L as measured by BCH uptake. Interestingly, when CLL lymphocytes are treated in vitro with phorbol esters, the cells are converted to a mature immunoglobulin-producing phenotype and the System L activity is restored to rates observed in normal cells treated with phorbol esters (173). Further experimentation is required to distinguish between the contribution of maturational level and transformation to the decreased transport.

SYSTEM $b^{o,+}$ A novel Na^+-independent system that accepts both neutral and cationic amino acids was first described by Van Winkle and his colleagues in mouse blastocysts (157, 158). The substrate specificity of System $b^{o,+}$ overlaps with those of Systems L and y^+ in that amino acids with bulky sidechains, but without branching on either the α or β carbon, are preferred. Interestingly, both organic and inorganic cations, including Na^+, compete for the cationic binding site and inhibit transport (159). The degree to which this effect serves to minimize the contribution of System $b^{o,+}$ in vivo is unknown.

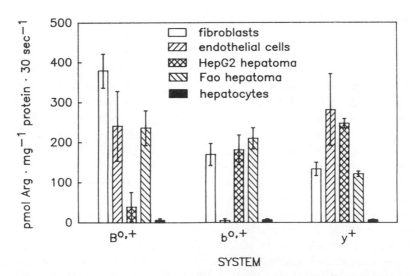

Figure 1 Transport of arginine by multiple pathways in mammalian cells. The uptake of 50 μM ^{3}H-arginine was measured for 30 sec at 37C in cultured cell monolayers as detailed previously (89). System $B^{o,+}$ was defined as the uptake rate in sodium-containing buffer minus the uptake rate in the absence of sodium. The Na^+-independent uptake rate that was inhibited by 10 mM leucine was defined as System $b^{o,+}$. System y^+ was the leucine insensitive Na^+-independent transport inhibited by 10 mM arginine. Each value represents the average ± standard deviations of at least three determinations.

The role of this and other systems during early development has been reviewed by (157). An extensive tissue distribution of System $b^{o,+}$ in the adult mammal has not been reported, but as shown in Figure 1 its presence in a number of cultured cells including human fibroblasts, rat or human hepatoma cells, and porcine endothelial cells suggests widespread occurrence. The existence of System $b^{o,+}$ in a variety of cell types cautions against the former practice of assigning all saturable Na^+-independent arginine uptake to System y^+.

SYSTEM y^+ Uptake of lysine by the Ehrlich cell was shown to be mediated by both neutral and cationic systems, depending on the net charge of the substrate (35). The process mediating uptake of the cationic form was designated System Ly^+ and later was shown to transport the net positively charged forms of lysine, arginine, and histidine. Recently, the term Ly^+ was changed to y^+ to underscore the breadth of acceptance for numerous cationic amino acids and related analogs (6).

An extensive review of System y^+ characteristics is published elsewhere (170). Four of its most interesting properties are as follows. (*i*) Tissue distribution appears to be widespread, but not ubiquitous (Figure 1; 170). (*ii*) Accumulation of amino acid against a concentration gradient occurs despite bidirectional transport because the cationic substrates respond to the membrane potential across the plasma membrane (20). (*iii*) Uptake is subject to trans-stimulation when substrate concentrations are sufficiently high on the opposite side of the membrane (171). (*iv*) A neutral amino acid plus a Na^+ can competitively inhibit System y^+ and participate in exchange reactions with the cationic substrates of this system (33, 170).

The cDNA for the System y^+ transporter was cloned serendipitously when researchers discovered that the corresponding protein, previously shown to be the murine ecotropic retrovirus receptor, exhibited all of the characteristics associated with this transport activity (92, 164). The following defining criteria were demonstrated: (*i*) injection of cRNA into oocytes produced a stimulation of transport activity for cationic amino acids only; (*ii*) certain neutral amino acids could inhibit if Na^+ was present; and (*iii*) among the substrates only histidine showed a sensitivity to pH. Consistent with previous observations that documented the lack of significant y^+ activity in adult rat liver (Figure 1; 170), Northern blot analysis yielded little or no detectable System y^+ mRNA in this tissue (92). Interestingly, System y^+ activity is expressed in both fetal and transformed hepatocytes (170). Figure 2 illustrates the relative amount of System y^+ mRNA for the rat Fao hepatoma cell line as well as newborn and adult rat liver tissue. The relative amounts of mRNA are in agreement with the transport activity within these cells and illustrate that cell-specific expression of System y^+ can occur at the transcriptional level. Given the hepatic catabolism of arginine via the urea cycle, the lack of System y^+ activity

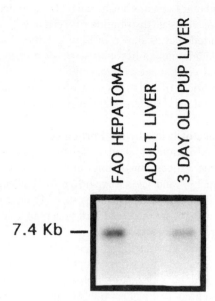

Figure 2 System y^+ mRNA content in adult or newborn rat liver, and a rat hepatoma. Total RNA was isolated from liver tissue or cultured rat Fao hepatoma cells. Size fractionation by agarose gel electrophoresis and subsequent Northern analysis was performed as described previously (136). Each lane contained 20 μg of total RNA and was probed with a cDNA provided by Dr. James Cunningham, Harvard University.

in the hepatocyte may at first seem illogical. However, in this way arginine efflux is prevented (other than by the nonsaturable route) and the cytoplasmic concentration is determined by cellular synthesis/degradation without potential fluctuations due to changes in the plasma levels.

REGULATORY SUBUNITS?   The possibility that mammalian amino acid transport activities are composed of multiple subunits or are regulated by associated membrane proteins is suggested by recent cDNA cloning reports from three laboratories (11, 103, 152, 168, 169). As a group these cDNAs code for putative proteins that are integral membrane proteins with a single transmembrane spanning domain. The latter property distinguishes them from many other Na^+-dependent and Na^+-independent organic solute transporters that have been cloned and contain 12–14 transmembrane domains. In vitro synthesis of cRNA from these cDNA clones and subsequent injection into oocytes resulted in stimulation of amino acid transport activities that resemble Systems y^+, $b^{o,+}$, or $B^{o,+}$. Tate et al (152) published the first of these sequences (NAA) and proposed that the corresponding protein mediated a System L-like activity. However, lysine served as an inhibitor of Na^+-inde-

Figure 3 Alignment of amino acid sequences for transport-associated membrane proteins. The predicted amino acid sequences deduced from the cloned cDNAs for 4F2, D2/NAA, or rBAT were aligned using the CLUSTAL program (77) within PC-GENE (IntelliGenetics, Mountain View, CA). The top two sequences compare 4F2 with D2/NAA, and the bottom two sequences compare D2/NAA and rBAT. Identical residues are marked with an asterisk (*) and conserved substitutions are indicated with a period (.) for each pair of sequences. Gaps (-) are inserted by the computer program to optimize the alignment.

pendent phenylalanine uptake by the expressed NAA activity in *Xenopus* oocytes, an observation consistent with the System $b^{o,+}$ assignment made for the same sequence (termed D2) later reported by Wells & Hediger (168). A cDNA isolated from rabbit kidney (rBAT) by Bertran et al (11) shows a high degree of homology to the rat sequence (NAA/D2) and also results in stimulation of amino acid transport activity similar to System $b^{o,+}$ when expressed in *Xenopus* oocytes (Figure 3). The putative rat proteins are 683 amino acids in length and have a molecular mass of 78 kDa. In vitro translation confirms this core protein size, whereas translation in the presence of microsomal membranes yields a product of 90–100 kDa, suggesting a significant amount of glycosylation (168). The rabbit clone (rBAT) codes for a protein of about 78 kDa as well, based on the deduced sequence of 677 amino acids (11, 103).

Both of these proteins show homology to the heavy chain (85 kDa) of a heterodimer membrane protein complex called the 4F2 cell surface antigen (169). Expression of the human 4F2 protein in oocytes results in stimulation of both Na^+-dependent and Na^+-independent transport of neutral and cationic amino acids. In contrast to the tissue specificity of NAA/D2 and rBAT, 4F2 is widely expressed in both mouse and human tissues. The exact function of these proteins is unclear; they may serve as necessary components for maximal constitutive activity of a given transporter or they may be strictly regulatory so as to alter the basal activity. At least in one example, System y^+, a putative protein that contains 12 transmembrane spanning domains is known to exhibit basal activity (92, 164).

Secondary Active Transporters

SYSTEM A   System A, originally described two decades ago in the Ehrlich cell (36, 113), has received a great deal of attention because of the availability of specific nonmetabolizable substrates (AIB or MeAIB) and its regulatory properties. For example, hormone-mediated induction of System A in liver occurs in response to a broad spectrum of hormones (138), and transcriptional control of a System A-associated gene is thought to be responsible for most of the enhanced transport observed.

Glucagon induction of hepatic System A transport activity is typical and will be used as an example. Enhanced System A activity (20–40%) occurs within a few minutes after addition of glucagon, but a much larger increase in activity is seen after a time lag of about 60 min. The increase detected during the first 60 min of exposure to hormone is cycloheximide-insensitive (50) and probably is the result of increased membrane potential (110). The majority of the elevated transport activity (five- to tenfold) is blocked by inhibitors of either RNA or protein synthesis (34, 41, 117). Supportive evidence for de novo synthesis of a System A-associated glycoprotein comes from Barber et al (7), who showed that tunicamycin blocked the glucagon induction of System A. As shown previously for cycloheximide or puromycin (34, 117), when tunicamycin was added to hepatocytes after the hormone-mediated induction of transport activity had begun, inhibition of further stimulation occurred within 1 hr (7). These results suggest that the System A-associated glycoprotein responsible for the increased uptake must be continuously synthesized. Following glucagon-dependent induction of transport in whole cells, isolated plasma membrane vesicles retain the activity (133) which also can be recovered following solubilization of plasma membrane proteins and reconstitution into artificial proteoliposomes (55).

More recent evidence for glucagon-dependent transcriptional control comes from exogenous RNA expression in *Xenopus* oocytes. Two independent studies have reported that rat liver RNA from glucagon-treated animals, when compared to RNA from control tissue, results in greater expression of System A activity following microinjection of oocytes (116, 151). Size fractionation of mRNA prior to injection into oocytes led both laboratories to conclude that the mRNA responsible was between 1.9 and 2.5 kb in length. The role of this product in initiating and maintaining the glucagon-induced transport is unknown and must await identification and characterization. Given the recent identification of putative transporter-associated regulators, the glucagon-stimulated mRNA may code for the System A transporter itself or for an associated regulatory protein. If it is solely regulatory in function, its action within the Golgi, as described below, must be explained.

Consistent with de novo membrane protein synthesis, Cariappa & Kilberg (22) have shown that glucagon-induced System A activity can be detected in transport-competent Golgi vesicles. Following glucagon treatment, a lag of 30–45 min occurred prior to detection of increased activity in cis Golgi, which then continued through the cellular machinery to include medial and trans Golgi, and finally the plasma membrane. If the newly synthesized protein is a regulator of basal or inactive System A carriers already present, this control must also occur for transporters in transit to the plasma membrane, given the ability to detect the hormone-induced activity in the Golgi compartment. Interestingly, the glucagon-stimulated transport activity present in cis or medial Golgi membranes was insensitive to inactivation by NEM, whereas after transfer to the trans Golgi or plasma membrane the sulfhydryl reagent produced rapid and irreversible inhibition of the carrier (22). This difference in NEM sensitivity was demonstrable even if the protein modification was performed on detergent-solubilized transport activity and then followed by proteoliposome reconstitution for transport measurements. The latter observation argues for an inherent change in the availability of a free sulfhydryl group during processing of a component of the System A transporter.

Studies on the trafficking of hepatic System A activity (23) revealed that the newly synthesized transporter arrives at the basolateral plasma membrane surface of the hepatocyte prior to its transfer, presumably by transcytosis (8), to the canalicular surface. Irreversible inactivation of the glucagon-stimulated basolateral activity with a cell-impermeant maleimide completely prevented transfer of the transport activity to the canalicular membrane.

SYSTEM GLY   Isolated rat hepatocytes have been shown to contain a glycine-specific system (31), similar to that originally described in pigeon erythrocytes (48) and rabbit reticulocytes (172). The hepatic System Gly is Na^+-dependent and appears to transport two sodium ions for each glycine. Glycine uptake by normal hepatocytes is not restricted to System Gly, however, as indicated by a sensitivity of a portion of its transport to inhibition by the System A-specific substrate MeAIB (31). Reichberg & Gelehrter have studied glycine transport in HTC cells in some detail, especially the regulation by hormones (121). In this hepatoma cell, glycine transport is mediated by two distinct systems, both of which are inhibited by glucocorticoid treatment. A Na^+-dependent glycine transporter has been described in the central nervous system, and two cDNAs encoding a putative transporter have been reported (63, 140). By Northern analysis, both laboratories demonstrated a high level of expression in spinal cord, brain stem, olfactory bulb, and cerebellum. The presence of significant glycine transport rates in other areas of the central nervous system may be indicative of related transporters.

SYSTEM N   The Na^+-dependent uptake of glutamine and histidine by isolated rat hepatocytes is not inhibited competitively by an excess of either the System A-specific substrate MeAIB or the System ASC-specific substrate cysteine (90). These and other results led Kilberg et al (90) to conclude that hepatocytes contained a Na^+-dependent transport system distinct from Systems A or ASC. Additional support for such a system had already been reported by Joseph et al (84), who showed that glutamine uptake did not occur by the same processes as uptake of alanine and serine. A detailed study demonstrated the presence of a previously undetected transport agency, called System N to reflect an apparent affinity for neutral amino acids containing nitrogen-bearing side-chains, which mediated the Na^+-dependent uptake of glutamine, histidine, and asparagine (90). In fact, in cells that contain basal System A activity, glutamine and histidine are specific substrates for System N. Contrary to the original report, glutamine uptake can occur via System A if this carrier's activity is induced by substrate starvation, thus requiring the continued inclusion of MeAIB to restrict glutamine or histidine to System N (67). System N does retain complete specificity for glutamine in the hepatoma cell line

H4-II-EC3 (also called H-35) as well as in hepatocytes isolated from rat fetuses (156).

The importance of System N in relation to glutamine metabolism in the liver has been the subject of a number of investigations (discussed below). The existence of System N-like activity in human placenta (88) and rat muscle (1, 81, 99, 122) has been documented. Dimaline et al (46) have suggested that a System N-like activity is an important component of histidine-induced gastric acid secretion, based on selective inhibition by glutamine and asparagine, and tolerance for lithium substitution for sodium.

Some progress has been made toward identifying the protein(s) responsible for hepatic System N activity. Following development of a procedure to efficiently solubilize the transport activity and subsequently reconstitute it into artificial proteoliposomes, enrichment of the transporter by nearly 600-fold was achieved through selective protein precipitation (150). Using this partially purified fraction as antigen, monoclonal antibodies were prepared that inhibited System N activity in rat hepatocytes and immunoprecipitated solubilized transporter (149). The antibodies revealed a broad band of immunoreactive protein at about 100 kDa on immunoblots of rat liver plasma membrane. A good correlation was observed between enrichment of this immunoreactive protein and System N activity during several steps of purification. Tissues known to lack System N activity do not contain immunoreactive material (B. K. Tamarappoo, unpublished data). Using a different approach, Taylor et al (153) have injected *Xenopus* oocytes with RNA from rat liver and demonstrated enhanced System N transport. Size fractionation of the RNA prior to injection suggested that the size of the mRNA responsible was approximately 1.9 kb. Further progress will require identifying an individual clone from a cDNA library prepared from this RNA fraction.

SYSTEM $B^{o,+}$ System $B^{o,+}$ is a Na^+-dependent activity that mediates uptake of both cationic and neutral amino acids (158). It was first described in mouse blastocysts (160) but also has been characterized in *Xenopus* oocytes (21) and in several other cell types (30). As shown in Figure 1, System $B^{o,+}$ is expressed in human fibroblasts, porcine endothelial cells, and rat Fao hepatoma cells; little or no activity is present, however, in the human hepatoma HepG2 or in normal rat hepatocytes. These data suggest that expression of $B^{o,+}$ activity is tissue and cell specific. The substrate specificity of the $B^{o,+}$ activity is somewhat broader than the Na^+-independent System $b^{o,+}$ because of its tolerance for branching in the α and β carbon positions. Hence, in some cells, a bicyclic analog formerly considered specific for System L, 2-aminobicyclo-(2,2,1)-heptane-2-carboxylic acid (BCH), may be transported by System $B^{o,+}$ in the presence of sodium. The activity of this transport system is developmentally regulated in the blastocyst (157). A possible variant of System $B^{o,+}$, called System B, exists in the brush border of absorptive epithelial cells (see below). The substrate specificity for System B is remarkably similar to those neutral amino acids accepted by System $B^{o,+}$ (145, 147).

Transporters of the Brain

A number of amino acids and related metabolites serve as neurotransmitters to mediate chemical transmission across the synapse. A hallmark of synaptic transmission is rapid termination of the signal by clearing the synaptic cleft of neurotransmitter. Specific Na^+-dependent transporters on the postsynaptic membrane mediate this process through active extraction of these compounds. A number of cDNAs that code for transport activities thought to function in this role have been cloned recently. One of the earliest advances was the purification of a Na^+-dependent GABA transport activity (120), which led to the subsequent cloning of the corresponding cDNA (64). Using oligonucleotides that have sequence homology to regions of the GABA transporter cDNA (sequences within or near a putative transmembrane domain), other laboratories have obtained clones by cDNA library screening or polymerase chain reaction (PCR) for Na^+-dependent transporters from neuronal tissue for norepinephrine (114), dopamine (62, 91, 137), serotonin (80), proline (59), and glycine (63, 140).

Sequence analysis of these cDNAs shows extensive homology, and they appear to represent a protein family (3, 134, 175). Figure 4 is a computer analysis of amino acid sequences coding for complete transmembrane domains for some of the family members. When each of the twelve putative transmembrane domains for the proline transporter is used to search for sequences of at least 60% identity among the other proteins, a number of relationships are revealed. Note, that the analysis shown in Figure 4 is based on the entire transmembrane sequence of each domain (approximately 20 amino acids); if shorter sequences are considered, as those used to obtain clone-related cDNAs, even stronger regions of identity are present (3, 59, 63, 134, 175). The most highly conserved of these sequences occurs within the first eight transmembrane domains. Within the family of transporters from the brain, the order of the transmembrane sequences appears to be conserved, but if one looks for similar sequences in transporters from other tissues (e.g. Na^+-dependent glucose or nucleotide transporters from brush border), reshuffling of these segments has occurred.

The evolutionary relationship between the proteins will require more extensive analysis, but such a high degree of conservation suggests a common ancestor. Interestingly, tissue-specific conservation may have been a factor in this evolution, because computer analysis using these same sequences shows that they are not as highly conserved within Na^+-dependent transporters

AA SEQUENCE HOMOLOGY FOR BRAIN TRANSPORTERS

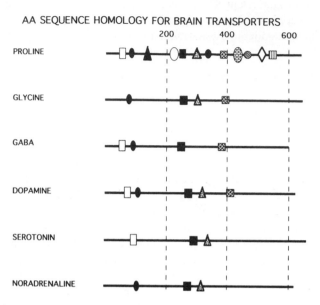

Figure 4 Conservation of transmembrane amino acid sequences for several Na$^+$-dependent transporters from the central nervous system. The deduced amino acid sequence was obtained for each transporter based on the published cDNA sequence. Using the HELIX MEM program (51) within PC-GENE (IntelliGenetics, Mountain View, CA), the putative 12 transmembrane spanning domains of the proline transporter were predicted in good agreement with those chosen by previous analyses (59). Each of these transmembrane segments was used to search for homologous sequences within the other transporters listed. Only when the amino acid identity was 60% or greater for the entire transmembrane sequence was the segment considered "conserved" and illustrated with a similar symbol.

present in other tissues. Evidence from radiation-inactivation studies suggests that Na$^+$-dependent organic solute transporters may exist as multiprotein complexes (9, 147). It has been suggested that transmembrane segment 2 for neuronal Na$^+$-dependent transporters may play a role in oligomerization of these proteins, because it contains a sequence similar to a leucine zipper (3). The leucine zipper motif has been documented within or near the voltage-sensing transmembrane domains of several ion channel proteins (106).

With specific regard to amino acid uptake, cDNAs coding for Na$^+$-dependent proline (59) and glycine (63, 140) transporters in the brain have been reported recently. At the present time it is unclear whether related glycine transporters are expressed in peripheral tissues. Northern analysis with one of the brain glycine transporter cDNAs revealed no detectable mRNA in spleen, kidney, or aorta, and only a weak signal in liver (140). Hepatocytes contain a glycine-specific Na$^+$-dependent transporter activity (31). Low stringency screening of cDNA libraries or PCR amplification using the sequences obtained from the brain may serve as useful strategies to clone cDNAs for homologous transporters in other tissues.

IMPACT OF TRANSPORT ON METABOLISM

Hepatic Zonal Heterogeneity

Division of labor, a basic concept of interorgan biology, is also reflected within the hepatocyte population of the liver through "functional hepatocyte heterogeneity" or "metabolic zonation" (71, 85, 155). With regard to nitrogen metabolism, hepatocytes along the acinus have been divided functionally into two cell populations, periportal and perivenous. Periportal hepatocytes are nearest the portal venules and comprise the vast majority (90%) of the total hepatocyte population. Perivenous cells account for less than 10% of the hepatocytes and are localized as a ring of one to three cells around the terminal central venules (61, 70). Based on a limited number of reports, selective expression of amino acid transporters likely occurs within the two cell populations (19, 74, 148).

Perfusion of rat liver shows significant hepatocyte heterogeneity for glutamate or aspartate uptake (148, 154). These observations are consistent with reports that glutamate uptake is significantly decreased after destruction of perivenous hepatocytes by carbon tetrachloride treatment (72, 154) and that ^{13}N-glutamate administered via the portal vein in vivo is preferentially accumulated by perivenous hepatocytes (40). Although Na^+-independent glutamate uptake was shown to be equal for isolated hepatocyte suspensions enriched in periportal or perivenous cells, a small Na^+-dependent glutamate transport component was 6- to 7-fold higher in perivenous compared to periportal cells (19). Studies using isolated rat liver plasma membrane vesicles from either the sinusoidal or canalicular domain reveal a relatively slow rate of Na^+-dependent glutamate transport by the canalicular membrane only (5, 23). The weak Na^+-dependent glutamate uptake by the plasma membrane vesicles may be the result of localization to the perivenous hepatocytes, which probably contribute proportionally (10% of hepatocytes) to the isolated membrane vesicles. Consistent with the observation of Na^+-independent glutamate transport by the sinusoidal membrane (5), uptake of glutamate by the perfused rat liver appears to occur primarily by an exchange mechanism (74).

Glutamine synthetase is expressed primarily by perivenous hepatocytes, whereas glutaminase activity is greatest in periportal cells (61, 69, 166). This striking change in expression of glutamine-metabolizing enzymes along the liver acinus is consistent with the "Intercellular Glutamine Cycle," described by Häussinger and his colleagues (74), which proposes net glutamine uptake by periportal cells and net glutamine release by perivenous cells. Apparently, glutamine extraction by the periportal hepatocytes largely involves Na^+-dependent System N (19, 54, 73, 90). In contrast, glutamine efflux from perivenous cells occurs via a facilitated transporter, (54, 127). W. W. Souba and his colleagues have recently obtained evidence for a Na^+-independent transport activity (tentatively termed System n) that exhibits the same narrow substrate specificity as the Na^+-dependent System N (unpublished data). If present in perivenous hepatocytes, this transporter may contribute to glutamine release. Isolated periportal and perivenous rat hepatocytes showed no difference in System N-mediated transport of histidine, but Na^+-independent uptake was higher in perivenous cells (19), consistent with the presence of either System L or System n.

Adaptive Regulation in Intestinal Brush Border

When faced with changing metabolite concentrations, cells can maintain their biochemical and physiological states by adjusting the rate of plasma membrane transport. This process was termed "adaptive regulation" and was originally used to describe increased activity of a specific transporter in response to starvation of substrates for that transporter (65, 138). However, adaptive regulation must be considered as a process capable of either up- or down-regulation in response to substrate availability, given the distinct regulatory differences among epithelial and nonepithelial membrane transporters (43, 87, 145). In general, a decreased extracellular concentration of certain amino acids leads to adaptive up-regulation of transporters in internal organs that maintain their own homeostasis and participate in interorgan nutrient flows. This process is exemplified by the induction of System A following substrate starvation. On the other hand, raising luminal amino acid concentrations induces adaptive up-regulation in epithelial cell apical membranes, as found in the small intestine or kidney. This control mechanism has been demonstrated for System y^+ and System B in enterocytes (M. Pan & B. R. Stevens, unpublished data). System B (formerly referred to as System NBB) is related to System $B^{o,+}$, as discussed above, and transports neutral amino acids. System B is expressed uniquely within the brush border membrane (Table 1; 102, 104, 146, 147).

In addition to absorbing organic nutrients for use by the whole organism, the intestinal mucosa utilizes its ready supply of amino acids for the tasks of Na^+ and water absorption (174), enterocyte volume regulation (100), and enterocyte nutrition. From the vantage point of the whole animal, intestinal transport represents the net vectorial transfer of amino acids from the environment to the body internal milieu, as coordinated by the asymmetric distribution of transporter species in the apical and basolateral membranes.

Table 1 Amino acid transport systems of the intestine

System	Membrane domain	Na$^+$-dependent	Typical substrates
B	Apical	Yes	Threonine, alanine
ASC	Apical	Yes	Alanine, glycine
IMINO	Apical	Yes	Proline, pipecolic acid
β	Apical	Yes, with Cl	β-Alanine
X$^-_{AG}$	Apical	Yes, with Cl	Glutamate, aspartate
A	Apical & basolateral	Yes	MeAIB
y$^+$	Apical & basolateral	No	Arginine, lysine
b$^{o,+}$	—	No	Lysine, leucine
L	Apical & basolateral	No	BCH, phenylalanine, leucine

Table 1 describes some of the well-studied membrane transport systems in enterocytes. Note that the basolateral membrane transporters are the same as those found in internal organ cells, while several of the apical membrane transporters are unique to this epithelial cell membrane. Kinetic analysis of intestinal transport illustrates that K_m values for a given amino acid are matched to those for transport by internal organs (18, 97). More detailed discussions of the kinetic mechanism and distribution of intestinal amino acid transporters are published elsewhere (45, 146).

The small intestine maintains an ontogenetically controlled baseline capacity to absorb amino acids in the starved state, and for many species this baseline value irreversibly declines over the course of the animal's development and maturity (17, 18). It is not clear whether constitutive expression of transporter proteins within the brush border is autonomously controlled or is maintained by localized regulatory signals from nutrients, growth factors, or hormones acting in a paracrine/autocrine manner. Nonetheless, when adult or infant epithelium is exposed to augmented amino acid concentrations, the absorptive capacity of the mucosa reversibly increases above the constitutive level, both acutely and chronically (87, 145). Physiologically, this adapative up-regulation prevents a precarious situation in which intestinal absorption would be the rate-limiting factor governing internal organ intermediary metabolism and the interorgan flow of amino acids. Thus, the intestine responds to increased luminal amino acid by maintaining a reserve absorptive capacity that exceeds the current dietary intake. Diamond (43) notes that this "safety margin" reserve for absorptive capacity only slightly exceeds dietary intake, as constrained by factors shaped by evolution, ecology, and cell energetics.

Down-regulation of intestinal amino acid transport is a return to the baseline absorptive capacity in the absence of a stimulating luminal nutrient. The decay of transport activity occurs over a period of days as absorptive villus enterocytes are sloughed off and replaced by differentiating stem cells migrating up from the crypts. The transport activity in the membranes of these maturing replacement cells represents the future transport capacity (18).

Both acute trans-effects and de novo protein synthesis of transporters contribute to increasing the intestinal absorptive capacity. Amino acids can acutely alter intestinal transport by the cycloheximide-insensitive process of trans-stimulation (145, 146). For Systems B, ASC, and L, acute increased uptake occurs as the result of an exchange reaction across the membrane with substrates sharing the same transporter. Interestingly, System X^-_{AG} is stimulated by all of the neutral amino acids except glycine (101). On the other hand, the intestinal basolateral membrane presents a unique phenomenon in which low concentrations of leucine stimulate dibasic amino acid transport (94). Cheeseman (26) recently explained this as an "allosteric" property of System y^+.

Alternatively, enterocytes up-regulate transport capacity by inducing de novo synthesis of specific amino acid transporters or transporter-associated regulatory proteins such as those discussed above for System $b^{o,+}$. A single amino acid substrate can increase the expression of its transport activity by 2- to 10-fold, as demonstrated in vivo or in vitro (43, 130, 131, 146). Using cultured enterocytes, B. R. Stevens and colleagues (unpublished data) have shown that substrate-dependent up-regulation of specific membrane transporter systems is cycloheximide-sensitive and follows a 10–24 hr lag period. Interestingly, reports indicate that individual amino acids can induce transporter systems that do not mediate the uptake of that substrate (12). For example, in mice fed a diet supplemented with either aspartate or aginine, both Systems X^-_{AG} and y^+ were induced (44, 56).

CELL PROLIFERATION AND TRANSPORT

Growth Factors, Cytokines, and Transformation

A number of growth factors modulate amino acid transport. Boerner et al (13) used rat kidney cells to demonstrate that epidermal growth factor (EGF) stimulated Systems A and L, but not System ASC. EGF also causes a rapid, but transient 30–40% stimulation of transport in isolated hepatocytes through plasma membrane hyperpolarization (111). Longer exposure to EGF increases basal AIB uptake by hepatocytes (10) and suppresses the glucagon-dependent (cAMP-mediated) stimulation of hepatic AIB transport (109). Visciano & Fehlmann (162) reported that de novo protein synthesis was required for this EGF-dependent antagonism of glucagon action.

In vivo treatment with either interleukin-1 (IL-1) or tumor necrosis factor α (TNFα) increased amino acid uptake by the liver (4, 115, 123), but neither IL-1 nor TNFα was effective with isolated hepatocytes in culture (123, 165). However, IL-6 alone does stimulate AIB uptake by isolated cells (4, 10). These data imply that the induction by IL-1 or TNFα in vivo is mediated via a secondary response, possibly involving release of other cytokines from nonepithelial cells within the liver. This conclusion is in agreement with studies of the regulation of acute phase protein synthesis by hepatocytes, which demonstrate that IL-6 acts directly (142), whereas TNFα and IL-1 do not (76). TNF administration in vivo may be accompanied by the release of hormonal mediators such as glucagon and glucocorticoid hormones that are known to stimulate Systems A and N. Pretreatment of rats with a glucocorticoid antagonist attenuates the TNF-stimulated increase in Na^+-dependent amino acid transport by approximately 50% (W. W. Souba et al, unpublished data).

Souba et al (144) have shown that, in contrast to hepatocytes, both TNF and IL-1 stimulate System ASC-mediated glutamine uptake by cultured porcine endothelial cells. The lag of 8–12 hr prior to induction of transport in the endothelial cells may reflect the time required for release of an autocrine-acting factor or, alternatively, for signal processing and de novo synthesis of transporter. The induction, one of the few examples of System ASC regulation, was prevented by blocking either RNA or protein synthesis. Although hepatocytes and endothelial cells exhibit cytokine-mediated increases in amino acid transport, the brush border of the intestine responds in an opposite manner. Studies in confluent monolayers of the human intestinal Caco-2 cell line indicate that interferon-γ decreases apical Na^+-dependent glutamine transport by about 30% (143). In contrast, TNF and IL-1 did not alter Na^+-dependent glutamine transport alone or in combination.

Transforming growth factor-β (TGF-β) suppresses the induction by IL-6 and inhibits basal hepatocyte AIB transport when it is administered alone (10). In contrast, TGF-β stimulates both Systems A and L activity in rat kidney cells (13). Extension of these studies on the regulation by cytokines and growth factors should provide considerable insight into the role that transport plays in cell and tissue growth.

The tumor-promoting compounds termed phorbol esters also alter System A–mediated transport. For example, Kitagawa et al (93) used 3T3 fibroblasts to demonstrate stimulation of AIB uptake following a 3-hr exposure to phorbol esters. Down-regulation of protein kinase C prior to tests for hormone induction of transport resulted in a decreased response to phorbol ester, platelet-derived growth factor (PDGF), or the calcium ionophore A23187 (93). These results suggest a common step in the mechanism of action, possibly protein kinase C activity. Boerner & Saier (15) showed that phorbol esters stimulate System A activity in Madin Darby Canine Kidney (MDCK) cells, whereas other investigators have reported no effect of either phorbol esters or diacylglycerol on uptake by primary cultures of renal proximal tubular cells (60). Dawson & Cook (42) reported stimulation of System A transport activity and redistribution of protein kinase C to the plasma membrane following treatment of LLC-PK$_1$ cells with phorbol esters. Both of these processes were prevented by the actin filament disruptor cytochalasin B, but only the induction of System A activity was prevented by inhibiting protein synthesis with cycloheximide. These results suggest that activation of protein kinase C is only one step in a sequence of events by which phorbol esters increase amino acid transport.

Induction of System A–mediated amino acid transport in response to transformation has been reported by a number of laboratories. The activity of System A–mediated transport is increased following chemical transformation of MDCK cells (14), despite the fact that the parent and transformed MDCK cell lines grow at similar rates (53). These results permit distinction between the effect of transport on growth rate and transformation per se. One potential step of the transformation mechanism was illustrated by Leister et al (96), who showed that turnover of System A activity in chemically transformed C3H-10T1/2 cells was significantly slower than in the parental line. This change in stability might account for elevated transport activity in the transformed cells, if the synthesis rates are similar for both cell types. Unfortunately, absolute rates of turnover and synthesis must await identification of protein(s) responsible for System A transport.

Beginning with the pioneering work of Foster & Pardee (57) many laboratories have demonstrated that viral transformation of mammalian cells increases Na$^+$-dependent AIB uptake. Plasma membrane vesicles isolated from virally transformed cells retain the increased transport activity observed in whole cells (98, 118). Borghetti et al (16) demonstrated that the enhanced System A and ASC activities in SV40-transformed 3T3 cells remained elevated in revertant cells that had regained density-dependent inhibition of growth. Like the results of Erlinger & Saier (53) mentioned above, these data illustrate that one can separate the changes in transport activity due to transformation from those due to cell growth.

A temperature-sensitive SV40 mutant used to transform rat hepatocytes has permitted investigators to shift cells from the "normal" to the "transformed" state simply by changing the incubation temperature (26a). At the permissive temperature of 33C, SV40-transformed hepatocytes exhibited rapid cell division and reduced synthesis of liver-specific proteins, but at the restrictive-temperature of 40C, functional T-antigen was no longer expressed, cell division was considerably reduced, and liver-specific proteins once again were produced. System A transport activity was expressed at high levels in rapidly growing cells maintained at 33C, but transport was considerably reduced in the slowly dividing cells (40C) (66). Transfer of the cells maintained at 40 to 33C resulted in both increased growth rate and transport activity over the following 72 hr. This induction of transport was prevented by protein synthesis inhibitors, and the elevated transport activity present in whole cells at 33C was retained when plasma membrane vesicles or reconstituted proteoliposomes were prepared (66). Collectively, the data suggest that transfer from 40 to 33C results in an increased de novo biosynthesis of a System A–associated membrane protein.

Cell Cycle and Regeneration

Sander & Pardee (132) monitored AIB uptake throughout the cell cycle in cultured cells. In early G phase a twofold increase in the transport rate, which preceded DNA synthesis by approximately 5–10 hr, was observed. The transport was elevated during the remainder of the cell cycle and returned to basal levels during mitosis. The relationship between System A transport and the cell cycle in vivo is suggested by monitoring AIB uptake following partial hepatectomy in the rat. A transient rise in AIB transport by whole tissue (163) or isolated hepatocytes (95) is observed 6–12 hr following 70% hepatectomy. This spike of System A activity following hepatectomy coincides with the initiation of cell replication and may reflect the increased transport observed during the cell cycle. It is likely that the normally quiescent hepatocytes in the liver remnant are initially synchronized by the signals that trigger regeneration. A second smaller peak in System A activity is usually detected 18–24 hr after the first one, and the diminished level of this induction probably reflects the gradual loss of cell synchronization. The return within 24 hr to a low basal rate of transport rather than the elevated levels typical of rapidly dividing hepatoma cells, despite continued liver growth, suggests that the transient elevation observed immediately following hepatectomy is not the same as the adaptation to an elevated growth rate that occurs following transformation. The increased transport activity following hepatectomy appears to reflect synthesis of a required System A-associated protein (47). Isolated plasma membrane vesicles from regenerating livers retained the increase in System A transport, and the specificity of the response was documented by the lack of any change in the activity of Systems ASC and N during the several days of liver regeneration (58).

AMINO ACID DELIVERY TO THE FETUS

Substrate Flux in Whole Animals

The placenta plays an integral role in the supply of nutrients to the developing fetus and serves as the interface between the maternal and fetal circulations

(139). Changes in the activity of specific placental amino acid transporters during the course of normal gestation remain largely unexplored (124). A number of studies have examined maternal and fetal serum amino acid levels at varying times throughout gestation (86, 108, 141), yet it is difficult to understand these data in terms of specific transporter activities. Placenta-specific transport systems have been the subject of a recent review (140), and therefore the present discussion focuses primarily on current concepts of transport regulation during normal gestation and in pathologic states. Fetal/maternal concentration ratios for most amino acids are greater than one, illustrating the concentrative transfer of specific amino acids (119).

The degree to which individual amino acids are transferred to the fetus depends on the level of expression and substrate competition for the numerous amino acid transport systems in basal and microvillous placental membranes. This supposition is supported by the classic observations of Christensen & Streicher (38), who noted in the guinea pig that high dietary intake of histidine, methionine, and proline resulted in a lower fetal/maternal ratio for glycine. These data imply competition between these amino acids for placental transporters. Recent reports showing competitive (proline, methionine) and noncompetitive (histidine) inhibition of System A (83) at the microvillous membrane, and competitive inhibition of System L (79) at the basal membrane, may account for the observed decrease in fetal glycine levels. Certainly, both placental and fetal metabolism also contribute to the steady state fetal/maternal ratios. Battaglia and coworkers utilized a fetal lamb model to demonstrate that glycine is avidly transferred from the maternal to the fetal circulation, where it is taken up by the fetal liver (105) and metabolized to serine (24). Interestingly, serine is then actively extracted from the fetal circulation. This observation is explained presumably by the presence of Na^+-dependent System ASC on the placental basal membrane (79).

The same group of investigators has similarly established the presence of a glutamine-glutamate cycle that transfers glutamine from the maternal to fetal circulation and subsequently to the fetal liver (105). Glutamine is metabolized to glutamate in the fetal liver and glutamate is then released into the fetal circulation to be transferred back to the placenta. The presence of Na^+-dependent System N in both placental microvillous membranes (88) and fetal hepatocytes (156) probably mediates the net transfer of glutamine to the fetus, whereas basal membrane localization of Na^+-dependent System X_{AG}^- activity allows transport of glutamate from the fetal circulation to the placenta (78). This glutamine/glutamate cycle represents a mechanism to shuttle nitrogen into the rapidly growing fetus, whereas the importance of the serine/glycine pathway is less obvious.

Impact on Fetal Development

Placental amino acid transfer during intrauterine growth retardation (IUGR) has been studied extensively. Several authors (25, 49, 75) have compared serum amino acid levels in IUGR infants to those from normal pregnancies; in general, levels of gluconeogenic amino acids are increased in IUGR fetuses, compared to those for "essential" amino acids. Rosso (125), and more recently Varma & Ramakrishnan (161), demonstrated decreased rates of AIB transfer to the fetus during IUGR in the malnourished rat dam. Similar findings have been reported in IUGR guinea pigs (82, 129). Ahokas et al (2) reported that placental transfer of AIB to the fetus was reduced in rat dams fed a diet that contained 50% less calories. Given that only a portion of these changes can be attributed to diminished placental blood flow (112, 126), they imply altered rates of intrinsic placental amino acid transport. Dicke & Henderson (45) prepared placental microvillous membranes derived from human IUGR pregnancies in which no prior risk factors for IUGR were known to exist. Rates of AIB transport were significantly decreased in this group, as compared with vesicles derived from normal pregnancies, and provided direct evidence for a reduction in amino acid transport during IUGR pregnancies. Collectively, the available data point to an inherent defect in placentofetal transfer in many examples of IUGR, but further work is required to delineate the molecular basis for these observations.

SUMMARY

During the last four decades, mammalian amino acid transport systems have been described at the cellular level through general properties such as ion-dependence, kinetics, substrate specificity, regulation of activity, and numerous other characteristics. These studies have allowed the definition of multiple transport systems for neutral, anionic, and cationic amino acids. Each system is distinct but exhibits overlapping substrate specificity. Direct measurement of transport has permitted a wealth of information to be accumulated regarding the regulation of overall activity, but the underlying molecular mechanisms have not been investigated because of a lack of the appropriate tools. Recent research designed to obtain these tools has proven fruitful, and the field of amino acid transport clearly is entering a new era. In the immediate future, transporter properties such as hormonal regulation, adaptive control, ion-dependence, and trans-effects will be studied at the molecular level by assaying mRNA or protein content and by analyzing results obtained with altered protein structures following site-directed mutagenesis.

Identification of specific proteins associated with activities already well described will provide answers to heretofore untestable questions. For example, is Na^+-independent transport mediated by the same proteins that mediate Na^+-dependent uptake except that their function in this mode does not require sodium binding? What is the protein composition of amino acid transporters? As discussed above, emerging evidence suggests that transporter proteins have different molecular structure, 12 versus 1 transmembrane domains, or that they exist as heterodimers or heterotetramers. Identification of certain transporter proteins and cloning of the respective genes also will provide valuable information about a number of inheritable diseases that are thought to be caused by defects in transporter synthesis or function. The opportunity to ask these questions will certainly generate renewed interest in the field of amino acid transport and lead to exciting advances in our knowledge.

ACKNOWLEDGMENTS

M. S. Kilberg acknowledges support from the Institute for Diabetes, Digestive, and Kidney Diseases, The National Institutes of Health (DK-28374 and DK-31580). The authors thank Marc Malandro, Mary Handlogten, and Jennifer Malandro for their contributions to this review.

Literature Cited

1. Ahmed, A., Taylor, P. M., Rennie, M. J. 1990. Characteristics of glutamine transport in sarcolemmal vesicles from rat skeletal muscle. *Am. J. Physiol.* 259:E284–91

2. Ahokas, R. A., Lahaye, E. B., Anderson, G. D., Lipshitz, J. 1981. Effect of maternal dietary restriction on fetal growth and placental transfer of alpha-amino isobutyric acid in rats. *J. Nutr.* 111:2052–58

3. Amara, S. G., Pacholczyk, T. 1991. Sodium-dependent neurotransmitter reuptake systems. *Curr. Opin. Neurobiol.* 1:84–90

4. Argiles, J. M., Lopez-Soriano, F. J., Wiggins, D., Williamson, D. H. 1989. Comparative effects of tumour necrosis factor-α (cachectin), interleukin-1-β and tumour growth on amino acid metabolism in the rat in vivo. *Biochem. J.* 261:357–62

5. Ballatori, N., Moseley, R. H., Boyer, J. L. 1986. Sodium gradient-dependent L-glutamate transport is localized to the canalicular domain of liver plasma membranes. *J. Biol. Chem.* 261:6216–21

6. Bannai, S., Christensen, H. N., Vadgama, J. V., Ellory, J. C., Englesberg, E., et al. 1984. Amino acid transport systems. *Nature* 311:308

7. Barber, E. F., Handlogten, M. E., Kilberg, M. S. 1983. Induction of amino acid transport System A in rat hepatocytes is blocked by tunicamycin. *J. Biol. Chem.* 258:11851–55

8. Bartles, J. M., Hubbard, A. L. 1988. Plasma membrane protein sorting in epithelial cells: do secretory pathways hold the key? *Trends Biochem. Sci.* 13:181–84

9. Beliveau, R., Demeule, M., Jette, M., Potier, M. 1990. Molecular sizes of amino acid transporters in the luminal membrane from the kidney cortex, estimated by the radiation-inactivation method. *Biochem. J.* 268:195–200

10. Bereta, J., Szuba, K., Fiers, W., Gauldie, J., Koj, A. 1990. Transforming growth factor-β and epidermal growth factor modulate basal and interleukin-6-induced amino acid uptake and acute phase protein synthesis in cultured rat hepatocytes. *FEBS Lett.* 266:48–50

11. Bertran, J., Werner, A., Moore, M. L., Stange, G., Markovich, D., et al. 1992. Expression cloning of a cDNA

from rabbit kidney cortex that induces a single transport system for cystine and dibasic and neutral amino acids. *Proc. Natl. Acad. Sci. USA* 89:5601–5

12. Bierhoff, M. L., Levine, G. M. 1988. Luminal and metabolic regulation of jejunal amino acid absorption in the rat. *Gastroenterology* 95:63–68

13. Boerner, P., Resnick, R. J., Racker, E. 1985. Stimulation of glycolysis and amino acid uptake in NRK-49F cells by transforming growth factor β and epidermal growth factor. *Proc. Natl. Acad. Sci. USA* 82:1350–53

14. Boerner, P., Saier, M. H. Jr. 1982. Growth regulation and amino acid transport in epithelial cells: Influence of culture conditions and transformation on A, ASC, and L transport activities. *J. Cell. Physiol.* 113:240–46

15. Boerner, P., Saier, M. H. Jr. 1988. Effects of 5-azacytidine, sodium butyrate, and phorbol esters on amino acid transport System A in a kidney epithelial cell line, MDCK: evidence for multiple mechanisms of regulation. *J. Cell. Physiol.* 137:117–24

16. Borghetti, A. F., Piedmonte, G., Tramacere, M., Severini, A., Ghiringhelli, P., et al. 1980. Cell density and amino acid transport in 3T3, SV3T3, and SV3T3 revertant cells. *J. Cell. Physiol.* 105:39–49

17. Buddington, R. K. 1992. Intestinal nutrient transport during ontogeny of vertebrates. *Am. J. Physiol.* 263:R503–9

18. Buddington, R. K., Diamond, J. M. 1989. Ontogenetic development of intestinal nutrient transporters. *Annu. Rev. Physiol.* 51:601–19

19. Burger, H.-J., Gebhardt, R., Mayer, C., Mecke, D. 1989. Different capacities for amino acid transport in periportal and perivenous hepatocytes isolated by digitonin/collagenase perfusion. *Hepatology* 9:22–28

20. Bussolati, O., Laris, P. C., Nucci, F. A., Dall'Asta, V., Longo, N., et al. 1987. Dependence of L-arginine accumulation on membrane potential in cultured human fibroblasts. *Am. J. Physiol.* 253:C1–C7

21. Campa, M. J., Kilberg, M. S. 1989. Characterization of neutral and cationic amino acid transport in *Xenopus* oocytes. *J. Cell. Physiol.* 141:645–52

22. Cariappa, R., and Kilberg, M. S. 1990. Hormone-induced System A amino acid transport activity in rat liver plasma membrane and golgi vesicles. *J. Biol. Chem.* 265:1470–75

23. Cariappa, R., Kilberg, M. S. 1992.

Plasma membrane domain localization, targeting, and transcytosis of the glucagon-induced hepatic system A carrier. *Am. J. Physiol.* 263:E1021–28

24. Cetin, I., Fennessey, P. V., Quick, A. N., Marconi, A. M., Meschia, G., et al. 1991. Glycine turnover and oxidation, and hepatic serine synthesis from glycine in fetal lambs. *Am. J. Physiol.* 260:E371–78

25. Cetin, I., Marconi, A. M., Bozzetti, P., Sereni, L. P., Corbetta, C., et al. 1988. Umbilical amino acid concentrations in appropriate and small-for-gestational-age infants: a biochemical difference present in utero. *Am. J. Obstet. Gynecol.* 158:120–26

26. Cheeseman, C. 1991. Molecular mechanisms involved in the regulation of amino acid transport. *Prog. Biophys. Mol. Biol.* 55:71–84

26a. Chou, J. Y. 1985. Establishment of rat fetal liver lines and characterization of their metabolic and hormonal properties: Use of temperature-sensitive SV40 virus. *Methods Enzymol.* 109: 385–96

27. Christensen, H. N. 1982. Interorgan amino acid nutrition. *Physiol. Rev.* 62:1193–1233

28. Christensen, H. N. 1984. Organic ion transport during seven decades. *Biochim. Biophys. Acta* 779:255–69

29. Christensen, H. N. 1985. On the strategy of kinetic discrimination of amino acid transport systems. *J. Membr. Biol.* 84:97–103

30. Christensen, H. N. 1990. Role of amino acid transport and countertransport in nutrition and metabolism. *Physiol. Rev.* 70:43–77

31. Christensen, H. N., Handlogten, M. E. 1981. Role of System Gly in glycine transport in monolayer cultures of liver cells. *Biochem. Biophys. Res. Commun.* 98:102–7

32. Christensen, H. N., Handlogten, M. E., Lam, I., Tager, H. S., Zand, R. 1969. A bicyclic amino acid to improve discriminations among transport systems. *J. Biol. Chem.* 244:1510–20

33. Christensen, H. N., Handlogten, M. E., Thomas, E. L. 1969. Na+ facilitated reactions of neutral amino acids with a cationic amino acid transport system. *Proc. Natl. Acad. Sci. USA* 63:948–55

34. Christensen, H. N., Kilberg, M. S. 1987. Amino acid transport across the plasma membrane: role of regulation in interorgan flows. In *Amino Acid Transport in Animal Cells*, ed. D. L. Yudilevich, C. A. R. Boyd, pp. 10–46. Manchester: Manchester Univ. Press

35. Christensen, H. N., Liang, M. 1966. Transport of diamino acids into the Ehrlich cell. *J. Biol. Chem.* 241:5542–51

36. Christensen, H. N., Oxender, D. L., Liang, M., Vatz, K. A. 1965. The Use of *N*-methylation to direct the route of mediated transport of amino acids. *J. Biol. Chem.* 240:3609–16

37. Christensen, H. N., Riggs, T. R., Fischer, H., Palatine, I. M. 1952. Amino acid concentration by a free cell neoplasm: Relations among amino acids. *J. Biol. Chem.* 198:1–22

38. Christensen, H. N., Streicher, J. A. 1948. Association between rapid growth and elevated cell concentrations of amino acids. *J. Biol. Chem.* 175:95–100

39. Collarini, E. J., Oxender, D. L. 1987. Mechanisms of transport of amino acids across membranes. *Annu. Rev. Nutr.* 7:75–90

40. Cooper, A J. L., Nieves, E., Rosenspire, K. C., Filc-DeRicco, S., Gelbard, A. S., et al. 1988. Short-term metabolic fate of 13-labeled glutamate, alanine, and glutamine(amide) in rat liver. *J. Biol. Chem.* 263:12268–73

41. Crettaz, M., Kahn, C. R., Fehlmann, M. 1983. Glucagon regulation of amino acid transport in hepatocytes: Effect of cell enucleation. *J. Cell. Physiol.* 115:186–90

42. Dawson, W. D., Cook, J. S. 1987. Parallel changes in amino acid transport and protein kinase C localization in LLC-PK1 cells treated with TPA or diradylglycerols. *J. Cell. Physiol.* 132:104

43. Diamond, J. M. 1991. Evolutionary design of intestinal nutrient absorption: enough but not too much. *NIPS* 6:92–96

44. Diamond, J. M., Karasov, W. H. 1987. Adaptive regulation of intestinal nutrient transporters. *Proc. Natl. Acad. Sci. USA* 84:2242–45

45. Dicke, J. M., Henderson, G. I. 1988. Rapid communication: Placental amino acid uptake in normal and complicated pregnancies. *Am. J. Med. Sci.* 295:223–27

46. Dimaline, R., Wilkinson, M., Talbot, S. J. 1990. Histidine-stimulated acid secretion in the conscious rat is mediated by amino acid uptake System N. *Exp. Physiol.* 75:717–20

47. Dolais-Kitabgi, J., Rey, J.-F., Fehlmann, M., Morin, O., Freychet, P. 1981. Effect of insulin and glucagon on amino acid transport in isolated hepatocytes after partial hepatectomy in the rat. *Endocrinology* 109:868–75

48. Eavenson, E., Christensen, H. N. 1967. Transport systems for neutral amino acids in the pigeon erythrocyte. *J. Biol. Chem.* 242:5386–96

49. Economides, D. L., Nicolaides, K. H., Gahl, W. A., Bernadini, I., Evans, M. I. 1989. Plasma amino acids in appropriate- and small-for-gestational age fetuses. *Am. J. Obstet. Gynecol.* 161:1219–27

50. Edmondson, J. W., Lumeng, L. 1980. Biphasic stimulation of amino acid uptake by glucagon in hepatocytes. *Biochem. Biophys. Res. Commun.* 96:61–68

51. Eisenberg, D., Schwarz, E., Komaromy, M., Wall, R. 1984. Analysis of membrane and surface protein sequences with the hydrophobic moment plot. *J. Mol. Biol.* 179:125–42

52. Englesberg, E., Moffett, J. 1986. A genetic approach to the study of neutral amino acid transport in mammalian cells in culture. *J. Membr. Biol.* 91:199–212

53. Erlinger, S., Saier, M. H. Jr. 1982. Decrease in protein content and cell volume of cultured dog kidney epithelial cells during growth. *In Vitro* 18:196

54. Fafournoux, P., Demigne, C., Remesy, C., LeCam, A. 1983. Bidirectional transport of glutamine across the cell membrane in rat liver. *Biochem. J.* 216:401–8

55. Fafournoux, P., Dudenhausen, E. E., Kilberg, M. S. 1989. Solubilization and reconstitution characteristics of hepatic System A-mediated amino acid transport. *J. Biol. Chem.* 264:4805–11

56. Ferraris, R. P., Diamond, J. M. 1989. Specific regulation of intestinal nutrient transporters by their dietary substrates. *Annu. Rev. Physiol.* 51:125–41

57. Foster, D. O., Pardee, A. B. 1969. Transport of amino acids by confluent and nonconfluent 3T3 and polyoma virus-transformed 3T3 cells growing on glass cover slips. *J. Biol. Chem.* 244:2675–81

58. Fowler, F. C., Banks, R. K., Mailliard, M. E. 1992. Characterization of sodium-dependent amino acid transport activity during hepatic regeneration. *Hepatology* 16:1187–94

59. Fremeau, R. T., Caron, M. G., Blakely, R. D. 1992. Molecular cloning and expression of a high affinity L-proline transporter expressed in putative glutamatergic pathways of rat brain. *Neuron* 8:915–26

60. Friedlander, G., Amiel, C. 1989. Protein kinase C activation has dissimilar effects on sodium-coupled uptakes in

renal proximal tubular cells in primary culture. *J. Biol. Chem.* 264:3935–41

61. Gebhardt, R., Mecke, D. 1983. Glutamate uptake by cultured rat hepatocytes is mediated by hormonally inducible, sodium-dependent transport systems. *FEBS Lett.* 161:275–78

62. Giros, B., Mestikawy, S. E., Bertrand, L., Caron, M. G. 1991. Cloning and functional characterization of a cocainesensitive dopamine transporter. *FEBS Lett.* 295:149–54

63. Guastella, J., Brecha, N., Weigmann, C., Lester, H. A., Davidson, N. 1992. Cloning, expression, and localization of a rat brain high-affinity glycine transporter. *Proc. Natl. Acad. Sci. USA* 89:7189–93

64. Guastella, J., Nelson, N., Nelson, H., Czyzyk, L., Keynan, S., et al. 1990. Cloning and expression of a rat brain GABA transporter. *Science* 249:1303–6

65. Guidotti, G. G. Borghetti, A. F., Gazzola, G. C. 1978. The regulation of amino acid transport in animal cells. *Biochim. Biophys. Acta* 515:329–66

66. Handlogten, M. E., Kilberg, M. S. 1988. Growth-dependent regulation of system A in SV40-transformed fetal rat hepatocytes. *Am. J. Physiol.* 255: C261–70

67. Handlogten, M. E., Kilberg, M. S., Christensen, H. N. 1982. Incomplete correspondence between repressive and substrate action by amino acids on transport systems A and N in monolayered rat hepatocytes. *J. Biol. Chem.* 257:345–48

68. Handlogten, M. E., Weissbach, L., Kilberg, M. S. 1982. Heterogeneity of Na⁺-independent 2-aminobicyclo-(2,2,1)-heptane-2-carboxylic acid and L-leucine transport in isolated rat hepatocytes in primary culture. *Biochem. Biophys. Res. Commun.* 104:307–13

69. Häussinger, D. 1983. Hepatocyte heterogeneity in glutamine and ammonia metabolism and the role of an intercellular glutamine cycle during ureogenesis in perfused rat liver. *Eur. J. Biochem.* 133:269–74

70. Häussinger, D. 1986. Regulation of hepatic ammonia metabolism: The intercellular glutamine cycle. *Adv. Enzyme Regul.* 25:159–80

71. Häussinger, D. 1990. Liver glutamine metabolism. *J. Parenter. Enter. Nutr.* 14:56S-62S

72. Häussinger, D., Gerok, W. 1983. Hepatocyte heterogeneity in glutamate uptake by isolated perfused rat liver. *Eur. J. Biochem.* 136:421–25

73. Häussinger, D., Soboll, S., Meijer, A.

J., Gerok, W., Tager, J. M., et al. 1985. Role of plasma membrane transport in hepatic glutamine metabolism. *Eur. J. Biochem.* 152:597–603

74. Häussinger, D., Stoll, B., Stehle, T., Gerok, W. 1989. Hepatocyte heterogeneity in glutamate metabolism and bidirectional transport in perfused rat liver. *Eur. J. Biochem.* 185:189–95

75. Haymond, M. W., Karl, I. E., Pagliara, A. S. 1974. Increased gluconeogenic substrates in the small-for-gestational-age infant. *N. Engl. J. Med.* 291:322–28

76. Heinrich, P. C., Castell, J. V., Andus, T. 1990. Interleukin-6 and the acute phase response. *Biochem. J.* 265:621–36

77. Higgins, D. G., Sharp, P. M. 1988. Clustal: a package for performing multiple sequence alignment on a microcomputer. *Gene* 73:237–44

78. Hoeltzli, S. D., Kelley, L. K., Moe, A. J., Smith, C. H. 1990. Anionic amino acid transport systems in isolated basal plasma membrane vesicles of human placenta. *Am. J. Physiol.* 259: C47–C55

79. Hoeltzli, S. D., Smith, C. H. 1989. Alanine transport systems in isolated basal plasma membranes of human placenta. *Am. J. Physiol.* 256:C630–37

80. Hoffman, B. J., Mezey, E., Brownstein, M. J. 1991. Cloning of a serotonin transporter affected by antidepressants. *Science* 254:579–80

81. Hundal, H. S., Rennie, M. J., Watt, P. W. 1987. Characteristics of L-Glutamine transport in perfused rat skeletal muscle. *J. Physiol.* 393:283–305

82. Jansson, T., Persson, E. 1990. Placental transfer of glucose and amino acids in intrauterine growth retardation: Studies with substrate analogs in the awake guinea pig. *Pediatr. Res.* 28:203–8

83. Johnson, L. W., Smith, C. H. 1988. Neutral amino acid transport systems of micovillous membrane of human placenta. *Am. J. Physiol.* 254:C773–80

84. Joseph, S. K., Bradford, N. M., McGivan, J. D. 1978. Characteristics of the transport of alanine, serine and glutamine across the plasma membrane of isolated rat liver cells. *Biochem. J.* 176:827–36

85. Jungermann, K., Katz, N. 1989. Functional specialization of different hepatocyte populations. *Physiol. Rev.* 69:708–64

86. Kamoun, P., Droin, V., Forestier, G., Daffos, F. 1985. Free amino acids in

human fetal plasma. *Clin. Chim. Acta* 150:227–30

87. Karasov, W. H. 1992. Tests of the adaptive modulation hypothesis for dietary control of intestinal nutrient transport. *Am. J. Physiol.* 263:R496–R502

88. Karl, P. I., Tkaczevski, H., Fisher, S. E. 1989. Characteristics of histidine uptake by human placental microvillous membrane vesicles. *Pediatr. Res.* 25: 19–26

89. Kilberg, M. S. 1989. Measurement of amino acid transport by hepatocytes in suspension or monolayer culture. *Methods Enzymol.* 173:564–75

90. Kilberg, M. S., Handlogten, M. E., Christensen, H. N. 1980. Characteristics of an amino acid transport system in rat liver for glutamine, asparagine, histidine, and closely related analogs. *J. Biol. Chem.* 255:4011–19

91. Kilty, J., Lorang, D., Amara, S. G. 1991. Cloning and expression of a cocaine-sensitive rat dopamine transporter. *Science* 254:78–79

92. Kim, J. W., Closs, E. I., Albritton, L. M., Cunningham, J. M. 1991. Transport of cationic amino acids by the mouse ecotropic retrovirus receptor. *Nature* 352:725–28

93. Kitagawa, K., Nishino, H., Iwashima, A. 1986. Possible involvement of protein kinase C in the stimulation of amino acid transport by phorbol ester, platelet-derived growth factor and A23187 in Swiss 3T3 cells. *Experientia* 42:1038–40

94. Lawless, K., Maenz, D., Cheeseman, C. 1987. Is leucine an allosteric modulator of the lysine transporter in the intestinal basolateral membrane? *Am. J. Physiol.* 253:G637–42

95. LeCam, A., Rey, J.-F., Fehlmann, M., Kitabgi, P., Freychet, P. 1979. Amino acid transport in isolated hepatocytes after partial hepatectomy in the rat. *Am. J. Physiol.* 236:E594–E602

96. Leister, K. J., Schenerman, M. A., Racker, E. 1988. Energetic mechanism of System A amino acid transport in normal and transformed mouse fibroblasts. *J. Cell. Physiol.* 135:163–68

97. Lerner, J., Larimore, D. L. 1986. Comparative aspects of the apparent Michaelis constant for neutral amino acid transport in several animal tissues. *Comp. Biochem. Physiol.* 84:235–48

98. Lever, J. E. 1976. Regulation of amino acid and glucose transport activity expressed in isolated membranes from untransformed and SV 40-transformed mouse fibroblasts. *J. Cell. Physiol.* 89:779–87

99. Low, S. Y., Taylor, P. M., Ahmed, A., Pogson, C. I., Rennie, M. J. 1991. Substrate-specificity of glutamine transporters in membrane vesicles from rat liver and skeletal muscle investigated using amino acid analogues. *Biochem. J.* 278:105–11

100. MacLeod, R. J., Hamilton, J. R. 1991. Volume regulation by Na^+-nutrient contransport in isolated mammalian villus enterocytes. *Am. J. Physiol.* 260: G26–G33

101. Maenz, D. D., Chenu, C., Breton, S., Berteloot, A. 1992. pH-dependent heterogeneity of acidic amino acid transport in rabbit jejunal brush border membrane vesicles. *J. Biol. Chem.* 267:1510–16

102. Maenz, D. D., Patience, J. F. 1992. L-Threonine transport in pig jejunal brush border membrane vesicles. Functional characterization of the unique System B in the intestinal epithelium. *J. Biol. Chem.* 267:22079–86

103. Magagnin, S., Bertran, J., Werner, A., Markovich, D., Biber, J., et al. 1992. Poly(A)+ RNA from rabbit intestinal mucosa induces $b^{o,+}$ and y^+ amino acid transport activities in *Xenopus laevis* oocytes. *J. Biol. Chem.* 267:15384–90

104. Malo, C. 1991. Multiple pathways for amino acid transport in brush border membrane vesicles isolated from the human fetal small intestine. *Gastroenterology* 100:1644–52

105. Marconi, A. M., Battaglia, F. C., Meschia, G., Sparks, J. W. 1989. A comparison of amino acid arteriovenous differences across the liver and placenta of the fetal lamb. *Am. J. Physiol.* 257:E909–15

106. McCormack, K., Campanelli, J. T., Ramaswami, M., Mathew, M. K., Tanouye, M. A., et al. 1989. Leucine-zipper motif update. *Nature* 340: 103

107. McGivan, J. D., Bradford, N. M., Mendes-Mourao, J. 1977. The transport of branched-chain amino acids into isolated rat liver cells. *FEBS Lett.* 80:380–84

108. McIntosh, N., Rodeck, C. H., Heath, R. 1984. Plasma amino acids of the mid-trimester human fetus. *Biol. Neonate* 45:218–24

109. Morin, O., Forest, C., Fehlmann, M. 1981. EGF inhibits glucagon stimulation of amino acid transport in primary cultures of adult rat hepatocytes. *FEBS Lett.* 127:109–11

110. Moule, S. K., Bradford, N. M., McGivan, J. D. 1987. Short-term stim-

ulation of Na$^+$-dependent amino acid transport by dibutyryl cyclic AMP in hepatocytes. *Biochem. J.* 241:737–43

111. Moule, S. K., McGivan, J. D. 1987. Epidermal growth factor, like glucagon, exerts a short-term stimulation of alanine transport in rat hepatocytes. *Biochem. J.* 247:233–35

112. Nylund, L., Lunell, N. O., Lewander, R., Sarby, B. 1983. Uteroplacental blood flow index in intrauterine growth retardation of fetal or maternal origin. *Br. J. Obstet. Gynecol.* 90:16–20

113. Oxender, D. L., Christensen, H. N. 1963. Distinct mediating systems for the transport of neutral amino acids by the Ehrlich cell. *J. Biol. Chem.* 238:3686–99

114. Pacholczyk, T., Blakely, R. D., Amara, S. G. 1991. Expression of cloning of a cocaine- and antidepressant-sensitive human noradrenaline transporter. *Nature* 350:350–54

115. Pacitti, A. J., Copeland, E. M. III, Souba, W. W. 1992. Stimulation of hepatocyte System-y$^+$-mediated L-Arginine transport by an inflammatory agent. *Surgery* 112:403–11

116. Palacin, M., Werner, A., Dittmer, J., Murer, H., Biber, J. 1990. Expression of rat liver Na$^+$/L-alanine co-transport in *Xenopus laevis* oocytes. *Biochem. J.* 270:189–95

117. Pariza, M. W., Butcher, F. R., Kletzien, R. F., Becker, J. E., Potter, V. R. 1976. Induction and decay of glucagon-induced amino acid transport in primary cultures of adult rat liver cells: Paradoxical effects of cycloheximide and puromycin. *Proc. Natl. Acad. Sci. USA* 73:4511–15

118. Parnes, J. R., Garvey, T. Q., Isselbacher, K. J. 1976. Amino acid transport by membrane vesicles of virally transformed and nontransformed cells: effects of sodium gradient and cell density. *J. Cell. Physiol.* 89:789–94

119. Phillipps, A. F., Holzman, I. R., Teng, C., Battaglia, F. C. 1978. Tissue concentration of free amino acids in term human placentas. *Am. J. Obstet. Gynecol.* 131:881–87

120. Radian, R., Bendahan, A., Kanner, B. I. 1986. Purification and identification of the functional sodium- and chloride-coupled gamma-aminobutyric acid transport glycoprotein from rat brain. *J. Biol. Chem.* 261:15437–41

121. Reichberg, S. B., Gelehrter, T. D. 1980. Glucocorticoid inhibition of two discrete glycine transport systems in rat hepatoma cells. *J. Biol. Chem.* 255:5708–14

122. Rennie, M. J., Ahmed, A., Low, S. Y., Hundal, H. S., Watt, P. W., et al. 1990. Transport of amino acids in muscle, gut and liver: relevance to metabolic control. *Biochem. Soc. Trans.* 18:1140–42

123. Roh, M. S., Moldawer, L. L., Ekman, L. G., Dinarello, C. A., Bistrian, B. R., et al. 1986. Stimulatory effect of interleukin-1 upon hepatic metabolism. *Metabolism* 35:419–24

124. Rosso, P. 1975. Changes in the transfer of nutrients across the placenta during normal gestation in the rat. *Am. J. Obstet. Gynecol.* 122:761–66

125. Rosso, P. 1975. Maternal malnutrition and placental transfer of alpha-aminoisobutyric acid in the rat. *Science* 187:648–50

126. Rosso, P., Kava, R. 1980. Effects of food restriction on cardiac output and blood flow to the uterus and placenta in the pregnant rat. *J. Nutr.* 110:2350–54

127. Said, H. M., Hollander, D., Khorchid, S. 1991. An Na$^+$-dependent and an Na$^+$-independent system for glutamine transport in rat liver basolateral membrane vesicles. *Gastroenterology* 101:1094–1101

128. Saier, M. H. Jr., Daniels, G. A., Boerner, P., Lin, J. 1988. Neutral amino acid transport systems in animal cells: Potential targets of oncogene action and regulators of cellular growth. *J. Membr. Biol.* 104:1–20

129. Saintonge, J., Rosso, P. 1981. Placental blood flow and transfer of nutrient analogs in large, average and small guinea pig littermates. *Pediatr. Res.* 15:152–56

130. Salloum, R. M., Souba, W. W., Fernandez, A., Stevens, B. R. 1990. Dietary modulation of small intestinal glutamine transport in intestinal brush border membrane vesicles of rats. *J. Surg. Res.* 48:635–38

131. Salloum, R. M., Stevens, B. R., Souba, W. W. 1991. Adaptive regulation of brush-border amino acid transport in a chronic excluded jejunal limb. *Am. J. Physiol.* 261:G22–G27

132. Sander, G., Pardee, A. B. 1972. Transport changes in synchronously growing CHO and L cells. *J. Cell. Physiol.* 80:267–72

133. Schenerman, M. S., Kilberg, M. S. 1986. Maintenance of glucagon-stimulated system A amino acid transport activity in rat liver plasma membrane vesicles. *Biochim. Biophys. Acta* 856:428–36

134. Schloss, P., Mayser, W., Betz, H.

1992. Neurotransmitter transporters—A novel family of integral plasma membrane proteins. *FEBS Lett.* 307:76–80

135. Segel, G. B., Simon, W., Lichtman, M. A. 1984. Multicomponent analysis of amino acid transport in human lymphocytes. *J. Clin. Invest.* 74:17–24

136. Shay, N. F., Nick, H. S., Kilberg, M. S. 1990. Molecular cloning of an amino acid-regulated mRNA (amino acid starvation-induced) in rat hepatoma cells. *J. Biol. Chem.* 265:17844–48

137. Shimada, S., Kitayama, S., Lin, C.-L., Patel, A., Nanthakumar, E., et al. 1991. Cloning and expression of a cocaine-sensitive dopamine transporter complementary DNA. *Science* 254: 576–78

138. Shotwell, M. A., Kilberg, M. S., Oxender, D. L. 1983. The regulation of neutral amino acid transport in mammalian cells. *Biochim. Biophys. Acta* 737:267–84

139. Smith, C. H. 1986. Mechanisms and regulation of placental amino acid transport. *Fed. Proc.* 45:2443–45

140. Smith, Q. R., Nagura, H., Takada, Y., Duncan, M. W. 1992. Facilitated transport of the neurotoxin, β-*N*-methylamino-L-alanine, across the blood-brain barrier. *J. Neurochem.* 58:1330–37

141. Soltesz, G., Harris, D., Mackenzie, I. Z., Aynsley-Green, A. 1985. The metabolic and endocrine millieu of the human fetus and mother at 18–21 weeks of gestation. I. Plasma amino acid concentrations. *Pediatr. Res.* 19:91–93

142. Sonne, O., Davidson, O., Moller, B., Munck-Petersen, C. 1990. Cellular targets and receptors for interleukin-6. I. In vivo and in vitro uptake of Il-6 in liver and hepatocytes. *Eur. J. Clin. Invest.* 20:366–76

143. Souba, W. W., Copeland, E. M. III 1992. Cytokine modulation of Na⁺-dependent glutamine transport across the brush border membrane of monolayers of human intestinal Caco-2 cells. *Ann. Surg.* 215:536–44

144. Souba, W. W., Salloum, R. M., Bode, B. P., Herskowitz, K. 1991. Cytokine modulation of glutamine transport by pulmonary artery endothelial cells. *Surgery* 110:295–302

145. Stevens, B. R. 1992. Vertebrate intestine apical membrane mechanisms of organic nutrient transport. *Am. J. Physiol.* 263:R458–63

146. Stevens, B. R. 1992. Amino acid transport in intestine. In *Mammalian Amino Acid Transport: Mechanisms and Con-*

trol, ed. M. S. Kilberg, D. Häussinger, pp. 149–64. New York: Plenum

147. Stevens, B. R., Kaunitz, J. D., Wright, E. M. 1984. Intestinal transport of amino acids and sugars: advances using membrane vesicles. *Annu. Rev. Physiol.* 46:417–33

148. Stoll, B., McNelly, S., Buscher, H.-P., Haussinger, D. 1991. Functional hepatocyte heterogeneity in glutamate, aspartate and α-ketoglutarate uptake: A histoautoradiographical study. *Hepatology* 13:247–53

149. Tamarappoo, B. K., Handlogten, M. E., Laine, R. O., Serrano, M. A., Dugan, J., et al. 1992. Identification of the protein responsible for hepatic system N amino acid transport activity. *J. Biol. Chem.* 267:2370–74

150. Tamarappoo, B. K., Kilberg, M. S. 1991. Functional reconstitution of the hepatic System N amino acid transport activity. *J. Biochem.* 274:97–101

151. Tarnuzzer, R. W., Campa, M. J., Qian, N.-X., Englesberg, E., Kilberg, M. S. 1990. Expression of the mammalian System A neutral amino acid transporter in *Xenopus* oocytes. *J. Biol. Chem.* 265:13914–17

152. Tate, S. S., Yan, N., Udenfriend, S. 1992. Expression cloning of a Na⁺-independent neutral amino acid transporter from rat kidney. *Proc. Natl. Acad. Sci. USA* 89:1–5

153. Taylor, P. M., Mackenzie, B., Low, S. Y., Rennie, M. J. 1992. Expression of rat liver glutamine transporters in *Xenopus laevis* oocytes. *J. Biol. Chem.* 267:3873–77

154. Taylor, P. M., Rennie, M. J. 1987. Perivenous localisation of Na⁺-dependent glutamate transport in perfused rat liver. *FEBS Lett.* 221:370–74

155. Traber, P. G., Chianale, J., Gumucio, J. J. 1988. Physiologic significance and regulation of hepatocellular heterogeneity. *Gastroenterology* 95:1130–43

156. Vadgama, J. V., Christensen, H. N. 1983. Investigation of L-Glutamine transport into rat hepatoma cells and fetal hepatocytes. In *Isolation, Characterization, and the Use of Hepatocytes,* pp. 233–38. New York: Elsevier Biomedical

157. Van Winkle, L. J. 1988. Amino acid transport in developing animal oocytes and early conceptuses. *Biochim. Biophys. Acta* 947:173–208

158. Van Winkle, L. J., Campione, A. L., Gorman, J. M. 1988. Na⁺ independent transport of basic and zwitterionic amino acids in mouse blastocysts by a shared system and by processes which

distinguish between these substrates. *J. Biol. Chem.* 263:3150–63

159. Van Winkle, L. J., Campione, A. L., Gorman, J. M. 1990. Inhibition of transport system b$^{o,+}$ in blastocysts by inorganic and organic cations yields insight into the structure of its amino acid receptor site. *Biochim. Biophys. Acta* 1025:215–24

160. Van Winkle, L. J., Christensen, H. N., Campione, A. L. 1985. Na$^+$-dependent transport of basic, zwitterionic, and bicyclic amino acids by a broadscope system in mouse blastocysts. *J. Biol. Chem.* 260:12118–23

161. Varma, D. R., Ramakrishnan, R. 1991. Effects of protein-calorie malnutrition on transplacental kinetics of aminoisobutyric acid in rats. *Placenta* 12:277–84

162. Visciano, G., Fehlmann, M. 1984. Mechanism of the inhibitory effect of EGF on cAMP-stimulated amino acid transport. *Mol. Cell. Endocrinol.* 37:103–7

163. Walker, P. R., Whitfield, J. F. 1978. Inhibition by colchicine of changes in amino acid transport and initiation of DNA synthesis in regenerating rat liver. *Proc. Natl. Acad. Sci. USA* 75:1394–98

164. Wang, H., Kavanaugh, M. P., North, R. A., Kabat, D. 1991. Cell-surface receptor for ecotropic murine retroviruses is a basic amino-acid transporter. *Nature* 352:729–31

165. Warren, R. S., Donner, D. B., Starnes, H. F. Jr., Brennan, M. F. 1987. Modulation of endogeneous hormone action by recombinant human tumor necrosis factor. *Proc. Natl. Acad. Sci. USA* 84:8619–22

166. Watford, M., Smith, E. M. 1990. Distribution of hepatic glutaminase activity and mRNA in perivenous and periportal rat hepatocytes. *Biochem. J.* 267:265–67

167. Weissbach, L., Handlogten, M. E., Christensen, H. N., Kilberg, M. S. 1982. Evidence for two Na$^+$-independent neutral amino acid transport systems in primary cultures of rat hepatocytes. *J. Biol. Chem.* 257:12006–11

168. Wells, R. G., Hediger, M. A. 1992. Cloning of a rat kidney cDNA that stimulates dibasic and neutral amino acid transport and has sequence similarity to glucosidases. *Proc. Natl. Acad. Sci. USA* 89:5596–5600

169. Wells, R. G., Lee, W.-S., Kanai, Y., Leiden, J. M., Hediger, M. A. 1992. The 4F2 antigen heavy chain induces uptake of neutral and dibasic amino acids in *Xenopus* oocytes. *J. Biol. Chem.* 267:15285–88

170. White, M. F. 1985. The transport of cationic amino acids across the plasma membrane of mammalian cells. *Biochim. Biophys. Acta* 822:355–74

171. White, M. F., Christensen, H. N. 1983. Simultaneous regulation of amino acid influx and efflux by System A in the hepatoma cell HTC. *J. Biol. Chem.* 258:8028–38

172. Winter, C. G., Christensen, H. N. 1965. Contrasts in neutral amino acid transport by rabbit erythrocytes and reticulocytes. *J. Biol. Chem.* 240:3594–3600

173. Woodlock, T. J., Segel, G. B., Lichtman, M. A. 1988. Phorbol ester restores L-system amino acid transport of B lymphocytes in chronic lymphocytic leukemia. *J. Clin. Invest.* 81:32–38

174. Wright, E. M., Gunther, R. D., Kaunitz, J. D., Stevens, B. R., Harms, V., et al. 1983. Mechanisms of sodium transport across brush border and basolateral membranes. In *Intestinal Transport,* ed. M. Gilles-Baillien, R. Gilles, pp. 122–32. Berlin: Springer-Verlag

175. Wright, E. M., Hager, K. M., Turk, E. 1992. Sodium cotransport proteins. *Curr. Opin. Cell Biol.* 4:696–702

Annu. Rev. Nutr. 1993. 13:167–89

FUNGAL TOXINS IN FOODS: Recent Concerns[1]

Ronald T. Riley, William P. Norred, and Charles W. Bacon

Toxicology and Mycotoxin Research Unit, United States Department of Agriculture/Agricultural Research Service, P.O. Box 5677, Athens, Georgia 30613

KEY WORDS: *Fusarium moniliforme,* fumonisins, mycotoxins

CONTENTS

INTRODUCTION 167
BIOLOGY OF *FUSARIUM MONILIFORME* 169
   Fungus Description and Taxonomy 169
   Occurrence and Pathogenicity in Plants 169
   Plant Toxicity 170
   Control Potentials 171
DISEASES ASSOCIATED WITH *FUSARIUM MONILIFORME* AND FUMONISINS 172
   Equine Leucoencephalomalacia 172
   Porcine Pulmonary Edema Syndrome 172
   Poultry Toxicity 173
   Human Esophageal Cancer 173
   Studies With Laboratory Animals 174
CHEMISTRY OF FUMONISINS AND RELATED COMPOUNDS 175
MODE OF ACTION OF THE FUMONISINS 176
   Inhibition of Sphingolipid Biosynthesis In Vitro 176
   Alterations in Free Sphingoid Bases In Vivo 177
   Altered Sphingolipid Biosynthesis and Animal Diseases 179
   Other Hypothesized Modes of Action 180
DETECTION AND OCCURRENCE OF FUMONISINS 181
   Analytical Methodology 181
   Results of Analyses of Feeds and Foods 182
   Potential Decontamination and Salvage Strategies 182
CONCLUSIONS 183

INTRODUCTION

Fusarium moniliforme, the fumonisins (toxins produced by *F. moniliforme*), and the health implications of their occurrence in corn and corn products are the focus of this review. The economic and health risks of other mycotoxins

---

[1]The US government has the right to retain a nonexclusive, royalty-free license in and to any copyright covering this paper.

were recently reviewed in great detail (26). In order to better understand what the future may hold for regulatory agencies and researchers, it is informative to consider how another fungus and its toxins, *Aspergillus flavus* and the aflatoxins, are perceived and acted upon by these groups. The interest of the scientific and regulatory community in both aflatoxins and fumonisins has grown in response to large increases in the incidence of unusual diseases in farm animals. For the aflatoxins this occurred in 1960 (15) and for the fumonisins, in 1989 (100). Aflatoxins (B_1, B_2, G_1, G_2) are currently the mycotoxins of greatest concern in the United States. However, the fumonisins have become the fastest growing area of mycotoxin research (93).

Perceived human health risks have spurred regulation of the aflatoxin content of foods and feeds. According to a recent General Accounting Office report to Congress concerning risks to humans, ". . . no cases of illness and/or death from eating aflatoxin have been documented in the United States" (33). In the United States the known effects on animals (26) and the perceived chronic risks to humans provide the pressure to regulate (93). The most obvious chronic risk is increased cancer incidence.

The United States is the world's major corn exporter. Three mycotoxins (or groups) commonly found on US corn are considered by the International Agency for Research on Cancer (35) to be either carcinogenic (class 1) or possibly carcinogenic (class 2B) to humans: aflatoxins (B_1 and G_1), zearalenone, and *Fusarium moniliforme* toxins (culture material and grains contaminated by *F. moniliforme* and containing fumonisins and fusarins). Currently, aflatoxin B_1 is the only mycotoxin for which the Food and Drug Administration (FDA) has set action levels in corn. An action level is the level of contamination at which the FDA may regard the food as adulterated. Action levels do not have the force of law and are not legally binding on the courts. States may set more stringent levels. In the United States, corn for use in human foods or for immature animals and dairy cows cannot exceed 20 ppb aflatoxin B_1. The action levels for aflatoxin in other animal feeds are higher; thus, corn that exceeds the 20-ppb action level is not destroyed but can often be used for various animal feeds. Recently, replacement of action levels with "regulatory limits," which are legally binding, has been discussed (34). Whether or not action levels or regulatory limits will be set for the other two carcinogenic mycotoxins on corn (zearalenone and *F. moniliforme* toxins) is uncertain. Possibly, domestic users or importing countries may set contractual specifications that could preempt any regulatory action by the FDA. Most importing countries have set aflatoxin limits that are lower than the action levels or regulatory limits set by exporting countries (31).

Human risk assessment plays a potentially important role in the economics of corn, an 8 billion bushel crop valued at $18 billion (124). Interestingly, less than 17% of the US corn supply is consumed as food by humans. Most corn in the US is consumed as animal feed or is exported (124) to other countries where it is used for animal feed. Nonetheless, the risk assessment of greatest significance pertains to humans. While the relationship between aflatoxin and liver cancer in humans in third world countries continues to be debated, there is much less debate about aflatoxin as a cause of liver cancer in the United States. According to a report by the General Accounting Office (33) the FDA Commissioner has stated ". . . the occasional consumption of the very few corn products that contain a measurable amount of aflatoxin are of little lifetime health consequence. . . ." However, the fact that the amount of aflatoxin consumed is small does not mean that the total amount of carcinogenic mycotoxins consumed is small. While the debate about the risks associated with consumption of aflatoxins continues, the fumonisins, a group of mycotoxins that induce cancer in laboratory rats, have been discovered. There is little doubt that the fumonisins will cause problems for producers and processors and that these problems may result in regulatory actions similar to those that govern the aflatoxins. The remainder of this review summarizes the current literature and research.

BIOLOGY OF *FUSARIUM MONILIFORME*

Fungus Description and Taxonomy

Fusarium moniliforme J. Sheldon [perithecial state *Gibberella fujikuroi* (Sawada) Ito in Ito & K. Kimura] belongs to the *Liseola* section of the genus *Fusarium*. The perithecial state of this fungus consists of a complex of biological species or mating populations (50) and is currently defined as having six different mating populations (63, 65) among which exist bisexual, self-sterile groups. Isolates of *G. fujikuroi* with members of the A and F mating population are the only fungi within the complex that are synonymous with *F. moniliforme* (65).

Occurrence and Pathogenicity in Plants

The fungi of mating popultions A and F, i.e. *F. moniliforme*, are distributed worldwide and are found primarily on cereal grasses in the warmer regions of the world (69). However, this distribution appears to be host species specific. Thus, fungi of mating population A and F are primarily found on corn and sorghum, respectively (50). The fungus on corn can exist as an endophyte; it may colonize portions of the developing plant but usually remains symptom-less (7, 49). This symptomless expression apparently is related to the genetic nature of the fungus, the cultivar of corn (49, 85, 104), and environmental factors. Aspects of the corn disease complex caused by *F. moniliforme* are stalk rot, seedling blight, root rot, and ear rot.

The points of entry into corn by the fungus vary, and the extent of infection as well as the nature of the expression depend on the route of entry. For example, a diseased plant might develop from a symptomless infection produced by the fungus located in the seedling root, the young shoot, or the nodal and other vegetative areas, but the corn kernels may also become infected by means other than vegetative parts. In the latter case, insects and wind may carry the fungus into the developing corn kernels, usually via the silk tracks (27). The results of ear infection vary: Some kernels are symptomless while others are obviously infected. The important point is that *F. moniliforme* is seed-borne. The fungus is located in the pedicel of kernels as a very small number of hyphae, but in kernels associated with animal toxicity the fungus is usually found as an extensive mass of sporulating hyphae that colonizes most of the internal section of the kernel, including the embryo (10). The fungus usually infects a seedling from the kernel within a two-week period. Death of the seedling may occur within three weeks (Bacon et al, manuscript submitted) or the infected seedling may show no disease symptoms as described above. In addition to being seed-borne, *F. moniliforme* is also soil-borne and survives in plant residues (83, 84), particularly roots (123a). This fungus does not produce sclerotia as survival structures; it can survive in the soil, however, as thickened hyphae within corn fragments buried 30-cm deep within a soil moisture range of 5–35%, at 5–10°C for 12 months.

Plant Toxicity

Both the A and the F mating populations of *F. moniliforme* are capable of producing mycotoxins such as the fumonisins (64), fusaric acid (C. W. Bacon, unpublished data), and fusarin C (9). The A mating population, however, is a much better producer of fumonisin B_1 than is the F population (65). The D mating population of *G. fujikuroi (F. proliferatum)* is also a good producer of FB_1 (65). *F. moniliforme* does not commonly produce moniliformin, whereas *F. proliferatum* can produce it (78). Another compound of interest that is produced by *F. moniliforme* is gibberellic acid, a plant growth regulator. Some of these compounds are phytotoxins and as such they may play important roles in the final pathology of the corn. At present, however, we have no specific information on any role these toxins play in disease expression on corn. The fumonisins are structurally similar to the tomato host-specific toxin, the AAL toxins, produced by *Alternaria alternata* f. sp. *lycopersici*. The AAL toxins produce stem canker disease in "Earlypak-7" and other susceptible cultivars of tomatoes (113). Similar disease symptoms are also produced on susceptible tomatoes by fumonisin B_1. However, *F. moniliforme* is not a natural pathogen of tomatoes, and all attempts at infecting tomatoes with it have failed (10, 42).

A growth-regulating response has also been observed by the addition of fumonisin B_1 to tomato plants (8). When fumonisin B_1 is applied to detached stems of resistant tomato cultivars, it induces de novo adventitious rooting. Plants dosed with a single application of fumonisin B_1 initiated callus tissue within a 24–48 hr period, and roots were produced as early as 72 hr after a dose of 10 μg per shoot. The induction of rooting was observed only in tomato cultivars that were resistant to the mycotoxin at amounts <50 μg per seedling. In one resistant cultivar, no rooting response was observed, but this cultivar showed no toxicity signs at the high doses, >50 μg per shoot, which suggests a permeability difference. The mechanism of induction may be complex and may be associated with an interaction of the rooting hormone indole acetic acid with calcium and related enzymes (14, 18). The effects of fumonisin B_1 on rooting of corn and other plants are unknown. However, it is toxic to jimsonweed (*Datura stramonium* L.) (3) and duckweed (2) (*Lemna minor* L.). This latter plant and susceptible genotypes of tomatoes (42) may be used as rapid assays for biological activity of the fumonisins and related compounds.

Control Potentials

F. moniliforme is a common cereal grain contaminant and control measures may prove difficult. Control of this pathogen on food stuff should focus on its complex infection cycle and/or the potential mechanisms for developing resistance to *F. moniliforme* in corn. Expression of the disease is highly variable, probably because of heterozygosity within a corn cultivar and genetic variation within the fungus species. Several aspects of infection appear to be under genetic control (28), and the genetics of the pericarp is considered a major determinant of resistance to air and insect transmission of the fungus into grain (104). Therefore, plant breeding is expected to be very helpful in preventing the fungus from entering the food chain. Possibly, control of soil-borne and kernel infection may be achieved with the use of microorganisms, particularly soil and endophytic bacteria (10). Of course, the successful utilization of biocontrol measures must be based on detailed knowledge of *F. moniliforme* and its association with corn—information that is not presently available.

Postharvest control of fumonisin production is possible. Two important factors are aeration and moisture content (61). Fumonisin production at low oxygen tension is minimal; thus, storage under modified atmospheres (e.g. N_2 or CO_2), or as silage, and low kernel moisture content $<22\%$ should reduce or prevent toxin production in storage (61).

DISEASES ASSOCIATED WITH *FUSARIUM MONILIFORME* AND FUMONISINS

Equine Leucoencephalomalacia

Equine leucoencephalomalacia (ELEM) syndrome is characterized by the presence of liquefactive necrotic lesions in the white matter of the cerebrum. The name is somewhat misleading, since the gray matter may also be involved (67). This fatal disease apparently occurs only in equids. The syndrome has been recognized since the nineteenth century as a sporadically occurring condition. In 1902 (21) ELEM was experimentally produced by feeding moldy corn obtained from a field case in Kansas. The disease was known as "moldy corn poisoning," but attempts to identify the responsible fungus failed.

Wilson & Maronpot (131) succeeded in establishing the causative agent when they isolated *F. moniliforme* as the predominant contaminant of moldy corn that had caused many cases of ELEM and when they reproduced ELEM by feeding *F. moniliforme* corn culture material. Many other investigators have since demonstrated the ability of *F. moniliforme* to duplicate the symptoms of ELEM.

Shortly after the isolation of fumonisins and the identification of their structures (13, 36), Marasas et al (67) successfully produced ELEM in a horse by the intravenous administration of fumonisin B_1. This was done by avoiding hepatotoxicity as much as possible. ELEM has also been produced in horses given pure fumonisin B_1 by stomach tube, again monitoring for liver toxicity (56). Researchers have suggested (67) that high dosage levels of fumonisins induce fatal hepatotoxicity with mild brain lesions, whereas low dosage levels cause mild hepatotoxicity and severe brain lesions. However, central nervous system signs and liver lesions in the absence of elevated serum parameters, and ELEM concurrent with significant liver disease have been observed in horses fed feeds naturally contaminated with fumonisins at low levels (133). The development of brain lesions in the absence of major liver lesions does not preclude biochemical dysfunction in nonbrain tissue from contributing to the brain lesions. Current evidence suggests that horses that consume feed containing levels as low as 8 ppm of fumonisin B_1 may be at risk for developing ELEM (133).

Porcine Pulmonary Edema Syndrome

In trials with cultures of *F. moniliforme,* Kriek et al (58) fed horses, pigs, sheep, rats, and baboons. Lung edema occurred only in pigs. In 1989–1990 outbreaks of porcine pulmonary edema (PPE) were reported in different parts of the United States (25, 86, 101). Corn screenings obtained from farms (46, 86) where PPE killed pigs were predominantly contaminated with *F.*

moniliforme. Feeding *F. moniliforme* culture material produced PPE in at least one study (86) since the report by Kriek et al (58), but not all such experiments have been successful (Billy M. Colvin, personal communication). Nevertheless, the association between *F. moniliforme* and PPE appears to be strong, especially since purified fumonisin B_1 has been shown to produce the disease when administered intravenously (46, 48, 86). Also, PPE (175 ppm, 14 days) and hepatotoxicity (≥ 23 ppm, 14 days) have been produced by feeding diets made with corn screenings naturally contaminated with fumonisins (11; G. Motelin et al, manuscript submitted).

As with ELEM, a strong correlation exists between the fumonisin content of feed obtained from different farms and outbreaks of PPE (100, 101). PPE has not yet been produced by oral administration of pure fumonisins; liver lesions have been observed, however, in swine orally dosed with pure fumonisin B_1 (47). The evidence gathered thus far suggests that the mycotoxin is responsible for PPE as well as for ELEM.

Poultry Toxicity

Several reports have been published implicating *F. moniliforme* contamination of feed in diseases of poultry (20, 30, 55). Immunosuppression in chickens was also produced in birds fed corn cultured with several different isolates of the fungus (71). Several recent studies have confirmed that *F. moniliforme, F. proliferatum,* fumonisin B_1, and moniliformin are toxic to broiler chicks (19, 29a, 52, 53, 62) and chicken embryos (54). The levels of fumonisins used in these studies were relatively high (75–644 ppm), and the co-occurrence of moniliformin in some studies posed an additional complication for interpretation. Studies at fumonisin levels closer to those found in naturally contaminated rations (1–20 ppm) should be conducted, and surveys to determine the prevalence of moniliformin in poultry diets are needed.

Human Esophageal Cancer

In some regions of the world the incidence of esophageal cancer (EC) far exceeds the "normal" occurrence of 5 or fewer cases per 100,000 population. The Transkei of South Africa has been the most extensively studied region (125) of high EC rate (50–200 per 100,000). The afflicted people consume corn as a staple, including a type of beer brewed with corn and a nonalcoholic fermented drink made with corn (98, 107). The corn is locally grown and harvested, is stored in open cribs, and is frequently visibly moldy (66). The moldiest ears of corn are hand selected for use in beer brewing (70), and *F. moniliforme* is the predominant fungus. Contamination of the corn with *F. moniliforme* (66, 94) and fumonisins (120) in the areas of high EC was statistically higher than that found in areas of the Transkei with low cancer rates (66, 94). The carcinogenic potential of fumonisin B_1 has been shown in laboratory rats (37). Whether fumonisins are responsible for the high rate of EC in regions of the Transkei cannot be determined conclusively, but the available evidence suggests that their presence may be at least partly responsible. Other areas of the world have high EC rates, but an association with *F. moniliforme* and/or fumonisins is not well documented (for a recent review see 79).

Studies With Laboratory Animals

In addition to studies designed to elucidate the relationship between *F. moniliforme*-induced diseases in farm animals and the fumonisins, numerous studies have been conducted with laboratory animals. Rats fed corn either contaminated with *F. moniliforme* naturally or with *F. moniliforme* culture materials develop liver tumors (51, 68, 132). Subsequent feeding studies showed that fumonisin B_1 (not <90% pure) fed at 50 ppm in a semi-purified rat diet for 18 to 26 months caused an increased incidence (10 of 15 rats) of hepatocellular carcinoma (37). Hepatotoxicity was evident after 6 months and progressed in severity with time (37). Short-term carcinogenesis studies using focal proliferation of heptocytes as an end point revealed that fumonisins B_2 and B_3 may also contribute to the toxicological and carcinogenic effects of *F. moniliforme* (39). Fumonisins were not mutagenic in the *Salmonella* mutagenicity assay (40) and they were not genotoxic in DNA repair assays using primary rat hepatocytes (80). Long-term feeding studies using pure fumonisin B_1 will be conducted by the National Toxicology Program in the near future (K. A. Voss, personal communication).

In some studies with rats, the kidney is an equal or more sensitive target for fumonisin B_1 fed either as naturally contaminated corn (127) or as pure fumonisin B_1 (126a). Interestingly, other reports for rats have indicated that the kidney is not an important target of fumonisin-induced toxicity (37, 38). The reason for these differences has yet to be explained.

Preliminary toxicokinetic studies in rats using fumonisin B_1 or [^{14}C]fumonisin B_1 have been reported (109, 110, 79a). The results indicate that orally dosed fumonisin B_1 is poorly absorbed, rapidly eliminated, and not appreciably metabolized. In the study by Norred & Plattner (79a), the liver and kidney were the organs that contained the greatest amount of radioactivity. Even though only a small amount of radioactivity was accumulated in liver and kidney, it remained constant for at least 96 hr (79a).

A study in which Vervet monkeys were fed low (0.25–to 1.0%) levels of *F. moniliforme* culture material in a corn-based, low-fat, high carbohydrate diet for periods up to 2 years indicated that *F. moniliforme* (and fumonisins) may cause atherosclerosis (32). However, the atherogenic potential was secondary to chronic hepatotoxicity as evidenced by liver fibrosis and elevated serum enzymes.

CHEMISTRY OF FUMONISINS AND RELATED COMPOUNDS

Isolates of *F. moniliforme* associated with disease outbreaks often produce large quantities of fumonisins (99, 122). It is reasonable to believe that the toxicities associated with consumption of *F. moniliforme* culture materials, or naturally contaminated corn, are a result of multiple toxins, toxin interactions, and synergies. However, the animal diseases associated with consumption of *F. moniliforme* culture materials or naturally contaminated corn have all been reproduced using pure fumonisin B_1 (see previous section). At the time that the structures of the fumonisins were first reported (13), two other groups had independently concluded that the hepatotoxic principle of *F. moniliforme* culture material was water soluble (60, 128) and of low molecular weight (60). The discovery of the fumonisins was made possible by the development of a short-term cancer initiation/promotion bioassay for screening the various fractions of the extracted corn culture materials (36). Interestingly, in 1981 a group of structurally similar, water-soluble compounds (AAL toxins) were isolated from culture filtrates of *Alternaria alternata* f. sp. *lycopersici* (17) after development of an appropriate plant bioassay (41). The chemistry and in vitro biological activity of these two groups of structurally related compounds are surprisingly similar. The AAL-toxins (T_A 2a and T_A 2b) are the monoesters of propane-tricarboxylic acid and 1-amino-11,15-dimethyl-2,4,5,13,14-pentahydroxyheptadecane (molecular weight = 521). The single propanetricarboxylic acid moiety is esterified at the C-13 (T_A 2a) or C-14 (T_A 2b) position of the 17 carbon aminopentol backbone. There is also a T_B series (2a and 2b), which differs from the T_A series because it lacks the C-5 hydroxyl and has a differing stereochemistry (17). Fumonisin B_1 is the diester of propane-1,2,3-tricarboxylic acid and 2-amino-12,16-dimethyl-3,5,10,14,15-pentahydroxyicosane (molecular weight = 721). The propanetricarboxylic acid moieties are esterified at the C-14 and C-15 positions of the 20-carbon aminopentol backbone.

Currently, the fumonisin family comprises fumonisins B_1, B_2, B_3, B_4, A_1, and A_2 (38). In naturally contaminated corn, the ratio of fumonisin B_1/fumonisin B_2 is approximately 3 and for fumonisin B_1/fumonisin B_3 it is 12 (100). Exceptions have been noted, but the isolated fungus is usually *F. proliferatum* (100). The fumonisins and AAL toxins are clearly "sphingosine-like" in their structures, and it has been suggested that the fumonisins follow a similar biosynthetic pathway (1, 91). However, other data suggest a polyketide-like pathway (77). Members of the B series differ in the number and location of the hydroxyl groups. Fumonisin B_1 is the most polar of the B series (22). Members of the A series are N-acetylated. There has been some speculation that the amides are artifacts of the extraction method (92).

The propanetricarboxylic acid moieties are easily removed by base hydrolysis (92, 111), and the amino group reacts readily with reagents commonly used for modification of protein amino groups (e.g. acetic anhydride, trinitrobenzenesulfonic acid, etc). Presumably, the carboxyl groups are equally reactive with reagents such as carbodiimide. Monomethyl and dimethylesters of fumonisin B_1 are produced during the isolation procedures when methanol is used for extraction (22). The fumonisins and AAL toxins have no ultraviolet or visible absorption, do not fluoresce, and are not easily volatilized.

Fumonisins can be purified from corn culture material (with difficulty) to a white powder (22); there is no published report of crystalline material. Often, fumonisin B_1 purified from corn culture material, which tests 100% pure based on mass comparison against a reference standard, is hygroscopic and slightly colored (B. Chamberlain, personal communication). Recently, methods have been developed for fermentation, extraction, and purification of fumonisins using liquid culture by stirred jar fermentation (77). Purification from liquid is reportedly much easier.

Nuclear magnetic resonance studies indicate that fumonisin B_1 interacts strongly with metal cations (59). In polar solvents fumonisin B_1 exists as a zwitterion, and it has been suggested that the structure favors intra and/or intermolecular hydrogen bonding and electrostatic interactions between the carboxyl and amino groups (59). Changes in chemical shifts of carbon and hydrogen of the propane-tricarboxylate esters, observed at pH 4.0, 5.7, and 7.0, are presumed to be a result of interaction between carbonyl groups (92). At present, little is known about the stereochemistry of the fumonisins; however, the chemical structures suggest a large number of possible stereoisomers (1,024 isomers, J. ApSimon, personal communication). Like sphingoid bases, which they resemble, some isomers may be biologically active and some inactive in various systems.

MODE OF ACTION OF THE FUMONISINS

Inhibition of Sphingolipid Biosynthesis In Vitro

The fumonisins (B_1, B_2, and hydrolyzed B_1) were shown to be the first naturally occurring specific inhibitors of de novo sphingolipid biosynthesis (129). The reader is directed to a recent paper describing this discovery and the implication for the diseases caused by fumonisins (76). In addition to inhibition of de novo biosynthesis, fumonisins also appear to inhibit the reacylation of sphingosine within the sphingolipid turnover pathway and may inhibit acylation of dietary sphingosine. This raises the interesting possibility that the animal diseases associated with the consumption of fumonisins, may result from altered sphingolipid biosynthesis. While other compounds and conditions can alter the kinetics and/or direction of carbon flux in the biosynthetic and turnover pathways, only fumonisins (including B_3 and AAL toxins; 76) have been shown to inhibit specifically ceramide synthases (sphinganine and sphingosine N-acyltransferase).

In primary rat hepatocytes, a consequence of in vitro inhibition of the sphinganine N-acyltransferase was the decrease in ceramide biosynthesis, and thus, de novo sphingosine biosynthesis (129), the rapid accumulation of sphinganine [the immediate precursor in the biosynthetic pathway of dihydroceramide (N-acylsphinganine)] (129), accumulation of sphingosine and sphinganine cleavage products (76), and depletion of complex sphingolipids (76, 129). In cultured cerebellar neurons, fumonisin B_1 inhibited de novo sphingomyelin biosynthesis to a greater extent than it inhibited glycosphingolipids, which suggests that fumonisins preferentially inhibit sphingomyelin biosynthesis in these cells (75). In cultured renal epithelial cells treated with fumonisin B_1, free sphingosine levels became significantly elevated but to a much lesser extent than free sphinganine (135). Unlike primary hepatocytes, the cytostatic and cytotoxic effects of fumonisin B_1 were well correlated with the inhibition of de novo sphingolipid biosynthesis (135). The accumulation of free sphingosine indicates that either reacylation of sphingosine derived from sphingolipid turnover or acylation of sphingosine derived from the serum component of the culture medium was also inhibited. The fact that sphinganine accumulated to a much greater extent than sphingosine suggested that the de novo pathway was the primary target for inhibition. As a result of this differential inhibition, the ratio of sphinganine to sphingosine increased after exposure to fumonisins, and these increases occurred long before any indication of decreased proliferation or cytotoxicity (135). In addition to implicating altered sphingolipid biosynthesis in the cytostatic and cytotoxic effects of fumonisins, the results suggested that changes in the relative amounts of free sphinganine and free sphingosine might be useful as a biomarker for animals consuming fumonisins.

Alterations in Free Sphingoid Bases In Vivo

Based on the specificity of fumonisin B_1 in inhibiting de novo sphingosine biosynthesis in primary rat hepatocytes (129), it was hypothesized that consumption of fumonisins would result in an elevated free sphinganine to free sphingosine ratio in serum. This hypothesis was first tested in horses. An increase in the serum free sphinganine to free sphingosine ratio was demonstrated, within 1 to 5 days, in ponies given feeds containing corn screenings naturally contaminated with 44 ppm fumonisin B_1 (130). The ratio became elevated before increases of serum enzymes indicative of cellular injury and in some ponies within 1 day after consuming fumonisin-contaminated feeds. The ratios returned to control levels when ponies voluntarily stopped eating the contaminated feed. However, the decrease in the ratio lagged by several days the decrease in fumonisin consumption. When animals resumed consumption of contaminated feed the ratios once again became elevated. In a pony given feed containing 15 to 22 ppm fumonisin B_1, no significant change in the ratio occurred until day 182 when the ratio increased dramatically and remained elevated until the animal died of equine leucoencephalomalacia on day 241. The increase in the ratio occurred at least 42 days before any other serum biochemical indices of cellular injury increased.

Similar results were obtained for pigs, confirming a dose-response relationship between the ratio of free sphinganine to free sphingosine in serum and tissues and the amount of fumonisin-contaminated feed consumed (95). Pigs were fed fumonisin-contaminated feed formulated from naturally contaminated corn screenings at 0 (<1), 5, 23, 39, 101, and 175 ppm total fumonisins (B_1 plus B_2). The results showed that the ratio was significantly elevated in liver, lung, and kidney from pigs consuming feeds containing ≥23 ppm fumonisins. Liver injury was observed in $\frac{1}{5}$ of pigs at 23 ppm, $\frac{3}{5}$ of pigs at 39 ppm, and all pigs at higher doses. However, injury to the kidney was not observed at any dose even though it contained equal or greater amounts of free sphingoid bases. In lung tissue, free sphingoid base content was elevated at doses ≥23 ppm, but lung lesions were only observed in pigs fed the diet containing 175 ppm fumonisins.

Possibly, different tissues have different tolerances to elevated levels of free sphingoid bases. Alternatively, (a) elevations in free sphingoid base concentrations may be a benign early response, (b) such elevations may not accurately gauge the extent of complex sphingolipid depletion, or (c) in some tissues sphingolipids may play more critical roles in maintaining cellular integrity and/or regulating cell function. In addition, many effects may be indirectly linked to sphingolipid alterations as has been proposed for pulmonary edema in swine (48). Nonetheless, it is very clear that alteration in free sphingoid bases is a very sensitive biomarker of fumonisin exposure.

In the same study with pigs (95), elevation of the ratio in serum paralleled the increase in tissues. This finding supported the earlier hypothesis (130) that the elevated ratio in serum was due to the movement of free sphinganine (accumulating as a result of inhibition of sphinganine N-acyltransferase) from tissues into the blood. Statistically significant increases in the serum ratio were observed at feed concentrations as low as 5 ppm total fumonisins (after 14 days) and in pigs (at higher concentrations) in which other serum biochemistry parameters were not elevated and in which there were no observable gross or microscopic lesions in liver, lung, or kidney. Thus, the increase in the sphinganine to sphingosine ratio appears to be a more sensitive indicator of fumonisin exposure than the development of detectable liver or lung lesions in pigs. It has been proposed that the ratio of free sphinganine to free sphingosine and the presence of elevated levels of free sphinganine in serum, urine, and tissue be used as an indicator for consumption of fumonisins by farm animals (97).

Pigs fed either naturally contaminated feed (27 ppm) or pure fumonisin B_1 at 1.5 mg/kg/day twice a day for 5 days showed qualitiatively similar alterations in free sphingoid bases in tissues and serum (47). Interestingly, in both groups, the increase in free sphingoid bases was greatest in the kidney. Liver, lung, and serum were also affected, but other tissues were only slightly or not at all altered (47).

In Sprague Dawley rats fed either *F. moniliforme* culture materials or pure fumonisin B_1 for 4 weeks (126a, 127), the kidney was a very sensitive target organ based on observed microscopic lesions. In the rats fed pure fumonisin B_1, elevation in free sphingoid bases in the kidney was closely correlated with the ultrastructural lesions (96). Rats fed *F. moniliforme* culture materials also had elevated free sphingoid bases in liver, the only organ analyzed (82).

Chickens fed feeds supplemented with *F. moniliforme* culture materials (T. S. Wiebking et al, manuscript submitted) or pure fumonisin B_1 (M. Henry, personal communication) exhibited elevated sphinganine levels and elevated ratios in tissues and serum. Thus, ingestion of fumonisins by every target animal tested to date results in elevation in free sphingoid bases in a manner consistent with inhibition of *N*-acyltransferases.

The following facts, when taken together, make a strong case for linkage between inhibition of de novo sphingolipid biosynthesis and the animal diseases shown to be caused by *F. moniliforme* culture materials and pure fumonisins. First, alterations in free sphingoid bases can be detected before or at the same time as ultrastructural lesions. Second, there is a close dose-response relationship between fumonisin levels in naturally contaminated diets or diets containing pure fumonisin B_1 and the degree of elevation of free sphingoid bases and depletion of complex sphingolipids. Third, changes in free sphingoid bases can usually be detected prior to elevation of serum biochemical parameters and at lower doses. And lastly, all the animals tested to date have responded to fumonisins with elevated levels of free sphingoid bases. However, the mechanism by which these sphingolipid alterations cause tissue damage is unknown.

Altered Sphingolipid Biosynthesis and Animal Diseases

The implications of fumonisin inhibition of sphingosine and sphinganine *N*-acyltransferases for diseases caused by fumonisins has been addressed in detail previously (76). A review of the sphingolipid literature is beyond the scope of this paper. Briefly, the maintenance of a low level of free sphingoid bases in tissues is important because these compounds have considerable intrinsic biological activity and can be cytotoxic in high concentrations (for review see 44, 72, 74). Thus, elevation of intracellular free sphingoid bases will disrupt the normal regulatory mechanisms within cells. In addition, complex sphingolipids have numerous important functions in cell membranes including stabilization of the membrane, sorting of lipids and proteins, binding to cytoskeletal elements, and cell-cell recognition (for review see 43, 44, 73, 114). Thus, depletion of complex sphingolipids in membranes will disrupt the normal function of the membrane. The regulated breakdown and turnover of complex sphingolipids such as sphingomyelin have been hypothesized to result in the formation of lipid second messengers (57). These hypothesized sphingolipid second messengers and effector systems (i.e. sphingosine and ceramide) may act as intracellular signals for turning on and turning off processes inside cells. Such processes include the expression of genes, activation or inactivation of specific proteins such as protein kinase C and phosphatidic acid phosphatase, the regulation of growth factor receptors, and other intracellular signalling systems (e.g. Ca^{2+}). All of the processes listed above are intimately connected to the processes of proliferation and differention of cells. Clearly, deciphering the observed in vivo effects of fumonisins in terms of altered sphingolipid biosynthesis will be complicated by the fact that there are potentially many mechanisms of action in cells.

Other Hypothesized Modes of Action

While the inhibition of de novo sphingolipid biosynthesis is a highly attractive hypothesis for explaining the diseases caused by fumonisins, it is quite possible that there are other mechanisms. Aside from one report that fumonisins interfered with calcium in atrial muscle, there is very little other mechanistic data (103).

Since fumonisins are neither genotoxic nor mutagenic (see above), and do not appear to be metabolized to any significant extent in vivo, the mechanism of carcinogenicity will probably be difficult to ascertain. In vitro studies with cell lines indicate that fumonisins are both cytostatic and cytotoxic (29, 112, 135). There have been no published reports that fumonisins have mitogenic activity in vitro. Yet, in vivo, proliferating foci are commonly observed in both liver and kidney of rats (36, 38, 39). Under appropriate conditions, low levels of free sphingoid bases are known to be mitogenic. Thus, possibly there are conditions that could promote increased cell proliferation, subsequent to fumonisin-induced tissue damage (76).

DETECTION AND OCCURRENCE OF FUMONISINS

Analytical Methodology

At the moment, two extraction methods are commonly cited for analysis of fumonisins in foods and feeds. Both methods involve extraction with polar solvents (methanol/water or acetonitrile/water) followed by clean-up on either strong anion-exchange column (SAX) (108) or via a C_{18} reverse phase Sep-Pak (Waters Associates, Milford, MA) (134). Use of the C_{18} method is more rapid than the SAX method; however, the SAX method produces cleaner fractions and thus detection at lower limits (B. Chamberlain, personal communication). Recovery of added fumonisins is good (>80%); however, how well these methods extract all fumonisins from natural matrices is unclear (16). Another current problem is that verified reference standards are not available.

Detection by liquid chromatography (108, 134) or thin layer chromatography (TLC) (36, 102) requires derivatization, whereas gas chromatography-mass spectrometry (GC-MS) (90) requires base hydrolysis to remove the tricarballylic acid groups and derivatization of the amino group to enhance volatility. The advantage of the GC-MS method is that it combines structural confirmation with quantification. Unfortunately, the method requires considerable time and equipment. The most frequently used method for quantification in foods and feeds is liquid chromatography, which utilizes o-phthaldialdehyde as the derivatizing agent (108, 118). The liquid chromatographic method can separate fumonisins B_1, B_2, and B_3 in 16 min using an isocratic solvent system, and the detection limit is 50 ppb using the methanol/water plus strong anion exchange extraction procedure (118). One problem is that the o-phthaldialdehyde-fumonisins derivative is not as stable as some other fluorescent derivatives (118) such as naphthalene-2,3-dicarboxaldehyde or 4-fluoro-7-nitrobenzofurazan (12, 105).

The least expensive and least sensitive method for detection of fumonisins is TLC (36). Using a two-step TLC development system made it possible to shorten the extraction procedure and quantify the para-anisaldehyde derivative using spectrophotodensitometry (61). The detection limit by this method was 50 ppm. Recently, a TLC method using fluorescamine instead of p-anisaldehyde allowed visualization of fumonisins from corn samples at concentrations as low as 0.1 ppm (101).

The most recent development for surveying foods and feeds is the production of monoclonal and polyclonal antibodies against fumonisins (5, 6). These antibodies have been used to screen fumonisins and related metabolites in foods, feeds, and tissues by competitive enzyme-linked immunoabsorbent assays and immunochromatography methods (88). Affinity columns have been used to isolate fumonisins from aqueous extracts of corn. Quantification of the eluate has been carried out by HPLC of the o-phthaldialdehyde-fumonisin derivative or by direct fluorescence measurement (45). The antibody methods are the basis for a commercially available affinity column (Vicam, Sumerville, MA) and a laboratory test kit (Neogen Corporation, Lansing, MI).

Results of Analyses of Feeds and Foods

All of the methods described above have been used to measure fumonisins in corn, corn-based feeds, and/or corn-based foods, or other corn-based products. The first natural occurrence of fumonisins in US corn was reported in 1989 in two corn samples associated with an outbreak of ELEM (80a). Soon thereafter it was reported that fumonisins were present in moldy home-grown corn from the Transkei in southern Africa, where the rate of esophageal cancer is high (116). Since these initial reports, numerous feeds and foods have been analyzed. Several general conclusions can be drawn. First, like *F. moniliforme,* the occurrence of fumonisins on corn is widespread. Fumonisins have been detected on corn and corn-based products from the United States and Canada, Europe, South America, and Africa (e.g. 89, 94, 101, 106, 115, 117, 119–121, 126). Second, fumonisins can co-occur with aflatoxin (23). Lastly, the concentrations of fumonisins in moldy corn or feeds associated with field cases of ELEM, PPE, and other animal diseases are usually much higher than in "clean feeds" that were not associated with field cases and in foods for human consumption (e.g. see 101, 121). Nonetheless, detection of total fumonisin concentrations greater than 0.5 ppm in foods destined for human consumption is not unusual. Trace amounts (<1 to 3 ppm) of fumonisins have been found in some commercial laboratory rat rations (24, 123). Analyses for fumonisins in diets used in long-term animal studies are clearly warranted.

Potential Decontamination and Salvage Strategies

The occurrence of fumonisins in foods and feeds indicates the need for development of methods for detoxification in order to salvage contaminated grains. Atmospheric ammoniation of corn does not appear to be an effective method for detoxification (81). Ammoniation at high pressure (60 psi) and low temperature (20°C) reduced detectable fumonisin B_1 levels in corn by 79%; however, the toxic potential of the ammoniated corn was not determined (87). The use of household bleach as a means of destroying fumonisin B_1 has been reported (134); however, no data were given. Boiling culture material for 30 min had no effect on fumonisin B_1 content of corn culture material nor did it reduce its toxic potential (4). A recent report indicated that thermal decomposition of fumonisin B_1 in corn culture material followed a first-order reaction with half-life times of 10, 38, and 175 min at 150, 125, and 100°C, respectively (61). The toxic potential of the heat-treated culture material was not tested. Baking of corn meal muffins also reduced detectable fumonisin content as did boiling of corn meal in lime water (106). Corn products from Peru and the United States that were treated with lime water as part of the processing were also found to contain very low amounts of fumonisins (119). Ethanol fermented from moldy corn contained no fumonisins; however, the fermented mash (beer) contained appreciable amounts (16).

CONCLUSIONS

F. moniliforme and the fumonisins are clearly an area of growing concern for producers and consumers. They are a unique problem for the following reasons: (*a*) The occurrence of the fungus and toxin in corn is widespread and can be symptomless in corn; (*b*) the toxicities associated with consumption of fumonisins by farm animals are quite varied; (*c*) fumonisins are often present in feeds in the ppm range and are sometimes found in food for human consumption at ppm levels; (*d*) the actual number of fumonisins, fumonisin-like compounds, and fumonisin precursors that occur in feeds and foods is unknown; and (*e*) the mode of action is unique and the role of sphingolipids in disease is poorly understood.

The health implication of low levels of fumonisins in human foods is unknown. The levels that are safe to feed to animals are also unknown. The Mycotoxin Committee of the American Association of Veterinary Laboratory Diagnosticians recommends that concentrations greater than 5 ppm, 10 ppm, 50 ppm, and 50 ppm should not be fed to equidae, swine, beef cattle, and poultry, respectively (P. F. Ross, personal communication). These recommendations will change as more data becomes available.

Literature Cited

1. Abbas, H. K., Shier, W. T. 1992. Evaluation of biosynthetic precursors for the production of radiolabeled fumonisin B₁ by *Fusarium moniliforme* on rice medium. *106th Annu. Assoc. Off. Anal. Chem. Meet.*, Cincinnati, Ohio, p. 236 (Abstr.)
2. Abbas, H. K., Tanaka, T., Duke, S. O., Gelderblom, W. C. A., Cawood, M. E. 1992. Comparison of phytotoxicities of fumonisins A & B with AAL-toxin using a duckweed (*Lemna pausicostata* L.) assay. *Phytopathology* 82:A209 (Abstr.)
3. Abbas, W. C. A., Gelderblom, M. E., Cawood, M. E., Shier, W. T. 1992. Biological activities of various fumonisins in jimsonweed and mammalian cell cultures. *Phytopathology* 82:A1 (Abstr.)
4. Alberts, J. F., Gelderblom, W. C. A.,

Thiel, P. G., Marasas, W. F. O., Van Schalkwyk, D. J., et al. 1990. Effects of temperature and incubation period on production of fumonisin B₁ by *Fusarium moniliforme*. *Appl. Environ. Microbiol.* 56:1729–33
5. Azcona-Olivera, J. I., Abouzied, M. M., Plattner, R. D., Norred, W. P., Pestka, J. J. 1992. Generation of antibodies reactive with fumonisins B₁, B₂, B₃ using cholera toxin as the carrier-adjuvant. *Appl. Environ. Microbiol.* 58:169–73
6. Azcona-Olivera, J. I., Abouzied, M. M., Plattner, R. D., Pestka, J. J. 1992. Production of monoclonal antibodies to the mycotoxins fumonisins-B₁, fumonisins-B₂, and fumonisins-B₃. *J. Agric. Food Chem.* 40: 531–34
7. Bacon, C. W., Bennett, R. M., Hinton,

D. M., Voss, K. A. 1991. Scanning electron microscopy of *Fusarium moniliforme* within symptomatic corn kernels, and kernels associated with equine leukoencephalomalacia. *Phytopathology* 76:144–48

8. Bacon, C. W., Hinton, D. M., Chamberlain, W. J., Norred, W. P. 1992. De novo induction of adventitious roots in excised shoots of tomatoes by fumonisin B$_1$, a metabolite of *Fusarium moniliforme*. *J. Plant Growth Regul.* In press

9. Bacon, C. W., Marijanovic, D. R., Norred, W. P., Hinton, D. M. 1989. Production of fusarin C on cereal and soybean by *Fusarium moniliforme*. *Appl. Environ. Microbiol.* 55: 2745–48

10. Bacon, C. W., Williamson, J. W. 1992. Interactions of *Fusarium moniliforme*, its metabolites and bacteria and corn. *Mycopathologia* 117:65–71

11. Beasley, V. R., Motelin, G., Ness, D. K., Hall, W. F., Harlin, K. S., et al. 1992. Fumonisin-contaminated corn screenings: Temporal and qualitative differences in the response of swine as a function of dose. *Toxicologist* 12:33 (Abstr.)

12. Bennett, G. A., Richard, J. L. 1992. High performance liquid chromatographic methods of analysis for fumonisins. See Ref. 1, p. 143

13. Bezuidenhout, S. C., Gelderblom, W. C. A., Gorst-Allman, C. P., Horak, R. M., Marasas, W. F. O., et al. 1988. Structure elucidation of the fumonisins, mycotoxins from *Fusarium moniliforme*. *J. Chem. Soc. Chem. Commun.*, pp. 743–45

14. Blakesley, D., Weston, G. D., Hall, J. F. 1991. The role of endogenous auxin in root initiation. *J. Plant Growth Regul.* 10:341–53

15. Blount, W. P. 1961. Turkey "X" disease. *Turkeys* 9:52

16. Bothast, R. J., Bennett, G. A., Vancauwenberge, J. E., Richard, J. L. 1992. Fate of fumonisin B$_1$ in naturally contaminated corn during ethanol fermentation. *Appl. Environ. Microbiol.* 58:233–36

17. Bottini, A. T., Bowen, J. R., Gilchrist, D. G. 1981. Phytotoxin II. Characterization of a phytotoxic fraction from *Alternaria alternata* f.sp. *lycopersici*. *Tetrahedron Lett.* 22:2723–26

18. Brock, T. G., Burg, J., Ghosheh, N. S., Kaufman, P. B. 1992. The role of calcium in growth induced by indole-3-acetic acid and gravity in the leaf-sheath pulvinum of oat *(Avena sativa)*. *J. Plant Growth Regul.* 11:99–103

19. Brown, T. P., Rottinghaus, G. E., Williams, M. E. 1992. Fumonisin mycotoxicosis in broilers: performance and pathology. *Avian Dis.* 36:450–54

20. Bryden, W. L., Love, R. J., Burgess, L. W. 1987. Feeding grain contaminated with *Fusarium graminearum* and *Fusarium moniliforme* to pigs and chickens. *Aust. Vet. J.* 64:225–26

21. Butler, T. 1902. Notes on a feeding experiment to produce leucoencephalitis in a horse, with positive results. *Am. Vet. Rev.* 26:748–51

22. Cawood, M. E., Gelderblom, W. C. A., Vleggaar, R., Behrend, Y., Thiel, P. G., et al. 1991. Isolation of the fumonisin mycotoxins: a quantitative approach. *J. Agric. Food Chem.* 39: 1958–62

23. Chamberlain, W. J., Norred, W. P., Bacon, C. W. 1992. Fumonisin B$_1$ found in aflatoxin-contaminated corn. See Ref. 1, p. 225

24. Chamberlain, W. J., Voss, K. A., Norred, W. P. 1992. Analysis of commercial laboratory rat rations for fumonisin, a mycotoxin produced on corn by *Fusarium moniliforme*. *Lab. Anim. Sci.* 32:26–28

25. Colvin, B. M., Harrison, L. R. 1992. Fumonisin-induced pulmonary edema and hydrothorax in swine. *Mycopathologia* 117:79–82

26. Council for Agricultural Science and Technology. 1989. *Mycotoxins: Economic and Health Risks, Rep. 116,* Ames, Iowa

27. Davis, R. M., Kegel, F. R., Sills, W. M., Farrar, J. J. 1989. *Fusarium* ear rot of corn. *Calif. Agric.* 43:4–5

28. De Leon, C., Pandey, S. 1989. Improvement of resistance to ear and stalk rots and agronomic traits in tropical maize gene pools. *Crop Sci.* 29:12–17

29. Dombrink-Kurtzman, M. A., Bennett, G. A., Richard, J. L. 1992. Cytotoxicity of fumonisins in avian lymphocytes. See Ref. 1, p. 145

29a. Dombrink-Kurtzman, M. A., Javid, J., Bennett, G. A., Richard, J. L., Cote, L. M., et al. 1992. Lymphocyte cytotoxicity and erythrocytic abnormalities induced in broiler chicks by fumonisin B$_1$ and B$_2$ and moniliformin from *Fusarium proliferatum*. See Ref. 1, p. 233

30. Engelhardt, J. A., Carlton, W. W., Tuite, J. F. 1989. Toxicity of *Fusarium moniliforme* var. *subglutinans* for

chicks, ducklings, and turkey poults. *Avian Dis.* 33:357–60

31. *Feedstuffs.* 1989. NGFA official contests media 'misinformation' campaign over aflatoxin. 61(16):8

32. Fincham, J. E., Marasas, W. F. O., Taljaard, J. J. F., Kriek, N. P. J., Badenhorst, C. J., et al. 1992. Atherogenic effects in an non-human primate of *Fusarium moniliforme* cultures added to a carbohydrate diet. *Atherosclerosis* 94:13–25

33. *Food Chemical News.* 1991. Aflatoxin controls are effective, GAO tells congress. 27 May:60–62

34. *Food Chemical News.* 1991. Regulatory limits for aflatoxin likely: Landa. 26 August:24–25

35. *Food Chemical News.* 1992. IARC classes aflatoxin B1 as class 1 human carcinogen. 3 August:62–64

36. Gelderblom, W. C. A., Jaskiewicz, K., Marasas, W. F. O., Thiel, P. G., Horak, R. M., et al. 1988. Fumonisins-novel mycotoxins with cancer-promoting activity produced by *Fusarium moniliforme*. *Appl. Environ. Microbiol.* 54:1806–11

37. Gelderblom, W. C. A., Kriek, N. P. J., Marasas, W. F. O., Thiel, P. G. 1991. Toxicity and carcinogenicity of the *Fusarium moniliforme* metabolite, fumonisin B₁, in rats. *Carcinogenesis* 12:1247–51

38. Gelderblom, W. C. A., Marasas, W. F. O., Vleggaar, R., Thiel, P. G., Cawood, M. E. 1992. Fumonisins: isolation chemical characterization and biological activity. *Mycopathologia* 117:11–16

39. Gelderblom, W. C. A., Semple, E., Marasas, W. F. O., Farber, E. 1992. The cancer-initiating potential of the fumonisin-B mycotoxins. *Carcinogenesis* 13:433–37

40. Gelderblom, W. C. A., Snyman, S. D. 1991. Mutagenicity of potentially carcinogenic mycotoxins produced by *Fusarium moniliforme*. *Mycotoxin Res.* 7:46–52

41. Gilchrist, D. G., Grogan, R. G. 1976. Production and nature of a host-specific toxin from *Alternaria alternata* f. sp. *lycopersici*. *Phytopathology* 66:165–71

42. Gilchrist, D. G., Ward, B., Moussato, V., Mirocha, C. J. 1992. Genetic and physiological response to fumonisin and AAL-toxin by intact tissue of a higher plant. *Mycopathologia* 117:57–64

43. Hakomori, S.-I. 1990. Bifunctional role of glycosphingolipids. *J. Biol. Chem.* 265:18713–16

44. Hannun, Y. A., Bell, R. M. 1989. Functions of sphingolipids and sphinoglipid breakdown products in cellular regulation. *Science* 243:500–7

45. Hansen, T. J., Zabe, N. A., Skipper, P. L. 1992. Immunoaffinity isolation of fumonisin B₁ and application to analysis in corn. See Ref. 1, p. 230

46. Harrison, L. R., Colvin, B. M., Greene, J. T., Newman, L. E., Cole, R. J. 1990. Pulmonary edema and hydrothorax in swine produced by fumonisin B₁, a toxic metabolite of *Fusarium moniliforme*. *J. Vet. Diagn. Invest.* 2:217–21

47. Haschek, W. M., Kim, H.-Y., Motelin, G. K., Stair, E. L., Beasley, W. J., et al. 1993. Pure fumonisin B₁, as well as fumonisin-contaminated feed, alters swine serum and tissue sphinganine and sphingosine levels, biomarkers of exposure. *Toxicologist* 13: In press (Abstr.)

48. Haschek, W. M., Motelin, G., Ness, D. K., Harlin, K. S., Hall, W. F., et al. 1992. Characterization of fumonisin toxicity in orally and intravenously dosed swine. *Mycopathologia* 117:83–96

49. Headrick, M., Pataky, J. K. 1989. Resistance to kernel infection by *Fusarium moniliforme* in inbred lines of sweet corn and the effect of infection on emergence. *Plant Dis.* 73:887–92

50. Jardine, D. J., Leslie, J. F. 1992. Aggressiveness of *Gibberella fujikuroi* (*Fusarium moniliforme*) isolates to grain sorghum under greenhouse conditions. *Phytopathology* 76:897–900

51. Jaskiewicz, K., van Rensberg, S. J., Marasas, W. F. O, Gelderblom, W. C. A. 1987. Carcinogenicity of *Fusarium moniliforme* culture material in rats. *JNCI* 78:321–25

52. Javed, T., Bennett, G. A., Richard, J. L., Dombrink-Kurtzman, M. A., Cote, L. M., et al. 1992. Mortality in broiler chicks on feed amended with a *Fusarium proliferatum* culture or with purified fumonisin B₁ and moniliformin. See Ref. 1, p. 232

53. Javed, T., Bunte, R. M., Bennett, G. A., Richard, J. L., Dombrink-Kurtzman, M. A., et al. 1992. Comparative pathologic changes in broiler chicks on feed amended with *Fusarium proliferatum* culture material or purified fumonisin B₁ and moniliformin. See Ref. 1, p. 230

54. Javed, T., Richard, J. L., Bennett, G. A., Dombrink-Kurtzman, M. A., Bunte, R. M., et al. 1992. Embryopathic and embryocidal effects of pu-

rified fumonisin B_1 or *Fusarium proliferatum* culture extract on chicken embryos. See Ref. 1, p. 231

55. Jeschke, N., Nelson, P. E., Marasas, W. F. O. 1987. Toxicity to ducklings of *Fusarium moniliforme* isolated from corn intended for use in poultry feed. *Poultry Sci.* 66:1619–23

56. Kellerman, T. S., Marasas, W. F. O., Thiel, P. G., Gelderblom, W. C. A., Cawood, M., et al. 1990. Leucoencephalomalacia in two horses induced by oral dosing of fumonisin B_1. *Onderstepoort J. Vet. Res.* 57:269–75

57. Kim, M.-Y., Linardic, C., Obeid, L., Hannun, Y. 1991. Identification of sphingomyelin turnover as an effector mechanism for the action of tumor necrosis factor and interferon. *J. Biol. Chem.* 266:484–89

58. Kriek, N. P. J., Kellerman, T. S., Marasas, W. F. O. 1981. A comparative study of the toxicity of *Furarium verticilliodies* (=*F. moniliforme*) to horses, primates, pigs, sheep and rats. *Onderstepoort J. Vet. Res.* 48:129–31

59. Laurent, D., Lanson, M., Goasdove, N., Kohler, F., Pellegrin, F., et al. 1990. Étude en RMN ¹H et ¹³C de la macrofusine, toxine isolée de maïs infesté par *Fusarium moniliforme* Sheld. *Analusis* 18:172–79

60. Laurent, D., Platzer, N., Kohler, F., Sauviat, M. P., Pellegrin, F. 1989. Macrofusine et micromoniline: deux nouvelles mocotoxine isolée de maïs infesté par *Fusarium moniliforme* Sheld. *Microbiologie Aliment Nutrition* 7:9–16

61. Le Bars, J., Le Bars, P., Dupuy, J., Boudra, H., Cassini, R. 1992. Biotic and abiotic factors in fumonisin production and accumulation. See Ref. 1, p. 106

62. Ledoux, D. R., Brown, T. P., Weibking, T. S., Rottinghaus, G. E. 1992. Fumonisin toxicity in broiler chicks. *J. Vet. Diagn. Invest* 4:330–33

63. Leslie, J. F. 1991. Mating populations in *Gibberella fujikuroi* (*Fusarium* section *Liseola*). *Phytopathology* 81:1058–60

64. Leslie, J. F., Doe, F. J., Plattner, R. D., Shackelford, D. D., Jonz, J. 1992. Fumonisin B_1 production and vegetative compatibility of strains from *Gibberella fujikuroi* mating population 'A' (*Fusarium moniliforme*). *Mycopathologia* 117:37–45

65. Leslie, J. F., Plattner, R. D., Desjardins, A. E., Klittich, C. J. R. 1992. Fumonsin B_1 production by

strains from different mating populations of *Gibberella fujikuroi* (*Fusarium* section *Liseola*). *Phytopathology* 82:341–45

66. Marasas, W. F. O., Jaskiewicz, K., Venter, F. S., Van Schalkwyk, D. J. 1988. *Fusarium moniliforme* contamination of maize in oseophageal cancer areas in Transkei. *S. Afr. Med. J.* 74:110–14

67. Marasas, W. F. O., Kellerman, T. S., Gelderblom, W. C. A., Coetzer, J. A. W., Thiel, P. G., et al. 1988. Leukoencephalomalacia in a horse induced by fumonisin B1 isolated from *Fusarium moniliforme*. *Onderstepoort J. Vet. Res.* 55:197–203

68. Marasas, W. F. O., Kriek, N. P. J., Fincham, J. E., van Rensberg, S. J. 1984. Primary liver cancer and oesophageal basal cell hyperplasia in rats caused by *Fusarium moniliforme*. *Int. J. Cancer* 34:383–87

69. Marasas, W. F. O., Nelson, P. E., Toussoun, T. A. 1984. *Toxigenic Fusarium Species*. University Park: Penn. State Univ. Press

70. Marasas, W. F. O., van Rensburg, S. J., Mirocha, C. J. 1979. Incidence of *Fusarium* species and the mycotoxins, deoxynivalenol and zearalenone, in corn produced in esophageal cancer areas in Transkei. *J. Agric. Food Chem.* 27:1108–12

71. Marijanovic, D. R., Holt, P., Norred, W. P., Bacon, C. W., Voss, K. A., et al. 1991. Immunosuppressive effects of *Fusarium moniliforme* corn cultures in chickens. *Poultry Sci.* 70:1895–1901

72. Merrill, A. H. Jr. 1991. Cell regulation by sphingosine and more complex sphingolipids. *J. Bioenerg. Biomembr.* 23:83–104

73. Merrill, A. H. Jr., Jones, D. 1990. An update of the enzymology and regulation of sphingomyelin metabolism. *Biochim. Biophys. Acta* 1044:1–12

74. Merrill, A. H. Jr., Stevens, V. L. 1989. Modulation of protein kinase C and diverse cell functions by sphingosine—a pharmacologically interesting compound linking sphingolipids and signal transduction. *Biochim. Biophys. Acta* 1010:131–39

75. Merrill, A. H. Jr., van Echten, G., Mandon, E. C., Rath, A., Ehses, I., et al. 1992. Inhibition of sphinganine N-acyltransferase and de novo sphingolipid synthesis in cultured cerebellar neurons by fumonisin. *Biophys. J.* 61:A492 (Abstr.)

76. Merrill, A. H. Jr., Wang, E., Gilchrist,

D. G., Riley, R. T. 1992. Fumonisin and other inhibitors of *de novo* sphingolipid biosynthesis. *Adv. Lipid Res.* In press

77. Miller, J. D. 1992. Production of fumonisins in liquid culture. See Ref. 1, p. 106

78. Nelson, P. E. 1992. Taxonomy and biology of *Fusarium moniliforme*. *Mycopathologia* 117:29–36

79. Norred, W. P. 1992. Fumonisins-mycotoxins produced by *Fusarium moniliforme J. Toxicol. Environ. Health*. In press

79a. Norred, W. P., Plattner, R. D. 1993. Excretion and distribution of [¹⁴C]fumonisin B₁ in male Sprague-Dawley rats. *Toxicologist* 13:(Abstr). In press

80. Norred, W. P., Plattner, R. D., Vesonder, R. F., Bacon, C. W., Voss, K. A. 1992. Effects of selected secondary metabolites on unscheduled synthesis of DNA by rat primary hepatocytes. *Food Chem. Toxicol.* 30: 233–37

80a. Norred, W. P., Plattner, R. D., Voss, K. A., Bacon, C. W., Porter, J. K. 1989. Natural occurrence of fumonisins in corn associated with equine leukoencephalomalacia. *Toxicologist* 9:258 (Abstr.)

81. Norred, W. P., Voss, K. A., Bacon, C. W., Riley, R. T. 1991. Effectiveness of ammonia treatment in detoxification of fumonisin-contaminated corn. *Food Chem. Toxicol.* 29:815–19

82. Norred, W. P., Wang, E., Yoo, H.-S., Showker, J. L., Voss, K., et al. 1992. Development of a diagnostic test for fumonisin toxicoses. *Toxicologist* 12: 189 (Abstr.)

83. Nyvall, R. F., Kommedahl, T. 1968. Individual thickened hyphae as survival structures of *Fusarium moniliforme* in corn. *Phytopathology* 58:1704–7

84. Nyvall, R. F., Kommedahl, T. 1970. Saprophytism and survival of *Fusarium moniliforme* in corn stalks. *Phytopathology* 6:1233–35

85. Ochor, T. E. 1987. Relationship of harvest date and host genotype to infection of maize kernels by *Fusarium moniliforme*. *Plant Dis.* 71:311–13

86. Osweiller, G. D., Ross, P. F., Wilson, T. M., Nelson, P. E., Witte, S. T., et al. 1992. Characterization of an epizootic of pulmonary edema in swine associated with fumonisin in corn screenings. *J. Vet. Diagn. Invest.* 4:53–59

87. Park, D. L., Rua, S. M., Mirocha, C. J., Abd-Alla, E.-S. A. M., Weng,

C. Y. 1992. Mutagenic potentials of fumonisin-contaminated corn following ammonia decontamination procedure. *Mycopathologia* 117:105–8

88. Pestka, J. J., Azcona-Olivera, J. I., Marovatsanga, L. T., Abouziel, M. M. 1992. Assessment of fumonisins in foods by immunochemical methods. See Ref. 1, p. 143

89. Pittet, A., Parisod, V., Schellenberg, M. 1992. Occurrence of fumonisins B₁ and B₂ in corn-based products from the Swiss market. *J. Agric. Food Chem.* 40:1352–54

90. Plattner, R. D., Norred, W. P., Bacon, C. W., Voss, K. A., Peterson, R., et al. 1990. A method of detection of fumonisins in corn samples associated with field cases of equine leukoencephalomalacia. *Mycologia* 82:698–702

91. Plattner, R. D., Shackelford, D. D. 1992. Biosynthesis of labeled fumonisins in liquid cultures of *Fusarium moniliforme*. *Mycopathologia* 117:17–22

92. Plattner, R. D., Weisleder, D., Shackelford, D. D., Peterson, R., Powell, R. G. 1992. A new fumonisin from solid cultures of *Fusarium moniliforme*. *Mycopathologia* 117:23–28

93. Pohland, A. E. 1991. Mycotoxins: a general overview. In *Emerging Food Safety Problem Resulting from Microbial Contamination*, ed. K. Mise, J. L. Richard, pp. 31–43. Tokyo: Minist. Health Welfare

94. Rheeder, J. P., Marasas, W. F. O., Thiel, P. G., Syndenham, E. W., Shephard, G. S., et al. 1992. *Fusarium moniliforme* and fumonisins in corn in relation to human esophageal cancer in Transkei. *Phytopathology* 82:353–57

95. Riley, R. T., An, N.-Y., Showker, J. L., Yoo, H.-S., Norred, W. P., et al. 1993. Alteration of tissue and serum sphinganine to sphingosine ratio: An early biomarker in pigs of exposure to fumonisin-containing feeds. *Toxicol. Appl. Pharmacol.* 118: 105–12

96. Riley, R. T., Hinton, D. M., Chamberlain, W. J., Bacon, C. W., Merrill, A. H. Jr., et al. 1993. Fumonisin (FB) inhibition of sphingolipid (SL) biosynthesis: a new mechanism of nephrotoxicity. *Toxicologist* 13:(Abstr). In press

97. Riley, R. T., Wang, E., Merrill, A. H. Jr. 1993. Liquid chromatography of sphinganine and sphingosine: use of the sphinganine to sphingosine ratio as a biomarker for consumption of

fumonisins. *J. Assoc. Off. Anal. Chem.* In press

98. Rose, E. F. 1982. Esophageal cancer in Transkei—The pattern and associated risk factors. In *Cancer of the Esophagus*, pp. 19–29. Boca Raton, Fla: CRC Press

99. Ross, P. F., Nelson, P. E., Richard, J. L., Osweiler, G. D., Rice, L. G., et al. 1990. Production of fumonisins by *Fusarium moniliforme* and *Fusarium proliferatum* isolates associated with equine leukoencephalomalacia and a pulmonary edema syndrome in swine. *Appl. Environ. Microbiol.* 56: 3225–26

100. Ross, P. F., Rice, L. G., Osweiler, G. D., Nelson, P. E., Richard, J. L., et al. 1992. A review and update of animal toxicoses associated with fumonisin-contaminated feeds and production of fumonisins by *Fusarium* isolates. *Mycopathologia* 117:109–14

101. Ross, P. F., Rice, L. G., Plattner, R. D., Osweiler, G. D., Wilson, T. M., et al. 1991. Concentrations of fumonisin B₁ in feeds associated with animal health problems. *Mycopathologia* 114: 129–35

102. Rottinghaus, G. E., Coatney, C. E., Minor, H. C. 1992. A rapid sensitive thin layer chromatographic procedure for detection of fumonisins B₁ and B₂. *J. Vet. Diagn. Invest.* 4:326–29

103. Sauviat, M. P., Laurent, D., Kohler, F., Pellegrin, F. 1991. Fumonisin, a toxin from the fungus *Fusarium moniliforme* Sheld, blocks both the calcium current and the mechanical activity in frog atrial muscle. *Toxicon* 29:1025–31

104. Scott, G. E., King, S. B. 1984. Site of action of factors for resistance to *Fusarium moniliforme* in Maize. *Plant Dis.* 68:804–6

105. Scott, P. M., Lawrence, G. A. 1992. Liquid chromatographic determination of fumonisins with 4-fluoro-7-nitrobenzofurazan. *J. Assoc. Off. Anal. Chem.* 75:829–34

106. Scott, P. M., Lawrence, G. A. 1992. Stability and problems in determination of fumonisins in foods. See Ref. 1, p. 144

107. Segal, I., Reinach, S. G., de Beer, M. 1988. Factors associated with oesophageal cancer in Soweto, South Africa. *Br. J. Cancer* 56:681–86

108. Shephard, G. S., Sydenham, E. W., Thiel, P. G., Gelderblom, W. C. A. 1990. Quantitative determination of fumonisins B₁ and B₂ by high pressure liquid chromatography with fluores-

cence detection. *J. Liquid Chromatogr.* 13:2077–87

109. Shephard, G. S., Thiel, P G., Sydenham, E. W. 1992. Initial studies on the toxicokinetics of fumonisins B₁ in rats. *Food Chem. Toxicol.* 30:277–79

110. Shephard, G. S., Thiel, P G., Sydenham, E. W., Albert, J. F., Gelderblom, W. C. A. 1992. Fate of a single dose of the ¹⁴C-labeled mycotoxin, fumonisin B₁ in rats. *Toxicon* 30:768–70

111. Shier, W. T., Abbas, H. K. 1992. A simple procedure for preparation of aminopentols (fumonisin hydrolysis products AP₁ and AP₂) from *Fusarium moniliforme* on solid media. See Ref. 1, p. 237

112. Shier, W. T., Abbas H. K., Mirocha, C. J. 1991. Toxicity of mycotoxins fumonisin B₁ and B₂ and *Alternaria alternata* f.sp. *lycopersici* toxin (AAL) in cultured mammalian cells. *Mycopathologia* 116:97–104

113. Siler, D. J., Gilchrist, D. G. 1983. Properties of host-specific toxins produced by *Alternaria alternata* f.sp. *lycopersici* in culture and in tomato plants. *Physiol. Plant Pathol.* 23:265–74

114. Simons, K., van Meer, G. 1988. Lipid sorting in epithelial cells. *Biochemistry* 27:6197–202

115. Stack, M. E., Eppley, R. M. 1992. Liquid chromatographic determination of fumonisins B₁ and B₂ in corn and corn products. *J. Assoc. Off. Anal. Chem.* 75:834–37

116. Sydenham, E. W., Gelderblom, W. C. A., Thiel, P. G., Marasas, W. F. O. 1990. Evidence for the natural occurrence of fumonisin B₁ in corn. *J. Agric. Food Chem.* 38:285–90

117. Sydenham, E. W., Marasas, W. F. O., Shephard, G. S., Thiel, P. G., Hirooka, E. Y. 1992. Fumonisin concentrations in Brazilian feeds associated with field outbreaks of confirmed and suspected animal mycotoxicoses. *J. Agric. Food Chem.* 40:994–97

118. Sydenham, E. W., Shepard, G. S., Thiel, P. G. 1992. Liquid chromatographic determination of fumonisins B₁, B₂, and B₃ in foods and feeds. *J. Assoc. Off. Anal. Chem.* 75:313–18

119. Sydenham, E. W., Shephard, G. S., Thiel, P. G., Marasas, W. F. O., Stockenström, S. 1991. Fumonisin contamination of commercial corn-based human foodstuffs. *J. Agric. Food Chem.* 39:2014–18

120. Sydenham, E. W., Thiel, P. G., Marasas, W. F. O., Shephard, G. S.,

van Schalkwyk, D. J., et al. 1990. Natural occurrence of some *Fusarium* mycotoxins in corn from low and high esophageal cancer prevalence areas of the Transkei, southern Africa. *J. Agric. Food Chem.* 38:1900–3

121. Thiel, P. G., Marasas, W. F. O., Sydenham, E. W., Shephard, G. S., Gelderblom, W. C. A. 1992. The implications of naturally occurring levels of fumonisins in corn for human and animal health. *Mycopathologia* 117: 3–10

122. Thiel, P. G., Shephard, G. S., Sydenham, E. W., Marasas, W. F. O., Nelson, P. E., et al. 1991. Levels of fumonisins B_1 and B_2 in feeds associated with confirmed cases of equine leukoencephalomalacia. *J. Agric. Food Chem.* 39:109–11

123. Thigpen, J. E., Locklear, J., Ross, P. F., Goelz, M. F., Stokes, W. S. 1992. The concentration, source, and significance of the fumonisins, a new class of recently recognized mycotoxins, in laboratory animal diets. *Lab. Animal Sci.* 42:424 (Abstr.)

123a. Thomas, M. D., Buddenhagen, I. W. 1980. Incidence and persistence of *Fusarium moniliforme* in symptomless maize kernels and seedlings in Nigeria. *Mycologia* 72:882–87

124. United States Department of Agriculture. 1991. Statistics of grains and feeds. In *Agricultural Statistics, 1991*, pp. 1–60. Washington, DC: Gov. Print. Off.

125. van Rensburg, S. J. 1985. Recent studies on the etiology of oesophageal cancer. *S. Afr. Cancer Bull.* 29:22–31

126. Visconti, A. 1992. Examination of European isolates of *Fusarium* for production of fumonisins. See Ref. 1, p. 107

126a. Voss, K. A., Chamberlain, W. J., Bacon, C. W., Norred, W. P. 1992. A preliminary investigation of renal and hepatic toxicity in rats fed purified fumonisin B_1. *Nat. Toxins.* In press

127. Voss, K. A., Norred, W. P., Plattner, R. D., Bacon, C. W. 1989. Hepato-

toxicity and renal toxicity in rats of corn samples associated with field cases of leukoencephalomalacia. *Food. Chem. Toxicol.* 27:89–96

128. Voss, K. A., Norred, W. P., Plattner, R. D., Bacon, C. W., Porter, J. K. 1989. Hepatotoxicity in rats of aqueous extracts of *Fusarium moniliforme* strain MRC 826 corn cultures. *Toxicologist* 9:258 (Abstr.)

129. Wang, E., Norred, W. P., Bacon, C. W., Riley, R. T., Merrill, A. H. Jr. 1991. Inhibition of sphingolipid biosynthesis by fumonisins: implications for diseases associated with *Fusarium moniliforme*. *J. Biol. Chem.* 266: 14486–90

130. Wang, E., Ross, P. F., Wilson, T. M., Riley, R. T., Merrill, A. H. Jr. 1992. Alteration of serum sphingolipids upon dietary exposure of ponies to fumonisins, mycotoxins produced by *Fusarium moniliforme*. *J. Nutr.* 122: 1706–16

131. Wilson, B. J., Maronpot, R. R. 1971. Causative fungal agent of leucoencephalomalacia in equine animals. *Vet. Rec.* 88:484–86

132. Wilson, T. M., Nelson, P. E., Knepp, C. R. 1985. Hepatic neoplastic nodules, adenofibrosis and cholangiocarcinomas in male Fischer 344 rats fed corn naturally contaminated with *Fusarium moniliforme*. *Carcinogenesis* 6:1155–60

133. Wilson, T. M., Ross, P. F., Owens, D. L., Rice, L. G., Green, S. A., et al. 1992. Experimental reproduction of ELEM—a study to determine the minimum toxic dose in ponies. *Mycopathologia* 117:115–20

134. Wilson, T. M., Ross, P. F., Rice, L. G., Osweiler, G. D., Nelson, H. A., et al. 1990. Fumonisin B_1 levels associated with an epizootic of equine leukoencephalomalacia. *J. Vet. Diagn. Invest.* 2:213–16

135. Yoo, H.-S., Norred, W. P., Wang, E., Merrill, A. H. Jr., Riley, R. T. 1992. Fumonisin inhibition of de novo sphingolipid biosynthesis and cytotoxicity are correlated in LLC-PK_1 cells. *Toxicol. Appl. Pharmacol.* 114:9–15

Annu. Rev. Nutr. 1993. 13:191–215

IMPACT OF PLANT GENETIC ENGINEERING ON FOODS AND NUTRITION

Luca Comai

Department of Botany KB-15, University of Washington, Seattle, Washington 98195

KEY WORDS: biotechnology, transformation, safety, storage, lipids, starch

CONTENTS

INTRODUCTION 191
THE TECHNOLOGIES OF PLANT GENETIC ENGINEERING 192
   Plant Transformation 192
   Gene Expression 194
   Gene Inactivation 195
GENETIC ENGINEERING FOR ENHANCED QUALITY 196
   Storage Ability of the Fresh Market Tomato 196
   Cold and Freeze Tolerance 198
   Plant Lipids 199
   From Sugars to Starch and Back 201
   Changes in Nutritionally Important Proteins 205
SAFETY AND PUBLIC ACCEPTANCE OF GENETICALLY ENGINEERED
     PLANT PRODUCTS 207
PROSPECTIVES AND CONCLUSION 210

INTRODUCTION

For the purpose of this review I define genetic engineering as the manipulation of plant genomes via the introduction of a characterized DNA segment. The novel genetic information in the introduced DNA will either specify a new protein or alter the expression level of an endogenous gene. This technology differs from somaclonal variation, protoplast fusion, selection of mutants in tissue culture, and other novel technologies, in that, although grouped under plant biotechnology, these techniques are not based on the introduction of defined DNA. I am limiting my review to genetic engineering because it is

191

0199-9885/93/0715-0191$02.00

responsible for the most impressive advances. Readers interested in the other technologies and their products should consult existing reviews (25, 71, 77).

During the last ten years plant genetic engineering has progressed to the point where most important crop species can now be manipulated (29–31). This new and powerful approach can improve agronomic and quality traits such as nutritional value, composition, flavor, and storage ability. The imminent inclusion of an increasing number of genetically engineered plant products in our diet has raised public awareness; people wonder whether this is a safe technology (16, 103). Safety concerns also interest nutrition experts who want to learn the scientific principles of this technology as well as the potential benefits and risks (54). This review is aimed primarily at the latter group although it should help inform the concerned public.

I have divided this review into three sections. In the first, I address the technological basis of plant genetic engineering; I emphasize its potential and limitations and explain the technical details needed to evaluate safety. In the second part, I review the progress made in quality traits improvement of plant products. I have not dealt in depth with agronomic improvements, since a number of exhaustive reviews have already been published on this topic (6, 9, 29–31, 48a, 69, 110). In the last section, I discuss the safety of genetically engineered foods, including agronomic improvements.

THE TECHNOLOGIES OF PLANT GENETIC ENGINEERING

Plant Transformation

Transformation is the process of introducing DNA into the genome of an organism. Although transient transformation can occur, for the purpose of this review I am only concerned with stable, i.e. inheritable, transformation. Three approaches are routinely used to transform crop plants; the chosen method depends on the target crop. The most common plant transformation method, and probably the preferred one because of its simplicity, employs *Agrobacterium tumefaciens* (49). This bacterium is able to introduce a segment of DNA, called the T-DNA (tumor DNA), into the plant nuclear genome. The wild type *Agrobacterium* T-DNA is a plant pathogenic element, since it carries genes for plant hormone production. Expression of these genes induces proliferation of transformed cells and results in tumor growth. However, in T-DNA-based vectors all *Agrobacterium* genes have been removed, leaving only regions of DNA needed in *cis* for transfer and called borders. The borders define the start and end of the T-DNA. The T-DNA used to engineer plants is usually 5 to 10 kb, and up to 50 kb in size, with the capacity to encode 2 to 20 genes. It is borne on a plasmid capable of transfer from *Escherichia coli* to *Agrobacterium*. It typically carries an antibiotic resistance gene for selection of transformed cells, called a selectable marker gene. The most common selectable marker confers resistance to the aminoglycoside antibiotic kanamycin and encodes the bacterial enzyme neomycin phosphotransferase (7, 50). Other genes for resistance to antibiotics or herbicides can be used for selection (22, 109). The T-DNA also carries one or rarely two additional genes. The nature of this additional gene varies according to the objective of each project.

For *Agrobacterium*-mediated plant transformation, a portion of plant material (explant) is exposed to *Agrobacterium* carrying the modified T-DNA. Proliferation and regeneration of the explant cells is induced by hormonal treatment in the presence of an antibiotic toxic to wild-type plant cells. Transformed cells expressing antibiotic resistance have a selective advantage and can regenerate into plants. Integration of the T-DNA in each transformed plant is most often at a single locus (chromosomal location), sometimes at two loci, and rarely at three or more loci (23). At each locus, one or more copies of the T-DNA can be found (68, 114).

Genetic mapping of T-DNAs inserted in plant chromosomes indicates that integration can occur at disparate positions in the genome. It is unlikely, however, that the choice of insertion sites is truly random. Rather, evidence from several laboratories indicates that insertion of the T-DNA occurs preferentially in or near genes, regardless of how much additional DNA is present in the target genome. This evidence is provided by gene fusions obtained by T-DNA insertion (64, 114). To detect gene fusions one places a promoterless reporter gene (a gene encoding an easily assayable product and lacking the region responsible for its transcription) in the proper orientation next to one terminus of the T-DNA. Upon insertion of this type of modified T-DNAs, transcriptional signals in the flanking plant DNA activated the promoterless gene in 25% of the resulting transformants. The frequency of these events is far greater than what would be expected by random insertion. Furthermore, several reports have described inactivation of genes by the T-DNA (114). Therefore, the T-DNA can function as an insertion mutagen.

Most monocotyledonous plants, like maize, wheat, and banana, cannot yet be transformed with *Agrobacterium*-based vectors (49). Instead, alternative methods using naked DNA transformation are necessary (19, 87, 88). Plants can stably incorporate exogenous DNA in their genome. However, since the cell wall prevents the entry of DNA into the cell, it must be bypassed. There are two approaches. In the first, plant cells are treated with cell wall-digesting enzymes to remove the cell wall (77). The resulting protoplasts are susceptible to transformation, although stably transformed cells are rare and must be selected. In addition, they must regenerate to form a plant, a process which is not possible with many species (77). The second approach consists of accelerating DNA-coated microscopic metal particles and impacting target cells at high velocity (90). Since the microprojectiles penetrate cell walls and deposit DNA inside cells, disparate cell types can be targeted. For example, if the microprojectiles hit the growing apex of a plant, a few rare cells will be transformed. If a transformed cell produces pollen or eggs in its lineage, a fraction of the progeny will be transformed. DNA introduced by micro-bombardment or protoplast transformation is inserted in apparently random and usually single loci as a few copies or a single copy per insertion site (15, 33, 91).

The use of T-DNA vectors or protoplast transformation requires that a selectable marker be present in the transforming DNA (49). A few highly regenerable crops, like tobacco, constitute an exception to the rule, in that one can, by patient screening, identify rare transformed plants among those regenerated from *Agrobacterium*-treated explants. The same requirement for a selectable marker applies to techniques where DNA is introduced in cultured regenerable cells. On the other hand, one does not need to incorporate a selectable marker in micro-bombardment of meristems, since this technique generates chimeric plants (composed of transformed and nontransformed tissue) and does not allow selection of the primary transformant (15). One can identify rare transformants among the progeny of bombarded plants by several screening approaches for DNA, RNA, or protein, or, if a selectable marker was used, one has the option to select transformed plants. Genes whose products can be easily assayed are useful detectable markers. A popular one is the *uidA* gene of *E. coli* encoding the enzyme beta-glucuronidase (Gus), which allows a sensitive and convenient histochemical assay (53).

Gene Expression

Plants follow a different developmental strategy from metazoans. Briefly, three basic tissues (epidermal, cortical, and ground) originate from groups of initial cells called meristems (105). The three tissues make up all organs, such as leaves, roots, petals, and fruits. Despite the underlying identities of these tissues, each organ expresses, in addition to a common set, a specialized set of genes. This specialization continues down to the cellular level. For example, unique sets of genes are expressed in specific cell types of anthers (63), the organs producing pollen. Cell specificity is usually conferred by *cis*-acting regulatory regions in the promoter, the region responsible for transcription initiation (8). Accordingly, foreign proteins can be expressed in an organ or in a subset of cells within that organ by fusing the coding region of their genes to a tissue- or cell-specific promoter. Although some transgenes (genes introduced by transformation) can function abnormally, properly expressed ones can be readily identified (60, 67). Transgenes are stable for many generations and probably indefinitely, behaving in every respect as native genes (74). Occasionally, difficulties are encountered in achieving sufficient expression of a foreign protein. The problem can be caused by incompatibility of the mRNA structure, of codon usage, or of the protein itself with the biochemical environment of the plant. For example, it was necessary to change the DNA sequence of a *Bacillus thuringiensis* insecticidal protein gene to achieve an expression level sufficient for insect control (84). Gene expression problems can be very serious. Often, failure to raise the expression level of a transgene prevents progress of a project from proof of concept stage to full implementation.

Gene Inactivation

The ability to remove a protein is as important as the ability to add a new protein. A gene product can be removed by conventional mutagenesis but, although there are examples of crop varieties derived by this approach, this is not always possible because of screening or mutagenesis limitations or because the same protein is encoded by more than one gene.

Genetic engineers working with fungi and mice have developed homology targeted gene inactivation, or replacement, to precisely and completely knock out target genes (26, 57). Regrettably, this approach has yet to be developed for plants although some progress has been described (43, 80, 81). Another technology, antisense RNA, has been successfully used for suppressing gene expression in plants (70). Antisense RNA refers to the transcription product of a gene whose coding region was inverted with respect to the promoter and termination regions and reintroduced into the plant. The antisense RNA molecule is complementary to the true mRNA produced by the endogenous gene. By a yet uncharacterized interaction, possibly the formation of a double-stranded RNA, the endogenous gene is suppressed in a fraction of transformants. A range of suppression phenotypes, from none to very strong, is found in different transformants and is probably caused by the influence of different neighboring chromosomal regions on the transgene. In most antisense RNA experiments reported there was no observable phenotype until expression of the target protein was decreased below 5 to 10% of wild type level. Since such a decrease can only be observed in a fraction of transformants and one is never certain of achieving complete suppression of the target locus, antisense RNA technology requires careful screening of transformed plants and is intrinsically more difficult to interpret than homology-targeted gene inactivation. On the other hand, antisense RNA suppression is effective even when multiple related genes encode identical enzymes.

Another approach to gene inactivation is called cosuppression and its basis is not understood. Simply stated, homology between an introduced gene and a resident one can lead, under certain circumstances, to mutual inactivation of the genes (56, 67). Because of developmental and epigenetic instability and because of its mysterious basis, it has not yet been incorporated in market-targeted genetic engineering.

GENETIC ENGINEERING FOR ENHANCED QUALITY

Storage Ability of the Fresh Market Tomato

All fresh plant products are stored between harvest and consumption. The length of storage and the quality of the product at the end of storage depend on the physiology of the stored produce. Quality loss occurs due to overmaturation or senescence, pathogenesis, and water and temperature stress. Overcoming any of these problems would increase the product's market value and deliver a higher quality product to the consumer. The fresh market tomato is a classic example. Most tomatoes are harvested when hard and green, allowing about two weeks for transit and storage. After maturation, the tomato can only be kept on display shelves for about a week. Premature harvesting prevents the full accumulation of sugars and organic acids, which are important flavor components (40). Controlling some maturation processes or delaying the onset of maturation would allow harvest after the proper amounts of sugars and acids have been reached, prolonged storage, and sale of a better product.

Maturation of the tomato fruit is a dramatic process (10, 40). It initiates with ethylene gas production followed by a number of responses including the production of cell wall-degrading enzymes, the synthesis of lycopene red pigments, increased respiration, the development of a distinct aroma, and numerous other cellular and biochemical changes. Until recently, causal relationships in the process were not known, including whether ethylene was the maturation trigger and what enzymes were responsible for softening of the fruit.

The first attempt to alter the maturation process was via suppression of the enzyme polygalacturonase (95, 99). Polygalacturonase was thought to participate in the softening of the ripe fruit by degrading pectin, a glue-like polymer, in the middle lamella, a structure connecting adjacent cells. Dissolution of the middle lamella would prevent adhesion between cells and result in tissue softening. To engineer a reduced level of polygalacturonase, its coding sequence was fused in an antisense orientation to a strong viral promoter, CaMV 35S, which is expressed in most plant tissues, and introduced into the tomato. Transformants exhibited a range of polygalacturonase levels in their mature fruits from wild type to below detection. There were no phenotypic effects in fruits with polygalacturonase levels higher than 10% of wild type. However, plants with very large reductions in polygalacturonase had lower pectin depolymerization in mature fruit and had juices with greater consistency and viscosity (39, 89). Two different groups disagree on the effect of decreased polygalacturonase on fruit softening. Smith et al (99) reported no difference in compressibility of wild type and engineered fruits exhibiting less than 1% of wild type polygalacturonase activity, while Redenbaugh et al (89) found highly significant reduction in compressibility of engineered tomatoes that had decreased polygalacturonase levels comparable to those reported by Smith et al. The two groups transformed different tomato varieties; this may account for the experimental discrepancies. Both groups, however, agree that the engineered tomato fruits were more resistant to mechanical damage and rotting by molds. There were no other phenotypic effects of polygalacturonase reduction on maturation. These studies indicate that polygalacturonase does not catalyze a crucial step of the maturation process and that softening of the tomato fruits is probably mediated by the concerted action of several cell wall-degrading enzymes, including polygalacturonase. In fact, ectopic expression of polygalacturonase in green, ripening-impaired mutant tomatoes was not sufficient to induce softening (35). While the changes in polygalacturonase-suppressed fruits were not large, they were nonetheless remarkable. Reduced softening and the increase in resistance to mechanical damage and to fungal rot will prove useful in allowing more efficient storage and distribution of vine-ripened tomatoes.

An alternative and possibly more powerful approach to engineering tomatoes for improved storage suppresses a step necessary for the initiation of ripening. The best suppression candidate was ethylene production, since its onset closely precedes ripening. Ethylene is synthesized in two steps from the precursor S-adenosylmethionine (SAM). Conversion of SAM into 1-aminocyclopropane-1-carboxylic acid (ACC) is catalyzed by ACC synthase; conversion of ACC into ethylene is catalyzed by ACC oxidase, also called ethylene-forming enzyme (117). To reduce ethylene one could either suppress a step in the biosynthesis or shunt or quench a biosynthetic intermediate. Oeller et al (79) introduced an antisense ACC synthase gene into tomato and found a transformant in which ACC synthase was severely repressed and ethylene evolution was less than 0.5% of the wild type. This plant's fruits had virtually arrested all major ripening responses including color and aroma development, softening, and increased respiration. Addition of exogenous ethylene restored the ripening process, leading to mature properties indistinguishable from normal fruits. The arrest in maturation demonstrated that ethylene is not merely associated with the onset of ripening but is a necessary signal. An attractive feature of manipulating ethylene production is that by choosing transformants with different levels of ACC synthase suppression it should be possible to obtain maturation phenotypes suitable for different marketing applications.

Hamilton et al (44) obtained suppression of ethylene formation by inhibiting the last step of the pathway. They engineered tomatoes with antisense expression of ACC oxidase and showed that ethylene synthesis and ripening were largely inhibited although not to the level obtained by Oeller et al. Klee et al (61) took a quenching approach to ethylene suppression. They cloned a gene encoding ACC deaminase from a soil *Pseudomonas*. This enzyme degrades ACC to alpha-ketobutyric acid. Plants expressing the ACC deaminase gene were inhibited in ethylene synthesis and ripening. This approach transfers from crop to crop more easily than antisense RNA, since the latter approach needs a high degree of nucleotide sequence similarity between antisense and target genes. Therefore, an antisense DNA construct must contain target sequences from the species to be engineered, thus requiring the isolation of the target gene from each new species chosen for engineering. The ACC deaminase does not have such a requirement and, as long as expression can be achieved in the new species, it will function in any genetic background. An enzyme converting ACC to malonyl-ACC has been described and could be used in a strategy similar to the one employed with ACC deaminase (61).

There are several available approaches to manipulating tomato ripening. The antisense engineering of ACC synthase has produced the most striking laboratory results and, in general, manipulation of ethylene biosynthesis seems more promising than manipulation of downstream responses. However, it is difficult to predict which strategy will impact the consumer market most. Product development and the connected engineering optimization may reveal unexpected strengths or weaknesses. Tomatoes engineered with antisense polygalacturonase are the first genetically engineered product that will appear on the consumer market and are discussed further in the section on safety.

Cold and Freeze Tolerance

Engineered cold or freeze tolerance in plants would apply to three problems. Firstly, losses due to cold and freeze damage often occur in the field in sensitive commodities such as citrus and strawberries. In addition, losses can occur during transport of the harvested product by accidental exposure to cold temperatures. Secondly, refrigeration (above 0 C) could retard spoilage in storage but its use may be prevented by sensitivity of the stored product. Thirdly, ice crystal formation and the resulting loss of membrane and cell wall integrity compromises the quality of some plant products that are marketed frozen.

Cold tolerance is developmentally induced in cold-tolerant plants by a process called acclimation during which several biochemical changes are observed (38, 41, 66). One change, found both in animals and in plants, is the production of organic compounds and antifreeze proteins (45), which lower the freezing temperature of tissue liquids. A well-characterized antifreeze

protein about fifty amino acids in length is produced by the winter flounder
(21, 72) and, interestingly, proteins with related properties have been described
in plants and are good candidates for key factors of acclimation (108). Georges
et al (32) expressed a fusion between chloramphenicol acetyl transferase and
a synthetic gene encoding the flounder antifreeze protein in maize tissue
culture cells. Hightower et al (46) described the transformation of tomato and
tobacco with a chimeric gene encoding a fusion protein between staphylococcal protein A and the winter flounder antifreeze protein. They observed that
tissue extracts, in which this protein could be detected immunologically,
displayed a reduction in ice crystal formation. Transformation of a gene
encoding the native winter flounder protein did not result in a detectable
protein, which suggests that the flounder gene or protein is not compatible
with some aspect of plant biochemistry. In general, expression in plants of
small heterologous proteins, such as the antifreeze protein, seems to be
difficult.

Information on the biochemical basis of cold tolerance is insufficient to
predict whether a single change, namely the introduction of an antifreeze
protein, will increase cold tolerance or keeping quality. A number of changes
are associated with acclimation (18, 34) and some of the genes induced by
acclimation have been cloned (42, 65). However, it is not known whether the
encoded products are synergistic or even necessary for the phenotype.
Mutation or antisense RNA analysis should test the contribution of each
biochemical change to the cold tolerance phenotype. For example, increased
desaturation of membrane lipids is also important to the establishment of cold
tolerance (75).

Plant Lipids

Plant lipids, major components of the human diet, are obtained from storage
organs of different crop plants and vary in composition depending on the
source (100). Even broader variations are found among wild species. Contrary
to what is seen in storage lipids, there is much less variation in membrane
lipids, probably because of functional constraints. The variety of storage oils
in different plants suggests that there should be no intrinsic barrier to changing
the composition of oils by genetic engineering. To do so, one must ascertain
what enzymes determine the composition of an oil. In the last ten years,
biochemical and genetic studies have furthered the understanding of lipid
synthesis, identifying the enzymes most likely to determine composition of a
storage oil (52, 98, 100). The genes encoding these enzymes are being cloned,
manipulated, introduced into oil crops, and expressed in tissues that synthesize
storage lipids.

The length and degree of fatty acid unsaturation in a storage oil triglyceride
determines its suitability for different applications. Fatty acid unsaturation in

storage lipids and membranes can be altered by mutations. Plant breeders are using a mutated sunflower line with storage lipids high in C18:1 fatty acids and a soybean line high in C18:0 (37). However, genetic engineering is preferable to mutation breeding because it would allow introduction of these desirable characteristics in any oil crop.

Knutzon et al (62) engineered a high stearate phenotype in rapeseed by an antisense RNA approach. Stearoyl-acyl carrier protein (stearoyl-ACP) desaturase is a soluble chloroplast enzyme that introduces a double bond in stearoyl-ACP (C18:0), converting it to oleyl-ACP (C18:1). The coding region of the gene (93, 107) for rapeseed desaturase was fused in an inverted position to the napin storage protein promoter and to the promoter of a seed-specific acyl carrier protein gene, and then introduced into rapeseed. The resulting production of antisense desaturase RNA was limited to the cotyledons (embryonic leaves), where both storage proteins and oils accumulate in the seed. The antisense RNA effectively suppressed expression of desaturase and caused the accumulation of stearate in storage triglycerides. Whereas little stearate is found in rapeseed oil, some of the antisense engineered plants had increased stearate up to 40% of total fatty acids with a corresponding decrease in oleate. A smaller but reproducible increase in longer chain fatty acids was also observed. It is not yet known whether this change affected the membrane composition of the seedling. Other changes were noted as well. In *Brassica rapa,* transformants exhibiting the highest repression of desaturase were impaired in total storage lipid accumulation and in germination. In *B. napus,* however, a comparable high stearate phenotype was not affected in germination and total lipid accumulation. These differences could be caused by the amount of desaturase suppression (complete suppression may be undesirable) or by the genetic background of the engineered plant. Whatever the cause, these observations highlight the general need to optimize the expression of engineered genes, as well as the importance of breeding a crop variety subsequent to its engineering. This experiment provided the first example of engineering plant oil composition. The high stearate oil may prove useful for production of margarine and cocoa butter substitutes.

Desaturation beyond the delta 9 position is catalyzed by membrane-bound desaturases that act on lipid esters rather than on ACP or CoA esters. Conversion of monoenoic into dienoic and further into trienoic fatty esters occurs both in the chloroplast and on the endoplasmic reticulum. However, triacylglycerols are mainly derived from the latter pathway. *Arabidopsis* mutants affected in the reticular desaturases result in major decreases not only in polyunsaturated fatty acids in storage lipids but also in the membranes of the whole plant. However, most oilseed crops appear to have seed specific desaturases that, if inactivated by mutations, reduce unsaturated fatty acid only in the storage oil and in the seed membranes without affecting the whole plant. The recent cloning of the fad3 gene (4), encoding the Δ 15 desaturase (C18:2 to C18:3), should allow manipulations of its level in oil crops to engineer low or high C18:3 oils. In combination with the fad2 gene (100), encoding the Δ 12 desaturase (C18:1 to C18:2), the fad3 gene may allow the engineering of C18:1 oils.

Yet another approach to altering the level of unsaturated fatty acids in membrane lipids was demonstrated by Murata et al (75), who introduced and expressed in tobacco the squash and *Arabidopsis* genes for the plastid glycerol-3-phosphate acyltransferase (51). This enzyme is responsible for choosing and esterifying fatty acids to the glycerol backbone. The transferase specificity differs from squash to *Arabidopsis* to tobacco. Overexpression of the squash enzyme in tobacco resulted in a large decrease in unsaturated fatty acids, while overexpression of the *Arabidopsis* enzyme resulted in a small but significant increase in the level of unsaturated fatty acids in membrane lipids and an associated increase in cold tolerance. Engineering of different transferases by itself, or in combination with an altered desaturation pathway, is a promising approach to altering storage oils composition.

Another key characteristic of fatty acids is their length, which varies from C8 to C24 in the storage lipids of different species. The enzymatic mechanism responsible for short-chain fatty-acid production was recently elucidated. Pollard et al (85) and Davies et al (20) demonstrated the presence in developing California bay seed of a thioesterase specific for C12:0 ACP esters. The appearance of the thioesterase coincided with the onset of accumulation of C10 and C12 acyl groups in storage triglycerides. Voelker et al (112) proved that this thioesterase is responsible for the accumulation of short-chain fatty acids in triglycerides by cloning the gene and expressing it in the developing seed of *Arabidopsis* where it caused the accumulation of C12 storage lipids. While the interest in a C12-rich oil is mainly for chemical feed stock, it would also have applications in confectionery production. The isolation and engineering of thioesterases with different specificities from wild plants promises to provide broad flexibility in the design of commercial oils with various chain length fatty acids.

The field of storage lipid modification via the engineering of the fatty acid biosynthesis enzymes promises to be a very fertile one that will contribute to production of healthier foods as well as to production of chemical feed stocks (76).

From Sugars to Starch and Back

Sugars and starches are the direct products of photosynthesis and constitute major flavor and nutritional components of foods. Sugar is produced from assimilated CO_2 and stored temporarily as starch in leaf chloroplasts (the source). At night, starch is depolymerized and sugars are translocated to the cytoplasm where sucrose is synthesized and exported through a vascular tissue called phloem to storage organs (the sink) which, depending on the plant, could be fruits, seeds, tubers, or roots. Storage organs convert sucrose to starch, or, in the case of grasses, into fructans (86).

The path of carbon interconversion from sugars to starch and vice versa and its interorgan transport is regulated at several steps (Figure 1). Plant physiologists formulated models explaining the role of different enzymes in the physiological network of sugar distribution from source to sink organs (47). Molecular biologists have recently tested these models by manipulating the properties and expression of the involved enzymes, in most cases confirming their proposed role (102). An unexpected finding is that plants are more tolerant than expected of altered sugar balances.

There are two major aims in manipulating sugars and starches: changes in

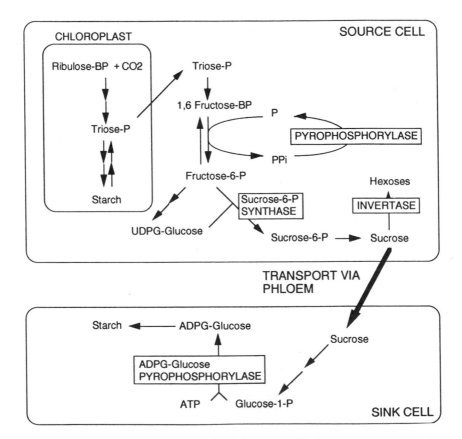

Figure 1   Interconversion and transport of assimilated carbon in plants.

concentration and changes in composition. I first review the changes in concentration.

Can sugars be increased in source tissues? Scientists reasoned that shifting the equilibrium of carbon flux toward sucrose synthesis in the source may result in an overall increase of sugars. Sucrose-P synthase converts UDPG-glucose to sucrose-6-phosphate, the direct precursor of sucrose, and it is tightly regulated in wild-type plants. Worrell et al (116) expressed the maize sucrose-P synthase gene in tomato leaves, doubling the total enzyme activity. As a result, in the engineered plants leaf starch was reduced and the sucrose level doubled. Sonnewald (101) decreased the cytosolic level of pyrophosphate in tobacco and potato leaves by expressing the *E. coli* inorganic pyro-phophatase gene. Since PPi is generated during the conversion of fructose-1,6-bisP to fructose-6P, it was hoped that by decreasing PPi one could shift the reaction equilibrium toward fructose-6P and, ultimately, sucrose. Indeed, both tobacco and potato showed an increased sugar/starch ratio but they differed in how it was achieved. In tobacco, sucrose increased up to 12-fold, glucose up to 68-fold, and starch up to 8-fold. In potato, sucrose increased 2-fold and starch decreased.

Can starch be increased in source organs? Presumably, this could be achieved by interrupting the flow of sucrose out of the leaf. Von Schaewen et al (113) and Dickinson et al (24) expressed a yeast invertase in cell walls of tobacco and tomato leaves and found that it strongly reduced the export of sucrose and that it increased starch concentration in the leaves. Thus, sucrose was the main mobile form of photosynthate and its degradation to exoses prevented its transport to sink organs.

Can starch be increased in sink organs? Starch is synthesized using ADP-glucose as a substrate. The synthesis of ADP-glucose, catalyzed by ADP-glucose pyrophosphorylase, is believed to be a rate-limiting step. Decreasing the expression of ADPG pyrophosphorylase in potato tuber by antisense RNA expression diminished the sink strength of these organs and starch accumulation (73). A mutant *E. coli* ADPG pyrophosphorylase is not subject to allosteric regulation by inorganic phosphate, contrary to the plant enzyme. Expression of an amyloplast-targeted *E. coli* pyrophosphorylase in potato tubers resulted in a dry matter increase, mostly starch, of 4% (102a). These experiments, taken together, illustrate how the source-sink relationships within a plant can be manipulated by acting at different steps of a synthetic and transport pathway. A few of the phenotypes described were associated with changes in growth habit or chlorophyll accumulation and may not be compatible with agricultural productivity. However, it is conceivable that these approaches will evolve in reliable and advantageous alterations of sugars and starch content in key crops.

Changes in composition of storage carbon could affect many characteristics of foods, including flavor and processing qualities. Changes as simple as the branching pattern of starch have important effects. There are two types of starch synthases in plants: One synthesizes a linear starch polymer (amylose) while the other synthesizes the branched polymer (amylopectin). Visser et al (111) repressed synthesis of the granule-bound starch synthase in potato by antisense RNA technology. Since this synthase is responsible for the synthesis of amylose, antisense engineered potato accumulated amylopectin. Knockout of amylose synthesis had already been achieved by mutation. However, antisense engineering established that manipulation of the two synthases should be a productive approach to obtaining variable ratios of linear to branched starch.

Changes in compositions caused by the synthesis of other polymers are also possible by introducing foreign enzymes. Bacteria produce a staggering variety of carbohydrate polymers, some of which are commonly used in food processing. Oakes et al (78) engineered production of cyclodextrins in potato tubers by expressing cyclodextrin glycosyltransferase from *Klebsiella*. Although the enzyme level was undetectable by direct assays, a measurable amount of cyclodextrins was found in the engineered tubers. Potato, being the quintessential starch crop, is a major target of genetic engineering manipulations. The prospects and potential for this important crop were recently reviewed by Vayda & Belknap (110).

A third type of composition change was described by Pen et al (82), who engineered *Bacillus licheniformis* α-amylase accumulation in the cell wall of tobacco. Since starch accumulates inside the cell, the amylase was physically separated from its substrate during the life of the plant. Contact between amylase and starch could be achieved by disrupting cell integrity, as when grinding the tissue, and starch depolymerization would occur. Compartmentation of an enzyme away from its substrate would be an effective strategy to prevent a deleterious reaction from taking place during plant growth and to initiate it during processing.

A last approach related to modifying sugar composition is to express sweet proteins in plants. Thaumatin and monellin are plant proteins that bind to taste receptors and induce a sweet response at very low concentrations. The genes for these proteins have been expressed in potato and tomato and are reported to increase the sweetness of the test tissues when they accumulated at levels of 10^{-6} to 10^{-7} M (10 to 50 μg per gram fresh weight) (83, 115). While these works demonstrate the feasibility of expressing sweet proteins in heterologous hosts, it is not yet clear which plant product would be the best target for sweetening. Another indirect approach to sweetening is the removal of bitter compounds. Citrus products such as grapefruit juice could be sweetened by the removal of flavanone glucosides, compounds responsible for bitterness.

This objective could be achieved by antisense suppression of a rhamno-syltransferase involved in flavanone glucosides synthesis (5).

Changes in Nutritionally Important Proteins

Plants storage compounds are oils, carbohydrates, and proteins. The latter class of compounds are especially important because human nutrition requires a balanced source of amino acids and the amino acid balance of many plant products is unsatisfactory. Many crops have storage proteins with unbalanced amino acids content. A second problem is the presence of antinutritional proteins in many seeds, a set of digestive enzyme inhibitors that probably evolved to deter herbivores (92). Ameliorating the nutritional quality of crops would thus involve three possible strategies (28, 97): expressing a desirable, heterologous storage protein; increasing the level of a desirable, but little expressed, endogenous protein; and suppressing the expression of antinutritional proteins.

An example of the first strategy is the cloning and expression in heterologous species of a sulfur-rich storage protein from Brazil nut (104). The Brazil nut protein contains 18% methionine and 8% cysteine and was expressed in tobacco and rapeseed seeds. In both species it accumulated to significant levels, increasing the total sulfur-containing amino acids by 300 and 30% respectively. In addition, Altenbach et al (2, 3) found that the protein was properly processed in both heterologous species from an 18,000 mol wt precursor to a 9,000 and 3,000 mol wt subunit heterodimer. The genetics and biochemistry of other storage proteins that are good candidates for engineering have been described (13, 14, 28, 59, 96).

A gene encoding a storage protein could also be modified by adding synthetic regions of DNA specifying peptides rich in desirable amino acids. Hoffman et al expressed a phaseolin gene artifically enriched in methionine residues in tobacco (48). Although this gene's mRNA was as abundant in tobacco as the mRNA of an unaltered phaseolin gene, the amount of accumulated methionine-rich phaseolin was much lower than that of native phaseolin. The engineered methionine-rich phaseolin appeared to be properly processed and was assembled in trimers. The reduced accumulation of the engineered protein must have been due to problems in a posttranscriptional process, such as transport, or protein turnover. This result emphasizes the need to understand the biochemistry of storage protein accumulation.

Could translation of a storage protein rich in a given amino acid be limited by the availability of that amino acid within the cell? While such an instance has not been reported, it may be possible to increase the synthesis of an amino acid by the engineering of a rate-limiting enzyme. For example, in a tobacco mutant lysine overproduction was caused by a lysine-insensitive dihydropicolinate synthase. Inspired by this observation, genetic engineers duplicated this situation by expressing in plant chloroplasts a bacterial dihydropicolinate synthase with reduced lysine feedback sensitivity and obtaining a 40-fold increase in free lysine (94).

A summary of all the discussed traits is presented in Table 1.

Table 1   Examples of genetically engineered quality traits in plants

Gene product manipulated[a]	Method[b]	Source[c]	Trait	Reference
Polygalacturonase	Antisense		Delayed softening	39, 89, 99
ACC synthase	Antisense		Delayed ripening	79
ACC oxidase	Antisense		Delayed ripening	44
ACC deaminase	Introduction	*Pseudomonas*	Delayed ripening	61
Antifreeze protein	Introduction	Flounder	Freeze tolerance	32, 46
Stearoyl-ACP desaturase	Antisense		High stearate oils	62
Δ15 desaturase[d]	Antisense or over-expression		Low or high poly-unsaturated oils	4
Glycerol-3-P acyltransferase	Introduction	Plant spp.	Low or high poly-unsaturated oils	75
Acyl-ACP thioesterase	Introduction	Bay	High laurate oils	112
Sucrose-P synthase	Introduction	Maize	Increased sugars	116
Pyrophosphatase	Introduction	*E. coli*	Increased sugars	101
Invertase	Introduction	Yeast	Increased starch	24, 113
ADPG pyrophosphorylase	Introduction	*E. coli*	Increased starch	102a
Starch synthase (granule)	Antisense		Increased amylopectin	111
Cyclodextrin glycosyl-transferase	Introduction	*Klebsiella*	Cyclodextrin synthesis	78
Alpha-amylase	Introduction	*Bacillus*	Starch depolymerization	82
Thaumatin, monellin	Introduction	Plant spp.	Sweetness	83, 115
S-rich storage protein	Introduction	Brazil nut	Increased S-amino acids	104
Dihydropicolinate synthase	Introduction	*E. coli*	Increased soluble lysine	94

[a] These examples range from projects at an early proof-of-concept phase to projects undergoing regulatory scrutiny in preparation for commercialization.
[b] Antisense mRNA production; introduction of a gene from another organism; overexpression of an existing gene.
[c] Source of the introduced gene.
[d] The fad3 gene has not been yet used to alter polyunsaturated fatty acids by genetic engineering, but it is included here because its potential appears high.

SAFETY AND PUBLIC ACCEPTANCE OF GENETICALLY ENGINEERED PLANT PRODUCTS

Most genetic engineering experiments to date have added three genetic components to the target plant: first, a novel DNA is inserted in the host genome; second, this DNA carries a selectable marker; third, the DNA carries an additional gene of various nature aimed at modifying a specific plant property. I will address the safety of each one of these components.

What risk is entailed by the insertion of a novel DNA in the host genome? This event could inactivate a resident gene. Upon self-fertilization, a mutated allele (the knocked-out gene) would become homozygous and, if the gene were to be active, not redundant and if it contributed to a relevant cellular function, it would cause a change in phenotype. That this change could result in a metabolic alteration or a pathway deregulation leading to a toxic product accumulating in harvested plant parts is possible, but extremely unlikely. Assuming that every insertion inactivates a gene and that there are 50,000 genes in a plant (58) the frequency of this event would be 1/50,000. This scenario is not a relevant risk factor for several reasons. First, a mutation rate of 1/50,000 is not different from the rate of spontaneous mutations (106), many of which are caused by plant transposable elements. Second, mutation breeding, a commonly used strategy in development of conventional varieties, is more likely to introduce deleterious mutations of this type because mutagenesis achieves mutation rates between 1/1000 to 1/10,000. Third, accumulation of a toxic product would most likely be detected during varietal testing.

A selectable marker is often a necessity for the isolation of transformants. The selectable marker gene typically encodes an antibiotic detoxifying enzyme of bacterial origin. Flavell et al (27) argued that the kanamycin detoxifying protein, encoded by the most common marker gene, is safe for human consumption, does not compromise the efficacy of oral kanamycin in humans, and that the probability that its gene may be transferred from plants to bacteria or any other organism is irrelevant. Their arguments were based on well-documented and scientifically sound evidence submitted by Calgene Inc. representatives in communications to the Foods and Drug Administration (FDA) (89). Flavell et al (27) concluded that regulations requiring the removal of the selectable marker gene from varieties destined to the market would be unjustified and would unduly complicate, or in some cases prevent, the production of such varieties. Bryant & Leather (12) agreed that the kanamycin resistance marker is safe. They concluded, however, that, for the sake of public perception, it should be removed. A technique that is capable of achieving such removal has been described by Dale & Ow (17). This technique is laborious in that it requires specific crosses to be made and it is not yet applicable to vegetatively propagated crops nor to selectable markers that are not engineered with specific recombination-target regions. I have concluded that there is no scientific argument justifying concerns for the safety of commonly used selectable markers.

The process of modifying a trait involves the introduction of a gene that expresses a protein or an antisense RNA. The safety of either type of modification can be assessed. An example of this process is represented by the documentation submitted to FDA by Calgene Inc. in support of the safety of the Flavr Savr[TM] Tomato (89). This fruit is the result of antisense engineering for suppression of the softening enzyme polygalacturonase. In general, one first addresses the safety of the protein being expressed: Is it toxic or allergenic? Second, does the protein directly or indirectly cause the formation of any toxic product? The direct products of a given enzyme activity are known and can be evaluated by standard procedures. Many crops have toxic products in nonconsumed plant parts such as in tomato and potato leaves. Other crops like cassava and beans have toxic products in consumed plant parts, but the toxic components are removed or inactivated by processing. Could the expression, or suppression, of a given gene indirectly induce enhanced accumulation of these compounds? While this is unlikely, it can easily be tested. In the case of tomato, the amount of toxic tomatine in genetically engineered fruits was shown to be no different than the amount found in common varieties.

Genetic engineers have introduced into crops genes conferring herbicide and pest resistance. The products of these genes will often be present in consumed plant organs. The safety of these modifications is also an important issue.

Genes for herbicide resistance function by either of two mechanisms (9, 69). They either encode altered enzyme targets of herbicide action, such as an altered EPSP synthase conferring tolerance to glyphosate or an altered acetolactate synthase conferring tolerance to sulfonylureas, or they encode a detoxifying enzyme, such as a nitrilase conferring tolerance to bromoxynil or an acetyl transferase conferring tolerance to gluphosinate. The toxicological effects of novel enzymes introduced in the plant can be addressed by processes similar to those used with neomycin phosphotransferase. The expression level of these proteins is usually below a tenth of one percent of the total soluble proteins. They either catalyze a normal reaction of plant metabolism or a new one where they only recognize the herbicide as a substrate. The most significant factor in their safety assessment is not the presence of a new enzyme, but rather the fate and concentration of the applied herbicide residues, and, with detoxifying enzymes, the toxicological properties of the reaction product. Thus, safety assessment follows the lines of herbicide certification. Genetically engineered herbicide tolerance will allow the use of broad range and effective herbicides when multiple applications of less effective herbicides would otherwise have been used, thereby reducing the chemical input in crop production.

Expressing viral coat protein genes in plants conferred resistance to several viral diseases (1, 6). In one case, expression of a portion of the viral replicase also effectively controlled tobacco mosaic virus (36). Many plant products sold on the consumer market are infected by plant viruses, and in some cases the titer of virus particles is very high. Thus, different coat proteins have been part of the human diet since evolutionary times and the risk to the consumer from coat protein-engineered plants seems to be very low.

A commonly used natural insecticide consists of *Bacillus thuringiensis* spores containing crystal proteins toxic to lepidopterans and certain cole-opterans (48a). This insecticide is probably one of the safest available, since the bacterial toxin, which interacts with an intestinal receptor in the insect, is very specific and nontoxic to humans. In the USA, its application is allowed up to harvest time. Expressing *Bacillus thuringiensis* crystal protein genes in plants resulted in resistance to certain insect pests. Given the toxicological properties of the *B. thuringiensis* protein and the expression level in plants, it seems likely that no adverse effects will be found. Scientists are searching for fungicidal and bactericidal proteins in plants and microbes: Both bean (11) and bacterial chitinase (55) expressed in plants conferred tolerance to the fungal pathogens *Rhizoctonia* and *Alternaria,* respectively. In the future, we can expect the expression of novel proteins with pesticidal properties to substitute for most pesticides.

In conclusion, I believe that the risk posed by the majority of genetic alterations is very low. Alterations that pose a significant risk can be rapidly identified, critically examined by the process exemplified by the Flavr Savr™ document, and subjected to a rigid risk versus benefit analysis.

Public perception and acceptance of plant genetic engineering is a fundamental issue. It has its roots in the relationship between scientists and society at large and is going to influence this relationship in the future. A portion of the public mistrusts genetic engineering. Their arguments originate from a philosophy that wants to protect the genetic integrity of nature's products, or from mistrust of technology and of the safety assurances of scientists, or from the dislike of "mingling" animal and bacterial proteins in plant food products. Genetic engineers have argued that manipulations of the genes of crops and domesticated animals has been carried out since prehistoric times, that genetic engineering can actually decrease the use of hazardous chemicals on foods, and that foreign proteins in quantities exceeding those made possible by genetic engineering are ingested daily with plant products colonized by a diverse and variable microbial flora.

A productive resolution of these concerns can only be achieved by frank and respectful communication among all involved parties.

PROSPECTIVES AND CONCLUSION

I have described advances made by plant genetic engineering in food and nutrition. The progress in this area has been substantial and suggests that any trait known to be conferred by one or few genes can be manipulated by introducing a foreign or modified gene, or by repressing an endogenous gene. I have refrained from compiling a long list of traits that are candidates for modification, because, given the theoretical premises above, the reader can easily identify such opportunities. While this is conceptually simple, it is certainly not easy to identify the combination of trait, gene, and market potential that will result in a successful new product. The reader may have been impressed by the variety of projects aimed at modifying plants for food and nutritional value. However, very few of the alterations described above will lead to commercialized products, at least in their present version.

Who will take the lead in developing new food products via quality manipulations? Genetic engineering companies are now painfully aware of the costs involved in inventing, developing, and testing new plant traits. Agronomic traits impact the seed market while quality traits address the much larger consumer market. The latter type of engineering is thus potentially more profitable and is attracting the attention of the industry (29). Public research institutions are also attracted to the modification of quality traits (100) and, while profitability will be important for them as well, they will clearly pursue the option of developing useful, but not necessarily profitable, quality traits.

An important component determining what traits will be developed is public response. Some people believe that genetic engineering is too risky to pursue, others feel that the benefits must clearly outweigh the risks. Some genetic engineering programs, such as the use of bovine growth hormone for enhanced milk production, have become very controversial because the benefits to society at large appear to be less significant than the benefits to the marketers. Developing novel products that clearly benefit the consumer is the best approach to ensure that this technology, which scientists believe is safe, will be accepted and understood by the public. Many of the projects described here would fit these parameters.

ACKNOWLEDGMENTS

I thank Lynnette Comai and Rene Fester for suggestions on manuscript style and Charlene Martinsen-Brannon for reviewing the manuscript. I also thank the following individuals for contributing useful information: John Browse, Chris Somerville, Jean Kridl, Toni Voelker, Charles Gasser, William Hiatt, and Martin Chrispeels.

Literature Cited

1. Abel, P. P., Nelson, R. S., De, B., Hoffmann, N., Rogers, S. G., et al. 1986. Delay of disease development in transgenic plants that express the tobacco mosaic virus coat protein gene. *Science* 232: 738–43
2. Altenbach, S. B., Kuo, C. C., Staraci, L. C., Pearson, K. W., Wainwright, C., et al. 1992. Accumulation of a Brazil nut albumin in seeds of transgenic canola results in enhanced levels of seed protein methionine. *Plant Mol. Biol.* 18:235–45
3. Altenbach, S. B., Pearson, K. W., Meeker, G., Staraci, L. C., Sun, S. M. 1989. Enhancement of the methionine content of seed proteins by the expression of a chimeric gene encoding a methionine-rich protein in transgenic plants. *Plant Mol. Biol.* 13:513–22
4. Arondel, V., Lemieux, B., Hwang, I., Gibson, S., Goodman, H., et al. 1992. Map-based cloning of a gene controlling omega-3 desaturation in *Arabidopsis. Science* 258:1353–55
5. Bar, P. M., Lewinsohn, E., Fluhr, R., Gressel, J. 1991. UDP-rhamnose: flavanone-7-O-glucoside-2'-O-rhamnosyltransferase. Purification and characterization of an enzyme catalyzing the production of bitter compounds in citrus. *J. Biol. Chem.* 266:20953–59
6. Beachy, R. N., Loesch-Fries, S., Tumer, N. E. 1990. Coat protein-mediated resistance against virus infection. *Annu. Rev. Phytopathol.* 28:738–43
7. Beck, E., Ludwig, G., Auerswald, E. A., Reiss, B., Schaller, H. 1982. Nucleotide sequence and exact localization of the neomycin phosphotransferase gene from transposon Tn5. *Gene* 19: 327–36
8. Benfey, P. N., Chua, N-H. 1989. Regulated genes in transgenic plants. *Science* 244:174–88
9. Botterman, J., Leemans, J. 1988. Engineering herbicide resistance in plants. *Trends Genet.* 4:219–22
10. Brady, C. F. 1987. Fruit ripening. *Annu. Rev. Plant Physiol.* 38:155–78
11. Broglie, K., Chet, I., Holliday, M., Cressman, R., Biddle, P., et al. 1991. Transgenic plants with enhanced resis-

tance of the fungal pathogen. *Rhizoctonia solani. Science* 254:1194–97
12. Bryant, J., Leather, S. 1992. Removal of selectable marker genes from transgenic plants: needless sophistication or social necessity. *Trends Biotech.* 10: In press
13. Ceriotti, A., Pedrazzini, E., Fabbrini, M. S., Zoppe, M., Bollini, R., et al. 1991. Expression of the wild-type and mutated vacuolar storage protein phaseolin in *Xenopus* oocytes reveals relationships between assembly and intracellular transport. *Eur. J. Biochem.* 202:959–68
14. Chee, P. P., Slightom, J. L. 1991. Molecular biology of legume vicilin-type seed storage protein genes. *Subcell. Biochem.* 17:31–52
15. Christou, P. 1992. Genetic transformation of crop plants using microprojectile bombardment. *Plant J.* 2:275–81
16. Council on Scientific Affairs. 1991. Biotechnology and the American agricultural industry. *J. Am. Med. Assoc.* 265:1429–36
17. Dale, E. C., Ow, D. W. 1991. Gene transfer with subsequent removal of the selection gene from the host genome. *Proc. Natl. Acad. Sci. USA* 88:10558–62
18. Danyluk, J., Sarhan, F. 1990. Differential mRNA transcription during the induction of freezing tolerance in spring and winter wheat. *Plant Cell Physiol.* 31:609–19
19. Davey, M. R., Rech, E. L., Mulligan, B. J. 1989. Direct DNA transfer to plant cells. *Plant Mol. Biol.* 13:273–85
20. Davies, H. M., Anderson, L., Fan, C., Hawkins, D. J. 1991. Developmental induction, purification, and further characterization of 12:0-ACP thioesterase from immature cotyledons of *Umbellularia californica. Arch. Biochem. Biophys.* 290:37–45
21. Davies, P. L., Roach, A. H., Hew, C. L. 1982. DNA sequence coding for an antifreeze protein precursor from winter flounder. *Proc. Natl. Acad. Sci. USA* 79:335–39
22. De Block, M., De Brouwer, D., Ten-

ning, P. 1989. Transformation of *Brassica napus* and *Brassica oleracea* using *Agrobacterium tumefaciens* and the expression of the bar and neo genes in the transgenic plants. *Plant Physiol.* 91:694–701

23. Deroles, S. C., Gardner, R. C. 1988. Expression and inheritance of kanamycin resistance in a large number of transgenic petunias generated by *Agrobacterium*-mediated transformation. *Plant Mol. Biol.* 11:355–64

24. Dickinson, S., Altabella, T., Chrispeels, M. 1991. Slow growth phenotype of transgenic tomato expressing apoplastic invertase. *Plant Physiol.* 95: 420–25

25. Evans, D. A. 1989. Somaclonal variation—genetic basis and breeding applications. *Trends Genet.* 5:46–50

26. Fincham, J. R. 1989. Transformation in fungi. *Microbiol. Rev.* 53:148–70

27. Flavell, R. B., Dart, E., Fuchs, R. L., Fraley, R. T. 1992. Selectable marker genes: safe for plants? *Bio-Technology* 10:141–44

28. Flavell, R. B., Payne, P. I. Thompson, R. D., Law, C. N. 1988. Strategies for the improvement of wheat-grain quality using molecular genetics. In *Biotechnology of Higher Plants*, ed. G. E. Russell, pp. 159–75. Dorset: Intercept

29. Fraley, R. T. 1992. Sustaining the food supply. *Bio-Technology*, 10:40–43

30. Gasser, C. S. 1992. Transgenic crops. *Sci. Am.* 266:62–69

31. Gasser, C. S., Fraley, R. T. 1989. Genetically engineered plants for crop improvement. *Science* 244:1293–99

32. Georges, F., Saleem, M., Cutler, A. J. 1990. Design and cloning of a synthetic gene for the flounder antifreeze protein and its expression in plant cells. *Gene* 91:159–65

33. Gharti-Chhetri, G. B., Cherdshewasart, W., Dewulf, J., Paszkowski, J., Jacobs, M., et al. 1990. Hybrid genes in the analysis of transformation conditions. 3. Temporal/spatial fate of NPTII gene integration, its inheritance and factors affecting these processes in *Nicotiana plumbaginifolia*. *Plant Mol. Biol.* 14:687–96

34. Gilmour, S. J., Hajela, R. K., Thomashow, M. F. 1988. Cold acclimation in *Arabidopsis* thaliana. *Plant Physiol.* 87:745–50

35. Giovannoni, J. J., Della Penna, D., Bennett, A. B., Fischer, R. L. 1989. Expression of chimeric polygalacturonase gene in transgenic rin (ripening inhibitor) tomato fruit results in poly-uronide degradation but not fruit softening. *Plant Cell* 1:53–63

36. Golemboski, D. B., Lomonosoff, G. P., Zaitlin, M. 1990. Plants transformed with a tobacco mosaic nonstructural gene sequence are resistant to the virus. *Proc. Natl. Acad. Sci. USA* 87:6311–15

37. Graef, G. L., Fehr, W. R., Hammond, E. G. 1985. *Crop Sci.* 25:1076–79

38. Graham, D., Patterson, B. D. 1982. Responses of plants to low, nonfreezing temperatures: proteins, metabolism, and acclimation. *Annu. Rev. Plant Physiol.*, 33:347–72

39. Gray, J., Picton, S., Shabbeer, J. Schuch, W., Grierson, D. 1992. Molecular biology of fruit ripening and its manipulation with antisense genes. *Plant Mol. Biol.* 19:69–87

40. Grierson, D., Kader, A. A. 1986. Fruit ripening and quality. In *The Tomato Crop*, ed. J. G. Atherton, J. Rudich, pp. 241–80. London: Chapman & Hall

41. Guy, C. L. 1990. Cold acclimation and freezing stress tolerance: role of protein metabolism. *Annu. Rev. Plant Physiol. Plant Mol. Biol.* 41:187–223

42. Hajela, R. K., Horvath, D. P., Gilmour, S. J., Thomashow, M. F. 1990. Molecular cloning and expression of cor (cold regulated) genes in *Arabidopsis* thaliana. *Plant Physiol.* 93:1246–52

43. Halfter, U., Morris, P. C., Willmitzer, L. 1992. Gene targeting in *Arabidopsis* thaliana. *Mol. Gen. Genet.* 231:186–93

44. Hamilton, A. J., Bouzayen, M., Grierson, D. 1991. Identification of a tomato gene for the ethylene-forming enzyme by expression in yeast. *Proc. Natl. Acad. Sci. USA* 88:7434–37

45. Hew, C. L., Yang, D. S. 1992. Protein interaction with ice. *Eur. J. Biochem.* 203:33–42

46. Hightower, R., Baden, C., Penzes, E., Lund, P., Dunsmuir, P. 1991. Expression of antifreeze proteins in transgenic plants. *Plant Mol. Biol.* 17:1013–21

47. Ho, L. C. 1988. Metabolism and compartmentation of imported sugars in sink organs in relation to sink strength. *Annu. Rev. Plant Physiol. Plant Mol. Biol.* 39:355–78

48. Hoffman, L. M., Donaldson, D. D., Herman, E. M. 1988. A modified storage protein is synthesized, processed, and degraded in the seeds of transgenic plants. *Plant Mol. Biol.* 11: 717–29

48a. Hofte, H., Whiteley, H. R. 1989. Insecticidal crystal proteins of *Bacillus thuringiensis*. *Microbiol. Rev.* 53:245–55

49. Hooykaas, P. J., Schilperoort, R. A.

1992. *Agrobacterium* and plant genetic engineering. *Plant Mol. Biol.* 19:15–38

50. Horsch, R. B., Fry, J. E., Hoffman, N. L., Eichholtz, D., Rogers, S. G., et al. 1985. A simple and general method for transferring genes into plants. *Science* 227:1229–31

51. Ishizaki, O., Nishida, I., Agata, K., Eguchi, G., Murata, M. 1988. Cloning and nucleotide sequence of cDNA for the plastid glycerol-3-phosphate acyltransferase from squash. *FEBS Lett.* 238:424–30

52. James, D. W., Dooner, H. K. 1991. Novel seed lipid phenotypes in combinations of mutants altered in fatty acid biosynthesis in *Arabidopsis*. *Theor. Appl. Genet.* 82:409–12

53. Jefferson, R. A., Kavanagh, T. A., Bevan, M. W. 1987. Gus fusions: beta-glucuronidase as a sensitive and versatile gene fusion marker in higher plants. *EMBO J.* 6:3901–7

54. Jones, D. D. 1988. Food safety aspects of gene transfer in plants and animal: pigs, potatoes, and pharmaceuticals. *Food Drug Cosmet. Law J.* 43:351–68

55. Jones, J., Dean, C., Gidoni, D., Gilbert, D., Bondnutter, D., et al. 1988. Expression of bacterial chitinase protein in tobacco leaves using two photosynthetic gene promoters. *Mol. Gen. Genet.* 212:536–42

56. Jorgensen, R. 1990. Altered gene expression in plants due to trans interactions between homologous genes. *Trends Biotechnol.* 8:340–44

57. Joyner, A. L. 1991. Gene targeting and gene trap screens using embryonic stem cells: new approaches to mammalian development. *Bioessays* 13:649–56

58. Juergens, G., Mayer, U., Torres-Ruiz, R. A., Berleth, T., Misera, S. 1991. Genetic analysis of pattern formation in the *Arabidopsis* embryo. *Dev. Suppl.* 1:27–38

59. Kho, C. J., de Lumen, B. O. 1988. Identification and isolation of methionine-cysteine rich proteins in soybean seed. *Plant Foods Hum. Nutr.* 38:287–96

60. Kilby, N. J., Leyser, H. M. O., Furner, I. J. 1992. Promoter methylation and progressive transgene inactivation in *Arabidopsis*. *Plant Mol. Biol.* 20:103–12

61. Klee, H. J., Hayford, M. B., Kretzmer, K. A., Barry, G. F., Kishore, G. M. 1991. Control of ethylene synthesis by expression of a bacterial enzyme in transgenic tomato plants. *Plant Cell* 3:1187–93

62. Knutzon, D. S., Thompson, G. A., Radke, S. E., Johnson, W. B., Knauf, V. C. et al. 1992. Modification of *Brassica* seed oil by antisense expression of a stearoyl-acyl carrier protein desaturase gene. *Proc. Natl. Acad. Sci. USA* 89:2624–28

63. Koltunow, A. M., Truettner, J., Cox, K. H., Wallroth, M., Goldberg, R. B. 1990. Different temporal and spatial gene expression patterns occur during anther development. *Plant Cell* 2:1201–24

64. Koncz, C., Martini, N., Mayerhofer, R., Koncz, K. Z., Korber, H., et al. 1989. High-frequency T-DNA-mediated gene tagging in plants. *Proc. Natl. Acad. Sci. USA* 86:8467–71

65. Kurkela, S., Franck, M. 1990. Cloning and characterization of a cold- and ABA-inducible *Arabidopsis* gene. *Plant Mol. Biol.* 15:137–44

66. Li, P. H. 1987. *Plant Cold Hardiness*. New York: Liss. 381 pp.

67. Matzke, M. A., Matzke, A. 1990. Gene interactions and epigenetic variation in transgenic plants. *Dev. Genet.* 11:214–33

68. Mayerhofer, R., Koncz, K. Z., Nawrath, C., Bakkeren, G., Crameri, A., et al. 1991. T-DNA integration: a mode of illegitimate recombination in plants. *EMBO J.* 10:697–704

69. Mazur, B. J. 1989. The development of herbicide resistant crops. *Annu. Rev. Plant Physiol. Plant Mol. Biol.* 40:441–70

70. Mol, J. N., van den Krol, A. R., van Tunen, A. J., van Blokland, R., de Lange, P., et al. 1990. Regulation of plant gene expression by antisense RNA. *FEBS Lett.* 268:427–30

71. Morrison, R. A., Evans, D. A., Fan, Z. 1991. Haploid plants from tissue culture. Application in crop improvement, *Subcell. Biochem.* 17:53–72

72. Mueller, G. M., McKown, R. L., Corotto, L. V., Hague, C., Warren, G. J. 1991. Inhibition of recrystallization in ice by chimeric proteins containing antifreeze domains. *J. Biol. Chem.* 266:7339–44

73. Mueller-Roeber, B., Sonnewald, U., Willmitzer, L. 1992. Inhibition of ADP-glucose pyrophosphorilase in transgenic potatoes leads to sugar-storing tubers and influences tuber formation and expression of tuber storage proteins. *EMBO J.* 11:1229–38

74. Muller, A. J., Mendel, R. R., Schiemann, J., Simoens, C., Inz'e, D. 1987. High meiotic stability of a foreign gene introduced into tobacco by *Agro-*

bacterium-mediated transformation. *Mol. Gen. Genet.* 207:171–75

75. Murata, N., Ishizaki-Nishizawa, O., Higashi, S., Hayashi, H., Tasaka, Y., et al. 1992. Genetically engineered alteration in the chilling sensitivity of plants. *Nature* 356:710–13

76. Murphy, D. J. 1992. Modifying oilseed crops for non-edible products. *Trends Biotechnol.* 10:84–87

77. Negrutiu, I., Hinnisdaels, S., Cammaerts, D., Cherdshewasart, W., Gharti-Chhetri, C. G., et al. 1992. Plant protoplasts as genetic tool: selectable markers for developmental studies. *Int. J. Dev. Biol.* 36:73–84

78. Oakes, J. V., Shewmaker, C. K., Stalker, D. M. 1991. Production of cyclodextrins, a novel carbohydrate, in the tubers of transgenic potato plants. *Bio-Technology* 9:982–86

79. Oeller, P. W., Lu, M. W., Taylor, L. P., Pike, D. A., Theologis, A. 1991. Reversible inhibition of tomato fruit senescence by antisense RNA. *Science* 254:437–39

80. Offringa, R., de Groot, M. J. A., Haagsman, H. J., Does, M. P., van den Elzen, P. J., Hooykaas, P. J. 1990. Extrachromosomal homologous recombination and gene targeting in plant cells after *Agrobacterium*-mediated transformation. *Embo J.* 9:3077–84

81. Paszkowski, J., Baur, M., Boguck, A., Potrykus, I. 1988. Gene targeting in plants. *EMBO J.* 7:4021–26

82. Pen, J., Molendijk, L., Quax, W. J., Sijmons, P. C., van Ooyen, A. J. J., et al. 1992. Production of active *Bacillus licheniformis* alpha-amylase in tobacco and its application in starch liquefaction. *Bio-Technology* 10:292–96

83. Penarrubia, L., Kim, R., Giovannoni, J., Kim, S.-H., Fischer R. L. 1992. Production of the sweet protein monellin in transgenic plants. *Bio-Technology* 10:561–64

84. Perlak, F. J., Fuchs, R. L., Dean, D. A., McPherson, S. L., Fischoff, D. A. 1991. Modification of the coding sequence enhances plant expression of insect control protein genes. *Proc. Natl. Acad. Sci. USA* 88:3324–28

85. Pollard, M. R., Anderson, L., Fan, C., Hawkins, D. J., Davies, H. M. 1991. A specific acyl-ACP thioesterase implicated in medium-chain fatty acid production in immature cotyledons of *Umbellularia californica*. *Arch. Biochem. Biophys.* 284:306–12

86. Pollock, C. J., Cairns, A. J. 1991. Fructan metabolism in grasses and ce-reals. *Annu. Rev. Plant Physiol. Plant Mol. Biol.* 42:77–101

87. Potrykus, I. 1990. Gene transfer to cereals. An assessment. *Bio-Technology* 8:535–42

88. Potrykus, I. 1991. Gene transfer to plants: assessment of published approaches and results. *Annu. Rev. Plant. Physiol. Plant Mol. Biol.* 42:205–25

89. Redenbaugh, K., Hiatt, W. R., Martineau, B., Kramer, M., Sanders, R. A., et al. 1992. Safety assessment of genetically engineered fruits and vegetables. A case study of the Flavr Savr™ tomato. Ann Arbor: CRC Press

90. Sanford, J. C. 1990. Biolistic plant transformation. *Physiol. Plant.* 79:205–9

91. Saul, M. W., Potrykus, I. 1990. Direct gene transfer to protoplasts: fate of the transferred genes. *Dev. Genet.* 11:176–81

92. Savelkoul, F. H., van der Poel, A. F., Tamminga, S. 1992. The presence and inactivation of trypsin inhibitors, tannins, lectins and amylase inhibitors in legume seeds during germination. A review. *Plant Foods, Hum. Nutr.* 42: 71–85

93. Shanklin, J., Somerville, C. 1991. Stearoyl-acyl-carrier-protein desaturase from higher plants is structurally unrelated to the animal and fungal homologs. *Proc. Natl. Acad. Sci. USA* 88:2510–14

94. Shaul, O., Galili, G. 1992. Increased lysine synthesis in tobacco plants that express high levels of bacterial dihydrodipicolinate synthase in their chloroplasts. *Plant J.* 2:203–9

95. Sheehy, R. E., Kramer, M., Hiatt, W. R. 1988. Reduction of poly-galacturonase activity in tomato fruit by antisense RNA. *Proc. Natl. Acad. Sci. USA* 85:8805–9

96. Shorrosh, B. S., Wen, L., Zen, K. C., Huang, J. K., Pan, J. S., et al. 1992. A novel cereal storage protein: molecular genetics of the 19 kDa globulin of rice. *Plant Mol. Biol.* 18:151–54

97. Shotwell, M. A., Larkins, B. A. 1991. Improvement of the protein quality of seeds by genetic engineering. In *Molecular Approaches to Crop Improvement,* ed. E. S. Dennis, D. J. Llewellyn, pp. 33–61. Wien: Springer-Verlag

98. Slabas, A. R., Fawcett, T. 1992. The biochemistry and molecular biology of plant lipid biosynthesis. *Plant Mol. Biol.* 19:169–91

99. Smith, C. J. S., Watson, C. F., Ray, J., Bird, C. R., Morris, P. C. et al.

1988. Antisense RNA inhibition of polygalacturonase gene expression in transgenic tomatoes. *Nature* 334:724–26

100. Somerville, C., Browse, J. 1991. Plant lipids: metabolism, mutants, and membranes. *Science* 252:80–87

101. Sonnewald, U. 1992. Expression of *E. coli* inorganic pyrophosphatase in transgenic plants alters photoassimilate partitioning. *Plant J.* 2:571–81

102. Sonnewald, U., Willmitzer, L. 1992. Molecular approaches to sink-source interactions. *Plant Physiol.* 99:1267–70

102a. Stark, D. M., Timmerman, K., Barry, G. F., Preiss, J., Kishore, G. M. 1991. Regulation of the amount of starch in plant tissues by ADP glucose pyrophosphorylase. *Science* 258:287–91

103. Straughan, R. 1990. Genetic manipulation for food production: social and ethical issues for consumers. *Br. Food. J.* 92:13–26

104. Sun, S. S., Altenbach, S. B., Leung, F. W. 1987. Properties, biosynthesis and processing of a sulfur-rich protein in Brazil nut (*Bertholletia excelsa* H.B.K.). *Eur. J. Biochem.* 162:477–83

105. Sussex, I. M. 1989. Developmental programming of the shoot meristem. *Cell* 56:225–29

106. Suzuki, D. T., Giffiths, A. J. F., Miller, J. H., Lewontin, R. 1989. *An Introduction to Genetic Analysis.* New York: Freeman. 768 pp.

107. Thompson, G. A., Scherer, D. E., Foxall, V. A. S., Kenny, J. W., Young, H. L., et al. 1991. Primary structures of the precursor and mature forms of stearoyl-acyl carrier protein desaturase from safflower embryos and requirement of ferredoxin for enzyme activity. *Proc. Natl. Acad. Sci. USA* 88:2578–82

108. Urrutia, M. E., Duman, J. G., Knight, C. A. 1992. Plant thermal hysteresis proteins. *Biochim. Biophys. Acta* 1121:199–206

109. van den Elzen, P. J., Townsend, J., Lee, K. Y., Bedbrook, J. R. 1985. A chimearic hygromycin resistance gene as a selectable marker in plant cells. *Plant Mol. Biol.* 5:299–302

110. Vayda, M. E., Belknap, W. R. 1992. The emergence of transgenic potatoes as commercial products and tools for basic science. *Transgenic Res.* 1:149–63

111. Visser, R. G. F., Somhorst, I., Kuipers, G. J., Ruys, N. J., Feenstra, W. J., et al. 1991. Inhibition of the expression of the gene for granule-bound starch synthase in potato by antisense constructs. *Mol. Gen. Genet.* 225:289–96

112. Voelker, T. A., Worrell, A. C., Anderson, L., Bleibaum, J., Fan, C., et al 1992. Fatty acid biosynthesis redirected to medium chains in transgenic oilseed plants. *Science* 257:72–74

113. von Schaewen, A., Stitt, M., Schmidt, R., Sonnewald, U., Willmitzer, L. 1990. Expression of a yeast-derived invertase in the cell wall of tobacco and *Arabidopsis* plants leads to accumulation of carbohydrate and inhibition of photosynthesis and strongly influences growth and phenotype of transgenic tobacco plants. *EMBO J.* 9:3033–44

114. Walden, R., Hayashi, H., Schell, J. 1991. T-DNA as a gene tag. *Plant J.* 1:281–88

115. Witty, M., Harvey, W. J. 1990. Sensory evaluation of transgenic *Solanum tuberosum* producing r-thaumatin II. *NZ J. Crop Hortic. Sci.* 18:77–80

116. Worrell, A. C., Bruneau, J-M., Summerfelt, K., Boersig, M., Voelker, T. 1991. Expression of maize sucrose phosphate synthase in tomato alters leaf carbohydrate partitioning. *Plant Cell* 3:1121–30

117. Yang, C. F. 1985. Biosynthesis and action of ethylene. *Hortic. Sci.* 20:41–45

Annu. Rev. Nutr. 1993. 13:217–41

BIOLOGICAL EFFECTS OF SHORT-CHAIN FATTY ACIDS IN NONRUMINANT MAMMALS

Maurice Bugaut and Marc Bentéjac

Laboratoire de Biologie Moléculaire et Cellulaire, Faculté des Sciences Mirande, Université de Bourgogne, BP 138, 21004 Dijon, France

KEY WORDS: butyrate, propionate, volatile fatty acids (VFAs), cholesterol, cell proliferation, human gastric lipase

CONTENTS

INTRODUCTION 217
OCCURRENCE IN THE DIGESTIVE TRACT 218
   Microbial Fermentation 218
   Bovine Milk Fat Digestion 219
ABSORPTION AND METABOLISM 221
BIOLOGICAL EFFECTS 223
   Propionate and Cholesterol Levels 223
   Trophic Effects on the Colon Mucosa 227
   Butyrate and Colon Cancer 228
CONCLUSION 230
   Contribution to Energy Requirements 230

INTRODUCTION

Dietary fibers from natural or semisynthetic sources have gained increasing attention because of their value as a supplement to the normal Western diet, which is poor in bulking substances, and as a therapeutic treatment of disorders such as atherosclerosis and colon cancer (31, 54, 62, 115, 116, 120, 128, 135). Over the last 50 years, numerous studies have shown that plant fibers are fermented in the gastrointestinal tract of mammals to short-chain fatty acids (SCFAs), also known as volatile fatty acids (VFAs), that are readily absorbed by the mucosa and metabolized by body tissues. Thus, production, absorption, and metabolism of SCFAs (acetate, propionate, and butyrate), as

217

0199-9885/93/0715-0217$02.00

well as their physiological effects, have been subjects of intense research and, consequently, of numerous published comments and reviews (22, 38, 65, 71, 185, 191, 193, 210, 225, 232). We therefore focus our attention here on some research areas that have benefited from recent developments and that are of interest in human nutrition and health. Bovine milk fat digestion as a source of butyrate, the effects of propionate on cholesterol homeostasis, and those of butyrate on cell proliferation are the major subjects emphasized in this review.

OCCURRENCE IN THE DIGESTIVE TRACT

Microbial Fermentation

Adult monogastric mammals of all species, including *Homo sapiens*, have a microbial flora indigenous to their alimentary canal and primarily localized in the hindgut (cecum and large intestine) (202). The microbial populations are composed of several hundred different microorganism species (prokaryotes and eukaryotes) and in aggregate can exceed 1×10^{11} cells per gram dry weight of intestinal content. They resemble rumen populations in their size and complexity. For example, the genera *Bacteroides, Bifidobacterium,* and *Enterococcus*, and the species *Escherichia coli,* are predominant in the feces of formula-fed babies (15). Substrates for microbial fermentation in the large intestine are macromolecules that come from endogenous (sloughed epithelial cells, lysed microbial cells. mucus, and other intestinal excretions) and exogenous (mostly fibrous components of food) sources and that cannot be digested by host enzymes (149). Dietary fibers are complex polysaccharide polymers that derive from the plant cell wall, which is made up of water-insoluble cellulose microfibrils coated with soluble hemicelluloses and embedded in a gel of pectins (62). Variable amounts of starch that escape digestion in the small intestine (this fraction is called resistant starch) also pass into the colon and become available as substrate for microbial fermentation, as does dietary fiber (166, 204, 229). Reflecting the anaerobic environment of the colon, most biochemical reactions catalyzed by microbial enzymes do not involve oxygen. The SCFAs acetate, propionate, and *n*-butyrate, and the gases H_2, CH_4, and CO_2, which can be detected in respiratory expiration (231), are major end products of microbial fermentation. Formate, valerate, caproate, and the branched-chain acids isobutyrate and isovalerate (144) also occur in the large intestine, though in smaller proportions (10–20 mol% of total SCFAs). SCFAs are present at total concentrations ranging from about 30 to 190 mM in the feces of individuals consuming an ordinary diet (202), irrespective of the hindgut size and the herbivorous status of mammalian species (22, 38, 185). SCFAs make up the predominant anions

Table 1   SCFA molar percents from 24-hr fermentation of dietary fibers in in vitro incubation systems inoculated with fresh human fecal flora[a]

Substrate	Acetate	Propionate	Butyrate
Pectin	81	11	8
Gum arabic	68	23	9
Oat bran[b]	65	19	16
Wheat bran[b]	63	16	21
Cellulose[c]	53	21	26

[a]Means recalculated from (2, 152, 222, 236, 240).
[b]α-cellulose and hemicelluloses are 7% and 19% dry total dietary fiber, respectively, in oat bran, and 19% and 38%, respectively, in wheat bran (36).
[c]48-hr fermentation.

in the large intestine of mammals and create a slightly acidic pH level (6.0–7.0) (38, 55, 73). The acids vary widely in their relative proportions, depending upon the fiber source in the diet (Table 1). SCFAs in human feces, following consumption of different defined polysaccharides, have been measured, on average, in the molar ratio of acetate:propionate:butyrate of 53:27:20 (202).

Bovine Milk Fat Digestion

Milk fat from domestic (cow, sheep, and goat) and wild ruminants is made up of triacylglycerols in excess of 95%. The chain length of the three acyl moieties esterified to glycerol ranges from 2 to 26 carbon atoms (146). Ruminant milk fat contains appreciable proportions of SCFAs, including butyric acid (10 mol%), caproic acid (5 mol%), and acetic acid as a minor component (168), but SCFAs are absent in the milk of other mammalian species, including humans. Bovine milk fat consists of thousands of individual stereospecific triacylglycerols (213), of which 223 molecular species were recently determined (93). We found that the three major triacylglycerols, 4-16-18:1 (4.2 mol%), 4-16-16 (3.2 mol%), and 4-14-16 (3.1 mol%), contained one butyric acid per molecule, as a result of the specific esterification of SCFA at the sn-3 position.

Bovine milk and dairy products contain small amounts of free fatty acids generated by endogenous lipoprotein lipase activity. Lipoprotein lipase, which is the major enzyme responsible for hydrolysis of serum triacylglycerols, is synthesized in extrahepatic organs, including the mammary gland (20, 238). The molecular cloning of bovine lipoprotein lipase cDNA was achieved by Senda et al (209). Lipoprotein lipase belongs to the lipase superfamily that also includes hepatic and pancreatic lipases (103). In the lactating mammary gland, the active enzyme is released partly in association with milk lipid globules from differentiated mammary epithelial cells (21, 44, 125), and thus bovine milk is an abundant source of the enzyme (6 mg liter^{-1} of skim milk). Although lipoprotein lipase preferentially attacks the ester bond in the *sn*-1 position, it catalyzes the rapid release of fatty acids, including butyric and caproic acids, in the primary position. Indeed, the rate of hydrolysis in vitro (176) or in vivo (173) is similar for triacylglycerols containing short chains (tributyrin), medium chains, long chains (Intralipid®: purified soybean oil emulsified with egg phosphatidylcholine), or mixed chains (milk fat globules) as substrates. The feature distinguishing lipoprotein lipase from other lipases is that it requires apolipoprotein C-II for maximal activity. The enzyme has maximal activity between pH 8.6 and 9.0 (176, 237). Thus, it is uncertain whether, in the stomach of humans swallowing bovine milk, lipoprotein lipase is still active in the absence of the serum factor and because of stomach acidity, and, therefore, whether it is important in milk fat digestion. The digestive enzyme bile salt-stimulated lipase has been found in the milk of humans, higher primates, and carnivores, but not in that of ruminants (217).

The first important step of dietary triacylglycerol lipolysis is catalyzed by a preduodenal acid lipase that is active in the stomach (95). The enzyme is known by various names, including lingual lipase (rat), gastric lipase (man and rabbit), and pregastric esterase (calf) (80). In each mammal, the preduodenal lipase activity is associated mainly with a single tissue, which is located in the lingual (mouse and rat), pharyngeal (calf and sheep), or gastric (horse, dog, cat, rabbit, guinea pig, hog, baboon, and macaque) area (59, 160). In humans, it was first believed that the lipase activity of the gastric juice originated from Ebner's lingual glands (95). More recently, it was clearly shown that human gastric lipase is mainly localized in the chief cells of the fundic mucosa (1, 58–60, 159, 161). The output of the enzyme is stimulated by intravenous infusion of pentagastrin (162, 163) or by gastric nutrient infusion (216) in healthy adults. Gastric lipolysis is of primary importance for milk fat digestion in infants because of the low pancreatic lipase level (137a). A 7-fold decrease in human gastric lipase activity of the fundic mucosa has been observed in persons over 60 years of age (161).

Human gastric lipase is a glycoprotein with an apparent molecular mass (MM) of ~50 kd as determined by SDS polyacrylamide gel electrophoresis (33, 158, 221). The amino acid sequence obtained from a cloned cDNA (33) consists of 379 amino acids (MM = 43 kd), including four potentially glycosylated asparagine residues and three cysteine residues, one of which is essential for the expression of enzyme activity (78, 79). Human gastric lipase is closely related to rat lingual lipase (377 amino acids) (61), with an overall homology of 78% (33), but is unrelated to porcine pancreatic lipase (56). The pH optimum of human gastric lipase is in the range of 3.5–5.5, which makes the enzyme ideally suited to act in the stomach, where the pH after the ingestion of a meal is in such a range (95). Human gastric lipase is remarkably stable at a low pH and remains active after incubation at pH values close to 1.0 (69, 160). It has often been reported that human gastric lipase displays a high specificity towards short-chain triacylglycerols in vitro, whereas the enzyme appears to be able to catalyze the hydrolysis of alimentary long-chain triacylglycerols in vivo. In fact, establishing the optimal assay conditions with short-chain (tributyrin) and long-chain (Intralipid) triacylglycerols, Gargouri et al (84) demonstrated that human gastric lipase had no intrinsic specificity for short-chain triacylglycerols and that the apparent specificity, when observed, depended on pH and the presence of amphiphile molecules (bile salts, bovine serum albumin, or dietary proteins such as β-lactoglobulin and ovalbumin) in the incubation medium (see also 58, 81, 82, 140, 221). Interestingly, Bernbäck et al (23) found that the rate of hydrolysis of human milk fat globule triacylglycerol, which is made up of about 6% medium-chain fatty acids (114), was comparable to that obtained with an artificial emulsion of long-chain triacylglycerol (25). It must be emphasized that the free fatty acids released by human gastric lipase hydrolysis of triacylglycerol strongly inhibit the enzyme activity when their chain length exceeds six carbons (23). This inhibition may be connected with the fact that, under in vivo conditions, only 10–20% of the hydrolysis of dietary lipids occurs within the stomach (14, 96). The enzyme appears to be partially specific for the sn-3 position when hydrolyzing synthetic long-chain triacylglycerols (119, 221).

To date, no data is available concerning human gastric lipase hydrolysis of bovine milk fat globule triacylglycerol. However, in view of the features of the enzyme, short-chain residues in bovine milk triacylglycerols, which are at the sn-3 position, probably are the first to be released to yield medium- and long-chain sn-1,2 diacylglycerols. The released SCFAs are rapidly absorbed by the gastric mucosa (27a, 201). Lipid digestion is completed in the proximal part of the small intestine by pancreatic colipase-dependent lipase, giving rise to sn-2 monoacylglycerols and free fatty acids, and more modestly by pancreatic bile salt-dependent lipase (88). It is now recognized that the generation of limited quantities of free long-chain fatty acids by the action of human gastric lipase on native milk fat globule triacylglycerols is of major importance in promoting the subsequent lipolysis by pancreatic lipase in the presence of colipase and bile salts (23, 24, 83). A concerted action of the different lipolytic enzymes in the gastrointestinal tract is probably one important mechanism responsible for the efficient digestion of dietary lipids (24, 141).

ABSORPTION AND METABOLISM

Daily production of SCFAs in the human colon is estimated to be greater than 300 mmol day^{-1}, but fecal excretion is only about 10 mmol day^{-1} (104). The colonic absorption rate of SCFAs is remarkably similar among nonruminant species, including humans, and ranges from 6 to 12 μmol $(cm^2)^{-1}$ h^{-1} (191). Thus, SCFAs in vivo appear to be absorbed rapidly and nearly completely. Clearance rates of SCFAs have generally been observed to increase with chain length, even though there are differences between rates in the distal and proximal colon (72, 186, 192). Several models have been proposed to explain SCFA transport and to account for the large number of observations describing the dependence of SCFA absorption rates on luminal pH and P_{CO_2}, as well as on fluxes of water, protons, and inorganic ions (Cl^-, HCO_3^-, Na^+ and K^+) through the colonic mucosa (38, 185, 223). It is widely believed that the transmural movement of SCFAs is a concentration-dependent, passive diffusion process, whereby SCFAs, at least in part, are transported in the protonated form. Hydrogen ions, which are needed for SCFA protonation because 99% of SCFAs (pKa $=$ 4.8) are in the ionized form at the colonic pH, may be available from Na^+-H^+ exchange and from hydration of luminal CO_2 to HCO_3^- and H^+. SCFAs may also be transported in the ionized form via an SCFA-HCO_3^- exchange mechanism. Most results from recent investigations in vivo (72, 148, 167, 186, 235) and in vitro (29, 30, 97, 98, 188, 192, 194, 208) in the colon of mammals agree with this outline. However, the precise mechanism for the absorptive process of SCFAs remains undefined.

Studies using in situ loops of rabbit hindgut (147), isolated colonocytes of rat (13, 52, 70, 74, 189), and biopsy specimens of human colon (242), all incubated in the presence of [^{14}C]substrates, have shown that SCFAs, once taken up, were metabolized at a high rate inside the cecal and colonic mucosal cells. Furthermore, butyrate was used as an important respiratory fuel in preference to acetate, propionate, and even to glutamine, glucose, and ketone bodies. Such findings have stimulated considerable research regarding the role of SCFAs in maintaining the health of colonic mucosa and in preventing colonic diseases (130, 215).

The SCFAs that escape colonic metabolization enter the hepatic portal blood, where their concentration varies in a wide range, depending on intestinal production rates and, therefore, on the diet. For example, values ranging from 0.3 to 3 mM have been reported in the rat (50, 110, 112, 157). In contrast, the relative proportions of the three major acids in the portal blood reflect quite well the relative proportions of those found in the intestinal contents. Table 2 shows that butyrate and propionate are extensively taken up by the liver, sometimes so much so that they are no longer detected (<2 μM) in the peripheral blood (57, 179, 181). There is also substantial clearance of acetate in the liver, with further uptake occurring in peripheral tissues. Indeed, utilization of SCFA in hepatocytes from rats fed a high fiber diet was 0.1, 0.6, and 0.9 μmol min^{-1} g^{-1} cells when incubated in the presence of 1.0 mM acetate, propionate, and butyrate, respectively (57). Propionate is used by the

Table 2 SCFA concentrations (μmol ml^{-1}) in rats fed a standard diet[a] and sudden-death human victims[b]

	Acetate	Propionate	Butyrate
Cecal content			
Rat	93.0	23.2	43.1
Man	69.1	25.3	26.1
Hepatic portal blood			
Rat	0.98	0.22	0.39
Man	0.258	0.088	0.029
Hepatic venous blood			
Rat	—	—	—
Man	0.115	0.021	0.012
Peripheral blood			
Rat (arterial blood)	0.40	0.02	0.03
Man (venous blood)	0.070	0.005	0.004

[a]Data from (111).
[b]Data from (55).

liver as a substrate for gluconeogenesis, and butyrate leads to ketone body production.

BIOLOGICAL EFFECTS

Propionate and Cholesterol Levels

Coronary heart disease is a leading cause of death in the Western countries. Epidemiological data show that elevated blood cholesterol, especially low-density-lipoprotein cholesterol, is a major risk factor. Dietary therapy is the mainstay in treatment of moderate hypercholesterolemia. Water-soluble dietary fibers, such as pectins, gums, and oat cereals, are widely believed to reduce total and low-density-lipoprotein cholesterol levels in serum of both hypercholesterolemic (6–9, 18, 19, 37, 45, 124, 126, 137, 153) and nonhypercholesterolemic (47, 187) humans, but insoluble fibers, such as wheat bran or cellulose, do not seem to lead to such reduction. Soluble fibers also decrease liver cholesterol levels, as observed in several species of laboratory animals (12, 68, 105, 122, 150, 212), and increase the hepatic LDL-receptor number (68, 226). Although fiber has an important sequestering effect (63, 113), the precise mechanism of cholesterol-lowering remains unclear. The decrease in serum cholesterol concentrations has been partially attributed to the ability of fibers to inhibit lipid absorption (35, 108, 249) and to increase biliary (67, 106, 109, 196) and fecal (10, 46, 109, 196) bile acid excretion. This would then cause the liver to convert more cholesterol to bile acids, thereby reducing body cholesterol. However, as some fibers are associated with a significant decrease in serum cholesterol without increasing fecal bile acid excretion (5, 46, 137, 155), we can conclude, as did Kritchevsky (135), that the "effects of fiber on bile acid metabolism represent, at best, a small part of the overall mechanism(s) related to hypolipidemia."

Researchers agree that the highly polymeric structure of fibers is a prerequisite for the potent cholesterol-lowering effect of nonabsorbable carbohydrates. However, Topping et al (227) reported that methylcellulose, a modified polysaccharide resistant to microbial metabolism, which therefore is not fermented in the colon to SCFAs, had no effect on plasma cholesterol, hepatic cholesterol synthesis, and fecal excretion of bile acids. Moreover, Ide et al (106) recently showed that guar gum hydrolysate had the same decreasing effects on cholesterol levels as did intact guar gum. In this experiment, tenfold increases in cecal SCFA contents were observed with both kinds of substrates. Such results suggest that the action of absorbed SCFAs on hepatic and peripheral metabolism of cholesterol may be an alternative mechanism for the effect of fermentable carbohydrates on body cholesterol concentrations (183). The idea that SCFAs (particularly propionate) derived from colonic fermentation may suppress liver cholesterol synthesis was based on the initial observation that 3-hydroxy-3-methylglutaryl-CoA (HMG-CoA) synthase in bovine liver was inhibited by 0.5 mM propionyl-CoA or 15 mM propionate (39). Moreover, it was known that the liver is the principal site of propionate metabolism and cholesterol synthesis (Figure 1). Ide et al (107) showed that feeding medium-chain triacylglycerols lowered the activity of rat liver HMG-CoA reductase, the rate-limiting enzyme in cholesterol synthesis, whereas feeding long-chain triacylglycerols did not. Thus, inhibition of cholesterol synthesis might be achieved in animals by the inclusion of propionate in the diet. The pig has often been chosen as a model because it is similar to the human in diet, lipoprotein profile, and responsiveness to hypercholesterolemic diets. In 1981, Boila et al (34) using young male, castrated pigs made hypercholesterolemic by addition of 15% tallow in the diet, were the first to observe an inhibitory effect of dietary propionate (5%) on the rate of cholesterol synthesis. Inhibition of cholesterol synthesis by propionate was confirmed in vitro by Anderson & Bridges (4) incubating isolated rat hepatocytes in the presence of 15–30 mM propionate. The same research group (49) reported that both serum and liver cholesterol levels were significantly lowered in rats when only 0.5% propionate was included in a 0.3% cholesterol-supplemented diet, but no effect was observed in rats fed a nonsupplemented diet. Propionate was thought to decrease cholesterol synthesis by inhibiting HMG-CoA reductase, but some studies in rat liver have

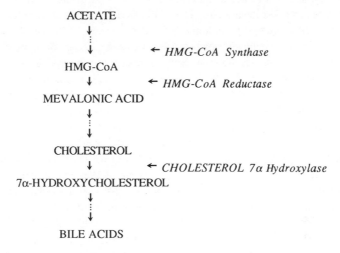

Figure 1   Key reactions in the cholesterol and bile acid biosynthetic pathways. HMG-CoA, 3-hydroxy-3-methylglutaryl-CoA. Modified from Shefer et al (211).

led to conflicting results (151, 182), like those obtained in studies of rats fed dietary fiber (68, 106, 171, 172, 184).

In contrast to the above data, Thacker and colleagues (218–220), who also used pigs fed diets containing high levels (3–9%) of propionate, noted reductions in serum cholesterol concentrations but slight increases in cholesterol concentrations of liver and backfat. The authors suggested that propionate may reduce the transport of cholesterol from peripheral tissues to the liver rather than reducing liver cholesterol synthesis. In keeping with these results, similar studies in vivo in the rat indicated that inhibition of hepatic and intestinal cholesterol synthesis was not responsible for the hypocholesterolemic effects of dietary propionate (111) or soluble dietary fibers (11, 66, 109, 226). Hepatic portal venous plasma propionate concentrations do not exceed 1 mM in animals fed high levels of propionate (111) or dietary fibers (10, 50, 109, 110, 157), or in patients after caecal lactulose instillation (179). Studies with perfused livers (111) or isolated hepatocytes (170, 245) from nonfasted rats indicated that propionate at a concentration of 1 mM or lower did not alter cholesterol synthesis, as measured by tritium incorporation into sterols from ^3H_2O. Sterologenesis was inhibited solely when nonphysiological concentrations (1 mM) of propionate were present in the medium (245), as originally observed (4). Although conflicting results have been obtained when using [^{14}C]acetate or ^3H_2O as the tracer (170), the cholesterol synthesis rate generally appears to be fairly independent of the substrate used, i.e. ^3H_2O, [^{14}C]acetate, or [^{14}C]mevalonate (143, 171, 245).

Recently, propionate supplements (7.5 g day^{-1}) were given to healthy human volunteers for one week (224) or seven weeks (223), and in both studies, total serum cholesterol was unchanged. Similar results were obtained in pigs (34) and rats (49) given standard diets supplemented with propionate but without lipids. Venter et al (234) designed a study in the baboon, which is regarded as a more suitable animal model for examining the association of fiber-depleted diets and atherosclerosis. Baboons were fed a Western diet, with or without supplements of 2% propionate or of 5% soluble dietary fiber concentrate, for periods of nine weeks. Total serum cholesterol values were increased in the baboons fed the unsupplemented Western diet, and soluble fiber prevented this increase while propionate did not. However, propionate and fiber increased the high-density-lipoprotein cholesterol concentration (234). Similar results were obtained in humans (233), and such an increase is considered to be a beneficial effect. Furthermore, the liver cholesterol concentration was lowered by propionate or fiber supplementation (234).

If we summarize data showing how propionate given orally to humans and animals (rat, pig, and baboon) affects cholesterol metabolism, conflicting results have been obtained regarding not only the rate of biosynthesis of cholesterol but also its serum and liver levels. The in vivo studies designed with propionate-supplemented diets have been criticized because whereas dietary propionate is rapidly absorbed in the upper gastrointestinal tract (stomach), as shown by Illman et al (111) in the rat and the pig, propionate arising by bacterial digestion of fiber is absorbed gradually in the lower part of the digestive tract (cecum + colon), and the metabolic effects of propionate may not be the same. Furthermore, the effects of propionate (or fiber) in oral supplementation cannot be studied independently from upper intestinal effects on digestibility of nutrients and enterohepatic bile acid metabolism. To overcome these difficulties, rectal or cecal infusions of propionate have been carried out in humans (243, 244) and in pigs with a cecal cannula (17). It was found that propionate either had no effect on, or raised, total serum cholesterol concentration. These results were in keeping with the findings of Ahrens et al (3), who had examined the effects on blood lipids of oral and intracecal pectin administration for four weeks in hypercholesterolemic minipigs. Total serum cholesterol concentration was lowered by 50% after feeding, while the intracecal infusion of the same amount of pectin had no effect. These studies demonstrated that the passage of fiber through the small intestine is necessary for its hypercholesterolemic action. To date, even if propionate concentrations in the hepatic portal vein of fiber-fed rats were found to be related to the cholesterol-lowering effect (109, 110), the hypothesis that propionate may mediate the hypercholesterolemic effects of high-fiber diets is becoming less and less satisfactory (66). Colonic fermentation of fiber also produces acetate and butyrate, but we cannot yet draw clear-cut conclusions from a few works concerning the effects of the two SCFAs on sterol synthesis (26, 27, 48, 85, 170) and serum cholesterol concentrations (27, 244).

Trophic Effects on the Colon Mucosa

Several laboratories have shown that ingestion of fiber or resistant starch exerts a trophic effect, when estimated by parameters such as mucosal weight or protein content, on the hindgut mucosa of rats (42, 64, 117). Conversely, fiber-free diets or total parenteral nutrition induce atrophy in the intestinal mucosa. Complex carbohydrates may also cause an increase in crypt cell proliferation when measured by various techniques including labeling with bromodeoxyuridine (64) or [^{3}H]thymidine (40, 73, 117, 145), counting of S phase cells by flow cytometry (64) or arrested metaphases (92), and assessing of thymidine kinase activity (42, 43, 139, 178). In fact, these studies have revealed that dietary fibers stimulated colonic cell proliferation more or less, depending on several factors, including the source and quantity of the dietary fiber and the intestinal site (cecum, proximal, or distal colon). Furthermore, some conflicting results have been reported. For example, high starch diets either increase (40, 42) or decrease (28, 40, 41) colonic crypt cell proliferation. Of the various possible explanations regarding the effects of dietary fibers on colonic cell proliferation, a hypothesis has emerged suggesting that these effects are mediated by SCFAs via luminal fermentation. Indeed, intraluminal infusions of SCFAs have a stimulatory effect on colonic mucosa proliferation under various experimental conditions in rats (134, 190, 197–200) and patients (165). Effects of SCFAs were dose-dependent and varied among the acids (butyrate   propionate   acetate) (198). Similar results were obtained in vitro by Scheppach et al (205) when cell proliferation was measured in biopsies of normal human cecal mucosa after labeling with [^{3}H]thymidine. However, a few differing results have been obtained. In patients with distal ulcerative colitis, the same authors (206) observed that 100-mM butyrate enemas resulted in amelioration of inflammation while upper crypt proliferation was diminished. Furthermore, when cecal tissue pieces of normal rats were incubated in the presence of SCFAs in a physiological range (0.01–100 mM) and then examined for frequencies of colchicine-arrested metaphases, epithelial proliferation was inhibited, and butyrate alone had an equivalent effect to that of a mixture of SCFAs (198). Lastly, no correlation has been established between cell proliferation and the consumed quantity of water-soluble dietary fibers (which are fermented to a greater extent than water-insoluble dietary fibers) or the SCFA concentrations in luminal contents (73, 145).

Trophic effects of SCFAs on the intestinal mucosa cannot be explained solely by direct luminal effects of the SCFAs absorbed and used as a major energy source in the mucosa. The in vivo effects of SCFAs are probably indirect, because intakes of short-chain triacylglycerols, which are rapidly hydrolyzed and absorbed in the upper digestive tract, have been shown to stimulate colonic mucosal growth in rats (133). Conversely, SCFAs infused into the rat hindgut lumen stimulate mucosal cell proliferation in the intact or disconnected jejunum (134, 198, 199). Moreover, parenteral or intravenous infusion of SCFAs reduces the mucosal atrophy associated with total parenteral nutrition in the rat (123, 131, 132). A humoral mechanism in which enteroglucagon may play a role has been suggested (92). The beneficial effect of SCFAs on mucosal cell trophicity may also be due, at least in part, to an increase in the mucosal blood flow (164). Stimulation of the microcirculation could result from a direct action on the resistance arteries, as demonstrated in vitro in the rat (174) and human (165), and vasorelaxation might be related to increases in artery tissue cAMP levels (174). In summary, a true cause-and-effect relationship between fermentable fiber or SCFAs and cell proliferation is still disputable, and the mechanism(s) of action of SCFAs on the intestinal mucosa remains uncertain.

Butyrate and Colon Cancer

Various human epidemiological and case-control studies have shown that colonic cancer is negatively correlated with fiber intake (31). In animal models of colorectal cancer with lesions induced by carcinogens such as 1,2-dimethylhydrazine (DMH), wheat bran and cellulose appear to have a consistently protective effect against chemical carcinogenesis, but no consensus exists for the water-soluble fibers, gums, and pectins (115, 116, 118). The suggestion that dietary fibers are protective in colorectal cancer is based on the fact that fibers increase large intestinal contents, speed up transit time, and bind carcinogens, which could reduce exposure of the mucosa to carcinogens. However, because dietary fibers differ in their physicochemical properties and because other dietary components, particularly fat, can induce reverse effects on the colonic mucosa, it remains difficult to identify a single mechanism by which fibers modify colon carcinogenesis. For example, some effects of fibers may be mediated via epidermal growth factor (EGF), since it has been reported that the addition of 10% wheat bran to a diet decreases the EGF level in the rat colon mucosa (203) and that the EGF receptor is overexpressed in human colonic carcinomas (246).

In cultured cell lines, butyrate is a well-recognized antitumor agent, whereas the other SCFAs are much less active in this respect (136). Some dietary fibers may therefore produce an antineoplastic effect through their fermentation products, especially butyrate. Microbial fermentation of insoluble fibers such as wheat bran is often associated with a higher production of butyrate than is fermentation of soluble fibers (Table 1; see also 154). Thus, in DMH-treated rats given diets supplemented with guar gum (85% soluble), oat bran (51% soluble), or wheat bran (25% soluble), Young et al (248) observed that the more insoluble the fibers, the more effective they are in elevating concentrations of butyrate in the distal large bowel and protecting against colorectal cancer. Conversely, when the SCFA distribution was investigated in enema samples taken from human subjects, a significantly lower ratio of butyrate to total SCFAs was found for polyp-colon cancer subjects than for normal subjects (239). Similarly, when studying SCFA production velocities from fiber in in vitro fecal incubation systems, Clausen et al (51) observed that the relative production rate of butyrate was reduced in patients with colonic cancer and adenomas, as compared to healthy controls. On the other hand, butyrate, when given orally, does not slow down the development of colonic neoplasia in DMH-treated rats (76). We can therefore conclude that high levels of luminal butyrate may have protective effects against colon cancer in vivo.

In vitro, the exposure of a number of cultured human colon cancer cell lines to butyrate induces alteration of several growth properties and morphological and biochemical changes consistent with a more differentiated phenotype. The changes generally include increased doubling times, reduced colony-forming ability in soft agar, morphological alterations, and increases in alkaline phosphatase and other enzymes (75, 94, 102, 121, 127, 169, 177, 230, 241). Induction of carcinoembryonic antigen (86, 169, 228, 230, 241), modifications in proto-oncogene expression (16, 53, 75, 207, 214), alterations in glycoprotein synthesis (16a, 86, 121, 127, 230), and an increase in the expression of the cytochrome c oxidase subunits encoded by mitrochondrial genes (99, 100) and of the basolateral Na^+/H^+ exchanger (32) have also been reported. These butyrate-induced alterations concern regulatory mechanisms of gene expression. Histone hyperacetylation, resulting from inhibition of histone deacetylase (101) and leading to weakening of histone/DNA interactions (175) and, then, to enhanced expression of some genes, is almost constantly observed (136, 180). Scaffold-attached regions may mediate the action of butyrate at the level of the chromatin structure (129). This description at the DNA level of the mechanisms that underlie the apparently pleiotropic effects of butyrate can suggest a nonspecific action of butyrate on gene expression. However, a more localized effect of butyrate, involving specific 5'-flanking DNA sequences that control butyrate-sensitivity of proximal genes, has been described in different genomic contexts (57a, 77, 89–91, 138, 247), and a 17-nucleotide consensus sequence has been identified (77). An explanation for the role of a specific 5'-upstream DNA sequence in butyrate-responsiveness may be that butyrate modifies the activity of transcriptional factors. That may, in turn, affect the interactions of these factors with proteins bound to the promoter. Because the molecular process of colon carcinogenesis likely involves both activated and repressed genes (195), it is of great interest to understand the molecular mechanisms involving the action of butyrate.

The intestinal epithelium can respond to a wide variety of stimuli by altering its rates of proliferation. We reported above that in many studies, but not all, dietary fibers increase colonic cell proliferation in healthy animals. Furthermore, despite some conflicting results, evidence exists that the products of hindgut fermentation, particularly butyrate, have a trophic effect on the normal intestinal epithelium in vivo. In contrast, epidemiological studies have revealed the protective role of some dietary fibers against the development of colon cancer in human subjects, and a few experimental studies have suggested that these effects may be mediated by butyrate, which is a potent antitumor agent in vitro. Moreover, according to some researchers, increased cellular proliferation may be a marker of gastrointestinal cancer risk (142). If butyrate does play a role in mediating the effects of fibers on the colonic mucosa, there is an apparent contradiction between the proliferating effects of fiber or butyrate in the normal mucosa, on the one hand, and their protective effects against colon cancer on the other hand. Recently, Gibson et al (86) compared the in vitro effects of butyrate on the differentiation of normal colonic epithelial cells (isolated cells and organ culture) with those on a colon cancer cell line. All the markers used to assess differentiation (glycoprotein synthesis, alkaline phosphatase activity, and carcinoembrionic antigen expression) were increased in neoplastic cells and unchanged or decreased in normal cells. These data indicate that butyrate has differing actions on normal and neoplastic cells.

CONCLUSION

Contribution to Energy Requirements

SCFAs can be an important source of carbon and energy for the nonruminant mammals. Bugaut (38) and Bergman (22) summarized estimates obtained in various species regarding the contribution of SCFAs to the basal energy requirements. Values from 5 to 30% were obtained; as expected, the highest figures were for herbivores such as rabbits and ponies, but they showed considerable variation, probably because of methodology used and assumptions made by the authors. In fact, substantially more energy would be available to nonruminants if fiber could be digested in the small intestine. In the case of farm animals, one of the applications of recombinant DNA technology would be to obtain the expression and secretion of heterologous cellulases and xylanases in the digestive tract of transgenic animals (87). As for humans, SCFA could contribute 6 to 10% of the energy requirements in developed countries (156). Dietary fiber intakes are often much higher in the

Third World, and it is likely, therefore, that greater amounts of energy via SCFAs are made available by large intestinal fermentation. Accurate studies need to be designed to assess the contribution of SCFAs to energy supplies in man.

Literature Cited

1. Abrams, C. K., Hamosh, M., Lee, T. C., Ansher, A. F., Collen, M. J., et al. 1988. Gastric lipase: localization in the human stomach. *Gastroenterology* 95:1460–64

2. Adiotomre, J., Eastwood, M. A., Edwards, C. A., Brydon, G. W. 1990. Dietary fiber: in vitro methods that anticipate nutrition and metabolic activity in humans. *Am. J. Clin. Nutr.* 52:128–34

3. Ahrens, F., Hagemeister, H., Pfeuffer, M., Barth, C. A. 1986. Effects of oral and intracecal pectin administration on blood lipids in minipigs. *J. Nutr.* 116:70–76

4. Anderson, J. W., Bridges, S. R. 1981. Plant-fiber metabolites alter hepatic glucose and lipid metabolism. *Diabetes* 30 (Suppl. 1):133A

5. Anderson, J. W., Chen, W., Story, L., Sieling, B., Story, J. 1983. Hypocholesterolemic effects of soluble-fiber rich foods for hypercholesterolemic men. *Am. J. Clin. Nutr.* 37:699 (Abstr.)

6. Anderson, J. W., Gilinsky, N. H., Deakins, D. A., Smith, S. F., O'Neal, D. S., et al. 1991. Lipid responses of hypercholesterolemic men to oat-bran and wheat-bran intake. *Am. J. Clin. Nutr.* 54:678–83

7. Anderson, J. W., Riddell-Lawrence, S., Floore, T. L., Dillon, D. W., Oeltgen, P. R. 1991. Bakery products lower serum cholesterol concentrations in hypercholesterolemic men. *Am. J. Clin. Nutr.* 54:836–40

8. Anderson, J. W., Riddell-Mason, S., Gustafson, N. J., Smith, S. F., Mackey, M. 1992. Cholesterol-lowering effects of psyllium-enriched cereal as an adjunct to a prudent diet in the treatment of mild to moderate hypercholesterolemia. *Am. J. Clin. Nutr.* 56:93–98

9. Anderson, J. W., Spencer, D. B., Hamilton, C. C., Smith, S. F., Tietyen, J., et al. 1990. Oat-bran cereal lowers serum total and LDL cholesterol in hypercholesterolemic men. *Am. J. Clin. Nutr.* 52:495–99

10. Arjmandi, B. H., Ahn, J., Nathani, S., Reeves, R. D. 1992. Dietary soluble fiber and cholesterol affect serum cholesterol concentration, hepatic portal venous short-chain fatty acid concentrations and fecal sterol excretion in rats. *J. Nutr.* 122:246–53

11. Arjmandi, B. H., Craig, J., Nathani, S., Reeves, R. D. 1992. Soluble dietary fiber and cholesterol influence in vivo hepatic and intestinal cholesterol biosynthesis in rats. *J. Nutr.* 122:1559–65

12. Assis, S. P., Basu, T. K. 1990. Effect of pectin on the lipid status in high cholesterol-fed mice. *Nutr. Res.* 10:99–108

13. Awad, A. B., Ferger, S. L., Fink, C. S. 1990. Effect of dietary fat on the lipid composition and utilization of short-chain fatty acids by rat colonocytes. *Lipids* 25:316–20

14. Balasubramanian, K., Zentler-Munro, P. L., Batten, J. C., Northfield, T. C. 1992. Increased intragastric acid-resistant lipase activity and lipolysis in pancreatic steatorrhoea due to cystic fibrosis. *Pancreas* 7:305–10

15. Balmer, S. E., Wharton, B. A. 1991. Diet and faecal flora in the newborn: iron. *Arch. Dis. Child.* 66:1390–94

16. Barnard, J. A., Warwick, G. 1992. Sodium butyrate rapidly induces "enterocyte-like" differentiation and growth inhibition of HT-29 cells. *Gastroenterology* 102:A199 (Abstr.)

16a. Bates, S. E., Currier, S. J., Alvarez, M., Fojo, A. T. 1992. Modulation of P-glycoprotein phosphorylation and drug transport by sodium butyrate. *Biochemistry* 31:6366–72

17. Beaulieu, K. E., McBurney, M. I. 1992. Changes in pig serum lipids, nutrient digestibility and sterol excretion during cecal infusion of propionate. *J. Nutr.* 122:241–45

18. Bell, L. P., Hectorne, K., Reynolds, H., Balm, T. K., Hunninghake, D. B. 1989. Cholesterol-lowering effects of psyllium hydrophilic mucilloid. Adjunct therapy to a prudent diet for patients with mild to moderate hyper-

cholesterolemia. *J. Am. Med. Assoc.* 261:3419–23

19. Bell, L. P., Hectorn, K. J., Reynolds, H., Hunninghake, D. B. 1990. Cholesterol-lowering effects of soluble-fiber cereals as part of a prudent diet for patients with mild to moderate hypercholesterolemia. *Am. J. Clin. Nutr.* 52:1020–26

20. Bensadoun, A. 1991. Lipoprotein lipase. *Annu. Rev. Nutr.* 11:217–37

21. Ben-Zeev, O., Doolittle, M. H., Davis, R. C., Elovson, J., Scholtz, M. C. 1992. Maturation of lipoprotein lipase. Expression of full catalytic activity requires glucose trimming but not translocation to the *cis*-golgi compartment. *J. Biol. Chem.* 267:6219–27

22. Bergman, E. N. 1990. Energy contributions of volatile fatty acids from the gastrointestinal tract in various species. *Physiol. Rev.* 70:567–90

23. Bernbäck, S., Bläckberg, L., Hernell, O. 1989. Fatty acids generated by gastric lipase promote human milk triacylglycerol digestion by pancreatic colipase-dependent lipase. *Biochim. Biophys. Acta* 1001:286–93

24. Bernbäck, S., Bläckberg, L., Hernell, O. 1990. The complete digestion of human milk triacylglycerol in vitro requires gastric lipase, pancreatic colipase-dependent lipase, and bile salt-stimulated lipase. *J. Clin. Invest.* 85:1221–26

25. Bernbäck, S., Hernell, O., Blackberg, L. 1985. Purification and molecular characterization of bovine pregastric lipase. *Eur. J. Biochem.* 148:233–38

26. Beynen, A. C., Buechler, K. F., van der Molen, A. J., Geelen, M. J. H. 1982. The effects of lactate and acetate on fatty acid and cholesterol biosynthesis by isolated rat hepatocytes. *Int. J. Biochem.* 14:165–69

27. Beynen, A. C., Lemmens, A. G. 1987. Dietary acetate and cholesterol metabolism in rats. *Z. Ernährungswiss.* 26:79–83

27a. Bezard, J., Bugaut, M. 1986. Absorption of glycerides containing short, medium, and long fatty acids. In *Fat Absorption*, ed. A. Kuksis, 1:119–58. Boca Raton, Fla: CRC Press

28. Bianchini, F., Caderni, G., Magno, C., Testolin, G., Dolara, P. 1992. Profile of short-chain fatty acids and rectal proliferation in rats fed sucrose or cornstarch diets. *J. Nutr.* 122:254–61

29. Binder, H. J., Mehta, P. 1989. Short-chain fatty acids stimulate active sodium and chloride absorption in vitro in the rat distal colon. *Gastroenterology* 96:989–96

30. Binder, H. J., Mehta, P. 1990. Characterization of butyrate-dependent electroneutral Na-Cl absorption in the rat distal colon. *Pflügers Arch.* 417:365–69

31. Bingham, S. A. 1990. Mechanisms and experimental and epidemiological evidence relating dietary fibre (non-starch polysaccharides) and starch to protection against large bowel cancer. *Proc. Nutr. Soc.* 49:153–71

32. Bishop, P. R., Warwick, G. J., Ghishan, F. K., Barnard, J. A. 1992. Sodium butyrate upregulates Na^+/H^+ exchanger mRNA and transport activity in CACO-2 cells. *Gastroenterology* 102:A201 (Abstr.)

33. Bodmer, M. W., Angal, S., Yarranton, G. T., Harris, T. J. R., Lyons, A., et al. 1987. Molecular cloning of a human gastric lipase and expression of the enzyme in yeast. *Biochim. Biophys. Acta* 909:237–44

34. Boila, R. J., Salomons, M. O., Milligan, L. P., Aherne, F. X. 1981. The effect of dietary propionic acid on cholesterol synthesis in swine. *Nutr. Rep. Int.* 23:1113–21

35. Borel, P., Martigne, M., Senft, M., Garzino, P., Lafont, H., et al. 1990. Effect of wheat bran and wheat germ on the intestinal uptake of oleic acid, monoolein, and cholesterol in the rat. *J. Nutr. Biochem.* 1:28–33

36. Bourquin, L. D., Titgemeyer, E. C., Garleb, K. A., Fahey, G. C. Jr. 1992. Short-chain fatty acid production and fiber degradation by human colonic bacteria: effects of substrate and cell wall fractionation procedures. *J. Nutr.* 122:1508–20

37. Bridges, S. R., Anderson, J. W., Deakins, D. A., Dillon, D. W., Wood, C. L. 1992. Oat bran increases serum acetate of hypercholesterolemic men. *Am. J. Clin. Nutr.* 56:455–59

38. Bugaut, M. 1987. Occurrence, absorption and metabolism of short chain fatty acids in the digestive tract of mammals. *Comp. Biochem. Physiol. B* 86:439–72

39. Bush, R. S., Milligan, L. P. 1971. Study of the mechanism of inhibition of ketogenesis by propionate in bovine liver. *Can. J. Anim. Sci.* 51:121–27

40. Caderni, G., Bianchini, F., Dolara, P., Kriebel, D. 1989. Proliferative activity in the colon of the mouse and its modulation by dietary starch, fat, and cellulose. *Cancer Res.* 49:1655–59

41. Caderni, G., Bianchini, F., Dolara, P., Kriebel, D. 1991. Starchy foods

and colon proliferation in mice. *Nutr. Cancer* 15:33–40

42. Calvert, R. J., Otsuka, M., Satchithanandam, S. 1989. Consumption of raw potato starch alters intestinal function and colonic cell proliferation in the rat. *J. Nutr.* 119:1610–16

43. Calvert, R. J., Reicks, M. 1988. Alterations in colonic thymidine kinase enzyme activity induced by consumption of various dietary fibers (42778). *Proc. Soc. Ex. Biol. Med.* 189:45–51

44. Camps, L., Reina, M., Llobera, M., Vilaro, S., Olivecrona, T. 1990. Lipoprotein lipase: cellular origin and functional distribution. *Am. J. Physiol.* 258:C673–81

45. Cara, L., Armand, M., Borel, P., Senft, M., Portugal, H., et al. 1992. Long-term wheat germ intake beneficially affects plasma lipids and lipoproteins in hypercholesterolemic human subjects. *J. Nutr.* 122:317–26

46. Cara, L., Borel, P., Armand, M., Senft, M., Riottot, M., et al. 1991. Effects of increasing levels of raw or defatted wheat germ on liver, feces and plasma lipids and lipoproteins in the rat. *Nutr. Res.* 11:907–16

47. Cara, L., Dubois, C., Borel, P., Armand, M., Senft, M., et al. 1992. Effects of oat bran, rice bran, wheat fiber, and wheat germ on postprandial lipemia in healthy adults. *Am. J. Clin. Nutr.* 55:81–88

48. Carmona, A., Freedland, R. A. 1989. Comparison among the lipogenic potential of various substrates in rat hepatocytes: the differential effects of fructose-containing diets on hepatic lipogenesis. *J. Nutr.* 119:1304–10

49. Chen, W.-J., Anderson, J. W., Jennings, D. 1984. Propionate may mediate the hypocholesterolemic effects of certain soluble plant fibers in cholesterol-fed rats. *Proc. Soc. Exp. Biol. Med.* 175:215–18

50. Cheng, B.-Q., Trimble, R. P., Illman, R. J., Stone, B. A., Topping, D. L. 1987. Comparative effects of dietary wheat bran and its morphological components (aleurone and pericarp-seed coat) on volatile fatty acid concentrations in the rat. *Br. J. Nutr.* 57:69–76

51. Clausen, M. R., Bonnen, H., Mortensen, P. B. 1991. Colonic fermentation of dietary fibre to short chain fatty acids in patients with adenomatous polyps and colonic cancer. *Gut* 32:923–28

52. Clausen, M. R., Mortensen, P. B. 1992. Metabolism of short-chain fatty acids and glucose in colonocytes isolated from fed and starved rats. *Gastroenterology* 102:A205 (Abstr.)

53. Collins, J. F., Herman, P., Schuch, C., Bagby, G. C. Jr. 1992. *c-myc* antisense oligonucleotides inhibit the colony-forming capacity of *Colo 320* colonic carcinoma cells. *J. Clin. Invest.* 89:1523–27

54. Cummings, J. H., Englyst, H. N. 1987. Fermentation in the human large intestine and the available substrates. *Am. J. Clin. Nutr.* 45:1243–55

55. Cummings, J. H., Pomare, E. W., Branch, W. J., Naylor, C. P. E., Macfarlane, G. T. 1987. Short chain fatty acids in human large intestine, portal, hepatic and venous blood. *Gut* 28:1221–27

56. De Caro, J., Boudouard, M., Bonicel, J., Guidoni, A., Desnuelle, P., et al. 1981. Porcine pancreatic lipase. Completion of the primary structure. *Biochim. Biophys. Acta* 671:129–38

57. Demigné, C., Yacoub, C., Rémésy, C. 1986. Effects of absorption of large amounts of volatile fatty acids on rat liver metabolism. *J. Nutr.* 116:77–86

57a. Deng, G., Liu, G., Hu, L., Gum, J. R. Jr., Kim, Y. S. 1992. Transcriptional regulation of the human placental-like alkaline phosphatase gene and mechanisms involved in its induction by sodium butyrate. *Cancer Res.* 52:3378–83

58. DeNigris, S. J., Hamosh, M., Kasbekar, D. K., Fink, C. S., Lee, T. C., et al. 1985. Secretion of human gastric lipase from dispersed gastric glands. *Biochim. Biophys. Acta* 836:67–72

59. DeNigris, S. J., Hamosh, M., Kasbekar, D. K., Lee, T. C., Hamosh, P. 1988. Lingual and gastric lipases: species differences in the origin of prepancreatic digestive lipases and in the localization of gastric lipase. *Biochim. Biophys. Acta* 959:38–45

60. DiPalma, J., Kirk, C. L., Hamosh, M., Colon, A. R., Benjamin, S. B., et al. 1991. Lipase and pepsin activity in the gastric mucosa of infants, children, and adults. *Gastroenterology* 101:116–21

61. Docherty, A. J. P., Bodmer, M. W., Angal, S., Verger, R., Riviere, C., et al. 1985. Molecular cloning and nucleotide sequence of rat lingual lipase cDNA. *Nucleic Acids Res.* 13:1891–1903

62. Eastwood, M. A. 1992. The physiological effect of dietary fiber: an update. *Annu. Rev. Nutr.* 12:19–35

63. Ebihara, K., Schneeman, B. O. 1989.

Interaction of bile acids, phospholipids, cholesterol and triglyceride with dietary fibers in the small intestine of rats. *J. Nutr.* 119:1100–6

64. Edwards, C. A., Wilson, R. G., Hanlon, L., Eastwood, M. A. 1992. Effect of the dietary fibre content of lifelong diet on colonic cellular proliferation in the rat. *Gut* 33:1076–79

65. Elsen, R. J., Bistrian, B. R. 1991. Recent developments in short-chain fatty acid metabolism. *Nutrition* 7:7–10

66. Evans, A. J., Hood, R. L., Oakenfull, D. G., Sidhu, G. S. 1992. Relationship between structure and function of dietary fibre: a comparative study of the effects of three galactomannans on cholesterol metabolism in the rat. *Br. J. Nutr.* 68:217–29

67. Everson, G. T., Daggy, B. P., McKinley, C., Story, J. A. 1992. Effects of psyllium hydrophilic mucilloid on LDL-cholesterol and bile acid synthesis in hypercholesterolemic men. *J. Lipid Res.* 33:1183–92

68. Fernandez, M. L., Trejo, A., McNamara, D. J. 1990. Pectin isolated from prickly pear (*Opuntia sp.*) modifies low density lipoprotein metabolism in cholesterol-fed guinea pigs. *J. Nutr.* 120:1283–90

69. Fink, C. S., Hamosh, P., Hamosh, M. 1984. Fat digestion in the stomach: stability of lingual lipase in the gastric environment. *Pediatr. Res.* 18:248–54

70. Firmansyah, A., Penn, D., Lebenthal, E. 1989. Isolated colonocyte metabolism of glucose, glutamine, *n*-butyrate, and β-hydroxybutyrate in malnutrition. *Gastroenterology* 97:622–29

71. Fleming, S. E., Arce, D. S. 1986. Volatile fatty acids: their production, absorption, utilization, and roles in human health. *Clin. Gastroenterol.* 15: 787–814

72. Fleming, S. E., Choi, S. Y., Fitch, M. D. 1991. Absorption of short-chain fatty acids from the rat cecum in vivo. *J. Nutr.* 121:1787–97

73. Fleming, S. E., Fitch, M. D., DeVries, S. 1992. The influence of dietary fiber on proliferation of intestinal mucosal cells in miniature swine may not be mediated primarily by fermentation. *J. Nutr.* 122:906–16

74. Fleming, S. E., Fitch, M. D., DeVries, S., Liu, M. L., Kight, C. 1991. Nutrient utilization by cells isolated from rat jejunum, cecum and colon. *J. Nutr.* 121:869–78

75. Foss, F. M., Veillette, A., Sartor, O., Rosen, N., Bolen, J. B. 1989. Alterations in the expression of pp60[c-src] and

p56[lck] associated with butyrate-induced differentiation of human colon carcinoma cells. *Oncog. Res.* 5:13–23

76. Freeman, H. J. 1986. Effects of differing concentrations of sodium butyrate on 1,2-dimenthylhydrazine-induced rat intestinal neoplasia. *Gastroenterology* 91:596–602

77. Frégeau, C. J., Helgason, C. D., Bleackley, C. R. 1992. Two cytotoxic cell proteinase genes are differentially sensitive to sodium butyrate. *Nucleic Acids Res.* 20:3113–19

78. Gargouri, Y., Moreau, H., Jain, M. K., de Haas, G. H., Verger, R. 1989. Ajoene prevents fat digestion by human gastric lipase in vitro. *Biochim. Biophys. Acta* 1006:137–39

79. Gargouri, Y., Moreau, H., Pieroni, G., Verger, R. 1988. Human gastric lipase: a sulfhydryl enzyme. *J. Biol. Chem.* 263:2159–62

80. Gargouri, Y., Moreau, H., Verger, R. 1989. Gastric lipases: biochemical and physiological studies. *Biochim. Biophys. Acta* 1006:255–71

81. Gargouri, Y., Pieroni, G., Ferrato, F., Verger, R. 1987. Human gastric lipase. A kinetic study with dicaprin monolayers. *Eur. J. Biochem.* 169:125–29

82. Gargouri, Y., Pieroni, G., Lowe, P. A., Sarda, L., Verger, R. 1986. Human gastric lipase. The effect of amphiphiles. *Eur. J. Biochem.* 156:305–10

83. Gargouri, Y., Pieroni, G., Rivière, C., Lowe, P. A., Saunière, J-F., et al. 1986. Importance of human gastric lipase for intestinal lipolysis: an in vitro study. *Biochim. Biophys. Acta* 879:419–23

84. Gargouri, Y., Pieroni, G., Rivière, C., Saunière, J-F., Lowe, P. A., et al. 1986. Kinetic assay of human gastric lipase on short- and long-chain triacylglycerol emulsions. *Gastroenterology* 91:919–25

85. Gibbons, G. F., Pullinger, C. R. 1979. Utilization of endogenous and exogenous sources of substrate for cholesterol biosynthesis by isolated hepatocytes. *Biochem. J.* 177:255–63

86. Gibson, P. R., Moeller, I., Kagelari, O., Folino, M. 1990. Contrasting effects of butyrate on the differentiation of normal and neoplastic colonic epithelial cells in vitro. *Gastroenterology* 98:A495 (Abstr.)

87. Gilbert, H. J., Hazlewood, G. P. 1991. Genetic modification of fibre digestion. *Proc. Nutr. Soc.* 50:173–86

88. Gjellesvik, D. R. 1991. Fatty acid specificity of bile salt-dependent lipase: enzyme recognition and super-substrate

effects. *Biochim. Biophys. Acta* 1086: 167–72

89. Glauber, J. G., Wandersee, N. J., Little, J. A., Ginder, G. D. 1991. 5′-Flanking sequences mediate butyrate stimulation of embryonic globin gene expression in adult erythroid cells. *Mol. Cell. Biol.* 11:4690–97

90. Goldberg, P. Y., Leaner, V. D., Parker, I. M. 1992. Elevation of large-T antigen production by sodium butyrate treatment of SV40-transformed WI-38 fibroblasts. *J. Cell. Biochem.* 49:74–81

91. Golub, E. I., Li, G., Volsky, D. J. 1991. Induction of dormant HIV-1 by sodium butyrate: involvement of the TATA box in the activation of the HIV-1 promoter. *Aids* 5:663–68

92. Goodlad, R. A., Lenton, W., Ghatei, M. A., Adrian, T. E., Bloom, S. R., et al. 1987. Effects of an elemental diet, inert bulk and different types of dietary fibre on the response of the intestinal epithelium to refeeding in the rat and relationship to plasma gastrin, enteroglucagon, and PYY concentrations. *Gut* 28:171–80

93. Gresti, J., Bugaut, M., Maniongui, C., Bezard, J. 1993. Composition of molecular species of triacylglycerols in bovine milk fat. *J. Dairy Sci.* In press

94. Gum, J. R., Kam, W. K., Byrd, J. C., Hicks, J. W., Sleisenger, M. H., et al. 1987. Effects of sodium butyrate on human colonic adenocarcinoma cells. Induction of placental-like alkaline phosphatase. *J. Biol. Chem.* 262: 1092–97

95. Hamosh, M., ed. 1990. *Lingual and Gastric Lipases: Their Role in Fat Digestion.* Boca Raton, Fla: CRC Press

96. Hamosh, M., Bitman, J., Liao, T. H., Mehta, N. R., Buczek, R. J., et al. 1989. Gastric lipolysis and fat absorption in preterm infants: effect of medium-chain triglyceride or long-chain triglyceride-containing formulas. *Pediatrics* 83:86–92

97. Harig, J. M., Knaup, S. M., Shoshara, J., Dudeja, P. K., Ramaswamy, K., et al. Transport of *N*-butyrate into human colonic luminal membrane vesicles. 1990. *Gastroenterology* 98:A543 (Abstr.)

98. Hatch, M. 1987. Short-chain fatty acid transport and its effects on ion transport by rabbit cecum. *Am. J. Physiol.* 253: G171–78

99. Heerdt, B. G., Augenlicht, L. H. 1991. Effects of fatty acids on expression of genes encoding subunits of cytochrome c oxidase and cytochrome c oxidase activity in HT29 human colonic ade-

nocarcinoma cells. *J. Biol. Chem.* 266: 19120–26

100. Heerdt, B. G., Halsey, H. K., Lipkin, M., Augenlicht, L. H. 1990. Expression of mitochondrial cytochrome c oxidase in human colonic cell differentiation, transformation, and risk for colonic cancer. *Cancer Res.* 50:1596–1600

101. Hendzel, M. J., Delcuve, G. P., Davie, J. R. 1991. Histone deacetylase is a component of the internal nuclear matrix. *J. Biol. Chem.* 266:21936–42

102. Herz, F., Halwer, M. 1990. Differential effects of sodium butyrate and hyperosmolality on the modulation of alkaline phosphatases of LoVo cells. *Exp. Cell Res.* 188:50–54

103. Hide, W. A., Chan, L., Li, W-H. 1992. Structure and evolution of the lipase superfamily. *J. Lipid Res.* 33: 167–78

104. Hoverstad, T. 1986. Studies of short-chain fatty acid absorption in man. *Scand. J. Gastroenterol.* 21:257–60

105. Hundemer, J. K., Nabar, S. P., Shriver, B. J., Forman, L. P. 1991. Dietary fiber sources lower blood cholesterol in C57BL/6 mice. *J. Nutr.* 121:1360–65

106. Ide, T., Moriuchi, H., Nihimoto, K. 1991. Hypolipidemic effects of guar gum and its enzyme hydrolysate in rats fed highly saturated fat diets. *Ann. Nutr. Metab.* 35:34–44

107. Ide, T., Okamatsu, H., Sugano, M. 1978. Regulation by dietary fats of 3-hydroxy-3-metylglutaryl-coenzyme A reductase in rat liver. *J. Nutr.* 108:601–12

108. Ikeda, I., Tomari, Y., Sugano, M. 1989. Interrelated effects of dietary fiber and fat on lymphatic cholesterol and triglyceride absorption in rats. *J. Nutr.* 119:1383–87

109. Illman, R. J., Topping, D. L. 1985. Effects of dietary oat bran on faecal steroid excretion, plasma volatile fatty acids and lipid synthesis in rats. *Nutr. Res.* 5:839–46

110. Illman, R. J., Topping, D. L., Dowling, K., Trimble, R. P., Russell, G. R., et al. 1991. Effects of solvent extraction on the hypocholesterolaemic action of oat bran in the rat. *Br. J. Nutr.* 65:435–43

111. Illman, R. J., Topping, D. L., McIntosh, G. H., Trimble, R. P., Storer, G. B., et al. 1988. Hypocholesterolaemic effects of dietary propionate: studies in whole animals and perfused rat liver. *Ann. Nutr. Metab.* 32:97–107

112. Illman, R. J., Trimble, R. P., Snoswell, A. M., Topping, D. L. 1982. Daily

variations in the concentrations of volatile fatty acids in the splanchnic blood vessels of rats fed diets high in pectin and bran. *Nutr. Rep. Int.* 26:439–46

113. Indira, M., Kurup, P. A. 1989. Effects of neutral detergent fiber from blackgram (*Phaseolus mungo*) in rats and rabbits. *J. Nutr.* 119:1246–51

114. Innis, S. M. 1992. Human milk and formula fatty acids. *J. Pediatr.* 120: S56–61

115. Jacobs, L. R. 1986. Modification of experimental colon carcinogenesis by dietary fibers. *Adv. Exp. Med. Biol.* 206:105–18

116. Jacobs, L. R. 1986. Relationship between dietary fiber and cancer: metabolic, physiologic, and cellular mechanisms. *Proc. Soc. Exp. Biol. Med.* 183:299–310

117. Jacobs, L. R., Lupton, J. R. 1984. Effect of dietary fibers on rat large bowel mucosal growth and cell proliferation. *Am. J. Physiol.* 246:G378–85

118. Jacobs, L. R., Lupton, J. R. 1986. Relationship between colonic luminal pH, cell proliferation, and colon carcinogenesis in 1,2-dimethylhydrazine treated rats fed high fiber diets. *Cancer Res.* 46:1727–34

119. Jensen, R. G., Clark, R. M., deJong, F. A., Hamosh, M., Liao, T. H., et al. 1982. The lipolytic triad: human lingual, breast milk, and pancreatic lipases: physiological implications of their characteristics in digestion of dietary fats. *J. Pediatr. Gastroenterol. Nutr.* 1:243–55

120. Johnson, I. T. 1990. Fibre sources for the food industry. *Proc. Nutr. Soc.* 49:31–38

121. Joshi, S. S., Jackson, J. D., Sharp, J. G. 1985. Differentiation inducing effects of butyrate and DMSO on human intestinal tumor cell lines in culture. *Cancer Detect. Prevent.* 8:237–45

122. Kahlon, T. S., Chow, F. I., Sayre, R. N., Betschart, A. A. 1992. Cholesterol-lowering in hamsters fed rice bran at various levels, defatted rice bran and rice bran oil. *J. Nutr.* 122:513–19

123. Karlstad, M. D., Killeffer, J. A., Bailey, J. W., DeMichele, S. J. 1992. Parenteral nutrition with short- and long-chain triglycerides: triacetin reduces atrophy of small and large bowel mucosa and improves protein metabolism in burned rats. *Am. J. Clin. Nutr.* 55:1005–11

124. Kashtan, H., Stern, H. S., Jenkins, D. J. A., Jenkins, A. L., Hay, K., et al. 1992. Wheat-bran and oat-bran supplements' effects on blood lipids and lipoproteins. *Am. J. Clin. Nutr.* 55:976–80

125. Keenan, T. W., Dylewski, D. P., Ghosal, D., Keon, B. H. 1992. Milk lipid globule precursor release from endoplasmic reticulum reconstituted in a cell-free system. *Eur. J. Cell Biol.* 57:21–29

126. Kestin, M., Moss, R., Clifton, P. M., Nestel, P. J. 1990. Comparative effects of three cereal brans on plasma lipids, blood pressure, and glucose metabolism in mildly hypercholesterolemic men. *Am. J. Clin. Nutr.* 52:661–66

127. Kim, Y. S., Tsao, D., Siddiqui, B., Whitehead, J. S., Arnstein, P., et al. 1980. Effects of sodium butyrate and dimenthylsulfoxide on biochemical properties of human colon cancer cells. *Cancer* 45:1185–92

128. Kingman, S. M. 1991. The influence of legume seeds on human plasma lipid concentrations. *Nutr. Res. Rev.* 4:97–123

129. Klehr, D., Schlake, T., Maass, K., Bode, J. 1992. Scaffold-attached regions (SAR elements) mediate transcriptional effects due to butyrate. *Biochemistry* 31:3222–29

130. Körber, J., Soudah, B., Schmidt, F. W. 1992. Effects of short chain fatty acids irrigation on excluded inflamed segments of the colon in Crohn's disease. *Gastroenterology* 102:A648 (Abstr.)

131. Koruda, M. J., Rolandelli, R. H., Settle, G. R., Zimmaro, D. M., Rombeau, J. L. 1988. Effect of parenteral nutrition supplemented with short-chain fatty acids on adaptation to massive small bowel resection. *Gastroenterology* 95:715–20

132. Koruda, M. J., Rolandelli, R. H., Zimmaro, D. M., Hastings, J., Rombeau, J. L., et al. 1990. Parenteral nutrition supplemented with short-chain fatty acids: effect on the small-bowel mucosa in normal rats. *Am. J. Clin. Nutr.* 51:685–89

133. Kripke, S. A., De Paula, J. A., Berman, J. M., Fox, A. D., Rombeau, J. L., et al. 1991. Experimental short-bowel syndrome: effect of an elemental diet supplemented with short-chain triglycerides. *Am. J. Clin. Nutr.* 53:954–62

134. Kripke, S. A., Fox, A. D., Berman, J. M., Settle, G. R., Rombeau, J. L. 1989. Stimulation of intestinal mucosal growth with intracolonic infusion of short-chain fatty acids. *J. Parenter. Enter. Nutr.* 13:109–16

135. Kritchevsky, D. 1988. Dietary fiber. *Annu. Rev. Nutr.* 8:301–28
136. Kruh, J. 1982. Effects of sodium butyrate, a new pharmacological agent, on cells in culture. *Mol. Cell. Biochem.* 42:65–82
137. Lampe, J. W., Slavin, J. L., Baglien, K. S., Thompson, W. O., Duane, W. C., et al. 1991. Serum lipid and fecal bile acid changes with cereal, vegetable, and sugar-beet fiber feeding. *Am. J. Clin. Nutr.* 53:1235–41
137a. Lebenthal, E., Lee, P. C. 1980. Development of functional response in human exocrine pancreas. *Pediatrics* 66:556–60
138. Lei, K.-J., Gluzman, Y., Pan, C.-J., Chou, J. Y. 1992. Immortalization of virus-free human placental cells that express tissue-specific functions. *Mol. Endocrinol.* 6:703–12
139. Levrat, M.-A., Behr, S. R., Rémésy, C., Demigné, C. 1991. Effects of soybean fiber on cecal digestion in rats previously adapted to a fiber-free diet. *J. Nutr.* 121:672–78
140. Liao, T. H., Hamosh, P., Hamosh, M. 1984. Fat digestion by lingual lipase: mechanism of lipolysis in the stomach and upper small intestine. *Pediatr. Res.* 18:402–9
141. Lindström, M. B., Persson, J., Thurn, L., Borgström, B. 1991. Effect of pancreatic phospholipase A_2 and gastric lipase on the action of pancreatic carboxyl ester lipase against lipid substrates in vitro. *Biochim. Biophys. Acta* 1084:194–97
142. Lipkin, M. 1988. Biomarkers of increased susceptibility to gastrointestinal cancer: new application to studies of cancer prevention in human subjects. *Cancer Res.* 48:235–45
143. Lutton, C., Ferezou, J., Sérougne, C., Verneau, C., Champarnaud, G., et al. 1990. Critical analysis of the use of ^{14}C-acetate for measuring in vivo rat cholesterol synthesis. *Reprod. Nutr. Dev.* 30:71–84
144. Macfarlane, G. T., Gibson, G. R., Beatty, E., Cummings, J. H. 1992. Estimation of short-chain fatty acid production from protein by human intestinal bacteria based on branched-chain fatty acid measurements. *FEMS Microbiol. Ecol.* 101:81–88
145. Malville-Shipan, K., Fleming, S. E. 1992. Wheat bran and corn oil do not influence proliferation in the colon of healthy rats when energy intakes are equivalent. *J. Nutr.* 122:37–45
146. Maniongui, C., Gresti, J., Bugaut, M.,

Gauthier, S., Bezard, J. 1991. Determination of bovine butterfat triacylglycerols by reversed-phase liquid chromatography and gas chromatography. *J. Chromatogr.* 543:81–103
147. Marty, J., Vernay, M. 1984. Absorption and metabolism of the volatile fatty acids in the hind-gut of the rabbit. *Br. J. Nutr.* 51:265–77
148. Mascolo, N., Rajendran, V. M., Binder, H. J. 1991. Mechanism of short-chain fatty acid uptake by apical membrane vesicles of rat distal colon. *Gastroenterology* 101:331–38
149. Mathers, J. C. 1991. Digestion of non-starch polysaccharides by non-ruminant omnivores. *Proc. Nutr. Soc.* 50:161–72
150. Mazur, A., Gueux, E., Felgines, C., Bayle, D., Nassir, F., et al. 1992. Effects of dietary fermentable fiber on fatty acid synthesis and triglyceride secretion in rats fed fructose-based diet: studies with sugar-beet fiber. *Proc. Soc. Exp. Biol. Med.* 199:345–50
151. Mazur, A., Rémésy, C., Gueux, E., Levrat, M.-A., Demigné, C. 1990. Effects of diets rich in fermentable carbohydrates on plasma lipoprotein levels and on lipoprotein catabolism in rats. *J. Nutr.* 120:1037–45
152. McBurney, M. I., Thompson, L. U. 1989. Effect of human faecal donor on in vitro fermentation variables. *Scand. J. Gastroenterol.* 24:359–67
153. McIntosh, G. H., Whyte, J., McArthur, R., Nestel, P. J. 1991. Barley and wheat foods: influence on plasma cholesterol concentrations in hypercholesterolemic men. *Am. J. Clin. Nutr.* 53:1205–9
154. McIntyre, A., Young, G. P., Taranto, T., Gibson, P. R., Ward, P. B. 1991. Different fibers have different regional effects on luminal contents of rat colon. *Gastroenterology* 101:1274–81
155. McLean Ross, A. H., Eastwood, M. A., Brydon, W. G., Anderson, J. R., Anderson, D. M. W. 1983. A study of the effects of dietary gum arabic in humans. *Am. J. Clin. Nutr.* 37:368–75
156. McNeil, N. I. 1984. The contribution of the large intestine to energy supplies in man. *Am. J. Clin. Nutr.* 39:338–42
157. Morand, C., Rémésy, C., Levrat, M.-A., Demigné, C. 1992. Replacement of digestible wheat starch by resistant cornstarch alters splanchnic metabolism in rats. *J. Nutr.* 122:345–54
158. Moreau, H., Abergel, C., Carrière, F., Ferrato, F., Fontecilla-Camps, J. C., et al. 1992. Isoform purification

of gastric lipases. Towards crystallization. *J. Mol. Biol.* 225:147–53

159. Moreau, H., Bernadac, A., Gargouri, Y., Benkouka, F., Laugier, R., et al. 1989. Immunocytolocalization of human gastric lipase in chief cells of the fundic mucosa. *Histochemistry* 91: 419–23

160. Moreau, H., Gargouri, Y., Lecat, D., Junien, J. L., Verger, R. 1988. Screening of preduodenal lipases in several mammals. *Biochim. Biophys. Acta* 959: 247–52

161. Moreau, H., Laugier, R., Gargouri, Y., Ferrato, F., Verger, R. 1988. Human preduodenal lipase is entirely of gastric fundic origin. *Gastroenterology* 95:1221–26

162. Moreau, H., Saunière, J. F., Gargouri, Y., Pieroni, G., Verger, R., et al. 1988. Human gastric lipase: variations induced by gastrointestinal hormones and by pathology. *Scand. J. Gastroenterol.* 23:1044–48

163. Moreau, J., Bouisson, M., Balas, D., Ravaud, A., Stupnik, S., et al. 1990. Gastric lipase in alcoholic pancreatitis. Comparison of secretive profiles following pentagastrin stimulation in normal adults and patients with pancreatic insufficiency. *Gastroenterology* 99: 175–80

164. Mortensen, F. V., Hessov, I., Birke, H., Korsgaard, N., Nielsen, H. 1991. Microcirculatory and trophic effects of short chain fatty acids in the human rectum after Hartmann's procedure. *Br. J. Surg.* 78:1208–11

165. Mortensen, F. V., Nielsen, H., Mulvany, M. J., Hessov, I. 1990. Short chain fatty acids dilate isolated human colonic resistance arteries. *Gut* 31: 1391–94

166. Muir, J. G., O'Dea, K. 1992. Measurement of resistant starch: factors affecting the amount of starch escaping digestion in vitro. *Am. J. Clin. Nutr.* 56:123–27

167. Murray, R. D., McClung, J. H., Li, U. B. K., Ailabouni, A. 1989. Stimulatory effects of short-chain fatty acids on colonic absorption in newborn piglets in vivo. *J. Pediatr. Gastroenterol. Nutr.* 8:95–101

168. Myher, J. J., Kuksis, A., Marai, L. 1988. Identification of the more complex triacylglycerols in bovine milk fat by gas chromatography-mass spectrometry using polar capillary colums. *J. Chromatogr.* 452:93–118

169. Niles, R. M., Wilhelm, S. A., Thomas, P., Zamcheck, N. 1988. The effect of sodium butyrate and retinoic acid on

growth and CEA production in a series of human colorectal tumor cell lines representing different states of differentiation. *Cancer Invest.* 6:39–45

170. Nishina, P. M., Freedland, R. A. 1990. Effects of propionate on lipid biosynthesis in isolated rat hepatocytes. *J. Nutr.* 120:668–73

171. Nishina, P. M., Freedland, R. A. 1990. The effects of dietary fiber feeding on cholesterol metabolism in rats. *J. Nutr.* 120:800–5

172. Nishina, P. M., Schneeman, B. O., Freedland, R. A. 1991. Effects of dietary fibers on nonfasting plasma lipoprotein and apolipoprotein levels in rats. *J. Nutr.* 121:431–37

173. Nordenström, J., Neeser, G., Olivecrona, T., Wahren, J. 1991. Effect of medium and long-chain triglyceride infusion on lipoprotein and hepatic lipase in healthy subjects. *Eur. J. Clin. Invest.* 21:580–85

174. Nutting, C. W., Islam, S., Daugirdas, J. T. 1991. Vasorelaxant effects of short chain fatty acid salts in rat caudal artery. *Am. J. Physiol.* 261:H561–67

175. Oliva, R., Bazett-Jones, D. P., Locklear, L., Dixon, G. H. 1990. Histone hyperacetylation can induce unfolding of the nucleosome core particle. *Nucleic Acids Res.* 18:2739–47

176. Olivecrona, T., Bengtsson, G. 1983. Lipoprotein lipase. In *The Adipocyte and Obesity: Cellular and Molecular Mechanisms,* ed. A. Angel, C. H. Hollenberg, D. A. K. Roncari, pp. 117–26. New York: Raven

177. Otaka, M., Singhal, A., Hakomori, S.-I. 1989. Antibody-mediated targeting of differentiation inducers to tumor cells: inhibition of colonic cancer cell growth in vitro and in vivo. A preliminary note. *Biochem. Biophys. Res. Commun.* 158:202–8

178. Otsuka, M., Satchithanandam, S., Calvert, R. J. 1989. Influence of meal distribution of wheat bran on fecal bulk, gastrointestinal transit time and colonic thymidine kinase activity in the rat. *J. Nutr.* 119:566–72

179. Peters, S. G., Pomare, E. W., Fisher, C. A. 1992. Portal and peripheral blood short chain fatty acid concentrations after caecal lactulose instillation at surgery. *Gut* 33:1249–52

180. Pfeffer, U., Vidali, G. 1991. Histone acetylation: recent approaches to a basic mechanism of genome organization. *Int. J. Biochem.* 23:277–85

181. Pomare, E. W., Branch, W. J., Cummings, J. H. 1985. Carbohydrate fermentation in the human colon and its

relation to acetate concentrations in venous blood. *J. Clin. Invest.* 75:1448–54

182. Proia, A. D., McNamara, D. J., Edwards, K. D. G., Anderson, K. E. 1981. Effects of dietary pectin and cellulose on hepatic and intestinal mixed-function oxidations and hepatic 3-hydroxy-3-methylglutaryl-coenzyme. A reductase in the rat. *Biochem. Pharmacol.* 30:2553–58

183. Propionate and cholesterol homeostasis in animals 1987. *Nutr. Rev.* 45:188–90

184. Qureshi, A. A., Burger, W. C., Peterson, D. M., Elson, C. 1985. Suppression of cholesterogenesis by plant constituents: review of Wisconsin contributions to NC-167. *Lipids* 20:817–24

185. Rechkemmer, G., Rönnau, K., von Engelhardt, W. 1988. Fermentation of polysaccharides and absorption of short chain fatty acids in the mammalian hindgut. *Comp. Biochem. Physiol. A* 90:563–68

186. Rechkemmer, G., von Engelhardt, W. 1988. Concentration- and pH-dependence of short-chain fatty acid absorption in the proximal and distal colon of guinea pig *(Cavia Porcellus). Comp. Biochem. Physiol. A* 91:659-63

187. Redard, C. L., Davis, P. A., Schneeman, B. O. 1990. Dietary fiber and gender: effect on postprandial lipemia. *Am. J. Clin. Nutr.* 52:837–45

188. Reynolds, D. A., Rajendran, V. M., Binder, H. J. 1991. Butyrate transport in rat distal colon basolateral membrane vesicles: evidence for bicarbonate/butyrate exchange. *Gastroenterology* 100: A838 (Abstr.)

189. Roediger, W. E. W. 1982. Utilization of nutrients by isolated epithetial cells of the rat colon. *Gastroenterology* 83: 424–29

190. Rolandelli, R. H., Koruda, M. J., Settle, G. R., Rombeau, J. L. 1986. Effects of intraluminal infusion of short-chain fatty acids on the healing of colonic anastomosis in the rat. *Surgery* 100:198–203

191. Rombeau, J. L., Kripke, S. A. 1990. Metabolic and intestinal effects of short-chain fatty acids. *J. Parent. Enter. Nutr.* 14:S181–85 (Suppl.)

192. Rönnau, K., Guth, D., von Engelhardt, W. 1989. Absorption of dissociated and undissociated short-chain fatty acids across the colonic epithelium of guinea-pig. *Q. J. Exp. Physiol.* 74:511–19

193. Rowe, W. A., Bayless, T. M. 1992. Colonic short-chain fatty acids: fuel from the lumen. *Gastroenterology* 103: 336–39

194. Rowe, W. A., Montrose, M. H. 1991. Short chain fatty acids activate multiple ion transport mechanisms in a human colon cell line. *Gastroenterology* 100: A701 (Abstr.)

195. Rustgi, A. K., Podolsky, D. K. 1992. The molecular basis of colon cancer. *Annu. Rev. Med.* 43:61–68

196. Sablé, R., Sicart, R., Berry, E. 1990. Steroid pattern of bile and feces in response to a fruit-enriched diet in hypercholesterolemic hamsters. *Ann. Nutr. Metab.* 34:303–10

197. Sakata, T. 1986. Effects of indigestible dietary bulk and short chain fatty acids on the tissue weight and epithelial cell proliferation rate of the digestive tract in rats. *J. Nutr. Sci. Vitaminol.* 32:355–62

198. Sakata, T. 1987. Stimulatory effect of short-chain fatty acids on epithelial cell proliferation in the rat intestine: a possible explanation for trophic effects of fermentable fibre, gut microbes and luminal trophic factors. *Br. J. Nutr.* 58:95–103

199. Sakata, T. 1989. Stimulatory effect of short-chain fatty acids on epithelial cell proliferation of isolated and denervated jejunal segment of the rat. *Scand. J. Gastroenterol.* 24:886–90

200. Sakata, T., von Engelhardt, W. 1983. Stimulatory effect of short chain fatty acids on the epithelial cell proliferation in rat large intestine. *Comp. Biochem. Physiol.* 74A:459–62

201. Saunders, D. R. 1991. Absorption of short-chain fatty acids in human stomach and rectum. *Nutr. Res.* 11: 841–47

202. Savage, D. C. 1986. Gastrointestinal microflora in mammalian nutrition. *Annu. Rev. Nutr.* 6:155–78

203. Schaudies, P. R., Satchithanandam, S., Calvert, R. J. 1991. Alteration in levels of immunoreactive epidermal growth factor in the gastrointestinal mucosa of fischer rats fed a diet containing 10% wheat bran. *J. Nutr.* 121: 800–5

204. Scheppach, W., Bach, M., Bartram, P., Christl, S., Bergthaller, W., et al. 1991. Colonic fermentation of potato starch after a freeze-thaw cycle. *Dig. Dis. Sci.* 36:1601–5

205. Scheppach, W., Bartram, P., Richter, A., Richter, F., Liepold, H., et al. 1992. Effect of short-chain fatty acids on the human colonic mucosa in vitro. *J. Parent. Enter. Nutr.* 16:43–48

206. Scheppach, W., Sommer, H., Kirchner, T., Paganelli, G.-M., Bartram, P., et al. 1992. Effect of butyrate enemas

on the colonic mucosa in distal ulcerative colitis. *Gastroenterology* 103:51–56

207. Schroy, P., Rustgi, A., Ikonomu, K., Polito, J., O'Keene, J. C. 1991. Growth inhibition and differentiation are independently regulated in HT29 colon cancer cells. *Gastroenterology* 100:A399 (Abstr.)

208. Sellin, J. H., DeSoignie, R. 1990. Short-chain fatty acid absorption in rabbit colon in vitro. *Gastroenterology* 99:676–83

209. Senda, M., Oka, K., Brown, V. W., Qasba, P. K. 1987. Molecular cloning and sequence of a cDNA coding for bovine lipoprotein lipase. *Proc. Natl. Acad. Sci. USA* 84:4369–73

210. Settle, R. G. 1988. Invited comment: short-chain fatty acids and their potential role in nutritional support. *J. Parenter. Enter. Nutr.* 12:S104–7 (Suppl.)

211. Shefer, S., Nguyen, L. B., Salen, G., Ness, G. C., Chowdhary, I. R., et al. 1992. Differing effects of cholesterol and taurocholate on steady state hepatic HMG-CoA reductase and cholesterol 7α-hydroxylase activities and mRNA levels in the rat. *J. Lipid Res.* 33:1193–1200

212. Shinnick, F. L., Ink, S. L., Marlett, J A. 1990. Dose response to a dietary oat bran fraction in cholesterol-fed rats. *J. Nutr.* 120:561–68

213. Small, D. M. 1991. The effects of glyceride structure on absorption and metabolism. *Annu. Rev. Nutr.* 11:413–34

214. Souleimani, A., Asselin, C. 1992. Regulation of proto-oncogene expression by sodium butyrate in the human colon carcinoma cell line CACO-2. *Gastroenterology* 102:A400 (Abstr.)

215. Steinhart, A. H., Brzezinski, A., Baker, J. P. 1992. Butyrate enemas in the treatment of refractory distal ulcerative colitis: an open label trial. *Gastroenterology* 102:A700

216. Sternby, B., Holtmann, G., Kelly, D. G., DiMagno, E. P. 1992. Effect of gastric or duodenal nutrient infusion on gastric and pancreatic lipase secretion. *Gastroenterology* 102:A292 (Abstr.)

217. Swan, J. S., Hoffman, M. M., Lord, M. K., Poechmann, J. L. 1992. Two forms of human milk bile-salt-stimulated lipase. *Biochem. J.* 283: 119–22

218. Thacker, P. A., Bowland, J. P. 1981. Effects of dietary propionic acid on serum lipids and lipoproteins of pigs fed diets supplemented with soybean meal or canola meal. *Can. J. Anim. Sci.* 61:439–48

219. Thacker, P. A., Bowland, J. P., Fenton, M. 1982. Effects of vitamin B_{12} on serum lipids and lipoproteins of pigs fed diets supplemented with propionic acid or calcium propionate. *Can. J. Anim. Sci.* 62:527–36

220. Thacker, P. A., Salomons, M. O., Aherne, F. X., Milligan, L. P., Bowland, J. P. 1981. Influence of propionic acid on the cholesterol metabolism of pigs fed hypercholesterolemic diets. *Can. J. Anim. Sci.* 61:969–75

221. Tiruppathi, C., Balasubramanian, K. A. 1982. Purification and properties of an acid lipase from human gastric juice. *Biochim. Biophys. Acta* 712:692–97

222. Titgemeyer, E. C., Bourquin, L. D., Fahey, G. C. Jr., Garleb, K. A. 1991. Fermentability of various fiber sources by human fecal bacteria in vitro. *Am. J. Clin. Nutr.* 53:1418–24

223. Titus, E., Ahearn, G. A. 1992. Vertebrate gastrointestinal fermentation: transport mechanisms for volatile fatty acids. *Am. J. Physiol.* 262:R547–53

224. Todesco, T., Rao, V. A., Bosello, O., Jenkins, D. J. A. 1991. Propionate lowers blood glucose and alters lipid metabolism in healthy subjects. *Am. J. Clin. Nutr.* 54:860–65

225. Topping, D. L. 1991. Soluble fiber polysaccharides: effects on plasma cholesterol and colonic fermentation. *Nutr. Rev.* 49:195–203

226. Topping, D. L., Illman, R. J., Roach, P. D., Trimble, R. P., Kambouris, A., et al. 1990. Modulation of the hypolipidemic effect of fish oils by dietary fiber in rats: studies with rice and wheat bran. *J. Nutr.* 120:325–30

227. Topping, D. L., Oakenfull, D., Trimble, R. P., Illman, R. J. 1988. A viscous fibre (methylcellulose) lowers blood glucose and plasma triacylglycerols and increases liver glycogen independently of volatile fatty acid production in the rat. *Br. J. Nutr.* 59:21–30

228. Toribara, N. W., Sack, T. L., Gum, J. R., Ho, S. B., Shively, J. E., et al. 1989. Heterogeneity in the induction and expression of carcinoembryonic antigen-related antigens in human colon cancer cell lines. *Cancer Res.* 49:3321–27

229. Tovar, J., Björck, I. M., Asp, N-G. 1992. Incomplete digestion of legume starches in rats: a study of precooked flours containing retrograded and physically inaccessible starch fractions. *J. Nutr.* 122:1500–7

230. Tsao, D., Morita, A., Bella, A. Jr., Luu, P., Kim, Y. S. 1982. Differential effects of sodium butyrate, dimethyl sulfoxide, and retinoic acid on membrane-associated antigen, enzymes, and glycoproteins of human rectal adenocarcinoma cells. *Cancer Res.* 42:1052–58

231. Tsuji, K., Shimizu, M., Nishimura, Y., Nakagawa, Y., Ichikawa, T. 1992. Simultaneous determination of hydrogen, methane and carbon dioxide of breath using gas-solid chromatography. *J. Nutr. Sci. Vitaminol.* 38:103–9

232. Venter, C. S., Vorster, H. H. 1989. Possible metabolic consequences of fermentation in the colon for humans. *Med. Hypotheses* 29:161–66

233. Venter, C. S., Vorster, H. H., Cummings, J. H. 1990. Effects of dietary propionate on carbohydrate and lipid metabolism in healthy volunteers. *Am. J. Gastroenterol.* 85:549–53

234. Venter, C. S., Vorster, H. H., van der Nest, D. G. 1990. Comparison between physiological effects of konjac-glucomannan and propionate in baboons fed "Western" diets. *J. Nutr.* 120:1046–53

235. Vernay, M. 1986. Colonic absorption of inorganic ions and volatile fatty acids in the rabbit. *Comp. Biochem. Physiol. A* 83:775–84

236. Vince A. J., McNeil, N. I., Wager, J. D., Wrong, O. M. 1990. The effect of lactulose, pectin, arabinogalactan and cellulose on the production of organic acids and metabolism of ammonia by intestinal bacteria in a faecal incubation system. *Br. J. Nutr.* 63:17–26

237. Wang, C-S. 1991. Structure and functional properties of apolipoprotein C-II. *Prog. Lipid Res.* 30:253–58

238. Wang, C-S., Hartsuck, J., McConathy, W. J. 1992. Structure and functional properties of lipoprotein lipase. *Biochim. Biophys. Acta* 1123:1–17

239. Weaver, G. A., Krause, J. A., Miller, T. L., Wolin, M. J. 1988. Short chain fatty acid distributions of enema samples from a sigmoidoscopy population: an association of high acetate and low butyrate ratios with adenomatous polyps and colon cancer. *Gut* 29:1539–43

240. Weaver, G. A., Krause, J. A., Miller, T. L., Wolin, M. J. 1992. Cornstarch fermentation by the colonic microbial community yields more butyrate than does cabbage fiber fermentation; cornstarch fermentation rates correlate negatively with methanogenesis. *Am. J. Clin. Nutr.* 55:70–77

241. Whitehead, R. H., Young, G. P., Bhathal, P. S. 1986. Effects of short chain fatty acids on a new human colon carcinoma cell line (LIM1215). *Gut* 27:1457–63

242. Williams, N. N., Brannigan, A., Fitzpatrick, J. M., O'Connell, P. R. 1992. Glutamine and butyric acid metabolism measurement in biopsy specimens (ex vivo): a method of assessing treatment on inflammatory bowel conditions. *Gastroenterology* 102:A713 (Abstr.)

243. Wolever, T. M. S., Brighenti, F., Royall, D., Jenkins, A. L., Jenkins, D. J. A. 1989. Effect of rectal infusion of short chain fatty acids in human subjects. *Am. J. Gastroenterol.* 84:1027–33

244. Wolever, T. M. S., Spadafora, P., Eshuis, H. 1991. Interaction between colonic acetate and propionate in humans. *Am. J. Clin. Nutr.* 53:681–87

245. Wright, S. R., Anderson, J. W., Bridges, S. R. 1990. Propionate inhibits hepatocyte lipid synthesis. *Proc. Soc. Exp. Biol. Med.* 195:26–29

246. Yasui, W., Sumiyoshi, H., Hata, J., Kameda, T., Ochiai, A., et al 1988. Expression of epidermal growth factor receptor in human gastric and colonic carcinomas. *Cancer Res.* 48:137–41

247. Yeivin, A., Tang, D-C., Taylor, M. W. 1992. Sodium butyrate selectively induces transcription of promoters adjacent to the MoMSV viral enhancer. *Gene* 116:159–64

248. Young, G. P., McIntyre, A., Taranto, T., Ward, P., Gibson, P. R. 1991. Butyrate production from dietary fiber protects against large bowel cancer in a rat model. *Gastroenterology* 100:A411 (Abstr.)

249. Zhang, J.-X., Hallmans, G., Andersson, H., Bosaeus, I., Aman, P., et al. 1992. Effect of oat bran on plasma cholesterol and bile acid excretion in nine subjects with ileostomies. *Am. J. Clin. Nutr.* 56:99–105

Annu. Rev. Nutr. 1993. 13:243–60

EFFECTS OF POLYUNSATURATED FATS ON BLOOD PRESSURE[1]

James M. Iacono and Rita M. Dougherty

US Department of Agriculture, ARS, Western Human Nutrition Research Center, Presidio of San Francisco, California 94129

KEY WORDS: hypertension, diet, n-6 fatty acids, n-3 fatty acids, prostaglandins

CONTENTS

INTRODUCTION 243
BLOOD PRESSURE IN ANIMALS: n-6 FATTY ACIDS AND PROSTAGLANDINS 244
BLOOD PRESSURE IN ANIMALS: n-3 FATTY ACIDS AND PROSTAGLANDINS 246
BLOOD PRESSURE IN HUMANS: n-6 FATTY ACIDS AND PROSTAGLANDINS 248
    Dietary Intervention Studies 248
    Epidemiological Studies 251
    Prostaglandin Studies 251
BLOOD PRESSURE IN HUMANS: n-3 FATTY ACIDS AND PROSTAGLANDINS 253
CONCLUSIONS 255

INTRODUCTION

Hypertension is recognized as an important risk factor for cardiovascular disease in industrialized societies. Much effort has been expended during the last 10–15 years pursuing both pharmacological and nonpharmacological approaches to reduce blood pressure. Because the nonpharmacological approach is a reasonable way of dealing with hypertension, serious efforts must be made to establish which environmental factors affect blood pressure. Several have been described; these include diet modification, weight reduction, alcohol control, stress management, and relaxation. When examining the

---

[1]The US government has the right to retain a nonexclusive, royalty-free license in and to any copyright covering this paper.

influence of diet on hypertension, one must determine which specific nutrients affect blood pressure and how to modify them.

Recent literature relating polyunsaturated fatty acids (PUFAs) to blood pressure regulation has been reviewed (34). This chapter emphasizes the role of linoleic (n-6), γ-linolenic (n-6), α-linolenic (n-3), eicosapentaenoic (EPA, n-3), and docosahexaenoic (DHA, n-3) acids. Focus is placed on the nutritional aspects of these fatty acids, their relationship to prostaglandin (PG) metabolism, and how the PGs may affect blood pressure (62, 74, 77). In this chapter, we also summarize the results of nutritional intervention studies conducted in man and animals consuming n-6 and n-3 PUFAs.

BLOOD PRESSURE IN ANIMALS: n-6 FATTY ACIDS AND PROSTAGLANDINS

Early evidence that a seminal extract lowered blood pressure of man and animals was demonstrated by Goldblatt (28) and von Euler (88). Evidence that a lipid-soluble seminal preparation was involved in regulating blood pressure came from the work of Bergström et al (4), who showed that the administration of prostaglandin E (PGE) to animals reduced blood pressure. Additional examples of this phenomenon were published (21, 83, 84, 94). Larsson & Änggård showed that rabbits infused with arachidonate had a dose-dependent decrease in blood pressure (45), which was associated with an increase in the urinary output of PGE_2. The output of PGs was blocked by indomethacin, a nonsteroidal anti-inflammatory agent that resulted in an increase in blood pressure.

An early study implicating linoleic acid in blood pressure control (63) reported that the deprivation of linoleic acid during a salt-loading study resulted in a significantly elevated blood pressure in the rat and that elevated blood pressure was mediated through an impairment of renal homeostasis, which affected water, sodium, and potassium excretion. Other studies have corroborated these findings (81, 82, 86). ten Hoor & van de Graaf (82) found that the urinary excretion of total PG metabolites was reduced substantially when linoleic acid intake was low. However, total PG metabolites increased in urine of rats after they were fed diets with increasing increments of linoleic acid for four months. Of the PGs analyzed, prostacyclin (PGI_2) metabolites were shown to have increased in isolated pulsation-perfused rat aorta. At about the same time, it was reported (48, 51, 75) that the development of an elevated systolic blood pressure was aggravated in rats by a relatively low level of dietary linoleic acid even when the dietary intake of sodium was low.

Cox et al (14) demonstrated that urinary excretion of PGE_2 was dependent on dietary linoleic acid. In support of these findings, Tobian et al (85) showed in a salt-loading study that feeding high levels of linoleic acid to salt-sensitive

Dahl rats increased PGE_2 levels of renal papilla and reduced blood pressure. The increased PGE_2 at the papilla was thought to facilitate the transport of sodium in both the ascending limb of the loop of Henle and the collecting tubule, thereby increasing capacity for sodium excretion and eventually lowering blood pressure (78, 79).

A study by Düsing et al (16) showed that a rise in arterial pressure in Sprague-Dawley rats fed a low level of linoleic acid was associated with a suppression of the vascular rise in circulating thromboxane A_2 (TxA_2) concentrations. A more recent study (15) showed that renal prostaglandins may play a role in blood pressure regulation by affecting renal excretory function and renal renin secretion. Generation of four metabolites, $PGF_{2\alpha}$, PGE_2, 6-keto-$PGF_{1\alpha}$, and TxB_2, by rat-isolated glomeruli and papillary homogenates decreased with the changes in linoleic acid and NaCl intake. This effect occurred in the absence of changes in renal blood flow, glomerular filtration rate, and urinary excretion of inorganic phosphate, which suggests an effect on tubular sodium reabsorption beyond the proximal tubule. Both "distal delivery" and "distal fractional chloride absorption" were affected by linoleic acid deprivation; this finding suggests that linoleic acid deprivation and subsequent renal prostanoid deficiency in the rat is associated with increased sodium absorption in the thick ascending limb of Henle and the distal portion of the nephron. Furthermore, linoleic acid deprivation was associated with an increase in papillary osmolality by raising tissue concentrations of sodium, chloride, and potassium. Papillary urea concentration was unchanged; thus increased papillary osmolality may be independent of changes in papillary blood flow.

Schoene et al (68) fed spontaneously hypertensive (SHR) and Wistar-Kyoto (WKY) rats semisynthetic diets containing 0, 5, and 10% corn oil for 12 weeks. Blood pressures of both species decreased as the corn oil content of the diet increased, while PGE_2 and $PGF_{2\alpha}$ increased in kidney medullae of these rats.

Weanling male Wistar rats were fed an essential fatty acid (EFA)-deficient diet for 25 weeks followed by an EFA-supplemented diet for 3 weeks (29). Towards the end of the EFA-deficient diet period, water consumption increased about 60%, and urinary output and PGE_2 excretion decreased about 45 and 70%, respectively. Feeding the EFA-deficient rats diets supplemented with EFA for 3 weeks decreased water consumption and raised the urine output to that observed in the controls.

Mills & Ward (54) compared four oils, including evening primrose oil, in borderline hypertensive rats (BHR) whose drinking water was replaced with 1% NaCl solution. They found that evening primrose oil (with 9% γ-linolenic acid) was the most hypotensive. Groups of rats who received MaxEPA and sunflowerseed oil had similar increases in blood pressure that were intermediate between the evening primrose oil and safflower oil groups. The olive oil–fed animals had the highest blood pressure. The protective effect of γ-linolenic acid seemed to be greater than that of the other fatty acids tested. The apparent explanation for this effect is that the γ-linolenic acid is more accessible to the cyclooxygenase enzymes since it bypasses the early desaturating enzymes in its conversion to arachidonic acid. Engler et al (19) also demonstrated in male Sprague-Dawley rats the hypotensive effects of dietary γ-linolenic acid from borage oil. They noted that the animals consuming the borage oil had attenuated in vivo pressor responses to norepinephrine and angiotensin II.

In summary, practically all the studies in which diets enriched with n-6 PUFA were consumed showed that blood pressure was decreased regardless of the strain of rat used. In general, the vasodilator PGs, PGI_2, and PGE_2 increased in either kidney, aorta, blood, or urine when linoleic acid was increased. Dietary linoleic acid also reduced blood pressure regardless of whether the rats were salt-loaded. The blood pressure lowering effect appeared to be mediated through the PG changes. The latter were promoted systemically and led to increased water and salt excretion from the kidney.

BLOOD PRESSURE IN ANIMALS: n-3 FATTY ACIDS AND PROSTAGLANDINS

Evidence suggests that n-3 fatty acids may also be important nutrients in regulating blood pressure. n-3 fatty acids are obtained in the diet as α-linolenic acid from plant leaves and seed oils such as linseed, soybean, and canola oils and as EPA and DHA from marine oils.

Schoene et al (66) reported the effect of feeding n-3 fatty acids from menhaden oil (high in EPA and DHA) on the in vitro production of PGs from arachidonic acid. The formation of PGE_2 and $PGF_{2\alpha}$ was impaired in homogenates of kidney medullae and cortices of SHR rats fed the menhaden oil diet. This effect was not observed in the WKY group of animals that served as a control. The reduction in the diene PGs produced in the kidney corresponded to the decreased level of arachidonic acid found in the tissue. Blood pressures in SHR rats and stroke-prone rats consuming diets containing corn oil plus menhaden oil were lower than in the corresponding corn oil–fed animals (67). In contrast to data reported above, Scherhag et al (65) reported elevated blood pressure in Sprague-Dawley rats after six weeks on diets containing either cod-liver oil, which is high in EPA and DHA, or linseed oil, which served as a source of α-linolenic acid. This effect was associated with a suppressed generation of vasodilator PGI_2 by vascular tissue. The authors concluded that the suppression of vascular PGI_2 promoted the hypertensive effect of the cod-liver oil and linseed oil supplements. It has been shown that EPA is readily incorporated into rabbit aorta phospholipids in vitro and that

EPA is a poor substrate for cyclooxygenase enzymes (92). Furthermore, increasing the amount of dietary α-linolenic acid suppressed the levels of arachidonic acid in tissue lipids. This finding suggests that the conversion of linoleic acid to arachidonic acid may be partially inhibited by α-linolenic acid because of its higher affinity to the desaturating enzymes (55).

Ziemlański et al (93) fed Wistar rats diets containing various fats along with 1.5% NaCl added to the drinking water to induce hypertension. The rise in blood pressure was greatest in the rats on the animal fat diet, and lower in the animals fed sunflowerseed oil or partially hydrogenated marine oil, and lowest in the rats consuming cod-liver oil diets. Elevated blood pressure was also found in salt-loaded SHR rats fed marine oil (MaxEPA) (11). In the absence of dietary NaCl, blood pressure was not affected and the 2-series prostanoids were suppressed in SHR and WKY rats. The hypertensive rats showed diminished excretion of 6-keto-$PGF_{1\alpha}$ and PGE_2 in urine. The ability of SHR rats to excrete a salt load was reduced when they were fed a diet enriched with MaxEPA; they exhibited mild sodium retention and increased vascular sensitivity. This effect was similar to that shown by salt-loaded EFA-deficient rats. In another study, DOCA-salt-loaded, unilaterally nephrectomized Sprague-Dawley rats were fed different fats in semisynthetic diets for 21 days. Webb et al (90) observed that blood pressure was lower in the marine oil-supplemented group than in the group consuming safflower oil. The amount of arachidonate in kidney phospholipid fatty acids was markedly lower in rats fed marine oil compared to levels in rats fed safflower oil. At the same time, an increase in EPA and DHA occurred in kidney phospholipids while only EPA was increased in plasma phospholipids.

Codde et al (12) showed that the suppression of the 2 series PG synthesis by a marine oil diet (MaxEPA) was not accompanied by accelerated DOCA-salt hypertension. Feeding PUFA (safflower oil) diminished DOCA-salt hypertension, but this effect could not be related specifically to PG synthesis. The lower pressures observed in rats that were fed n-3 or n-6 and that had DOCA or 1-kidney, 1-clip hypertension suggest that volume-dependent forms of hypertension are sensitive to increased dietary PUFA intake. Although the mechanism for this attenuation of hypertension is obscure, it did not seem to involve the renin-angiotensin system, which was suppressed in both models, and thus must be due to effects of PUFA on other vasoactive mechanisms. Hui et al (32) showed that linoleic acid and marine oil fatty acids were equally potent in reducing systolic arterial pressure induced by the chronic infusion of angiotensin II in Sprague-Dawley rats. Systemic and renal synthesis of PGI_2 and the renal formation of PGE_2 were unaffected. Indomethacin inhibited the biosynthesis of PGI_2, but not PGE_2, and only partially neutralized the antihypertensive effects of linoleic acid or marine oil fatty acids. Apparently, linoleic acid and marine oil fatty acids exerted equivalent antihypertensive effects in angiotensin II-induced hypertension that appeared to be independent of the prostaglandin system. When McIntosh et al (52) fed a commercial diet supplemented with various fats to Hooded Wistar rats for eight months, they found that arterial blood pressure was elevated by sheep fat and lowered by sunflowerseed oil and tuna oil.

Sunflowerseed oil, linseed oil, and evening primrose oil were shown to attenuate hypertension in SHR rats (30) when the feeding regimen was started immediately after suckling. During the prehypertensive period, the reduction in blood pressure was most pronounced in the rats treated with α-linolenic acid, and the decreased blood pressures were not explained by changes in prostanoid production. Hoffmann & Förster (31) showed that semisynthetic diets enriched with n-3 and n-6 PUFA reduced the development of hypertension in SHR rats compared to those consuming chow in the third and fourth generations of a four generation feeding period. PGI$_2$-like production from isolated pulsating perfused aortic preparations was reduced in rats fed linseed oil, but not in those fed sunflowerseed oil. These effects disappeared when regular chow was substituted for the PUFA diets during the fifth and sixth generations.

In summary, the studies generally showed decreases in blood pressure in rats fed either linseed oil containing α-linolenic acid or marine oils containing EPA and DHA. Additional dietary studies are necessary to explain the mechanism for lowering blood pressure by n-3 fatty acids.

BLOOD PRESSURE IN HUMANS: n-6 FATTY ACIDS AND PROSTAGLANDINS

Dietary Intervention Studies

FREE-LIVING STUDIES   A series of studies reviewed in this section attempt to define the effect of diets enriched with n-6 fatty acids (primarily linoleic acid) on blood pressure in human subjects. The effects of linoleic acid feeding on PG levels of tissue or on urinary excretion products in relation to blood pressure are discussed.

A dietary intervention study in which all foods were weighed or measured was conducted with 10 men and 11 women (normo- to high-normotensive), 40–60 years old (39). During the first 40 days the diets contained 25% of total calories (en%) from fat with a polyunsaturated to saturated fatty acid ratio (P:S) of 1.0. The linoleic acid content of the diet rose from 3.8 en% during the pre-study period to 6.5 en% during the 25-en% period. The saturated fatty acids decreased from 17 en% to 6.7 en% during these periods. A significant decrease of 13 mm Hg systolic and 7 mm Hg diastolic blood pressure was observed for all subjects. No further change was observed in blood pressure when the fat content of the diet was increased to 35 en% during the second 40 days.

In studying 8 mild hypertensives over a 4-week period, Comberg et al (13) also observed a decrease of 8 mm Hg diastolic blood pressure when the volunteers consumed linoleic acid-enriched diets containing sunflowerseed oil and soybean oil. Systolic blood pressure also decreased, but not significantly.

In a crossover study (37), 10 hypertensive males were compared to 10 normotensive males. All foods were prepared in a metabolic kitchen and were weighed. The intervention diet contained 25 en% total fat of which 6.6 en% was n-6 PUFA. Systolic and diastolic blood pressure was significantly lower in the hypertensives during the low-fat, higher P:S intervention period than during ingestion of a typical USA diet. The normotensives showed no significant changes during either dietary period. Sodium and potassium excretion and urine volume in the hypertensives showed a progressive increase during the low-fat, higher P:S dietary period. When the diets were reversed, sodium excretion and urine volume decreased progressively to initial levels, but potassium changes were variable (38).

Four groups of males selected on the basis of their blood pressures, i.e. normal to slightly elevated, participated in a study where they consumed natural diets containing 2 levels of fat, 44 and 25 en%, at P:S of 0.3 and 1.0 (41). All of the foods consumed were weighed. Regardless of the level of fat, systolic and diastolic blood pressures decreased when the subjects consumed the P:S 1.0 diets. When the subjects consumed the higher fat P:S 1.0 diet, systolic blood pressure decreased by 8 mm Hg and diastolic pressure decreased by 7 mm Hg. On the low fat, high P:S diet, systolic and diastolic blood pressure decreased by 6 mm Hg. These data suggested that linoleic acid was the nutrient that reduced blood pressure.

Rao et al (61) supplemented PUFA in the diets of normotensive and hypertensive subjects for 6 weeks. When safflower oil was added to the diet, a significant decrease of 5 mm Hg in both systolic and diastolic blood pressure occurred. Groundnut oil (peanut oil) produced a decrease of 8 mm Hg in diastolic blood pressure only. A third group of subjects, unresponsive to antihypertensive therapy, had a reduction of 7 mm Hg in systolic and diastolic blood pressure when they were supplemented with safflower oil for 6 weeks.

When Margetts et al (49) placed normotensive subjects on either high or low P:S diets, no change in blood pressure was observed. Data obtained from this study appeared to agree with the lack of dietary effect of linoleic acid on blood pressure for normotensives in other studies (9, 27, 37, 53, 60, 64). However, Mutanen et al (57) investigated the effects of sunflowerseed-oil and rapeseed-oil enriched diets on blood pressures of normotensive males and females and found a significant decrease of 1.3 mm Hg in diastolic pressure when the 59 subjects consumed the sunflowerseed-oil diet. No effect on blood pressure was observed when the subjects consumed the high α-linolenic acid (rapeseed-oil) diet.

In an attempt to define which fatty acid influenced the reduction in blood pressure, a study was conducted on a metabolic research unit (33, 35) in which mildly hypertensive men consumed a diet containing ~ 10 en% of each saturated and monounsaturated fatty acid. In addition, 3 en% linoleic acid was fed for 6 weeks and then was increased to ~ 10 en% for an additional 6 weeks. A significant decrease in systolic and diastolic blood pressure of 7 mm Hg and 5 mm Hg, respectively, was observed during the 10-en% linoleic acid feeding period.

COMMUNITY-BASED STUDIES   The effects on blood pressure of reducing the amount of fat and increasing the P:S of the dietary fat were reported in a dietary intervention study of a rural Finnish population (40). Fifty-nine high normotensive subjects, 30 men and 29 women, aged 40 to 50 years, participated. A significant decrease in both systolic (7.7 mm Hg) and diastolic (6.3 mm Hg) blood pressure was observed for all subjects on the lower fat (24 en%)-higher P:S diet. The intervention diet contained 8.5 en% linoleic acid, 7.6% saturated, and 6.3 en% monounsaturated fatty acids. Blood pressures returned to initial levels when the subjects reverted to their customary diets.

A follow-up intervention study in 2 other communities in North Karelia, Finland was conducted (59) with 57 normal to moderately hypertensive couples, aged 20 to 50 years. The low-fat diet (6.4 en% n-6 PUFA) group had a reduction in both systolic and diastolic blood pressure. During the switchback period their blood pressures rose progressively to the initial levels. Only small differences were observed in systolic and diastolic blood pressures in the control (4.3 en% n-6 PUFA) and low-salt (3.4 en% n-6 PUFA) groups throughout the study.

In a community-based study in Italy, Strazzullo et al (80) investigated the effects of modifying the typical Mediterranean diet to mimic the typical Western diet in a healthy, rural population in Southern Italy. Fifty-seven normotensive volunteers (29 males and 28 females, aged 30–50 years) were studied. Systolic and diastolic blood pressure increased significantly in males (2.7 mm Hg and 3.6 mm Hg) and females (3.3 mm Hg and 4.0 mm Hg). After a return to their customary diet for another 5 weeks, the blood pressures of the participants returned to baseline levels.

Adolescents (15–18 years) were the focus of a community-based study conducted by Stern et al (76) in North Carolina. Within 6 weeks, the students receiving the dietary supplements (mainly from corn oil) had an 11-mm Hg decrease in systolic blood pressure, while the control group had a decrease of 6 mm Hg. A slight decrease was observed in diastolic blood pressure in both groups. In another community-based intervention study, Vartiainen et al (87) reported that systolic and diastolic blood pressures were decreased by 4 mm Hg and 3 mm Hg, respectively, in children and adolescents (8–18 years) when dietary fat was decreased and P:S levels were increased to either 0.4 or 0.9 (60).

In summary, in all studies where hypertensive subjects were fed n-6 fatty acids, significant reductions in blood pressure were observed. This occurred in free-living and community-based intervention studies and in a metabolic unit study. When normotensive subjects were studied, most authors reported no significant reductions in blood pressure related to dietary linoleic acid.

Epidemiological Studies

Additional supporting evidence relating dietary fat to blood pressure comes from epidemiological studies. A pilot epidemiological study was conducted (36) in farmers, aged 40 to 50 years, in Italy, Finland, and the USA. The Finns, who consumed a diet high in saturated fat and very low in linoleic acid, had significantly higher systolic and diastolic blood pressures than the Italian and USA farmers.

In an epidemiological survey of 650 healthy men, Oster et al (58) found a highly significant negative correlation between the linoleic acid composition of adipose tissue and blood pressure. Dietary linoleic acid intake was positively correlated with urinary sodium concentration and urine volume and negatively correlated with serum sodium concentration. Berry & Hirsch (5) studied the long-term effects of dietary fat on blood pressure by analyzing adipose tissue fatty acid composition of 399 free-living male subjects (average age, 47 years). Stepwise-regression analysis revealed that α-linolenic acid in adipose tissue was associated with a decrease in systolic and diastolic blood pressure and that a 1% increase of α-linolenic acid in adipose tissue was associated with a 5-mm Hg decrease in mean arterial blood pressure.

Prostaglandin Studies

A number of studies have dealt with precursors of PGs and their effects on kidney function, on levels of PGs in plasma, and excretion of PGs, but only a few have taken into account blood pressure regulation. PGs are not stored in the body but are synthesized as needed and degraded in minutes. It is thought that the major end products of circulating PGs are excreted in the urine in the form of polar metabolites. The pharmacological effects of PGs have been studied extensively in the last decade, yet their clinical and nutritional importance is still far from clear. Little is known about the daily synthesis and turnover of PGs or the daily production of PGs in the body as they are affected by n-6 or n-3 fatty acid intake and the degree to which they are related to a variety of physiological functions. The mechanisms of the vasodilatory effect of fatty acids on renal circulation in man remains unclear. Changes in renal eicosanoid metabolism with alterations in the balance of the vasodilatory eicosanoids PGE_2 and PGI_2 and the vasconstrictor TxB_2 remain a likely explanation.

A study showing that cortex and medulla have differing roles in the synthesis of PGs through the cyclooxyengenase pathway was conducted by Frölich & Walker (26). They described results in hypertensive subjects in which PGI_2 was shown to be the compound most characteristic of the cortex and the one that promoted renin release from the kidney. They found that PGE_2 was characteristic of the kidney medulla and that it was involved in water and salt regulation. In vivo and in vitro studies by Weber et al (91) demonstrated that renal formation of PGs in the vasculature of the cortex, PGI_2 and $PGF_{1\alpha}$, represented an important step in describing the mechanism of renin secretion, which is influential in controlling electrolyte and volume balance.

Friedman et al (25) reported decreased turnover of PGE_2 levels in infants on a linoleic acid–deficient diet. The influence of linoleic acid intake on PG formation has been studied (1–3, 95) in healthy volunteers, mainly females. The subjects consumed liquid formula diets containing 0, 3, 3.5, 4, 6, 8, 13, 18, or 20 en% of linoleic acid for 2-week periods. Tetranorprostanedioic acid (TNPDA) levels in urine increased with increasing amounts of linoleic acid. TNPDA in urine represents the sum total of the end products of PG metabolism and includes PGE_1, PGE_2, 6-keto-$PGF_{1\alpha}$, and $PGF_{2\alpha}$. In one of these studies (1), systolic blood pressure decreased by 10 mm Hg during the corpus luteum phase of the subjects' menstrual cycles. Although these were short-term dietary intervention studies, the authors demonstrated that linoleic acid stimulated levels of PGs in urine and influenced blood pressure.

The effects of acute administration of linoleic acid on the production of urinary PGE_2 and 6-keto-$PGF_{1\alpha}$ were monitored by Epstein et al (20). Six normal subjects were infused with 1.5 g/kg body weight of safflower oil (Liposyn®) containing approximately 77% linoleic acid over an 8-h period. The Liposyn induced a profound increase in 6-keto-$PGF_{1\alpha}$ while PGE_2 excretion increased modestly.

Ferretti et al (23) investigated the effects of marine oil supplementation on the level of the urinary metabolite of PGE-M (PGE_2 + PGE_1). They found a 14% reduction in PGE-M after 10 weeks of marine oil supplementation, which suggests an inhibition of PG synthesis by marine oil. The occurrence of the trienoic derivatives of PGs, PGI_3, and PGE_3 in humans as a result of marine oil intake has been demonstrated by GC-mass spectroscopy. These PGs were found in urine when marine oils were fed. The mechanism for the reduction in blood pressure appears to be the vasodilatory effect of n-3 fatty acid supplements within the renal circulation (17, 18, 22, 24). Results of a study by Judd et al (42) suggest that the amount of dietary linoleic acid is important in the regulation of PG synthesis. These authors observed significant reductions in the excretion of $PGF_{2\alpha}$ and 6-keto $PGF_{1\alpha}$ when linoleic acid intake was reduced from 6.5 en% to 3.2 en%. Systolic and diastolic blood pressures were lowered by 9 mm Hg and 4 mm Hg when the total fat was reduced from 37 en% to 25 en%. These changes were not related to the level of linoleic acid. The authors show that $PGF_{2\alpha}$ and 6-keto-$PGF_{1\alpha}$ were positively correlated with the blood pressure changes.

Blair et al (7) studied the levels of PGs in urine after subjects consumed 3 or 10 en% linoleic acid. All foods consumed in this study were weighed. At 10 en% linoleic acid, the female subjects excreted significantly higher levels of PGE_2 while the excretion of 2,3-dinor TxB_2 decreased.

BLOOD PRESSURE IN HUMANS: n-3 FATTY ACIDS AND PROSTAGLANDINS

One of the earliest reports on the effect of marine oils on blood pressure was by Mortensen et al (56). In studies of marine oil supplementation to Western diets, they administered either 10 g of vegetable oil (a mixture of corn oil and olive oil) or 10 g of marine oil (MaxEPA) to healthy volunteers for 10 weeks. Each oil contained approximately 40% of either n-6 or n-3 PUFA. During the n-3 PUFA feeding period, systolic blood pressure decreased. The intake of the n-3 or n-6 fatty acid supplements represented less than 1 en% of the daily intake. No dietary control was exerted, but the subjects were asked not to change their dietary habits.

Lorenz et al (47) added 40 ml/day of cod-liver oil to the diets of 8 volunteers for 25 days. This amount of cod-liver oil provided about 10 g of n-3 fatty acids per day and represented about 4.5 en% of the total calories. The n-3 PUFA was incorporated into platelet and erythrocyte membrane phospholipids at the expense of n-6 PUFA. Systolic blood pressure decreased by $\sim$ 10 mm Hg and blood pressure response to norepinephrine fell by $\sim$ 11 mm Hg. This reaction was reversed 4 weeks after the cod-liver oil supplementation was stopped. Formation of PGs derived from EPA, and the interference of EPA with formation and action of PGs derived from arachidonic acid, were evident in vitro.

A series of short-term (2 weeks) studies were conducted by Singer et al (69–73) in which mackerel or herring was added to the diets of normotensive and hypertensive subjects. Lower systolic and diastolic blood pressures were usually observed in the subjects consuming the mackerel supplements. von Houwelingen et al (89) attempted to determine the effect of the intake of fish on specific cardiovascular risk factors in the Netherlands and Norway. Healthy male normotensive volunteers, ranging in age from 28 to 45 years, were given a dietary supplement of $\sim$ 135 g/day of either mackerel or meat for 6 weeks. Systolic blood pressure dropped slightly in both groups to a comparable degree; therefore, no specific effect of the fish supplement was observed. The fish-supplemented group had prolonged bleeding times (8.43 min vs 7.72 min for the control group) along with decreased platelet counts (218×10^9 per liter vs 231×10^9 per liter).

Knapp & Fitzgerald (44) studied blood pressure and eicosanoid production during supplementation with n-3 or n-6 dietary fats for 4 weeks. Thirty two men with mild essential hypertension participated in this study. They reported a reduction in systolic and diastolic blood pressure in subjects who took a supplement of 50 ml/day of MaxEPA, but no changes in the groups consuming 50 ml/day of safflower oil or a mixture of oils similar to that consumed in the USA diet. A significant reduction in TxB_2 metabolites was observed at the end of the high marine oil period. Significant increases in PGE_2 metabolites were found in the group receiving safflower oil, suggesting improved kidney function. Biermann & Herrmann (6) reported that when 125 male subjects consumed either 2 or 6 g/day of marine oil or equivalent amounts of n-6 PUFA, the marine oil contributed to a decrease in blood pressure whereas the n-6 fatty acids did not. In a double-blind study conducted by Kestin et al (43), 33 normotensive men were randomly assigned to diets containing supplements of oil high in either linoleic acid, α-linolenic acid, or EPA + DHA. After 6 weeks of supplementation, the group consuming the high EPA + DHA showed a significant decrease in systolic blood pressure. No effect was shown on diastolic blood pressure.

Margolin et al (50) compared the blood pressure lowering effects of either 9 g of marine oil or 9 g of corn oil. Forty-six elderly hypertensive subjects were randomized into dietary groups in a double-blind crossover study. During the first treatment period, both marine oil and corn oil lowered blood pressure. After a washout period, blood pressures were not lowered any further during the second period. An interesting part of this study was that many of the subjects took the fat supplements in addition to one or more antihypertensive drugs. Apparently, an interaction between the dietary fats and the antihypertensive drugs effectively lowered blood pressure. Bønaa et al (8) demonstrated in hypertensive subjects that dietary supplementation with 6 g/day of marine oil EPA and DHA lowered blood pressure more than did supplementation with 6 g/day corn oil in a control group. The blood pressure response correlated to changes in plasma levels of phospholipid n-3 fatty acids.

Levinson et al (46) studied male and female hypertensives, 18–75 years of age, supplemented with either MaxEPA or palm oil + corn oil. Diastolic blood pressure decreased during treatment in the marine oil group. The amount of n-3 fatty acids used in this study added up to about 21 g/day. This would be equivalent to consuming about 14 kg of fatty fish per day. In this study, serum aldosterone, plasma renin activity, and plasma catecholamine levels did not change with either n-3 or n-6 fatty acid supplementation. Overall, these findings suggest that the renin-angiotensin-aldosterone system, the sympathetic nervous system, and fluidity of cell membranes were not primary mediators of the hypotensive effect of the marine oil.

A study by Cobiac et al (10), found that a combination of 8 g marine oil (Himega®) and sodium restriction reduced blood pressure in elderly normotensive subjects. The phenomenon of reducing salt intake while administering marine oil has not been studied to a great extent.

In summary, the results of the studies reported here show that n-3 fatty acids of marine origin generally reduced blood pressure. Of concern in most n-3 fatty acid studies on blood pressure is that capsules of oil were given as supplements at pharmacological levels. Furthermore, when n-6 fatty acids were given as supplements in capsule form to serve as the control fat in a number of n-3 fatty acid studies reported here, the group taking the n-6 fatty acid supplement showed no changes in blood pressure. The lack of effect of the n-6 fatty acids on blood pressure could be due to the low levels of n-6 fatty acids given as supplements and, hence, to low levels of total n-6 fatty acids in the diet. The feeding of high levels of compounds with unsaturated double bonds from marine or plant sources to control blood pressure may be harmful to the degree to which lipid peroxidation occurs under these conditions.

CONCLUSIONS

Dietary n-6 and n-3 fatty acids play a role in blood pressure regulation. Both classes of fatty acids have been shown to reduce blood pressure in rats and hypertensive subjects. Until studies are conducted in which these fatty acids as well as other dietary components are controlled, their role in blood pressure regulation will remain unclear.

Only a few well-designed nutritional studies on the effect of n-3 fatty acids on blood pressure have utilized fish as the primary source of the n-3 fatty acids. These studies were conducted in normotensive individuals and the results were negative, i.e. they did not lower blood pressure. In the case of n-6 fatty acids, a number of studies have been conducted on the metabolic unit, as free-living studies, or as community-based dietary intervention studies in which food intake was carefully controlled. These studies have demonstrated the lowering of blood pressure in hypertensives by dietary means.

The studies where n-3 and n-6 fatty acids were given as supplements (usually in the form of capsules) can be described as pharmacological trials, because the levels of the n-3 fatty acids administered were well beyond what could possibly be eaten as fish. Hence, any interpretation of the data must take into account the fact that these are drug trials. When n-6 fatty acids were given as the so-called control placebo for the n-3 fatty acid studies, the amount of n-6 fatty acid given was usually below the quantity required in the usual diet, i.e. 5 to 10 en%. Moreover, there generally was no attempt to assess the amount of n-6 fatty acids in the diet. Interpretation of the data of n-6 fatty acids supplements to lower blood pressure is difficult if not impossible. On the other hand, the data for the n-3 fatty acid supplement intake suggests a lowering of blood pressure in hypertensive subjects.

PG production in kidney and other tissue from dietary PUFA is also involved in the regulation of blood pressure. At the present time, it is not possible to relate how n-6 or n-3 fatty acids affect PG production, owing to the lack of adequate techiques for assessing PG output in urine. Clearly, only a sophisticated chemical approach will yield the information needed to arrive at reasonable conclusions. The methods currently being adapted to give this type of information include extraction, chromatography, and mass spectrographic analysis of the urinary metabolites of PGs. Most of the data presently cited in the literature are based on radioimmunoassay techniques for determining the level of PGs in tissue and urine. These techniques, although sensitive, lack specificity. As the spectrographic techniques become available for routine usage, we should be better able to assess the relative roles of n-6 and n-3 fatty acids in controlling blood pressure as well as in other physiological functions.

Further research is needed to understand the relationship between dietary n-6 and n-3 PUFAs and PG metabolism as well as their interaction with other metabolic processes in the regulation of blood pressure.

The level of dietary n-6 fatty acids required to reduce blood pressure in hypertensives appears to be in the range of 5 to 10 en%. This amount of n-6 fatty acids agrees with the recommendations of most health groups for the reduction of blood lipids. The level of n-3 fatty acids required in order to lower blood pressure is not clear, but levels ranging from <3 to about 21 g/day have been reported to reduce blood pressure in hypertensives.

The study of diet and hypertension is still in its infancy and will require a far greater effort to elucidate the role of fat and fatty acids on blood pressure.

Literature Cited

1. Adam, O. 1989. Effects of linoleic and alpha linolenic acids intake on blood pressure in man. *Prog. Clin. Biol. Res.* 301:523–28
2. Adam, O., Wolfram, G. 1984. Effect of different linoleic acid intakes on prostaglandin biosynthesis and kidney function in man. *Am. J. Clin. Nutr.* 40:763–70
3. Adam, O., Wolfram, G., Zöllner, N. 1982. Prostaglandin formation in man during intake of different amounts of linoleic acid in formula diets. *Ann. Nutr. Metab.* 26:315–23
4. Bergström, S., Dunér, H., von Euler, U. S., Pernow, B., Sjövall, J. 1959. Observations on the effects of infusion of prostaglandin E in man. *Acta Physiol. Scand.* 45:145–51
5. Berry, E. M., Hirsch, J. 1986. Does dietary linolenic acid influence blood pressure? *Am. J. Clin. Nutr.* 44:336–40
6. Biermann, J., Herrmann, W. 1990. Modification of selected lipoproteins and blood pressure by different dosages of n-3 fatty acids. *Z. Gesamte Inn. Med.* 45:540–44
7. Blair, I. A., Prakash, C., Phillips, M. A., Dougherty, R. M., Iacono, J. M. 1993. Dietary modification of ω6 fatty acid intake and its effect on urinary eicosanoid excretion. *Am. J. Clin. Nutr.* 57:154-60
8. Bønaa, K. H., Bjerve, K. S., Straume, B., Gram, I. T., Thelle, D. 1990. Effect of eicosapentaenoic and docosahexaenoic acids on blood pressure in hypertension: A population-based in-

tervention trial from the Tromsø Study. *N. Engl. J. Med.* 322:795–801

9. Brussaard, J. H., van Raaij, J. M. A., Stasse-Wolthuis, M., Katan, M. B., Hautvast, J. G. A. J. 1981. Blood pressure and diet in normotensive volunteers: absence of an effect of dietary fiber, protein, or fat. *Am. J. Clin. Nutr.* 34:2023–29

10. Cobiac, L., Nestel, P. J., Wing, L. M. H., Howe, P. R. C. 1992. A low-sodium diet supplemented with fish oil lowers blood pressure in the elderly. *J. Hypertens.* 10:87–92

11. Codde, J. P., Croft, K. D., Beilin, L. J. 1986. Effect of salt loading on blood pressure and eicosanoid metabolism of spontaneously hypertensive rats fed a fish oil enriched diet. *Clin. Exp. Pharmacol. Physiol.* 13:371–75

12. Codde, J. P., Croft, K. D., Beilin, L. J. 1987. Dietary suppression of prostaglandin synthesis does not accelerate DOCA/salt hypertension in rats. *Clin. Exp. Pharmacol. Physiol.* 14:513–23

13. Comberg, H. U., Heyden, S., Hames, C. G., Vergroesen, A. J., Fleischman, A. I. 1978. Hypotensive effect of dietary prostaglandin precursor in hypertensive man. *Prostaglandins* 15:193–97

14. Cox, J. W., Rutecki, G. W., Francisco, L. L., Ferris, T. F. 1982. Studies on the effects of essential fatty acid deficiency in the rat. *Circ. Res.* 51:694–702

15. Düsing, R., Scherf, H. 1990. Dietary linoleic acid deprivation: An experimental model of salt-sensitive hypertension. *Klin. Wochenschr.* 68 (Suppl. 20):4–10

16. Düsing, R., Scherhag, R., Glänzer, K., Budde, U., Kramer, H. 1983. Dietary linoleic acid deprivation: effects on blood pressure and PGI_2 synthesis. *Am. J. Physiol.* 244:H228–33

17. Düsing, R., Struck, A., Göbel, B. O., Weisser, B., Vetter, H. 1990. Effects of n-3 fatty acids on renal function and renal prostaglandin E metabolism. *Kidney Int.* 38:315–19

18. Dyerberg, J., Jørgensen, K. A., Arnfred, T. 1981. Human umbilical blood vessel converts all cis-5,8,11,14,17 eicosapentaenoic acid to prostaglandin I_3. *Prostaglandins* 22:857–62

19. Engler, M. M., Engler, M. B., Paul, S. M. 1992. Effects of dietary borage oil rich in gamma-linolenic acid on blood pressure and vascular reactivity. *Nutr. Res.* 12:519–28

20. Epstein, M., Lifschitz, M., Rappaport,

K. 1982. Augmentation of prostaglandin production by linoleic acid in man. *Clin. Sci.* 63:565–71

21. Ferreira, S. H., Vane, J. R. 1967. Prostaglandins: Their disappearance from the release into the circulation. *Nature* 216:868–73

22. Ferretti, A., Flanagan, V. P., Reeves, V. B. 1988. Occurrence of prostaglandin E_3 in human urine as a result of marine oil ingestion: gas chromatographic-mass spectrometric evidence. *Biochim. Biophys. Acta* 959:262–68

23. Ferretti, A., Judd, J. T., Ballard-Barbash, R., Nair, P. P., Taylor, P. R., et al. 1991. Effect of fish oil supplementation on the excretion of the major metabolite of prostaglandin E in healthy male subjects. *Lipids* 26:500–3

24. Fischer, S., Weber, P. C. 1984. Prostaglandin I_3 is formed in vivo in man after dietary eicosapentaenoic acid. *Nature* 307:165–68

25. Friedman, Z., Seyberth, H., Lamberth, E., Oates, J. 1978. Decreased prostaglandin E turnover in infants with essential fatty acid deficiency. *Pediatr. Res.* 12:711–14

26. Frölich, J. C., Walker, L. A. 1980. Determination, source, metabolism, and functional role of renal prostaglandins. *Clin. Exp. Hypertens.* 2:709–28

27. Goldberg, R. J., Ellison, R. C., Hosmer, D. W. Jr., Capper, A. L., Puleo, E., et al. 1992. Effects of alterations in fatty acid intake on the blood pressure of adolescents: the Exeter-Andover Project. *Am. J. Clin. Nutr.* 56:71–76

28. Goldblatt, M. W. 1935. Properties of human seminal plasma. *J. Physiol.* 84:208–18

29. Hansen, H. S. 1981. Essential fatty acid supplemented diet increases renal excretion of prostaglandin E_2 and water in essential fatty acid deficient rats. *Lipids* 16:849–54

30. Hoffmann, P., Block, H. U., Beitz, J., Taube, C., Förster, W., et al. 1986. Comparative study of the blood pressure effects of four different vegetable fats on young, spontaneously hypertensive rats. *Lipids* 21:733–37

31. Hoffmann, P., Förster, W. 1986. Antihypertensive effect of dietary sunflowerseed oil and linseed oil in spontaneously hypertensive rats during a multigeneration feeding study. *Prostaglandins Leukotr. Med.* 25:65–70

32. Hui, R., St.-Louis, J., Falardeau, P. 1989. Antihypertensive properties of linoleic acid and fish oil omega-3

fatty acids independent of the prostaglandin system. *Am. J. Hypertens.*
2:610–17

33. Iacono, J. M., Dougherty, R. M. 1987.
Dietary polyunsaturated fat and blood
pressure regulation. In *AIN Symposium
Proceedings, Nutrition '87*, ed. O. A.
Levander, pp. 105–9. Bethesda, MD:
Am. Inst. Nutr.

34. Iacono, J. M., Dougherty, R. M. 1990.
Blood pressure and fat intake. In *Hy-
pertension: Pathophysiology, Diagno-
sis, and Management*, ed. J. H. Laragh,
B. M. Brenner, pp. 257–76. New
York: Raven

35. Iacono, J. M., Dougherty, R. M. 1991.
Lack of effect of linoleic acid on
the high-density-lipoprotein-cholesterol
fraction of plasma lipoproteins. *Am J.
Clin. Nutr.* 53:660–64

36. Iacono, J. M., Dougherty, R. M.,
Paoletti, R., Galli, C., Carvalho, A.
C. A., et al. 1978. Pilot epidemiolog-
ical studies in thrombosis. In *The
Thrombotic Process in Atherogenesis*,
ed. A. B. Chandler, K. Eurenius, G.
C. McMillan, C. B. Nelson, C. J.
Schwartz, et al, pp. 309–27. New
York: Plenum

37. Iacono, J. M., Judd, J. T., Marshall,
M. W., Canary, J. J., Dougherty, R.
M., et al. 1981. The role of dietary
essential fatty acids and prostaglandins
in reducing blood pressure. *Prog. Lipid
Res.* 20:349–64

38. Iacono, J. M., Marshall, M. W., Dougherty, R. M., Kliman, P., Weinland,
B. T., et al. 1978. *Proc. 11th Int.
Congr. Nutr.* Rio de Janeiro, Brazil,
101 (Abstr.)

39. Iacono, J. M., Marshall, M. W., Dougherty, R. M., Wheeler, M. A., Mac-
kin, J. F., et al. 1975. Reduction in
blood pressure associated with high
polyunsaturated fat diets that reduce
blood cholesterol in man. *Prev. Med.*
4:426–43

40. Iacono, J. M., Puska, P., Dougherty,
R. M., Pietinen, P., Vartiainen, E.,
et al. 1983. Effect of dietary fat on
blood pressure in a rural Finnish population. *Am. J. Clin. Nutr.* 38:860–69

41. Judd, J. T., Marshall, M. W., Canary,
J. J. 1981. Changes in blood pressure
and blood lipids of adult men consum-
ing modified fat diets. In *Beltsville
Symposia in Agricultural Research.
Human Nutrition Research*, ed. G. R.
Beecher, 4:129–41. Totowa, NJ: Al-
lanheld, Osmun

42. Judd, J. T., Marshall, M. W., Dupont,
J. 1989. Relationship of dietary fat to
plasma fatty acids, blood pressure, and

urinary eicosanoids in adult men. *J.
Am. Coll. Nutr.* 8:386–99

43. Kestin, M., Clifton, P., Belling, G.
B., Nestel, P. J. 1990. n-3 fatty acids
of marine origin lower systolic blood
pressure and triglycerides but raise LDL
cholesterol compared with n-3 and n-6
fatty acids from plants. *Am. J. Clin.
Nutr.* 51:1028–34

44. Knapp, H. R., Fitzgerald, G. A. 1989.
The antihypertensive effects of fish oil:
A controlled study of polyunsaturated
fatty acid supplements in essential hypertension. *N. Engl. J. Med.* 320:1037–
43

45. Larsson, C., Änggård, E. 1973.
Arachidonic acid lowers and indomethacin increases the blood pressure of
the rabbit. *J. Pharm. Pharmacol.* 25:
653–55

46. Levinson, P. D., Iosiphidis, A. H.,
Saritelli, A. L., Herbert, P. N., Steiner,
M. 1990. Effects of n-3 fatty acids in
essential hypertension. *Am. J. Hypertens.* 3:754–60

47. Lorenz, R., Spengler, U., Fischer, S.,
Duhm, J., Weber, P. C. 1983. Platelet
function, thromboxane formation and
blood pressure control during supplementation of the Western diet with
cod liver oil. *Circulation* 67:504–11

48. MacDonald, M. C., Kline, R. L.,
Mogenson, G. J. 1981. Dietary linoleic
acid and salt-induced hypertension.
Can. J. Physiol. Pharmacol. 59:872–75

49. Margetts, B. M., Beilin, L. J., Armstrong, B. K., Rouse, I. L.,
Vandongen, R., et al. 1985. Blood
pressure and dietary polyunsaturated
and saturated fats: a controlled trial.
Clin. Sci. 69:165–75

50. Margolin, G., Huster, G., Glueck, C.
J., Speirs, J., Vandegrift, J., et al.
1991. Blood pressure lowering in elderly subjects: a double-blind crossover
study of ω-3 and ω-6 fatty acids. Am.
J. Clin. Nutr. 53:562–72

51. McGiff, J. C., Quilley, J. 1981. Prostaglandins, hypertension, and the cardiovascular system. In *Prostaglandins
and Cardiovascular Disease*, ed. R.
J. Hegyeli, pp. 101–7. New York:
Raven

52. McIntosh, G. H., McLennan, P. L.,
Lawson, C. A., Bulman, F. H., Charn-
ock, J. S. 1985. The influence of
dietary fats on plasma lipids, blood
pressure and coagulation indices in the
rat. *Atherosclerosis* 55:125–34

53. Mensink, R. P., Stolwijk, A. M.,
Katan, M. B. 1990. Effect of a
monounsaturated diet vs a polyunsaturated fatty acid-enriched diet on blood

pressure in normotensive women and men. *Eur. J. Clin. Invest.* 20:463–69

54. Mills, D. E., Ward, R. P. 1987. Dietary n-6 and n-3 fatty acids and salt-induced hypertension in the borderline hypertensive rat. In *Proceedings of the AOCS Short Course on Polyunsaturated Fatty Acids and Eicosanoids,* ed. W. E. M. Lands, pp. 346–48. Champaign, Ill.: Am. Oil Chem. Soc.

55. Mohrhauer, H., Holman, R. T. 1963. Effect of linolenic acid upon the metabolism of linoleic acid. *J. Nutr.* 81: 67–74

56. Mortensen, J. Z., Schmidt, E. B., Nielsen, A. H., Dyerberg, J. 1983. The effect of N-6 and N-3 polyunsaturated fatty acids on hemostasis, blood lipids and blood pressure. *Thromb. Haemost.* 50:543–46

57. Mutanen, M., Kleemola, P., Valsta, L. M., Mensink, R. P., Räsänen, L. 1992. Lack of effect on blood pressure by polyunsaturated and monounsaturated fat diets. *Eur. J. Clin. Nutr.* 46:1–6

58. Oster, P., Arab, L., Schellenberg, B., Kohlmeier, M., Schlierf, G. 1980. Linoleic acid and blood pressure. *Prog. Food Nutr. Sci.* 4:39–40

59. Puska, P., Iacono, J. M., Nissinen, A., Korhonen, H. J., Vartiainen, E., et al. 1983. Controlled, randomised trial of the effect of dietary fat on blood pressure. *Lancet* 1:1–5

60. Puska, P., Iacono, J. M., Nissinen, A., Vartiainen, E., Dougherty, R., et al. 1985. Dietary fat and blood pressure: an intervention study on the effects of a low-fat diet with two levels of polyunsaturated fat. *Prev. Med.* 14:573–84

61. Rao, R. H., Rao, U. B., Srikantia, S. G. 1981. Effect of polyunsaturate-rich vegetable oils on blood pressure in essential hypertension. *Clin. Exp. Hypertens.* 3:27–38

62. Romero, J. C., Knox, F. G. 1988. Mechanisms underlying pressure-related natriuresis: The role of renin-angiotensin and prostaglandin systems. *Hypertension* 11:724–38

63. Rosenthal, J., Simone, P. G., Silbergleit, A. 1974. Effects of prostaglandin deficiency on natriuresis, diuresis, and blood pressure. *Prostaglandins* 5:435–40

64. Sacks, F. M., Stampfer, M. J., Munoz, A., McManus, K., Canessa, M., et al. 1987. Effect of linoleic and oleic acids on blood pressure, blood viscosity, and erythrocyte cation transport. *J. Am. Coll. Nutr.* 6:179–85

65. Scherhag, R., Kramer, H. J., Düsing, R. 1982. Dietary administration of eicosapentaenoic and linolenic acid increases arterial blood pressure and suppresses vascular prostacyclin synthesis in the rat. *Prostaglandins* 23:369–82

66. Schoene, N. W., Ferretti, A., Fiore, D. 1981. Production of prostaglandins in homogenates of kidney medullae and cortices of spontaneously hypertensive rats fed menhaden oil. *Lipids* 16:866–69

67. Schoene, N. W., Fiore, D. 1981. Effect of a diet containing fish oil on blood pressure in spontaneously hypertensive rats. *Prog. Lipid Res.* 20:569–70

68. Schoene, N. W., Reeves, V. B., Ferretti, A. 1980. Effects of dietary linoleic acid on the biosynthesis of PGE_2 and $PGF_{2\alpha}$ in kidney medullae in spontaneously hypertensive rats. *Adv. Prostaglandin Thromboxane Res.* 8:1791–92

69. Singer, P., Jaeger, W., Wirth, M., Voigt, S., Naumann, E., et al. 1983. Lipid and blood pressure-lowering effect of mackerel diet in man. *Atherosclerosis* 49:99–108

70. Singer, P., Wirth, M., Berger, I., Voigt, S., Gerike, U., et al. 1985. Influence on serum lipids, lipoproteins and blood pressure of mackerel and herring diet in patients with type IV and V hyperlipoproteinemia. *Atherosclerosis* 56:111–18

71. Singer, P., Wirth, M., Gödicke, W., Heine, H. 1985. Blood pressure lowering effect of eicosapentaenoic acid-rich diet in normotensive, hypertensive and hyperlipemic subjects. *Experientia* 41:462–64

72. Singer, P., Wirth, M., Mest, H. J., Taube, C., Richter-Heinrich, E., et al. 1986. Changes in blood pressure and serum lipids with fish diets in patients with mild essential hypertension. *Z. Gesamte Inn. Med.* 41:38–44

73. Singer, P., Wirth, M., Voigt, S., Richter-Heinrich, E., Gödicke, W., et al. 1985. Blood pressure- and lipid-lowering effect of mackerel and herring diet in patients with mild essential hypertension. *Atherosclerosis* 56:223–35

74. Smith, M. C., Dunn, M. J. 1985. The role of prostaglandins in human hypertension. *Am. J. Kidney Dis.* 5:A32–39

75. Smith-Barbaro, P., Fisher, H., Quinn, M. R., Hegsted, D. M. 1980. The effect of varying polyunsaturated to saturated fat ratios on salt-induced hypertension in rats. *Nutr. Rep. Int.* 22: 759–70

76. Stern, B., Heyden, S., Miller, D., Latham, G., Klimas, A., et al. 1980. Intervention study in high school students with elevated blood pressures. Dietary experiment with polyunsaturated fatty acids. *Nutr. Metab.* 24:137–47

77. Stoff, J. S. 1986. Prostaglandins and hypertension. *Am. J. Med.* 80:56–61

78. Stokes, J. B. 1979. Effect of prostaglandin E_2 on chloride transport across the rabbit thick ascending limb of Henle. Selective inhibitions of the medullary portion. *J. Clin. Invest.* 64:495–502

79. Stokes, J. B., Kokko, J. P. 1977. Inhibition of sodium transport by prostaglandin E_2 across the isolated, perfused rabbit collecting tubule. *J. Clin. Invest.* 59:1099–1104

80. Strazzullo, P., Ferro-Luzzi, A., Siani, A., Scaccini, C., Sette, S., et al. 1986. Changing the Mediterranean diet: effects on blood pressure. *J. Hypertens.* 4:407–12

81. ten Hoor, F. 1980. Cardiovascular effects of dietary linoleic acid. *Nutr. Metab.* 24 (Suppl. 1):162–80

82. ten Hoor, F., van de Graaf, H. M. 1978. The influence of a linoleic acid-rich diet and of acetyl salicylic acid on NaCl-induced hypertension, Na^{+-} and H_2O—balance and urinary prostaglandin excretion in rats. *Acta Biol. Med. Ger.* 37:875–77

83. Terragno, D. A., Crowshaw, K., Terragno, N. A., McGiff, J. C. 1975. Prostaglandin synthesis by bovine mesenteric arteries and veins. *Circ. Res.* 36/37(Suppl.1):1–76–80

84. Terragno, N. A., Terragno, D. A., McGiff, J. C. 1977. Contribution of prostaglandins to the renal circulation in conscious, anesthetized, and laparotomized dogs. *Circ. Res.* 40:590–95

85. Tobian, L., Ganguli, M., Johnson, M. A., Iwai, J. 1985. The influence of renal prostaglandins and dietary linoleate on hypertension of Dahl salt-sensitive rats. In *Proc. NIH Workshop, Nutrition and Hypertension,* ed. M. J. Horan, M. Blaustein, J. B. Dunbar, W. Kachadorian, N. M. Kaplan, et al, pp. 349–59. New York: Biomed. Info.

86. Triebe, G., Block, H. U., Förster, W. 1976. Über das Blutdruckverhalten kochsalzbelasteter Ratten bei unterschiedlichem Linolsäuregehalt des Futters. *Acta Biol. Med. Ger.* 35:1223–24

87. Vartiainen, E., Puska, P., Pietinen, P., Nissinen, A., Leino, U., et al. 1986. Effects of dietary fat modifications on serum lipids and blood pressure in children *Acta Paediatr. Scand.* 75:396–401

88. von Euler, U. S. 1939. Weitere Untersuchungen über Prostaglandin, die physiologisch aktive Substanz gewisser Genitaldrusen. *Skand. Arch. Physiol.* 81:65–80

89. von Houwelingen, R., Nordøy, A., van der Beek, E., Houtsmuller, U., de Metz, M., et al. 1987. Effect of a moderate fish intake on blood pressure, bleeding time, hematology, and clinical chemistry in healthy males. *Am. J. Clin. Nutr.* 46:424–36

90. Webb, P., Bond, V., Kotchen, T., Bruckner, G. 1987. Lipid compositional changes in hypertensive (DOCA-salt loaded) rats fed fish oil, safflower oil, or soluble fiber supplemented diets. See Ref. 54, pp. 329–33

91. Weber, P. C., Siess, W., Scherer, B. 1980. Possible significance of renal prostaglandins in essential hypertension. *Clin. Exp. Hypertens.* 2:741–60

92. Whitaker, M. O., Wyche, A., Fitzpatrick, F., Sprecher, H., Needleman, P. 1979. Triene prostaglandins: prostaglandin D_3 and icosapentaenoic acid as potential antithrombotic substances. *Proc. Natl. Acad. Sci. USA* 76:5919–23

93. Ziemlański, S., Panczenko-Kresowska, B., Okolska, G., Wielgus-Serafińska, E., Żelakiewicz, K. 1985. Effect of dietary fats on experimental hypertension. *Ann. Nutr. Metab.* 29:223–31

94. Zins, G. R. 1975. Renal prostaglandins. *Am. J. Med.* 58:14–24

95. Zöllner, N., Adam, O., Wolfram, G. 1979. The influence of linoleic acid intake on the excretion of urinary prostaglandin metabolites. *Res. Exp. Med.* 175:149–53

Annu. Rev. Nutr. 1993. 13:261–86

NEW TETRAHYDROBIOPTERIN-DEPENDENT SYSTEMS*

Seymour Kaufman

Laboratory of Neurochemistry, National Institute of Mental Health, Bethesda, Maryland 20892

KEY WORDS: tetrahydrobiopterin, nitric oxide, indoleamine dioxygenase, neopterin, phenyl-ketonuria

CONTENTS

INTRODUCTION 261
ROLE OF TETRAHYDROBIOPTERIN (BH4) AS THE COENZYME FOR THE
    AROMATIC AMINO ACID HYDROXYLASES 262
PHENYLKETONURIA AND ITS VARIANTS 264
BH4 AND CELL PROLIFERATION 266
BH4 AND CELL-MEDIATED IMMUNITY 269
    Studies with Indoleamine Dioxygenase 272
    Studies with Nitric Oxide Synthase 274
BH4 AS A NEUROTRANSMITTER-RELEASING FACTOR 279
CONCLUDING REMARKS 280

INTRODUCTION

In 1955–1956, two lines of research with apparently nothing in common culminated in the independent discovery of biopterin. The starting point for one of these studies was the observation that maximum growth of an obscure protozoan, *Crithidia fasiculata,* in a chemically defined medium required exceptionally high concentrations of folic acid (9). In 1955, this growth-promoting substance was isolated from 4000 liters of human urine and characterized as 2-amino-4-hydroxy-6-(1,2-dihydroxypropyl) pteridine (83, 84). These workers suggested that this unconjugated pteridine be called "biopterin." All that remained to be determined about the structure of biopterin was its optical configuration. Chemical synthesis established that the *Crithidia* factor is 2-amino-4-hydroxy-6-[1,2-dihydroxypropyl (L-*erythro*)] pteridine (85). In addition to biopterin, the structurally related unconjugated pterin neopterin (6-trihydroxypropylpterin), a derivative of the biological precursor of tetrahydrobiopterin (BH₄), can also support the growth of *Crithidia fasiculata*.

The other line of research that led to the independent discovery of biopterin originated with structural studies of the eye color pigments in *Drosophila melanogaster*. During the course of these studies, Forrest & Mitchell isolated several pteridines including a blue fluorescent compound that they characterized as biopterin (22).

These early investigations established one role for biopterin—that of pigment—and, based on the finding that it is essential for the growth of *Crithidia fasiculata*, hinted at others. A clue to what these other roles might be, at least for this organism, was provided by the observation that certain pyrimidines such as uracil and cytosine and some unsaturated fatty acids such as a mixture of oleic and linoleic acid can spare the growth requirement of *Crithidia fasiculata* for an unconjugated pteridine (52). These findings suggested that an unconjugated pteridine like biopterin might be essential for the synthesis of certain pyrimidines and unsaturated fatty acids, but this possibility was never fully realized. Thus, although preliminary evidence indicated that in *Crithidia fasiculata* the conversion of dihydroorotic acid to orotic acid involves a tetrahydropterin-dependent hydroxylation of the dihydro compound and subsequent dehydration of the hydroxylated product to orotic acid (53), this pathway appears to be unique for *Crithidia fasiculata*: In all other organisms, the conversion of dihydroorotic acid to orotic acid is catalyzed by an NAD-dependent, iron-containing flavoprotein (for literature citations, see 53). As for the possibility that BH₄ might be essential for the desaturation of long-chain fatty acids by a sequence of hydroxylation-dehydration reactions, no evidence supports such a role for this pterin.

ROLE OF BH₄ AS THE COENZYME FOR THE AROMATIC AMINO ACID HYDROXYLASES

The first metabolic role for BH₄ was established when it was shown that the enzymatic conversion of phenylalanine to tyrosine catalyzed by the multi-enzyme hepatic phenylalanine hydroxylating system is completely dependent on a new coenzyme isolated from rat liver extracts. In 1963, structural studies carried out on the naturally occurring hydroxylation coenzyme that had been isolated from rat liver proved that it is tetrahydrobiopterin, 2-amino-4-hydroxy-6-[1,2-dihydroxy(L-*erythro*)]-5,6,7,8-tetrahydropteridine, whose structure is shown in Figure 1 (40). Several synthetic unconjugated pteridines like

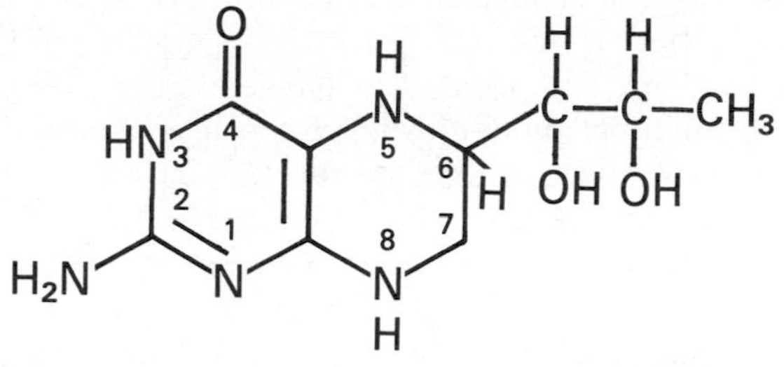

Figure 1   Structure of tetrahydrobiopterin (BH₄).

2-amino-4-hydroxy-6-methyltetrahydropteridine (6MPH₄) were also shown to be active in the system (38, 48).

In addition to the tetrahydropterin coenzyme ("pterin" is the trivial name for a 2-amino-4-hydroxy-pteridine), the phenylalanine hydroxylating system was shown to consist of three enzymes. The role of each component of the system is illustrated in Figure 2 with 6MPH₄ as the coenzyme. Phenylalanine hydroxylase (PAH) catalyzes a coupled reaction in which phenylalanine is oxidized to tyrosine and the tetrahydropterin is oxidized to the corresponding 4a-hydroxytetrahydropterin; molecular oxygen, which is the source of the oxygen in the newly synthesized tyrosine, is normally reduced to water. At neutral pH, the 4a-hydroxytetrahydropterin product is unstable and breaks down rapidly to the quinonoid dihydropterin derivative; this reaction is also catalyzed by an enzyme that originally was called PAH-stimulating protein (abbreviated "PHS") (42) and later was shown to be a dehydratase (31, 43, 58). The cycle is completed by the action of the third enzyme, dihydropteridine reductase (DHPR), which catalyzes the reduction of the quinonoid dihydropterin to the tetrahydropterin. NADH is the preferred electron donor in vitro. This last reaction allows the pterin coenzyme to function catalytically in the hydroxylating system (47).

The elucidation of the roles of the individual components in the phenylalanine hydroxylating system facilitated subsequent studies showing that BH₄ and DHPR function in the same way in the tyrosine and tryptophan hydroxylating systems (reviewed in 47). Since the end products of these hydroxylase-catalyzed reactions are the tyrosine-derived neurotransmitters, dopamine and norepinephrine, and the tryptophan-derived neurotransmitter serotonin, these studies indicated that BH₄ and DHPR, are essential for normal brain development and functioning. BH₄ was also shown to be the essential

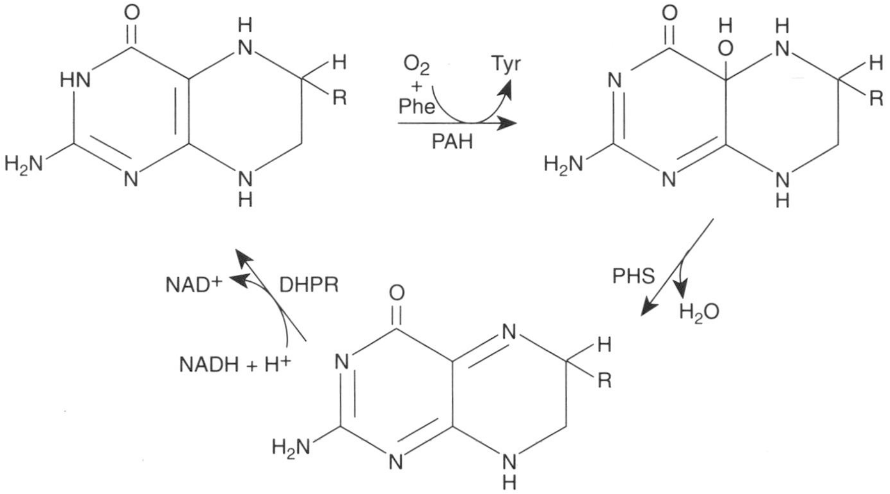

Figure 2 The enzymatic conversion of phenylalanine to tyrosine catalyzed by the multi-component phenylalanine hydroxylase system.

coenzyme in the system that catalyzes the oxidative cleavage of glyceryl ethers (49, 103).

PHENYLKETONURIA AND ITS VARIANTS

Before discussing new roles for BH$_4$, it is worth noting that progress in our understanding of the biochemistry of the BH$_4$-dependent aromatic amino acid hydroxylating systems led to parallel progress in our understanding of aspects of phenylketonuria (PKU), a genetic disease known to be caused by a defect in the hydroxylation of phenylalanine (21, 33). The demonstration that the phenylalanine hydroxylating system consists of three essential components led to the prediction of three distinct forms of PKU, each caused by the lack of one of the essential components (41). After PAH had been identified as the missing component in the most common form of this disease, called "classical" PKU (37), researchers described several variant forms of PKU that were caused by a lack of either DHPR or BH$_4$; the latter condition is a consequence of a deficiency of one of the enzymes involved in the de novo synthesis of BH$_4$ from GTP [for review, see (45, 94)].

Note that observations made on patients who are deficient in BH$_4$, either because they cannot synthesize it or regenerate it (owing to a lack of DHPR), are relevant to a discussion of new roles for BH$_4$ because it is reasonable to expect that the BH$_4$ deficiency in these patients underlies most of their pathological signs. So far, however, clinical experience with these variants, including the more-or-less successful outcome of replacement therapy with BH$_4$ or the products of the affected tyrosine hydroxylase- and tryptophan hydroxylase-catalyzed reactions (i.e. 3,4-dihydroxyphenylalanine and 5-hydroxytryptophan) or a combination (reviewed in 45, 94), has not provided useful clues to new roles for BH$_4$. Some reasons for the failure to realize this expectation have been discussed (46); others are considered below.

The original prediction that three variant forms of PKU might exist, each caused by the lack of one of the three essential components of the PAH system, was made before the role of the dehydratase in the system had been elucidated. Because the reaction catalyzed by this enzyme occurs rapidly nonenzymatically under physiological conditions (43), it was predicted that a complete lack of the dehydratase, unlike the lack of any of the other three essential components, would probably lead to only a partial defect in phenylalanine metabolism and, hence, to only mild hyperphenylalaninemia (HPA) (44).

Recent evidence is coherent with this view. Several patients with mild HPA appear to be distinct from any that have been described previously. Their distinguishing feature is the excretion of abnormally high amounts of 7-biopterin, an isomer of biopterin with the dihydroxypropyl substituent in the 7, rather than in the 6, position of the pterin ring (6, 11, 18).

Feeding BH$_4$ to these patients led to the parallel increase in the excretion of both biopterin and 7-biopterin, suggesting that the 7-isomer is derived from BH$_4$ (12). The possibility that the patients who excrete 7-biopterin might be deficient in the dehydratase was raised by the results of in vitro experiments. These experiments demonstrated that in the absence of the dehydratase the initial pterin product of the PAH-catalyzed hydroxylation of phenylalanine, 4a-hydroxytetrahydrobiopterin, not only breaks down to its major product, quinonoid dihydrobiopterin, as shown in Figure 2, but also rearranges to give rise to small amounts of 7-biopterin, which is probably derived from the corresponding 7-quinonoid dihydrobiopterin. Furthermore, addition of the dehydratase markedly decreased the amount of 7-biopterin found (15). Qualitatively similar results were reported by Curtius et al 1990 (10). These in vitro findings suggest a possible link between excretion of 7-biopterin and a deficiency of the dehydratase, but the validity of this suggestion must await the proof that these patients actually lack the dehydratase.

The cause of the mild HPA in patients who excrete 7-biopterin has not been established. In this regard, it has been observed that 7-BH$_4$ is utilized inefficiently by pure rat liver PAH. Most of the 7-BH$_4$ is oxidized non-productively in a reaction in which oxidation of the tetrahydropterin is largely uncoupled from hydroxylation of the amino acid (13). Additionally, in the presence of high concentrations of phenylalanine, 7-BH$_4$ is a potent inhibitor of PAH (16). Either or both of these effects of 7-BH$_4$ on PAH could account for the impaired hydroxylation of phenylalanine and the consequent HPA seen in patients who excrete 7-biopterin.

BH$_4$ AND CELL PROLIFERATION

The earliest indication that BH$_4$ has metabolic roles in addition to that of coenzyme for the aromatic amino acid hydroxylases came from the observation, mentioned earlier, that biopterin or a structurally related unconjugated pterin like neopterin, is essential for the growth of *Crithidia fasiculata*. This dependence, together with the finding that this organism has an absolute requirement for tyrosine (9), and therefore cannot synthesize it, and is also unlikely to synthesize the tyrosine hydroxylase- and tryptophan hydroxylase-derived neurotransmitters, provided strong, albeit indirect, evidence for other roles for BH$_4$.

That BH$_4$ might also have other roles in higher organisms was indicated by the finding that the pterin is present in cells and tissues such as blood, spleen, and lung, which have negligible amounts of the aromatic amino acid hydroxylases (24).

Some insight into how biopterin may function in the physiology and development of red blood cells came from the observation that cellular levels of biopterin increase in proliferating hemopoietic cells during bone marrow transplantation in beagle dogs (118). An essential connection between biopterin synthesis and hemopoietic cell proliferation was proposed.

Also pointing in the same direction was the finding that both the content of total biopterin and the levels of GTP cyclohydrolase, the enzyme that catalyzes the first step in the *de novo* synthesis of BH$_4$ (See Figure 3), are strikingly higher in young rat erythrocytes, than in older erythrocytes (101). These results suggested that BH$_4$ levels in reticulocytes, the precursors of erythrocytes, might be high. This possibility was examined in rats treated with phenylhydrazine to stimulate the production of erythrocyte precursor cells. The biopterin concentration and the levels of GTP cyclohydrolase were found to be 17.5-fold and 23-fold higher, respectively, in hemolysates prepared from phenylhydrazine-treated rats (reticulocyte content more than 80% of total erythrocytes) than in comparable preparations from control rats (1–2% reticulocytes) (101). Very similar results were obtained with phenylhydrazine-treated mice (50).

The possibility raised by these results, i.e. that BH$_4$ may regulate the proliferation of erythroid cells, was examined in greater detail in murine erythroleukemia (MEL) cells as a model for erythrogenesis. In culture, these cells have a very low level of spontaneous erythroid differentiation. Treatment with certain agents, such as hexamethylene bisacetamide (HMBA), leads to

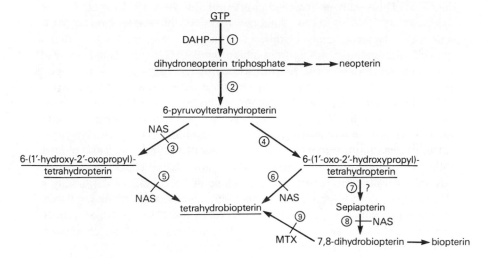

Figure 3 Proposed scheme for the biosynthesis of tetrahydrobiopterin from guanosine triphosphate (GTP).

The intermediates on the *de novo* pathway are underlined. The scheme shows two alternate routes for the conversion of 6-pyruvoyltetrahydropterin to BH_4. One involves the successive reductions of this diketo intermediate; each reduction is catalyzed by sepiapterin reductase (reactions 3 and 5). The other pathway, first demonstrated in brain tissue (68, 69), proceeds with the reduction of the 2'-oxo group of the diketo intermediate, catalyzed by an aldose reductase (reaction 4) to form the 1'-oxo-2'-hydroxy intermediate (also called 6-lactoyltetrahydropterin) and followed by reduction of the 1'oxo group, also catalyzed by sepiapterin reductase. The sepiapterin shown in the scheme is probably formed during the nonenzymatic oxidation of 6-lactoyltetrahydropterin. Conversion of sepiapterin to BH_4 through the successive actions of sepiapterin reductase and dihydrofolate reductase (reactions 8 and 9) constitutes the so-called salvage pathway for the synthesis of BH_4 (71).

The key reactions are catalyzed by the following enzymes: reaction 1, GTP cyclohydrolase; reaction 2, 6-pyruvoyltetrahydropterin synthase; reactions 3, 5, 6, 8, sepiapterin reductase; reaction 4, 6-pyruvoyltetrahydropterin-(2'-oxo)-reductase, an aldose reductase (69); reaction 9, dihydrofolate reductase. The abbreviations used are DAHP, 2,4-diamino-6-hydroxypyrimidine, an inhibitor of GTP cyclohydrolase; NAS, *N*-acetylserotonin, an inhibitor of sepiapterin reductase; MTX, methotrexate, an inhibitor of dihydrofolate reductase.

induction of differentiation culminating in terminal cell divisions and hemoglobin synthesis (62).

During a 96-hr period of exposure of MEL cells to HMBA, a progressive decrease in the initially high levels of BH_4 and GTP cyclohydrolase was accompanied by a marked increase in hemoglobin content that was detectable after 72 hr of exposure to the inducing agent (101). Cellular content of BH_4 was decreased by inhibition of its synthesis. This was accomplished by treatment of the cells with *N*-acetylserotonin (NAS), an inhibitor of sepiapterin reductase, which is the terminal enzyme in the BH_4 biosynthetic pathway (See

Figure 3). This treatment inhibited proliferation of the cells, as measured by a decrease in DNA synthesis. Although inhibition of proliferation of MEL cells is usually accompanied by differentiation, the decreased DNA synthesis and cell proliferation resulting from inhibition of BH_4 synthesis did not lead to an increase in differentiation as measured by the appearance of hemoglobin-positive cells. Inhibition of proliferation caused by treatment of the MEL cells with NAS was not due to an irreversible toxic effect of NAS on the cells, since repletion of the BH_4 content of the NAS-treated cells, by treatment with the BH_4 precursor sepiapterin, completely restored DNA synthesis (101). Indeed, increasing the BH_4 content of MEL cells that had not been treated with NAS increased DNA synthesis above control values (101).

Similar results were reported in a subclone of MEL cells (F4N); addition of either BH_4 or its precursor, sepiapterin, significantly increased DNA synthesis (51). In this subclone, in contrast to the MEL cells, only trace amounts of biopterin and GTP cyclohydrolase are present and induction (with dimethyl sulfoxide) significantly increased their levels (51).

These results indicate that BH_4 plays a role in proliferation and differentiation of murine erythroid cells. The observation that inhibition of cell proliferation by depletion of BH_4 does not culminate in hemoglobin synthesis suggests that the presence of BH_4 may enable MEL cells to enter the erythroid program that commits them to a terminal differentiation.

How BH_4 regulates the growth of these cells has not been elucidated. One possibility is based on the finding that biopterin and BH_4 inhibit the guanine: queuine tRNA transglycosylase from rabbit reticulocytes (20). This enzyme is responsible for the synthesis of the modified tRNA species in which the hypermodified base queuine is substituted for guanine. Evidence suggests that the ratio of tRNA queuine ($tRNA_Q$) to tRNA guanine ($tRNA_G$) decreases in tumor tissues during cell transformation (73, 76) and that the ratio also changes during erythroid differentiation of MEL cells. In one study, a continual decrease in $tRNA_G$ was observed during differentiation (95), whereas Lin et al (60) found an initial increase in $tRNA_G$ followed by a decrease.

Recently, the relationship between changes in cellular content of BH_4 and those of $tRNA_G$ was studied during the course of tetramethylurea-induced differentiation of MEL cells (82). Changes in levels of BH_4 and $tRNA_G$ followed similar patterns: An initial increase after the first 12 to 24 h was followed by a decrease, i.e. levels of $tRNA_G$ were high when BH_4 levels were high and these levels decreased when BH_4 levels were decreasing. Such a temporal relationship would not be expected if BH_4 was acting to inhibit the incorporation of guanine into tRNA in the MEL cells. While these results are of interest, the possibility that the BH_4 regulation of proliferation of erythroid cells is mediated by changes in the ratio of $tRNA_Q$ to $tRNA_G$ remains to be established.

These results with erythroid cells raised the possibility that BH_4 might be a general regulator of cell proliferation. Preliminary results indicate that BH_4 may also regulate proliferation of cultured neonatal rat brain astrocytes (70). On the other hand, attempts to demonstrate a similar role for BH_4 in proliferation of hamster ovary cells were negative (S. Milstien & K. Tanaka, unpublished results). Thus, it is unlikely that BH_4 is involved in the regulation of the growth of all cells.

The role of BH_4 in the proliferation of erythrocyte precursor cells is complex. Not only is there strong evidence, reviewed above, supporting the conclusion that BH_4 is necessary for the growth of these cells, but, in addition, there are indications of a reciprocal relationship, i.e. the rate of *de novo* synthesis of BH_4 is high during periods of rapid proliferation of the cells.

BH_4 AND CELL-MEDIATED IMMUNITY

Our understanding of this kind of reciprocal relationship has been advanced by studies of the relationship between pterin metabolism and activation of the immune system.

Some of the earliest evidence for such a connection came from reports that urinary levels of pterins such as neopterin (derived from the BH_4 precursor dihydroneopterin triphosphate (see Figure 3) (88, 105) and blood levels of BH_4 (54) are elevated in cancer patients. This increase was not specifically related to malignancy, but rather was part of a much broader response, involving a variety of conditions associated with activation of the immune system. Reports indicated that urinary neopterin levels are also elevated in patients suffering from viral (105) and bacterial (23) infections, including acquired immune deficiency (AIDS) (1,104), as well as from such conditions as rheumatoid arthritis and systemic lupus erythematosus (26). Thus, increased urinary excretion of neopterin is a marker for activation of the cell-mediated immune system.

These in vivo studies did not identify the cellular source of the elevated urinary neopterin. A subsequent in vitro study showed, upon stimulation with factors derived from activated T cells [activated by treatment with alloantigens or phytohemaglutinin (PHA)], that human monocytes and macrophages release neopterin into the cell culture medium and that interferon gamma (IFNγ) is the most active stimulating factor. Researchers concluded that this cytokine is the mediator of the response, because monoclonal antibodies against IFNγ were able to completely block the increased neopterin release that was induced by activated T cells (32). Macrophages and their precursors, monocytes, therefore, are probably major sources of the elevated urinary excretion of neopterin that is associated with activation of the immune system.

The mechanism for the IFNγ-induced increase in synthesis and release of neopterin was the induction of GTP cyclohydrolase. Treatment of human macrophages with supernatants from mitrogen (PHA)-activated or alloantigen-activated T cells or with recombinant IFNγ resulted in a 10–20 fold increase in GTP cyclohydrolase activity. A comparable increase in the activity of the enzyme in the T cells, themselves, was noted after they had been activated. In T cells, the increase in GTP cyclohydrolase activity was accompanied by a modest (50–100%) increase in levels of neopterin and an increase of both biopterin and pterin (a breakdown product of BH_4) (4, 14), neither of which was detectable in unactivated T cells. By contrast, in human macrophages the elevation in neopterin induced by either activated T cell supernatants or IFNγ was not accompanied by any increase in either biopterin or pterin (92).

These results with activated T cells agree with previous reports that activation of both murine and human T lymphocytes leads to large increases in the formation and release of pteridines, including biopterin (115, 116). It was also reported that BH_4 and its biological precursors, 7,8-dihydrobiopterin and sepiapterin, are co-stimulators of concanavalin A–mediated lymphocyte proliferation, which perhaps affects the interaction of the lymphocytes with interleukin 2 (117, 119). These results suggest that in its effects on lymphocytes BH_4 is part of an autocrine signaling process in which cells respond to substances that they themselves release.

The finding that IFNγ induces in human macrophages a striking increase in neopterin, whereas biopterin remains at undetectable levels, was paradoxical because, in contrast to BH_4, no physiological function has ever been ascribed to neopterin or its derivatives.[1]

This selective effect of IFNγ on human macrophages is coherent with the observation that humans and nonhuman primates are peculiar because they have relatively large amounts of neopterin in their body fluids (19). Studies with macrophages from other species, as well as those with human cells other than macrophages, showed that the selective IFNγ-mediated increase in neopterin is unique to human macrophages. In mouse peritoneal macrophages stimulated with lipopolysaccharide and in a murine T cell line stimulated with interleukin-2, cell content of biopterin was increased twofold and four- to sevenfold, respectively, whereas neopterin was not detectable (93), i.e. this

---

[1]Regarding possible biological activity of this pterin, note that it is potentially active as a hydroxylase coenzyme in vivo; however, no reports have suggested that its coenzyme activity is comparable to that of BH_4. Thus, although the biosynthetic intermediate, dihydro-(D-*erythro*)-neopterin triphosphate, is not a substrate for DHFR, this enzyme does catalyze the reduction of the dephosphorylated compound, dihydroneopterin, to its tetrahydro form (74), a finding that has recently been confirmed (3). Furthermore, it has been known since 1962 that tetrahydroneopterin has high coenzyme activity with rat liver PAH (39). The maximum activity of tetrahydroneopterin, however, is only about one third that of BH_4 (77). In the case of rat brain tryptophan hydroxylase, the relative activity of tetrahydroneopterin is even less favorable—only about 5% that of BH_4 (36).

pterin pattern is just the reverse of the one seen in stimulated human macrophages.

A more detailed study of the effect of cytokines on murine macrophages, which was also extended to murine fibroblasts, showed that treatment of these cells with tumor necrosis factor (TNFα) alone increased intracellular biopterin 2-fold (macrophages) to 13-fold (fibroblasts); treatment with IFNγ alone led to modest increases, and treatment with both led to greater increases than treatment with either factor alone (109).

In human fibroblasts, in contrast to human macrophages, IFNγ increased the cell content of *both* neopterin and biopterin, with the levels of biopterin actually exceeding those of neopterin; activity of GTP cyclohydrolase increased more than 10-fold (107). In this study, unlike an earlier one (93), treatment of human macrophages with IFNγ modestly increased their biopterin content, although the amount of neopterin contained in the treated cells was about 80-times greater than that of bioperin.

The unique response to IFNγ treatment of human macrophages, leading to a selective increase in neopterin, has been traced to differences in the levels of the post-cyclase enzymes that are essential for BH$_4$ synthesis, particularly 6-pyruvoyltetrahydropterin synthase (Figure 3). Thus, in human macrophages, synthase activity is extremely low, and unlike GTP cyclohydrolase, is unaffected by IFNγ treatment. After this treatment, cyclohydrolase activity was about 40-times higher than that of the synthase. Sepiapterin reductase, the terminal enzyme in the BH$_4$ synthetic pathway, is constitutive and is in huge excess over the activities of the synthase and hydrolase (108). The ability of IFNγ to induce GTP cyclohydrolase, together with the low-constitutive levels of the synthase and its lack of response to IFNγ, account for the selective cytokine-mediated increase in neopterin in human macrophages. On the other hand, in murine macrophages as well as in nonmacrophage, cytokine-sensitive human cells that have been studied, the constitutive level of the synthase far exceeds even the elevated induced level of the hydrolase. In murine fibroblasts, for example, synthase activity is about 10 times higher than the maximally induced levels of cyclohydrolase; (109). In this enzyme pattern, where the synthase, the enzyme utilizing the neopterin derivative and converting it to BH$_4$, is in vast excess over the enzyme synthesizing it, the stimulation of the cyclohydrolase leads to a selective increase in biopterin rather than neopterin.

A paradoxical question was raised by the results with human macrophages: What is the physiological sense of turning on the BH$_4$ biosynthetic pathway only to have it almost completely short-circuited because of severely limiting amounts of the key enzyme in the pathway, 6-pyruvoyltetrahydropterin synthase? Although this question has not been answered, recent studies have uncovered possible functional connections between the immune response and increased synthesis of BH$_4$.

The compass for this search was provided by the observation that IFNγ plays a key role in the process. This observation focused attention on BH_4-dependent enzymes that are also induced by IFNγ and of which two are known: indoleamine-2,3-dioxygenase (IDO) and nitric oxide synthase (NOS).

Studies with Indoleamine Dioxygenase

There were several early indications that indoleamine dioxygenase, which in nonhepatic tissues catalyzes the superoxide ion-dependent, oxygenative ring cleavage of various indoleamine derivatives, may be involved in the immune response. In mammals, the enzyme catalyzes the first step in the major catabolic pathway of L-tryptophan in which the amino acid is converted to kynurenine via the formation of N-formyl kynurenine. The enzyme occurs in two entirely distinct forms, one in liver and one in many nonhepatic tissues. Activity of the extrahepatic enzyme in tissues such as lung and stomach was found to be markedly increased in mice under some pathological conditions e.g. after intraperitoneal injection of bacterial lipopolysaccharide, whereas the activity of the hepatic enzyme was decreased by this treatment (113). Subsequently, it was demonstrated that exposure of mouse lung slices to mouse IFN increased the activity of IDO 10- to 15-fold (114). Induction of IDO by IFNγ was also demonstrated in human peripheral blood monocytes (78).

The mechanism by which IDO mediates some of the physiological effects of IFNγ, such as its ability to fight viral and nonviral intracellular infections, was suggested by the finding that the effectiveness of this cytokine in suppressing the growth of an intracellular protozoan parasite in human fibroblasts was blocked by high levels of tryptophan in the culture medium. This observation and the finding that the IFNγ-treated fibroblasts could degrade this amino acid led to the suggestion that the increased degradation of tryptophan could limit growth of the organism either because tryptophan metabolites could be toxic to the parasite or because degradation of tryptophan could decrease the intracellular concentration of this commonly limiting amino acid (86).

Studies of the antiproliferative effects of IFNγ on a variety of human neoplastic cell lines also support the conclusion that the antiproliferative, antitumor effect of the cytokine, like its effect on growth of intracellular parasites, is due to the IFNγ-induction of IDO, with consequent starvation of the cells for tryptophan (79).

The demonstration that, in certain cells, IFNγ could induce both BH_4 synthesis and IDO appeared to make sense in light of the earlier report that BH_4 and $DMPH_4$ have cofactor activity with IDO purified from rabbit small intestine (72). The enzyme had previously been shown to require ascorbic acid and methylene blue for maximum activity. The dye was believed to be responsible for the generation of superoxide ion, which was known to participate as a reactant in the reaction (30). The possibility that BH_4 might be the preferred coenzyme was supported by the finding that the K_m for BH_4 is lower (70 μM) (72) than the K_m for ascorbate (200 μM) (30); the values for V_{max}/K_m for the two potential coenzymes are similar (72).

Subsequent studies with IDO purified from mouse epididymis, however, made it less likely that BH_4 might function as the physiological coenzyme with this enzyme. Reduced flavin mononucleotide at 0.005 mM (with an $FMNH_2$ regenerating system) supports reaction rates that are about 40-fold higher than reaction rates in which 0.1 mM BH_4 is in the presence of its regenerating system, i.e. DHPR and NADPH (80). These in vitro data indicated that reduced flavin mononucleotide is, in all probability, the physiological coenzyme for IDO, at least for this tissue.

Despite these in vitro results, the notion that BH_4 may function in vivo as the coenzyme for IDO continues to be put forward. Recently, apparent support for this possibility was provided by the finding that both IDO and BH_4 synthesis (as measured by GTP cyclohydrolase activities and intracellular concentrations of neopterin and biopterin) are induced together by IFNγ in six human cancer cell lines, as well as in human fibroblasts and macrophages (107). As mentioned above, the level of BH_4 attained in macrophages was very low, equal to only 1–2% that of neopterin. Also suggestive of a possible functional link between IDO and pterin synthesis was the finding in macrophages that at a fixed dose of IFNγ, both IDO activity (measured by kynurenine formation) and pterin biosynthesis (measured by neopterin formation) were increased in parallel fashion by increases in L-tryptophan in the culture medium. In this study, the cofactor activity of BH_4 with IDO, originally reported with the enzyme from rabbit intestine (72), was also demonstrated with crude extracts of an IFNγ-treated human bladder carcinoma cell line. This study confirmed the observation that BH_4 showed little activity in the absence of methylene blue. The relative activities of BH_4 and ascorbate were essentially the same as in the earlier study. By contrast, the coenzyme activity of reduced flavin mononucleotide reported with IDO from mouse epididymis (80) could not be replicated with the enzyme from the human bladder carcinoma cells (107).

Despite the parallel induction by IFNγ of BH_4 biosynthesis and IDO activity in a variety of human cell lines (107) and the reported coenzyme activity of BH_4 with IDO in vitro (72, 107), the evidence does not strongly support the notion that, when the immune system is activated, BH_4 synthesis is turned on because BH_4 is the physiological coenzyme for IDO. In particular, the near-absolute dependence of the coenzyme activity of BH_4 on the presence of methylene blue, and the finding that, at least in one tissue, $FMNH_2$ is far more active than BH_4 (78), weaken support for the postulated connection.

Indeed, recent evidence has seriously undermined the IFN-IDO-BH_4

postulate. Treatment of human macrophages with IFNγ led to the expected increase in formation of kynurenine and neopterin, but treatment of the cells with 2,4-diamino-6-hydroxypyrimidine (DAHP), an inhibitor of the BH_4 biosynthetic pathway that completely prevented the IFNγ-mediated increase in neopterin, had no effect on the amount of kynurenine formed. Similar results were obtained with DAHP-treated human fibroblasts (N. Sakai, K. Saito, M. P. Heyes, et al, unpublished results)

In fibroblasts devoid of BH_4 that were obtained from patients who are deficient in 6-pyruvoyltetrahydropterin synthase, treatment with cytokines still leads to induction of IDO, as measured by kynurenine formation (N. Sakai, K. Saito, M. P. Heyes, et al, unpublished results). These results, which show that increased IDO activity can be expressed even in the absence of detectable amounts of BH_4, provide persuasive evidence against the proposal that BH_4, is the physiological cofactor for IDO.

Studies with Nitric Oxide Synthase

The other candidate enzyme that could be the link between activation of the immune system and the BH_4 biosynthetic pathway is nitric oxide synthase (NOS). This enzyme catalyzes the NADPH-dependent conversion of L-arginine to L-citrulline and nitric oxide (•NO). The enzyme is classified as an oxygenase or mixed function oxidase, since molecular oxygen, rather than water, is the source of the ureido oxygen in citrulline (56).

•NO, a highly reactive radical, has been shown to be a mediator in a bewildering array of biological processes. Not only has it been identified as the endothelium-derived relaxing factor, which is active as a smooth muscle relaxant, but it also acts as a neurotransmitter, prevents platelet aggregation, and, as part of the cell-mediated immune response, destroys or halts the growth of some tumor and bacterial cells (reviewed in 61, 63).

The synthase occurs in two distinct forms with different properties: a constitutive form, present in tissues like cerebellum, endothelial cells, and platelets, and a cytokine-inducible form, present in cells like macrophages and hepatocytes (97).

Inducible cytosolic NOS, partially purified from a murine macrophage cell line after stimulation of the cells by treatment with interferon γ and *E. coli* lipopolysaccharide, was shown to be absolutely dependent on L-arginine and on NADPH and to be partially dependent (two- to threefold stimulation) on BH_4 (57, 102), FAD, and a thiol such as glutathione (98).

The constitutive enzyme from rat cerebellum, like the inducible macrophage enzyme, also requires L-arginine and NADPH, but unlike the former enzyme, it is also dependent on exogenous Ca^{2+} and calmodulin (7). Like the macrophage enzyme, NOS from brains of various species, including rat (25, 91), porcine (67), and human (90), is stimulated by BH_4.

Both the constitutive and macrophage enzymes are homodimers, composed of identical subunits, $M_r = 279,000$ (7, 66, 90). The macrophage enzyme appears to be somewhat smaller (96). Both enzymes contain bound flavins [flavin adenine dinucleotide (FAD) and flavin mononucleotide (FMN)] and tightly bound BH4. The presence of bound BH4 may account for the fact that NOS has considerable activity in the absence of added BH4. NOS from murine macrophages contains heme-bound iron, and is sensitive to inhibition by CO (111). Although originally reported to contain nonheme iron (67), recent evidence indicates that like the macrophage enzyme, the brain enzyme is sensitive to CO (111), thereby indicating that it is also a heme-iron protein (see also 61).

It has been demonstrated that N$^\omega$-hydroxyl-L-arginine is an intermediate in the conversion of L-arginine to L-citrulline and •NO (96). The overall reaction has been formulated as shown in Figure 4: 1.5 mol of NADPH is oxidized for each mole of arginine converted to •NO (measured as nitrate plus nitrite), whereas only 0.5 mol of NADPH is consumed for each mole of hydroxyarginine converted to •NO (96). Although Figure 4 depicts BH4 as being involved only in the latter step, there is no evidence in support of this assignment.

One of the most striking differences between NOS and hepatic PAH is that the K_m for BH4 for the NOS (0.02–0.03 μM) (25, 97) is orders of magnitude smaller than that for PAH (2 μM) (2).

The extremely low K_m of NOS for BH4 is relevant to our understanding of the clinical picture presented by patients with variant forms of PKU caused by an inability to either regenerate or synthesize BH4 (94). The discovery that BH4 is a cofactor for nitric oxide synthase raised questions about why these BH4-deficient patients do not show signs that might be expected if the BH4 deficiency led to diminished activity of NOS with consequent impairment of

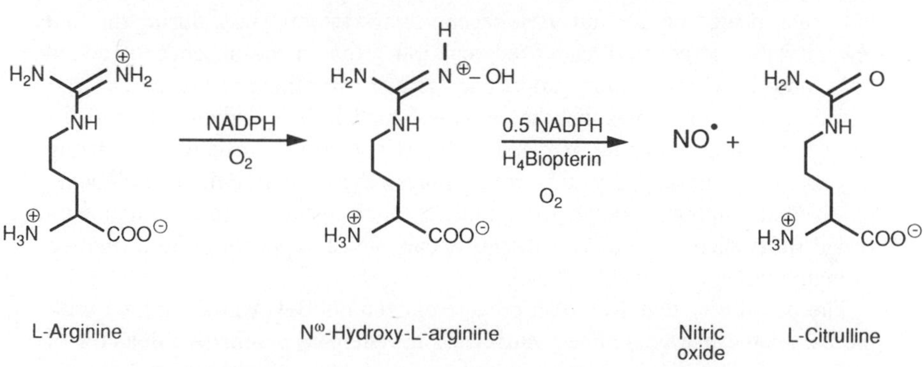

Figure 4   The reaction sequence for the enzymatic conversion of L-arginine to L-citrulline and •NO showing N$^\omega$ hydroxy-L-arginine as an intermediate [adapted from (99)].

the myriad physiological processes that appear to be mediated by this biofactor. To mention only one example, why do not BH_4-deficient patients exhibit signs of impaired immune function (34)? One explanation for this apparent paradox is that the deficiency of BH_4 and the consequent decrease in tissue levels of BH_4 in these patients is severe enough to impair the function of an enzyme like PAH, with a K_m for BH_4 of 2 μM, but is not severe enough to impair the function of enzyme like NOS, with a K_m for BH_4 of 0.02 μM.

Another sharp difference between NOS and PAH is that the requirement for BH_4 by the former enzyme is much more specific than it is for the latter. Thus, whereas synthetic model tetrahydropterins like $6MPH_4$ have about the same coenzyme activity for PAH as does BH_4 [i.e. the same V_{max}/K_m value (2)], $6MPH_4$ at 0.2–0.5 μM (i.e. ~ 10–20 × the K_m for BH_4) is inactive with both macrophage (57) and brain NOS (25), although it does show some activity at 50–100 μM (25, 57).

Given the large number of redox cofactors that are, or can be, bound to NOS—NADPH, FMN, FAD, heme-iron, and BH_4—the question of what role BH_4 plays in this built-in electron-transport system is of special interest. It has been postulated (57) that BH_4 functions in the NOS system in precisely the same way that it has been shown to function with the aromatic amino acid hydroxylating systems (Figure 2); the only difference is that the proposed scheme for the NOS-catalyzed reaction does not include the formation of 4a-hydroxytetrahydropterin as an intermediate in the reaction, as shown in Figure 2. If, indeed, BH_4 does function with NOS as it does with PAH (and the other aromatic amino acid hydroxylases), BH_4 must cycle between the tetrahydro and dihydro states during •NO synthesis.

There are indications, however, that BH_4 does not function with NOS in exactly the same way as it does with PAH. One difference is that both bound and exogenous BH_4 appear to function catalytically during •NO synthesis even in the absence of any obvious BH_4-regenerating system. Thus, during the first few minutes of the NOS-catalyzed reaction, even in the absence of added BH_4, about 18 times more product is formed than the amount of enzyme added. This result shows that the enzyme-bound BH_4 is functioning catalytically, and that if it is being oxidized during the reaction, it is capable of being regenerated. Alternatively, this result may indicate that BH_4 is not being oxidized to support product formation. Similar results were obtained with added BH_4; each mole of added BH_4 is capable of supporting the formation of many moles of citrulline (25).

The possibility that NOS can recycle exogenous BH_4 was examined with the use of the phenylalanine hydroxylation system as a sensitive detector of recycling. To function catalytically in that system, the quinonoid dihydropterin product must be reduced back to the tetrahydro level (see Figure 2). Under conditions where any possibility of chemical regeneration of BH_4 from its quinonoid dihydro derivative was minimized, there was no evidence for BH_4 recycling in the presence of a complete NOS system (25). Additional evidence against recycling of BH_4 was provided by the observation that methotrexate, an inhibitor of all enzymes known to convert dihydrobiopterin to BH_4, does not inhibit BH_4-dependent NOS activity (25). Strictly speaking, these results only provide evidence against the recycling of exogenous BH_4. But unless the assumption is made that enzyme-bound and added BH_4 stimulate the reaction by different mechanisms, the data also make it unlikely that the enzyme-bound BH_4 recycles during the reaction, i.e. that the bound BH_4 is stoichiometrically oxidized (each mole of product formed is supported by the oxidation of an equivalent of BH_4) and then reduced.

Either or both of the following mechanisms have been proposed to explain these results (25). First, BH_4 may be needed to reduce NOS from an inactive to an active form, as has been demonstrated with PAH (64). In this reaction, BH_4 is oxidized but the oxidation is stoichiometric with the amount of enzyme and not with the amount of product formed. The observation that BH_4 is not an absolute requirement suggests that the purified enzyme is at least partially in the reduced, active form and that, on incubation in the absence of added BH_4, the reduced form is oxidized. Secondly, BH_4 may be an allosteric effector of NOS that is necessary to maintain the enzyme in an active form. In this regard, BH_4 has been shown to be an effector, albeit a negative one, in the activation of PAH by cyclic AMP-dependent protein kinase (87). In summary, NOS may require reduction by BH_4 to activate it, or it may require the mere presence of BH_4 to maintain it in an active form, or BH_4 may be needed to both reductively and allosterically activate the enzyme (25).

The conclusion of Giovanelli et al (25) that enzyme-bound BH_4 functions catalytically in the NOS-catalyzed reaction, as well as their proposal that one of the functions of BH_4 may be to reduce NOS to an active form, have been endorsed by other workers (27). In a further elaboration of their views, Hevel & Marletta (27) have cited results of experiments with 6-methyl-5-deaza-tetrahydropterin showing that this analogue of $6MPH_4$ has no coenzyme activity with NOS but is an inhibitor of the $6MPH_4$-stimulated NOS-catalyzed reaction. On the basis of these results, they have concluded that bound-BH_4 functions in one of the two hydroxylation steps in the NOS-catalyzed reaction in a manner similar to that observed with the amino acid hydroxylases, a conclusion that implies that oxidation of BH_4 is stoichiometric with product formation. Although it is possible that future work will prove that this is the role of BH_4, this particular argument is not persuasive. Some deazatetra-hydropterins inhibit tetrahydropterin-dependent enzymes when the pterin coenzyme does not function in a redox capacity, e.g. 5,10-dideaza-5,6,7,8-tetrahydrofolate inhibits glycinamide ribonucleotide transformylase (5). Following the same line of reasoning as that used for deazapterin and NOS, one might conclude that the pterin coenzyme in the transformylase reaction, 10-formyltetrahydrofolate, is involved in a redox reaction with this enzyme. This conclusion, however, would be incorrect.

In contrast to the unsuccessful attempts to demonstrate a functional connection between cytokine-mediated increases in IDO activity and BH_4 levels, reviewed above, similar attempts to link NOS and BH_4 have succeeded. Evidence suggestive of such a link first came from studies of the effect of cytokine treatment on murine fibroblasts which showed that IFNγ alone, or preferably in combination with TNFα or lipopolysaccharide (LPS), induced the synthesis of NOS (measured by enhanced formation of its products, nitrite plus nitrate) and increased the intracellular content of total biopterin (110). Inhibition of the cytokine-induced increase in BH_4 synthesis by treatment of the cells with DAHP prevented almost completely the increase in BH_4 content and decreased NOS activity to 57% of the high induced levels obtained in the absence of DAHP. The effect of DAHP on NOS activity was reversed by increasing intracellular BH_4 levels by treatment of the cells with the BH_4 precursor sepiapterin. These results indicate that about half of the cytokine-induced NOS activity is dependent on the concomitant increase in BH_4 synthesis and suggest, but do not prove, that the other half may also be dependent on the BH_4 that is present prior to cytokine treatment. Evidence was also presented that DAHP could partially prevent the cytokine-induced decrease in the viability of the fibroblasts (110) and that the effect on viability was mediated by the well-established cytotoxic action of •NO (28).

A more striking dependence of NOS activity on BH_4 levels has been demonstrated in a murine macrophage cell line (RA264). Treatment of these cells with IFNγ and LPS increased BH_4 levels above the relatively high constitutive level and, in agreement with previous results (100), stimulated the synthesis of NO as measured by nitrite production (89). Incubation of the cells with DAHP in the presence or absence of cytokines resulted in 90% depletion of intracellular levels of BH_4 within 6 hr but only marginally decreased nitrite production. Depletion of total cellular BH_4 by 96% inhibited the cytokine-stimulated production of nitrite by only 52%. Nitrite formation was dramatically inhibited only after BH_4 content was depleted by more than 99% [by treatment with DAHP plus NAS, an inhibitor of sepiapterin reductase (35)]. This sharp decrease in nitrite production was largely reversed by repletion of the BH_4 content of the cells. These results indicate that BH_4 is indeed an absolute requirement for cytokine-stimulated •NO production in murine macrophages, and probably in other cells, and suggest that only a small fraction of the total intracellular pool of BH_4 in macrophages is used in the induction and expression of NOS (89).

The first indication that humans also possess a cytokine-activated NOS system came from the report that a human subject on a low nitrate diet developed an increase in nitrate production (9-fold over basal levels) that coincided with the onset of fever and diarrhea (106). There is evidence that both the basal (59) and cytokine-mediated increased production of nitrate (29) are derived from L-arginine.

These results with humans have set the stage for what is proving to be the second unsolved mystery in this area (the first is the role of the cytokine-stimulated production of neopterin): In humans, what cell is the site of the cytokine-induced increase in NOS? To date, attempts to induce increased •NO synthesis in cultured human cells with the use of various cytokine protocols that are effective in rodent cells have been unsuccessful (8, 29, 81).

Limited success has been reported by Denis (17); upon treatment with TNFα, human monocyte-derived macrophages restricted the growth of the virulent form of *Mycobacterium avium* and enhanced the killing of the avirulent form of this organism. Granulocyte macrophage-colony stimulating factor (GM-SF) was as effective as TNFα in increasing the bacteriostatic activity of macrophages on *M. avium,* and the combination of TNFα plus GM-SF was more effective than either treatment alone. Significantly, the ability of TNFα to enhance the killing of the avirulent form of the organism was sensitive to N^G-monomethylarginine, an inhibitor of NOS, thus implicating •NO in the killing process. Also pointing to the same conclusion is the finding that the mycobacteridal activity of the macrophages correlated with nitrite production. These results appear to be peculiar to macrophages infected with *M. avium,* since nitrite production was not detectable in uninfected, cytokine-treated macrophages. Whether conditions can be found that will allow generalization of these findings to include the response of human cells to a wider variety of organisms and other invading cells remains to be seen.

BH4 AS A NEUROTRANSMITTER-RELEASING FACTOR

An in vivo dialysis technique in which a microdialysis probe is implanted in a specific brain area, e.g. the striatum, thereby allowing perfusion of the area and the quantitative measurement of metabolites in the dialysate, has demonstrated the novel activity of (6R)-BH4 as a dopamine-releasing agent in rat striatum (55). The addition of (6R)-BH4 (0.25, 0.5, 1.0 mM) to the perfusion fluid increased dopamine levels in the striatal dialysates in a concentration-dependent manner. The possibility that this effect of (6R)-BH4 was due to the stimulation by the pterin of tyrosine hydroxylase activity, leading to faster conversion of tyrosine to dopa and ultimately to more rapid formation of dopamine, is unlikely because most of the effect of BH4 was not blocked by inhibition of tyrosine hydroxylase activity with α-methyl-*p*-tyrosine. The ability of BH4 to stimulate the release of dopamine appears to depend on neural impulses reaching nerve terminals, since the effect was virtually abolished by pretreatment with tetrodotoxin, a drug that inhibits neuronal activity by blocking sodium channels in neuronal tissues.

The same technique was used to show that the activity of (6R)-BH$_4$ as a releasing agent extends to the release of dopamine, serotonin, and glutamate from rat striatum and frontal cortex (65). The BH$_4$-stimulated release of glutamate was almost completely suppressed after destruction of striatal dopaminergic terminals by treatment with the neurotoxin 6-hydroxydopamine.

(6R)-BH$_4$ was also reported to enhance the release of acetylcholine in vivo in the rat hippocampus (75). The BH$_4$-induced increase in release of acetylcholine was also eliminated after inhibition of voltage-dependent Na$^+$ channels by tetrodotoxin, but not after depletion of catecholamines by reserpine; this would indicate that the effect of BH$_4$ on acetylcholine release is direct and not secondary to the effects of BH$_4$ on release of dopamine.

An attempt to demonstrate BH$_4$-mediated release of serotonin from isolated synaptosomes was unsuccessful (112). Although the reasons why this in vitro experiment failed are not known with certainty, one likely reason is that no attempt was made to inhibit re-uptake of any serotonin that might have been released. Under these conditions, therefore, a BH$_4$-stimulation of release would have been difficult to detect.

CONCLUDING REMARKS

One only has to think back to one of the historically important early discoveries in this field, i.e. the growth requirement of *Crithidia fasiculata* for biopterin, to be reminded that more new roles for BH$_4$ remain to be discovered. This conclusion follows because none of the established roles for BH$_4$ can readily explain why it is essential for the growth of this organism.

In addition to the likelihood that other new functions for BH$_4$ will be uncovered, many questions remain about how this pterin functions in the recently described BH$_4$-dependent systems. With respect to these systems, in particular the one responsible for the synthesis of NO, every one of the myriad functions of this biofactor represents a new physiological role for BH$_4$. Clearly, therefore, this field, which just a few years ago appeared to be reaching maturity, has now entered a new and exciting growth spurt.

Literature Cited

1. Abita, J. P., Cost, H., Milstien, S., Kaufman, S., Saimot, G. 1985. Urinary neopterin and biopterin levels in patients with AIDS and AIDS-related complex [letter]. *Lancet* 2:51–52
2. Abita, J. P., Parniak, M., Kaufman, S. 1984. The activation of rat liver phenylalanine hydroxylase by limited proteolysis, lysolecithin, and tocopherol phosphate. Changes in conformation and catalytic properties. *J. Biol. Chem.* 259:14560–66
3. Adler, C., Ghisla, S., Rebrin, I., Haavik, J., Heizmann, C. W., et al. 1992. 7-Substituted pterins in humans with suspected pterin-4a-carbinolamine dehydratase deficiency. *Eur. J. Biochem.* 208:139–44

4. Armarego, W. L. F., Randles, D., Taguchi, H. 1983. Peroxidase catalyzed aerobic degradation of 5,6,7,8-tetrahydrobiopterin at physiological pH. *Eur. J. Biochem.* 135:393–403

5. Beardsley, G. P., Moroson, B. A., Taylor, E. C., Moran, R. G. 1989. A new folate antimetabolite, 5,10-dideaza-5,6,7,8-tetrahydrofolate is a potent inhibitor of *de novo* purine synthesis. *J. Biol. Chem.* 264:328–33

6. Blau, N., Curtius, H.-C., Kuster, T., Matasovic, A., Schoedon, G., et al. 1989. Primapterinuria: A new variant of atypical phenylketonuria. *J. Inherit. Metab. Dis.* 12:335–38

7. Bredt, D. S., Snyder, S. H. 1990. Isolation of nitric oxide synthetase, a calmodulin-requiring enzyme. *Proc. Natl. Acad. Sci. USA* 87:682–85

8. Cameron, M. L., Granger, D. L., Weinberg, J. B., Kozumbo, W. J., Koren, H. S. 1990. Human alveolar and peritoneal macrophages mediate fungistasis independently of L-arginine oxidation to nitrite or nitrate. *Am. Rev. Respir. Dis.* 142:1313–19

9. Cowperthwaite, J., Weber, M. M., Packer, L., Hutner, S. H. 1953. Nutrition of *Herpetomonas (Strigomonas) culicidarum. Ann. NY Acad. Sci.* 56: 972–81

10. Curtius, H.-C., Adler, C., Rebrin, I., Heizmann, C., Ghisla, S. 1990. 7-Substituted pterins: Formation during phenalanine hydroxylation in the absence of dehydratase. *Biochem. Biophys. Res. Commun.* 172: 1060–66

11. Curtius, H.-C., Kuster, T., Matasovic, A., Blau, N., Dhondt, J.-L. 1988. Primapterin, anapterin, and 6-oxoprimapterin, three new 7-substituted pterins identified in a patient with hyperphenylalaninemia. *Biochem. Biophys. Res. Commun.* 153:715–21

12. Curtius, H.-C., Matasovic, A., Schoedon, G., Kuster, T., Guibaud, P., et al. 1990. 7-Substituted pterins. *J. Biol. Chem.* 265:3923–30

13. Davis, M. D., Kaufman, S. 1991. 7-Tetrahydrobiopterin is an uncoupled cofactor for rat hepatic phenylalanine hydroxylase. *FEBS Lett.* 285:17–20

14. Davis, M. D., Kaufman, S., Milstien, S. 1988. The auto-oxidation of tetrahydrobiopterin. *Eur. J. Biochem.* 173: 345–51

15. Davis, M. D., Kaufman, S., Milstien, S. 1991. Conversion of 6-substituted tetrahydropterins to 7-isomers via phenylalanine hydroxylase-generated intermediates. *Proc. Natl. Acad. Sci. USA* 88:385–89

16. Davis, M. D., Ribeiro, P., Tipper, J., Kaufman, S. 1992. 7-Tetrahydrobiopterin, a naturally-occurring analogue of tetrahydrobiopterin, is a cofactor for and a potential inhibitor of the aromatic acid hydroxylases. *Proc. Natl. Acad. Sci. USA* 89:10109–13

17. Denis, M. 1991. Tumor necrosis factor and granulocyte macrophage-colony stimulating factor stimulate human macrophages to restrict growth of virulent *Mycobacterium avium* and to kill avirulent *M. avium:* Killing effector mechanism depends on the generation of reactive nitrogen intermediates. *J. Leukocyte Biol.* 49:380–87

18. Dhondt, J. L., Forzy, G., Hayte, J. M. 1987. Impaired biopterin synthesis in a patient with mild hyperphenylalaninemia. A new variant? In *Unconjugated Pterins and Related Biogenic Amines,* ed H.-C. Curtius, N. Blau, R. A. Levine, pp. 257–63. Berlin/New York: de Gruyter

19. Duch, D. S., Bowers, S. W., Woolf, J. H., Nichol, C. A. 1984. Biopterin cofactor synthesis: GTP cyclohydrolase, neopterin and biopterin in tissues and fluids of mammalian species. *Life Sci.* 35:1895–1901

20. Farkas, W. R., Jacobson, K. B., Katze, J. R. 1984. Substrate and inhibitor specificity of tRNA-guanine ribosyltransferase. *Biochim. Biophys. Acta* 781: 64–75

21. Fölling, A. 1934. Über Ausscheidung von Phenylbrenztraubensäure in den harn als Stoffwechselanomalie in Verbindung mit Imbezillitat. *Z. Physiol. Chem.* 227:169–76

22. Forrest, H. S., Mitchell, H. K. 1955. Pteridines from *Drosophila.* 3. Isolation and identification of three more pteridines. *J. Am. Chem. Soc.* 77:4865–69

23. Fuchs, D., Hausen, A., Knosp, O., Reibnegger, G., Wachter, H., et al. 1983. Neopterin evaluation in patients with pulmonary tuberculosis. In *Biochemical and Clinical Aspects of Pteridines,* ed. H.-C. Curtius, W. Pfleiderer, H. Wachter, 2:281–91. Berlin/New York: de Gruyter

24. Fukushima, T., Nixon, J. 1980. Analysis of reduced forms of biopterin and biological tissues and fluids. *Anal. Biochem.* 102:176–88

25. Giovanelli, J., Campos, K. L., Kaufman, S. 1991. Tetrahydrobiopterin, a cofactor for rat cerebellar nitric oxide synthase, does not function as a reactant in the oxygenation of arginine. *Proc. Natl. Acad. Sci. USA* 88:7091–95

26. Hausen, A., Fuchs, D., Reibnegger, G., Wachter, H., Egg, D., et al. 1983. Neopterin an index for activity of disease in patients with rheumatoid arthritis. See Ref. 23, pp. 245–54

27. Hevel, J. M., Marletta, M. A. 1992. Macrophage nitric oxide synthase: relationship between enzyme-bound tetrahydrobiopterin and synthase activity. *Biochemistry* 31:7160–65

28. Hibbs, J. B. Jr., Taintor, R. R., Vavrin, Z., Rachlin, E. M. 1988. Nitric oxide: A cytotoxic activated macrophage effector molecule. *Biochem. Biophys. Res. Commun.* 157:87–94

29. Hibbs, J. B. Jr. Westenfelder, C., Taintor, R., Vavrin, Z., Kablitz, C., et al. 1992. Evidence for cytokine-inducible nitric oxide synthesis from L-arginine in patients receiving interleukin-2 therapy. *J. Clin. Invest.* 89:867–77

30. Hirata, F., Hayaishi, O. 1977. Superoxide anion as an intermediate or a substrate for certain oxygenases. In *Superoxide and Superoxide Dismutases,* ed. A. M. Michelson, J. M. McCord, I. Fridovich, pp. 395–406. London: Academic

31. Huang, C. Y., Kaufman, S. 1973. Studies on the mechanisms of action of phenylalanine hydroxylase and its protein stimulator. I. Enzyme concentration dependence of the specific activity of phenylalanine hydroxylase due to a nonenzymatic step. *J. Biol. Chem.* 248:4242–51

32. Huber, C., Batchelor, J. R., Fuchs, D., Hausen, A., Lang, A., et al. 1984. Immune-response-associated production of neopterin. *J. Exp. Med.* 160:310–16

33. Jervis, G. A. 1947. Studies on phenylpyruvic oligophrenia. The position of the metabolic error. *J. Biol. Chem.* 169:651–56

34. Joller, P. W., Blau, N., Atares, M., Niederwieser, A., Cardesa-Garcia, J. 1983. Guanosine-triphosphate cyclopydrolase deficiency: analysis of the influence on immune parameters in a girl. See Ref. 23, pp. 167–76

35. Katoh, S., Sueoka, T., Yamada, S. 1982. Direct-inhibition of brain sepiapterin reductase by a catecholamine and an indoleamine. *Biochem. Biophys. Res. Commun.* 105:75–81

36. Kato, T., Yamaguchi, T., Nagatsu, T., Sugimoto, T., Matsuura, S. 1980. Effects of structures of tetrahydropterin cofactors on rat brain tryptophan hydroxylase. *Biochim. Biophys. Acta* 611:241–50

37. Kaufman, S. 1958. Phenylalanine hydroxylation cofactor in phenylketonuria. *Science* 128:1506–8

38. Kaufman, S. 1959. Studies on the mechanism of the enzymatic conversion of phenylalanine to tyrosine. *J. Biol. Chem.* 234:2677–82

39. Kaufman, S. 1962. On the structure of the phenylalanine hydroxylation cofactor. *J. Biol. Chem.* 237:2712–13

40. Kaufman, S. 1963. The structure of phenylalanine hydroxylation cofactor. *Proc. Natl. Acad. Sci. USA* 5:1085–93

41. Kaufman, S. 1967. Unanswered questions in the primary metabolic block in phenylketonuria. In *Phenylketonuria and Allied Metabolic Diseases, Proc. Conf., April 6–8, 1966,* ed. J. A. Anderson, K. F. Swaiman, pp. 205–13. Washington, DC: US Gov. Print. Off.

42. Kaufman, S. 1970. A protein that stimulates rat liver phenylalanine hydroxylase. *J. Biol. Chem.* 245:4751–59

43. Kaufman, S. 1975. Studies on the mechanism of phenylalanine hydroxylase: detection of an intermediate. In *Chemistry and Biology of Pteridines,* ed. W. Pfleiderer, pp. 291–304. Berlin: de Gruyter

44. Kaufman, S. 1977. Phenylketonuria: biochemical mechanisms. *Adv. Neurochem.* 2:1–132

45. Kaufman, S. 1983. Phenylketonuria and its variants. *Adv. Hum. Genet.* 13:217–97

46. Kaufman, S. 1986. The metabolic role of tetrahydrobiopterin. In *Chemistry and Biology of Pteridines,* ed. B. A. Cooper, V. M. Whitehead, pp. 185–200. Berlin: de Gruyter

47. Kaufman, S., Fisher, D. B. 1974. Pterin-requiring aromatic amino acid hydroxylases. In *Molecular Mechanisms of Oxygen Activation,* ed. O. Hayaishi, pp. 285–369. New York: Academic

48. Kaufman, S., Levenberg, B. 1959. Further studies on the phenylalanine hydroxylation cofactor. *J. Biol. Chem.* 234:2683–88

49. Kaufman, S., Pollock, R. J., Summer, G. K., Das, A. K., Hajra, A. K. 1990. Dependence of an alkyl glycol-ether monooxygenase activity upon tetrahydropterins. *Biochim. Biophys. Acta* 1040:19–27

50. Kerler, F., Hültner, L., Ziegler, I., Katzenmaier, G., Bacher, A. 1990. Analysis of the tetrahydrobiopterin synthesizing system during maturation of

murine reticulocytes. *J. Cell Physiol.* 142:268–71

51. Kerler, F., Ziegler, I., Schmid, C., Bacher, A. 1990. Synthesis of tetrahydrobiopterin in Friend erythroleukemia cells and its modulator effect on cell proliferation. *Exp. Cell Res.* 189:151–56

52. Kidder, G. W., Dewey, V. C. 1963. Relationship between pyrimidine and lipid biosynthesis and unconjugated pteridine. *Biochem. Biophys. Res. Commun.* 12:280–83

53. Kidder, G. W., Nolan, L. L. 1973. Pteridine-requiring dihydroorotate hydroxylase from *Crithidia fasciculata*. *Biochem. Biophys. Res. Commun.* 53: 929–36

54. Kokolis, N., Ziegler, I. 1977. On the levels of phenylalanine, tyrosine and tetrahydrobiopterin in the blood of tumor-bearing organisms. *Can. Biochem. Biophys.* 2:79–85

55. Koshimura, K., Miwa, S., Lee, K., Fujiwara, M., Watanabe, Y. 1990. Enhancement of dopamine release in vivo from the rat striatum by dialytic perfusion of 6R-L-erythro-5,6,7,8-tetrahydrobiopterin. *J. Neurochem.* 54: 1391–97

56. Kwon, N. S., Nathan, C. F., Gilker, C., Griffith, O. W., Matthews, D. E., et al. 1990. L-citrulline production from L-arginine by macrophage nitric oxide synthase. *J. Biol. Chem.* 265:13442–45

57. Kwon, N. S., Nathan, C. F., Stuehr, D. J. 1989. Reduced biopterin as a cofactor in the generation of nitrogen oxides by murine macrophages. *J. Biol. Chem.* 264:20496–20501

58. Lazarus, R. A., Benkovic, S. J., Kaufman, S. 1983. Phenylalanine hydroxylase stimulator protein is a 4a-carbinolamine dehydratase. *J. Biol. Chem.* 258:10960–962

59. Leaf, C. D., Wishnok, J. S., Tannenbaum, S. R. 1989. L-arginine is a precursor for nitrate biosynthesis in humans. *Biochem. Biophys. Res. Commun.* 163:1032–37

60. Lin, V. K., Farkas, W. R., Agris, P. F. 1980. Specific changes in Q-ribonucleoside containing transfer RNA species during Friend leukemia cell erythroid differentiation. *Nucleic Acids Res.* 8:3481–89

61. Lowenstein, C. J., Snyder, S. H. 1992. Nitric oxide, a novel biologic messenger. *Cell* 70:705–7

62. Marks, P. A., Rifkind, R. A. 1978. Erythroleukemic differentiation. *Annu. Rev. Biochem.* 47:419–48

63. Marletta, M. 1989. Nitric oxide: biosynthesis and biological significance. *Trends Biochem. Sci.* 14:488–92

64. Marota, J. J. A., Shiman, R. 1984. Stoichiometric reduction of phenylalanine hydroxylase by its cofactor: a requirement for enzymatic activity. *Biochemistry* 23:1303–11

65. Mataga, N., Imamura, K., Watanabe, Y. 1991. 6R-Tetrahydrobiopterin perfusion enhances dopamine, serotonin, and glutamate outputs in dialysate from rat striatum and frontal cortex. *Brain Res.* 551:64–71

66. Mayer, B., John, M., Bohme, E. 1990. Purification of Ca^{2+}/calmodulin-dependent nitric oxide synthase from porcine cerebellum. *FEBS Lett.* 277:215–19

67. Mayer, B., John, M., Heinzel, B., Werner, E. R., Wachter, H., et al. 1991. Brain nitric oxide synthase is a biopterin- and flavin-containing multifunctional oxido-reductase. *FEBS Lett.* 288:187–91

68. Milstien, S., Kaufman, S. 1989. The biosynthesis of tetrahydrobiopterin in rat brain. Purification and characterization of 6-pyruvoyl tetrahydropterin (2'-oxo)reductase. *J. Biol. Chem.* 264: 8066–73

69. Milstien, S., Kaufman, S. 1989. Immunological studies on the participation of 6-pyruvoyl tetrahydropterin (2'-oxo) reductase, an aldose reductase, in tetrahydrobiopterin biosynthesis. *Biochem. Biophys. Res. Commun.* 165: 845–50

70. Milstien, S., Kaufman, S., Tanaka, K. 1990. Regulation of cellular proliferation by tetrahydrobiopterin. In *Chemistry and Biology of Pteridines*, ed. H.-C. Curtius, S. Ghisla, N. Blau, pp. 506–10. Berlin: de Gruyter

71. Nichol, C. A., Lee, C. L., Edelstein, M. P., Chao, J. Y., Duch, D. S. 1983. Biosynthesis of tetrahydrobiopterin by de novo and salvage pathways in adrenal medulla extracts, mammalian cell cultures and rat brain in vivo. *Proc. Natl. Acad. Sci. USA* 80:1546–50

72. Nishikimi, M. 1975. A function of tetrahydropteridines as cofactors for indoleamine 2,3-dioxygenase. *Biochem. Biophys. Res. Commun.* 63:92–98

73. Nishimura, S. 1983. Structure, biosynthesis and function of quenosine in transfer RNA. *Prog. Nucleic Acids Res. Mol. Biol.* 28:49–73

74. Nixon, J. C., Lee, C. L., Milstien, S., Kaufman, S., Bartholome, K. 1980. Neopterin and biopterin levels in pa-

tients with atypical forms of phenyl-ketonuria. *J. Neurochem.* 35:898–904

75. Ohue, T., Koshimura, K., Lee, K., Watanabe, Y., Miwa, S. 1991. A novel action of 6R-L-*erythro*-5,6,7,8-tetrahydrobiopterin, a cofactor for hydroxylases of phenylalanine, tyrosine and tryptophan; enhancement of acetylcholine release in vivo in the rat hippocampus. *Neurosci. Lett.* 128:93–96

76. Okada, N., Shindo-Okada, N., Sato, S., Itoh, Y. H., Oda, K.-I., et al. 1978. Detection of unique tRNA species in tumor tissues by *Escherichia coli* guanine insertion enzyme. *Proc. Natl. Acad. Sci. USA* 75:4247–51

77. Osanai, M., Rembold, H. 1971. Cofactor specificity of L-*erythro*-tetrahydrobiopterin rat liver phenylalanine 4-hydroxylase. *Hoppe-Seyler's Z. Physiol. Chem.* 352:1359–62

78. Ozaki, Y., Edelstein, M. P., Duch, D. S. 1987. The actions of interferon and antiinflammatory agents on induction of indoleamine 2,3-dioxygenase in human peripheral blood monocytes. *Biochem. Biophys. Res. Commun.* 144:1147–53

79. Ozaki, Y., Edelstein, M. P., Duch, D. S. 1988. Induction of indoleamine 2,3-dioxygenase: A mechanism of the antitumor activity of interferon γ. *Proc. Natl. Acad. Sci. USA* 85:1242–46

80. Ozaki, Y., Reinhard, J. F. Jr., Nichol, C. A. 1986. Cofactor activity of dihydroflavin mononucleotide and tetrahydrobiopterin for murine epididymal indoleamine 2,3-dioxygenase. *Biochem. Biophys. Res. Commun.* 137:1106–11

81. Padgett, E. L., Pruett, S. B. 1992. Evaluation of nitrite production by human monocyte-derived macrophages. *Biochem. Biophys. Res. Commun.* 186:775–81

82. Parniak, M. A., Kleiman, L., Marx, S., Andrejchyshyn, S. 1989. Changes in the level of biopterin and of queuine-containing tRNA during erythroid differentiation of murine erythroleukemia cells. In *Chemistry and Biology of Pteridines,* ed. H.-C. Curtius, S. Ghisla, N. Blau, pp. 364–67. Berlin: de Gruyter

83. Patterson, E. L., Broquist, H. P., Albrecht, A. M., von Saltza, M. H., Stokstad, E. L. 1955. A new pteridine in urine required for the growth of the protozoan *Crithidia fasciculata. J. Am. Chem. Soc.* 77:3167–68

84. Patterson, E. L., Milstrey, R.,

Stokstad, E. L. 1956. The synthesis of a pteridine required for the growth of *Crithidia faciculata. J. Am. Chem. Soc.* 78:5868–71

85. Patterson, E. L., von Saltza, M. H., Stokstad, E. L. 1956. The isolation and characterization of a pteridine required for the growth of *Crithidia fasiculata. J. Am. Chem. Soc.* 78:5871–73

86. Pfefferkorn, R. 1984. Interferon γ blocks the growth of *Toxoplasma gondii* in human fibroblasts by inducing the host cells to degrade tryptophan. *Proc. Natl. Acad. Sci. USA* 81:908–12

87. Phillips, R. S., Kaufman, S. 1984. Ligand effects on the phosphorylation state of hepatic phenylalanine hydroxylase. *J. Biol. Chem.* 259:2474–79

88. Rokos, H., Rokos, K., Frisius, H., Kirstaedter, H.-J. 1980. Altered urinary excretion of pteridines in neoplastic disease. Determination of biopterin, neopterin, xanthopterin, and pterin. *Clin. Chim. Acta* 105:275–86

89. Sakai, N., Kaufman, S., Milstien, S. 1992. Tetrahydrobiopterin is required for cytokine-induced nitric oxide production in a murine macrophage cell line (RAW 264). *Mol. Pharmacol.* In press

90. Schmidt, H. H. H. W., Pollack, J., Nakane, M., Gorsky, L., Forstermann, U., et al. 1991. Purification of a soluble isoform of guanylyl cyclase-activating-factor synthase. *Proc. Natl. Acad. Sci. USA* 88:365–69

91. Schmidt, H. H. H. W., Smith, R., Nakane, M., Murad, F. 1992. Ca²⁺/Calmodulin-dependent NO synthase Type I: A biopteroflavoprotein with Ca²⁺/Calmodulin-independent diaphorase and reductase activities. *Biochemistry* 31:3243–49

92. Schoedon, G., Groppmair, J., Adolf, G., Huber, C., Niederwieser, A. 1986. Interferon-γ enhances biosynthesis of pterins in peripheral blood mononuclear cells by induction of GTP-cyclohydrolase I activity. *J. Interferon Res.* 6:697–703

93. Schoedon, G., Troppmain, J., Fontana, A., Huber, C., Curtius, H.-C., et al. 1987. Biosynthesis and metabolism of pterins in peripheral blood mononuclear cells and leukemia cell lines of man and mice. *Eur. J. Biochem.* 166:303–10

94. Scriver, C. R., Kaufman, S., Woo, S. L. C. 1989. The hyperphenylalaninemias. In *The Metabolic Basis of Inherited Disease,* ed. C. R. Scriver, A.

L. Beaudet, W. S. Sly, D. Valle, pp. 495–546. New York: McGraw-Hill
95. Shindo-Okada, N., Terada, M., Nishimura, S. 1981. Changes in amount of hypo-modified tRNA having guanine in place of quenine during erythroid differentiation of murine erythroleukemia cells. *Eur. J. Biochem.* 115:423–28
96. Stuehr, D. J., Cho, H. J., Kwon, N. S., Weise, M. F., Nathan, C. F. 1991. Purification and characterization of the cytokine-induced macrophage nitric oxide synthase: an FAD- FMN-containing flavoprotein. *Proc. Natl. Acad. Sci. USA* 88:7773–77
97. Stuehr, D. J., Griffith, O. W. 1992. Mammalian nitric oxide synthases. In *Adv. Enzymol.* 65:287–346
98. Stuehr, D. J., Kwon, N. S., Nathan, C. F. 1990. FAD and GSH participate in macrophage synthesis of nitric oxide. *Biochem. Biophys. Res. Commun.* 168:558–65
99. Stuehr, D. J., Kwon, N. S., Nathan, C. F., Griffith, O. W., Feldman, P. L., et al. 1991. N^ω-hydroxy-L-arginine is an intermediate in the biosynthesis of nitric oxide from L-arginine. *J. Biol. Chem.* 266:6259–63
100. Stuehr, D. J., Marletta, M. A. 1987. Synthesis of nitrite and nitrate in murine macrophage cell lines. *Cancer Res.* 47:5590–94
101. Tanaka, K., Kaufman, S., Milstien, S. 1989. Tetrahydrobiopterin, the cofactor for aromatic amino acid hydroxylases, is synthesized by and regulates proliferation of erythroid cells. *Proc. Natl. Acad. Sci. USA* 86:5864–67
102. Tayeh, M. A., Marletta, M. A. 1989. Macrophage oxidation of L-arginine to nitric oxide, nitrite, and nitrate. Tetrahydrobiopterin is required as a cofactor. *J. Biol. Chem.* 264:19654–58
103. Tietz, A., Lindberg, M., Kennedy, E. P. 1964. A new pteridine-requiring enzyme system for the oxidation of glyceryl ethers. *J. Biol. Chem.* 239:4081–90
104. Wachter, H., Fuchs, D., Hausen, A., Huber, C., Knosp, O., et al. 1983. Elevated urinary neopterin levels in patients with the acquired immunodeficiency syndrome (AIDS). *Hoppe-Seyler's Z. Physiol. Chem.* 364:1345–46
105. Wachter, H., Hausen, A., Grassmayr, K. 1979. Erhöhte Ausscheidung von Neopterin im Harn von Patienten mit malignen Tumoren und mit Viruserkrankungen. *Hoppe-Seyler's Z. Physiol. Chem.* 360:1957–60
106. Wagner, D. A., Tannenbaum, S. R. 1982. Enhancement of nitrate biosynthesis by *E. coli* lipopolysaccharide In *Nitrosamines and Human Cancer,* ed. P. N. Magee, 12:437–43. Cold Spring Harbor, NY: Cold Spring Harbor Lab. Banbury Rep.
107. Werner, E. R., Werner-Felmayer, G., Fuchs, D., Hausen, A., Reibnegger, G., et al. 1989. Parallel induction of tetrahydrobiopterin biosynthesis and indoleamine 2,3-dioxygenase activity in human cells and cell lines by interferon γ. *Biochem. J.* 262:861–66
108. Werner, E. R., Werner-Felmayer, G., Fuchs, D., Hausen, A., Reibnegger, G., et al. 1990. Tetrahydrobiopterin biosynthetic activities in human macrophages, fibroblasts, THP-1, and T 24 cells. *J. Biol. Chem.* 265:3189–92
109. Werner, E. R., Werner-Felmayer, G., Fuchs, D., Hausen, A., Reibnegger, G., et al. 1991. Impact of tumour necrosis factor-α and interferon-γ on tetrahydrobiopterin synthesis in murine fibroblasts and macrophages. *Biochem. J.* 280:709–14
110. Werner-Felmayer, G., Werner, E. R., Fuchs, D., Hausen, A., Reibnegger, G., et al. 1990. Tetrahydrobiopterin-dependent formation of nitrite and nitrate in murine fibroblasts. *J. Exp. Med.* 172:1599–1607
111. White, K. A., Marletta, M. A. 1992. Nitric oxide synthase is a cytochrome P-450 type hemoprotein. *Biochemistry* 31:6627–31
112. Wolf, W. A., Anastasiadis, P. Z., Kuhn, D. M., Levine, R. A. 1990. Influence of tetrahydrobiopterin on serotonin synthesis, metabolism and release in synaptosomes. *Neurochem. Int.* 16:335–40
113. Yoshida, R., Hayaishi, O. 1978. Induction of pulmonary indoleamine 2,3-dioxygenase by intraperitoneal injection of bacterial lipopolysaccharide. *Proc. Natl. Acad. Sci. USA* 75:3998–4000
114. Yoshida, R., Urade, Y., Sayama, S., Takikawa, O., Ozaki, Y., et al. 1982. Indoleamine 2,3-dioxygenase: A new mediator of interferon actions. In *Oxygenases and Oxygen Metabolism,* ed. M. Nozaki, S. Yamamoto, Y. Ishimuri, M. J. Coon, L. Ernster, R. W. Esterbrook, pp. 569–79. New York: Academic
115. Ziegler, I. 1985. Pteridine formation during lectin-induced lymphocyte activation. *J. Cell. Biochem.* 28:197–206
116. Ziegler, I. 1985. Synthesis and interferon-γ controlled release of pteridines

during activation of human peripheral blood mononuclear cells. *Biochem. Biophys. Res. Commun.* 132:404–11

117. Ziegler, I., Hamm, U., Berndt, J. 1983. Participation of pterins in the control of lymphocyte stimulation and lymphoblast proliferation. *Can. Res.* 43:5356–59

118. Ziegler, I., Kolb, H. J., Bodenberger, U., Wilmanns, W. 1982. Biopterin level in blood cells as a marker for hemopoietic cell proliferation during autologous bone marrow transplantation in beagle dogs. *Blut* 44:261–70

119. Ziegler, I., Schwulera, U. 1989. Modulation of interleukin 2 high-affinity binding by lymphocyte-derived tetrahydrobiopterin: Pterins as potential participants in the control of interleukin 2 receptor assembly. *J. Cell. Biochem.* 41:103–11

Annu. Rev. Nutr. 1993. 13:287–316

NUTRITIONAL FACTORS IN OSTEOPOROSIS

Robert P. Heaney

Creighton University, Omaha, Nebraska 68178

KEY WORDS: fragility fractures, calcium, vitamin D, bone mass/density, hip fracture

CONTENTS

OVERVIEW OF OSTEOPOROSIS 287
    Fraility and Injury 288
    Intrinsic Bony Strength and Fragility 289
    Bone Mass/Density 290
CALCIUM 290
    The Requirement for Calcium 295
    Primary Prevention: The Acquisition of Genetically Programmed Bone Mass . . . 296
    Secondary Prevention: The Conservation of Acquired Bone Mass 299
    Calcium Intake and Risk of Fracture 302
    Calcium as a Component of Treatment of Established Osteoporosis 303
    Nutrient-Nutrient Interactions 303
VITAMIN D 306
VITAMIN K 308
TRACE MINERALS 310
NUTRITION AND HIP FRACTURE 310

OVERVIEW OF OSTEOPOROSIS

Osteoporosis is a multifactorial disorder in which the skeleton is sufficiently fragile so that it fractures when exposed to the mechanical forces and accidents that are a routine part of ordinary living. Nutrition is only one of several factors that influence bone strength. To understand adequately where nutrition fits in, it will be helpful, first, to provide a general description of the complex domain of osteoporotic fragility.

Fracture is almost always due to an interaction of bony fragility with injury. Fragility, in turn, is due not simply to decreased bone mass, but to accumulated fatigue damage and to critical trabecular disconnections, as well. Reduced bone mass also has many contributing causes, of which inadequate nutrition

287

0199-9885/93/0715-0287$02.00

is one. Others include a genetically small skeletal program, gonadal hormone deficiency, physical inactivity, and many life-style, co-morbid, and pharmacologic agencies.

Nutritional factors important for bone health include calcium, phosphorus, protein, vitamins C, D, and K, and various trace minerals. Of these, calcium has been the most extensively studied. Intake of calcium may be inadequate for the obvious reason that it is low; however, even when statistically "normal," it may still be inadequate because of subnormal absorption (60) or greater than normal excretory losses.

Frailty and Injury

Almost all fractures, even those we term "low-trauma," occur as a result of some injury—the application of more force to the bone than it is able to sustain. Usually this is a result of a fall or the application of bad body mechanics. Although fracture incidence patterns differ somewhat from site to site, the risk of virtually all fractures rises with age, and all fractures contribute to the burden of illness, disability, and expense that the elderly (and society) bear. Hip fracture is perhaps the most serious of the fragility fractures, inasmuch as it carries an excess mortality, is expensive, and causes significant deterioration in quality of life for many of its survivors. It is, as well, a good example of the many interacting factors that constitute this fracture domain.

First, there is the fall itself. Normally, postural reflexes work to get the arms into position to break the force of the fall, or to swing the body so that it lands on the buttocks (or both). These reflexes almost always operate effectively in younger individuals, but commonly fail in the elderly. As a result, young people rarely strike the lateral portion of the trochanteric region of the hip when they fall, whereas the fragile elderly more commonly do so. Additionally, hip fracture is a particularly serious problem in undernourished elderly individuals who have less muscle and fat mass around the hip, and therefore less soft tissue through which the force of the impact can be distributed to a larger area of the lateral surface of the trochanter. The force of the impact, when falling from standing height, may well be sufficient to break even a healthy femur if that force is concentrated in a small enough impact area (117).

Nutrition enters into this region of the fracture domain primarily through its effect on maintenance of the soft tissue mass that serves to cushion the impact of falls. In some cases nutrition may also influence central nervous system processing time or contribute to the general feebleness that predisposes to falling. But energy dissipation by soft tissue at the point of impact is the major factor here.

Intrinsic Bony Strength and Fragility

Strength in bone, as in most engineering structures, is dependent upon its mass density, upon the arrangement of its material in space, and upon the intrinsic strength of its component material (particularly as influenced over long periods of use by the accumulation of unrepaired fatigue damage). All three factors play some role in most low trauma fractures, and it is not possible to say which may be the most important in any given case. Nevertheless, most of the effort in this regard in the past 30 years has been devoted to the measurement of bone mass and density, and hence much of what we know about bone strength in living individuals comes from our observation of this facet of the bone strength triad. The general consensus is that decreased bone mass produces a decrease in bone strength (26), but there is disagreement about how much of a strength reserve bone possesses and whether it usually takes more than a simple decrease in mass to produce a fragility fracture.

Whatever the final answer, it is an inescapable fact that most elderly individuals have bone mass values that are more than two standard deviations below the young adult mean and hence they are *all* at increased risk for fragility fracture. Why some older persons do fracture and some do not appears to be explainable, at least in part, by differences in bony architecture and in the effectiveness of repair of universally occurring fatigue damage. These factors and their interplay have been reviewed extensively elsewhere (53).

Briefly, individuals with compression fractures of the vertebrae have been found to have excessive loss of horizontal, cross-bracing trabeculae in their cancellous bone, whereas other individuals with the same overall degree of bone loss, but with the bracing trabeculae maintained intact, do not fracture. Women, particularly, are more prone to lose their horizontal trabeculae than are men, and this fact is probably the explanation for the 6:1 to 8:1 female:male sex differential in vertebral osteoporosis. Similarly, studies of elderly individuals with fractures of the femoral neck have shown localized failure of bone remodeling in the region concerned (40) as well as cytochemical abnormalities of osteocytes in the fracture region (33). The ultimate significance of such findings is not known, but they suggest a sluggishness of the bone remodeling process which, other things being equal, might have removed accumulated fatigue damage and better maintained the strength of the bony structures.

Nutrition enters into this portion of the fracture domain predominantly through its influence on bone density. However, trace nutrients such as certain vitamins (e.g. D and K), or the trace minerals such as manganese, copper, and zinc, may directly influence the remodeling process and hence affect bone strength through their impact on the repair of inevitable fatigue damage. However, little is known about these possibilities, and in most of the following discussion, the emphasis is on the nutritional factors that influence bone *mass*.

Bone Mass/Density

Bone mass and density are themselves influenced by many factors. The three most important, overall, are physical activity, gonadal hormones, and calcium intake. Manganese, zinc, copper, vitamin C, vitamin K, phosphorus, and protein are also essential for building a healthy skeleton, but, except for calcium, their effects are usually seen most clearly during growth. Once built, however, the skeleton tends to be relatively insulated from many subsequent nutritional deficiencies. In addition, a number of other factors also influence bone mass, such as smoking, alcohol abuse, and various drugs used to treat a variety of medical illnesses, as well as those illnesses themselves.

The effects of each of these factors are largely independent and therefore one cannot substitute for, or compensate for, the other. Thus, a high calcium intake will not offset the loss of bone that occurs immediately following menopause in women or castration in men. Nor will vigorous physical activity alter menopausal loss, for that matter. Similarly, physical activity will not compensate for an inadequate calcium intake. Neither will a high calcium intake offset the effects of alcohol abuse or smoking. Much of the apparent confusion in the bone field over the past 20 years could have been avoided if we had better understood that these factors, while interactive, are largely independent.

Finally, although much of the following discussion focuses on calcium, it is necessary to stress, what should perhaps go without saying, that calcium is not an isolated nutrient; it occurs in foods along with other nutrients, and diets low in calcium tend also to be nutritionally poor, generally (7). Thus, while it is necessary to deal with nutrients one at a time in an analysis such as this, the disorders in patients are likely to be more complex.

CALCIUM

The topic of calcium and osteoporosis has been reviewed in these pages by Avioli in 1984 (3) and again by Arnaud & Sanchez in 1990 (2). Cumming in 1990 published a metaanalysis (28) of all studies up through 1988 relating calcium intake and bone status and concluded that the evidence supported a positive relationship between the two variables. Given this prior work, this review focuses mainly on studies published since 1988. Interestingly, the quantity of such studies is surprisingly large and their quality, overall, is gratifyingly high. The majority view among members of the nutritional scientific community now appears to be that calcium intake, within the range of plausible intakes, has a positive influence on bone status (2, 9, 82, 96). There have also been dissenting views (71). However, while several questions remain unanswered, previous controversy can be said to be resolved, and the results of disparate studies can be satisfactorily explained within a comprehensive model of bone metabolism.

In the discussion of published studies it is helpful to highlight certain methodological problems which inevitably are a part of studies of this topic and which may explain prior disagreement:

1. Multifactorial character of age-related change in bone mass and of bone fragility.
2. Differing calcium intake distributions in various study populations.
3. Inability in most types of studies to address the several causes of calcium deficiency; i.e. while calcium deficiency may be caused by low intake, it may also be due to decreased absorptive performance or high obligatory excretory loss.
4. Insufficient power to detect plausible population-level correlations, if they exist, in many published studies.
5. Failure in most studies of the postmenopausal period to recognize the special circumstances created by estrogen withdrawal in the few years immediately following hormone loss and, in the analysis of published reports, to separate studies on the basis of proximity to menopause.
6. Use of weak or inaccurate tools for estimating calcium intake in all studies except for intervention or metabolic studies, and the seeming failure to recognize this limitation.

1. Multifactorial character of change in bone mass and of bone fragility. Calcium, to the extent that it plays a role in bone health, is only one of many interacting factors (54, 55). Some of these factors remain unknown, or at least inadequately explored; hence it is difficult to control for them. While exercise, hormonal status, heredity, co-morbidity, medications, smoking, and alcohol consumption are all recognized in a general way, they are seldom adequately quantified in observational studies. Finally, as already noted, bony fragility, which underlies low-trauma fractures, is due only partly to reduced bone mass. While the nonmass fragility factors may yet prove to have nutritional correlates, little is known of these possibilities to date. Calcium deficiency, to the extent that it plays a role in this complex context, is postulated to have an effect only on bone mass. Hence the connection of calcium intake to fracture risk can be no stronger than the connection between bone mass and fracture.

2. Differing calcium intake distributions in various populations. Reported studies need to be interpreted against the national background of the individuals studied. To the extent that low calcium intake contributes to the osteoporotic fracture problem, one would expect to find the evidence most clearly presented in populations with intakes that span the range from low to

high, not in populations with predominantly high intakes. Beaton, in his McCollum lecture (11), dealt clearly with this problem for nutrients generally. For example, most of the reported studies from the Netherlands, where calcium intakes are comparatively high, have shown little or no relationship between calcium intake and bone mass (126, 127). The two studies of Elders et al. (37, 38) are comparative exceptions for Dutch studies.

In general, osteoporosis occurring in populations with high calcium intakes would be expected to have causes other than calcium deficiency, and one would not look to studies in such countries for evidence bearing on this question. Even the discrepancy between the hip fracture studies of Holbrook et al (67), who found a protective effect of high calcium intake, and of Wickham et al (130), who did not, may be due to differences in distribution of calcium intake between their respective populations. Mean calcium intake in the Wickham study was well into the upper tertile of intakes for the Holbrook study.

3. Inability in most studies to address the several bases for calcium deficiency. Calcium deficiency may be caused not only by low intakes but also by inefficient absorption (60) or by high obligatory losses, neither of which is quantified in most observational or even intervention studies. (For the most part, these causes of calcium deficiency can be satisfactorily measured only in metabolic studies.) The net result of ignoring them is a misclassification bias. Individuals classified as having high intakes may still be actually deficient if their absorptive or renal excretory performances are not appropriate for their intake. Conversely, other individuals with lower absolute intakes may be fully calcium-replete if their absorptive and excretory processes have adapted sufficiently. If these misclassifications occur equally in both directions (which seems unlikely from the evidence available), the result would be only a loss of power (see below). But if the misclassification of deficient subjects as high intake individuals dominates, the result will be a bias against finding a calcium effect.

4. Insufficient power. Power is a well-understood, if sometimes ignored, problem in studies testing an hypothesis. What has been little appreciated until recently is the relative magnitude of the calcium effect to be expected in observational studies in a free-living population, and the impact that that magnitude has on investigational power. For example, the longitudinal study of Riggs et al (114), widely quoted as showing no benefit from calcium, had a stated power to detect a population level correlation with a value in the range of 0.6 or higher. But even given zero errors in estimating either bone loss or calcium intake (which are not even remotely possible), Avioli & Heaney (4) calculated that the highest plausible population level correlation would be less than 0.4. Given the problems discussed below inherent in assessing calcium intake, it seems clear that the correlation likely to be detectable would have

been less than 0.30—far smaller than Riggs et al could reliably have detected. This is a problem to which Cumming (28) also referred in his metaanalysis.

5. Failure to recognize the special characteristics of the immediate postmenopausal period. It now seems increasingly clear that bone loss in the immediate postmenopausal period is due almost exclusively to loss of gonadal hormones. This point is discussed at greater length below. Its importance in the context of interpreting published studies lies in the fact that the effect of gonadal hormone loss is relatively short-lived. Studies that either concentrated upon or failed to exclude early postmenopausal women generally failed to find a calcium effect or underestimated its magnitude. On the basis of current understanding, this is exactly what would be expected, and the ineffectiveness of calcium at this time is not relevant to the need for calcium at earlier and later life stages.

In a cross-sectional investigation Elders et al (37), found habitual calcium intake to be a significant determinant of perimenopausal bone mass, but their data suggested that calcium probably exerted its effect by influencing peak bone mass, rather than by influencing menopausal bone loss. This conclusion is consistent with the findings in the study by Hansen et al (49): calcium intake was highly correlated with bone density both before and after menopause, but it had no effect on the quantity of bone lost across menopause. In their intervention study Elders et al (38), using daily supplements of 25 and 50 mmol of calcium in addition to a basal diet averaging about 29 mmol per day, found a dose-related, stepwise reduction in rate of bone loss before menopause, in the early postmenopause, and in the late postmenopause as well. However, in their early postmenopausal women, mean rates of bone change were still negative, even at the highest calcium intake (79 mm/day), though slightly less so than at lower intakes. These latter findings may reflect what Kanis & Passmore (71) have termed a pharmacologic effect of calcium, i.e. a suppression of the basic remodeling process itself, which thereby slows change in bone mass irrespective of its cause.

6. Use of weak and inaccurate instruments for assessing calcium intake. Most observational studies have assessed calcium intake at one or, rarely, two points in time, using a food frequency questionnaire (FFQ) limited in some studies to as few as seven food items. Others used one-day recall, three-day diaries, and a few, seven-day diaries. The accuracy of these assessments is a problem of underappreciated importance, at least among many workers in the bone health field, if not among dietitians and nutritional scientists. Only a few of the problems with assessing calcium intake by such tools can be touched upon here.

Even when one knows to the gram exactly how much of what foods went into an individual's mouth, chemical analysis invariably reveals a somewhat different figure from the entries in food database estimates for those same foods. (This, of course, is because the nutrient content of food varies, lot-to-lot.) Charles (23) found, under metabolic ward conditions, a correlation of only 0.87 between database values for calcium content of various diets and the actually analyzed contents. This means that fully one fourth of the actual interindividual variation in intakes could not be explained by knowledge of the precise quantities of foods eaten. In similar studies performed in my own laboratory the correlation was better ($r = 0.98$), but it still was not perfect, and can never be. The problem becomes even more difficult when one moves from subjects studied under metabolic ward conditions to a free-living population, where we no longer can measure, but only can estimate, quantities consumed. Even seven-day diaries fall short of capturing adequately the full details of intake (54, 57). Given typical day-to-day variation in calcium intake, diaries extending as long as 13–17 days may be needed for an acceptably small error estimate. These are plainly impracticable for most studies.

FFQs, the most commonly used tool, are attractive for their simplicity and ease of administration, but are generally less accurate than multiple-day diaries. In any event, in several studies in which they are compared with other methods, they produced substantially higher intake estimates than did diet diaries taken at the same time in the same individuals. Bergman et al (13) reported that a FFQ produced more than 50% higher figures for some nutrients, notably calcium, than did a 3-day food record. The validation usually cited in published reports is that the FFQ value correlated with some other measure of calcium intake. For example, Musgrave et al (93) reported a correlation coefficient of 0.73 between a FFQ value for calcium intakes and a concurrently developed food record. But one would expect correlation. That is not the issue. What is at stake is substitution. It is this chain of substitutions (FFQ for multiple day food record; food record for actual quantities of foods consumed; data base values of foods consumed for actual food content) that degrades the estimate produced by the measures actually employed in most observational studies, whether cross-sectional or longitudinal.

A further problem is one-point sampling. Heaney et al (57) have documented the quite considerable extent to which individual intakes vary over time. To the extent that bone density is affected by calcium intake, it would be the integrated intake over many years which would be important. Yet, very few published studies have used multiple point sampling. Finally, there is the general failure to include, in estimates of intake, the calcium content of excipients in medications or supplements taken for some reason other than their (generally unrecognized) calcium content (57). The error so introduced will generally be small, but in perhaps 5–10% of middle-aged or elderly women it will result in a substantial misclassification bias, i.e. counting people as having low intakes when they are actually high.

What may be considered surprising in all this is the contrast between the great attention paid to the accuracy, sensitivity, and specificity of bone mass

Table 1   Categorization of studies of the relation of calcium intake to bone status in Caucasian women

		Investigator-controlled calcium intake?		
		No	Yes	Total
Women from 0-5 years postmenopausal excluded?	No	0/8	4/7	4/15
	Yes	11/16	12/12	23/28
	Total	11/24	16/19	27/43

measurements and the low accuracy of the means to quantify what is postulated to be the independent variable in the hypothesis being tested. What should not be surprising, therefore, is that some studies fail to support the hypothesis.

In summary, Table 1 presents a classification of the 43 relevant studies in Caucasian women published since 1987. To facilitate analysis, studies are categorized first by menopausal age of the subjects and then by degree of investigator control over, and/or knowledge of, calcium intake.

The Table shows that about 60% of the studies reported a benefit from calcium (27 of 43). But this simple tallying of successes and failures treats all studies equally and does not do full justice to the data. For reasons already discussed, studies in which calcium intake is not investigator-controlled are biased toward the null hypothesis. When such studies find an effect, therefore, the result is more convincing than when they do not. In a similar way, as also discussed, endogenous calcium released from bone in the wake of gonadal hormone loss substitutes for, or displaces, exogenous calcium. For that reason, studies performed within the first five years after menopause also tend to show no benefit of dietary and supplemental calcium.

The 4-way breakdown presented in the Table is the result of applying these two criteria. As can be seen, the proportion of positive studies rises with the rigor and salience of the scientific design. Twenty-three of 28 studies excluding early postmenopausal women were positive, as were 16 of 19 in which the investigators controlled the calcium intake. And without exception all 12 studies meeting both criteria showed a calcium benefit.

The Requirement for Calcium

Within cells, calcium is a nearly universal second messenger mediating such diverse responses as muscle contraction, mitosis, and secretion. Extracellularly, it is essential for blood coagulation and neuromuscular signal transmission. The cells themselves regulate the concentration of free calcium ions in their cytosol, keeping it at least three orders of magnitude lower than in the surrounding extracellular fluid (ECF). They do this both by pumping calcium up a concentration gradient out to the ECF and by sequestering calcium in intracellular vesicles, such as the sarcoplasmic reticulum in muscle. In turn, ECF $[Ca^{2+}]$ is rigidly controlled at about 1.2 mM, mainly through the actions of parathyroid hormone, calcitriol, and calcitonin. The secretion of all three hormones is responsive directly or indirectly to changes in ECF $[Ca^{2+}]$ levels.

The primary metabolic functions of calcium are as outlined, and if calcium were like most other nutrients, its requirement would be defined as the intake needed to sustain those functions. But true nutrient deficiency in that sense is essentially never encountered in humans. This is because the skeleton serves as a very large—essentially inexhaustible—reserve of calcium for these critical biochemical functions. Over the millennia of vertebrate evolution, the skeleton has acquired important mechanical functions as well. It is for these mechanical functions of the skeleton, rather than in relation to the metabolic activity of calcium, that the notion of a requirement has meaning. Apart from fat, which in addition to being an energy reserve, provides insulation for animals living in cold environments, bone is the only known instance of a nutrient reserve having an important function in its own right. In fact, the size of the reserve (i.e. bone mass), as has just been seen, is one of the main determinants of bone strength. Thus, unlike most other nutrients, the requirement for calcium is related to building and maintaining the largest reserve possible within the individual genetic program.

Primary Prevention: The Acquisition of Genetically Programmed Bone Mass

Calcium is a threshold nutrient (as, for example, is iron). Forbes et al (43) showed in growing rats that femur bone mass was a linear function of diet calcium content up to values of about 0.6%. Above that intake, bone mass remained constant. Long bone growth was not limited in these animals at subthreshold levels of calcium intake, but bone *mass* was. Current models of bone metabolism explain this effect by a relative excess of bone resorption on the subthreshold diets, resulting in a tearing down of some of the bone deposited so that its calcium could support the demands of continuing linear growth. The resulting bone is thus of normal external size and shape, but of increased internal porosity and/or decreased cortical and trabecular thickness.

No evidence suggests that dietary calcium itself affects the mineralization process so long as serum calcium levels are maintained, either during growth or later, although some data suggest that low calcium intakes may limit linear growth. This may occur in some growing animal models with very low calcium intakes, and has been reported for Scottish school children (78), in whom addition of 12 oz of milk per day to the diet of one group resulted in substantially greater linear growth. But in such experiments it is not possible to tease apart the effects due specifically to calcium from the effects of the associated extra protein and energy intake. In general, it seems probable that the effect of low calcium intake on the growing skeleton is mediated largely through modulation of the balance between bone formation and bone resorption and is confined to an effect on bone density.

Clearly, while sufficient exogeneous calcium must be present to sustain density during growth and to maintain skeletal mass later in life, additional calcium above the threshold (whatever its value may be) will not produce more bone than is required either by the genetic program or by current levels of mechanical loading. The notion of a requirement is thus tied to this threshold. An individual's requirement would be the inflection point of the curve relating bone mass to intake, i.e. the threshold. A recommended dietary allowance (RDA) would be the corresponding point for a population. In both, further increases in intake produce no additional benefit or confer no additional protection. The following discussion therefore centers around new evidence in humans as to where the inflection point of the curve relating calcium intake to bone mass is located.

Matkovic assembled all studies, performed in healthy growing subjects, of calcium balances which had been published since 1922 and eliminated only those which tested altered intake or evaluated experimental foods or diets (83). He was able to find over 500 such studies, a number sufficiently large to detect threshold behavior if present. He and Heaney (85) analyzed these data by age group and found clear evidence of a balance threshold at all stages of growth from infancy up through the skeletal consolidation years (ages 18–30). The threshold calcium intake in children ages 2–8 was 35 mmol/day; in adolescents aged 9–17, 37 mmol/day; and in young adults aged 18–30, 24 mmol/day. These values are somewhat above the current RDAs for the ages concerned (20–30 mmol/day).

Johnston and colleagues, in a 3-year double-blind placebo-controlled trial in identical twins, found significantly augmented skeletal density in children receiving 17.5 mmol of supplemental calcium in addition to their normal diets (70). Mean intakes in the unsupplemented twins were between 21 and 22 mmol, already above the RDA for prepubertal children. Using a similar design, but a more modest supplement dose (8.75 mmol.day), Lloyd et al (80) found augmented bone gain in adolescent females, relative to unsupplemented controls whose intake averaged about 22 mmol/day. These findings thus confirm the conclusions drawn by Matkovic & Heaney in their metaanalysis (85).

Finally, Recker et al (108), in a four year longitudinal study of women aged 19–30, found continued augmentation of skeletal mass and density at total body, forearm, and spine, on diets averaging about 17.5 mmol/day. Bone acquisition was positively correlated with physical activity and with calcium intake, and negatively correlated with protein intake and age. Regressing rate of skeletal gain on age, these investigators found X-axis intercepts (zero gain) for the various bony sites to be at about age 29. The single most powerful factor influencing this skeletal consolidation was the calcium:protein ratio of the diet.

In a cross-sectional study Hirota et al (65) found a positive association between calcium intake and bone mass in Japanese college women aged 19–25, as did Fehily et al (41) in young Irish women. Prentice et al (104), in another cross-sectional study, found gain in bone mass until sometime in the fourth decade in Gambian women and noted in passing that, though rates of gain seemed slower, they remained positive in British women, as well, until sometime in the fourth decade.

On the other hand, Bonjour and colleagues (15), in cross-sectional studies of Swiss children, found substantial slowing of skeletal acquisition by age 18 and suggested that there was no further accumulation after that age. However, these authors did not specifically evaluate women in the third decade. It may also be that, with higher national calcium intakes, Swiss adolescents reach their genetic maximum earlier than do North American youngsters.

Thus, from both longitudinal and cross-sectional data, most studies show continuing skeletal consolidation throughout most of the third decade, dietary intake permitting. These studies also suggest that current estimates for the RDA may be low. Note in this regard that the RDA for children and adolescents is explicitly based on an assumption that calcium absorption efficiency at these ages is at least 50% (111). Recent studies of absorption by Miller et al (91, 92) using double tracer, stable isotope methods, showed that, in the ages concerned, absorption fraction averages only about 35%, or nearly one-third lower than the RDA Committee assumed.

A further reason for a higher than expected requirement during growth is seen in the observation of high urinary calcium loss, particularly in adolescents, noted first by Matkovic et al (84), and then found in the balances assembled by Matkovic & Heaney (85). During growth, urine calcium is a function mainly of body size, and during adolescence, particularly, it is quite independent of calcium intake. While a high urinary calcium loss might be taken as evidence of calcium sufficiency in an adult, that is not a tenable conclusion in a growing adolescent. Yet in both studies (84, 85) urinary calcium values in adolescent girls were high even on very restricted intakes— so restricted that no skeletal acquisition was possible. Hence this loss through the kidneys must be considered obligatory, and coupled with the lower than presumed absorption efficiency, explains why the threshold intake may be higher than estimated in the current RDAs.

Current nutritional thinking about this issue presumes that the body would conserve calcium during times of need—such as during the rapid growth of adolescence. Thus, the finding of values as low as those of adults for absorption and excretion at this age comes as a surprise. That reaction may reflect some degree of nutritional provincialism. Eaton & Konner (35) and Eaton & Nelson (36) point out that the calcium nutrient density of the diets of both the chimpanzee and contemporary hunter-gatherers is in the range of 1.75–2.0 mmol of calcium/100 kCal, two to four times what typical Western diets provide. They suggest that human physiology has adapted to such calcium-rich diets, and that the time that has elapsed from the agricultural revolution to the present has been insufficient to have allowed substantial evolutionary resetting of the basic physiological mechanisms involved.

Secondary Prevention: The Conservation of Acquired Bone Mass

Because of critical physiological differences at various life-stages, conservation of acquired bone mass is discussed under three temporal headings: premenopause, early postmenopause, and late postmenopause. While these three terms explicitly refer to women, available evidence suggests that the situation for aging men is similar to that for late postmenopausal women.

PREMENOPAUSE   Most authors have suggested that bone mass declines slowly with age after the adult peak is reached at age 30–35, and cross-sectional studies have tended to be consistent with that presumption. However, most such studies have inappropriately applied linear models across significant watershed events (e.g. menopause), and cross-sectional studies are also prone to the confounding of cohort effects (109). When they measured it directly, Mazess & Barden (87) found no measurable loss with age at any bony site in premenopausal women, and Recker et al, in a longitudinal study of over 70 late premenopausal women, found no measurable loss over periods up to three years in duration (110). These two observations suggest that ambient dietary calcium intakes (averaging above 700 mg for the Recker study) were sufficient to prevent calcium deficiency-related bone loss in premenopausal women.

Only one study suggests that augmented calcium intake may be beneficial in premenopausal women. Baran et al (5) found no loss in women supplemented with two additional servings of dairy products daily, but substantial loss in unsupplemented control subjects. However, the difference was detectable only at the third year study point, at which time there had been substantial losses of sampling units; and so it is hard to know how much of the apparent effect was a consequence of these losses.

This period of life has received much less attention than other phases of a woman's life, but the available data are consistent with a conclusion that intakes in the range of the current RDA are adequate to prevent intake-related bone loss in healthy premenopausal women.

EARLY POSTMENOPAUSE   Typical women lose roughly 15% of their bone mass following menopause. The loss is well described as an exponential function with a rate constant of about -0.25 yr^{-1} (55). Thus, most of the loss will occur within the first 5 yr after menopause, and by 15 yr postmenopause, the estrogen withdrawal loss merges into the slow, age-related loss of senescence, seen in both men and women. The early postmenopausal change in the skeleton is clearly due to withdrawal of gonadal hormones, and is preventable indefinitely by estrogen replacement therapy. An apparently very similar loss occurs in castrated males.

The mechanism of this shift is uncertain but has been plausibly explained as a resetting of the putative bone density "mechanostat," the bony apparatus that adjusts bone density through a canonical feedback loop that responds to sensed mechanical loading. Ostensibly, the setpoint is lowered in the presence of gonadal hormones, and accordingly bone density increases to reduce the load-induced strains. The shift from high estrogen to low estrogen levels at menopause thus produces a down-sizing of bones exactly analogous to what would be produced by decreased exercise.

Virtually all published studies show little or no effect of dietary calcium during this five-year period following menopause (39, 71, 114–116, 121). Before the centrality of the load-density feedback system and its sensitivity to gonadal hormones were appreciated, this failure of calcium was over-interpreted to mean that calcium intake had no role in age-related bone loss at any age. It is now clear that the situation is rather different.

During the first few years after menopause, so much calcium is made available from downward revision of bone density that in effect there may be no external calcium requirement whatsoever. Only with intakes high enough to suppress remodeling would an effect of calcium intake be expected. Elders and co-workers (38), in fact, show exactly such an effect in controlled trials with intakes of 29, 54, and 79 mmol/day. And, while the highest intakes in early postmenopausal women delayed menopausal loss, they did not prevent it.

The early postmenopausal years are, of course, the time when bone loss is the most rapid and the value of successfully intervening is most evident, which may explain why so many previous studies of calcium effect chose to address the early postmenopausal period (39, 71, 114–116, 121). But loss at that life stage is best prevented by estrogen. This topic has been extensively explored elsewhere (55) and is elucidated clearly in the study by Dawson-Hughes et al (31), in which, with the same investigational design, the same measurement methods, and the same calcium sources, a modest calcium supplement abolished age-related bone loss in women six or more years postmenopausal, but was quite without effect in women within 0–5 years following menopause. This point is also illustrated by Prince et al (106), who studied women an average of 5–6 years after menopause. Their subjects thus straddle the age-dividing line used by Dawson-Hughes et al (31) and would be predicted to exhibit only a partial response to increased calcium intake. Prince et al, in fact, found a significant reduction in rate of loss in the calcium-supplemented group, but the effect was less than produced by estrogen, precisely as predicted for a group this close to menopause.

LATE POSTMENOPAUSE/SENESCENCE   As just noted, women more than five years postmenopausal, and middle-aged and older men generally, show decreased bone loss with age if they have high calcium intakes (28, 56). The double-blind, placebo-controlled study by Dawson-Hughes et al, (31) already cited, makes that point clear, as do other studies, which, though mainly observational, nevertheless all come to the same conclusion. The Dawson-Hughes study concentrated on women with calcium intakes below 16 mmol/day, and it is sometimes interpreted as showing a benefit of calcium supplements only in those women with intakes below 10 mmol/day, and even that the threshold intake itself must be below 22 mmol/day. Both interpretations go well beyond the data. What the study clearly shows is that women with low intakes lose bone, that calcium supplements reduce or prevent that loss, and that the effect is not seen in women less than five years postmenopausal but becomes quite clear at six or more years after menopause. The study was not designed to provide more quantitative information. In fact, the data show a clear, dose-related effect, with women below 10 mmol/day losing bone most rapidly, women supplemented with calcium losing not at all, and placebo-treated women with intakes between 10 and 16 mmol/day, losing at a rate intermediate between the two. While the loss in the latter group was not significantly different from the loss in women with the lowest intake, this is nearly always true for adjacent groups in any continuous variable. Again, as Beaton pointed out for nutrients generally (11), there must be a range of intake if one is to find a statistically significant relationship.

Similarly, the absence of loss in this study in the supplemented women, whose intakes averaged about 22 mmol/day, is interpreted as indicating that 22 mmol is sufficient. This also would overinterpret the data. Calcium supplements (or any remodeling suppressor, for that matter) induce a remodeling transient that interferes with the ability to measure new steady state rates. Only changes beginning after one year or more of therapy can safely be used to infer the new steady state. The Dawson-Hughes study was not designed to address such questions.

That the effective response threshold may well be higher than the levels achieved by Dawson-Hughes is indicated both by the older metabolic balance studies of Heaney et al (61) and the more recent, very similar metabolic studies of Charles et al (23, 50), both of which point to equilibrium intakes well in excess of 25 mmol/day. Reid et al (112) in a design similar to that of the Dawson-Hughes study, but starting with women with higher basal intakes and supplementing with 25 mmol/day, rather than 12.5 mmol, found results essentially similar to those of Dawson-Hughes et al (31). Furthermore, their data indicated that the effect continued into the second year of treatment and thus showed that the much higher calcium intake had induced a new steady state—in other words, that women with higher basal intakes were nevertheless responsive to additional calcium. Finally, in older adults, and even in those with prior hip fracture, calcium supplementation has been shown to slow or prevent further bone loss (22a, 24).

Calcium Intake and Risk of Fracture

For reasons of feasibility, most studies of nutrition and bone health have used bone mass (or change in bone mass over time) as a surrogate for bone strength, which is the ultimate focus of our interest. And, while there is an undoubted relation between the two, it is important to bear in mind that low trauma fractures and their prevention must ultimately be the focus of interest.

The study of Matkovic and colleagues (86) was perhaps the first to demonstrate anti-fracture efficacy for high calcium intakes. However, the authors found protection only for hip fracture, not for the equally common wrist fracture; and because it was both observational and cross-sectional, the study did not control for many possibly confounding variables. However, Holbrook et al, in a 14-year longitudinal study, also found that hip fracture rates were lower in individuals ingesting higher calcium diets (67). Three other epidemiological studies have been reported (27, 77, 130), one showing that high calcium intakes protect both men and women, one showing protection for men only, and one showing protection for neither.

In perhaps the largest and best controlled study using fracture itself as the endpoint, Chapuy and colleagues have shown substantial reductions in fracture rate in a large group of institutionalized elderly given supplements of both calcium and vitamin D (22a). Protection became apparent after 6–12 months of treatment, and by 18 months, fractures were reduced by more than 30% in the treated individuals. Heikinheimo et al (64), using vitamin D alone in a randomized controlled trial, also found a substantial reduction in all fractures in the elderly.

Three studies in elderly individuals have reported decreased hip fracture risk in patients receiving thiazide diuretics, an effect presumably due to thiazide-induced reduction of urinary calcium losses (42, 76, 107). Nordin and colleagues have reported a tendency to a renal calcium leak in post-menopausal women (98), and, as has already been noted, renal conservation of calcium is an important determinant of the intake requirement. Hence these results complement the data from direct studies of calcium intake. Finally, while fractures in the elderly are the main concern, it is worth noting that Chan and colleagues, in a long-running series of studies, have shown fracture rates and bone density in children inversely proportional to calcium intake (20–22). So, at all life-stages, other things being equal, the higher the calcium intake, the stronger the skeleton.

Calcium as a Component of Treatment of Established Osteoporosis

The goals of treatment of osteoporosis, in addition to symptom control and rehabilitation, include arrest of further bone loss and, where possible, restoration of lost bone mass. Estrogen, the bisphosphonates, and calcitonin act mainly to arrest bone loss, although they often produce a small increase in mass that is probably at least in part a remodeling transient. Fluoride and PTH, both still experimental, increase trabecular bone density more dramatically, sometimes restoring it to young adult values.

However, for any of these modalities to produce these effects, calcium intakes must be sufficient to prevent further bone loss and/or to support the laying down of new bone, without taking calcium from other regions of the skeleton. Both PTH and fluoride will increase spine trabecular density irrespective of intake, and both agents are thus capable of producing an intra-body shift of bone from appendicular cortical sites to axial, trabecular sites. This seems to be a part of the reason why, in some studies, appendicular bone mass has actually declined while spine density was improving and why peripheral fracture rates increased under these therapies. In this connection, Dure-Smith and colleagues have demonstrated a striking degree of bone hunger in patients responding to fluoride treatment (34).

Hence, calcium supplementation, usually beyond what can feasibly be provided by diet alone, constitutes an essential component of virtually every therapeutic regimen for this disorder. Given the relatively poor absorption efficiency found in the elderly, intakes of at least 40–60 mmol/day seem necessary. Adequate attention needs to be paid, as well, to vitamin D status (see below).

Nutrient-Nutrient Interactions

FIBER   The term *fiber* refers to a varied group of plant polymers that are not hydrolyzed by human digestive enzymes and therefore pass intact through the principal absorptive region of the intestine. These polymers frequently contain multiple, negatively charged groups capable of complexing with cations. In theory, therefore, they might interfere with the availability of co-ingested calcium, at least until the intestinal contents reach the colon where bacterial hydrolysis of the polymer chains may free bound cations. Barger-Lux et al (8), in examining the time course of tracer absorption from labeled calcium intakes, noted that 95% of the calcium that will be absorbed from a mixed food meal is absorbed by 4 to 5 hr after ingestion, and that the remaining 5% is slowly absorbed over the next 20 hr. This performance is consistent with the notion of release of bound calcium after entry into the colon. At the same time it also indicates that not much calcium is made available that way in the typical adult human.

Contemporary diets typically contain from 5 to 15 g fiber. Current recommendations are for intakes in the range of 15–20 g/day. This increase, if realized, might be expected to interfere to some extent with calcium absorption. While such interference can be demonstrated in various animal models, it has been harder to show in humans. When reviewing various aspects of calcium nutrition in the elderly in 1982, Heaney et al (58) concluded that only large increases in fiber intake were likely to produce much effect, and an expert panel, in reviewing the topic more recently (101), came to much the same conclusion.

Knox et al (73) found that increasing the fiber content of a test meal from 0.5 to 10.5 g (using raw wheat bran as the fiber source), resulted in a decrease in apparent calcium absorption (measured by whole body tracer retention) from about 25–26% for the low fiber meal to about 19–20% for the high fiber meal. Weaver et al (129) found that 40 g of wheat bran cereal (containing 12 g of bran) reduced calcium absorption from co-ingested milk by about one third—from a value of 37.5% to 25.8%. On the other hand, the same paper reported higher absorption for the calcium contained in whole wheat bread than for milk ingested at a comparable calcium load. The same authors (62, 63) also report good absorbability for calcium from kale and from low phytate soybeans, both of which contain significant amounts of fiber. Consistent with this finding are the data of Wisker et al (131), who found that a large addition (15 g/day) of a low phytate barley fiber concentrate did not interfere with either calcium absorption or calcium balance in normal adults. Apparently, the various forms of fiber contained in different food sources do not interfere with calcium absorption to an equivalent extent.

It may be concluded that at least certain fiber sources, such as wheat bran, do interfere with absorption of co-ingested calcium, though the effect over an intake range typically encountered in adult diets is not likely to be very great. The experiments of Knox et al (73) and of Weaver et al (129) are concordant and can be summarized to predict a decrease in absorbability of about 20–30% upon going from an intake of 0–1 g bran fiber per day to roughly 30 g per day, values that span the plausible range of fiber intakes for most adults. Thus, an adult with a basal intake of 10 g per day, who chooses to double that intake, might therefore expect a 6–10% decrease in food calcium availability. This is not negligible, particularly if calcium intake is already low. Still, it could be easily compensated for by relatively small increases in dietary calcium intake. Finally, it must be stressed that these calculations apply only to wheat bran fiber. At least some other plant fibers interfere not at all.

PHOSPHORUS   Phosphorus is as important for bone health as is calcium. As phosphate, it makes up roughly half the weight of bone mineral and hence must be present in adequate quantities in the diet both to mineralize and to maintain the skeleton. Phosphorus is generally present in relatively adequate quantities in the US diet, and most of the recent concern of the nutrition community has centered on the question of whether its presence in the diet might be excessive, with consequent harm (25).

Increased phosphorus intake transiently depresses ionized calcium and thereby leads to increased secretion of PTH, which could clearly influence bone. However, the effect wanes in a few days (118), unless calcium intake is also suppressed, in which case PTH levels remain high (17, 18). Under steady state conditions, an increased phosphorus intake reduces urinary calcium loss and increases digestive juice secretion of calcium (25). The two effects are approximately equal in magnitude; hence total body calcium balance tends not to be affected.

Calvo et al (18) placed young adults on high phosphorus, low calcium diets, and noted elevations of iPTH and urinary hydroxyproline lasting for at least four weeks. However, Barger-Lux & Heaney (6), found identical changes in both variables when *both* calcium and phosphorus intake were lowered. Thus, it seems unlikely that the effects noted by Calvo et al are due specifically to high phosphorus intakes, as these authors suggested.

Increased phosphorus intake also powerfully suppresses renal synthesis of calcitriol, which could lead to decreased calcium absorption (103). At the same time, as already noted, increased phosphorus intake suppresses urinary calcium loss and is used for that purpose in patients with renal stone disease. The effect appears to be direct, since it can readily be demonstrated by adjusting phosphate loads in patients on total parenteral nutrition (133).

Although low phosphorus intakes are less common in the United States, low intakes may limit the body's utilization of calcium for building and remodeling bone. According to NHANES II (19), only about 10 to 15% of women aged 65 to 74 have phosphorus intakes less than two-thirds the RDA. The proportion is probably higher for the old elderly. Low phosphorus intakes lead to excessive urinary calcium loss and hence could aggravate the effect of low calcium intakes. Conversely, large calcium supplements will lower absorbed phosphorus and, in individuals who already have low phosphorus intakes, this effect could produce phosphate deficiency. Individually, these interactions are generally well studied, but taken together in the very old elderly, who may have other problems (such as declining renal function, which will affect ECF phosphorus levels), they present complexities that have not been adequately explored.

PROTEIN AND SODIUM   Dietary excesses of both protein and sodium increase urinary calcium loss and hence interfere with calcium conservation in response to a restricted calcium intake. Protein is a powerful determinant of urine calcium, partly, at least, because of the associated increase in acid load (1, 79, 132). At least three different groups of investigators have found that a doubling of protein intake results in roughly a 50% increase in urine calcium loss (59). Hence, protein intake is an important determinant of calcium requirement. This is shown clearly, for example, by the finding cited above that the calcium:protein ratio of the diet was the most important measured determinant of the rate of bone acquisition in third-decade women (108).

While excess protein intake (relative to calcium) is more of a problem in the US than is protein insufficiency, the relationship is biphasic, and low intake is also important for bone health, especially in the elderly. Bone mineral density has been reported to be positively correlated with protein intake in elderly Caucasian and Asian women (75, 125), and protein intake was inversely correlated with rates of bone loss (46) in older women. Many other variables are involved in these studies, and by themselves they are only suggestive. However, in view of the clear benefit from protein supplements at the time of repair of hip fracture (10, 32, 69), it seems reasonably clear that in some patients, particularly the very old elderly, insufficient protein intake may contribute importantly to the osteoporosis problem.

Urine calcium rises by 1–2 mmol for every 100 mmol increment of ingested sodium (97). The sodium effect appears more marked at low calcium intakes and may be less important at intakes above 25 mmol/day. It is as if a large renal sodium load interferes with ability to reabsorb calcium from the tubular lumen under conditions when calcium is being conserved, but has less effect when excess calcium is being excreted.

VITAMIN D

That vitamin D is important for absorption of calcium from the diet has long been recognized. Its role lies in facilitating active transport, in part by inducing the formation of calcium-binding protein in intestinal mucosal cells. This function is particularly important for adaptation to low intakes. However, passive transport occurs by other means, not as well elucidated, which are not dependent upon vitamin D. The proportion of absorption by the two mechanisms varies with intake and is not well characterized; at high calcium intakes (above 60–75 mmol/day) absorption fraction approaches that observed in anephric individuals ($\sim$10–15% of intake). Under these circumstances it is likely that active transport contributes relatively little to the total absorbed load. Nevertheless, it is generally recognized that vitamin D status can influence absorptive performance and hence effective calcium requirement.

A principal storage form of the vitamin is 25-hydroxyvitamin D [25(OH)D], and its plasma level is the best clinical indicator of vitamin D status. Although orders of magnitude less potent than calcitriol in promoting active transport, 25(OH)D may possess physiological functions in its own right (12). Vitamin D status commonly deteriorates in the elderly, whose plasma 25(OH)D levels are generally lower than in young adults (44, 88). These elderly persons, without histological or biochemical evidence of osteomalacia, nevertheless exhibit high PTH levels and low absorptive performance, both of which change when they are given physiological amounts of supplemental vitamin D (30, 52, 74). Low dosage vitamin D supplementation of ostensibly healthy postmenopausal women significantly slows wintertime bone loss and reduces the annual parathyroid-mediated activation of the bone remodeling system that occurs in winter through late spring (30). The rate of age-related loss of bone has been found to be inversely correlated to dietary vitamin D (81). Heikinheimo et al (64) in a 4-yr, randomized, controlled trial found a substantial reduction in all fractures in elderly Finns given a single injection of 150,000–300,000 IU vitamin D in the fall of each year. And, in a 3-yr randomized controlled trial, combined supplementation with calcium and vitamin D in 3,270 institutionalized elderly significantly reduced both bone loss and fracture rate after the first year of treatment (22a). The latter study is particularly noteworthy because it concentrated on the most vulnerable population, used the ultimate endpoint (fracture), and employed a strong design (randomized controlled trial).

The foregoing studies, and many others as well, lead inexorably to the conclusion that vitamin D insufficiency is prevalent in the middle-aged and elderly of Europe and North America. In virtually none of these studies was frank osteomalacia a significant feature of the problem. Hence this criterion for true vitamin D deficiency may well be much too strict to be nutritionally useful.

Low 25(OH)D levels in the elderly are partly due to decreased solar exposure, partly to decreased efficiency of skin vitamin D synthesis, and partly to decreased intake of milk, the principal dietary source of the vitamin in the US. Moreover, the elderly exhibit other abnormalities of the vitamin D endocrine system that may further impair their ability to adapt to reduced calcium intake. These include decreased responsiveness of the renal 1-α-hydroxylase to parathyroid hormone (120) and decreased mucosal responsiveness to calcitriol (45). For all these reasons there is a growing body of opinion that the requirement for vitamin D rises with age (48, 52, 100, 124).

How much of the effect of vitamin D in the above studies is due to facilitating gut adaptation to marginal calcium intakes and how much may represent an extra-intestinal effect of the vitamin in its own right is not clear. Calcitriol receptors are widely distributed in many tissues, and calcitriol enhances PTH-mediated bone resorption, exhibits autocrine action in cell differentiation and in the immune response, and inhibits parathyroid hormone synthesis by direct action on the parathyroid gland. Furthermore, calcitriol elicits a prompt and sizable increase in osteoblast synthesis of osteocalcin (105). Nevertheless, patients with vitamin D–dependent rickets Type II, who lack functional calcitriol receptors, show essentially complete remission of their pathophysiological processes with intravenous calcium infusions alone (14). Furthermore, while subtle impairment of immune function can be demonstrated in nutritional vitamin D deficiency, the defects appear to be sufficiently mild to be of little or no clinical consequence. Hence the issue remains quite unclear.

Nevertheless, whether solely through an effect on calcium absorption, or through other mechanisms as well, a growing body of data strongly suggests that relative vitamin D deficiency plays a role in several components of the osteoporosis syndrome.

VITAMIN K

Vitamin K was reviewed in 1984 (99) and its role in the synthesis of bone proteins in 1988 (105). Thus the current review focuses mainly on developments since 1988.

Vitamin K is necessary for the gamma-carboxylation of glutamic acid residues in a large number of proteins, and the vitamin K-dependent carboxylase is widely distributed in many tissues. At least seven vitamin K dependent proteins are involved in one way or another in blood coagulation. The gamma-carboxyglutamic acid residues in the peptide chain bind calcium, either free or on the surface layers of crystals, and are thought to function in varying ways—from inhibiting mineralization (as in urine) (95) to serving as osteoclast chemotactic signals (51). Vitamin K deficiency classically produces bleeding disorders, but the liver, where the clotting factors are produced, is highly efficient in extracting vitamin K from the circulation, and gamma-carboxylation declines substantially in other tissues before the deficiency is serious enough to result in bleeding disorders. Thus the bleeding tendencies that have been the hallmark of vitamin K deficiency may, in fact, be the last manifestation of deficiency. If so, the other clinical manifestations of vitamin K deficiency remain uncertain.

Two vitamin K-dependent proteins are of special interest in the context of this review: osteocalcin [bone Gla protein (BGP)] and a kidney Gla protein (nephrocalcin) (94), both of which are dependent upon vitamin K for their synthesis. BGP is the principal noncollagenous protein of bone. It is synthesized and gamma-carboxylated by osteoblasts as they synthesize bone matrix. Roughly 30% of the synthesized BGP is not incorporated into matrix but is released instead into the circulation, where, like alkaline phosphatase, it can be measured and used as an indicator of bone formation. In vitamin K deficiency, as would occur with coumarin anticoagulants, serum BGP levels decline, and the degree of carboxylation of the circulating BGP protein falls dramatically. Further, binding to hydroxyapatite of the BGP synthesized under these conditions to hydroxyapatite falls precipitously soon after starting anticoagulant therapy. It would seem, therefore, that vitamin K deficiency would have detectable skeletal effects. The problem is that they have been very hard to find. Rats reared and sustained to adult life under near total suppression of BGP gamma-carboxylation show only minor skeletal abnormalities (105). Hauschka et al have suggested that BGP bound to hydroxyapatite is chemotactic for osteoclasts, and that the absence of such binding might impede remodeling (51)—an effect that may not be apparent in the rat, which does not remodel bone the way larger animals do.

Various vitamin K-related abnormalities have been described in association with osteoporosis, but their significance remains unclear. Circulating vitamin K and menaquinone levels are low in hip fracture patients (66). BGP is under-carboxylated in osteoporotics, and this defect responds to physiological doses of vitamin K (102). Finally, Vermeer and colleagues have reported that urine calcium is high in osteoporotics and falls in response to physiological doses of vitamin K (72, 128). In the same subjects, urine hydroxyproline, an indicator of bone resorption, was also high and fell after vitamin K treatment. The urinary effects could plausibly be explained as a defect first in a calcium transport protein, with resulting renal leak of calcium, and a consequent PTH-mediated increase in bone resorption (reflected in the increased hydroxyproline excretion).

Whether or not vitamin K is important for bone health, vitamin K levels are indicators of general nutritional status; the observation of low vitamin K levels in osteoporotics, especially in those with hip fracture, may simply reflect the often poor nutrition of these individuals (47, 113). Clearly, however, much about vitamin K and bone health remains an enigma, and more work must be done before the picture will become clear.

TRACE MINERALS

Several trace minerals, notably zinc, manganese, and copper, are essential metallic cofactors for enzymes involved in synthesis of various bone matrix constituents. In growing animals, diets deficient in these elements produce definite skeletal abnormalities (29, 89). Additionally, zinc deficiency is well known to produce growth retardation and other abnormalities in humans. But it is not known with certainty whether significant deficiencies of these elements occur in previously healthy adults, or at least, if they do, whether such deficiencies contribute to the osteoporosis problem. Copper deficiency is said to be associated with osteoporotic lesions in sheep, cattle, and rats (29, 122). Copper has not been much studied in connection with human osteoporosis, but in one study serum copper levels were negatively correlated with lumbar spine BMD, even after adjusting for body weight and dietary calcium intake (68). Further, in one four-way, randomized intervention trial, copper, as a part of a trace mineral cocktail including also zinc and manganese, slowed bone mineral loss in postmenopausal women, when given either with or without supplemental calcium (123). Most of the effect in this study was shown to be due to the calcium supplement, but there appeared to be a small additional benefit from the extra trace minerals. Since both osteoporotic and age-related bone loss are multifactorial, and since there was no way to select subjects for inclusion on the basis of presumed trace mineral need, the findings of this study, while inconclusive, have to be considered strongly suggestive.

NUTRITION AND HIP FRACTURE

The impact of nutrition on the problem of hip fracture is twofold: in predisposing to fracture and in recovery from and repair of the injury. Fractures in the very old elderly, and particularly hip fractures, are concentrated in institutionalized persons with multiple disabilities (119). The osteoporotic elderly generally have depleted lean body mass and fat mass (113), as well as low circulating values for several key nutritional indicator variables, from serum albumin to ferritin and vitamin A (32). Survival two years after injury is four times higher in patients with serum albumin values above 3.5 g/dl than in patients with values below 3.0 g (16).

Additionally, patients with hip fracture often have low calcium intakes, and dietary calcium earlier in life has been inversely associated with hip fracture risk. Moreover, it is likely that there are other intrinsic abnormalities in the bone at the femoral neck (40). Thus hip fracture occurs in multiply compromised individuals, and the prospect of successfully intervening to reduce risk of fracture has proved daunting.

However, one aspect of the problem may be more amenable to control. The relative malnutrition of patients suffering hip fracture and coming to hospital for repair may contribute significantly to the often unsatisfactory outcomes for this common fracture (15–20% excess mortality; 50% institutionalization of the survivors). If so, appropriate nutritional treatment could improve outcomes. Exactly such improvement was found by Delmi et al (32) in a randomized trial of a protein-based nutrient supplement given to patients newly hospitalized for hip fracture. Only 26% of unsupplemented individuals had outcomes classified as good at six months after injury, whereas nearly 60% of supplemented individuals had good outcomes. The investigators noted that the hospital diets offered the unsupplemented individuals were nutritionally adequate, but were frequently unconsumed, whereas the investigators saw to the ingestion of the supplement. Subsequent work from this same group both confirmed these dramatic benefits and narrowed the effect of the supplement to its protein content. This is not an isolated observation; others had earlier found qualitatively similar benefit from nutritional supplementation in these patients (10, 69). Thus the consistency of these findings presents a challenge to the medical profession to apply these basic nutritional principles in the management of their patients.

Literature Cited

1. Adams, N. D., Gray, R. W., Lemann, J. Jr. 1979. The calciuria of increased fixed acid production in humans: evidence against a role for parathyroid hormone and 1,25(OH)2-vitamin D. Calcif. Tissue Int. 28:233–38

2. Arnaud, C. D., Sanchez, S. D. 1990. The role of calcium in osteoporosis. Annu. Rev. Nutr. 10:397–414

3. Avioli, L. V. 1984. Calcium and osteoporosis. Annu. Rev. Nutr. 4:471–91

4. Avioli, L. V., Heaney, R. P. 1991. Calcium intake and bone health (editorial). Calcif. Tissue Int. 48:221–23

5. Baran, D., Sorensen, A., Grimes, J., Lew, R., Karellas, A., et al. 1990. Dietary modification with dairy products for preventing vertebral bone loss in premenopausal women: a three-year prospectve study. J. Clin. Endocrinol. Metab. 70:264–70

6. Barger-Lux, M. J., Heaney, R. P. 1993. Metabolic characteristics of premenopausal women after calcium restriction or calcium supplementation. J. Clin. Endocrinol. Metab. 76:103–7

7. Barger-Lux, M. J., Heaney, R. P., Packard, P. T., Lappe, J. M., Recker, R. R. 1992. Nutritional correlates of low calcium intake. Clinics Appl. Nutr. 2:39–44

8. Barger-Lux, M. J., Heaney, R. P., Recker, R. R. 1989. Time course of calcium absorption in humans: evidence for a colonic component. Calcif. Tissue Int. 44:308–11

9. Barrett-Connor, E. 1989. The RDA for calcium in the elderly: too little, too late (editorial). Calcif. Tissue Int. 44:303–7

10. Bastow, M. D., Rawlings, J., Allison, S. P. 1983. Benefits of supplementary tube feeding after fractured neck of femur. Br. Med. J. 287:1589–92

11. Beaton, G. H. 1986. Toward harmonization of dietary, biochemical, and clinical assessments: the meanings of nutritional status and requirements. Nutr. Rev. 44:349–58

12. Bell, N. H., Epstein, S., Shary, J., Greene, V., Oexmann, M. J., Shaw, S. 1988. Evidence of a probable role for 25-hydroxyvitamin D in the regulation of calcium metabolism. J. Bone Miner. Res. 3:489–95

13. Bergman, E. A., Boyungs, J. C., Erickson, M. L. 1990. Comparison of a food frequency questionnaire and a 3-day diet record. J. Am. Diet. Assoc. 90:1431–33

14. Bliziotes, M., Yergey, A. L., Nanes, M. S., Muenzer, J., Begley, M. G., et al. 1988. Absent intestinal response to calciferols in hereditary resistance to 1,25-dihydroxyvitamin D; documentation and effective therapy with high dose intravenous infusions. *J. Clin. Endocrinol. Metab.* 66:294–300

15. Bonjour, J.-P., Theintz, G., Buchs, B., Slosman, D., Rizzoli, R. 1991. Critical years and stages of puberty for spinal and femoral bone mass accumulation during adolescence. *J. Clin. Endocrinol. Metab.* 73:555–63

16. Bruyere, A., Rapin, C. H., Dirren, H. 1984. Nutritional blood values in patients with femoral neck fracture. A comparative study. In *Nutrition, Immunity and Illness in the Elderly*, ed. R. K. Chandra, pp. 242–46. London: Pergamon

17. Calvo, M. S., Kumar, R., Heath, H. III. 1988. Elevated secretion and action of serum PTH in young adults consuming high phosphorus, low calcium diets assembled from common foods. *J. Clin. Endocrinol. Metab.* 66:823–29

18. Calvo, M. S., Kumar, R., Heath, H. III. 1990. Persistently elevated PTH secretion and action in young women after four weeks of ingesting high phosphorus, low calcium diets. *J. Clin. Endocrinol. Metab.* 70:1334–40

19. Carroll, M. D., Abraham, S., Dresser, C. M. 1983. Dietary intake source data: US, 1976–80. *Vital & Health Statistics, Ser. 11-NO. 231, DHHS. Publ. No. (PHS) 83-PHS, March.* Washington, DC: Gov. Print. Off.

20. Chan, G. M. 1991. Dietary calcium and bone mineral status of children and adolescents. *Am. J. Dis. Child.* 145:631–34

21. Chan, G. M., Hess, M., Hollis, J., Book, L. S. 1984. Bone mineral status in childhood accidental fractures. *Am. J. Dis. Child.* 138:569–70

22. Chan, G. M., McMurry, M., Westover, K., Engelbert-Fenton, K., Thomas, M. R. 1987. Effects of increased dietary calcium intake upon the calcium and bone mineral status of lactating adolescent and adult women. *Am. J. Clin. Nutr.* 46:319–23

22a. Chapuy, M. C., Arlot, M. E., Duboeuf, F., Brun, J., Crouzet, B., et al. 1992. Vitamin D3 and calcium to prevent hip fractures in elderly women. *New Engl. J. Med.* 327:1637–42

23. Charles, P. 1989. Metabolic bone disease evaluated by a combined calcium balance and tracer kinetic study. *Dan. Med. Bull.* 36:463–79

24. Chevalley, T., Rizzoli, R., Nydegger, V., Slosman, D. O., Rapin, C.-H., et al. 1992. Effects of calcium supplement on femoral bone mineral density and vertebral fracture rate in vitamin D replete elderly patients with and without a recent hip fracture. *J. Bone Miner. Res.* 7:S322. (Abstr.)

25. Chinn, H. I. 1981. Effects of dietary factors on skeletal integrity in adults: calcium, phosphorus, vitamin D, and protein. Report prepared for the Bureau of Foods, Food and Drug Admin. (FDA), Sept. Life Sciences Research Office, FASEB, Bethesda, Md.

26. Consensus Development Conference: prophylaxis and treatment of osteoporosis. 1991. *Am. J. Med.* 90:107–10

27. Cooper, C., Barker, D. J. P., Wickham, C. 1988. Physical activity, muscle strength, and calcium intake in fracture of the proximal femur in Britain. *Br. Med. J.* 297:1443–46

28. Cumming, R. G. 1990. Calcium intake and bone mass: a quantitative review of the evidence. *Calcif. Tissue Int.* 47:194–201

29. Davis, G. K., Mertz, W. 1987. Copper. See Ref. 89, pp. 301–64

30. Dawson-Hughes, B., Dallal, G. E., Krall, E. A., Harris, S., Sokoll, L. J., Falconer, G. 1991. Effect of vitamin D supplementation on wintertime and overall bone loss in healthy postmenopausal women. *Ann. Int. Med.* 115:505–12

31. Dawson-Hughes, B., Dallal, G. E., Krall, E. A., Sadowski, L., Sahyoun, N., Tannenbaum, S. 1990. A controlled trial of the effect of calcium supplementation on bone density in postmenopausal women. *New Engl. J. Med.* 323:878–83

32. Delmi, M., Rapin, C.-H., Bengoa, J.-M., Delmas, P. D., Vasey, H., Bonjour, J.-P. 1990. Dietary supplementation in elderly patients with fractured neck of the femur. *Lancet* 335: 1013–16

33. Dodds, R. A., Emery, R. J. H., Klenerman, L. 1990. Selective depression of metabolic activities in cortical osteoblasts at the site of femoral neck fractures. *Bone* 11:157–61

34. Dure-Smith, B. A., Farley, S. M., Linkhart, S. G., Baylink, D. J. 1992. Evidence that increased bone formation leads to calcium deficiency and peripheral bone loss in fluoride treated patients: correction with 1,25 vitamin D. *J. Bone Miner. Res.* 7:S188 (Abstr.)

35. Eaton, S. B., Konner, M. 1985. Paleolithic nutrition. A consideration of

its nature and current implications. *New Engl. J. Med.* 312:283–89

36. Eaton, S. B., Nelson, D. A. 1991. Calcium in evolutionary perspective. *Am. J. Clin. Nutr.* 54:S281–87

37. Elders, P. J. M., Netelenbos, J. C., Lips, P., Khoe, E., van Ginkel, F. C., et al. 1989. Perimenopausal bone mass and risk factors. *Bone Miner.* 7:289–99

38. Elders, P. J. M., Netelenbos, J. C., Lips, P., van Ginkel, F. C., Khoe, E., et al. 1991. Calcium supplementation reduces vertebral bone loss in perimenopausal women: a controlled trial in 248 women between 46 and 55. *J. Clin. Endocrinol. Metab.* 73: 533–40

39. Ettinger, B., Genant, H. K., Cann, C. E. 1987. Postmenopausal bone loss is prevented by treatment with low-dosage estrogen with calcium. *Ann. Intern. Med.* 106:40–45

40. Eventov, I., Frisch, B., Cohen, Z., Hammel, I. 1991. Osteopenia, hematopoiesis and osseous remodeling in iliac crest and femoral neck biopsies: a prospective study of 102 cases of femoral neck fractures. *Bone* 12:1–6

41. Fehily, A. M., Coles, R. J., Evans, W. D., Elwood, P. C. 1992. Factors affecting bone density in young adults. *Am. J. Clin. Nutr.* 56:579–86

42. Felson, D. T., Sloutskis, D., Anderson, J. J., Anthony, J. M., Kiel, D. P. 1991. Thiazide diuretics and the risk of hip fracture. Results from the Framingham Study. *J. Am. Med. Assoc.* 265:370–73

43. Forbes, R. M., Weingartner, K. E., Parker, H. M., Bell, R. M., Erdman, J. Jr. 1979. Bioavailability to rats of zinc, magnesium and calcium in: casein-, egg- and soy protein-containing diets. *J. Nutr.* 109:1652–60

44. Francis, R. M., Peacock, M., Storer, J. H., Davies, A. E. J., Brown, W. B., Nordin, B. E. C. 1983. Calcium malabsorption in the elderly: the effect of treatment with oral 25-hydroxy-vitamin D3. *Eur. J. Clin. Invest.* 13:391–96

45. Francis, R. M., Peacock, M., Taylor, G. A., Storer, J. H., Nordin, B. E. C. 1984. Calcium malabsorption in elderly women with vertebral fractures: evidence for resistance to the action of vitamin D metabolites on the bowel. *Clin. Sci.* 66:103–7

46. Freudenheim, J. L., Johnson, N. E., Smith, E. L. 1986. Relationships between usual nutrient intake and bone-mineral content of women 35–65 years of age: longitudinal and cross-sectional analysis. *Am. J. Clin. Nutr.* 44:863–76

47. Geinoz, G., Rapin, C. H., Rizzoli, R., Kraemer, R., Buchs, B., et al. 1993. Relationship between bone mineral density and dietary intakes in elderly. *Osteoporosis Int.* In press

48. Gloth, F. M. III, Tobin, J. D., Sherman, S. S., Hollis, B. W. 1991. Is the recommended daily allowance for vitamin D too low for the homebound elderly? *J. Am. Geriatr. Soc.* 39:137–41

49. Hansen, M. A., Overgaard, K., Riis, B. J., Christiansen, C. 1991. Potential risk factors for development of postmenopausal osteoporosis—examined over a 12-year period. *Osteoporosis Int.* 1:95–102

50. Hasling, C., Charles, P., Jensen, F. T., Mosekilde, L. 1990. Calcium metabolism in postmenopausal osteoporosis: the influence of dietary calcium and net absorbed calcium. *J. Bone Miner. Res.* 5:939–46

51. Hauschka, P. V., Lian, J. B., Cole, D. E. C., Gundberg, C. M. 1989. Osteocalcin and matrix gla protein: vitamin K-dependent proteins in bone. *Physiol. Rev.* 69:990–1047

52. Heaney, R. P. 1986. Calcium, bone health, and osteoporosis. In *Bone and Mineral Research, Annual IV,* ed. W. A. Peck, pp. 255–301. Amsterdam: Elsevier Sci.

53. Heaney, R. P. 1989. Osteoporotic fracture space: an hypothesis. *Bone Miner.* 6:1–13

54. Heaney, R. P. 1989. Nutritional factors in bone health in elderly subjects: methodological and contextual problems. *Am. J. Clin. Nutr.* 50:S1181–89

55. Heaney, R. P. 1990. Estrogen-calcium interactions in the postmenopause: a quantitative description. *Bone Miner.* 11:67–84

56. Heaney, R. P. 1992. Calcium intake and bone health in an aging population. *Clin. Appl. Nutr.* 2:10–29

57. Heaney, R. P., Davies, K. M., Recker, R. R., Packard, P. T. 1990. Long-term consistency of nutrient intakes in humans. *J. Nutr.* 120:869–75

58. Heaney, R. P., Gallagher, J. C., Johnston, C. C. Jr., Neer, R., Parfitt, A. M., Whedon, G. D. 1982. Calcium nutrition and bone health in the elderly. *Am. J. Clin. Nutr.* 36:986–1013

59. Heaney, R. P., Recker, R. R. 1982. Effects of nitrogen, phosphorus, and caffeine on calcium balance in women. *J. Lab. Clin. Med.* 99:46–55

60. Heaney, R. P., Recker, R. R. 1986. Distribution of calcium absorption in

middle-aged women. *Am. J. Clin. Nutr.* 43:299–305

61. Heaney, R. P., Recker, R. R., Saville, P. D. 1978. Menopausal changes in calcium balance performance. *J. Lab. Clin. Med.* 92:953–63

62. Heaney, R. P., Weaver, C. M. 1990. Calcium absorption from kale. *Am. J. Clin. Nutr.* 51:656–57

63. Heaney, R. P., Weaver, C. M., Fitzsimmons, M. L. 1991. Soybean phytate content: effect on calcium absorption. *Am. J. Clin. Nutr.* 53:741–44

64. Heikinheimo, R. J., Inkovaara, J. A., Harju, E. J., Haavisto, M. V., Kaarela, R. H., et al. 1992. Annual injection of vitamin D and fractures of aged bones. *Calcif. Tissue Int.* 51:105–10

65. Hirota, T., Nara, M., Ohguri, M., Manago, E., Hirota, K. 1992. Effect of diet and lifestyle on bone mass in Asian young women. *Am. J. Clin. Nutr.* 55:1168–73

66. Hodges, S. J., Pilkington, M. J., Stamp, T. C. B., Catterall, A., Shearer, M. J., et al. 1991. Depressed levels of circulating menaquinones in patients with osteoporotic fractures of the spine and femoral neck. *Bone* 12:387–89

67. Holbrook, T. L., Barrett-Connor, E., Wingard, D. L. 1988. Dietary calcium and risk of hip fracture: 14-year prospective population study. *Lancet* 2: 1046–49

68. Howard, G., Andon, M., Bracker, M., Saltman, P., Strause, L. 1992. Low serum copper, a risk factor additional to low dietary calcium in postmenopausal bone loss. *J. Trace Elements Exp. Med.* 5:23–31

69. Jensen, J. E., Jensen, T. G., Smith, T. K., Johnson, D. A., Dudrick, S. J. 1982. Nutrition in orthopaedic surgery. *J. Bone Joint Surg.* 64A:1263–72

70. Johnston, C. C. Jr., Miller, J. Z., Slemenda, C. W., Reister, T. K., Hui, S., et al. 1992. Calcium supplementation and increases in bone mineral density in children. *New Engl. J. Med.* 327:82–87

71. Kanis, J. A., Passmore, R. 1989. Calcium supplementation of the diet—I and II. *Br. Med. J.* 298:137–40; 205–8

72. Knapen, M. H. J., Hamulyak, K., Vermeer, C. 1989. The effect of vitamin K supplementation on circulating osteocalcin (bone gla protein) and urinary calcium excretion. *Ann. Int. Med.* 111:1001–5

73. Knox, T. A., Kassarjian, Z., Dawson-Hughes, B., Golner, B. B., Dallal, G. E., et al. 1991. Calcium absorption in elderly subjects on high- and low-fiber diets: effect of gastric acidity. *Am. J. Clin. Nutr.* 53:1480–86

74. Krall, E. A., Sahyoun, N., Tannenbaum, S., Dallal, G. E., Dawson-Hughes, B. 1989. Effect of vitamin D intake on seasonal variations in parathyroid hormome secretion in postmenopausal women. *New Engl. J. Med.* 321:1777–83

75. Lacey, J. M., Anderson, J. J. B. 1991. Correlates of cortical bone mass among premenopausal and postmenopausal Japanese women. *J. Bone Miner. Res.* 6:651–59

76. LaCroix, A. Z., Wienpahl, J., White, L. R., Wallace, R. B., Scherr, P. A., et al. 1990. Thiazide diuretic agents and the incidence of hip fracture. *New Engl. J. Med.* 322:286–90

77. Lau, E., Donnan, S., Barker, D. J. P., Cooper, C. 1988. Physical activity and calcium intake in fracture of the proximal femur in Hong Kong. *Br. Med. J.* 297:1441–43

78. Leighton, G., McKinlay, P. L. 1930. Milk consumption and the growth of schoolchildren. Dept. of Health for Scotland H.M.S.O.

79. Lemann, J. Jr., Gray, R. W., Maierhofer, W. J., Cheung, H. S. 1986. The importance of renal net acid excretion as a determinant of fasting urinary calcium excretion. *Kidney Int.* 29:743–46

80. Lloyd, T., Andon, M. B., Rollings, N., Demers, L. M., Eggli, D. F., et al. 1992. The effect of calcium supplementation on total body bone mineral density in adolescent females. *J. Bone Miner. Res.* 7:S136 (Abstr.)

81. Lukert, B., Higgins, J., Stoskopf, M. 1992. Menopausal bone loss is partially regulated by dietary intake of vitamin D. *Calcif. Tissue Int.* 51:173–79

82. Marcus, R. 1987. Calcium intake and skeletal integrity: is there a critical relationship? *J. Nutr.* 117:631–35

83. Matkovic, V. 1991. Calcium metabolism and calcium requirements during skeletal remodeling and consolidation of bone mass. *Am. J. Clin. Nutr.* 54:S245–60

84. Matkovic, V., Fontana, D., Tominac, C., Goel, P., Chesnut, C. H. III. 1990. Factors that influence peak bone mass formation: A study of calcium balance and the inheritance of bone mass in adolescent females. *Am. J. Clin. Nutr.* 52:878–88

85. Matkovic, V., Heaney, R. P. 1992. Calcium balance during human growth. Evidence for threshold behavior. *Am. J. Clin. Nutr.* 55:992–96

86. Matkovic, V., Kostial, K., Simonovic, I., Buzina, R., Brodarec, A., Nordin, B. E. C. 1979. Bone status and fracture rates in two regions of Yugoslavia. *Am. J. Clin. Nutr.* 32:540–49

87. Mazess, R. B., Barden, H. S. 1991. Bone density in premenopausal women: effects of age, dietary intake, physical activity, smoking, and birth-control pills. *Am. J. Clin. Nutr.* 53:132–42

88. McKenna, J. M., Freaney, R., Meade, A., Muldowney, F. P. 1985. Hypovitaminosis D and elevated serum alkaline phosphatase in elderly Irish people. *Am. J. Clin. Nutr.* 41:101–9

89. Mertz, W., ed. 1987. *Trace Elements in Human and Animal Nutrition,* Vol. 1. San Diego: Academic. 5th ed.

90. Deleted in proof

91. Miller, J. Z., Smith, D. L., Flora, L., Peacock, M., Johnston, C. C. Jr. 1989. Calcium absorption in children estimated from single and double stable calcium isotope techniques. *Clin. Chem. Acta* 183:107–13

92. Miller, J. Z., Smith, D. L., Flora, L., Slemenda, C., Jiang, X., Johnston, C. C. Jr. 1988. Calcium absorption from calcium carbonate and a new form of calcium (CCM) in healthy male and female adolescents. *Am. J. Clin. Nutr.* 48:1291–94

93. Musgrave, K. O., Giambalvo, L., Leclerc, H. L., Cook, R. A., Rosen, C. J. 1989. Validation of a quantitative food frequency questionnaire for rapid assessment of dietary calcium intake. *J. Am. Diet. Assoc.* 89:1484–88

94. Nakagawa, Y., Abram, V., Kezdy, F. J., Kaiser, E. T., Coe, F. L. 1983. Purification and characterization of the principal inhibitor of calcium monohydrate crystal growth in human urines. *J. Biol. Chem.* 258:12594–12600

95. Nakagawa, Y., Ahmed, M. A., Hall, S. L., Deganello, S., Coe, F. L. 1987. Isolation from human calcium oxalate renal stones of nephrocalcin, a glycoprotein inhibitor of calcium oxalate crystal growth. *J. Clin. Invest.* 79:1782–87

96. Nordin, B. E. C., Heaney, R. P. 1990. Calcium supplementation of the diet: justified by present evidence. *Br. Med. J.* 300:1056–60

97. Nordin, B. E. C., Need, A. G., Morris, H. A., Horowitz, M. 1991. Sodium, calcium, and osteoporosis. In *Nutritional Aspects of Osteoporosis, Serono Symp. Publ.* ed. P. Burckhardt, R. P. Heaney, 85:279–95. New York: Raven

98. Nordin, B. E. C., Need, A. G., Morris, H. A., Horowitz, M., Robertson, W. G. 1991. Evidence for a renal calcium leak in postmenopausal women. *J. Clin. Endocrinol. Metab.* 72:401–7

99. Olson, R. E. 1984. The function and metabolism of vitamin K. *Annu. Rev. Nutr.* 4:281–337

100. Parfitt, A. M., Gallagher, J. C., Heaney, R. P., Johnston, C. C. Jr., Neer, R., Whedon, G. E. 1982. Vitamin D and bone health in the elderly. *Am. J. Clin. Nutr.* 36:1014–31

101. Pilch, S. M. 1987. Physiological effects and health consequences of dietary fiber. Prepared for Center for Food Safety Appl. Nutr. FDA, Dept. Health Hum. Serv., Washington, DC. LSRO, FASEB

102. Plantalech, L. C., Chapuy, M. C., Guillaumont, M., Chapuy, P., Leclerq, M., Delmas, P. D. 1990. Impaired carboxylation of serum osteocalcin in elderly women: Effect of vitamin K1. In *Osteoporosis 1990,* ed. C. Christiansen, K. Overgaard, pp. 345–47. Copenhagen: Osteopress

103. Portale, A. A., Halloran, B. P., Morris, R. C. Jr. 1989. Physiologic regulation of the serum concentration of 1,25-dihydroxyvitamin D by phosphorus in normal man. *J. Clin. Invest.* 83:1494–99

104. Prentice, A., Shaw, J., Laskey, M. A., Cole, T. J., Fraser, D. R. 1991. Bone mineral content of British and rural Gambian women aged 18–80 + years. *Bone Miner* 12:201–14

105. Price, P. A. 1988. Role of vitamin-K-dependent proteins in bone metabolism. *Annu. Rev. Nutr.* 8:565–83

106. Prince, R. L., Smith, M., Dick, I.M., Price, R. I., Webb, P. G., et al. 1991. Prevention of postmenopausal osteoporosis. *New Engl. J. Med.* 325:1189–95

107. Ray, W. A., Griffin, M. R., Downey, W., Melton, L. J. III. 1989. Long-term use of thiazide diuretics and risk of hip fracture. *Lancet* 1:687–90

108. Recker, R. R., Davies, K. M., Hinders, S. M., Heaney, R. P., Stegman, M. R., Kimmel, D. B. 1992. Bone gain in young adult women. *J. Am. Med. Assoc.* 268:2403–8

109. Recker, R. R., Heaney, R. P. 1990. Age-related bone loss (editorial). *J. Bone Miner. Res.* 4:795–96

110. Recker, R. R., Lappe, J. M., Davies, K. M., Kimmel, D. B. 1992. Change in bone mass immediately before menopause. *J. Bone Miner. Res.* 7:857–62

111. *Recommended Dietary Allowances.* 1989. Washington, DC: Natl. Acad. Press. 10th ed.

112. Reid, I. R., Ames, R. W., Evans, M.

C., Gamble, G. D., Sharpe, S. J. 1993. Effect of calcium supplementation on bone loss in late postmenopausal women. *New Engl. J. Med.* 328: In press

113. Rico, H., Revilla, M., Villa, L. F., Hernandez, E. R., Fernandez, J. P. 1992. Crush fracture syndrome in senile osteoporosis: a nutritional consequence. *J. Bone Miner. Res.* 7:317–19

114. Riggs, B. L., Wahner, H. W., Melton, L. J. III, Richelson, L. S., Judd, H. L., O'Fallon, W. M. 1987. Dietary calcium intake and rates of bone loss in women. *J. Clin. Invest.* 80:979–82

115. Riis, B. J., Nilas, L., Christiansen, C. 1987. Does calcium potentiate the effect of estrogen therapy on postmenopausal bone loss? *Bone Miner.* 2:1–9

116. Riis, B. J., Thomsen, K., Christiansen, C. 1987. Does calcium supplementation prevent postmenopausal bone loss? *New Engl. J. Med.* 316:173–77

117. Robinovitch, S. N., Hayes, W. C., McMahon, T. A. 1991. Prediction of femoral impact forces in falls on the hip. *J. Biomech. Eng.* 113:366–74

118. Silverberg, S. J., Shane, E., Clemens, T. L., Dempster, D. W., Segre, G. V., et al. 1986. The effect of oral phosphate administration on major indices of skeletal metabolism in normal subjects. *J. Bone Miner. Res.* 1:383–88

119. Simonen, O. 1991. Incidence of femoral neck fractures: senile osteoporosis in Finland in the years 1970–1985. *Calcif. Tissue Int.* 49:S8–S10

120. Slovik, D. M., Adams, J. S., Neer, R. M., Holick, M. F., Potts, J. T. Jr. 1981. Deficient production of 1,25-dihydroxyvitamin D in elderly osteoporotic patients. *New Engl. J. Med.* 305:372–74

121. Stevenson, J. C., Whitehead, M. I., Padwick, M., Endacott, J. A., Sutton, C., et al. 1988. Dietary intake of calcium and postmenopausal bone loss. *Br. Med. J.* 297:15–17

122. Strain, J. J. 1988. A reassessment of diet and osteoporosis—possible role for copper. *Med. Hypotheses* 27:333–38

123. Strause, L., Saltman, P., Smith, K., Andon, M. 1991. The role of trace elements in bone metabolism. See Ref. 97, pp. 223–33

124. Suter, P. M., Russell, R. M. 1987. Vitamin requirements of the elderly. *Am. J. Clin. Nutr.* 45:501–12

125. Tylavsky, F. A., Anderson, J. J. B. 1988. Dietary factors in bone health of elderly lactoovovegetarian and omnivorous women. *Am. J. Clin. Nutr.* 48:842–49

126. van Beresteijn, E. C. H., van't Hof, M. A., Schaafsma, G., de Waard, H., Duursma, S. A. 1990. Habitual dietary calcium intake and cortical bone loss in perimenopausal women: a longitudinal study. *Calcif. Tissue Int.* 47:338–44

127. van Beresteijn, E. C. H., van't Hof, M. A., de Waard, H., Raymakers, J. A., Duursma, S. A. 1990. Relation of axial bone mass to habitual calcium intake and to cortical bone loss in healthy early postmenopausal women. *Bone* 11:7–13

128. Vermeer, C., Hamulyak, K. 1991. Pathophysiology of vitamin K-deficiency and oral anticoagulants. *Thromb. Haemostas.* 66:153–59

129. Weaver, C. M., Heaney, R. P., Martin, B. R., Fitzsimmons, M. L. 1991. Human calcium absorption from whole wheat products. *J. Nutr.* 121:1769–75

130. Wickham, C. A. C., Walsh, K., Cooper, C., Barker, D. J. P., Margetts, B. M., et al. 1989. Dietary calcium, physical activity, and risk of hip fracture: a prospective study. *Br. Med. J.* 299:889–92

131. Wisker, E., Nagel, R., Tanudjaja, T. K., Feldheim, W. 1991. Calcium, magnesium, zinc, and iron balances in young women: effects of a low-phytate barley-fiber concentrate. *Am. J. Clin. Nutr.* 54:553–59

132. Wood, R. J., Sitrin, M. D., Rosenberg, I. H. 1984. Calciuria in total parenteral nutrition: effects of amino acids and glucose in rats. *Am. J. Clin. Nutr.* 40:101–6

133. Wood, R. J., Sitrin, M. D., Rosenberg, I. H. 1988. Effect of phosphorus on endogenous calcium losses during total parenteral nutrition. *Am. J. Clin. Nutr.* 48:632–36

Annu. Rev. Nutr. 1993. 13:317–35

BIOLOGICAL NITROGEN FIXATION

Robert H. Burris[1] *and Gary P. Roberts*[2]

Department of Biochemistry[1] and Department of Bacteriology,[2] College of
Agricultural and Life Sciences, University of Wisconsin-Madison, Madison,
Wisconsin 53706

KEY WORDS: legumes, nitrogenase, mechanism, genetics, control

CONTENTS

INTRODUCTION   318
CHEMICAL FIXATION OF N_2   318
BIOLOGICAL FIXATION OF N_2   318
   Agents   319
   Agronomic Applications   319
ROLE OF BIOLOGICAL N_2 FIXATION IN NUTRITION   320
MECHANISM OF BIOLOGICAL N_2 FIXATION   321
   "Key" Intermediate   321
   Dinitrogenase and Dinitrogenase Reductase   322
   Energetics and Electron Transfer   322
EVOLUTION OF NITROGENASE SYSTEMS   324
   Similarity of Nitrogenases from Diverse Sources   324
   Adaptation of Nitrogenase to Different Organisms
      and Environments   326
ORGANIZATION OF GENES ENCODING NITROGENASE SYSTEMS   327
   Linkage of Known nif *Genes*   327
   Cotranscription and Coregulation of nif *Genes*   327
   Genome Rearrangements in nif *Regions*   328
CONTROL OF NITROGENASE   328
   Transcriptional Control by "Global" Regulators   329
   nif-*Specific Transcriptional Control*   330
   Posttranslational Control of Nitrogenase   330
CONCLUSION   332

0199-9885/93/0715-0317$02.00

INTRODUCTION

Nitrogen is a key macro element required by all living organisms. However, a broad spectrum of nitrogenous compounds are usable by different organisms. Higher plants and bacteria can utilize diverse organic and inorganic nitrogenous compounds, and some prokaryotic organisms can use N_2 via biological N_2 fixation. Animals are the most demanding organisms and require eight to ten preformed amino acids for their nutrition. They discard nitrogenous metabolic products that serve as excellent sources of nitrogen for the growth of microorganisms and plants. Not only are the animals of the planet directly dependent upon the photosynthetic activity of plants for their energy, but they also are dependent directly or indirectly upon plants for many of their nitrogenous compounds as well. The higher plants in turn depend upon nitrogenous compounds derived from N_2 by chemical fixation (primarily through the Haber-Bosch process) or by biological N_2 fixation.

CHEMICAL FIXATION OF N_2

Chemical fixation of N_2 requires the use of fossil fuels as a source of H_2 and of energy. Natural gas commonly provides both H_2 as reductant and, by combustion, the high temperature required for the catalytic production of NH_3 from N_2 at high pressure. The supply of natural gas is finite, and coal probably will be substituted as the feed stock for chemical N_2 fixation when natural gas is exhausted.

BIOLOGICAL FIXATION OF N_2

Biological N_2 fixation, like chemical fixation, is energy demanding, but solar energy can be tapped by green plants and some bacteria to fuel fixation. Thus any increase in exploitation of biological N_2 fixation can help to slow the depletion of our fossil fuels. Chemical fixation of N_2 yields about 60×10^6 metric tons of fixed nitrogen per year (29), but this major chemical industry contributes much less fixed nitrogen to the earth's nitrogen cycle than does biological fixation. Estimation of annual biological fixation of N_2 is very difficult, and hence estimates vary widely—from 100×10^6 to 180×10^6 metric tons per year (8, 16, 47). Although disagreement on the magnitude of biological N_2 fixation is widespread, there is agreement that it is two or more times greater than chemical fixation.

If we examine the nitrogen cycle on earth, we recognize that the atmosphere constitutes an enormous reservoir of N_2. It can be chemically or biologically reduced so that it can function in living organisms. It can be discharged as soluble nitrogenous compounds that are lost from the terrestrial reservoir to the sea or it can be bound to particles, primarily in the soil. Denitrification can return N_2 to the atmosphere from the terrestrial cycle.

Agents

Centuries ago farmers recognized empirically that it was beneficial to mix N_2-fixing crops with crops incapable of fixing N_2, although the basis of the enhanced growth was not apparent. In the 1830s Boussingault (67) reported that leguminous plants fix N_2. This was contested by Liebig (67) in Germany, and Lawes, Gilbert & Pugh (67) in Great Britain. Experiments of Ville (67) in France and tests elsewhere did not resolve the problem to everyone's satisfaction. Finally, Hellriegel & Wilfarth reported in 1886 and published in 1888 (67) convincing evidence for N_2 fixation in leguminous plants, and they localized fixation in the root nodules of pea plants. Their findings sparked interest in the agronomic application of inoculation for legumes and in studies of the process of nodulation and the structure of root nodules. These nodules contain large numbers of the rhizobia in a modified form referred to as bacteroids. They receive abundant photosynthate from the plant to supply their energy requirements for N_2 fixation.

Somewhat later, biological N_2 fixation was demonstrated in free-living microorganisms: anaerobic fixation in *Clostridium pasteurianum* (68), and aerobic fixation in *Azotobacter chroococcum* (4). Since then a variety of other prokaryotic organisms (but no eukaryotes) have been added to the list of N_2 fixers. These include cyanobacteria, photosynthetic bacteria, *Klebsiella* spp., archaebacteria, *Desulfovibrio* spp., etc. (70). Symbiotic systems in which nodules are formed and fix N_2 on the root systems of nonleguminous plants (e.g. on the roots of alders by *Frankia* spp.) are widespread (53). In recent years considerable interest has focused on associative fixation between a nonsymbiotic microorganism (e.g. *Azospirillum* spp.) growing on the root system of a nonleguminous plant but without forming nodules (19). Young (70) has discussed the great variety of prokaryotes that reportedly are capable of fixing N_2.

Agronomic Applications

Soon after Hellriegel & Wilfarth (67) published their findings in 1888 on N_2 fixation by leguminous plants in symbiotic association with rhizobia, it was recognized that inoculation of seed with rhizobia would help ensure that the leguminous roots would nodulate and fix N_2. The practice of inoculation became widespread and the production of inoculum was commercialized (23).

ROLE OF BIOLOGICAL N2 FIXATION IN NUTRITION

Most leguminous plants are nodulated by root nodule bacteria and fix N_2 in symbiotic association with these bacteria. There are more than 13,000 described species of legumes, and they constitute a major source of protein in approximately the order listed: dry beans, dry peas (about 3 kg of each of these produced per person per year), chickpeas, broad beans, vetch, pigeon peas, cowpeas, lentils, amd lupines (9). Peanuts and soybeans are the dominant sources of cooking oils, and soybeans are used as a major food source in much of eastern Asia. Tofu and tempeh have been introduced to US markets in recent years. Areas of highest consumption of legumes as food are the former USSR, South and Central America, Mexico, India, Turkey, and Greece; Brazil produces about five times as much beans per person as we produce in the US. It is estimated that about 20% of food protein worldwide is derived from legumes. N_2-fixing nonleguminous plants are not significant sources of food.

Although diets in the United States supply only about 3% of the protein requirement as legumes, the percentage in many countries is far greater (22). As indicated, the diets in Mexico and in South and Central America are highly dependent upon legume seeds. There is a marked preference for specific legumes in these countries; some groups prefer black beans, whereas others may favor kidney beans or navy beans. The nutritional differences among these are not great, so preference appears to be based on local customs and how well the legume grows in a given area.

Leguminous plants that fix N_2 well will grow on soils that are poor in fixed nitrogen, thus making it unnecessary to add expensive nitrogenous fertilizers. However, it may be necessary to add potassium and phosphate and to lime the soil to raise the pH.

The amino acid balance of leguminous seeds commonly shows a deficiency of methionine, but combining legumes with cereal proteins usually offers a proper amino acid balance. Beans and other legume seeds thus can furnish an inexpensive, high-quality food that complements some of the deficiencies of a grain diet.

A number of toxic substances have been reported in legume seeds, and some can produce serious diseases such as neurolathyrism. Fortunately, most of the toxic materials are destroyed during cooking and hence pose little hazard.

Because of recent concerns that high fat diets may promote coronary heart disease and certain types of cancer, the public has been admonished to reduce fat intake and substitute other nutrients. As stated in *Diet and Health* (22), "Diets high in plant foods—i.e., fruits, vegetables, legumes and whole grain cereals—are associated with a lower occurrence of coronary heart disease and cancer of the lung, colon, esophagus and stomach. . . . By using plant products (e.g., cereals and legumes) instead of animal products as sources of protein, one can also reduce the amount of saturated fatty acids and cholesterol in the diet. . . . Foods highest in dietary fiber include whole (unrefined) grains and breads made from them, legumes, vegetables, fruits, nuts and seeds." In 1985 about 18 pounds of dry beans, peas, nuts and soybeans were available per person per year in the United States.

Leguminous plants also are very important as animal feed. Alfalfa, clovers, and other legumes are grown over extensive areas as forage crops and are fed as dry hay or as silage. Maize and alfalfa are dominant as silage crops; the latter furnishes not only roughage and high quality protein but also a variety of vitamins, minerals, and other nutrients. The anaerobic ensiling process supports a rapid fermentative acidification of the plant material, and this serves to preserve its nutritional quality.

MECHANISM OF BIOLOGICAL N_2 FIXATION

Meyerhof & Burk (41) initiated biochemical investigations when they studied how N_2 fixation in *Azotobacter chroococcum* was influenced by the partial pressure of N_2 and O_2. Wilson (67) extended these studies by investigating the symbiotic N_2-fixing system of red clover and *Rhizobium trifolii*. Although the symbiotic system was difficult to manipulate, they established that half-saturation of the nitrogenase in the association occurred at a pN_2 of about 0.05 atmosphere. O_2 at high pressures cause a nonspecific inhibition of fixation. A surprising observation was that H_2 functioned as a specific, competitive inhibitor of nitrogenase. In the symbiotic system maintenance of a proper balance between fixed nitrogen and carbohydrate was necessary to support vigorous fixation of N_2 (67).

"Key" Intermediate

Arguments about the mechanism of biological N_2 fixation centered about the "key" intermediate of N_2 fixation. This was defined as the nitrogenous compound derived from N_2 that was the inorganic product of fixation that was assimilated into an organic nitrogenous compound (e.g. ammonium assimilated into glutamine or glutamic acid). Evidence for any key intermediate was scanty, although A. I. Virtanen made a strong plea for hydroxylamine in many publications (64). There is evidence that hydrazine appears as a bound intermediate (62a), but no free intermediate with a reduction level between N_2 and NH_3 has been demonstrated. When concentrated ^{15}N became available as a tracer (10), it facilitated more critical tests of potential intermediates. Exposure of various N_2-fixing organisms to $^{15}N_2$ established a pattern of assimilation suggesting that newly fixed N accumulated in glutamic acid, and this in turn suggested NH_4^+ as the key intermediate (11). *C. pasteurianum*, in contrast to other N_2-fixing organisms, excreted NH_4^+, and when it was exposed to $^{15}N_2$ its NH_4^+ had a far higher ^{15}N concentration than any other product recovered (71). When consistent cell-free fixation of N_2 was achieved (12, 13), the product of the reaction clearly was shown to be NH_4^+ (52).

Dinitrogenase and Dinitrogenase Reductase

The achievement of consistent cell-free N_2 fixation made it feasible to purify nitrogenase. Nitrogenase consists of two proteins: an MoFe protein and an Fe protein (44, 45). These were purified essentially to homogeneity (63), and each had the same general properties when isolated from different organisms. The MoFe proteins are $\alpha_2\beta_2$ proteins of about 240,000 daltons molecular mass, whereas the Fe proteins are α_2 complexes of about 60,000 daltons molecular mass. These component proteins have been described under a variety of names (protein 1 and protein 2, fraction 1 and fraction 2, molybdoferredoxin and azoferredoxin, azofermo and azofer, etc), but we prefer the terms dinitrogenase and dinitrogenase reductase for the MoFe and Fe proteins, respectively, as these terms suggest the function of each protein (dinitrogenase binds and reduces N_2, whereas dinitrogenase reductase functions specifically to reduce dinitrogenase).

For many years scientists thought that the active site in nitrogenase centers at the Mo on dinitrogenase, but current evidence on the tertiary structure raises questions about this assumption (24a, 34a). Shah & Brill (55) demonstrated that they could dissociate and isolate an Fe- and Mo-containing center from dinitrogenase, which was designated FeMoco (for iron molybdenum cofactor). This unit could be reinserted into the apoprotein to regenerate an active dinitrogenase (51). The active site still is not defined completely, but a plausible structure of FeMoco has been presented (38). Recent crystallographic data at about 2.9 Å resolution has given a close approximation of the tertiary structure of the dinitrogenase active site (24a, 34a, 34b). The reader should refer to the original references to obtain a proper picture of the structures.

Energetics and Electron Transfer

The path of electron transfer in the nitrogenase system (Figure 1) was defined primarily by electron paramagnetic resonance (EPR) measurements at low temperatures (46). Both dinitrogenase and dinitrogenase reductase have characteristic EPR spectra that change with their oxidation-reduction state. Studies with purified nitrogenase components indicated that an external reductant (e.g. reduced ferredoxin or $Na_2S_2O_4$) passed electrons first to dinitrogenase reductase, from which they moved to dinitrogenase. The dinitrogenase then bound and reduced N_2. Each interaction of the proteins

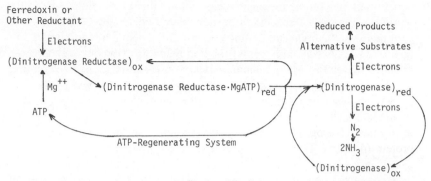

Figure 1 Electron transfer in the nitrogenase system. Electrons from ferredoxin or another reductant are passed to dinitrogenase reductase, which in turn binds 2 MgATP to yield the reduced MgATP-dinitrogenase reductase complex. This process alters the conformation of dinitrogenase reductase and drops its oxidation-reduction potential so that it can transfer an electron to dinitrogenase. Dinitrogenase and dinitrogenase reductase form a complex; one electron is passed to dinitrogenase and MgATP is hydrolyzed. Because N_2 reduction requires 8 electrons (6 electrons for N_2 and 2 electrons for the obligatory reduction of 2 protons to H_2), the dinitrogenase reductase must recycle to reduce dinitrogenase to a level adequate to reduce N_2. Only 1 electron is passed per cycle, and 2 MgATP are hydrolyzed per electron transferred.

results in the transfer of only a single electron, and as reduction of N_2 to $2NH_3$ requires 6 electrons (plus 2 electrons for obligatory reduction of 2 H^+ to H_2), the electron shuttle must operate several times before any reduction of N_2 can occur.

It was reported incorrectly that ATP inhibited cell-free fixation of N_2 (13); the ADP derived from ATP actually is the inhibitor. Therefore, the report that ATP was required as the energy source for the nitrogenase system (39) was met initially with some skepticism. Two MgATP are required for each electron transferred from dinitrogenase reductase to dinitrogenase, so a minimum of 16 MgATP are needed to drive the reaction:

$$N_2 + 8\,H^+ + 8\,e^- \rightarrow 2\,NH_3 + H_2$$

Under natural conditions, probably 20–30, rather than 16, MgATP are needed, as the process is less efficient than when optimized under laboratory conditions. The limiting step in the N_2 fixation process (Figure 1) appears to be the dissociation of the dinitrogenase-dinitrogenase reductase complex after each electron transfer (35).

As indicated, the production of H_2 that accompanies fixation of N_2 is obligatory. In the limiting case of greatest efficiency of the system, 1 H_2 (required 4 MgATP) is released for each N_2 reduced to 2 NH_3 (requires 12 MgATP). This means that 25% of the energy from MgATP is dissipated in production of H_2. As the organism cannot block this production of H_2 (58), its only recourse is to recapture a portion of the energy by reoxidizing the H_2. In this way the organism has the potential to generate a reduced electron carrier or MgATP required in the N_2 fixation reaction. Albrecht et al (2) have shown that hup^+ *Bradyrhizobium japonicum* (soybean-infecting bacteria that contain an uptake hydrogenase) support a higher yield of soybeans than do hup^- *B. japonicum* strains that are genetically identical except for the absence of hydrogenase.

EVOLUTION OF NITROGENASE SYSTEMS

As described below, both genetic and biochemical evidence indicates that all nitrogenases are homologous. This capability is so broadly distributed among prokaryotes that it is thought to have evolved very early and, indeed, the ability to fix N_2 might be considered a "typical" rather than an unusual attribute of prokaryotes. Regardless of the correctness of this view, it seems surprising that nature has not developed completely different enzyme systems, given both the biological importance of the enzyme's activity and the relatively slow turnover rate of the known nitrogenases.

There is little doubt that the common ancestor of all known nitrogenases was the product of substantial evolution. The α and β subunits of dinitrogenase, which make up the $\alpha_2\beta_2$ tetramer, are homologous to each other, reflecting an ancient gene duplication. These proteins are also homologous to another protein involved in nitrogen fixation, the NifNE protein, which functions in the synthesis of FeMoco (6, 62). (The term *nif* refers to genes involved in nitrogen fixation, and NifNE to the protein products of the *nifN* and *nifE* genes.) Future analysis of the structure-function relationships within these two complexes should provide some interesting insights into the evolution of protein function.

Similarity of Nitrogenases From Diverse Sources

N_2-fixing systems from diverse organisms seem to be very similar, i.e. they all require dinitrogenase and dinitrogenase reductase, all require a strong reductant, and all require MgATP as an energy source. The homology among the dinitrogenases and dinitrogenase reductases from diverse N_2-fixing organisms is very striking. Detroy et al (17, 18) first showed that the dinitrogenase reductase from one N_2-fixing organism could be combined with the dinitrogenase from another organism to reconstitute a functional nitrogenase. This observation was extended (20) to preparations from 8 N_2-fixing organisms; these furnished 64 possible dinitrogenase-dinitrogenase reductase combinations, 8 of which were homologous. Among the 56 nonhomologous crosses,

85% produced active nitrogenases. These represented proteins from aerobic, anaerobic, facultative, photosynthetic, free-living, and symbiotic N_2-fixing organisms.

There are variations on this theme, however. Some dinitrogenases have a different subunit composition and are devoid of molybdenum. In these "alternate" dinitrogenases molybdenum may be replaced by vanadium, and in others it is proposed that iron replaces the molybdenum (5).

Clearly, different nitrogenase systems have developed slightly different mechanisms for addressing the maturation and functioning of the enzyme. The fundamental similarity of the underlying biochemical mechanisms is, however, more striking than the differences.

The ability to fix N_2 has been found in a broad range of bacteria, including representatives of both the archaebacteria and eubacteria (70). This diversity of organisms, when contrasted with the remarkable conservation of nitrogenase itself, immediately suggests the possibility of horizontal transfer. The data, while not unequivocal, suggest otherwise. Generally speaking, a phylogeny of diazotrophs based on their 16S RNA yields a tree similar to one based on the sequence of *nifH* (30, 70), which suggests that if horizontal transfer did occur it was between relatively related organisms.

Other arguments against horizontal transfer based on *nifH* sequences appear less strong. Although it is true that *nifH* sequences have the same GC content as the rest of the chromosome and employ "typical" codon usage (59, 70), this merely suggests that there will be a strong selection for each of these features in the case of a gene that must be so highly expressed (57). As our data bases grow, it will be interesting to see if the same points will hold for the less abundantly expressed *nif* genes. Finally, phylogeny arguments based on *nifH* are complicated by the organisms that have multiple *nifH* sequences (65). Some of these encode dinitrogenase reductases for alternate nitrogenase systems. Others may not even express a functional product, but their presence makes it difficult to choose the appropriate gene for the phylogenetic analysis.

The structural genes for dinitrogenase and dinitrogenase reductase are much more conserved than the other *nif* genes; this is revealed most directly by sequence comparison, but also by the relative ability to detect the genes by hybridization with heterologous gene probes. It seems plausible that the first two proteins have a number of biochemical features that must be maintained if they are to remain biochemically functional. These include domains for protein-protein interactions to form their own multimers, domains for binding the various necessary metal clusters and for interactions with each other, and domains for binding with the low potential electron donor and with the various gene products involved in their maturation. In contrast, it is likely that the other *nif* gene products require a much smaller number of domains for their function, thereby freeing the genes to evolve more rapidly. In the case of other *nif* genes, examples of gene splitting (66) and gene fusion (15) suggest significant plasticity in their gene products.

Adaptation of Nitrogenase to Different Organisms and Environments

The fundamental problem facing any diazotroph is how to protect its extremely O_2-labile nitrogenase proteins from O_2. Secondary problems are the availability of ATP and securing a supply of low potential electrons and a source of metal for the active sites of dinitrogenase.

Anaerobic diazotrophy removes the problem of O_2-sensitivity, and fermentation provides an abundance of reductant for N_2 fixation. To solve the problem of sufficient ATP levels to support N_2 fixation, the "typical" free-living diazotroph oxidizes organic compounds, but alternative sources include photosynthesis, H_2 oxidation, and chemolithotrophic metabolism (32).

Given the O_2 lability of nitrogenase, the growth of any diazotroph in the presence of O_2 is beset with problems. Nitrogenase must be protected from the O_2, and nitrogenase and respiration will compete for reductant. The advantage of aerobic N_2 fixation is that respiration provides an abundance of energy. The general strategies for fixing N_2 in the presence of O_2 require physical protection of the enzyme. In many cases, this involves the construction of a specialized cell or cell compartment. Such compartments include the heterocysts of the cyanobacteria discussed below as well as the nodule that is characteristic of most symbiotic diazotrophs. In the nodule, the level of free O_2 is effectively controlled by the presence of leghemoglobin. For energy, symbiotic N_2-fixers rely on photosynthate supplied by their host plant, typically in the form of carbohydrates and organic acids.

As photosynthetic organisms, the cyanobacteria (or blue-green algae) liberate O_2 and still maintain an active nitrogenase (28). Most commonly, they accomplish this by producing heterocysts, which are specialized cells that differentiate to lose their photosynthetic capacity to generate O_2 while gaining the capability to fix N_2. The vegetative cells in the filament maintain active photosynthesis and transfer photosynthate to heterocysts to supply the energy needed by the heterocysts to fix N_2. Seldom are more than 10% of the cells differentiated into heterocysts, although in an association between a small water fern *(Azolla)* and a blue-green alga *(Anabaena azollae)* about 30% of the cells in the alga may be heterocysts (48). This productive *Azolla-Anabaena azollae* system has been used for centuries to add fixed nitrogen in rice culture in southeast Asia. In another adaptation certain filamentous marine cyanobacteria have adopted a diurnal cycle that alternates photosynthesis in the day with fixation of N_2 at night when there is no photosynthetic production of O_2 (42). These systems furnish models for those who are attempting to introduce the O_2-sensitive nitrogenase system into O_2-generating photosynthetically active plants.

Although the aerobes in the genus *Azotobacter* are among the most intensively studied organisms both biochemically and genetically, the basis for their O_2 tolerance is not well understood. When purified, their nitrogenase components are as O_2-labile as those from any other source (54). Shethna found that very gentle cell breakage allowed the isolation of the nitrogenase activity in a large complex (56). This complex showed substantial O_2-tolerance in vitro and appeared to contain other proteins including an iron-sulfur protein, often termed the Shethna protein. Unfortunately, these observations have not been actively pursued. Another basis for the O_2-tolerance of the azotobacters might well be their extremely high respiration rate, which potentially could reduce the O_2 concentration within the cell (49).

Given the amount of dinitrogenase necessary to sustain growth on N_2, it is not surprising that the supply of metals for the active site of the enzyme might occasionally be limiting. Those diazotrophs that possess more than one nitrogenase respond to such limitation by expressing their alternate nitrogenases. Although the actual mechanism of the response is not entirely clear, apparently the products of a set of regulatory genes recognize metal availability and activate the set of genes appropriate to that metal (5). Another layer of regulation, apparently involving the various dinitrogenase reductases themselves, also serves to further shut down expression of the "nonfunctional" nitrogenases (33).

ORGANIZATION OF GENES ENCODING NITROGENASE SYSTEMS

Linkage of Known nif Genes

Whereas the genes encoding dinitrogenase and dinitrogenase reductase have been cloned and sequenced from a wide variety of organisms, the other *nif* genes have been studied in only a few organisms. In these cases, the *nif* genes have been found in one or two gene clusters (15). Again, the presence of the alternate nitrogenases complicates the story, especially because they utilize at least some of the proteins involved in maturation of the Mo-containing dinitrogenases.

Cotranscription and Coregulation of nif Genes

While substantial clustering of *nif* genes is the rule, there is little consistency in their transcriptional organization (15). Presumably, the cotranscription of different genes allows their expression to be regulated identically in timing and in amount, although different types of post-transcriptional regulation certainly also could affect synthesis of the protein product (25).

In the case of the *nif* genes, however, it is unclear what selections have created the transcriptional units that are found. For example, differential timing of expression of *nif* transcripts has not been demonstrated other than of the regulatory genes themselves. The data on the actual accumulation level of most of the *nif* products is incomplete, so an explanation of cotranscription based on comparable product synthesis cannot be tested. Our current limited understanding of *nif* gene product function also makes it difficult to fully rationalize the transcriptional organization on this basis. Certainly the genes encoding the major components of nitrogenase tend to be cotranscribed, but *B. japonicum* (1) and others provide exceptions. That other genes are present in the same transcript as the structural genes for nitrogenase is also puzzling (3).

Genome Rearrangements in nif *Regions*

Genome rearrangements, including inversions and amplifications, have been identified in a number of bacteria, but two of the best-studied cases of site-specific deletions are in the *nif* operon (26, 27). Deletions are unique among rearrangements because they are irreversible. Thus, it is not surprising that the examples of *nif* deletions have only been detected in the "terminally differentiated" heterocyst cells of *Anabaena*. In these cells, two deletion events must occur for the proper transcription of two different *nif* operons (26, 27). These events take place during differentiation and eventually allow these cells to produce functional nitrogenase. Such deletions would not be an acceptable regulatory mechanism for growing cells, but it is unclear why they should be useful to the terminally differentiated cells in which they occur.

The aforementioned duplications of *nifH* in some organisms also might play a role in the physiology of the cell, though that role currently is unclear.

CONTROL OF NITROGENASE

N_2 is an unattractive nitrogen source, largely because of the high activation energy required for its reduction. This accounts for the high energy demand for the process and may contribute to the relative "slowness" of nitrogenase itself and the need to accumulate large amounts of nitrogenase to supply the cell's nitrogen requirements. The implications of these constraints are twofold. First, cells are "reluctant" to derepress the *nif* system until it is very clear that there are no better nitrogen sources. Then, after the system has been elaborated, the presence of a better nitrogen source, or changes in the environment that preclude N_2 fixation, must be addressed by shutting down

N_2 fixation. These constraints have given rise to various levels of regulation that differ in both the timing and the degree of their effects.

Transcriptional Control by "Global" Regulators

All diazotrophs must determine if N_2 is their best available nitrogen source, and apparently this question is resolved predominately by the global nitrogen regulatory system (the products of the *ntr* genes) (50). In contrast to most catabolic systems, the substrate N_2 is not required for induction. As N_2 is normally present, the cell instead seeks other available nitrogen sources. This is accomplished by elements of the *ntr* system that appear to use levels of such metabolically central compounds as glutamate and glutamine to determine if nitrogen is limiting (50). It is curious, and often ignored, that the interval between the onset of starvation and the induction of *nif* expression is protracted (usually one to two hours). It is unclear whether this is the time required to deplete sufficiently all available nitrogenous compounds within the cell or whether it is a deliberate regulatory device to preclude derepression of nitrogenase when its presence would be unnecessary.

The actual mechanism of the *ntr*-mediated regulation of *nif* is rather well understood, at least in the case of *K. pneumoniae*. The *ntr* gene products signal the activation of the NtrC protein by a phosphorylation mechanism (34), which follows the paradigm of other two-component regulatory systems (61). This activated NtrC, in concert with the sigma factor RpoN, activates transcription of *nifLA*, with *nifA* encoding the *nif*-specific regulator discussed below. Because this regulation involves activation of a regulatory transcript, it does not provide an obvious mechanism for shutting down *nif* expression rapidly when a better nitrogen source becomes available. Other diazotrophs appear to use slight variations on this theme; often the NtrC homolog is not the general transcription regulator that it appears to be in *K. pneumoniae*.

In those organisms that regulate *nif* expression in response to O_2, the effect of O_2 seems to be to regulate the expression of the *nif*-specific transcriptional activator. An obvious candidate for such an effector would be the protein product of the *fnr* gene, which is known to activate the expression of a number of anaerobically regulated genes (59). Unfortunately, experiments to test the involvement of the *fnr* product in *nif* regulation were performed in a heterologous background, so the negative results obtained must be accepted with caution (31).

An entirely different proposal for anaerobic regulation posits that the degree of supercoiling reflects the aerobicity of the cell and that, in turn, it directly affects the functionality of specific promoters and transcription factors (69). The basis of the model is the effect of specific inhibitors of gyrase in blocking anaerobic gene expression. This model has received much support, largely through identical experiments performed in different organisms. However, an entirely different mode of analysis of anaerobic gene expression has found no such "anaerobic-specific" effects of supercoiling (14), so the issue should be considered undecided until new experimental approaches are tried.

nif-*Specific Transcriptional Control*

If the global systems described above are capable of determining both nitrogen starvation as well as anaerobiosis, why should the cell have one or more *nif*-specific regulatory proteins? First, a specific factor probably is useful for coordinating the expression of the numerous *nif* operons. Second, nitrogenase is a slow enzyme and when the cell is in nitrogen-excess, a minimal level of nitrogenase is advantageous; under nitrogen-limiting conditions, however, the cell needs massive amounts of the nitrogenase proteins. Thus, a single level of regulation might not be sufficient to provide the huge difference seen in nitrogenase activity under these two conditions (10^5-fold at least). Finally, at least in some organisms, the *nif*-specific regulators provide another level for sensing and responding to the nitrogen and O_2 status of the cell. Since these are *nif*-specific, their useful range can be tuned to rather lower levels of O_2 or fixed nitrogen than those typically addressed by a global system. Such a *nif*-specific response also supports a much more rapid transcriptional response than would be provided by the global systems.

In studied organisms, the *nif*-specific activator is either NifA or its homolog; it apparently acts by binding to an "Upstream Activator Sequence" (7) and facilitates the isomerization of RNA polymerase (including the RpoN sigma factor) from a closed to an open complex (43). In some diazotrophs, another regulatory factor, NifL, appears to interfere with the activation by NifA when O_2 or fixed nitrogen is present (40). The mechanism by which NifL senses these compounds is completely unknown, as is the precise way it blocks NifA function. In other diazotrophs, the NifA homolog appears to be an O_2-sensor itself (21).

Posttranslational Control of Nitrogenase

Although transcriptional regulation is important, it necessarily effects a slow response to a change in the environment. Some diazotrophs have developed posttranslational systems that allow a much more rapid turn-off of the energy-demanding nitrogenase system. One of the most thoroughly studied of these is covalent modification of the dinitrogenase reductase by ADP ribosylation.

Rhodospirillum rubrum is a photosynthetic purple nonsulfur bacterium that is capable of N_2 fixation. Although *R. rubrum* yielded N_2-fixing cell-free preparations (52), consistently active preparations were difficult to obtain. Ludden & Burris found (36) that the organism possessed an enzyme that would convert inactive to active preparations. Subsequently it was observed (37) that *R. rubrum* also had an inactivating enzyme. Thus it had the capability to switch nitrogenase activity on and off.

The system was explored in detail (37) and is depicted in Figure 2. The activation-inactivation affects dinitrogenase reductase, apparently without participation of dinitrogenase. The enzyme that inactivates nitrogenase activity, termed dinitrogenase reductase ADP-ribosyl transferase (DRAT), uses NAD as a source of an ADP-ribosyl group, which it transfers to a particular arginine on one of the two subunits of dinitrogenase reductase. Nicotinamide is released and the reaction can be followed with ^{32}P-labeled NAD (51).

Dinitrogenase reductase activating glycohydrolase (DRAG) removes the ADP-ribosyl group from the arginine residue, and thus restores activity to dinitrogenase reductase. This change also can be followed on gels, as the band from the modified subunit loses its ADP-ribosyl group and regains its original mobility.

The DRAT-DRAG system will turn off nitrogenase activity in response to addition of NH_4^+ (24), and, in some organisms, to the presence of O_2. In some photosynthetic organisms it also responds to darkness, because photosynthetic energy is required for fixation of N_2. In microaerobic *Azospirillum* spp. the system responds to anaerobiosis because low respiration is necessary to support N_2 fixation.

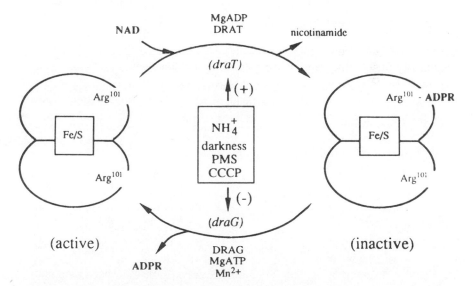

Figure 2   Control of dinitrogenase reductase activity by ADP-ribosylation as depicted by Ludden & Roberts (37). ADPR, ADP-ribose; PMS, phenazine methosulfate; CCCP, chlorocarbonyl-cyanide phenylhydrazone.

Not all N_2-fixing organisms possess a posttranslational regulatory system, but some that do appear to use mechanisms other than ADP ribosylation. An interesting case is presented by the *Azospirillum* spp. The azospirilla are a group of microaerobic N_2-fixing organisms that are described as associative N_2-fixing bacteria. They do not function in a tight symbiosis as do rhizobia in the nodules of leguminous plants, but rather they grow on the roots (and sometimes within the roots) and utilize excreted or sloughed material as their energy source in support of N_2 fixation. *Azospirillum brasilense* and *Azospirillum lipoferum* have well-developed DRAT and DRAG systems for the reversible control of N_2 fixation (72). However, *Azospirillum amazonense* from the same genus lacks the system according to the following criteria: it lacks DNA homologous to *draT* and *draG* probes, it lacks detectable DRAG and DRAT antigens, and it does not alter the mobility of dinitrogenase reductase upon switch-off of activity.

CONCLUSION

The stability of the N_2 bond has dictated constraints on the enzymatic and biochemical mechanisms of biological N_2 fixation. Different microorganisms, many of them serving critical functions in world agriculture, have developed a fascinating range of adaptations within these constraints. One hundred years after the clear demonstration of biological N_2 fixation, we still are seeking to understand and to utilize fully this important process.

ACKNOWLEDGMENTS

This work was supported by the College of Agricultural and Life Sciences, University of Wisconsin-Madison, Department of Energy grant DE-FG02-87ER13707 to R. H. B., and Department of Agriculture grant 91-37305-6664 to G. P. R.

Literature Cited

1. Adams, T. H., McClung, C. R., Chelm, B. K. 1984. Physical organization of the *Bradyrhizobium japonicum* nitrogenase gene region. *J. Bacteriol.* 159:857–62
2. Albrecht, S. L., Maier, R., Hanus, F. J., Russell, S. A., Emerich, D. W., et al. 1979. *Science* 203: 1255–57
3. Arnold, W., Rump, A., Klipp, W., Preifer, U. B., Pühler, A. 1988. Nucleotide sequence of a 24,206-base-pair DNA fragment carrying the entire nitrogen fixation gene cluster of *Klebsiella pneumoniae. J. Mol. Biol.* 203:715–38
4. Beijerinck, M. W. 1901. Über oligonitrophile Mikroben. *Zentralbl. Bakteriol. Parasitenkd. Abt.* II 7:561–82
5. Bishop, P. E., Premakumar, R. 1992. Alternative nitrogen fixation systems. See Ref. 60, pp. 736–62
6. Brigle, K. E., Weiss, M. C., Newton, W. E., Dean, D. R. 1987. Products of the iron-molybdenum cofactor-specific biosynthetic genes, *nifN* and *nifE*, are structurally homologous to the prod-

ucts of the nitrogenase molybdenum-iron protein genes, *nifD* and *nifK*. *J. Bacteriol.* 169:1547–53

7. Buck, M., Miller, S., Drummond, M., Dixon, R. 1986. Upstream activator sequences are present in the promoters of nitrogen fixation genes. *Nature* 320: 374–78

8. Burns, R. C., Hardy, R. W. F. 1975. Nitrogen fixation in bacteria and higher plants. In *Molecular Biology, Biochemistry and Biophysics*, Vol. 21. New York: Springer-Verlag. 189 pp.

9. Burr, H. K. 1975. Pulse proteins. In *Protein Nutritional Quality of Foods and Feeds,* ed. M. Friedman, Pt. 2: 119–34. New York: M. Dekker

10. Burris, R. H., Miller, C. E. 1941. Application of ¹⁵N to the study of biological nitrogen fixation. *Science* 93: 114–15

11. Burris, R. H., Wilson, P. W. 1946. Ammonia as an intermediate in nitrogen fixation by *Azotobacter*. *J. Bacteriol.* 52:505–12

12. Carnahan, J. E., Mortenson, L. E., Mower, H. F., Castle, J. E. 1960. Nitrogen fixation in cell-free extracts of *Clostridium pasteurianum*. *Biochim. Biophys. Acta* 38:188–89

13. Carnahan, J. E., Mortenson, L. E., Mower, H. F., Castle, J. E. 1960. Nitrogen fixation in cell-free extracts of *Clostridium pasteurianum*. *Biochim. Biophys. Acta* 44:520–35

14. Cook, D. N., Armstrong, G. A., Hearst, J. E. 1989. Induction of an-aerobic gene expression in *Rhodobacter capsulatus* is not accompanied by a local change in chromosomal super-coiling as measured by a novel assay. *J. Bacteriol.* 171:4836–43

15. Dean, D. R., Jacobson, M. R. 1992. Biochemical genetics of nitrogenase. See Ref. 60, pp. 763–834

16. Delwiche, C. C. 1970. The nitrogen cycle. *Sci. Am.* 223:136–46

17. Detroy, R. W., Witz, D. F., Parejko, R. A., Wilson, P. W. 1967. Comple-mentary functioning of two components required for the reduction of N_2 from four nitrogen-fixing bacteria. *Science* 158:526–27

18. Detroy, R. W., Witz, D. F., Parejko, R. A., Wilson, P. W. 1968. Reduction of N_2 by complementary functioning of two components from nitrogen-fixing bacteria. *Proc. Natl. Acad. Sci. USA* 61:537–41

19. Döbereiner, J., Pedrosa, F. O. 1987. *Nitrogen-Fixing Bacteria in Non-legu-minous Crop Plants.* Madison, Wisc: Sci. Tech. 155 pp.

20. Emerich, D. W., Burris, R. H. 1978. Complementary functioning of the com-ponent proteins of nitrogenase from several bacteria. *J. Bacteriol.* 134:936–43

21. Fisher, H-M., Bruderer, T., Hennecke, H. 1988. Essential and nonessential domains in the *Bradyrhizobium japonicum* NifA protein: Identification of indispensible cysteine residues po-tentially involved in redox activity and/or metal binding. *Nucleic Acids Res.* 16:2207–24

22. Food and Nutrition Board. 1989. *Diet and Health.* Washington, DC: Natl. Acad. Sci. Press. 749 pp.

23. Fred, E. B., Baldwin, I. L., McCoy, E. 1932. *Root Nodule Bacteria and Leguminous Plants.* Madison: Univ. Wisc. Press. 343 pp.

24. Fu, H., Burris, R. H. 1989. Ammonium inhibition of nitrogenase activity in *Herbaspirillum seropedicae*. *J. Bacte-riol.* 171:3168–75

24a. Georgiadis, M. M., Komiya, H., Chakrabarti, P., Woo, D., Kornuc, J. J., Rees, D. C. 1992. Crystallographic structure of the nitrogenase iron protein from *Azotobacter vinelandii*. *Science* 257:1653–59

25. Gold, L. 1988. Posttranscriptional reg-ulatory mechanisms in *Escherichia coli*. *Annu. Rev. Biochem.* 57:199–233.

26. Golden, J. W., Carrasco, C. D., Mul-ligan, M. E., Schneider, G. J., Haselk-orn, R. 1985. Deletion of a 55-kilobase-pair DNA element from the chromosome during heterocyst dif-ferentiation of *Anabaena* sp. strain PCC 7120. *J. Bacteriol.* 170:5034–41

27. Golden, J. W., Robinson, S. J., Haselk-orn, R. 1985. Rearrangement of nitro-gen fixation genes during heterocyst differentiation in the cyanobacterium *Anabaena. Nature* 314:419–23

28. Haselkorn, R., Buikema, W. J. 1992. Nitrogen fixation in cyanobacteria. See Ref. 60, pp. 166–90

29. Hauck, R. D. 1985. Agronomic and technological approaches to improving the efficiency of nitrogen use by crop plants. In *Nitrogen and the Environ-ment,* ed. K. A. Malik, S. H. M. Naqvi, M. I. H. Aleem, pp. 317–26. Faisalabad, Pakistan: Nuclear Inst. Agric. Biol. 440 pp.

30. Hennecke, H., Kaluza, K., Thöny, B., Fuhrmann, M., Ludwig, W., et al. 1985. Concurrent evolution of nitroge-nase genes and 16S rRna in *Rhizobium* species and other nitrogen fixing bac-teria. *Arch. Microbiol.* 142:342–48

31. Hill, S. 1985. Redox regulation of

enteric *nif* expression is independent of the *fnr* gene product. *FEMS Microbiol. Lett.* 29:5–9

32. Hill, S. 1992. Physiology of nitrogen fixation in free-living heterotrophs. See Ref. 60, pp. 87–134

33. Joerger, R. D., Wolfinger, E. D., Bishop, P. E. 1991. The gene encoding dinitrogenase reductase 2 is required for expression of the second alternative nitrogenase from *Azotobacter vinelandii. J. Bacteriol.* 173:4440–46

34. Keener, J., Kustu, S. 1988. Protein kinase and phosphoprotein phosphatase activities of nitrogen regulatory proteins NTRB and NTRC of enteric bacteria: Roles of the conserved amino-terminal domain of NTRC. *Proc. Natl. Acad. Sci. USA* 85:4976–80

34a. Kim, J., Rees, D. C. 1992. Structural models for the metal centers in the nitrogenase molybdenum-iron protein. *Science* 257:1677–82

34b. Kim, J., Rees, D. C. 1992. Crystallographic structure and functional implications of the nitrogenase molybdenum-iron protein from *Azotobacter vinelandii. Nature* 360:553–60

35. Lowe, D. J., Thorneley, R. N. F. 1984. The mechanism of *Klebsiella pneumoniae* nitrogenase action. Presteady-state kinetics of H_2 formation. *Biochem. J.* 224:877–86

36. Ludden, P. W., Burris, R. H. 1976. Activating factor for the iron protein of nitrogenase from *Rhodospirillum rubrum. Science* 194:424–26

37. Ludden, P. W., Roberts, G. P. 1989. Regulation of nitrogenase activity by reversible ADP ribosylation. *Curr. Top. Cell. Regul.* 30:23–56

38. Madden, M. S., Krezel, A. M., Allen, R. M., Ludden, P. W., Shah, V. K. 1992. Plausible structure of the iron-molybdenum cofactor of nitrogenase. *Proc. Natl. Acad. Sci. USA* 89:6487–91

39. McNary, J. E., Burris, R. H. 1962. Energy requirements for nitrogen fixation by cell-free preparations from *Clostridium pasteurianum. J. Bacteriol.* 84:598–99

40. Merrick, M. S., Hill, S., Hennecke, H., Hahn, M., Dixon, R., et al. 1982. Repressor properties of the *nifL* gene product of *Klebsiella pneumoniae. Mol. Gen. Genet.* 185:65–81

41. Meyerhof, O., Burk, D. 1928. Über die Fixation des Luftstickstoffs durch Azotobacter. *Z. Phys. Chem. Abt. A* 139:117–42

42. Mitsui, A., Kumazawa, S., Takahashi, A., Ikemoto, H., Cao, S., et al. 1986.

Strategy by which nitrogen-fixing unicellular cyanobacteria grow photoautotrophically. *Nature* 323:720–22

43. Morett, E., Cannon, W., Buck, M. 1988. The DNA-binding domain of the transcriptional activator protein NifA resides in its carboxy terminus, recognizes the upstream activator sequences of *nif* promoters and can be separated from the positive control function of NifA. *Nucleic Acids Res.* 16:11469–88

44. Mortenson, L. E. 1965. Nitrogen fixation in extracts of *Clostridium pasteurianum.* In *Non-heme Iron Proteins: Role in Energy Conversion,* ed. A. San Pietro, pp. 243–59. Yellow Springs, Ohio: Antioch. 473 pp.

45. Mortenson, L. E. 1966. Components of cell-free extracts of *Clostridium pasteurianum* requited for ATP-dependent H_2 evolution from dithionite and for N_2 fixation. *Biochim. Biophys. Acta* 127:18–25

46. Orme-Johnson, W. H., Hamilton, W. D., Ljones, T., Tso, M-Y. W., Burris, R. H., et al. 1972. Electron paramagnetic resonance of nitrogenase compounds from *Clostridium pasteurianum* W5 and *Azotobacter vinelandii* OP. *Proc. Natl. Acad. Sci. USA* 69:3142–45

47. Paul, E. A. 1978. Contribution of nitrogen fixation to ecosystem functioning and nitrogen fluxes on a global basis. In *Enviromental Role of Nitrogen-Fixing Blue-Green Algae and Asymbiotic Bacteria. Ecol. Bull.* ed. U. Granhall, 26:282–93. Stockholm: Swedish Natl. Sci. Res. Council. 391 pp.

48. Peters, G. A., Meeks, J. C. 1989. The *Azolla-Anabaena* symbiosis: Basic biology. *Annu. Rev. Plant Physiol.* 40:193–210

49. Ramos, J. L., Robson, R. L. 1985. Isolation and properties of mutants of *Azotobacter chroococcum* defective in aerobic nitrogen fixation. *J. Gen. Microbiol.* 131:1449–58

50. Reitzer, L. J., Magasanik, B. 1987. Ammonium assimilation and the biosynthesis of glutamine, glutamate, aspartate, asparagine, L-alanine, and D-alanine. In *Escherichia coli and Salmonella typhimurium: Cellular and Molecular Biology,* ed. F. C. Neidhardt, 1:302–20. Washington, DC: Am. Soc. Microbiol. 806 pp.

51. Roberts, G. P., Ludden, P. W. 1992. Nitrogen fixation by photosynthetic bacteria. See Ref. 60, pp. 135–65

52. Schneider, K. C., Bradbeer, C., Singh, R. N., Wang, L. C., Wilson, P. W.,

et al. 1960. Nitrogen fixation by cell-free preparations from microorganisms. *Proc. Natl. Acad. Sci. USA* 46:726–33

53. Schwintzer, C. R., Tjepkema, J. D. 1990. *The Biology of Frankia and Actinorhizal Plants*. San Diego: Academic. 408 pp.

54. Shah, V. K., Brill, W. J. 1973. Nitrogenase IV. Simple method of purification to homogeneity of nitrogenase components from *Azotobacter vinelandii*. *Biochim. Biophys. Acta* 305: 445–54

55. Shah, V. K., Brill, W. J. 1977. Isolation of an iron-molybdenum cofactor from nitrogenase. *Proc. Natl. Acad. Sci. USA* 74:3249–53

56. Shethna, Y. I. 1970. Non-heme iron (iron-sulfur) proteins of *Azotobacter vinelandii*. *Biochim. Biophys. Acta* 205: 58–62

57. Shpaer, E. G. 1986. Constraints on codon context in *Escherichia coli* genes: their possible role in modulating the efficiency of translation. *J. Mol. Biol.* 188:555–64

58. Simpson, F. B., Burris, R. H. 1984. A nitrogen pressure of 50 atmospheres does not prevent evolution of hydrogen by nitrogenase. *Science* 224:1095–97

59. Spiro, S., Guest, J. R. 1990. FNR and its role in oxygen-regulated gene expression in *Escherichia coli*. *FEMS Microbiol. Rev.* 75:399–428

60. Stacey, G., Burris, R. H., Evans, H. J., eds. 1992. *Biological Nitrogen Fixation*. New York: Chapman & Hall. 943 pp.

61. Stock, J. B., Ninfa, A. J., Stock, A. M. 1989. Protein phosphorylation and regulation of adaptive responses in bacteria. *Microbiol. Rev.* 53:450–90

62. Thöny, B., Kaluza, K., Hennecke, H. 1985. Structural and functional homology between the α and β subunits of the nitrogenase MoFe protein as revealed by sequencing the *Rhizobium japonicum nifK* gene. *Mol. Gen. Genet.* 198:441–48

62a. Thorneley, R. N. F., Eady, R. R.,

Lowe, D. J. 1978. Biological nitrogen fixation by way of an enzyme-bound dinitrogen-hydride intermediate. *Nature* 272:557–58

63. Tso, M-Y. W., Ljones, T., Burris, R. H. 1972. Purification of the nitrogenase proteins from *Clostridium pasteurianum*. *Biochim. Biophys. Acta* 267: 600–4

64. Virtanen, A. I. 1938. *Cattle Fodder and Human Nutrition*. London: Cambridge Univ. Press. 108 pp.

65. Wang, S-Z., Chen, J-S., Johnson, J. L. 1988. The presence of five *nifH*-like sequences in *Clostridum pasteurianum*: Sequence divergence and transcription properties. *Nucleic Acids Res.* 16:439–53

66. Wang, S-Z., Dean, D. R., Chen, J-S., Johnson, J. L. 1991. The N-terminal and C-terminal portions of NifV are encoded by two different genes in *Clostridium pasteurianum*. *J. Bacteriol.* 173:3041–46

67. Wilson, P. W. 1940. *The Biochemistry of Symbiotic Nitrogen Fixation*. Madison: Univ. Wisc. Press. 302 pp.

68. Winogradsky, S. 1893. Sur l'assimilation de l'azote gazeux de l'atmosphere par les microbes. *C. R. Acad. Sci. Paris* 116:1385–88

69. Yamamoto, N., Droffner, M. L. 1985. Mechanisms determining aerobic or anaerobic growth in the facultative anaerobe *Salmonella typhimurium*. *Proc. Natl. Acad. Sci. USA* 82:2077–81

70. Young, J. P. W. 1992. Phylogenetic classification of nitrogen-fixing organisms. See Ref. 60, pp. 43–86

71. Zelitch, I., Rosenblum, E. D., Burris, R. H., Wilson, P. W. 1951. Isolation of the key intermediate in biological nitrogen fixation by *Clostridium*. *J. Biol. Chem.* 191:295–98

72. Zhang, Y-P., Burris, R. H., Roberts, G. P. 1992. Cloning, sequencing, mutagenesis and functional characterization of *draT* and *draG* genes from *Azospirillum brasilense*. *J. Bacteriol.* 174:3364–69

Annu. Rev. Nutr. 1993 13:337–54

GENETICS OF OBESITY

Claude Bouchard and Louis Pérusse

Physical Activity Sciences Laboratory, Laval University, Ste-Foy, Québec, Canada
G1K 7P4

KEY WORDS: heritability, major genes, temporal trends, genotype-environment interactions,
fat distribution

CONTENTS

INTRODUCTION 337
HUMAN GENETIC RESEARCH STRATEGIES 338
EXCESS BODY FAT 340
REGIONAL FAT DISTRIBUTION 342
ENERGY AND NUTRIENT INTAKE 343
METABOLIC RATE AND ENERGY EXPENDITURE 344
   Resting Metabolic Rate 344
   Thermic Effect of Food 345
   Physical Activity Level 345
NUTRIENT PARTITIONING 346
MAJOR GENE EFFECTS 346
TEMPORAL TRENDS 348
GENETIC-ENVIRONMENT INTERACTION 348
   Response to Overfeeding 348
   Response to Negative Energy Balance 349
CONTRIBUTION OF SINGLE GENES: A BEGINNING 350

INTRODUCTION

The field was reviewed by us five years ago in the 1988 issue of this publication
(11). The emphasis was on genetic epidemiologic data concerning total body
fat content, amount of subcutaneous fat, regional fat distribution, and
subcutaneous fat patterning. Since then, much research that is relevant to the
general topic of the genetics of obesity has been reported and a new review
of the field is warranted.

The present review deals not only with the genetics of body fat content and
regional fat distribution phenotypes but also with the genetics of some of the

337

main affectors of these phenotypes such as energy intake, resting metabolic rate, level of habitual physical activity, and nutrient partitioning. Additive genetic effects, major gene and single gene effects, temporal trends, and genotype-environment interaction effects are considered.

A complex phenotype, obesity is not readily reduced to simple Mendelian segregation patterns primarily for two reasons. First, body fat content, and more specifically an excessive amount of body fat, results from an intricate network of additive and interactive causes that may be related to DNA sequence variation but may also be associated with behavioral and lifestyle characteristics. Second, obesity is a heterogeneous phenotype, and evidence is growing that each phenotypic entity is modulated by a different set of causal factors. Recently, we have proposed that it would be useful to distinguish a minimum of four obesity phenotypes for the study of the etiology and the causes of human obesities as well as for the investigation of their clinical implications (7–9). These four phenotypes were defined as an excessive total amount of body fat (Type I), an excessive amount of subcutaneous fat on the trunk and abdominal area (Type II), an excessive amount of abdominal visceral fat (Type III), and an excessive amount of gluteo-femoral fat (Type IV). Very few studies have dealt with the genetics of obesity-related phenotypes as defined in this scheme. Indeed, as was observed in our 1988 review, most recent studies have again relied on the body mass index (weight in kilograms divided by height in meter squared) as a surrogate measurement for total amount of body fat (Type I).

HUMAN GENETIC RESEARCH STRATEGIES

Geneticists rely on a large number of traditional and innovative research designs and procedures in the current massive effort to define the genetic and molecular basis of common complex and multifactorial diseases that bear a striking similarity to the case of human obesities. Ultimately, the goal is to identify DNA sequence variants that impact on the various obesity phenotypes and to understand the mechanisms by which they exert these influences on body fat content and fat topography. Four broad categories of research strategies are commonly used to define the genetic basis of such phenotypes. The division is somewhat arbitrary and hybrid approaches are becoming the rule rather than the exception.

The first class of methods is one in which inference about heritability, the quantitative nature of the genetic effects, segregation patterns, and single gene effects is obtained from nuclear family, extended pedigree, twin, or adoption data without any information on genetic polymorphism. These methods have been classified as a so-called "top-down" approach to the problem (65). Alternatively, one may begin from genetic variation at a given locus or at several genes and proceed in the opposite direction by a variety of procedures that attempt to relate genetic polymorphisms to the variance in the phenotype of interest. Collectively, this second class of methods has been labelled as the "bottom-up" strategy (65). A more productive strategy that has evolved recently is to combine both methods in the same study design (3).

Progress can be anticipated also through a very different approach in which a great number of experimental and analytical techniques can be used to examine the positional cloning strategy. Positional cloning (the third class of methods) can be useful in a variety of circumstances, several of which are particularly relevant to human obesities. In broad terms, positional cloning will enable the precise localization of the chromosomal region that seems to include the gene(s) responsible for the undesirable phenotype characteristics. In some cases, the investigation may begin with an animal model of the human phenotype and evolve toward definition of the human chromosomal region homologous to the animal genome segment encoding the deficient gene (30). In other cases, the research may focus on a segment of a human chromosome known to segregate with some or all of the phenotype manifestations in an attempt to identify progressively the position of the gene by a combination of several techniques. Animal crosses and backcrosses from informative strains and transgenic animal models are very valuable resources in an elaborate positional cloning strategy. The recently developed "quantitative trait loci" (37, 45) approach is rapidly becoming an important technique in the efforts to identify genes or coding sequences relevant to a complex multifactorial phenotype and to assist in localizing them on the genomic map.

One of the most important goals of genetic research is to identify the relevant gene(s) and the DNA sequence variant(s) that are involved (the fourth class of methods). Many of the genes that have been implicated so far in complex multifactorial diseases or clinical conditions exhibit several different DNA mutations, which has led to the recognition that genetic heterogeneity may exist for many entities. Sequencing the gene or appropriate DNA fragments in informative individuals will ultimately provide the evidence that one or several DNA base pairs are implicated and will provide the molecular information to investigate the mechanisms relating DNA sequence alteration(s) to the gene product and to the phenotype of interest. Short of sequencing the whole DNA, techniques have also become available to identify DNA variation and provide information on the physical position of the variant in the DNA sequence [single-standed conformation polymorphism (SSCP), RNAse cleavage mismatch methods, heteroduplex analysis, etc].

Finally, it is important to recognize that major progress in understanding the genetics of obesity and other complex human disease phenotypes is likely to come about with the development of transgenic animals. Although research with transgenic animal models is not, strictly speaking, an investigative tool specific to human genetic issues, the power of the technology is such that it will have a major influence on human genetics in the future. The development of transgenic animals has received a great deal of attention in the recent past, and a number of approaches can now be used in a variety of circumstances (41).

EXCESS BODY FAT

Although the familial nature of obesity is well established (11, 32, 44, 57), there is still some disagreement among researchers regarding the importance of genetic factors in this familiality. Most studies on the genetics of obesity used the body mass index (BMI) or the sum of skinfold thicknesses at only two or three sites as measures of excess body fat. Heritability estimates ranging from almost zero to values as high as 90% have been reported for BMI (1a, 11, 69). Given the use of different designs (twin, family, and adoption studies); a large variation in age of subjects; studies of only a few types of relatives; and, very often, a small sample size, such a wide variation in the reported heritabilities of type I obesity is not unexpected. With few exceptions, these studies could not separate the effects of genes from those of the environment shared by relatives living together in the same household. The comparison of monozygotic (MZ) twins reared apart with MZ twins reared together represents an interesting design to assess the role of heredity without the confounding influence of shared family environment. The results of three recent studies (39, 55, 70) using this design are summarized in Table 1. Except for the 24 female twin pairs from the study by MacDonald & Stunkard (39), the correlations of MZ twins reared apart are very similar to those of MZ twins reared together and suggest that shared familial environment did not

Table 1 Intraclass correlations between monozygotic twins reared apart or together for the body mass index

| | Monozygotic twins | | | |
| | Reared apart | | Reared together | |
Reference	N pairs	r	N pairs	r
Stunkard et al (70)				
Males	49	0.70	66	0.74
Females	44	0.66	88	0.66
MacDonald & Stunkard (39)				
Males	14	0.64	14	0.68
Females	24	0.39	25	0.76
Price & Gottesman (55)[a]	34	0.61	38	0.75

[a]Data adjusted for the effects of age and gender.

contribute to the variation in BMI. The correlations of MZ twins reared apart provide a direct estimate of the genetic effect if we assume that these twins were not placed in similar environments and that intrauterine factors did not influence variation in BMI. According to these studies, the heritability of body mass index would be in the range of 40 to 70%.

Five recent adoption studies (54, 66–68, 71) in which BMI data were available from both the biologic as well as the adoptive relatives of the adoptees reported that the effect of shared family environment on BMI was negligible. In a recent review of behavior genetic studies relevant to obesity, Grilo & Pogue-Geile (33) also concluded that experiences shared among family members appear largely irrelevant in determining individual differences in weight and obesity. These findings are somewhat at odds with the strong familiality of the major affectors of excess body fat, i.e. energy intake (47) and energy expenditure (12), and should be interpreted with caution.

The role of genes in type I obesity has also been studied with the strategy of path analysis. Path analysis is a method used in genetic epidemiology to assess the relative contribution of genetic and environmental factors based on correlations computed among various pairs of relatives by descent or adoption. We used this strategy in two different population-based samples (the Quebec Family Study and the 1981 Canada Fitness Survey) to determine the contribution of heredity in BMI, subcutaneous fat (sum of 6 skinfold thicknesses), and percent body fat derived from underwater weighing (13, 49). The total transmission effect across generations reached 35% for BMI and amount of subcutaneous fat and 55% for percent body fat and total fat mass, but most of this transmission effect was cultural, as the genetic effect (heritability) reached only 5% for BMI and amount of subcutaneous fat and 25% for percent body fat and total fat mass.

More recently, BMI measurements obtained in a Norwegian sample of about 75,000 individuals were used to compute familial correlations in a large

Table 2 Familial correlations for body mass index in various types of relatives[a]

Relative	N pairs	r
Spouses	23,936	0.123
Father-offspring	19,632	0.193
Mother-offspring	23,954	0.202
Brothers	6,017	0.262
Sisters	3,858	0.258
Brother-sister	9,278	0.206
MZ twins	79	0.576

[a]Adapted from Tambs et al (72). Age- and gender-adjusted data.

number of first- and second-degree relatives (72). Correlations obtained in first-degree relatives are summarized in Table 2. As indicated in this table, correlations were about 0.12 for spouses, 0.20 for parent-offspring, opposite-sexed siblings, and dizygotic (DZ) twins, 0.26 for same-sexed siblings, and 0.58 for MZ twins. Correlations among second-degree relatives (not shown in table) were close to zero. By fitting a path model to these data, the authors found a heritability level of 40% for BMI plus a moderate, but significant effect of cultural transmission. These results, derived from path analysis and based on the largest number of relatives ever used in genetic studies of BMI, suggest that heritability accounts for a maximum of 40% of the variance in BMI.

REGIONAL FAT DISTRIBUTION

The increased interest in the genetics of human obesities observed in the last few years is in part attributable to the fact that regional fat distribution has been shown to be an important determinant of the relationship between obesity and health and an independent risk factor for various morbid conditions such as cardiovascular diseases or noninsulin-dependent diabetes.

Evidence for familial resemblance in body fat distribution has been reported (23). Using skinfold measurements obtained in 173 monozygotic and 178 dizygotic pairs of male twins, Selby et al (63) recently reported heritability estimates of 0.77 (p 0.0001) for subscapular skinfold, 0.29 (p 0.05) for the difference between subscapular and triceps skinfolds, and 0.17 (p 0.05) for the subscapular to triceps skinfolds ratio. After adjustment for body mass index, heritability levels were reduced and remained significant only for subscapular skinfold ($h^2 = 0.44$, $p = 0.002$). Thus, the authors concluded that there was a significant genetic influence on central deposition of body fat.

Using data from the Canada Fitness Survey and the strategy of path analysis, we have shown (49) that the transmissible effect across generation reached about 40% for trunk skinfolds (sum of subscapular and suprailiac skinfolds), extremity skinfolds (sum of biceps, triceps, and medial calf skinfolds), the trunk to extremity skinfolds ratio (TE ratio), and 28% for the waist to hip ratio (WHR). If we assume that all transmissible effects are genetic, these results suggest that heredity accounts for a maximum of 40% of the phenotypic variance for various indicators of type II obesity. The biological and cultural components of transmission in regional fat distribution were assessed with data from the Quebec Family Study (13). Two indicators of regional fat distribution were considered: the TE ratio and the subcutaneous fat to fat mass ratio obtained by dividing the sum of the 6 skinfolds by fat mass derived from body density measurements. A genetic effect of 25% was found for the TE ratio with a slightly higher genetic effect of 30% for subcutaneous fat to fat mass ratio. These results suggest that the pattern of subcutaneous fat distribution is partly determined by the genotype. When the influence of total body fat was taken into account, the profile of subcutaneous fat deposition was characterized by higher heritability estimates reaching about 40 to 50% of the residual variance (6, 7). These results imply that for a given level of fatness some individuals store more fat on the trunk or abdominal area (type II) while others store primarily on the lower body (type IV). No heritability estimates have been reported so far for abdominal visceral fat or type III obesity.

ENERGY AND NUTRIENT INTAKE

Energy and nutrient intakes have long been shown to aggregate in families, with significant resemblance observed between spouses as well as between parents and their children (47). Several twin studies have been undertaken to assess the role of heredity in energy intake, and most studies have reported greater similarities in dietary intakes between MZ twins than between DZ twins, which suggests that genetic factors might contribute to interindividual differences. However, these findings must be interpreted with caution, as some authors (25, 35) observed that MZ twins tended to get together and eat together more regularly than DZ twins, which immediately suggests that the greater similarity in energy intake among MZ twin pairs could be partly explained by a greater degree of shared environment.

We studied the role of heredity in energy intake using familial correlations computed in several types of relatives by descent or adoption from the Quebec Family Study and the BETA model of path analysis (51). Energy intake measurements were derived from a 3-day dietary record filled out by each family member and checked by trained nutritionists during individual interviews to ensure completeness. Food intake was recorded during two weekdays and one weekend day. The transmission effect across generations was found to be almost entirely cultural, as no significant genetic effect was observed for total energy intake. If one considers the large intra-individual day-to-day variation in energy intake in subjects followed over a one-year period (73), the absence of genetic effect for energy intake is not surprising. However, when intakes of carbohydrate, fat, and protein were expressed in percent of total energy intake, the contribution of genetic factors increased, ranging from 11% for percent of energy derived from protein to 20% for percent of energy derived from carbohydrate (51). If we assume that the fraction of energy derived from macronutrients is an indicator of food selection, these results suggest that food selection may be partially under genetic control. If excess body fat is often associated with a lipid-rich diet, food selection may be one of the factors determining the susceptibility of some individuals to be in positive energy balance over a long period of time. Several peptides reportedly stimulate or inhibit food intake and intake of specific macronutrients in animal models (20). Although their role in the regulation of human energy intake is unclear, these peptides represent promising candidate genes for studying the genetic basis of individual differences in energy and macronutrient intakes.

METABOLIC RATE AND ENERGY EXPENDITURE

Reduced energy expenditure for a given energy intake level causes positive energy balance and may eventually lead to excess body weight and obesity. The causes of interindividual differences in energy expenditure are important to consider in the study of the genetic basis of obesity. Several studies have reported that most obese subjects do not seem to have higher energy intake than their lean counterparts. Energy expenditure is a complex phenotype that includes various components: basal and resting metabolic rates, thermic effect of food, energy expenditure of activities, and energy cost for given activities. Little is known about the contribution of genetic factors to these various components of energy expenditure, although both total daily (24-hour) energy expenditure (61) and resting metabolic rate (2) were found to aggregate in families.

Resting Metabolic Rate

Resting metabolic rate (RMR) is the largest component of energy expenditure and accounts for about 70% of daily energy expenditure. We have published two studies regarding the heritability of RMR using parent-child and MZ and DZ twin data (19, 28). Results of these studies reveal that correlations are always higher in MZ twins than in DZ twins, whether RMR is expressed per kilogram of body weight or fat free mass. Heritability estimates derived from these results by doubling the difference between MZ and DZ twin correlations suggest that 40 to 80% of the variance in RMR, after adjustment for age, gender, body mass, and body composition, could be inherited. Heritability of 42% has recently been reported for casual metabolic rate measured at rest in 40 pairs of MZ and 40 pairs of DZ male twins (16 to 24 years), but this significant genetic effect was found to be entirely accounted for by body weight (36). However, when metabolic rate was measured under psychological stress, the authors found evidence for a significant genetic effect, independent of the genetic effect on body weight, accounting for 22% of the variance in the augmented energy expenditure measured during the stress. Metabolic rate was measured during a very short period of time (4 min) and in the late afternoon or evening. Even though the data cannot be considered as valid estimates of

RMR, the findings of Hewitt et al (36) support the notion of a genotype-dependent response of metabolic rate to environmental stimulus.

Thermic Effect of Food

The thermic effect of food (TEF) is the integrated increase of energy expenditure after food ingestion. To our knowledge, only one study (19) has considered the heritability of TEF. In that study, energy expenditure was measured during 4 consecutive hours after ingestion of a 1000 kcal carbohydrate meal in 31 parent-child pairs as well as in 21 pairs of DZ twins and 37 pairs of MZ twins. Correlations of 0.30, 0.35, and 0.52 in parent-child, DZ, and MZ pairs, respectively, were found, which suggest a heritability level of 40 to 60% for TEF.

Physical Activity Level

Studies on the genetic effect of energy expenditure associated with physical activity are also limited. Using data from the 1981 Canada Fitness Survey, we studied the importance of familial resemblance in leisure-time energy expenditure (48). A total of 18,073 individuals living in thousands of households across Canada completed a questionnaire on their physical activity habits. Detailed information on frequency, duration, and intensity of activities performed on a daily, weekly, monthly, and yearly basis was obtained and used to determine average daily energy expenditure (kJ/day/per kg body weight). Familial correlations of 0.28, 0.12, and 0.21 were obtained in spouses ($N = 1024$ pairs), parent-offspring ($N = 1622$ pairs), and siblings ($N = 1036$), respectively, suggesting a weak genetic contribution to interindividual differences in leisure-time energy expenditure (48).

More recently, the familial resemblance in the level of habitual physical activity was investigated with the Caltrac accelerometer in 100 children, 4 to 7 years of age, 99 mothers, and 92 fathers from the Framingham Children's Study (43). Data were obtained with the accelerometer for about 10 hours per day for an average of 9 days in children and 8 days in fathers and mothers. Active (accelerometer counts per hour above the median) fathers or active mothers were more likely to have active children than inactive fathers or mothers, with odds ratios of 3.5 and 2.0, respectively. When both parents were active, the children were 5.8 times more likely to be active than children of two inactive parents.

Results from a few twin studies suggest that physical activity level as behavior (person having an active temperament) and leisure-time physical activity could be partly inherited (12). With data from the Quebec Family Study and the strategy of path analysis we assessed the role of heredity in two different indicators of physical activity derived from a 3-day activity record filled out by 1610 individuals of 375 families encompassing 9 types of relatives by descent or adoption (50). Two indictors were used: "habitual physical activity" included all activities of each day, while "exercise participation" included only sport activities, i.e. activities of a higher intensity. Most of the variance in these two indicators of physical activity level was explained by nontransmissible environmental factors with values of 71% for habitual physical activity and 88% for exercise participation. The transmission effect across generation was significant but entirely accounted for by genetic factors for habitual physical activity, with a value of 29%, and by cultural transmission (12%) for exercise participation with no genetic effect. These results were interpreted as an indication of inherited differences in the propensity towards being spontaneously active.

NUTRIENT PARTITIONING

Nutrient partitioning can be defined as the propensity to store the ingested energy in the form of fat or lean tissue. Only one report has dealt with the heritability of nutrient partitioning characteristics in humans and it is based on data from the Quebec Family Study (15). A total transmission effect of about 50%, with a genetic transmission of approximately 20% after adjustment for the proper concomitants, was reported.

MAJOR GENE EFFECTS

The results reviewed thus far indicate a wide range of heritability levels for the various body composition phenotypes and their affectors. This variability in the contribution of genetic factors is expected if one considers the very different nature of all the phenotypes involved, but what appears more surprising is the large variation observed in the heritability of some obesity phenotypes. Heritabilities ranging from about 5 to 90%, for example, are reported for BMI. In interpreting these findings, one must keep in mind that several factors could influence the heritability of a given phenotype. Different designs and methods will obviously give different estimates, but, within a given method, values could differ not only from one population to another but also within a given population, depending on the age of the subjects and on other circumstances. In that context, knowing the exact heritability value of an obesity phenotype is not the most important issue, as most researchers in the field will agree that genes are undoubtedly involved to some extent in the development of obesity. Other issues like the identification of major genes and the recognition that genes may influence not only the level of the phenotype but also its response to growth and aging (temporal trends) and to changes in the environment (G × E effect) are more important in the quest for understanding the genetic basis of obesity.

The genetic effect reported above for the various obesity phenotypes was assumed to be polygenic; that is, it resulted from the additive effects of a large number of genes with each having small effects on the phenotypes. Recent research reported over the last few years provided evidence that, in addition to a polygenic component, some obesity phenotypes are influenced by major gene effects. Most of the evidence for the contribution of major genes in measures of body fat comes from commingling and segregation analyses. Commingling analysis is used to obtain preliminary evidence of major gene effects by testing the hypothesis that the distribution of a variable is best fitted by a mixture of two or three distributions rather than one. Although evidence of commingling or mixture of distributions is compatible with a major gene effect on the phenotype, it is not sufficient to conclude that a major locus genotype exists, because commingling can also result from the influence of nongenetic factors. More direct evidence for a major gene effect can be obtained with segregation analysis, a method used by geneticists to evaluate alternative models of genetic transmission by analysis of pedigree data.

A summary of the current evidence for major gene effects in body fat phenotypes is presented in Table 3. Evidence of commingling has been reported for all indicators of body fat and fat distribution. Results from segregation analyses support the hypothesis that a major gene contributes to percent body fat, subcutaneous fat to fat mass, trunk to extremity skinfolds, and subscapular to sum of subscapular and suprailiac skinfolds ratios. Results for BMI are conflicting: Three studies provided support for a major gene effect (42, 56, 58), whereas another (T. Rice et al, submitted) did not. As for percent body fat, results from a recent study provided evidence for a major locus genotype accounting for 45% of the phenotypic variance with another 22 to 26% of the variance attributable to a multifactorial component (62). Results from two studies also suggest the influence of major genes on regional fat distribution phenotypes. In one study, Hasstedt et al (34) reported a major gene effect explaining 42% of the variance in a relative fat pattern index

Table 3 Evidence from commingling and segregation analyses for major gene effects in body composition phenotypes[a]

Phenotype	Commingling	Segregation
BMI	Yes	Yes/no
Percent body fat	Yes	Yes
Subcutaneous fat/fat mass	Yes	Yes
Trunk/extremity skinfolds	Yes	Yes
Subscapular/subscapular and suprailiac skinfolds	Yes	Yes

[a]Adapted from References (5, 21, 34, 42, 56, 58, 59, 61a, 62) and from I. B. Borecki et al (submitted) and T. Rice et al (submitted).

defined as the ratio of the subscapular skinfold to the sum of the subscapular and suprailiac skinfold thicknesses. Recent results from the Quebec Family Study suggest major gene effects for the amount of subcutaneous fat (sum of 6 skinfolds) as well as for the trunk to extremity skinfolds ratio, both adjusted for total fat mass and accounting for about 35% of the phenotypic variance (I. B. Borecki et al, submitted).

TEMPORAL TRENDS

Commingling analyses undertaken on body composition measurements obtained in individuals from the Quebec Family Study (5) revealed the presence of commingling for BMI and percent body fat, but only in the parental generation and not in offspring. This finding raises the possibility that the effects of some genes could be different in children and adults. This issue of temporal trends has received little attention from geneticists, but is increasingly recognized as an important component of the genetic basis of obesity (4). Using path analysis models that incorporate parameters defined as a function of time, investigators have observed significant temporal trends in the transmissibility of BMI (60). More recently, a longitudinal study performed on a cohort of 514 adult male twin pairs, who were examined 3 times over a 43-year period of time, concluded that changes in BMI across adulthood were largely genetic (24). These results suggest that genetic factors may be involved in determining the changes of body mass, and perhaps body fat, over time and, consequently, may put some individuals at increased risk of developing obesity as they progressively age.

GENETIC-ENVIRONMENT INTERACTION

We all know that some individuals are susceptible to excessive accumulation of fat and are always trying to lose these extra pounds while others seem relatively well protected against the extra calories they ingest. We recently tried to test whether such differences could be explained by genetic factors by comparing the intrapair (within genotype) and interpair (between genotypes) resemblances in the response of MZ twins to overfeeding and negative energy balance or, in other words, by testing for the presence of genotype-environment interaction effect.

Response to Overfeeding

Two experiments were undertaken to study individual differences when exposed to a positive energy balance protocol. In both experiments, subjects had to eat a caloric surplus of 4.2 MJ (1000 kcal) per day for a period of 22 days, in a short-term overfeeding experiment (17, 52), and 100 days in a long-term overfeeding experiment (16). Both experiments resulted in significant changes in the various obesity phenotypes, but considerable interindividual differences in the adaptation to the extra calories were observed. In the long-term overfeeding experiment (16), the mean body mass gain of the 24 subjects (12 pairs of MZ twins) was 8.1 kg, but the range of weight gain was from 4 to 13 kg. However, the variation observed was not randomly distributed: Variance in response between pairs was about three times greater than within pairs for gains in body weight and fat mass, and was about six times greater between pairs than within pairs for changes in visceral fat (assessed by computerized tomography) after adjustment for gains in fat mass (16). These results suggest that the amount of fat stored in response to a caloric surplus is significantly influenced by the genotype of the individual. This genotype-overfeeding interaction effect appears to be more important for fat topography than for the amount of fat gained as indicated by higher F ratios for the amount of abdominal visceral fat gained. These findings suggest that genes may determine not only the gain in fat mass or body energy when subjected to positive energy balance but also the pattern of fat deposition among the various fat depots of the body. This has important implications for health because truncal-abdominal fat and, particularly, visceral fat are associated with greater health risks than total amount of body fat.

Response to Negative Energy Balance

In two other experiments, exercise was used to induce an energy deficit in MZ twins in order to test for the contribution of the genotype in the response to negative energy balance sustained for 22 days (53) or 100 days (18). In both experiments, the energy deficit was obtained by exercising twins on a cycle ergometer twice a day for about 50 min per session. The exercise prescription was designed to induce an extra energy expenditure of 4.2 MJ (1000 kcal) while maintaining energy intake at the baseline level throughout the study. Results from the long-term experiment revealed a significant within-pair resemblance for the reduction in body weight and fat mass as well as for the changes in regional fat distribution phenotypes, while results from the short-term study revealed that only fat-free mass changes were characterized by a significant MZ twin resemblance.

Thus, results from both overfeeding and negative energy balance experiments generally suggest that undetermined genetic characteristics specific to each individual are associated with the response to changes in energy balance. The use of the measured genotype approach could be helpful in the identification of some of the genes involved in determining variation in responsiveness. Genetic variation at some apolipoprotein gene loci has been used to study the role of genetic factors in the response of blood lipids and lipoproteins to changes in the diet (1) or the response of aerobic performance and markers of aerobic metabolism to exercise training (10), but no study has been published yet for phenotypes associated with obesity.

CONTRIBUTION OF SINGLE GENES: A BEGINNING

The definition of the genetic architecture of excess body fat in humans has just begun. It is likely that the human obesity genotypes will be complex multigenic systems with networks of gene-gene and gene-environment interactions (9). Already, some promising data, primarily derived from animal models, are highly suggestive of significant contributions from single gene mutations.

Some studies had suggested that allelic variation at the class I loci of the HLA system (chromosomal assignment: 6p21.3) was associated with the BMI as a marker of obesity (22, 26, 31). However, a study with relatively large samples of males and females and more elaborate assessments of body fat has not confirmed these results (14).

Sib-pair linkage analysis data obtained in four large families have suggested significant associations between a subcutaneous fat pattern index and the adenylate kinase 1 locus (9q34) as well as the glutamic-pyruvate transaminase locus (8q24) (64). Erythrocyte acid phosphatase (locus 1) (2p25) phenotypes exhibiting low enzyme activity levels (ACP_1A and BA) were reported to be associated with excess body mass for age, height, and gender among 75 children, 3 to 14 years of age (38). On the other hand, mitochondrial DNA sequence variation was also found to be nonrandomly related to body fat content and fat topography in 42 women (J. Truchon et al, submitted). Thus, carriers of the EcoRV morph 2 in the D-loop region were leaner than noncarriers, whereas carriers of the morph 1 generated by the Kpnl in the D-loop were markedly fatter than the noncarriers.

The augmented expression of adipocyte genes was studied in overfed primates and rats in an attempt to identify candidate genes that could be used in genetic studies of body weight regulation and obesity (76). A subtractive cDNA cloning strategy allowed investigators to identify a 5-kilobase message expressed preferentially in the adipose tissue of overfed macaques and rats. The 5-kb mRNA was also found in human subcutaneous fat. The precise nature of the protein encoded by this message and potential polymorphism of the gene have not yet been established to our knowledge.

The relationship between rodent obesity genes and human obesity is being considered by several investigators. Friedman et al (30) have reported that five mouse mutations that cause obesity in the animals are encoded on five different mouse chromosomes. However, these mouse obesity genes seem to be part of coding regions that have homologous counterparts on human chromosomes. These human homologous regions are also located on five different human chromosomes (1p31-ter; 7q31; 11p15.1; 16q22-24; 20q13). Interestingly, the mouse *db* gene may be homologous to the rat *fa* obesity gene (74), and they both appear to have a human counterpart on chromosome 1p31 (29).

Two putative new loci for excessive body fat content have been identified in backcross mice by quantitative trait loci mapping with restriction fragment length polymorphism (75). Backcross progeny from crosses between mouse strains C57BL/6J and *Mus spretus* exhibit a body fat content ranging from almost zero to 50% (27). One locus on chromosome 1 and one on chromosome 10 were identified by these procedures (75).

A transgenic mouse with impaired corticosteroid receptor function was created by partially knocking out gene expression with type II glucocorticoid receptor (5q31-32) antisense RNA (46). The transgenic animals had increased fat deposition and a body mass that by about 6 months of age was twice as high as that of controls. An elevated body fat content was observed despite the fact that transgenic animals ate about 15% less than the normal mice.

The results reported thus far suggest that several genes have the potential to cause obesity in humans. It seems likely that the obesity genotype is a complex multigenic system; perhaps the more severe cases carry mutations at several loci and the less affected individuals carry one or only a few of the mutant genes. Each of the putative single gene effects reviewed here seems to be encoded on a different human chromosome region, including 1p31, 2p25, 5q31-32, 6p21.3, 7q31, 8q24, 9q34, 11p15.1, 16q22-24, 20q13. Moreover, we know that another putative obesity gene, causing the paternally imprinted Prader-Willi syndrome, is encoded on human chromosome 15q11-13 (40).

The growing number of obesity-related or obesity-causing genes does not bode well for the single gene hypothesis. It implies, however, that genetic heterogeneity is likely to become a major challenge in future genetic studies of this complex phenotype.

Literature Cited

1. Abbey, M. 1992. The influence of apolipoprotein polymorphism on the response to dietary fat and cholesterol. *Curr. Opin. Lipidol.* 3:12–16

1a. Bodurtha, J. N., Mosteller, M., Hewitt, J. K., Nance, W. E., Eaves, L. J., et al. 1990. Genetic analysis of anthropometric measures in 11-year-old twins: the Medical College of Virginia Twin Study. *Pediatr. Res.* 28:1–4

2. Bogardus, C., Lillioja, S., Ravussin, E., Abbott, W., Zawadkzi, J. K., et al. 1986. Familial dependence of the resting metabolic rate. *N. Engl. J. Med.* 315:96–100

3. Bonney, G. E., Lathrop, G. M., Lalouel, J. M. 1988. Combined linkage and segregation analysis using regressive models. *Am. J. Hum. Genet.* 43: 29–37

4. Borecki, I. B., Province, M. A., Bouchard, C., Rao, D. C. 1993. Genetics of obesity: etiologic heterogeneity and temporal trends. In *Genetics of Obesity*, ed. C. Bouchard. Boca Raton: CRC Press. In press

5. Borecki, I. B., Rice, T., Bouchard,

C., Rao, D. C. 1991. Commingling analysis of generalized body mass and composition measures: the Québec Family Study. *Int. J. Obes.* 15:763–73

6. Bouchard, C. 1988. Inheritance of human fat distribution. In *Fat Distribution During Growth and Later Health Outcomes,* ed. C. Bouchard, F. E. Johnson, 17:103–25. New York: Liss. 363 pp

7. Bouchard, C. 1990. Variation in human body fat: the contribution of the genotype. In *Obesity: Towards a Molecular Approach, UCLA Symp. Mol. Cell. Biol. New Ser.,* ed. G. A. Bray, D. Ricquier, B. M. Spiegelman, 132:17–28. New York: Wiley-Liss. 307 pp

8. Bouchard, C. 1991. Current understanding of the etiology of obesity: genetic and nongenetic factors. *Am. J. Clin. Nutr.* 53:1561S–65S

9. Bouchard, C. 1992. Human obesities: chaos or determinism? In *Obesity in Europe 91, Proc. 3rd Eur. Congr. Obes.,* ed. G. Ailhaud, B. Guy-Grand, M. Lafontan, D. Ricquier, pp. 7–14. Paris: Libbey

10. Bouchard, C., Dionne, F. T., Simoneau, J. A., Boulay, M. R. 1992. Genetics of aerobic and anaerobic performances. *Exerc. Sport Sci. Rev.* 20:27–58

11. Bouchard, C., Pérusse, L. 1988. Heredity and body fat. *Annu. Rev. Nutr.* 8:259–77

12. Bouchard, C., Pérusse, L., Dériaz, O., Després, J. P., Tremblay, A. 1993. Genetic influences on energy expenditure in humans. In *Child and Adolescent Obesity: What, How and Who?,* ed. L. J. Filer. Washington, DC: Int. Life Sci. Inst. In press

13. Bouchard, C., Pérusse, L., Leblanc, C., Tremblay, A., Thériault, G. 1988. Inheritance of the amount and distribution of human body fat. *Int. J. Obes.* 12:205–15

14. Bouchard, C., Pérusse, L., Rivest, J., Morissette, J., Allard, C., et al. 1985. HLA system, body fat and fat distribution in children and adults. *Int. J. Obes.* 9:411–22

15. Bouchard, C., Tremblay, A., Després, J. P., Dériaz, O., Dionne, F. T. 1992. The genetics of body energy content and energy balance: an overview. See Ref. 20, pp. 3–21

16. Bouchard, C., Tremblay, A., Després, J. P., Nadeau, A., Lupien, P. J., et al. 1990. The response to long-term overfeeding in identical twins. *N. Engl. J. Med.* 302:1477–82

17. Bouchard, C., Tremblay, A., Després, J. P., Poehlman, E. T., Thériault, G.,

et al. 1988. Sensitivity to overfeeding: the Quebec experiment with identical twins. *Prog. Food Nutr. Sci.* 12:45–72

18. Bouchard, C., Tremblay, A., Després, J. P., Thériault, G., Nadeau, A., et al. 1992. The response to exercise with constant energy intake in identical twins. *FASEB J.* 6:A1647 (Abstr.)

19. Bouchard, C., Tremblay, A., Nadeau, A., Després, J. P., Thériault, G. 1989. Genetic effect in resting and exercise metabolic rates. *Metabolism* 38:364–70

20. Bray, G. A. 1992. The effect of peptides on nutrient intake and the sympathetic nervous system. In *The Science of Food Regulation: Food Intake, Nutrient Partitioning and Energy Expenditure,* ed. G. A. Bray, D. H. Ryan, pp. 257–76. Baton Rouge: Louisiana State Univ. Press. 408 pp

21. Byard, P. J., Siervogel, R. M., Roche, A. F. 1989. X-linked pattern of inheritance for serial measures of weight/stature. *Am. J. Hum. Biol.* 1:443–49

22. Digy, J. P., Raffoux, C., Pointel, J. P., Perrier, P., Drouin, P., et al. 1985. HLA and familial obesity: evidence for a genetic origin. In *Recent Advances on Obesity Research,* ed. J. Hirsch, T. Van Italie, pp. 171–75. London: Libbey. 402 pp.

23. Donahue, R. P., Prineas, R. J., Gomez, O., Hong, C. P. 1992. Familial resemblance of body fat distribution: the Minneapolis Children's blood pressure study. *Int. J. Obes.* 16:161–67

24. Fabsitz, R. R., Carmelli, D., Hewitt, J. K. 1992. Evidence for independent genetic influences on obesity in middle age. *Int. J. Obes.* 16:657–66

25. Fabsitz, R. R., Garrison, R. J., Feinleib, M., Hjortland, M. 1978. A twin analysis of dietary intake: evidence for a need to control for possible environmental influences in MZ and DZ twins. *Behav. Genet.* 8:15–25

26. Fabsitz, R. R., Nam, J. M., Gart, J., Stunkard, A., Price, A. R., et al. 1989. HLA associations with obesity. *Hum. Hered.* 39:156–64

27. Fisler, J. S., Pace, M. J., Warden, C. H., Lusis, A. J. 1991. Spretus/B6: A new mouse model of polygenic obesity. *Int. J. Obes.* 15(Suppl. 3):54 (Abstr.)

28. Fontaine, E., Savard, R., Tremblay, A., Després, J. P., Poehlman, E. T., et al. 1985. Resting metabolic rate in monozygotic and dizygotic twins. *Acta Genet. Med. Gemellol.* 34:41–47

29. Friedman, J. M., Leibel, R. L. 1992. Tackling a weighty problem. *Cell* 69:217–20

30. Friedman, J. M., Leibel, R. L., Bahary,

N. 1991. Molecular mapping of obesity genes. *Mammalian Genome* 1:130–44

31. Fumeron, F., Apfelbaum, M. 1981. Association between HLA-B18 and the familial obesity syndrome. *N. Engl. J. Med.* 305:645

32. Garn, S. M., Sullivan, T. V., Hawthorne, V. M. 1989. Fatness and obesity of the parents of obese individuals. *Am. J. Clin. Nutr.* 50:1308–13

33. Grilo, C. M., Pogue-Geile, M. F. 1991. The nature of environmental influences on weight and obesity: a behavior genetic analysis. *Psychol. Bull.* 110:520–37

34. Hasstedt, S. J., Ramirez, M. E., Kuida, H., Williams, R. R. 1989. Recessive inheritance of a relative fat pattern. *Am. J. Hum. Genet.* 45:917–25

35. Heller, R. F., O'Connell, D. L., Roberts, D. C. K., Allen, J. C., Knapp, P. L., et al. 1988. Lifestyle factors in monozygotic and dizygotic twins. *Genet. Epidemiol.* 5:311–21

36. Hewitt, J. K., Stunkard, A. J., Carroll, D., Sims, J., Turner, J. R. 1991. A twin study approach towards understanding genetic contributions to body size and metabolic rate. *Acta Genet. Med. Gemellol.* 40:133–46

37. Lander, E. S., Botstein, D. 1989. Mapping mendelian factors underlying quantitative traits using RFLP linkage maps. *Genetics* 121:185–99

38. Lucarini, N., Finocchi, G., Gloria-Bottini, F., Macioce, M., Borgiani, P. 1990. A possible genetic component of obesity in childhood. Observations on acid phosphatase polymorphism. *Experientia* 46:90–91

39. MacDonald, A., Stunkard, A. J. 1990. Body mass indexes of British separated twins. *N. Engl. J. Med.* 322:1530

40. McKusick, V. A. 1992. *Mendelian Inheritance in Man. Catalogs of Autosomal Dominant, Autosomal Recessive, and X-linked phenotypes.* Baltimore: Johns Hopkins Univ. Press. 2320 pp. 10th ed

41. Merlino, G. T. 1991. Transgenic animals in biomedical research. *FASEB J.* 5:2996–3001

42. Moll, P. P., Burns, T. L., Lauer, R. M. 1991. The genetic and environmental sources of body mass index variability: The Muscatine Ponderosity Family Study. *Am. J. Hum. Genet.* 49:1243–55

43. Moore, L. L., Lombardi, D. A., White, M. J., Campbell, J. L., Oliveria, S. A., et al. 1991. Influence of parents' physical activity levels on activity levels of young children. *J. Pediatr.* 118:215–19

44. Mueller, D. F. 1983. The genetics of human fatness. *Yearb. Phys. Anthropol.* 26:215–30

45. Paterson, A. H., Lander, E. S., Hewitt, J. D., Peterson, S., Lincoln, S. E. 1988. Resolution of quantitative traits into mendelian factors by using a complete linkage map of restriction fragment length polymorphisms. *Nature* 335:721–26

46. Pépin, M. C., Pothier, F., Barden, N. 1992. Impaired type II glucocorticoid-receptor function in mice bearing antisense RNA transgene. *Nature* 235: 725–28

47. Pérusse, L., Bouchard, C. 1993. Genetics of energy intake and food preferences. In *Genetics of Obesity,* ed. C. Bouchard. Boca Raton: CRC Press. In press

48. Pérusse, L., Leblanc, C., Bouchard, C. 1988. Familial resemblance in lifestyle components: results from the Canada Fitness Survey. *Can. J. Public Health* 79:201–5

49. Pérusse, L., Leblanc, C., Bouchard, C. 1988. Inter-generation transmission of physical fitness in the Canadian population. *Can. J. Sport Sci.* 13:8–14

50. Pérusse, L., Tremblay, A., Leblanc, C., Bouchard, C. 1989. Genetic and environmental influences on level of habitual physical activity and exercise participation. *Am. J. Epidemiol.* 129: 1012–22

51. Pérusse, L., Tremblay, A., Leblanc, C., Cloninger, C. R., Reich, T., et al. 1988. Familial resemblance in energy intake: contribution of genetic and environmental factors. *Am. J. Clin. Nutr.* 47:629–35

52. Poehlman, E. T., Tremblay, A., Després, J. P., Fontaine, E., Pérusse, L., et al. 1986. Genotype-controlled changes in body composition and fat morphology following overfeeding in twins. *Am. J. Clin. Nutr.* 43:723–31

53. Poehlman, E. T., Tremblay, A., Marcotte, M., Pérusse, L., Thériault, G., et al. 1987. Heredity and changes in body composition and adipose tissue metabolism after short-term exercise-training. *Eur. J. Appl. Physiol.* 56:398–402

54. Price, R. A., Cadoret, R. J., Stunkard, A. J., Troughton, E. 1987. Genetic contributions to human fatness: an adoption study. *Am. J. Psychiatry* 144:1003–8

55. Price, R. A., Gottesman, I. I. 1991. Body fat in identical twins reared apart: roles for genes and environment. *Behav. Genet.* 21:1–7

56. Price, R. A., Ness, R., Laskarzewski,

P. 1990. Common major gene inheritance of extreme overweight. *Hum. Biol.* 62:747–65

57. Price, R. A., Stunkard, A. J., Ness, R., Wadden, T., Heshka, S., et al. 1990. Childhood onset (age 10) obesity has high familial risk. *Int. J. Obes.* 14:185–95

58. Province, M. A., Arnqvist, P., Keller, J., Higgins, M., Rao, D. C. 1990. Strong evidence for a major gene for obesity in the large, unselected, total community health study of Tecumseh. *Am. J. Hum. Genet.* 47(Suppl.):A143 (Abstr.)

59. Province, M. A., Keller, M., Higgins, M., Rao, D. C. 1991. A commingling analysis of obesity in the Tecumseh Community Health Study. *Am. J. Hum. Biol.* 3:435–45

60. Province, M. A., Rao, D. C. 1985. Path analysis of family resemblance with temporal trends: application to height, weight and Quetelet index in Northeastern Brazil. *Am. J. Hum. Genet.* 37:178–92

61. Ravussin, E., Lillioja, S., Knowler, W. C., Christin, L., Freymond, D., et al. 1988. Reduced rate of energy expenditure as a risk factor for body weight gain. *N. Engl. J. Med.* 318:467–72

61a. Rice, T., Borecki, I. B., Bouchard, C., Rao, D. C. 1992. Commingling analysis of regional fat distribution measures: the Quebec Family Study. *Int. J. Obes.* 16:831–44

62. Rice, T., Borecki, I. B., Bouchard, C., Rao, D. C. 1993. Segregation analysis of fat mass and other body composition measures derived from underwater weighing *Am. J. Hum. Genet.* In press

63. Selby, J. V., Newman, B., Quesenberry, C. P. Jr., Fabsitz, R. R., King, M. C., et al. 1989. Evidence of genetic influence on central body fat in middle-aged twins. *Hum. Biol.* 61:179–93

64. Siervogel, R. M., Wilson, A. F., Baumgartner, R. N., Elston, R. C. 1991. Evidence of possible genetic linkage for a postulated fat patterning gene and marker genes using the robust sib-pair method. *Am. J. Hum. Biol.* 3:67

65. Sing, C. F., Boerwinkle, E. A., Moll, P. P., Templeton, A. R. 1988. Characterization of genes affecting quantitative traits in humans. In *Proceedings of the 2nd International Conference on Quantitative Genetics,* ed. B. S. Weir, E. J. Eisen, M. M. Goodman, G. Namkoong, pp. 250–69. Sunderland:Sinauer. 704 pp.

66. Sorensen, T. I. A., Holst, C., Stunkard, A. J. 1992. Childhood body mass index—genetic and familial environmental influences assessed in a longitudinal adoption study. *Int. J. Obes.* 16:705–14

67. Sorensen, T. I. A., Holst, C., Stunkard, A. J., Theil, L. 1992. Correlations of body mass index of adult adoptees and their biological relatives. *Int. J. Obes.* 16:227–36

68. Sorensen, T. I. A., Price, R. A., Stunkard, A. J., Schulsinger, F. 1989. Genetics of obesity in adult adoptees and their biological siblings. *Br. Med. J.* 298:87–90

69. Stunkard, A. J., Foch, T. T., Hrubec, Z. 1986. A twin study of human obesity. *J. Am. Med. Assoc.* 256:51–54

70. Stunkard, A. J., Harris, J. R., Pedersen, N. L., McClearn, G. E. 1990. The body mass index of twins who have been reared apart. *N. Engl. J. Med.* 322:1483–87

71. Stunkard, A. J., Sorensen, T. I. A., Hannis, C., Teasdale, T. W., Chakraborty, R., et al. 1986. An adoption study of human obesity. *N. Engl. J. Med.* 314:193–98

72. Tambs, K., Moum, T., Eaves, L., Neale, M., Midthjell, K., et al. 1991. Genetic and environmental contributions to the variance of the body mass index in a Norwegian sample of first- and second-degree relatives. *Am. J. Hum. Biol.* 3:257–67

73. Tarasuk, V., Beaton, G. H. 1991. The nature and individuality of within-subject variation in energy intake. *Am. J. Clin. Nutr.* 54:464–70

74. Truett, G. E., Bahary, N., Friedman, J. M., Leibel, R. L. 1991. Rat obesity gene fatty (fa) maps to chromosome 5: Evidence for homology with the mouse gene diabetes (db). *Proc. Natl. Acad. Sci. USA* 88:7806–9

75. Warden, C. H., Fisler, J. S., Pace, M. J., Diep, A., He, K. Y., et al. 1991. Identification of two loci underlying polygenic obesity in mice. *Int. J. Obes.* 15(Suppl. 3):54 (Abstr.)

76. Wilson, B. E., Meyer, G. E., Cleveland, J. C., Weigle, D. S. 1990. Identification of candidate genes for a factor regulating body weight in primates. *Am. J. Physiol.* 259:R1148–55

Annu. Rev. Nutr. 1993. 13:355–81

REGULATION OF PLASMA LDL-CHOLESTEROL LEVELS BY DIETARY CHOLESTEROL AND FATTY ACIDS

D. K. Spady, L. A. Woollett, and J. M. Dietschy

Department of Internal Medicine, University of Texas Southwestern Medical Center, Dallas, Texas 75235

KEY WORDS: liver cholesterol synthesis, LDL receptors, LDL production, cholesteryl esters, atherosclerosis

CONTENTS

Introduction and Scope	355
General Features of Cholesterol and LDL Metabolism	356
Types of Lipids Present in the Western Diet	358
Tissue Sites for Cholesterol Synthesis in Different Species	360
Tissue Sites for LDL-C Transport out of the Plasma in Different Species	362
Quantitative Considerations in the Regulation of LDL-C Levels in Plasma	364
Effect of Dietary Cholesterol on LDL Receptor Activity and LDL-C Production . .	368
Effect of Different Fatty Acids on LDL Receptor Activity and LDL-C Production in	
* Animals*	369
A Model for the Interaction of Dietary Cholesterol and Triacylglycerol	371
Effect of Cholesterol and Different Fatty Acids on Plasma LDL-C Levels in Man .	374
Summary	376

Introduction and Scope

Abundant data now support the conclusion that atherosclerotic disease in Western countries is related to a number of factors such as the level of circulating lipids, hypertension, smoking, and glucose intolerance (2, 25). Of these various factors, the concentration of cholesterol carried in low density lipoproteins (LDL-C) is one of the most important. Thus, the incidence of various complications of atherosclerosis appears to be directly related to the level of this specific class of plasma lipids (2, 25, 57). Lowering this level by dietary and/or pharmacological means decreases the incidence of these events

355

0199-9885/93/0715–0355$02.00

(34, 44) and, in some instances, may even lead to a reduction in the size of the atherosclerotic lesion (8, 10).

Considerable data also support the conclusion that the relatively high levels of LDL-C found in these same countries are associated, in some manner, with the intake of large quantities of dietary lipids including both cholesterol and triacylglycerol. Furthermore, innumerable studies in both experimental animals and humans have elucidated certain general principles that describe the effects of these lipids on the plasma cholesterol levels. First, the concentration of LDL-C usually increases as the level of dietary cholesterol is increased (46). Second, in general, triacylglycerols containing predominantly saturated fatty acids further increase the concentration of cholesterol carried in this lipoprotein fraction while those containing predominantly unsaturated fatty acids lower these levels. Third, when fed at equal levels, saturated fatty acids are more active in increasing the LDL-C concentration than are unsaturated lipids in reducing the level of concentration (33, 41).

While these principles appear to be valid for most species, until very recently relatively little has been known about which specific fatty acids are responsible for these effects, which organ(s) these lipids act in to regulate the plasma LDL-C concentration, and how cholesterol and fatty acids interact biochemically in this (these) tissue(s) to alter plasma cholesterol levels. This chapter reviews recent information on those organs in various species, including humans, that are involved in the synthesis and excretion of cholesterol and in the synthesis and degradation of LDL-C. The quantitative relationships between these processes are also described, and the manner in which dietary cholesterol and triacylglycerol alter these processes is reviewed. Finally, to the extent that data are available, a model is presented that suggests how fatty acids and cholesterol interact biochemically to bring about the marked changes in the steady-state concentration of LDL-C observed in both experimental animals and humans.

General Features of Cholesterol and LDL Metabolism

The general characteristics of cholesterol and LDL-C metabolism have been elucidated over the past few years, and some of the key features of these processes are shown diagrammatically in Figure 1. A portion of the cholesterol that is present in the diet is absorbed by the small intestine (A), incorporated into the chylomicron particle, and delivered to the liver (C) after partial degradation of the chylomicron to its remnant (31, 69). The arrival of dietary cholesterol in the liver is signaled by an increase in the level of cholesteryl esters (CE) and partial suppression of the rate of hepatic cholesterol synthesis from acetyl-CoA (56). Nearly all of the other extrahepatic tissues (B) are also capable of synthesizing cholesterol, although the rates vary markedly among the different organs (62). Each day an amount of cholesterol equal to that

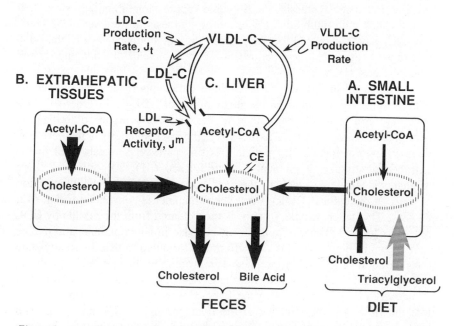

Figure 1 A model showing the central role of the liver in maintaining both net cholesterol balance and plasma low density lipoprotein-cholesterol (LDL-C) levels in animals and humans. The *solid arrows* are meant to show, in a semiquantitative manner, the rates of cholesterol synthesis in the three tissue compartments and the rate of intestinal sterol absorption, as well as the flow of this cholesterol to the liver and out of the body in the feces. The steady-state concentration of cholesterol carried in LDL is also primarily determined by the rate of conversion of very low density lipoprotein-cholesterol (VLDL-C) to LDL-C and the subsequent clearing of this particle from the plasma through the intervention of LDL receptors located primarily in the liver. The exact magnitude of each of these processes in maintaining cholesterol and LDL-C balance in the intact animal and man is discussed in detail in the text. CE represents the inert storage pool of cholesteryl esters in the liver.

which is synthesized in these extrahepatic tissues must be transported to the liver for excretion. This process of "reverse" cholesterol transport presumably involves high density lipoproteins (HDL) (24). Other than small losses of cholesterol through the sloughing of skin and endothelial cells and the synthesis of steroid hormones, most sterol is excreted from the body as biliary cholesterol and bile acids (7, 76). Thus, in the steady state the rate at which sterol is excreted in the feces as cholesterol and bile acid must equal the rate at which cholesterol is synthesized in all of the tissues and absorbed from the diet. The rate of synthesis in the liver, but not in the extrahepatic tissues, will change to accommodate any alteration in net sterol balance in the animal. An increase in fecal sterol excretion, for example, will invariably lead to an increase in hepatic synthesis (75, 79) while suppression of net fecal sterol loss is associated with inhibition of cholesterol synthesis in the liver (13). Thus, the liver plays the central role in maintaining net sterol balance in the body and rapidly responds to any perturbation of this balance by changing its rate of cholesterol synthesis.

As is also illustrated in Figure 1, recent data support the concept that the liver is similarly important in the metabolism of LDL-C. In order to move triacylglycerol from the hepatocyte to the peripheral organs of utilization (muscle) or storage (adipose tissue) (31), the liver synthesizes the very low density lipoprotein (VLDL) particle. As this particle is metabolized in the extrahepatic tissues, a remnant is also formed (31). A portion of these remnants is taken up directly by the liver, apparently through the intervention of the LDL receptor (LDL-R), while the remainder is converted to LDL (42, 84, 85). This latter particle, in turn, is then cleared from the plasma by LDL receptors located primarily in the liver, but also in some extrahepatic tissues (not shown in Figure 1). It is clear from this formulation that the steady-state concentration of LDL-C in the plasma is profoundly influenced by both the rate at which LDL-C is formed, i.e. the LDL-C production rate, and the level of activity of LDL receptors in the liver. However, it should also be noted that the flow of cholesterol out of the liver, through VLDL and LDL, and back to the liver does not alter net sterol balance in this organ. Only if there is net transfer of some of the sterol newly synthesized in the extrahepatic tissues to LDL or VLDL (24, 38) will the uptake of these particles make a net contribution to the hepatic cholesterol pools.

From these general considerations, it is clear that the liver is uniquely situated to integrate the metabolic effects of dietary lipids on both net sterol balance in the body and the level of circulating LDL-C. Much of the dietary cholesterol and at least a portion of the dietary triacylglycerol is delivered to this organ. These lipids alter the pools of cholesterol in the hepatocyte and even change the distribution of fatty acids in the phospholipids, triacylglycerols, and cholesteryl esters that comprise the membranous and bulk lipid compartments of the liver cell. These changes, in turn, are associated with marked alterations in both LDL-R activity and the LDL-C production rate.

Types of Lipids Present in the Western Diet

The diet of the average individual in Western countries typically contains several hundred milligrams of cholesterol and 80–130 g of triacylglycerol. Even though the great majority of the sterol in the diet is unesterified, it is, nevertheless, very poorly absorbed. Because cholesterol contains only a single hydrophilic group, the 3β-hydroxyl group, its absorption is very sensitive to the size of the bile acid pool in the small intestine, the relative hydrophobicity of this pool, the resistance of the intestinal diffusion barrier, the relative hydrophobicity of the microvillus membrane, and the rate at which cholesterol is esterified once it reaches the interior of the intestinal epithelial cell (69). Hence, in many species, including man, only about 40–60% of the mass of cholesterol reaching the intestinal lumen is absorbed. However, it is equally clear that this percentage is highly variable among individual members of any species (30) so that the same dietary challenge may elicit a wide range of LDL-C concentrations in different individuals (4).

The physiological behavior of fatty acids in the diet is much more complicated. Because of the complex chemistry of these compounds, individual fatty acids vary markedly in their physical characteristics, absorbability, metabolic fate, and regulatory effects. The first variable is the length of the hydrocarbon chain. Whereas most biological tissues contain fatty acids with 16 or 18 carbon atoms, saturated fatty acids containing virtually any number of carbon atoms can be chemically synthesized. In general, those with less than 10–12 carbon atoms, e.g. the 4:0, 6:0, 8:0, and 10:0 fatty acids, have low melting points, are readily absorbed across the gastrointestinal tract, and are not incorporated into the chylomicron particle. They are carried directly to the liver through the portal vein and rapidly oxidized to acetyl-CoA. In contrast, the longer chain saturated fatty acids, e.g. the 16:0 and 18:0 fatty acids, have higher melting points, may be less well absorbed, and are incorporated into the chylomicron particle. They eventually reach the liver, through uptake of the chylomicron remnant and plasma free fatty acids, where they enrich the lipids present in the various metabolic pools (82).

The second variable in the chemistry of these compounds concerns the number of double bonds present in the hydrocarbon chain. Again, while an almost infinite number of isomers is possible, dietary lipids most commonly contain fatty acids with one, two, or three double bonds in the *cis* configuration at the 6, 9, or 12 positions. In general, the addition of a double bond to a saturated fatty acid lowers the melting point of that compound and increases its absorbability. These unsaturated, long chain fatty acids, e.g. the 18:1(*c*9) and 18:2(*c*9, *c*12) compounds, are also incorporated into the chylomicron particle after absorption and eventually reach the liver where they also can enrich the various metabolic pools (16).

The third variable in fatty acid structure is introduced largely during the commercial preparation of edible oils. During the process of hydrogenation the double bonds in the fatty acids may migrate longitudinally along the hydrocarbon chain, and, in addition, may be rotated from their normal *cis* configuration to the *trans* configuration. This chemical change raises the melting point of the lipid (23). Nevertheless, these long chain *trans* fatty acids are absorbed and incorporated into the chylomicron and reach the liver where they can be identified within the various lipid pools (23).

Finally, these various fatty acids may be esterified to the glycerol molecule in a highly specific manner. Not only does the stereospecific structure of the triacylglycerol molecule affect its physical characteristics and the absorbability of the constituent fatty acids (59), but, in addition, the location of a given fatty acid on the triacylglycerol molecule may determine whether it is predominantly delivered to the liver or to the extrahepatic tissues. Thus, the stereospecific structure of a fat could markedy influence whether a particular triacylglycerol influences LDL-C metabolism or not.

While the types of fatty acids in the diet and their location on the triacylglycerol molecule can, in theory, vary enormously, in practice the great majority of dietary fats contain predominantly two saturated fatty acids, i.e. the 16:0 and 18:0 compounds, and two unsaturated fatty acids, i.e. the 18:1(*c*9) and 18:2(*c*9, *c*12) compounds. In addition, processed and specialty fats may contain *trans* long chain fatty acids as well as the 12:0 and 14:0 compounds. Triacylglycerols containing these various fatty acids are essentially completely absorbed and reach the metabolic pools of lipids in the liver where they potentially can regulate those processes dictating sterol and LDL-C balance across the liver.

Tissue Sites for Cholesterol Synthesis in Different Species

To begin to understand these regulatory processes, one must first review the quantitative importance of the liver to sterol synthesis in the whole animal and man. The rates of cholesterol synthesis in whole animals have now been measured in at least 15 species, including humans, under circumstances where there is essentially no intake of dietary cholesterol. In general, the rate of whole animal synthesis markedly decreases as body weight increases. Thus, for example, the mouse synthesizes approximately 50 mg of cholesterol per day per kg of body weight. In other species such as the hamster, rabbit, dog, and various nonhuman primates, this rate decreases by about 10 mg/day per kg for each 10-fold increase in body weight. Thus, the typical 70-kg human synthesizes approximately 9 mg/day per kg or about 600–800 mg/day (76).

A persistent misconception is that much of this de novo synthesis takes place in the liver. This concept comes from older studies in which rates of sterol synthesis were quantified in vitro using various ^{14}C-labeled substrates (20, 22). Subsequent investigations, however, demonstrated that these in vitro techniques systematically underestimated rates of cholesterol synthesis in the extrahepatic organs and, consequently, overestimated the importance of the liver to whole animal sterol synthesis (1). Newer methods have been developed that obviate these artifacts and allow measurement of absolute rates of cholesterol synthesis in the individual organs of the live animal (1, 37). These new methods have now been applied to a number of species, and the results of these studies are summarized in Figure 2. This figure illustrates the percentage of whole animal cholesterol synthesis that can be accounted for

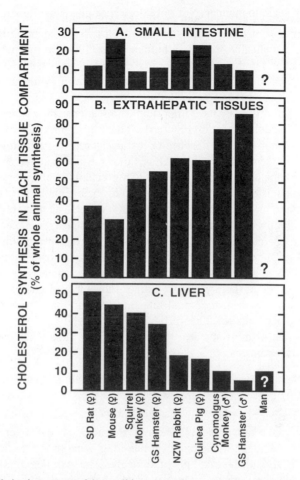

Figure 2 Relative importance of the small intestine, other extrahepatic tissues, and liver as sites for cholesterol synthesis. Rates of cholesterol synthesis were measured in all of the organs of live animals maintained on diets essentially free of cholesterol and triacylglycerol using [³H]water. The data in humans were estimated from rates of synthesis measured in liver biopsy specimens in vitro. SD, GS, and NZW refer to the Sprague-Dawley, Golden Syrian, and New Zealand White strains, respectively, of rats, hamsters, and rabbits. These data come from both published and unpublished observations in this laboratory (18, 19, 62, 68, 77).

by synthesis in the small intestine (*A*), liver (*C*), and remaining extrahepatic organs (*B*) (18, 19, 68, 77).

In some species such as the rat, mouse, and squirrel monkey, cholesterol synthesis in the liver occurs at relatively high rates and so accounts for 40–50% of whole animal sterol synthesis (*C*). In most other species, however, including the rabbit, guinea pig, Cynomolgus monkey, hamster, and apparently, man, the liver accounts for only about 5–20% of whole animal synthesis. Furthermore, when any of these species is placed on a diet containing the amounts of cholesterol typically present in human diets (100–300 mg per/1,000 kcal intake), synthesis in the liver, but not in the extrahepatic tissues, is suppressed so that in such animals 90% of whole animal sterol synthesis takes place in the extrahepatic tissue compartment.

These quantitative data have important implications when superimposed on the general model shown in Figure 1. The higher the rate of cholesterol synthesis in the liver in the absence of dietary sterol, the more tolerant is that species of cholesterol feeding. Thus, the rat and squirrel monkey, by suppressing hepatic synthesis can adapt to a greater load of dietary cholesterol than can the hamster and Cynomologus monkey before cholesteryl esters begin to accumulate in the liver and alterations in LDL-C metabolism occur. Obviously, the liver of the squirrel monkey that synthesizes cholesterol at 800 nmol/hr per g, can adapt to the inflow of a greater amount of dietary cholesterol than can the liver of the Cynomolgus monkey that normally synthesizes sterol at only 50 nmol/hr per g (62). Nevertheless, in the presence of small amounts of dietary sterol, the net movement of cholesterol into the liver (Figure 1, C) from the small intestine (A) and the extrahepatic tissues (B) probably accounts for 90% of the cholesterol that is moving through the system, so that in most species the liver is only a minor net contributor to whole animal synthesis.

Tissue Sites for LDL-C Transport out of the Plasma in Different Species

The second aspect of the scheme shown in Figure 1, and for which there is much new quantitative data, concerns the role of the liver in LDL-C metabolism. Although the hepatocyte has long been known to be the site of origin of VLDL and, hence, LDL, the mechanism(s) of degradation of these particles was (were) poorly understood until the seminal studies of Brown & Goldstein in which the LDL receptor was described (11). With the further observation that interaction between the LDL particle and its receptor could be blocked by chemical modification of the lipoprotein (45, 80), a second, receptor-independent mechanism for the removal of LDL from the plasma was defined. The importance of these two transport processes for the removal of LDL-C from the plasma has now been established in a number of different species. Animals on diets that are low in both cholesterol and triacylglycerol have plasma LDL-C concentrations that typically are only 10–30 mg/dl, and receptor-dependent transport usually accounts for 75% of the LDL-C that is removed from the plasma and degraded each day (61, 65, 66, 70). When lipids are added to the diet and the plasma concentration of LDL-C increases to 75–200 mg/dl, this percentage decreases and, in man, equals 65–80% (6,

40). In animals or humans that genetically lack LDL-R activity, essentially 100% of LDL-C removal from the plasma takes place by the receptor-independent mechanism (6, 65).

As methods for measuring the rates of both receptor-dependent and receptor-independent LDL-C uptake into the various tissues of the live animal have been developed (58, 61), the quantitative importance of the different organs for the degradation of LDL-C has been defined in a number of species and is summarized in Figure 3. LDL-C uptake by either mechanism can be

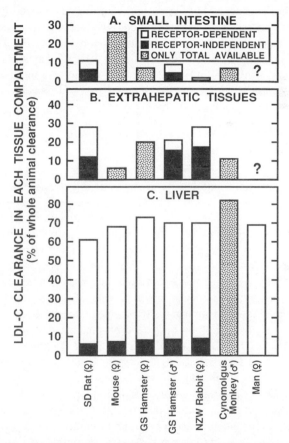

Figure 3 Relative importance of the small intestine, other extrahepatic tissues, and liver in the uptake of LDL-C. Rates of homologous LDL-C uptake were measured in all of the organs of live animals maintained on diets essentially free of cholesterol and triacylglycerol. In some species both the receptor-dependent and receptor-independent components of this LDL-C transport process were quantified and are also shown. The human data were calculated from LDL-C turnover studies in a patient receiving a liver transplant (5). These data come from both published and unpublished observations in this laboratory (61, 65, 66).

detected in many organs (61, 65, 66). However, because of the high rate of LDL-C transport per unit weight in the liver and because of its large size, hepatic uptake accounts for about 70% of the LDL-C degradation that can be detected in every species in which data are available (C) (61, 65, 66). A similar value can be calculated indirectly for humans (5). In most of these species the small intestine accounts for the clearance of approximately 10% of the LDL-C (A) while the remaining extrahepatic organs account for only about 20% of LDL-C degradation (B). Furthermore, insofar as data are available, the liver is also the tissue site that accounts for the great majority of the receptor-dependent LDL-C transport that can be detected in the whole animal (C). In contrast, 60–70% of the receptor-independent transport detected in the whole animal takes place in extrahepatic organs (A, B). Thus, in the absence of dietary lipids where the circulating LDL-C concentration is low, most cholesterol synthesis takes place in the extrahepatic organs (Figure 2) while the great majority of LDL-C is cleared from the plasma by receptor-dependent transport into the liver (Figure 3).

Quantitative Considerations in the Regulation of LDL-C Levels in Plasma

Unfortunately, this relatively simple scheme has little application when the diet contains cholesterol and triacylglycerol and where there are significant alterations in both the rates of sterol synthesis and receptor-dependent LDL-C clearance. Therefore, we need to define the quantitative, kinetic relationships that exist between the rates of LDL-C formation and these two transport systems that are responsible for LDL removal from the plasma.

Such relationships are illustrated in Figure 4 for a hypothetical animal weighing ~0.5 kg. These same relationships are seen in all species that have been studied, including humans; however, the absolute values for these transport parameters vary from species to species. Panel A illustrates how the absolute rate of LDL-C transport out of the plasma space varies as a function of the concentration of LDL-C in the plasma. Panel B expresses these same transport data as either the LDL-C fractional catabolic rate (FCR) or the clearance rate. These three transport parameters are all interchangeable, but are measured experimentally using different techniques. The first point illustrated by these curves is that the rate of LDL-C transport out of the plasma by the receptor-independent process is a linear function of the plasma LDL-C concentration (A). This relationship has been demonstrated in both animals and humans (6, 65, 66). Because of this linear relationship, the FCR and clearance rate for the receptor-independent process is constant at any level of plasma LDL-C (B). In contrast, the receptor-dependent transport process that is occurring simultaneously is saturable (A) (65, 66). Consequently, the value of the FCR and clearance rate for this component of LDL-C transport

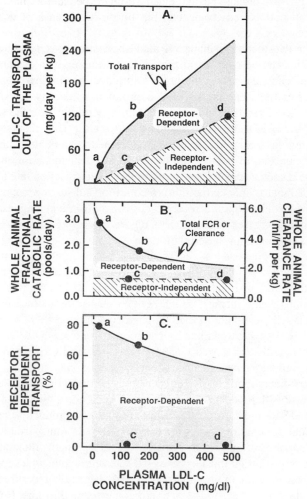

Figure 4 The kinetic relationships between the rates of LDL-C transport out of the plasma by the receptor-dependent and receptor-independent processes in the whole animal and the concentration of LDL-C in the plasma. These rates are expressed in panels *A* and *B* in three ways: (*i*) as the absolute rate of LDL-C taken up by the various tissues each day (mg/day per kg body weight), (*ii*) as the fraction of the plasma LDL-C pool removed each day (pools per day), and (*iii*) as the milliliters of plasma cleared entirely of their LDL-C content each hour (ml/hr per kg). Panel *C* shows the percentage of LDL-C transport out of the plasma that is receptor dependent. In constructing these curves, the level of LDL-R activity in the body was kept constant while the LDL-C production rate was systematically increased to raise the LDL-C concentration in the plasma. The experimental points labeled a, b, c, and d in the three panels represent specific, theoretical situations that may occur in such animals and are discussed in detail in the text. These curves apply to an animal weighing about 0.5 kg but were adapted from curves determined experimentally in the rat, hamster, and man (48, 50, 64, 66).

progressively decreases (B) as the plasma LDL-C concentration is increased, even though LDL-R activity in this illustration has been kept constant (50, 64).

The four data points in Figure 4 also show how these relationships are altered with extreme changes in the LDL-C formation or receptor activity. Point a, for example, shows the typical situation in an experimental animal on a lipid-free diet. The rate of LDL-C production, and its rate of transport out of the plasma, are shown as about 30 mg/day per kg, and the steady-state concentration of LDL-C in the plasma as 25 mg/dl. This absolute transport rate of 30 mg/day per kg (A) can also be expressed as an FCR of 2.8 pools/day or a clearance rate of about 5 ml/hr per kg (B). In this case, 80% of the transport is receptor-dependent (C). If the LDL-C production rate is increased 4-fold to 120 mg/day per kg (point b), the FCR and clearance rate both decline (B), about 67% of transport is receptor-dependent (C), and the plasma LDL-C concentration increases to about 150 mg/dl. Points c and d, respectively, illustrate the changes in these relationships that would occur if all receptor-dependent transport were lost but the LDL-C production rate remained either 30 or 120 mg/day per kg. In both cases the FCR and clearance rates would decrease to the same fixed values (B), and the steady-state plasma LDL-C concentrations would increase to the high levels necessary to drive receptor-independent LDL-C uptake at the two respective rates of LDL-C production. Thus, for example, the plasma LDL-C concentration would have to reach almost 500 mg/dl to achieve a rate of LDL-C removal through the receptor-independent process equal to 120 mg/day per kg (point d).

These considerations clearly indicate that the steady-state plasma LDL-C concentration is dependent upon four variables (49, 50, 64, 66): (a) the rate at which LDL-C enters the plasma space, the LDL-C production rate (J_t), (b) the maximal achievable rate of receptor-dependent transport (J^m), (c) the functional affinity of the LDL particle for its receptor (K_m), and (d) the proportionality constant that describes the rate of receptor-independent transport (P). Since each of these variables can be measured directly in the experimental animal (21) and they have been estimated in man (48), one can calculate how the steady-state concentration of LDL-C (C_1) will change under circumstances where dietary components have altered one or more of these variables using the following equation:

$$C_1 = \frac{J_t - J^m - PK_m + [(J_t - J^m - PK_m)^2 + 4PK_mJ_t]^{1\!/\!2}}{2P}. \qquad 1.$$

Although environmental factors such as diet might, in theory, change any one of these four variables, in practice dietary cholesterol and triacylglycerol primarily alter the level of LDL-R activity in the body (J^m) and the rate of LDL-C production (J_t). Such dietary manipulations have relatively little effect, if any, on the values of K_m or P.

Using this equation, one can calculate how changes in either J^m or J_t, or both, will alter the steady-state concentration of LDL-C. These relationships are illustrated, in the case of the male hamster, by the two solid curves shown in Figure 5. Similar curves may be generated for other species, including humans, by substituting the appropriate values for the four variables into Equation 1 (21). In this figure, the absolute values for J^m and J_t measured in control animals fed a lipid-free diet have both been set equal to 100% (*open circle*). The two *solid curves* show how the plasma LDL-C concentration will

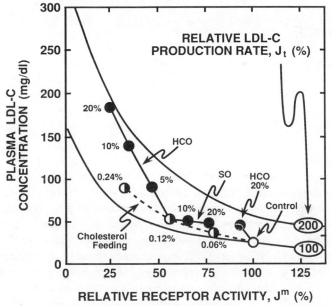

RELATIVE RECEPTOR ACTIVITY, J^m (%)

Figure 5 Relationship between the steady-state concentration of LDL-C and whole animal receptor activity and production rates. These curves were constructed by entering into equation #1 the appropriate rate constants for J^m, J_t, K_m, and P as experimentally determined in the male hamster. The lower curve (100% LDL-C production) was then constructed by systematically reducing receptor activity to 0% while keeping the other three parameters constant. The upper curve (200% LDL-C production) was similarly constructed after doubling the value of J_t. To simplify this diagram, the absolute values of the receptor activity and production rate found in the control animals fed a lipid-free diet are each set equal to 100%. Superimposed upon these two theoretical curves are experimental data obtained after feeding different amounts of cholesterol alone *(dashed line)* or a constant level of cholesterol along with different amounts of hydrogenated coconut oil (HCO) or safflower oil (SO) *(solid lines)*. The numbers represent the amounts of cholesterol and triacylglycerol present in each diet expressed as percentages by weight (grams per 100-gram diet).

increase as LDL-R activity is reduced to 0% under circumstances where the LDL-C production rate is set at either 100 or 200% of the control value. Two general principles are evident from these curves. First, the plasma LDL-C concentration does not increase as an inverse, linear function of J^m. Rather, loss of receptor activity has relatively little effect on the circulating cholesterol level until 50% of receptor-dependent transport is suppressed. Second, the level of receptor activity does, however, profoundly affect the response of the steady-state plasma LDL-C concentration to changes in LDL-C production. Doubling J_t, for example, raises the plasma LDL-C level by only about 30 mg/dl if receptor activity is 100%, but by nearly 125 mg/dl if J^m is only 25% of control. Thus, the most profound elevations in plasma LDL-C will be seen with dietary manipulations that suppress J^m and increase J_t.

Effect of Dietary Cholesterol on LDL Receptor Activity and LDL-C Production

Having defined the theoretical relationships between these two parameters and the plasma LDL-C concentration, one can review the metabolic effects of the two dietary lipids, cholesterol and triacylglycerol, on J^m and J_t. The addition of cholesterol alone to a lipid-free diet is associated with major metabolic alterations in the liver of every species, including humans, for which data are available. As the sterol reaches the liver in the chylomicron remnant, hepatic cholesterol synthesis is rapidly suppressed and cholesteryl esters increase to levels that are dependent on the amount of sterol absorbed (Figure 1) (56, 64). If such cholesterol feeding is continued, the circulating LDL-C concentration increases more slowly until a new steady-state level is achieved, the latter is also dependent upon the amount of cholesterol absorbed through the intestine (63, 64). Thus, for example, in the young male hamster, the plasma LDL-C level will increase from ~25 mg/dl to new steady-state values of ~40, 55, and 90 mg/dl when 0.06, 0.12, and 0.24% cholesterol, respectively, is added to the diet. Similarly, the human infant increases its LDL-C level from ~25 to 90 mg/dl as the content of sterol in its milk is progressively raised from 0 to 15 mg/dl (15); the human adult increases its LDL-C concentration from about 50 to 120 mg/dl as the daily intake of cholesterol is raised from 20 to 160 mg (14). Note that these increments in LDL-C concentration in the hamster require the daily intake of amounts of cholesterol (~160 mg/kg) that are 4 times higher than the daily synthesis rate in this species (~40 mg/kg); similar increases in LDL-C can be induced in the human infant and adult at much lower intakes of sterol (~24 and 2 mg/day per kg, respectively) relative to whole animal synthesis rates (~25 and 9 mg/day per kg, respectively) (27, 76). However, even though primates, including man, are more sensitive to dietary cholesterol than many smaller animals, nevertheless, virtually every species will respond to dietary cholesterol feeding by elevating its LDL-C level.

The mechanisms responsible for this elevation are also illustrated in Figure 5 in the case of the hamster. As the amount of cholesterol in the diet is increased, sterol synthesis in the liver is essentially fully suppressed, a new level of cholesteryl esters is established in the hepatocyte that is proportional to the amount of cholesterol absorbed, and LDL-R activity is reduced (64). Thus, as shown by the *dashed line* in Figure 5, when diets are fed that contain 0.06 to 0.24% cholesterol and new steady states are achieved, J^m at the highest dose is reduced to only about 30% of the activity found in the control animals and J_t increases slightly to approximately 130% of control. These two changes alone fully account for the modest increases in LDL-C levels from ~27 to 90 mg/dl. Thus, the primary effect of cholesterol feeding is to expand the storage pool of cholesteryl esters in the hepatocyte and reduce the level of hepatic receptor activity. These changes, in turn, reduce the percentage of LDL-C cleared by the receptor-dependent process and reduce both the FCR and clearance rate of LDL-C observed in the whole animal (Figure 4). Little or no change is found in the small fraction of receptor-dependent uptake that occurs in the extrahepatic tissues or in receptor-independent LDL-C transport.

Effect of Different Fatty Acids on LDL Receptor Activity and LDL-C Production in Animals

The addition of commercial triacylglycerols to the diets of various experimental animals results in further changes in the steady-state LDL-C concentrations. The magnitude and direction of these changes depend upon the amount of cholesterol also present in the diet and the types of fatty acids in the triacylglycerols. For example, in the hamster, feeding predominantly longer chain saturated fatty acids (~40% of caloric intake) elevates the LDL-C levels by only about 25 mg/dl if no cholesterol is in the diet but by nearly 160 mg/dl if 0.12% cholesterol is present (81). In virtually all species, when the cholesterol content of the diet is kept constant, feeding increasing amounts of triacylglycerol containing mainly long chain saturated fatty acids markedly elevates the plasma LDL-C levels in a dose-dependent manner (32, 39, 83), whereas triacylglycerols containing medium chain-length saturated fatty acids have virtually no effect on the plasma cholesterol level (81). Triacylglycerols containing predominantly long chain unsaturated fatty acids tend to lower the plasma LDL-C levels below those seen with cholesterol feeding alone, although the absolute magnitude of this effect is small compared to the effect of the saturated fatty acids in raising these levels (39, 63, 64, 83).

The mechanisms responsible for these changes are also illustrated in Figure 5. When the cholesterol content of the diet is kept constant at 0.12%, the addition of 5, 10, and 20% (by weight) of a triacylgycerol containing predominantly long chain saturated fatty acids (HCO) causes further suppression of receptor activity and a near doubling of the LDL-C production rate. This decrease in J^m to only 25% of control and the increase in J_t to nearly 200% of control fully accounts for the rise in the LDL-C concentration from about 55 to 190 mg/dl. Figure 5 also shows that such changes do not occur in the control animal fed a cholesterol-free diet. When the animals fed 0.12% cholesterol are also fed triacylglycerol containing predominantly unsaturated fatty acids (SO), receptor activity is partially restored (83) so that the plasma LDL-C concentration decreases slightly to about 45 mg/dl. Note, however, that if the dietary load of triacylglycerol is kept constant at 20% and the unsaturated triacylglycerol is systematically substituted for the saturated lipid, then the plasma LDL-C concentration falls dramatically, from ~190 to 55 mg/dl (83). This type of substitution is commonly carried out in human studies and obscures the fact that saturated and unsaturated lipids have independent and oppositely directed effects on receptor activity (83). These effects are primarily manifest in the liver, although small changes also occur in receptor-dependent transport in the extrahepatic tissues (81). While cholesterol feeding markedly increases the level of cholesteryl esters in the liver, paradoxically, the suppression of hepatic LDL-R activity seen with saturated lipids is associated with a marked reduction in the cholesteryl ester (CE) content of the hepatocyte (63, 64, 81, 83).

The next question of importance is which specific fatty acids in commercial triacylglycerols are responsible for these regulatory effects. This question has been addressed in animal studies using synthesized triacylglycerols that contain only a single species of fatty acid. Although such studies are not complete, it is becoming clear that fatty acids fall into three different groups. In the first group are short and medium chain-length compounds such as the 4:0, 6:0, 8:0, and 10:0 saturated fatty acids that are rapidly oxidized by the liver to acetyl-CoA. These fatty acids do not alter the composition of the lipid pools in the liver, do not change the concentration of free or esterified cholesterol in the hepatocyte, and do not alter J^m or J_t from those values attributable to the cholesterol also present in the experimental diets (82). Thus, such fatty acids are biologically neutral with respect to regulation of the concentration of LDL-C in the plasma. The long chain 18:0 fatty acid also belongs to this biologically neutral group (82). A second category of lipids includes the 12:0, 14:0, and 16:0 saturated fatty acids that do enrich the hepatic lipid pools, including the pool of fatty acids esterified to cholesterol. When fed with sterols, they suppress steady-state cholesteryl ester levels in the hepatocyte, lower hepatic receptor activity, and markedly increase the rate of LDL-C formation (16, 82). Therefore, these three saturated fatty acids, when fed with cholesterol, are biologically very active and markedly elevate the plasma LDL-C concentration.

The third group of fatty acids is best exemplified by the 18:1(c9) compound which, when fed with cholesterol, markedly increases the steady-state cholesteryl ester fraction in the liver, restores hepatic receptor activity, and reduces the rate of LDL-C production (16). Thus, such compounds significantly reduce the circulating level of LDL-C. However, even though the 18:1(c9) fatty acid is just as effective in raising J^m as is the 14:0 fatty acid in suppressing this activity nevertheless, when fed with cholesterol the unsaturated fatty acid will only lower the LDL-C concentration modestly from ~70 to 30 mg/dl while the 14:0 fatty acid will raise this level from ~70 to 200 mg/dl (16). This very different quantitative response is due to the nonlinear relationship that exists between receptor activity in the animal and the steady-state LDL-C concentrations (Figure 5). Finally, when the 18:1(c9) compound is converted to the 18:1(t 9) fatty acid or when a second double bond is introduced into the molecule to form the 18:2(c9, c12) fatty acid, the new compounds become biologically much less regulatory and essentially lose their ability to markedly increase receptor activity and lower the LDL-C concentration, i.e. they become nearly neutral.

Regardless of whether such studies are carried out with mixed, commercial triacylglycerols or with fats containing a single fatty acid, there usually is a reciprocal relationship between changes in LDL-R activity and LDL-C formation. Thus, the possibility exists that fatty acids may regulate two separate processes that independently dictate the values of J^m and J_t. However, fat feeding does not increase mRNA levels for apo B in the liver (43, 60). Furthermore, there is no increase in apo B secretion from the perfused liver of the fat-fed monkey (60) or the receptor-deficient rabbit (35), even though LDL-C production is elevated in both of these situations. Since the LDL receptor is involved in the clearance of VLDL remnants (42), as well as LDL, the most likely explanation for these findings is that suppression of J^m leads to increased conversion of VLDL remnants to LDL and, hence, to an increase in J_t (Figure 1). Conversely, restoration of receptor activity would be associated with a decrease in LDL-C production. If this explanation is correct, then these findings are consistent with the view that fatty acids, working in conjunction with dietary cholesterol, regulate a single event within the liver, i.e. the level of LDL-R activity. The reciprocal changes observed in LDL-C production rates presumably are only the secondary consequences of these changes in receptor activity.

A Model for the Interaction of Dietary Cholesterol and Triacylglycerol

All of these observations of the seemingly contradictory effects of cholesterol and fatty acids on hepatic cholesterol levels and LDL-R activity can be incorporated into a single, unified model for the regulation of plasma LDL-C levels. The major assumptions of this model are illustrated in the insert in Figure 6. At any level of cholesterol flux through the liver cell, presumably an equilibrium is established between the sterol that acts as a regulator of hepatic receptor activity (C^R) and the inert storage pool of cholesteryl esters (CE). The size of this putative regulatory pool of cholesterol or a metabolite of cholesterol, acting through the sterol regulatory elements on the LDL-R gene (17, 73, 74), presumably dictates the level of LDL-R mRNA in the cell and, ultimately, the activity of receptor-dependent LDL-C transport in the liver. C^R must represent only a very small part of the unesterified pool of cholesterol in the cell and cannot be identified or measured at this time.

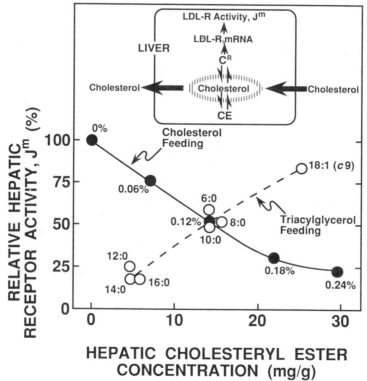

Figure 6   A model illustrating the possible mechanisms of interaction of dietary cholesterol and fatty acids in regulating LDL-R activity in the liver. The insert shows the specific steps involved in this regulation: CE refers to the steady-state concentration of cholesteryl esters in the cell, and C^R is the small component of unesterified cholesterol that is the putative regulator of LDL-R mRNA transcription in the cell nucleus. The *solid curve* illustrates the relationship between J^m and CE when increasing amounts of cholesterol alone are added to the diet for prolonged periods of time. The *dashed line* illustrates this same relationship when the cholesterol content of the diet is kept constant and a constant level of triacylglycerols containing different fatty acids is also fed. The concepts and data presented in this figure are derived from Reference 16.

However, all other parameters of this model, including net cholesterol balance across the liver and the steady-state level of cholesteryl esters, LDL-R mRNA, and receptor-dependent transport, can be measured under circumstances in which the experimental animals have been fed varying amounts of sterol and triacylglycerol.

The first major mechanism that alters the parameters of this system is a change in net sterol balance across the liver. When a particular level of cholesterol is fed in the diet for a prolonged period of time, a new steady state is achieved in which cellular cholesterol levels are elevated and the LDL-R mRNA level and activity are partially suppressed (36, 64). In this case, the equilibrium between C^R and CE is presumably constant so that LDL-R activity varies inversely with the concentration of CE (and, presumably, with C^R) as the level of sterol fed in the diet is progressively increased (*solid line,* Figure 6) (16). This inverse relationship between J^m and CE is invariably seen where there is a demonstrable change in net sterol balance across the liver such as can be induced by feeding cholesterol (64, 81) or bile acids (67), or by feeding agents that block the intestinal absorption of either of these two sterols.

The second mechanism that alters this system is the flow of specific fatty acids into the lipid pools of the liver. When the amount of sterol in the diet is constant, feeding the saturated fatty acids apparently shifts the equilibrium of the excess cholesterol in the liver cell out of the ester pool and into the putative regulatory pool, which, in turn, markedly suppresses the LDL-R mRNA level and activity (16, 36). In contrast, unsaturated fatty acids like the 18:1(*c*9) compound shift this equilibrium out of the regulatory pool towards the cholesteryl ester pool so that receptor-dependent transport is markedly increased (16). Thus, as illustrated by the *dashed line* in Figure 6, when sterol intake is constant and the type of fatty acid in the diet is varied, a direct relationship is found between the steady-state concentration of cholesteryl esters and LDL-R activity in the liver. The magnitude of this effect is markedly diminished when there is little cholesterol in the diet. It should be emphasized that not only is this relationship between CE and J^m diametrically opposed to that observed with cholesterol feeding, but, in addition, these marked changes in LDL-R activity seen with fatty acid feeding occur under circumstances where no measurable change in net sterol balance across the liver has taken place (16). Thus, the most detrimental change in the plasma LDL-C concentration occurs when the liver cell is loaded with cholesterol by feeding sterol in the diet, and this cholesterol is then shifted into the putative regulatory pool by also feeding one of the long chain saturated fatty acids. This combination leads to marked suppression of LDL-R activity, a large increase in the LDL-C production rate, and a marked rise in the LDL-C concentration in the plasma.

One of the key questions raised by this model is what enzyme(s) is (are) responsible for determining the equilibrium between C^R and CE. Several lines of evidence suggest that this key role is played by acylCoA:cholesterol acyltransferase (ACAT), the enzyme that catalyzes the esterification of cholesterol to a variety of fatty acids (26). The rate of this reaction is clearly influenced by both the mass of cholesterol and the types of fatty acids that are available in the liver cell. Apparently, this enzyme is usually present in excess so that when only cholesterol is entering the cell, the level of apparent ACAT activity varies directly with the mass of sterol available for esterification (71, 72). In the absence of dietary triacylglycerol, this cholesterol is esterified to the 18:1(c9) and other fatty acids that are synthesized endogenously (16). Thus, in this situation both C^R and CE presumably increase in proportion to the amount of cholesterol absorbed from the intestine, and the ratio of C^R to CE remains relatively constant. However, this reaction is also exquisitely sensitive to the types of fatty acid that enter the liver during triacylglycerol feeding. For example, feeding the 14:0 fatty acid, which is a poor substrate for ACAT (26), markedly reduces the level of CE in the liver cell, and these esters become very enriched with the 14:0 and 16:0 fatty acids (16). Apparently, these particular fatty acids inhibit ACAT activity by entering the substrate pool of fatty acids used by this enzyme. In contrast, feeding the 18:1(c9) fatty acid, which is the preferred substrate for this enzyme (26), markedly increases the level of CE in the cell, and these esters become even more enriched with the 18:1(c9) compound. Thus, these data are consistent with the view that flooding the liver with fatty acids such as the 14:0 compound inhibits cholesterol esterification and elevates the C^R/CE ratio, whereas the 18:1(c9) fatty acid shifts this equilibrium in the opposite direction so that C^R is relatively reduced. This model, therefore, suggests that all of the observed consequences of dietary cholesterol and triacylglycerol can be explained by the effects of these lipids on ACAT activity; these effects, in turn, alter the distribution of excess cellular cholesterol in the liver between the storage pool of cholesteryl esters and the metabolically active, regulatory pool. Whether this concept is correct must await new methods that allow direct quantification of C^R in all of these experimental situations.

Effect of Cholesterol and Different Fatty Acids on Plasma LDL-C Levels in Man

Virtually all of the effects of cholesterol and triacylglycerol feeding that have been seen in experimental animals have also been observed in man. Obvious limitations in studying these regulatory processes in human populations, however, make it difficult to interpret the results of such studies in quantitative terms. For example, many such studies use subjects of different sex, age, ethnicity, and responsiveness to dietary lipids. Such variation in genetic background adds considerable variability to the experimental results obtained in such groups. Second, in studying triacylglycerol effects, the background level of dietary cholesterol sometimes has not been controlled or else varies markedly in different studies. Third, the quantitative alterations that can be made in the lipid content of human diets are relatively limited. Thus, it is often difficult to discriminate between the effects of two lipids that have subtle differences in metabolic effects. Fourth, comparisons are usually carried out by substituting one active triacylglycerol for another, rather than by substituting an active triacylglycerol for a biologically neutral fat. This often obscures the true effect of a particular fatty acid because such experiments do not make clear whether a change in the LDL-C level was brought about by removal of the active fatty acid from the diet or by the addition of the second triacylglycerol. Fifth, most human studies are necessarily carried out over a period of only 4–8 weeks. In one month, a hamster will turn over approximately 120 pools of LDL-C and come into a new steady state, while a human will metabolize only about 12 pools of LDL-C during this same period. Thus, the results obtained after such relatively short experiments can only indicate the trends in serum lipid levels and not new steady-state values. Sixth, human studies usually yield only very limited experimental data, i.e. changes in the LDL-C concentration. As illustrated in Figure 5, however, the LDL-C level is a poor measure of what is happening with respect to the LDL-C receptor activity and production rate. Finally, one of the most serious limitations in human studies is failure to define the "neutral" LDL-C concentration, i.e. the level of LDL-C dictated by the content of cholesterol and other nutrients in a particular diet. Thus, it becomes nearly impossible to distinguish whether the substitution of a particular triacylglycerol into the diet lowers or raises the LDL-C level because that lipid actively increases or decreases J^m or, alternatively, whether that lipid is biologically inactive and the LDL-C level is merely drifting upwards or downwards towards the neutral value dictated by the level of cholesterol in that experimental diet.

In spite of these limitations, however, several generalizations can be made concerning the effects of various lipids on LDL-C levels in man based on data that have recently been extensively reviewed (29, 55). In the presence of large quantities of dietary triacylglycerol, the plasma cholesterol level in man increases about 10 mg/dl for every 250 mg of cholesterol that is added to the diet (29). This amount of sterol corresponds to a daily intake of ~3–4 mg/kg or about 35% of the amount of sterol synthesized in the body each day. To obtain a similar increase in the plasma cholesterol concentration in a small animal such as the triacylglycerol-fed hamster would require a cholesterol intake of ~10–15 mg/kg or, again, about 35% of the amount of cholesterol synthesized each day. Saturated fatty acids added to these cholesterol-containing diets invariably elevate the plasma cholesterol (and LDL-C) concentration in humans and, as in animals, the active compounds appear to be the 12:0,

14:0, and 16:0 fatty acids while the 18:0 compound is almost certainly biologically neutral with respect to the regulation of J^m and J_t (9, 47, 55).

Triacylglycerols containing predominately unsaturated fatty acids are quantitatively less effective in changing the plasma total and LDL-C levels, although these reductions are clearly evident when comparisons are made to a neutral control diet in which carbohydrate has been isocalorically substituted for the lipid (3, 12, 28, 51–53, 78). The implication in humans, as in animals (Figure 5), is that these lipids actively increase LDL-R activity. Several studies also suggest, but do not prove, that the 18:1($c9$) monounsaturated compound is more active than the 18:2($c9$, $c12$) polyunsaturated fatty acid in this regard (53, 78). In contrast to the effect of these two unsaturated fatty acids, the 18:1($t9$) monounsaturated fatty acid appears to be biologically neutral and results in plasma LDL-C levels indistinguishable from those observed after feeding the 18:0 saturated compound but higher than those observed after feeding the 18:1($c9$) fatty acid (54, 86). Based on data reported in experimental animals, the 18:1($t9$) and 18:0 fatty acids are not likely to actively raise the LDL-C concentration in humans, but, rather, are biologically neutral in the regulation of J^m. It is the 18:1($c9$) compound that is actively increasing J^m and so reducing the LDL-C level below that observed after feeding the 18:1($t9$) and 18:0 lipids.

Summary

Extensive data obtained in both experimental animals and humans demonstrate that steady-state plasma LDL-C concentrations are determined largely by the rate of LDL-C formation, J_t, and the level of LDL-R activity, J^m, located primarily in the liver. An increase in net cholesterol delivery to the liver suppresses J^m, slightly elevates J_t, and modestly raises the LDL-C level. Feeding lipids such as the 12:0, 14:0, and 16:0 saturated fatty acids further suppresses J^m, increases J_t, and markedly elevates the plasma LDL-C concentration. Feeding triacylglycerols containing the 18:1($c9$) fatty acid restores hepatic receptor activity, decreases J_t, and modestly reduces the concentration of LDL-C in the plasma. The 18:2($c9$, $c12$) compound has similar effects, although it is quantitatively less active than the monounsaturated fatty acid in restoring J^m. In contrast to these fatty acids that actively raise or lower hepatic receptor activity, a large group of compounds including the 4:0, 6:0, 8:0, 10:0, 18:0, and 18:1($t9$) fatty acids have no demonstrable effect on any parameter of LDL-C metabolism. These fatty acids, therefore, can be added to animal and human diets with relative impunity. They will alter plasma LDL-C levels only to the extent that they replace the active saturated fatty acids (in which case they lower the LDL-C concentration) or unsaturated compounds (in which case they raise the plasma cholesterol level). All of these effects of cholesterol and the various fatty acids can be explained by the effects of these lipids in altering the size of the regulatory pool of cholesterol in the hepatocyte. However, many aspects of the cellular and molecular biology of these regulatory processes require additional investigation. In particular, new studies should focus on how the genetic background of an individual animal or human alters the quantitative response of its plasma LDL-C concentration to the dietary challenge of each of these types of lipids.

ACKNOWLEDGMENTS

The work reviewed in this manuscript from the authors' laboratories was supported by National Institutes of Health Research Grants HL-09610 and HL-38409. Additional support was provided by the Moss Heart Fund, the Institute of Shortening and Edible Oils, and the National Livestock and Meat Board.

Literature Cited

1. Anderson, J. M., Dietschy, J. M. 1979. Absolute rates of cholesterol synthesis in extrahepatic tissues measured with ³H-labeled water and ¹⁴C-labeled substrates. *J. Lipid Res.* 20: 740–52
2. Anderson, K. M., Wilson, P. W. F., Odell, P. M., Kannel, W. B. 1991. In *Cholesterol and Coronary Heart Disease,* ed. P. Gold, S. Grover, D. A. K. Roncari, pp. 3–17. Park Ridge: Parthenon
3. Baggio, G., Pagnan, A., Muraca, M., Martini, S., Opportuno, A., et al. 1988. Olive-oil-enriched diet: effect on serum lipoprotein levels and biliary cholesterol saturation. *Am. J. Clin. Nutr.* 47:960–64
4. Beynen, A. C., Katan, M. B., Van Zutphen, L. F. M. 1987. Hypo- and hyperresponders: Individual differences in the response of serum cholesterol concentration to changes in diet. *Adv. Lipid Res.* 22:115–71
5. Bilheimer, D. W., Goldstein, J. L., Grundy, S. M., Starzl, T. E., Brown, M. S. 1984. Liver transplantation to provide low-density-lipoprotein receptors and lower plasma cholesterol in a child with homozygous familial hypercholesterolemia. *N. Engl. J. Med.* 311:1658–64
6. Bilheimer, D. W., Stone, N. J., Grundy, S. M. 1979. Metabolic studies in familial hypercholesterolemia. *J. Clin. Invest.* 64:524–33
7. Björkhem, I. 1992. Mechanism of degradation of the steroid side chain in the formation of bile acids. *J. Lipid Res.* 33:455–71
8. Blankenhorn, D. H., Nessim, S. A., Johnson, R. L., Sanmarco, M. E., Azen, S. P., Cashin-Hemphill, L. 1987. Beneficial effects of combined colestipol-niacin therapy on coronary atherosclerosis and coronary venous bypass grafts. *J. Am. Med. Assoc.* 257:3233–40
9. Bonanome, A., Grundy, S. M. 1988. Effect of dietary stearic acid on plasma cholesterol and lipoprotein levels. *N. Engl. J. Med.* 318:1244–48
10. Brown, G., Albers, J. J., Fisher, L. D., Schaefer, S. M., Lin, J.-T., et al. 1990. Regression of coronary artery disease as a result of intensive lipid-lowering therapy in men with high levels of apolipoprotein B. *N. Engl. J. Med.* 323:1289–98
11. Brown, M. S., Goldstein, J. L. 1986. A receptor-mediated pathway for cholesterol homeostasis. *Science* 232:34–47
12. Brussaard, J. H., Dallinga-Thie, G., Groot, P. H. E., Katan, M. B. 1980. Effects of amount and type of dietary fat on serum lipids, lipoproteins and apolipoproteins in man. *Atherosclerosis* 36:515–27
13. Carrella, M., Dietschy, J. M. 1977. Comparison of the effects of cholic acid and chenic acid feeding on rates of cholesterol synthesis in the liver of the rat. *Am. J. Dig. Dis.* 22:318–26
14. Connor, W. E., Cerqueira, M. T., Connor, R. W., Wallace, R. B., Malinow, M. R., Casdorph, H. R.

1978. The plasma lipids, lipoproteins, and diet of the Tarahumara Indians of Mexico. *Am. J. Clin. Nutr.* 31:1131–42

15. Cruz, M. L., Mimouni, F., Wong, W., Hachey, D. L., Klein, P., Tsang, R. C. 1991. Effects of infant nutrition on cholesterol synthesis rates in infancy. *Pediatr. Abstr. Clin. Res.* 39(3):689 (Abstr.)

16. Daumerie, C. M., Woollett, L. A., Dietschy, J. M. 1992. Fatty acids regulate hepatic low density lipoprotein receptor activity through redistribution of intracellular cholesterol pools. *Proc. Natl. Acad. Sci. USA* 89:10797–10801

17. Dawson, P. A., Hofmann, S. L., van der Westhuyzen, D. R., Südhof, T. C., Brown, M. S., Goldstein, J. L. 1988. Sterol-dependent repression of low density lipoprotein receptor promoter mediated by 16-base pair sequence adjacent to binding site for transcription factor Sp1. *J. Biol. Chem.* 263:3372–79

18. Dietschy, J. M., Gamel, W. G. 1971. Cholesterol synthesis in the intestine of man: Regional differences and control mechanisms. *J. Clin. Invest.* 50:872–80

19. Dietschy, J. M., Kita, T., Suckling, K. E., Goldstein, J. L., Brown, M. S. 1983. Cholesterol synthesis in vivo and in vitro in the WHHL rabbit, an animal with defective low density lipoprotein receptors. *J. Lipid Res.* 24:469–80

20. Dietschy, J. M., Siperstein, M. D. 1967. Effect of cholesterol feeding and fasting on sterol synthesis in seventeen tissues of the rat. *J. Lipid Res.* 8:97–104

21. Dietschy, J. M., Spady, D. K., Meddings, J. B. 1988. A quantitative approach to low density lipoprotein metabolism in man and in various experimental animals. In *Hyperlipidaemia and Atherosclerosis*, ed. K. E. Suckling, P. H. E. Groot, pp. 17–32. London/San Diego/New York/Boston/Sydney/Tokyo/Toronto: Academic

22. Dietschy, J. M., Wilson, J. D. 1968. Cholesterol synthesis in the squirrel monkey: Relative rates of synthesis in various tissues and mechanisms of control. *J. Clin. Invest.* 47:166–74

23. Emken, E. A., Dutton, H. J., eds. 1979. *Geometrical and Positional Fatty Acid Isomers*, pp. 1–344. Peoria, Ill: Am. Oil Chem. Soc.

24. Fielding, C. J. 1987. Factors affecting the rate of catalyzed transfer of cholesteryl esters in plasma. *Am. Heart J.* 113:532–37

25. Goodman, D. S. 1988. Report of the national cholesterol program expert panel on detection, evaluation and treatment of high blood cholesterol in adults. *Arch. Intern. Med.* 148:36–68

26. Goodman, D. S., Deykin, D., Shiratori, T. 1964. The formation of cholesterol esters with rat liver enzymes. *J. Biol. Chem.* 239:1335–45

27. Grobe, R. 1982. Vergleichende Untersuchung über gallensaeuren-und Cholesterinsynthese in Kleinkindesalter bei gesunden und bei Kindern mit cystischer Fibrose. Hohen Medizinischen Fakultät Dissertation. Rheinischen Friedrich-Wilhelms-Universität zu Bonn, Bonn, Germany. 30 pp.

28. Grundy, S. M. 1986. Comparison of monounsaturated fatty acids and carbohydrates for lowering plasma cholesterol. *N. Engl. J. Med.* 314:745–48

29. Grundy, S. M., Barrett-Connor, E., Rudel, L. L., Miettinen, T., Spector, A. A. 1988. Workshop on the impact of dietary cholesterol on plasma lipoproteins and atherogenesis. *Arteriosclerosis* 8:95–101.

30. Gylling, H., Miettinen, T. A. 1992. Cholesterol absorption and synthesis related to low density lipoprotein metabolism during varying cholesterol intake in men with different apoE phenotypes. *J. Lipid Res.* 33:1361–71

31. Havel, R. J. 1986. Functional activities of hepatic lipoprotein receptors. *Annu. Rev. Physiol.* 48:119–34

32. Hayes, K. C., Pronczuk, A., Lindsey, S., Diersen-Schade, D. 1991. Dietary saturated fatty acids (12:0, 14:0, 16:0) differ in their impact on plasma cholesterol and lipoproteins in nonhuman primates. *Am. J. Clin. Nutr.* 53:491–98

33. Hegsted, D. M. 1989. Unanswered questions. In *Proceedings from the Conference on the Effects of Dietary Fatty Acids on Serum Lipoproteins and Hemostasis*, ed. R. J. Nicolosi, pp. 103–14. Washington, DC: Am. Heart Assoc.

34. Holme, I. 1990. An analysis of randomized trials evaluating the effect of cholesterol reduction on total mortality and coronary heart disease incidence. *Circulation* 82:1916–24

35. Hornick, C. A., Kita, T., Hamilton, R. L., Kane, J. P., Havel, R. J. 1983. Secretion of lipoproteins from the liver of normal and Watanabe heritable hyperlipidemic rabbits. *Proc. Natl. Acad. Sci. USA* 80:6096–100

36. Horton, J. D., Cuthbert, J. A., Spady, D. K. 1992. Regulation of hepatic LDL receptor activity and mRNA levels

by dietary fatty acids. *Circulation* 86: 1745

37. Jeske, D. J., Dietschy, J. M. 1980. Regulation of rates of cholesterol synthesis in vivo in the liver and carcass of the rat measured using [³H]water. *J. Lipid Res.* 21:364–76

38. Jiang, X. C., Agellon, L. B., Walsh, A., Breslow, J. L., Tall, A. 1992. Dietary cholesterol increases transcription of the human cholesteryl ester transfer protein gene in transgenic mice. *J. Clin. Invest.* 90:1290–95

39. Johnson, F. L., St. Clair, R. W., Rudel, L. L. 1985. Effects of degree of saturation of dietary fat on the hepatic production of lipoproteins in the African green monkey. *J. Lipid Res.* 26:403–17

40. Kesaniemi, Y. A., Witztum, J. L., Steinbrecher, U. P. 1983. Receptor-mediated catabolism of low density lipoprotein in man. Quantitation using glucosylated low density lipoprotein. *J. Clin. Invest.* 71:950–59

41. Keys, A., Anderson, J. T., Grande, F. 1957. Serum-cholesterol response to dietary fat. *Lancet* 1:787

42. Kita, T., Brown, M. S., Bilheimer, D. W., Goldstein, J. L. 1982. Delayed clearance of very low density and intermediate density lipoproteins with enhanced conversion to low density lipoprotein in WHHL rabbits. *Proc. Natl. Acad. Sci. USA* 79:5693–97

43. Kushwaha, R. S., McMahan, C. A., Mott, G. E., Carey, K. D., Reardon, C. A., et al. 1991. Influence of dietary lipids on hepatic mRNA levels of proteins regulating plasma lipoproteins in baboons with high and low levels of large high density lipoproteins. *J. Lipid Res.* 32:1929–40

44. Lipid Research Clinic Program. 1984. The lipid research clinics coronary primary prevention trial results. II. The relationship of reduction in incidence of coronary heart disease to cholesterol lowering. *J. Am. Med. Assoc.* 251:365–74

45. Mahley, R. W., Weisgraber, K. H., Melchior, G. W., Innerarity, T. L., Holcombe, K. S. 1980. Inhibition of receptor-mediated clearance of lysine and arginine-modified lipoproteins from the plasma of rats and monkeys. *Proc. Natl. Acad. Sci. USA* 477:225–29

46. Mattson, F. H., Erickson, B. A., Kligman, A. M. 1972. Effect of dietary cholesterol on serum cholesterol in man. *Am. J. Clin. Nutr.* 25:589–94

47. Mattson, F. H., Grundy, S. M. 1985. Comparison of effects of dietary satu-rated, monounsaturated, and polyunsaturated fatty acids on plasma lipids and lipoproteins in man. *J. Lipid Res.* 26: 194–202

48. Meddings, J. B., Dietschy, J. M. 1986. Regulation of plasma levels of low-density lipoprotein cholesterol: interpretation of data on low-density lipoprotein turnover in man. *Circulation* 74:805–14

49. Meddings, J. B., Dietschy, J. M. 1987. Low density lipoproteins and atherogenesis: Implications for modification through alterations in diet and new drug designs. In *Contributions of Chemistry to Health, Proc. 5th Chemrawn Conf., Heidelberg* 1986, ed. H. Machleidt, 2:269–82. Winheim: Verlagsgesellschaft

50. Meddings, J. B., Dietschy, J. M. 1987. Regulation of plasma low density lipoprotein levels: New strategies for drug design. In *Progress in Clinical Biochemistry and Medicine*, 5:1–24. Berlin/Heidelberg: Springer-Verlag

51. Mensink, R. P., de Groot, M. J. M., van den Broeke, L. T., Severijnen: Nobels, A. P., Demacker, P. N. M., Katan, M. B. 1989. Effects of monounsaturated fatty acids *v* complex carbohydrates on serum lipoproteins and apoproteins in healthy men and women. *Metabolism* 38:172–78

52. Mensink, R. P., Katan, M. B. 1987. Effect of monounsaturated fatty acids versus complex carbohydrates on high-density lipoproteins in healthy men and women. *Lancet* 1:122–25

53. Mensink, R. P., Katan, M. B. 1989. Effect of diet enriched with monounsaturated or polyunsaturated fatty acids on levels of low-density and high-density lipoprotein cholesterol in healthy women and men. *N. Engl. J. Med.* 321:436–41

54. Mensink, R. P., Katan, M. B. 1990. Effect of dietary trans fatty acids on high-density and low-density lipoprotein cholesterol levels in healthy subjects. *N. Engl. J. Med.* 323:439–45

55. Mensink, R. P., Katan, M. B. 1992. Effect of dietary fatty acids on serum lipids and lipoproteins. *Arterioscler. Thromb.* 12:911–19

56. Nervi, F. O., Weis, H. J., Dietschy, J. M. 1975. The kinetic characteristics of inhibition of hepatic cholesterogenesis by lipoproteins of intestinal origin. *J. Biol. Chem.* 250:4145–51

57. Newman, W. P. III, Freemand, D. S., Voors, A. W., Gard, P. D., Srinivasan, S. R., et al. 1986. Relation of serum lipoprotein levels and systolic

blood pressure to early atherosclerosis. *N. Engl. J. Med.* 314:138–44

58. Pittman, R. C., Attie, A. D., Carew, T. E., Steinberg, D. 1979. Tissue sites of degradation of low density lipoprotein: Application of a method for determining the fate of plasma proteins. *Proc. Natl. Acad. Sci. USA* 76:5345–49

59. Small, D. M. 1991. The effects of glyceride structure or absorption and metabolism. *Annu. Rev. Nutr.* 11:413–34

60. Sorci-Thomas, M., Wilson, M. D., Johnson, F. L., Williams, D. L., Rudel, L. L. 1989. Studies on the expression of genes encoding apolipoproteins B100 and B48 and the low density lipoprotein receptor in nonhuman primates. *J. Biol. Chem.* 264:9039–45

61. Spady, D. K., Bilheimer, D. W., Dietschy, J. M. 1983. Rates of receptor-dependent and -independent low density lipoprotein uptake in the hamster. *Proc. Natl. Acad. Sci. USA* 80:3499–3503

62. Spady, D. K., Dietschy, J. M. 1983. Sterol synthesis in vivo in 18 tissues of the squirrel monkey, guinea pig, rabbit, hamster, and rat. *J. Lipid Res.* 24:303–15

63. Spady, D. K., Dietschy, J. M. 1985. Dietary saturated triacylglycerols suppress hepatic low density lipoprotein receptor activity in the hamster. *Proc. Natl. Acad. Sci. USA* 82:4526–30

64. Spady, D. K., Dietschy, J. M. 1988. Interaction of dietary cholesterol and triglycerides in the regulation of hepatic low density lipoprotein transport in the hamster. *J. Clin. Invest.* 81:300–9

65. Spady, D. K., Huettinger, M., Bilheimer, D. W., Dietschy, J. M. 1987. Role of receptor-independent low density lipoprotein transport in the maintenance of tissue cholesterol balance in the normal and WHHL rabbit. *J. Lipid Res.* 28:32–41

66. Spady, D. K., Meddings, J. B., Dietschy, J. M. 1986. Kinetic constants for receptor-dependent and receptor-independent low density lipoprotein transport in the tissues of the rat and hamster. *J. Clin. Invest.* 77:1474–81

67. Spady, D. K., Stange, E. F., Bilhartz, L. E., Dietschy, J. M. 1986. Bile acids regulate hepatic low density lipoprotein receptor activity in the hamster by altering cholesterol flux across the liver. *Proc. Natl. Acad. Sci. USA* 83:1916–20

68. Stange, E. F., Dietschy, J. M. 1984. Age-related decreases in tissue sterol acquisition are mediated by changes in

cholesterol synthesis and not low density lipoprotein uptake in the rat. *J. Lipid Res.* 25:703–13

69. Stange, E. F., Dietschy, J. M. 1985. Cholesterol absorption and metabolism by the intestinal epithelium. In *New Comprehensive Biochemistry: Sterols and Bile Acids,* ed. H. Danielsson, J. Sjövall, 12:121–49. Netherlands: Elsevier Sci.

70. Steinbrecher, U. P., Witztum, J. L., Kesaniemi, Y. A., Elam, R. L. 1983. Comparison of glucosylated low density lipoprotein with methylated or cyclohexanedione-treated low density lipoprotein in the measurement of receptor-independent low density lipoprotein catabolism. *J. Clin. Invest.* 71:960–64

71. Suckling, K. E., Stange, E. F. 1985. Role of acyl-CoA:cholesterol acyltransferase in cellular cholesterol metabolism. *J. Lipid Res.* 26:647–71

72. Suckling, K. E., Stange, E. F., Dietschy, J. M. 1983. Dual modulation of hepatic and intestinal acyl-CoA: cholesterol acyltransferase activity by (de-) phosphorylation and substrate supply in vitro. *FEBS Lett.* 151:111–16

73. Südhof, T. C., Goldstein, J. L., Brown, M. S., Russell, D. W. 1985. The LDL receptor gene: A mosaic of exons shared with different proteins. *Science* 228:815–22

74. Südhof, T. C., Russell, D. W., Brown, M. S., Goldstein, J. L. 1987. 42 bp element from LDL receptor gene confers end-product repression by sterols when inserted into viral TK promoter. *Cell* 48:1061–69

75. Turley, S. D., Daggy, B. P., Dietschy, J. M. 1991. Cholesterol-lowering action of psyllium mucilloid in the hamster: Sites and possible mechanisms of action. *Metabolism* 40:1063–73

76. Turley, S. D., Dietschy, J. M. 1988. The metabolism and excretion of cholesterol by the liver. In *The Liver: Biology and Pathobiology,* ed. I. M. Arias, W. B. Jakoby, H. Popper, D. Schachter, D. A. Shafritz, pp. 617–41. New York: Raven. 2nd ed.

77. Turley, S. D., Spady, D. K., Dietschy, J. M. 1983. Alteration of the degree of biliary cholesterol saturation in the hamster and rat by manipulation of the pools of preformed and newly synthesized cholesterol. *Gastroenterology* 84:253–64

78. Valsta, L. M., Jauhiainen, M., Aro, A., Katan, M. B., Mutanen, M. 1992. Effects of a monounsaturated rapeseed oil and a polyunsaturated sunflower oil

diet on lipoprotein levels in humans. *Arterioscler. Thromb.* 12:50–57

79. Weis, H. J., Dietschy, J. M. 1974. Adaptive responses in hepatic and intestinal cholesterogenesis following ileal resection in the rat. *Eur. J. Clin. Invest.* 4:33–41

80. Weisgraber, K. H., Innerarity, T. L., Mahley, R. W. 1978. Role of the lysine residues of plasma lipoproteins in high affinity binding to cell surface receptors on human fibroblasts. *J. Biol. Chem.* 153:9053–62

81. Woollett, L. A., Spady, D. K., Dietschy, J. M. 1989. Mechanisms by which saturated triacylgycerols elevate the plasma low density lipoprotein-cholesterol concentration in hamsters. *J. Clin. Invest.* 84:119–28

82. Woollett, L. A., Spady, D. K., Dietschy, J. M. 1992. Regulatory effects of the saturated fatty acids 6:0 through 18:0 on hepatic low density lipoprotein receptor activity in the hamster. *J. Clin. Invest.* 89:1133–41

83. Woollett, L. A., Spady, D. K., Dietschy, J. M. 1992. Saturated and unsaturated fatty acids independently regulate low density lipoprotein receptor activity and production rate. *J. Lipid Res.* 33: 77–88

84. Yamada, N., Shames, D. M., Stoudemire, J. B., Havel, R. J. 1986. Metabolism of lipoproteins containing apolipoprotein B-100 in blood plasma of rabbits: Heterogeneity related to the presence of apolipoprotein E. *Proc. Natl. Acad. Sci. USA* 83:3479–83

85. Zhang, S. H., Reddick, R. L., Piedrahita, J. A., Maeda, N. 1992. Spontaneous hypercholesterolemia and arterial lesions in mice lacking apolipoprotein E. *Science* 258:468–71

86. Zock, P. L., Katan, M. B. 1992. Hydrogenation alternatives: effects of trans fatty acids and stearic acid versus linoleic acid on serum lipids and lipoproteins in humans. *J. Lipid Res.* 33: 399–410

Annu. Rev. Nutr. 1993. 13:383–403

IS OXYGEN AN ESSENTIAL NUTRIENT?

Robert E. Forster

Department of Physiology, University of Pennsylvania School of Medicine, Philadelphia, Pennsylvania 19104-6085

Ronald W. Estabrook

Department of Biochemistry, University of Texas Southwestern Medical Center, Dallas, Texas 75235-9038

KEY WORDS: gaseous nutrient, oxygen demand, cytochromes, oxygen paradox

CONTENTS

THE CHALLENGE 383
THE SOURCES OF OXYGEN 384
THE UNIQUENESS OF OXYGEN 386
NUTRITIONAL REQUIREMENTS AND THE BALANCE OF OXYGEN UPTAKE 387
   Oxygen as a Gaseous Nutrient 387
   The Delivery of Oxygen 389
   Meeting the Demand for Oxygen 390
OXYGEN-REACTING ENZYMES 391
   Cytochrome Oxidase 392
   Cytochrome P450s 393
   Other Oxygen-Reacting Enzymes 395
NUTRITIONAL DISEASES 395
   Malnutrition or the Limitation of Oxygen Supplied To Tissues 395
   Overnutrition or Oversupply of Oxygen to Cells 397
THE OXYGEN PARADOX 398
CONCLUDING REMARKS 398

THE CHALLENGE

Oxygen is essential for the survival of almost all eukaryotes. One can argue that oxygen is responsible for the development of cellular compartmentation and that it serves as the engine of morphogenesis in higher animals. For the

383

0199-9885/93/0715-0383$02.00

development of cellular organelles, membranes are needed to segregate oxygen-susceptible reactants in a milieu of oxygen, albeit at low and varying partial pressures. The organs of gas exchange, e.g. lungs and gills, the heart and circulatory system, and the peripheral capillary bed, have developed primarily to provide oxygen to cells. The concomitant development of unique hemoproteins, such as hemoglobin and myoglobin, augments the oxygen transport capacity of the circulatory fluid and provides for the transport and transient storage of oxygen. A large variety of oxygen-utilizing enzymes play central roles in the diverse functions of different cells. They range from oxygen-reacting enzymes that are required for generation of energy by the mitochondrial respiratory chain to other enzymes that aid in the synthesis of humoral regulators and mediators, such as the prostaglandins and physiologically active steroid hormones, to name but a few examples.

However, can one consider oxygen as a nutrient? Webster's dictionary (103) defines a *nutrient* as *furnishing nourishment; promoting growth*. By this definition one might consider oxygen as a nutrient. It not only promotes growth but also often serves as a regulatory molecule for metabolism. On the other hand, in a recently published textbook on nutrition (70) was the following statement: "One may partition the nutrients into six categories: proteins, carbohydrates, lipids, vitamins, major minerals, and trace elements. This excludes a consideration of water and oxygen as nutrients, since no special efforts are required to produce and provide them." This difference of interpretation stimulated us to answer the challenge by Robert E. Olson (the editor of this series) to write this review.

Oxygen is ubiquitous on the Earth's surface and it is the subject of immense chemical, physiological, and clinical literature. A recent computer search identified 130,718 bibliographic references in the last 25 years that responded to the search term "oxygen." The rich history of research involving oxygen stems from the original observations of Lavoisier (68), Priestley (89), and Scheele (94). In the intervening two centuries, oxygen has attracted the attention of leading scientists and has often played a fundamental role in their contributions to chemistry and biology (35). Therefore, any attempt to summarize the current status of research on oxygen is necessarily biased and superficial. In this brief article we have selected those aspects of oxygen chemistry and physiology that we know best and that we believe provide new insights on the role of oxygen in eukaryotes—in particular, its role as a nutrient.

THE SOURCES OF OXYGEN

The energy for life derives from the large free energy difference between hydrogen and oxygen. The energy of radiation from the sun is used in the photosynthetic processes of plants to separate water into oxygen and hydrogen. The hydrogen is stored combined with carbon in what are classically called nutrients (i.e. fat, carbohydrate, and protein) while the oxygen is released to the atmosphere as a diatomic molecule. Practically all living organisms that occupy the surface of planet Earth today, including the plants themselves, require molecular oxygen for the metabolism of the macro-nutrients to obtain the energy needed for growth, reproduction, movement, and survival. Thus, to designate one of these two reactants, hydrogen, as a more important nutrient than the other reactant, oxygen, is not logical.

The original atmosphere of the Earth presumably contained the lighter elements in approximately the same proportions as found in the universe, namely hydrogen at 86.687%, helium 13.18%, oxygen 0.09%, carbon 0.03%, and nitrogen 0.01% (69). Because hydrogen was predominant, it combined with all the other elements, except He, to produce an atmosphere consisting primarily of H_2, He, H_2O, CH_4, and NH_3. The lighter elements, H_2 and He, escaped from the Earth's gravitational field first; loss of the former is equivalent to oxidation of the Earth. Radiation reaching the Earth, over a period of time, dissociated hydrogen from combination with the other elements; some bound as well as free hydrogen also was lost, leaving an enrichment of the heavier, more abundant elements, i.e. oxygen, carbon, and nitrogen. There was no free O_2 in the atmosphere. The subsequent outgassing of the outer layers of the Earth then contributed to the atmosphere the small amount of oxygen required for initiating life processes in which oxygen combined with carbon to form CO_2 (51). CO_2, with N_2, formed the next stage of our atmosphere. Understanding the evolution of the atmosphere of Earth and the complex chemistry associated with progressive changes remains an active area of speculation (69). The linkage to the development of life, as we understand it, in particular the key role played by oxygen, remains a challenge for scientific investigation. Life presumably developed in the original reducing atmosphere using oxidation-reduction reactions dependent on such elements as sulfur and iron; but at some point photosynthesis developed and reactions were established for the dissociation of water, thereby markedly increasing the availability of oxygen for chemical and biological reactions (60). The oxygen in the atmosphere is believed to represent but 0.1% of the oxygen content of the Earth. The greatest store of oxygen remains combined with minerals in the solid crust and in water.

Oxygen in the atmosphere is continually being replenished by photosynthesis but consumed by oxidation of organic compounds, including respiration by living organisms including the small plants that produce it, in the sea as well as on land, at a rate of about 0.04% per year. Since the concentration of O_2 in the atmosphere is constant over time (based on measurements taken during a limited time scale of less than 100 years), and presumably uniform over the Earth's surface, production and consumption are considered equal. Therefore if photosynthesis stopped and the consumption of oxygen remained constant, presumably the concentration of atmospheric oxygen would fall at this same rate, requiring 2500 years to disappear. What forces have led to the current "steady state" level of 21% oxygen in the atmosphere? What were the kinetics of transition from the original reducing atmosphere of primordial Earth to the present time and can one anticipate further increases in oxygen concentration in the atmosphere? Immense amounts of oxygen are available in mineral compounds. It is the energy available from the oxygen and hydrogen that is needed for life, rather than the molecules themselves.

THE UNIQUENESS OF OXYGEN

In 1964 P. George (34) summarized the advances in our understanding of the physical chemistry of oxygen by writing a tribute for the fiftieth anniversary of the publication of *The Fitness of the Environment* by L. J. Henderson (50). George's classic presentation itemizes the remarkable advances in our understanding of the physical-chemical properties of oxygen that justify its role as the ideal agent to serve as the terminal oxidant for life processes. George concludes that the physical properties of oxygen, combined with its thermodynamic and kinetic properties, place oxygen in a unique position so "that no other element could effectively replace it." Central to this theme is the large free energy release available in discrete increments that occurs during the reduction of oxygen to water. The four one-electron equivalent stepwise reduction of molecular oxygen to water results in a great variety of chemical species as intermediates (48, 65).

In biological systems the one-electron reduction of oxygen results in (*a*) the formation of the free radical superoxide anion, $O_2^{\cdot-}$. For example, during the reaction of some flavoproteins or hemoproteins with oxygen or during the redox cycling of quinones, significant amounts of superoxide are formed. The microbicidal role of superoxide formed during the "oxygen burst" of phagocytosis is an essential component of the response to inflammation. The protonated form of the superoxide anion, the perhydoxy radical, is the dominant form at neutral pH and is more invidious because of its increased lipid solubility. (*b*) The two-electron reduction state of molecular oxygen is hydrogen peroxide. This compound is generally formed by a dismutation of the perhydroxy radical in a reaction catalyzed by the enzyme superoxide dismutase (32, 74). Hydrogen peroxide can dissociate (in the presence of a suitable metal) to form an electrophilic oxene intermediate together with water (7, 47). Of course, this highly reactive form of oxygen can also arise from the heterolytic cleavage of molecular oxygen. (*c*) Most reactive of the reduction intermediates of molecular oxygen is the strongly oxidizing hydroxyl radical, HO˙, i.e. the three-electron reduced state of molecular oxygen (16). Classic Fenton reaction chemistry or the metal (iron) catalyzed Haber-Weiss reaction leads to this species of oxygen. Lastly, (d) the four-electron reduced form of molecular oxygen is water.

Although oxygen radicals are recognized to be short-lived, their destructive potential is frequently stabilized in the form of organic peroxides (ROOH) that can lead to peroxy radicals (ROO˙) by hydrogen abstraction or alkoxy radicals (RO˙) following interaction of the peroxide radical with an electron-rich molecule, such as a polyunsaturated fatty acid.

For many years, the study of these intermediates has been the predominant activity of those concerned with oxygen metabolism. Intense interest in this area has resulted in a rapid proliferation of Symposia and the establishment of new scientific societies (The Oxygen Society, The Society for Free Radical Research, to name but two) and associated journals dedicated to understanding the role of oxygen intermediates in chemistry and biology. The reactivity and associated toxicity of the highly reactive oxygen species formed during the reduction of oxygen may be major contributors to the pathogenesis of many chronic degenerative diseases (21).

NUTRITIONAL REQUIREMENTS AND THE BALANCE OF OXYGEN UPTAKE

The uniqueness of molecular oxygen is due to (a) its omnipresence as a gas; (b) its limited solubility in water, and (c) its specialized kinetic properties, particularly in association with metal ions such as iron and copper. Although molecular oxygen is used by higher animals in the synthesis of a great variety of important chemical compounds that serve as constituents and regulators of cellular metabolism, the amount of oxygen used for these reactions is minor compared to that consumed for energy production. A certain amount of oxygen is present in carbohydrate and protein (less in fat) and of course in water, but it is present in a reduced state with a limited potential for energy release. For example, the daily water intake of a normal adult human contains about three times as many molecules of oxygen as are consumed in respiratory metabolism. Oxygen-containing functional groups are present in most organic chemicals where they provide the necessary sites for recognition (by enzymes, immune cells, and receptors), as well as sites for conjugation (to increase the hydrophilicity of molecules) or for esterification (for storage or targeting signals).

Oxygen As a Gaseous Nutrient

A specified amount of O_2 is required for all energy needs by mammals. Any transient anaerobic energy used is eventually replaced from aerobic sources.

As a nutrient, O_2 has no substitute—unlike fat, carbohydrate, and protein, which are metabolically interchangeable. Furthermore, oxygen has a relatively limited concentration, in terms of moles per unit volume, in the ambient atmosphere and a relatively low solubility in water. Whereas an individual can ingest more solid and liquid nutrients than needed immediately and store these in the body as fat or glycogen, sufficient to maintain nutrition for days, the total possible body stores of molecular oxygen in humans can support metabolism for only several minutes. This property places stringent require-ments on O_2 transport from the environment to cells. It also means that O_2 delivery must be adjusted within seconds for any changes in metabolic rate in order to maintain cell pO_2 and avoid cell death.

Within a cell, O_2 is transported by physical diffusion at a rate that is proportional to, and in the direction of, the concentration gradient of the oxygen multiplied by the diffusion coefficient of the O_2 in the cytoplasm (33, 88). If the innermost region of a cell is to be adequately supplied with O_2, its distance from the surface is restricted by the following equation (29, 31):

$$[O_2]_{surface} - [O_2]_r = \frac{metabolic\ rate}{6d}\ (r_{surface} - r).$$

1.

For this calculation the cell is considered as a sphere, $[O_2]_{surface}$ is the oxygen concentration at the surface of the cell, and $[O_2]r$ is the concentration inside the cell at radius r; both are in moles per cubic centimeter. Metabolic rate is in moles/(cc $\times$ sec) and is considered uniform throughout the cell; ($r_{surface}$) is the radius of the spherical cell and r is a radial distance from the center, inside the cell, both in centimeters; and d is the diffusion coefficient of O_2 inside the cell in cm^2/sec and is also considered homogenous. This equation dictates that the radius of such a cell can be no larger than the value obtained when pO_2 at the center of the cell is so low that the rate of O_2 reduction by the mitochondria falls to zero. The minimal pO_2 at which a mitochondrion will continue to reduce O_2 is thought to be low, possibly less than 1 mm Hg, but this value is in dispute (14, 17, 53, 82, 92, 106–110). One can approximate this condition by setting $[O_2]$ at the center equal to 0 mm Hg; this will give the maximal radius for the cell. Choosing average values for a normal human kidney cell exposed to air, the pO_2 at the cell surface = 150 mm Hg, i.e. $[O_2]_{surface}$ of the cell = 1.2×10^{-4} mol/cc; the metabolic rate = 5.8×10^{-8} mol/cc, and the diffusion of oxygen $d = 1.03 \times 10^{-5}$ $cm^2 \cdot$ sec (29, 30). Substituting these values in Equation 1 and solving for radius r, one obtains a value of 60 μm.

However, two other considerations must be applied when evaluating the slope of the oxygen gradient within the cell. Inspection of Equation 1 shows that decreasing the metabolic rate of the cell increases its maximal possible size proportionally (52). First, as O_2 diffuses into a metabolizing cell, it is consumed at each point and reduces the pO_2, which in turn reduces the diffusion gradient for further flux into the cell. Thus the higher the metabolic rate, the steeper the pO_2 gradient and the larger the pO_2 difference between the surface of the cell and the center. One might consider exceptions to this rule: For example, plant cells, whose rate of metabolism is slow, or fat cells, in which metabolism takes place only in the thin layer of cytoplasm surrounding the lipid droplet, may become much larger. Some cells have developed in their cytoplasm O_2-binding pigments such as myoglobin, which are believed to facilitate O_2 flux and thus increase the effective diffusion constant and reduce the pO_2 gradients in the cell. Second, the concentration of the oxygen-reacting enzymes in a cell may not be trivial. For example, in a liver cell the average concentration of cytochrome c oxidase is about 15 nmol per gram wet weight of tissue (15 μM) and of cytochrome P450 is about 50 nmol per gram wet weight of tissue (50 μM). Thus as the oxygen diffuses from the surface to the center of a cell, the rate of oxygen utilization rapidly becomes dependent on the concentration of the oxygen-reacting enzyme, i.e. the first-order reaction velocity constant changes to a second-order constant.

The Delivery of Oxygen

As life forms evolved into multicellular organisms with convective systems that in effect surround each cell with an oxygen-containing environment, they were able to grow in size. Claude Bernard immortalized this concept in his "millieu interieur" (6). Pasteur (86) noted that lack of O_2 produced changes in the structure of yeast, and he concluded that O_2 was the key to differentiation. Warburg (102) later extended this principle, believing that the lack of O_2 caused cells to de-differentiate. Certainly the need to maintain an optimum pO_2 at the cell surface is the prime determinant of the mechanical systems that maintain the milieu interieur in multicellular animals. For example, some insects conduct ambient air to the cells with small tubes (tracheoles) (76); some marine animals pump sea water to each cell (55). Higher vertebrates have developed a closed double-capillary exchange system that equilibrates a circulant (e.g. blood, hemolymph) with the surrounding air or liquid and moves this equilibrated transport fluid to capillaries around each cell where O_2 diffuses from the circulant to each cell (97). The most highly developed O_2 exchange systems include: (a) an external exchanger (lungs, gills, skin, etc.) that equilibrates ambient oxygen with a (b) circulant that is convected mechanically (heart and circulatory system) to (c) an internal exchanger, the tissue capillary beds, which equilibrate O_2 with the cell surfaces. The circulant in higher animals contains pigmented proteins that react reversibly with O_2, taking up and releasing a large amount of O_2 for a relative small change in O_2 partial pressure. In mammals this pigment, hemoglobin, is contained within cells (erythrocytes) and raises the blood O_2 concentration to some 100 times the concentration of dissolved O_2. CO_2, which is produced in the cells, is carried in the opposite direction by the blood, mainly as HCO_3^-. This gives the blood a CO_2-carrying capacity even greater than that for O_2. The uptake of O_2 and the release of CO_2 in the lungs, and the reverse in the peripheral capillaries, mutually facilitate each other in an integrated physicochemical process. The O_2-carrying capacity of the blood can be regulated by altering the concentration of erythrocytes.

The mechanisms of O_2 uptake from the ambient are closely controlled to maintain constant blood pO_2 (30), but in a manner ensuring that unnecessary ventilatory effort is not exerted. The rate of pumping air or water past the external capillary exchange bed depends on the metabolic demand (30, 35). Although the ventilatory rate in humans decreases in sleep, a minimal level has to be maintained for survival. Water-breathing animals are further compromised by the low solubility of O_2 in water. Sea water equilibrated with the air contains about one thirtieth as much O_2 as the atmosphere and thus requires that 30 times as great a volume of sea water flow past the gill capillaries as the volume of air pumped in and out of the lung of an equivalent air-breathing animal. Active fish, such as the tuna, must keep swimming to force water past their gill capillaries fast enough to maintain their metabolism (22).

Meeting the Demand for Oxygen

The rate of metabolism is set by the organisms's need for energy for maintenance, movement, and growth; the transport system is subsidiary and is required to provide whatever O_2 is demanded by the cells. Sensors for O_2, the chemoreceptors of the carotid and aortic bodies (20, 56, 79), monitor the arterial blood and regulate minute ventilation of the lungs (or gills) so as to oxygenate the blood regardless of the cardiac output and pulmonary blood flow (28). The control of respiration acts to keep arterial blood pO_2 and pCO_2 constant, rather than regulating the amount of oxygen taken up. The activity of tissue cells is controlled independently by the volitional or vegetative nervous systems, which alter oxygen consumption and carbon dioxide production while the transport system adjusts to these needs. The mechanism by which the peripheral chemoreceptors sense blood pO_2 is not clear at this time (83). An extremely sensitive center in the medulla oblongata monitors arterial pCO_2 and can cause a doubling of ventilation for a rise in pCO_2 of only 1 mm Hg. Regulation of O_2 delivery is hierarchical at successive levels of arborization throughout the circulatory systems in order to maintain pO_2 in the individual cells within the required range.

The transport of O_2 from the peripheral capillaries to cell mitochondria is poorly understood; many experimental approaches have been used (40–43,

54, 66, 71, 87, 98), and a worldwide organization, the International Society for Oxygen Transport in Tissue (ISOTT) is dedicated to its study. The pO_2 in blood entering the cellular capillary bed is normally 100 mm Hg while the pO_2 at the mitochondria is certainly less than 15 mm Hg (19). This drop of pO_2 of some 85 mm Hg within the cells is the largest decline in the entire path from ambient air to the mitochondrial cytochrome c oxidase. The capillary walls, which are one cell thick, are so thin that their resistance to gaseous diffusion is negligible, or at least technically immeasurable (although some investigators disagree) (33, 54). Increased metabolic demand or decreased local O_2 from other causes produces increased capillary blood flow, but the most effective change is the opening up of closed or resting capillaries (95). Skin blood flow, which can be much greater than nutritional needs in order to promote heat loss, can vary more than 100-fold. Peripheral skeletal muscles have extremely low resting capillary blood flow, but with exercise and the associated metabolic demands the blood flow increases enormously (41, 53). Athletic training increases muscle capacity for work by increasing the number of mitochondria and, of necessity, the capillary bed to supply them.

Can one establish a similarity between the demand for oxygen and other nutrients? Other nutrients are taken into the body and transported from the environment to the cells by a system similar to that used by O_2, except that the blood-ambient exchanger is in the intestinal wall. Transport of other nutrients across the epithelium is by active and passive transport and endocytosis, and not simply by diffusion as in the alveolar capillary. However owing primarily to their much higher concentration in ingestates, the movement of nutrients from the absorption site to the cells is hardly ever a critical problem. A cell may die from lack of oxygen long before it can starve because of a failure of nutrient transport. For example, the normal arterial concentration of glucose is 5.5 mM and the normal arterial pO_2 is 100 mm Hg, equivalent to 0.12 mM O_2. In addition, 6 molecules of O_2 are required to oxidize 1 molecule of glucose so that from the viewpoint of supplying metabolic needs, the concentration of glucose is 275 times greater than that of O_2 in the extracellular fluid at the surface of the cell. Thus, oxygen turnover is the highest among essential nutrients.

OXYGEN-REACTING ENZYMES

The relative amounts of oxygen consumed by the tissues of an adult human male are directly related to the content and capacity of the mitochondrial respiratory chain (100). Skeletal muscle, which makes up about 42% of body weight, uses about 30% of oxygen consumed at rest, and over 86% of oxygen consumed during heavy work. The abdominal organs use 25% and the brain uses 20% of the oxygen consumed at rest. Their relative contributions proportionately decrease during heavy work. Thus one can quantify the respiratory activity of organs and cells under different conditions of stress and physical challenge. Of interest is the relationship, first described by Drabkin (23), that correlates the percent distribution of cytochrome c in organs of the body with the relative amounts of oxygen utilized by various organs during heavy work, i.e. 82.6% of the cytochrome c of man is located in skeletal muscle. A similar relationship exists for heart, brain, and abdominal organs.

Howard Mason (personal communication) has cataloged over 350 different classes of enzymes in biology that react with oxygen. Of these about 150 different types may be present in mammals, although many are shared with lower forms of life. This calculation does *not* include the large number of isoforms (isoenzymes) that subdivide a specific class of oxygen-reacting enzyme. These enzymes include oxidases, oxygenases, hydroxylases, and peroxidases. They consist of hemoproteins, flavoproteins, copper proteins, and proteins containing metals such as molybdenum, manganese, cobalt, vanadium, etc. Clearly, Nature has devised many different approaches to capture the potential energy present in oxygen.

Cytochrome Oxidase

Quantitatively, mitochondria are the major consumers of oxygen in most organisms. In mammals more than 90% of the oxygen utilized is thought to be consumed via cytochrome oxidase of the mitochondrion. Understanding the enzymology and physiological role of the respiratory chain electron transport carriers of mitochondria, in particular the reaction with oxygen of cytochrome c oxidase, has served as a driving force in biochemical research for the last 70 years, since the pioneering observations of Warburg (101) and Keilin (62).

How does cytochrome oxidase reduce molecular oxygen to water? Understanding the mechanism(s) by which a single electron transfer pathway provides the needed four electrons for this reaction has challenged researchers and has commanded the most sophisticated techniques of biophysics and biochemistry (15). Knowledge of the metal content of mammalian cytochrome oxidase has been well established for over three decades. Four prosthetic groups are present: two heme-containing domains, a and a_3, and two copper-containing domains, Cu_A and Cu_B. But how do these oxidation-reduction centers relate to one another and to the overall reaction of oxygen reduction? In spite of ingenious and demanding efforts, a detailed description of the intermediary events associated with the oxidation of reduced cytochrome c, concomitant with the reduction of oxygen to water, is not yet available. Controversy surrounds findings proposing the existence of a peroxy-intermediate (105), the formation of a reactive hydroxyl radical ($OH^{\cdot}$) intermediate (77), or linkage to a proton-motive "O-cycle" (78, 80).

Introduction of the techniques of molecular biology has revealed the structural complexity of mammalian cytochrome c oxidase (12). Two decades ago, one would never have guessed that cytochrome oxidase is a mega-protein composed of 13 polypeptides (58, 75) of which some subunits are encoded by the mitochondrial genome while other subunits are coded by the nuclear genome (10). Clearly, coordination of synthesis of these different peptides and the intricacies of import and assembly of the subunits are central to understanding the function of cytochrome oxidase. Identification of the protein subunits associated with the heme and copper metal centers has been facilitated by comparison of orthologous proteins in prokaryotes (e.g. *Paracoccus denitrificans*, which contains only three subunits) with the cytochrome c oxidases of eukaryotes (9). But this comparison has identified a function for only four of the thirteen subunits. What are the roles of the remaining subunits and how do they contribute to the mechanism of electron transport and the associated reactions of energy conservation (111)?

An unexpected finding is that isoforms of at least three subunits of mammalian cytochrome oxidase exist and are expressed in a tissue-specific manner (57, 63). Recent studies have defined a heart form (H), with one set of subunits dominant in heart and skeletal muscle, and a liver form (L) with a different set of subunits present in liver, kidney, and brain. And these differences appear to influence the catalytic activities of the respective cytochrome c oxidases.

A thorough consideration of oxygen as an essential nutrient must include a discussion of its metabolism and the properties of the enzymes that interact with it. Clearly, we have much more to learn about cytochrome oxidase, the central enzyme of oxygen metabolism.

Cytochrome P450s

Another class of hemoproteins present in many cells is the cytochrome P450 superfamily. These hemoproteins catalyze an oxygenase reaction for the incorporation of molecular oxygen into a wide spectrum of organic chemicals (26, 39, 73). At present, there is detailed knowledge of 209 members of the P450 gene superfamily (81). The P450 superfamily is composed of 35 different gene families of which 12 families exist in all mammals examined to date. (A P450 is assigned to a specific gene family when its protein sequence has greater than 40% similarity to the protein sequence of a related P450.) These 12 families can be further dissected into 23 subfamilies, of which 17 have been mapped to human chromosomes. (A P450 is assigned to a specific gene subfamily when its protein sequence has greater than 55% similarity to the protein sequence of a related P450.) This inventory of the P450s represents only those P450s that have been cloned and sequenced. One can predict that three- to four-times as many P450s remain to be characterized.

The P450s are oxygenases, specifically monooxygenases. They function by activating molecular oxygen to form an electrophilic species of oxygen [proposed to be a caged hydroxyl radical (104)], concomitant with the oxidation of reduced pyridine nucleotide (NADPH). The P450s contain cysteine as a ligand for the iron of the heme. The thiolate coordination bond that is formed is an identifying signature for this type of hemoprotein, and it is responsible for the absorbance band at about 450 nm that is formed when carbon monoxide reacts with the reduced hemoprotein (85).

Most interesting is the diversity of oxygen-dependent reactions catalyzed by different P450s. These reactions touch nearly every aspect of biology and medicine. An exhaustive listing of reactions catalyzed would reveal the central role that specific P450s play in cell development, differentiation, and death. Briefly, P450s catalyze critical biosynthetic reactions in plants leading to the formation of natural pesticides and insecticides (the phytoalexins) or the synthesis of plant hormones responsible for flavors, coloring pigments, flowering, or fruit ripening (64). In insects the P450s confer resistance to insecticides and they are responsible for the omega hydroxylation of fatty acids in the synthesis of waxes (1, 91). But it is in mammalian tissues that the P450s have been best studied and where we understand in greatest detail their role in the metabolism of endogenous as well as exogenous chemicals (39, 44). Initial studies revealed the role of adrenal P450s in the regio- and stereo-specific hydroxylation of steroids (25). Today one recognizes that the cascade of oxygen-dependent reactions associated with the metabolism of cholesterol to androgens and estrogens or to mineralo- or glucocorticoids involves at least five different P450s present in steroidogenic tissues (27). Of primary importance are the large number of different P450s with broad substrate specificity that participate in the metabolism of xenobiotics. The P450s play a critical role in the metabolic activation of chemicals for the initiation of chemical carcinogenesis or cellular toxicity (38). Of equal importance is the role of specific P450s in the metabolism of polyunsaturated fatty acids, such as arachidonic acid, to unique epoxides or the omega oxidation of prostaglandins, leukotrienes, and medium chain-length fatty acids (13). P450s catalyze the hydroxylation of vitamin D to its physiologically active form (8) as well as the oxidation of retinoids (90). The P450s may play a role in the odorant response of nasal tissue (93) and the mood-modifying role of neurosteroids in brain (2).

Genetic polymorphism is now recognized as a significant contributor to alterations in the function of specific P450s (37). The presence of varient alleles may explain the genetic susceptibility of individuals for lung cancer (61) or sensitivity to specific drugs (72). Clearly, those enzymes that react with oxygen are not immune from genetic variability in a manner that would alter their contribution to metabolism.

One of the most compelling arguments favoring identification of oxygen as an essential nutrient is the listing of oxygen-dependent reactions catalyzed by different P450s and the recognition of the role played in cellular homeostasis by many of the metabolites that are formed.

Other Oxygen-Reacting Enzymes

Regrettably, neither time nor space permits us to describe the fascinating enzymology and biology associated with the many other enzymes present in mammalian tissues that react with oxygen. Textbooks and journals are dedicated to many of these physiologically important enzymes. Knowledge of their presence and the key role that they play in metabolism reinforces the premise that oxygen is necessary for life.

NUTRITIONAL DISEASES

Malnutrition or the Limitation of Oxygen Supplied to the Tissues

Nutritional diseases are generally caused by a reduction of an essential nutrient at the cellular level resulting from a failure of some step in its uptake from the environment, distribution to the site of need, or function in the cell. Well-known examples are the avitaminoses—diseases caused by lack of a vitamin in the diet, or failure to absorb or use it. Is there an equivalent nutritional disease associated with a lack or limitation of oxygen? Most cells in higher eukaryotes are delicately balanced between anaerobiosis and aerobiosis. Interference with the supply of blood to an organ results in hypoxia and the rapid onset of ischemia leading to a shifting of metabolism from a highly efficient energy-producing mode to the deleterious outpouring of acidic metabolites. A concomitant shift in ion distribution accompanies this collapse of the "energy charge" in the cell. One must conclude that the concept of malnutrition can be applied to oxygen depletion and that the consequences can be as insidious and devastating as the lack of a vitamin, essential fatty acid, or amino acid.

Reduction in the intake of food, starvation, can be tolerated by humans for weeks; limitation of water uptake can be tolerated for days; but a limitation of oxygen can result in irreversible changes after a few minutes. If the uptake of one foodstuff (glucose) is restricted, the body can call upon its reserves of other foodstuffs, including stored fat and protein. If water intake is reduced, the body can draw on fluid stored in the extracellular space. No such alternative sources exist as a backup for oxygen depletion. Some tissues, particularly muscle, can turn to glycolysis for a transient alternate source of energy, of ATP, while other critical organs, such as the brain, cannot.

The condition of limited oxygen uptake can be caused by a dysfunction at any step in the transport of oxygen from inspired air to the cell. Some examples of a limited oxygen uptake where physiological adaptation has occurred are (30):

1. Reduced oxygen tension in the inspired air: This occurs at high altitude or breathing a polluted atmosphere.
2. Decreased alveolar ventilation of the lungs: Examples are the reduced minute ventilation in poliomyelitis, hemothorax, or pleural effusion.
3. Reduced O_2 content of the blood leaving the lungs: This can result from incomplete equilibration of O_2 between alveolar gas and blood leaving the individual capillaries such as in chronic pulmonary disease (52) or emphysema.
4. Decreased oxygen delivery to the capillaries: Anemia, obstruction of flow at the arterial level as in atherosclerosis or failure to pump the blood due to cardiac failure can limit delivery of oxygen to cells. This may result in angina pectoris and myocardial infarction; in the brain, it results in stroke; and in peripheral muscles, it results in intermittent claudication.
5. Handicapped transport from capillary blood to mitochondria: This process is primarily diffusion controlled, so the flux of O_2 is basically proportional to dpO_2/dx, but its local metabolism slows down the flux. Myoglobin, which binds O_2 reversibly and may act as a carrier molecule in a facilitated diffusion schema, can be poisoned.

O_2 lack can be acute or chronic. An acute fall in arterial pO_2 produces an increased rate of lung ventilation and increased cardiac output and arterial blood pressure in seconds. A similar decrease in tissue pO_2 causes dilation of peripheral arterioles in order to supply more O_2 to the cells. If the regulatory response is not rapid enough, or the stress is too great, there will be cell damage and ultimately death.

Chronic nonfatal reduction in the oxygen supply to a cell produces slower changes in the oxygen delivery system—an adaption. The blood hemoglobin concentration is increased by increasing the number of red cells. This takes days to weeks and is mediated through pO_2-sensing cells primarily in the kidney medulla that detect the lowered pO_2 and produce a hormone, erythropoietin, which stimulates bone marrow to produce more red blood cells. The affinity of hemoglobin for O_2 can be altered; the ventilation of the lungs can increase as well as the strength of the heart. Chronically lowered pO_2 in muscles produces an increased capillary bed. In athletic training, the metabolic reserve of the muscles rises because the concentration of mitochondria per cell increases and this demands more capillaries.

In recent years emphasis has shifted from seeking an understanding of the consequences of limiting the supply of oxygen to defining the deleterious effects of reestablishment of oxygen to a tissue that has been subjected to anoxia. Oxygen radicals are generated during the reintroduction of oxygen to a tissue, such as the reperfusion of the ischemic myocardium (59). As a result, a peroxidation of cellular lipids may modify the properties of cellular membranes or an oxidation of key cellular proteins may produce conformational change or denaturation with a concomitant loss of enzymatic activity. The result of these irreversible injuries to the cell is necrosis. The source of oxygen radicals may be the infiltration of the tissue by phagocytes (4), the reestablishment of a functional mitochondrial electron transport system (84), or purine catabolism by xanthine oxidase (5). Clearly, a complex series of intracellular events occurs when oxygen is reintroduced to a cell, and more than one causative agent contributes to the resultant death of a cell. Oxygen radicals may play a similar role in the posttraumatic neuronal necrosis following brain or spinal cord injury (99).

A variant of the situation in which the supply of oxygen to a cell is limited occurs when a modification of the mitochondrial respiratory chain impedes the utilization of oxygen (45). The consequences of inhibition of cytochrome oxidase by carbon monoxide or cyanide are well known. In recent years there has been an increased recognition of mitochondrial dysfunction caused by genetic changes that result in a failure of the mitochondrial respiratory chain to express competent proteins (24). This mitochondrial pathophysiology and the associated clinical manifestations, called mitochondrial diseases, now number in the hundreds, and many are associated with changes of cytochrome c oxidase (11, 24, 36, 49). Deficiencies of both nuclear-encoded as well as mitochondrial-encoded subunits of cytochrome oxidase have been identified as causative agents of these pathological conditions. Of interest is the possible linkage of these deficiencies in cytochrome c oxidase to the role of cardiolipin and coenzyme Q in the function of the respiratory chain.

Overnutrition or Oversupply of Oxygen to Cells

An excess of some nutrients can be harmful and can produce a nutritional disease. Obesity might be called such a condition. An increase in tissue pO_2 can damage cells and is a disease of modern technology resulting from an increase of inspired pO_2. After the discovery of oxygen by Priestley in 1777 and the recognition that it supported life, physicians began to use it as therapy—just as many foodstuffs have been used—but the therapeutic effects were minimal so enthusiasm declined quickly, particularly since some toxic effects were noted. The O_2 transport system regulates the delivery of O_2 to peripheral cells to maintain pO_2 within a narrow range, from about 1 mm Hg to about 15 mm Hg (18).

If a healthy adult breathes essentially pure O_2 at sea level, his lungs become irritated (67); a rat exposed in the same way will die in a matter of hours;

newborn humans will develop retrolental fibrodysplasia. Chronic exposure of rats to high oxygen can diminish or destroy the ability of the carotid bodies to monitor low arterial blood pO_2 (79). These are but a few examples of the deleterious effects of inspiring higher than normal O_2 concentrations. Which of these undesirable effects is simply a result of high $[O_2]$ and which are the result of the action of oxygen radicals produced by the higher pO_2 is the subject of intense research (16). In either case, O_2 is both an absolute requirement for life and at the same time a toxin, giving rise to the oxygen paradox.

THE OXYGEN PARADOX

Ames & Gold (3) estimate that "the DNA hits per cell per day from endogenous oxidants are normally $\sim 10^5$ in the rat and $\sim 10^4$ in humans." Oxygen radicals are thought to account for the major share of agents causing this damage. Thus, there is a paradox. Oxygen is essential to life, yet we must balance this positive effect with the recognition that oxygen may also limit life processes. The literature on the potential negative effects of oxygen radicals is vast (21). Oxygen radicals reportedly contribute to the processes of aging, the promotion of cancer, the establishment of atherosclerosis, the initiation of inflammation and the consequent rheumatoid diseases, and on and on. The term "oxygen (or oxidative) stress" (96) has been coined to encompass the physiological and pathological situations that result from increased cellular loads of oxygen radicals. No cellular constituent is immune to oxidative modification initiated by oxygen radicals. Lipids, proteins, nucleic acids, and carbohydrates all fall victim to damage following exposure to radical or oxidant exposure (21, 46).

CONCLUDING REMARKS

This review is a blend of two different scientific approaches to the question of whether or not molecular oxygen fulfills the definition of an essential nutrient. The physiologist approaches the question from the perspective of cellular and subcellular physiology with emphasis on the availability, transport, and distribution of oxygen. The biochemist focuses on the molecular aspects of oxygen and its role in enzymology and metabolism. We remain divided in our conclusion: The physiologist, from his perspective of organismic biology, favors including oxygen as an essential nutrient. Its delivery to cells and mitochondria is the most critical of all nutrients; the stores of it in the body are enough for only a few seconds of metabolism. On the other hand, the biochemist notes that oxygen is involved in a plethora of reactions that extend well beyond those of a classical nutrient. Thus, oxygen is too important to life to be categorized simply as a nutrient.

As a nutrient oxygen is unique. The circulatory-respiratory transport system monitors and regulates arterial pO_2 in order to supply the body's needs continuously and rapidly. O_2 can be viewed as the architect of phylogenetic development. The critical balance of an "oxygen limited" cellular metabolism places oxygen at the fulcrum point for dictating the energy charge required for homeostasis. One is struck by the diversity of reactions in which oxygen participates during the synthesis of hormonal mediators and structural elements and in xenobiotic metabolism. Lastly, one must consider the dualism of oxygen. Oxygen is essential for life, although it carries the risk of destroying the very life for which it serves as the source of useful energy.

The challenge has been met, but the question remains unanswered.

We apologize to our many friends and colleagues for the failure to cite their many contributions to oxygen metabolism and physiology, but it would be an impossible task to highlight even a small portion of the elegant science that has contributed to our present understanding of oxygen chemistry and physiology, and thus we have, of necessity, been highly selective and somewhat arbitrary in our focus.

ACKNOWLEDGMENTS

The preparation of this review was supported in part by grants HL 47815 (R. E. F.) and GM 16488 (R. W. E.) from the National Institutes of Health.

Literature Cited

1. Agosin, M., Srivatsan, J. 1991. Role of microsomal cytochrome P-450 in the formation of ecdysterone in larval house fly. *Comp. Biochem. Physiol. B* 99:271–74

2. Akwa, Y., Young, J., Kabbabj, K., Sancho, M. J., Zucman, D., et al. 1991. Neurosteroids: biosynthesis, metabolism and function of pregnenolone and dehydroepiandrosterone in the brain. *J. Steroid Biochem. Mol. Biol.* 40:71–81

3. Ames, B. N., Gold, L. S. 1991. Endogenous mutagens and the causes of aging and cancer. *Mutat. Res.* 250:3–16

4. Bannister, J. V., Bannister, W. H. 1985. Production of oxygen-centered radicals by neutrophils and macrophages as studied by electron spin resonance (ESR). *Environ. Health Perspect.* 64:37–43

5. Bannister, J. V., Bannister, W. H., Hill, H. A., Thornalley, P. J. 1982. Enhanced production of hydroxyl radicals by the xanthine-xanthine oxidase reaction in the presence of lactoferrin. *Biochim. Biophys. Acta* 715:116–20

6. Bernard, C. 1878. *Lecons sur les Phenomenes de la Vie Communs aux Animaux et aux Vegetaux*, Vol. 1. Paris: Bailliere

7. Bruice, T. C. 1988. In *Mechanistic Principles of Enzyme Action*, ed. J. F. Liebman, A. Greenberg, pp. 227–78. New York: VCH

8. Burgos-Trinidad, M., Ismail, R., Ettinger, R. A., Prahl, J. M., DeLuca, H. F. 1992. Immunopurified 25-hydroxyvitamin D_1-alpha-hydroxylase and 1,25-dihydroxyvitamin D 24-hydroxylase are closely related but distinct enzymes. *J. Biol. Chem.* 267:3498–3505

9. Buse, G., Steffens, G. C. 1991. Cytochrome c oxidase in *Paracoccus denitrificans*. Protein, chemical, structural, and evolutionary aspects. *J. Bioenerg. Biomembr.* 23:269–89

10. Cao, X. N., Hengst, L., Schlerf, A., Droste, M., Mengel, T., Kadenbach, B. 1988. Complexity of nucleus-encoded genes of mammalian cytochrome

c oxidase. *Ann. NY Acad. Sci.* 550:337–47

11. Capaldi, R. A. 1990. Tissue specificity and defects in human cytochrome c oxidase. *Biochim. Biophys. Acta* 1018:223–24

12. Capaldi, R. A. 1990. Structure and function of cytochrome c oxidase. *Annu. Rev. Biochem.* 59:569–96

13. Capdevila, J. H., Falck, J. R., Estabrook, R. W. 1992. Cytochrome P450 and the arachidonate cascade. *FASEB J.* 6:731–36

14. Chance, B. 1977. Molecular basis of O_2 affinity for cytochrome oxidase. In *Oxygen and Physiological Function,* ed. F. F. Jobsis, pp. 14–25. Dallas: Prof. Info. Libr.

15. Chance, B. 1981. The cycling of oxygen through intermediates in the cytochrome oxidase-oxygen reaction. *Curr. Top. Cell. Regul.* 18:343–60

16. Ciba Foundation Symposium. 1979. *Oxygen Free Radicals and Tissue Damage,* Vol. 65. Amsterdam: Excerpta Med.

17. Clark, A. Jr., Clark, P. A., Connett, R. J., Gayeski, T. E., Honig, C. R. 1987. How large is the drop in pO_2 between cytosol and mitochondrion? *Am. J. Physiol.* 252:C583–87

18. Coburn, R. F., Eppinger, R., Scott, D. P. 1986. Oxygen-dependent tension in vascular smooth muscle. Does the endothelium play a role? *Circ. Res.* 58:341–47

19. Coburn, R. F., Mayers, L. B. 1974. Myoglobin O_2 tension determined from measurements of carboxyhemoglobin in sketal muscle. *Am. J. Physiol.* 220:66–74

20. Cross, A. R., Henderson, L., Jones, O. T., Delpiano, M. A., Hentschel, J., Acker, H. 1990. Involvement of an NAD(P)H oxidase as a pO_2 sensor protein in the rat carotid body. *Biochem. J.* 272:743–47

21. Davis, K. J. A. 1991. *Oxidative Damage and Repair: Chemical, Biological, and Medical Aspects.* Oxford/New York: Pergamon. 899 pp.

22. Dejours, P. 1981. *Principles of Comparative Respiratory Physiology.* Elsevier: Amsterdam. 265 pp. 2nd ed.

23. Drabkin, D. 1950. The distribution of the chromoproteins, hemoglobin, myoglobin, and cytochrome c, in the tissues of different species, and the relationship of the total content of each chromoprotein to body mass. *J. Biol. Chem.* 182:317–33

24. Ernster, L., Lee, C-P. 1990. Thirty years of mitochondrial pathophysiology: From Luft's disease to oxygen toxicity. In *Bioenergetics,* ed. C. H. Kim, T. Ozawa, pp. 451–65. New York: Plenum

25. Estabrook, R. W., Cooper, D. Y., Rosenthal, O. 1963. The light reversible carbon monoxide inhibition of the steroid C21-hydroxylase system of the adrenal cortex. *Biochem. Z.* 338:741–55

26. Estabrook, R. W., Peterson, J. A., Mason, J. I., Simpson, E. R., Waterman, M. R. 1990. The cytochrome P450 superfamily: Impact on biology and medicine. In *Biological Oxidations Systems: Proceedings of The International Symposium on Biological Oxidations, Indian Inst. Sci., Bangalore, India,* ed. C. C. Reddy, G. A. Hamilton, K. M. Madyastha, 1:19–38. New York: Academic

27. Estabrook, R. W., Trant, J. M., Methew, P. A., Mason, J. I., Waterman, M. R. 1992. Designer membranes: Construction of a cell containing multiple membrane-bound cytochromes P450s. *Curr. Top. Cell. Regul.* 33:419–31.

28. Fitzgerald, R. S., Dehghani, G. A., Sham, J. S., Shirahata, M., Mitzner, W. A. 1992. Peripheral chemoreceptor modulation of the pulmonary vasculature in the cat. *J. Appl. Physiol.* 73:20–29

29. Forster, R. E. 1964. Factors affecting the rate of exchange of O_2 between blood and tissue. In *Oxygen in the Animal Organism,* pp. 393–409. New York: Pergamon. 694 pp.

30. Forster, R. E., DuBois, A. B., Briscoe, W. A., Fisher, A. B. 1986. *The Lung: Physiological Basis of Pulmonary Function Tests.* Chicago: Year Book. 329 pp.

31. Forster, R. E., Goodwin, G. W., Itada, N. 1976. A new approach to the experimental measurement of mean tissue pO_2. *Adv. Exp. Med. Biol.* 75:41–46

32. Fridovich, I. 1989. Superoxide dismutases. An adaptation to a paramagnetic gas. *J. Biol. Chem.* 264:7761–64

33. Gayeski, T. E., Honig, C. R. 1983. Direct measurement of intracellular O_2 gradients: role of convection and myoglobin. *Adv. Exp. Med. Biol.* 159:613–21

34. George, P. 1964. The fitness of oxygen. In *Oxidases and Related Redox Systems,* ed. T. E. King, H. S. Mason, M. Morrison, pp. 3–32. New York: Wiley

35. Gilbert, D. L. 1981. Perspective on the history of oxygen and life. In *Oxygen and Living Processes: An Interdisciplinary Approach,* ed. D. L.

Gilbert, pp. 1–12. New York: Springer-Verlag

36. Glerum, D. M., Yanamura, W., Capaldi, R. A., Robinson, B. H. 1988. Characterization of cytochrome-c oxidase mutants in human fibroblasts. *FEBS Lett.* 236:100–4

37. Gonzalez, F. J. 1990. Molecular genetics of the P-450 superfamily. *Pharmacol. Ther.* 45:1–38

38. Gonzalez, F. J., Crespi, C. L., Gelboin, H. V. 1991. DNA-expressed human cytochrome P450s: a new age of molecular toxicology and human risk assessment. *Mutat. Res.* 247:113–27

39. Gonzalez, F. J., Gelboin, H. V. 1991. Human cytochromes P450: evolution, catalytic activities and interindividual variations in expression. *Prog. Clin. Biol. Res.* 372:11–20

40. Grieb, P., Forster, R. E., Strome, D., Goodwin, C. W., Pape, P. C. 1985. O_2 exchange between blood and brain tissues studied with 1802 indicator-dilution technique. *J. Appl. Physiol.* 58:1929–41

41. Grieb, P., Pape, P. C., Forster, R. E., Goodwin, C. W., Nioka, S., Labbatte, L. 1985. Oxygen exchanges between blood and resting skeletal muscle: a shunt-sink hypothesis. *Adv. Exp. Med. Biol.* 191:309–24

42. Groebe, K. 1990. A versatile model of steady state O_2 supply to tissue. Application to skeletal muscle. *Biophys. J.* 57:485–98

43. Groebe, K., Thews, G. 1990. Calculated intra- and extracellular pO_2 gradients in heavily working red muscle. *Am. J. Physiol.* 259:H84–92

44. Guengerich, F. P., Shimada, T. 1991. Oxidation of toxic and carcinogenic chemicals by human cytochrome P-450 enzymes. *Chem. Res. Toxicol.* 4:391–407

45. Haller, R. G., Lewis, S. F., Estabrook, R. W., DiMauro, S., Servidei, S., Foster, D. W. 1989. Exercise intolerance, lactic acidosis, and abnormal cardiopulmonary regulation in exercise associated with adult skeletal muscle cytochrome c oxidase deficiency. *J. Clin. Invest.* 84:155–61

46. Halliwell, B. 1991. Reactive oxygen species in living systems: source, biochemistry, and role in human disease. *Am. J. Med.* 91:14S–22S

47. Hamilton, G. A. 1974. In *Molecular Mechanisms of Oxygen Activation*, ed. O. Hayaishi, pp. 405–57. New York: Academic

48. Hamilton, G. A. 1990. Mechanisms of biological oxidation reactions involving oxygen and reduced oxygen derivatives. See Ref. 26, pp. 3–19

49. Hayasaka, K., Brown, G. K., Danks, D. M., Droste, M., Kadenbach, B. 1989. Cytochrome c oxidase deficiency in subacute necrotizing encephalopathy (Leigh syndrome). *J. Inherit. Metab. Dis.* 12:247–56

50. Henderson, L. J. 1913. *The Fitness of the Environment.* New York: Macmillan. Republished 1958. Boston: Beacon

51. Herbig, G. H. 1981. The Origin and astronomical history of terrestrial oxygen. See Ref. 35, pp. 65–73

52. Holland, R. A., Forster, R. E. 1966. The effect of size of red cells on the kinetics of their oxygen uptake. *J. Gen. Physiol.* 49:727–42

53. Honig, C. R., Connett, R. J., Gayeski, T. E. 1992. O_2 transport and its interaction with metabolism: a systems view of aerobic capacity. *Med. Sci. Sports Exerc.* 24:47–53

54. Honig, C. R., Gayeski, T. E., Federspiel, W., Clark, A. Jr., Clark, P. 1984. Muscle O_2 gradients from hemoglobin to cytochrome: new concepts, new complexities. *Adv. Exp. Med. Biol.* 169:23–38

55. Hughes, G. M. 1965. *Comparative Physiology of Vertebrate Respiration.* Cambridge: Harvard Univ. 146 pp.

56. Iturriaga, R., Rumsey, W. L., Lahiri, S., Spergel, D., Wilson, D. F. 1992. Intracellular pH and oxygen chemoreception in the cat carotid body in vitro. *J. Appl. Physiol.* 72:2259–66

57. Kadenbach, B., Hartmann, R., Glanville, R., Buse, G. 1982. Tissue-specific genes code for polypeptide VIa of bovine liver and heart cytochrome c oxidase. *FEBS. Lett.* 138:236–38

58. Kadenbach, B., Jarausch, J., Hartmann, R., Merle, P. 1983. Separation of mammalian cytochrome c oxidase into 13 polypeptides by a sodium dodecyl sulfate-gel electrophoretic procedure. *Anal. Biochem.* 129:517–21

59. Kako, K. J. 1987. Free radical effects on membrane protein in myocardial ischemia/reperfusion injury, *J. Mol. Cell. Cardiol.* 19:209–11

60. Kamen, M. P. 1963. *Primary Processes in Photosynthesis.* New York: Academic

61. Kawajiri, K., Nakachi, K., Imai, K., Yoshii, A., Shinoda, N., Watanabe, J. 1990. Identification of genetically high risk individuals to lung cancer by DNA polymorphisms of the cytochrome P4501A1 gene, *FEBS Lett.* 263:131–33

62. Keilin, D. 1929. Cytochrome and re-

spiratory enzymes. *Proc. R. Soc. London Ser. B* 104:206–52

63. Kennaway, N. G., Carrero-Valenzuela, R. D., Ewart, G., Balan, V. K., Lightowlers, R., et al. 1990. Isoforms of mammalian cytochrome c oxidase: correlation with human cytochrome c oxidase deficiency. *Pediatr. Res.* 28:529–35

64. Kochs, G., Werck-Reichhart, D., Grisebach, H. 1992. Further characterization of cytochrome P450 involved in phytoalexin synthesis in soybean: cytochrome P450 cinnamate 4-hydroxylase and 3,9-dihydroxypterocarpan 6α-hydroxylase. *Arch. Biochem. Biophys.* 293:187–94.

65. Koppenol, W. H. 1988. The paradox of oxygen: thermodynamics versus toxicity. In *Oxidases and Related Redox Systems, Progress in Clinical and Biological Research*, ed. T. E. King, H. S. Mason, M. Morrison, pp. 93–109. New York: Liss

66. Kreuzer, F., Turek, Z., Hoofd, L. 1991. Oxygen transfer from blood to mitochondria. In *The Lung: Scientific Foundations*, ed. R. G. Crystal, J. B. West, et al, pp. 1479–88. New York: Raven

67. Lambertsen, C. J., Kaugh, R. H., Cooper, D. V., Emmel, G. L., Loeschche, H. H., Schmidt, C. F. 1953. Oxygen toxicity. Effects in man of oxygen inhalation at 1 and 3.5 atmospheres upon blood gas transport, cerebral circulation, and cerebral metabolism. *J. Appl. Physiol.* 5:471–86

68. Lavoisier, A.-L. 1777. Experiences sur la respiration des animaux et sur les changements qui arrivent a l'air en passant par leur poumon. *Mem. Acad. Sci.*, p. 185. Republished 1862 in *Oeuvres de Lavoisier, Memoires de Chimie et de Physique*, 2:174–83. Paris: Imp. Imperiale

69. Levine, J. S. 1988. The origin and evolution of atmospheric oxygen. See Ref. 65, pp. 111–26

70. Linder, M. C. 1991. *Nutritional Biochemistry and Metabolism with Clinical Applications*, p. 10. New York: Elsevier. 2nd ed.

71. Londraville, R. L., Sidell, B. D. 1990. Maximal diffusion-distance within skeletal muscle can be estimated from mitochondrial distributions. *Respir. Physiol.* 81:291–301

72. Mahgoub, A., Idle, J. R., Dring, L. G., Lancaster, R., Smith, R. L. 1977. Polymorphic hydroxylation of debrisoquine in man. *Lancet* 2:584–86

73. Mason, H. S., North, J. C., Vanneste, M. 1965. Microsomal mixed-function oxidations: the metabolism of xenobiotics. *Fed. Proc.* 24:1172–80

74. McCord, J. M., Fridovich, I. 1988. Superoxide dismutase: the first twenty years (1968–1988). *Free Radic. Biol. Med.* 5:363–69

75. Merle, P., Kadenbach, B. 1980. The subunit composition of mammalian cytochrome c oxidase. *Eur. J. Biochem.* 105:499–507

76. Miller, P. L. 1964. Respiration—aerial gas transport. In *The Physiology of Insecta*, ed. M. Rockstein, 3:558–617. New York: Academic

77. Mitchell, P. 1987. A new redox loop formality involving metal-catalysed hydroxide-ion translocation. A hypothetical Cu loop mechanism for cytochrome oxidase. *FEBS Lett.* 222:235–45

78. Mitchell, R., Mitchell, P., Rich, P. R. 1992. Protonation states of the catalytic intermediates of cytochrome c oxidase. *Biochim. Biophys. Acta* 1101:188–91

79. Mokashi, A., Lahiri, S. 1991. Aortic and carotid body chemoreception in prolonged hyperoxia in the cat. *Respir. Physiol.* 86:233–43

80. Muller, M., Azzi, A. 1991. Cytochrome c oxidase metal centers: location and function. *J. Bioenerg. Biomembr.* 23:291–302

81. Nebert, D. W., Nelson, D. R., Coon, M. J., Estabrook, R. W., Feyereisen, R., et al. 1991. The P450 superfamily: update on new sequences, gene mapping, and recommended nomenclature. *DNA Cell. Biol.* 10:1–14.

82. Nishiki, K., Erecinska, M., Wilson, D. F. 1978. Energy relationships between cytosolic metabolism and mitochondrial respiration in rat heart. *Am. J. Physiol.* 234:C73–81

83. Nuutinen, E. M., Wilson, D. F., Erecinska, M. 1984. Mitochondrial oxidative phosphorylation: tissue oxygen sensor for regulation of coronary flow. *Adv. Exp. Med. Biol.* 169:351–57

84. Okuda, M., Ikai, I., Chance, B., Kumar, C. 1991. Oxygen radical production during ischemia-reperfusion in the isolated perfused rat liver as monitored by luminol enhanced chemiluminescence. *Biochem. Biophys. Res. Commun.* 174:217–21

85. Omura, T., Sato, R. 1964. The carbon monoxide-binding pigment of liver microsomes. I. Evidence for its hemoprotein nature. *J. Biol. Chem.* 239:2370–78

86. Pasteur, L. 1861. Animalicules infusoires vivant sans gaz oxygene libre

et determinant des fermentations. *C. R. Acad. Sci.* 52:344–47

87. Piiper, J., Scheid, P. 1991. Diffusion limitation of O_2 supply to tissue in homogeneous and heterogeneous models. *Respir. Physiol.* 85:127–36

88. Popel, A. S. 1989. Theory of oxygen transport to tissue. *Crit. Rev. Biomed. Eng.* 17:257–321

89. Priestley, J. 1775. An account of further discoveries in air. *Philos. Trans.* 65:384–94

90. Roberts, E. S., Vaz, A. D., Coon, M. J. 1992. Role of isozymes of rabbit microsomal cytochrome P-450 in the metabolism of retinoic acid, retinol, and retinal. *Mol. Pharmacol.* 41:427–33

91. Ronis, M. J., Hodgson, E. 1989. Cytochrome P-450 monooxygenases in insects. *Zenobiotica* 19:1077–92

92. Rumsey, W. L., Robiolio, M., Wilson, D. F. 1989. Contribution of diffusion to the oxygen dependence of energy metabolism in human neuroblastoma cells. *Adv. Exp. Med. Biol.* 248:829–33

93. Sarkar, M. A. 1992. Drug metabolism in the nasal mucosa. *Pharmacol. Res.* 9:1–9

94. Scheele, C. W. 1777. Chemische abhandlung von der luft und dem feuer. Uppsala and Liepzig. Section 2. Chemical treatise on air and fire. In *The Collected Papers of Carl Wilhelm Scheele*. Transl. L. Dobbs, 1931. London: G. Bell. Republished 1971, pp. 85–178. New York: Kraus Reprint

95. Schumacker, P. T., Samsel, R. W. 1989. Analysis of oxygen delivery and uptake relationships in the Krogh tissue model. *J. Appl. Physiol.* 67:1234–44

96. Sies, H. 1991. Oxidative stress: from basic research to clinical application. *Am. J. Med.* 91:31S–38S

97. Silverton, S. F., Pacifici, M., Haselgrove, J. C., Colodny, S. H., Forster, R. E. 1990. Two-dimensional model of tissue oxygen gradients in avian growth cartilage. *Adv. Exp. Med. Biol.* 277:759–65

98. Silverton, S. F., Wagerle, L. C., Robiolo, M. E., Haselgrove, J. C., Forster, R. E. 1989. Oxygen gradients in two regions of the epiphyseal growth plate. *Adv. Exp. Med. Biol.* 248:809–15

99. Smith, D. S., Levy, W., Maris, M., Chance, B. 1990. Reperfusion hyperoxia in brain after circulatory arrest in humans. *Anesthesiology* 73:12–19

100. Tyler, D. D. 1992. *The Mitochondrion in Health and Disease,* Cambridge, UK: VCH

101. Warburg, O. 1949. *Heavy Metal Prosthetic Groups and Enzyme Action.* London: Oxford Univ. Press

102. Warburg, O., Geissler, A. W., Lorenz, S. 1968. Oxygen the creator of differentiation. In *Aspects of Yeast Metabolism,* ed. A. K. Mills, H. A. Krebs, pp. 327–37. Oxford: Blackell. 345 pp.

103. Webster's Third New International Dictionary of the English Language, Unabridged. 1976. Ed. P. B. Gove. Springfield, Mass: G. & C. Merriam. 1552 pp.

104. White, R. E., Coon, M. J. 1980. Oxygen activation by cytochrome P-450. *Annu. Rev. Biochem.* 49:315–56

105. Wikstrom, M., Morgan, J. E. 1992. The dioxygen cycle. Spectral, kinetic, and thermodynamic characteristics of ferryl and peroxy intermediates observed by reversal of the cytochrome oxidase reaction. *J. Biol. Chem.* 267:10266–73

106. Wilson, D. F. 1990. Contribution of diffusion to the oxygen dependence of energy metabolism in cells. *Experientia* 46:1160–62

107. Wilson, D. F., Erecinska, M., Drown, C., Silver, I. A. 1977. Effect of oxygen tension on cellular energetics. *Am. J. Physiol.* 233:C135–40

108. Wilson, D. F., Erecinska, M., Drown, C., Silver, I. A. 1979. The oxygen dependence of cellular energy metabolism. *Arch. Biochem. Biophys.* 195:485–93

109. Wilson, D. F., Erecinska, M., Nuutinen, E. M., Silver, I. A. 1984. Dependence of cellular metabolism and local oxygen delivery on oxygen tension. *Adv. Exp. Med. Biol.* 180:629–34

110. Wilson, D. F., Owen, C. S., Erecinska, M. 1979. Quantitative dependence of mitochondrial oxidative phosphorylation on oxygen concentration: a mathematical model. *Arch. Biochem. Biophys.* 195:494–504

111. Zhang, Y. Z., Ewart, G., Capaldi, R. A. 1991. Topology of subunits of the mammalian cytochrome c oxidase: relationship to the assembly of the enzyme complex. *Biochemistry* 30:3674–81

Annu. Rev. Nutr. 1993. 13:405–36

CLINICAL PHYSIOLOGY OF TASTE AND SMELL

Susan S. Schiffman and Carol A. Gatlin

Department of Psychiatry, Duke University Medical Center, Durham, North Carolina 27706

KEY WORDS: taste, smell, disease, drugs, aging

CONTENTS

INTRODUCTION   406
CLASSIFICATION OF CHEMOSENSORY DISORDERS   406
ANATOMY AND PHYSIOLOGY OF TASTE AND SMELL   407
   Taste   407
   Smell   408
TYPES OF CHEMOSENSORY LOSSES   408
CLINICAL EVALUATION   409
   Patient History   409
   Physical Examination   409
   Psychophysical Testing   410
   Medical Imaging   410
DYSFUNCTIONS RESULTING FROM DRUGS   410
DYSFUNCTIONS ASSOCIATED WITH DISEASES   414
DYSFUNCTIONS ASSOCIATED WITH NORMAL AGING   415
   Taste: Threshold Losses   416
   Taste: Suprathreshold Losses   417
   Taste: Causes of Perceptual Losses   417
   Smell: Threshold Losses   418
   Smell: Suprathreshold Losses   418
   Smell: Causes of Perceptual Losses   420
DYSFUNCTIONS ASSOCIATED WITH ALZHEIMER'S DISEASE   421
DYSFUNCTIONS ASSOCIATED WITH ENVIRONMENTAL POLLUTION   422
   Offensive Tastes and Odors Associated With Pollution   422
   Pollutants That Alter the Olfactory and Taste Systems   423
TREATMENT OR COMPENSATION FOR CHEMOSENSORY LOSSES   423

0199-9885/93/0715-0405$02.00

INTRODUCTION

A report to the National Advisory Neurological and Communicative Disorders and Stroke Council (198) estimates that a significant number of Americans (approximately 2,000,000 people) suffer from losses, diminution, or distortion of their senses of taste, smell, or both. Although these disorders are seldom life-threatening, they can influence the health and well-being of the person who suffers from them (229). Taste and smell not only play a role in protection against harmful substances but they also contribute significantly to nutritional status as well as to the quality of life.

The senses of taste and smell convey the attractive properties of foods that promote and maintain food intake. When chemosensory disorders diminish or distort these senses, the taste and smell of foods can become uninteresting or even repugnant, which may lead to reduced food intake and compromised nutritional status. Persons with reduced taste and smell sensitivity may overcompensate for losses by increasing intake of substances that can be harmful if ingested in excess. For example, the increased taste thresholds for sweet sensation that commonly accompany aging can lead elderly diabetic patients to ingest too much sugar (229). Age-related losses in NaCl perception can be harmful to persons with hypertension. Decrements in taste and smell may also expose patients to harmful substances such as environmental contaminants and spoiled food. Overall, chemosensory dysfunction can reduce quality and enjoyment of life, deprive the individual of protective mechanisms, and can even contribute to stress, depression, and anorexia.

CLASSIFICATION OF CHEMOSENSORY DISORDERS

Disorders of taste and smell can be classified into five broad categories, depending on the degree or type of symptoms (270). These disorders are diagnosed by psychophysical evaluation in which patients are tested with a variety of chemical compounds.

1. Ageusia: total loss of taste sensitivity to some or all stimulants (tastants).
2. Hypogeusia: decreased taste sensitivity to some or all stimulants (tastants).
3. Dysgeusia (parageusia): distortion of taste for some or all tastants, or the perception of taste in the absence of any tastants (gustatory hallucination).
4. Hypergeusia: increased taste sensitivity to some or all stimulants (tastants).
5. Taste agnosia: complete or partial inability to identify, classify, or contrast a tastant verbally despite ability to recognize and distinguish between tastants.

Smell disorders fall into five similar categories:

1. Anosmia: total loss of sensitivity to odors.
2. Hyposmia: decreased sensitivity to odors.
3. Dysosmia: distortion of smell for some or all odorants, or the perception of odor in the absence of any odorants (olfactory hallucination).
4. Hyperosmia: increased odor sensitivity to some or all stimulants (odorants).
5. Smell agnosia: complete or partial inability to identify, classify, or contrast an odorant verbally despite ability to recognize and distinguish between odorants.

ANATOMY AND PHYSIOLOGY OF TASTE AND SMELL

To gain an understanding of taste and smell disorders, it is helpful to be familiar with the anatomy and physiology of chemosensory systems (see 249 for a review).

Taste

The sensory organs that mediate the sense of taste are the taste buds. These pear-shaped organs are found on the tongue, soft palate, pharynx, larynx, epiglottis, uvula, the upper third of the esophagus, and (especially in infants) the lips and cheeks. Taste buds on the tongue are contained in small specialized structures called papillae. There are three types of papillae: fungiform, circumvallate, and foliate. Fungiform papillae are elevated structures located on the anterior two thirds of the tongue; each fungiform papilla contains an average of 1 to 18 taste buds, although many fungiform papillae contain no buds at all. Circumvallate papillae are large mushroom-shaped structures arranged in a V shape on the posterior tongue and are surrounded by a "moat." Foliate papillae are vertical folds on the lateral border of the tongue, just anterior to the circumvallate papillae. Taste buds consist of about 50 cells that have a life span of approximately 10 to 10 $\frac{1}{2}$ days. Taste cells are constantly replaced by division of epithelial cells that surround the bud.

Three cranial nerves transmit taste signals from taste buds. The taste buds on the fungiform papillae, the anterior foliate papillae, and most buds on the soft palate are innervated by the seventh cranial nerve. Buds on the circumvallate papillae and posterior foliate papillae are innervated by the ninth cranial nerve. Buds on the pharynx, larynx, epiglottis, and uvula are innervated by the tenth cranial nerve. Taste information is transmitted to the cortex (cortical taste area) via the nucleus of the solitary tract and thalamus. Some taste information is also transmitted to the hypothalamus, which is integral to the feeding system in the brain. The three cranial nerves also contain some axons that terminate in the spinal trigeminal nucleus, and it is presumed that these fibers convey thermal and tactile information from the oral cavity.

The taste system is stimulated by a wide range of chemicals including organic and inorganic compounds. The range of taste sensations is broad and includes not only sweet, sour, salty, and bitter qualities but "umami" (glutamate), astringent, and other tastes that are difficult to describe in words.

Smell

The receptors for smell are located in the olfactory epithelium in the pigmented upper part of the superior turbinate, the nasal septum, and the roof in between these regions. These receptors are specialized bipolar neurons with cilia that protrude into the mucus that covers the olfactory epithelium. Like taste cells, the receptor portion of the bipolar olfactory cells is constantly renewed from basal cells, but the turnover time is three times longer, approximately 30 days (191).

The very thin axons of bipolar neurons are aggregated in bundles that traverse small holes in the cribriform plate to reach the olfactory bulb where they form small bushy masses called glomeruli. With age, the glomeruli deteriorate and assume a moth-eaten appearance as the fibers disappear. Projections from the olfactory bulb then project to the primitive cortex including the pyriform lobe and hippocampal formation. The areas of primitive cortex not only process olfactory information but also process emotional information. The neurons in the hippocampus and pyriform cortex degenerate with age sooner than other parts of the brain. Like the taste system, olfactory information also projects to the hypothalamic feeding centers.

TYPES OF CHEMOSENSORY LOSSES

While taste and smell disorders are associated with a wide variety of conditions (including drug therapy, disease states, normal aging, Alzheimer's disease, and pollution), they can generally be classified by three major types of losses: transport losses, sensory losses, and neural losses (268). The term *sensorineural losses* is used in situations in which it is difficult in practice to distinguish between sensory and neural disorders.

Transport losses interfere with the access of a chemical stimulus to the taste or smell receptors. A common example in the case of smell is nasal airway blockage by swollen membranes or structural abnormalities such as polyps and a deviated septum. In taste, transport losses can result from blockage of taste buds by bacterial colonizations, xerostomia, inflammation of the oral cavity, or poor oral hygiene.

Sensory losses are caused by damage to the sensory organs themselves (229). Toxic chemicals, radiation therapy, medications, neoplasms, endocrine and viral infections that reduce cell turnover or directly modify cells, can impair taste and smell functioning. For example, radiation treatment can reduce cell turnover and cause aberrations in the sense of taste. Medications with sulfhydryl groups in their molecular structure such as penicillamine (antirheumatic drug) and captopril (antihypertensive agent) probably cause taste disorders because they interfere with receptor proteins on the surface of taste cells.

Neural losses result from damage to either the peripheral neural pathways that mediate taste and smell information or to the central nervous system. Common causes include head trauma, neoplasms, and surgical procedures. For example, head trauma resulting from an automobile accident can sever the nerve pathways through the cribriform plate to produce olfactory dysfunction.

CLINICAL EVALUATION

The clinical evaluation of a patient who presents with symptoms of chemosensory dysfunction normally consists of four components: (*a*) a history, (*b*) a physical examination, (*c*) psychophysical testing, and (*d*) medical imaging (269). The general strategy is first to make an anatomic diagnosis and then to make an etiologic diagnosis.

Patient History

The first step in diagnosis is the patient history. The patient is asked to describe the events associated with the onset of a taste or smell disorder. Patients are encouraged to recall events that coincided with the time of onset of the symptoms such as viral infections and head injuries. They are given ample opportunity to describe their chemosensory symptoms in detail. It is important to determine the following points: (*a*) whether the onset of symptoms was sudden or gradual; (*b*) whether the sensory loss applies to selected stimuli or all stimuli; (*c*) whether the changes are qualitative or quantitative; (*d*) whether the loss is intermittent (temporary losses suggest a transport problem) or continuous; (*e*) whether the sense is lost, diminished, enhanced, or distorted; (*f*) whether other symptoms accompany the disorder such as nasal or oral dryness, excess salivation, burning tongue, dental pain, or headache; (*g*) whether the patient is taking medications; (*h*) whether the patient has medical problems that may cause a chemosensory disorder. The patient's history should include family medical history and patient's social and occupational history including occupational exposures, substance abuse, and dietary history.

Physical Examination

The second step in diagnosis is a complete examination of the head and neck, including ears and upper respiratory tract. A neurologic examination of the cranial nerves is also necessary.

The nasal airways are examined to identify any obstructions that may interfere with transport of olfactory stimuli to the receptors in the olfactory epithelium. After initial visual examination, a vasoconstrictor is applied to improve visualization. The nasal mucous membrane is examined for abnormal conditions including inflammation, swelling, erosion, ulceration, epithelial metaplasia, and purulent discharge. Examination of the olfactory neuroepithelium itself is difficult even with the smallest of modern instruments.

The mucous membranes of the oral cavity should be examined for inflammation, swelling, dryness, abnormal texture, exudate, edema, atrophy erosion, ulceration, leukoplakia, and erythroplasia. Changes in the fungiform or circumvallate papillae should be noted.

Psychophysical Testing

All patients who report chemosensory dysfunction should be subjected to psychophysical evaluation of both taste and smell. Subjects often confuse a smell disorder with a taste disorder. The reason for this is that food is placed in the oral cavity and hence the patient attributes losses to taste rather than smell. However, the flavor of food is based on combined responses of the taste buds, olfactory neurons, and free nerve endings in the nose, mouth, and throat. Odor from food placed in the oral cavity reaches the olfactory receptors via the nasal pharnyx. A variety of psychophysical tests at threshold concentrations and suprathreshold concentrations are described in later sections on chemosensory losses in aging and Alzheimer's disease.

Medical Imaging

Computed tomography of the head provides important diagnostic information, expecially for olfactory disorders, by providing details about the structure of the nasal cavities, the cribriform plates, and the anterior cranial fossa (150). The presence of sinusitis and neoplasms of the nose, paranasal sinuses, and cranial cavity are diagnosed with computed tomography techniques. Magnetic resonance imaging can also be helpful in evaluating the contents of the cranial cavity, but computed tomagraphy is superior in providing detail on the bony structures.

DYSFUNCTIONS RESULTING FROM DRUGS

Medications that have been reported to alter chemosensory functioning are given in Tables 1 and 2. The drugs that alter chemosensory functioning have been shown to produce their effects after oral administration, systemic injection, or direct application to the chemosensory receptors. However, our current understanding of the mechanisms by which these pharmaceutical

Table 1 Drugs that interfere with the taste system

Classification	References
Amebicides and antihelmintics	
Metronidazole	283
Niridazole	209
Anesthetics (local)	
Benzocaine	295
Procaine hydrochloride (novocain)	295
Lidocaine	306
Anticholesteremic	
Clofibrate	105
Anticoagulants	
Phenindione	253
Antihistamines	
Chlorpheniramine maleate	229
Antimicrobial agents	
Amphotericin B	216
Ampicillin	134
Bleomycin	273
Cefamandole	125
Griseofulvin	78
Ethambutol hydrochloride	216
Lincomycin	105
Sulfasalazine	216
Tetracyclines	168, 229
	271
Antiproliferative, including immunosuppressive agents	
Doxorubicin and methotrexate	60, 96
Azathioprine	216
Carmustine	211
Vincristine sulfate	275
Antirheumatic, analgesic-antipyretic, antiinflammatory	
Allopurinol	216
Colchicine	15
Dexamethasone	72
Gold	216
Hydrocortisone	72
Levamisole	219
D-penicillamine	147, 277
Phenylbutazone	216
Salicylates	19, 102
Sodium fluoride	288
5-Thiopyridoxine	130
Antiseptics	
Hexetidine	208

Table 1 (*continued*)

Classification	References
Antithyroid agents	
Carbimazole	66
Methimazole	66, 98
Methylthiouracil	250
Propylthiouracil	94
Thiouracil	216
Agents for dental hygiene	
Sodium lauryl sulfate	216, 50
Chlorhexidine digluconate mouth rinses	157
Diuretics and antihypertensive agents	
Acetazolamide	45, 91
Amiloride and its analogs	177, 237, 241
Captopril	180, 181, 294
Diazoxide	229
Diltiazem	17
Enalapril	180
Ethacrynic acid	85
Nifedipine	162
Hypoglycemic drugs	
Glipizide	154
Phenformin and derivatives	74, 216
Muscle relaxants and drugs for treatment of Parkinson's disease	
Baclofen	216
Chlormezanone	216
Levodopa	261
Psychopharmacologic agents	
Carbamazepine	97
Lithium carbonate	23, 59
Phenytoin	229
Psilocybin	75, 76
Trifluoperazine	75, 76
Sympathomimetic drugs	
Amphetamines	176
Vasodilators	
Bamifylline hydrochloride	216
Dipyridamole	90
Nitroglycerin patch	69
Oxyfedrine	210, 303
Others	
Etidronate	139
Germine monoacetate	34
Idoxuridine	262
Iron sorbitex	179
Vitamin D	216, 229

Table 2 Drugs that intefere with the smell system

Classification	References
Anesthetics, local	
Cocaine hydrochloride and tetracaine hydrochloride	307
Antihypertensive drugs	
Diltiazem	17
Nifedipine	162
Antimicrobial agents	
Allicin	18
Streptomycin	308
Tyrothricin	258
Antithyroid agents	
Carbimazole	66
Methimazole	66, 98
Methylthiouracil	250
Propylthiouracil	94
Opiates	
Codeine	166
Hydromorphone hydrochloride	166
Morphine	166
Psychopharmacologic drugs	
Amitriptyline	35, 71
Radiation therapy	
Radiation to head	30
Sympathomimetic drugs	
Amphetamines	87, 229, 290
Phenmetrazine theoclate with fenbutrazate hydrochloride	290
Vasodilators	
Diltiazem	17
Other	
Acetylcholine-like substances	265
Strychnine	265

agents modify the taste and olfactory systems is limited, and there are several reasons for our lack of knowledge. First, most drugs that cause chemosensory dysfunctions affect only a small minority of patients. Thus, well-controlled clinical trials to establish the cause of a taste or smell dysfunction are impractical because they would require such a large number of subjects. Second, persons taking medications have concomitant diseases that may contribute to the chemosensory disorder. Third, the transduction mechanisms for taste and smell at the receptor level are not fully understood; thus it is premature in most cases to speculate on the mechanisms by which drugs alter chemosensory functioning. Fourth, the neurotransmitters responsible for relaying taste and olfactory information from the periphery to the brain are not well documented. Hence, the interference with the transmission of neural signals by drugs is not well understood.

Many taste complaints resulting from medications are simply due to the taste of the drug itself rather than to some modification of the taste system. The drug may be administered in a dosage form that does not mask its unpleasant taste. The drug may also reach the taste receptors by excretion into the saliva or by an intravascular route (21). In order to determine if the taste of the drug itself is the source of the complaint, the drug can be dissolved in water (or alcohol and water if necessary to achieve solubility) to determine if the taste sensation matches the taste of the solution. Odor complaints are seldom due to the odor of a drug, but this can be determined by a simple sniff test.

Drugs may also produce pharmacologic changes in chemosensory systems. The mechanism by which the drug alters the taste or smell systems may be identical to or different from the mechanisms by which it produces its pharmacologic effect on other tissues. Numerous medications given in Tables 1 and 2 have been shown to affect turnover of cells in other biological systems and thus may also affect turnover of taste and olfactory cells by the same mechanism.

DYSFUNCTIONS ASSOCIATED WITH DISEASES

A broad range of medical conditions leads to losses in taste and smell (see Tables 3 and 4). These medical conditions can affect chemosensory functioning in a multitude of ways. First, decreased turnover of receptors may be the cause in many of these illnesses. Decreased turnover in the chemosensory systems would be consistent with decreased cell proliferation that has been found in small-bowel epithelium after fasting (including starvation and protein deprivation), uremia, ionizing irradiation, and administration of methotrexate. Endocrine factors, including adrenalectomy, hypophysectomy, thyroidectomy, and castration, also lead to reduced cell renewal in small-bowel epithelium (229). Decreased levels of vitamins and minerals such as niacin and zinc respectively may also contribute to reduced turnover in malnourished patients.

The most frequent causes of losses in olfaction are viral infections, normal aging, head injuries that sever neurons coursing through the cribriform plate, and local obstructions (229, 232). For taste, the most common offenders are viral infections, dental problems, and drugs, especially those containing sulfhydryl groups in their chemical structures (229). Some odorants can also cause pain by increasing nasal resistance and blood flow to the nasal cavity (54).

Table 3   Medical conditions that affect the sense of taste

Condition	Reference	Condition	Reference
Nervous			
Alzheimer's disease	233	Gonadal dysgenesis (Turner's syndrome)	103
Bell's palsy	62		
Damage to chorda tympani	136	Pseudohypoparathyroidism	104
Guillain-Barre syndrome	274	Local	
Familial dysautonomia	110	Facial hypoplasia	108
Head trauma	223	Glossitis and other oral disorders	22, 137
Multiple sclerosis	31, 39	Leprosy	272
Raeder's paratrigeminal syndrome	77	Oral Crohn's disease	80
Tumors and lesions	63, 197	Radiation therapy	40, 143
Nutritional		Sjögren's syndrome	116
Cancer	52, 82	Cushing's syndrome	107
Chronic renal failure	37	Cretinism	259
Liver disease including cirrhosis	28, 83, 267	Viral and infectious	
Niacin deficiency	92	Influenza-like infections	112
Thermal burn	38	Other	
Zinc deficiency	201	Amyloidosis and sarcoidosis	225, 291
Endocrine		Cystic fibrosis	51, 113, 118
Adrenal cortical insufficiency	107	High altitude	146
Congenital adrenal hyperplasia	107	Hypertension	70, 106, 293
Panhypopituitarism	107	Laryngectomy	145
Hypothyroidism	178, 222	Psychiatric disorders	4
Diabetes mellitus	99		

DYSFUNCTIONS ASSOCIATED WITH NORMAL AGING

A general decline in both taste and smell perception occurs during aging with losses at both threshold and suprathreshold levels. Both detection thresholds and recognition thresholds are elevated in elderly individuals. A detection threshold is the absolute threshold of sensation; it is the lowest concentration of a tastant or odorant at which it is first detected. A recognition threshold is the lowest concentration at which the stimulus is correctly identified. Taste and olfactory losses also occur at suprathreshold concentrations.

The age at which these losses occur is not well established because individual subjects have never been followed longitudinally to determine the rate or extent of loss over the life span. However, cross-sectional studies suggest that a systematic decrement in olfaction begins around sixty years of

Table 4 Medical conditions that affect the sense of smell

Condition	Reference	Condition	Reference
Nervous			
Alzheimer's disease	184, 233, 256, 257	Pseudohypoparathyroidism	104, 301
Down's syndrome	298	X-linked ichthyosis due to	6, 285
Epilepsy	44	steroid sulfatase deficiency	
Head trauma	159, 161, 189, 223,	Local	
	284	Adenoid hypertrophy	84
Korsakoff's syndrome	138, 170	Allergic rhinitis, atopy,	36, 73
Migraine	43, 305	and bronchial asthma	
Multiple sclerosis	207	Crouzon's syndrome	46
Parkinson's disease	7, 55, 297	Leprosy	14
Tumors and lesions	12, 81, 135, 203	Ozena	282
Nutritional & metabolic		Paranasal sinus exenteration	127
Chronic renal failure	244	Sinusitis and polyposis	73, 126, 221
Liver disease including cirrhosis	28, 83	Sjögren's syndrome	116
Trimethylaminuria	160	Viral and infectious	
Vitamin B_{12} deficiency	218	Acute viral hepatitis	115
Endocrine		HIV infection	26
Adrenal cortical insufficiency	107	Influenza-like infections	112
Cushing's syndrome	107	Other	
Hypothyroidism	178, 222	Amyloidosis and sarcoidosis	48, 225
Diabetes mellitus	140	Cystic fibrosis	113, 118
Gonadal dysgenesis (Turner's	103	Familial (genetic)	264
syndrome)		Laryngectomy	109, 111
Hypogonadotropic hypogo-	142, 171	Psychiatric disorders	182
nadism (Kallman's syndrome)			
Primary amenorrhea	175		

age and becomes significantly worse after seventy (57, 248). Taste losses may occur slightly later.

Taste: Threshold Losses

Increased taste thresholds in elderly persons have been reported for salty tastes (95, 192, 235, 300), sweet tastes (188, 192, 240), sour tastes (86, 192, 231), bitter tastes including phenythiourea-type compounds (41, 86, 144, 192, 236, 300), amino acids (238), glutamate salts (236), and weak galvanic currents (129).

An examination of recent threshold data (231) reveals that losses at threshold levels are not uniform across tastants. Average losses varied across different taste qualities. The average detection threshold in elderly individuals was 2.72 times higher than in young persons for sweeteners, 11.58 times higher for sodium salts, 4.29 times higher for acids, 6.94 times higher for bitter compounds, 2.48 times higher for amino acids, and 5.04 times higher for glutamate salts presented alone or when mixed with the taste enhancer inosine-5'-monophosphate. Across all of these qualities, the average loss is 5.51-fold. Within each of these categories, there is considerable variability. For example, the average detection threshold for sodium carbonate is only 3.79 times higher in elderly persons than in young individuals; however, the detection thresholds for sodium succinate, sodium citrate, and sodium sulfate are 16.2, 24.5, and 28.8 times higher, respectively, in older persons. Schiffman et al (235) have found that the degree of loss is related to the molar conductivity of the anion.

Taste: Suprathreshold Losses

Suprathreshold sensitivity to taste compounds as measured by magnitude estimation and identification experiments shows a decline in elderly subjects.

MAGNITUDE ESTIMATION   In magnitude estimation experiments, numbers are assigned to tastes in proportion to their perceived intensities. Applications of magnitude estimation techniques suggest that the growth in perceived intensity with increases in concentration is blunted by the aging process. Reduced suprathreshold intensities have been found for a range of common tastes including sweeteners, amino acids, and tomato juice (42, 164, 234, 240). The slopes of the lines that relate the log of the concentration (abscissa) to the perceived intensity (ordinate) for a series of sweeteners were compared for young and elderly subjects (240). The average decrement in slope with age was 48.7%; however, there was considerable variation among compounds. The greatest age-related losses in sweeteners were for thaumatin, rebaudioside, and neohesperidin dihydrochalcone, which are relatively large molecules that are capable of concerted intermolecular hydrogen bonding. There is also variability in the depression in slope for amino acids (234); the greatest depression is for glutamic and aspartic acid. This is noteworthy because alterations in glutamate binding have been found in individuals with Alzheimer's disease (93).

IDENTIFICATION TASKS   Identification tasks indicate that elderly subjects are less able to identify sweet, sour, salty, and bitter compounds (29, 117) and foods that involve cooperative functioning of taste and smell (227, 228). In food tests, elderly subjects have more complaints including weakness in sensation than do young subjects (227, 228).

Taste: Causes of Perceptual Losses

The underlying physiologic changes responsible for taste decrements in the elderly are not well understood. The prevailing theory until recently was that an aged person has suffered a loss in the number of papillae and taste buds over a lifetime. Losses in the mean number of taste buds per circumvallate papillae from adulthood to old age range from 40 to 57% (8, 185). A 20% decrease has been found in the mean number of taste buds on foliate papillae (186). The reduction in density of fungiform papillae per cm^2 on the anterior tongue of persons from 4 to 55 years of age has also been reported (190).

More recent studies contradict these earlier findings of age-related losses associated with fungiform, foliate, or circumvallate papillae. Arvidson (9) reported that there was no correlation between the number of buds per fungiform papillae and age over the life span. Studies in rhesus monkeys also show no age-related losses in buds on fungiform, foliate, or circumvallate papillae from 4 to 31 years. Further work is necessary to standardize methods of sampling, status of autopsy material, and statistical procedures before any final conclusions can be drawn. Little is known about degenerative changes in gustatory neural pathways (245).

Smell: Threshold Losses

Elderly subjects show elevated detection and recognition thresholds for olfactory and trigeminal stimulants. Threshold losses have been reported for n-butanol (149), coal gas (32, 33), coffee and citral (183), food odors (228, 242), menthol (193), pyridine and thiophene (206), 18 purified odorants (292), citralva (248), and geraniol, guaiacol, and benzaldehyde (248). The degree of loss found in elderly subjects varies widely depending on the study. However, on average, the thresholds for elderly persons in their 70s are from 2 to 10 times higher than for young persons in their 20s. Persons who are ill and are taking multiple drugs tend to have the highest thresholds.

Smell: Suprathreshold Losses

Suprathreshold losses in the sense of smell have been determined by a variety of measurement techniques including magnitude estimation, identification, and discrimination tasks. Loss in sensitivity to suprathreshold concentrations of trigeminal stimulants also occurs with age.

MAGNITUDE ESTIMATION   Magnitude estimation experiments, in which numbers are assigned to odors in proportion to their perceived intensities, suggest that persons over 70 years of age perceive suprathreshold odors on average as one half as intense as persons in their 20s. Reductions in perceived intensity in older individuals have been reported for odors that range from pleasant to foul: benzaldehyde, d-limonene, pyridine, ethyl alcohol, isoamyl alcohol (280), isoamyl butyrate (279, 280, 281), menthol (193), and 8 odorants including citralva, geraniol, citronellal, 2-methoxy-3-isobutyl-pyrazine, benzaldehyde, 2-methoxypyrazine, limonene, and acetic acid (248). Losses in trigeminal sensitivity to CO_2 (281) have also been reported.

IDENTIFICATION TASKS   The elderly also show a decrement in odor identifi-cation experiments. In identification tasks using 9 odors of moderate intensity (248), the scores for healthy persons over 70 years of age are from 60% to 75% of those for young subjects (248). Losses in the ability to identify coffee, peppermint, coal tar, and oil of almonds (5), a wide range of foods (194, 227), 40 common substances (226), a microencapsulated battery of 40–50 odors (57, 58), and 9 chemicals with characteristic odors (248) have been found.

DISCRIMINATION TASKS INCLUDING MULTIDIMENSIONAL SCALING TECHNIQUES Schiffman & Warwick (248) found that persons grouped by decade—10–19, 20–29, 30–39, 40–49, 50–59, 60–69, and 70–79 years—lost the ability to discriminate among 9 odors (benzaldehyde, n-butanol, caproic acid, citral, citronellal, geraniol, guaiacol, menthol, and methyl salicylate) with advancing age. The discrimination task entailed two steps, a confusability task and a similarity task. In the first (confusability) task, subjects sniffed three bottles one at a time; two of the bottles contained the same odorant. One of the six possible combinations of stimuli (AAB, ABA, ABB, BAA, BAB, and BBA) was selected randomly for each subject. In a second step, subjects considered the qualitative range for the odorants and marked the similarity of the two diferent odorants on a nine point scale from "identical" to "completely different." The confusability scores are represented as percentiles by decade in Table 5. Subjects in the seventh decade performed significantly worse than those in the younger decade groupings. It can be seen that a score of 54.2% correct would place a 75-year-old in the seventy-fifth percentile; however, the same score would relegate an 18-year-old to the first percentile. The highest score for the elderly (77.8% correct) is the average score (fiftieth percentile) for the entire group of 143 subjects.

Table 5 Percentile in which a person would be classified by decade and by subject based on percent correct score

%tile	10s	20s	30s	40s	50s	60s	70s	Composite (all decades)
99	91.7	100.0	97.2	100.0	97.2	91.7	77.8	100.0
95	91.6	99.7	96.9	99.4	96.7	91.7	77.8	94.4
90	88.9	94.4	91.7	93.9	91.1	91.7	72.8	91.7
75	85.4	91.0	88.4	87.4	88.9	83.3	54.2	86.1
50	80.6	79.2	83.3	77.8	86.1	69.4	47.2	77.8
25	75.7	72.9	66.7	63.9	68.1	66.7	38.9	61.1
10	66.9	61.8	53.1	42.2	61.6	58.3	30.3	45.5
5	64.0	61.1	50.1	29.2	58.6	50.0	23.0	39.5
1	63.9	61.1	50.0	27.8	58.3	50.0	22.2	24.7

While the confusability data suggest that persons in their 60s retain the ability to select within a triad the stimulus that differs from the other two, the similarity data indicate that these same persons have a diminished capacity to discriminate the *degree* of difference among the odorants on ratings along similarity scales. The multidimensional scaling procedure ALSCAL (individual differences option) was applied to the mean similarity matrices for each decade; these matrices were computed by averaging the ratings of each pair along the 9-point scale. Stimuli were arranged by ALSCAL so that stimuli rated similar to one another were located closer to one another than stimuli rated different from one another. Individual multidimensional spaces based on mean scores for the sixth and seventh decades indicate that subjects in the 60s and 70s have difficulty rating the degree of similarity between two different odor stimuli. However, the degree of loss in this ability is considerably greater in the 70s than in the 60s. No gender differences were found when males and females were analyzed separately.

Other multimensional scaling experiments are consistent with these findings that elderly subjects have reduced ability to discriminate suprathreshold odors. Reduced discrimination has been reported for food odors (246), common odors (278), and pyrazines (239).

Smell: Causes of Perceptual Losses

The decrements in odor perception that occur with aging can result from a variety of anatomic and physiologic losses. Structural and physiologic changes throughout the olfactory system occur in old age from the periphery (olfactory epithelium) to the olfactory bulb and to the olfactory cortex including the limbic structures. These changes include reduced protein synthesis and structural alterations in olfactory epithelium (53, 196), atrophy in olfactory bulb and nerve (25, 120, 121–124, 163, 266), presence of senile plaques and neurofibrillary tanges in hippocampus and amygdaloid complex (224, 289), hypothalamic degeneration including disruption of hypothalamic architecture paralleled by deterioration and loss of dendritic surface (165), altered calcium homeostasis in hippocampus leading to elevated intracellular calcium (155), and hippocampal pathology including increase in reactive astrocytes associated with elevated plasma adrenocorticoids (156). These structural and physiologic losses can result from normal aging, diseases, medications, and pollutants (229, 230). A theoretical model (245) based on the "across-fiber pattern" theory of Erickson (65), suggests that losses in chemosensory neurons from a variety of causes degrade the pattern of neural activity for stimuli. This degradation diminishes the ability of a person to discriminate between two stimuli.

DYSFUNCTIONS ASSOCIATED WITH ALZHEIMER'S DISEASE

Severe olfactory losses have been found in elderly persons with Alzheimer's disease (see Table 6). In 1974, Waldton (296) reported that patients with a general diagnosis of senile dementia had marked impairment of olfactory functioning and that this decrement became more severe as the disease progressed. More recent studies have found that patients with Alzheimer's disease (AD) exhibit a diminished capacity to recognize and identify supra-threshold odorants compared to that of age-matched controls. These losses in the recognition and identification of odorants are very salient in the earliest phases of the disease (153, 299). Prominent losses in the ability to remember odorants have also been reported by Moberg et al (184) in early AD. Losses in olfactory sensitivity at the threshold level tend to develop as the symptoms progress but can be present at the early stages. The degree of loss in olfactory functioning in Alzheimer's disease is greatest for olfactory memory where scores often reflect performance at the level of chance. Recognition and identification experiments indicate that persons with AD generally perform below the twenty-fifth percentile for their age group. The degree of threshold losses has not been well-established.

Decrements in olfactory perception in AD are not surprising because the morphological and neurochemical changes in this disease are especially prominent in neural pathways related to olfaction, including the olfactory epithelium (287), olfactory bulbs (202), anterior olfactory nucleus (10, 68, 141, 202), olfactory tubercle (263), amygdala (27, 119), prepiriform cortex (212), hippocampus (13, 27, 131, 141, 205), entorhinal cortex (27, 131), uncus (27), and subiculum (131). The impairment of olfactory and limbic structures of the temporal lobe produces decrements in the ability to identify, recognize, and remember odorants. Impairment closer to the periphery produces losses in the ability to detect the presence of odorants. This was clearly demonstrated by Eichenbaum et al (61) who studied the olfactory

Table 6   Deficits in Alzheimer's disease

Task	References
Recognition and identification of odors	56, 128, 148, 151–153, 204, 213, 254, 255–257, 296, 299
Odor memory	148, 184
Olfactory threshold	56, 151–153, 195, 213, 276

capacities in a patient with bilateral medial temporal lobe resection. This procedure involved bilateral removal of the amygdala, uncus, and the anterior two-thirds of the hippocampus and parahippocampal gyrus. The pyriform cortex was affected as well. This patient performed normally on a battery of tests of odor detection, intensity discrimination, and adaptation. However, the patient was unable to discriminate or identify odors in match-to-sample tasks or in same-different discriminations. Although olfactory losses do occur in other conditions that afflict the elderly, it should be emphasized here that a decrement in olfactory functioning is always associated with AD. The olfactory system may be the site of initial pathology in AD (205). Roberts (214) has suggested that the causative agent for AD may act through a nasal route. There is evidence for transneural transport in the olfactory system for such diverse materials as viruses (67, 187), dyes (133), gold (49, 133), aluminosilicates (214), and wheat-germ agglutinin-horseradish peroxidase conjugate (260). These compounds may be transported from the external environment via olfactory receptor neurons to the olfactory bulb and beyond into gustatory and other areas. This could disrupt the functioning of neurons known to be associated with AD and produce long-term changes or degeneration in these regions. The recent finding by Schiffman et al (233) that the degree of olfactory loss was related to a family history of senile dementia raises the question whether vulnerability to transneuronal transport in the olfactory system may have a genetic component.

Histopathologic changes in olfactory circuits occur in AD. However, the losses in neurotransmitters in AD may also be responsible in part for the losses in identification, recognition, and memory of odors. Neurotransmitter deficits in glutamic acid (100, 101, 173), acetylcholine (47, 132, 302), serotonin (132, 172, 304), somatostatin (215, 217), noradrenaline (16, 79, 132), and dopamine (89, 174) have been found in the brains of patients with Alzheimer's disease.

DYSFUNCTIONS ASSOCIATED WITH ENVIRONMENTAL POLLUTION

Losses in taste and smell sensations are also caused by a broad range of environmental pollutants (243). The chemical senses are especially vulnerable to environmental contaminants in water and air because taste and smell receptors are strategically situated to contact and monitor our external chemical environment. Pollutants not only produce offensive tastes and odors in and of themselves but they also damage chemosensory tissue.

Offensive Tastes and Odors Associated With Pollution

Offensive tastes and odors associated with pollution are often due to the sensory properties of the pollutants themselves rather than to pathologic changes in the chemosensory systems. For example, petroleum and petrochemical waste, bacterial contamination of food and water, chemicals concentrated in indoor air, and industrial chemicals such as fumigants can trigger taste and smell complaints.

Sensory irritants inhaled through the nose elicit a variety of chemosensory complaints because irritants can increase permeability of blood vessels, alter secretions from mucoserous glands, alter flow patterns of nasal mucus, decrease ciliary activity on respiratory epithelial cells, and suppress breathing rate.

Persons who report hypersensitivity to airborne chemicals do not necessarily have lower taste, smell, or irritation thresholds. Rather, persons who are hypersensitive to pollutants may experience more nasal swelling and thus more irritation than normal individuals.

Pollutants That Alter the Olfactory and Taste Systems

Both acute and chronic exposure to a variety of chemical agents including industrial substances can cause losses in olfactory sensitivity. These agents include metallic compounds, nonmetallic inorganic compounds, organic compounds, dusts, and other airborne chemicals (see Table 7). Losses may occur after brief or prolonged exposure and may be either temporary or permanent. Pollutants can alter olfactory functioning in a variety of ways including modification of neurotransmitter levels and physiologic or anatomic damage to the olfactory epithelium, bulbs, or tract. Some pollutants such as methylmercury can actually accumulate in the olfactory bulbs.

Less is known about pollution-induced disturbances in taste perception. Schiffman & Nagle (243) reported that persistent metallic or bitter taste complaints occur in some individuals after exposure to insecticides. Pesticides have been shown to bind extensively to the tongue (24) and to alter taste bud morphology.

TREATMENT OR COMPENSATION FOR CHEMOSENSORY LOSSES

There are no standard treatments for chemosensory dysfunctions because little is known about the mechanisms by which they occur. While enhancement of taste or smell perception by pharmacologic means has been attempted, no studies suggest that drug treatments of any kind have broad efficacy in restoring chemosensation. Exogenous application of acetylcholine or substance P (20) apparently increases olfactory receptor cell activity, and administration of the cholinergic agonists methacholine (110) and bethanechol (11) reportedly restores taste acuity in some patients with familial dysautonomia. Dietary zinc supplementation can correct taste disorders related to zinc deficiency (169) or the zinc may combine with –SH groups in an offending molecule (e.g. captopril or D-penacillamine, see 229). However, in a controlled study, dietary supplementation with zinc sulfate was no more effective than a placebo for

Table 7 Compounds, dusts and processes associated with permanent anosmia or hyposmia in humans with chronic exposure

Compounds, dusts, and processes	References
Metallurgical compounds and processes	
Cadmium compounds including oxides	3
Chromium, including chromate salts and chromium plating	3
Lead	3
Magnet production, includes iron, aluminum, nickel, cobalt, and chromium powders	3
Mercury	3
Nickel, including nickel hydroxide, nickel plating and refining	3
Silver plating	3
Steel production	3
Zinc, including zinc chromate, zinc production	3
Dusts	
Ashes, incinerator	200
Cement	3
Chemicals	3
Coke	200
Grain	200
Hardwoods	3
Lime	3
Printing	3
Silicosis	3, 200
Nonmetallic inorganic compounds	
Ammonia	3
Carbon disulfide	3, 200
Carbon monoxide	3
Chlorine	3
Hydrazine	3
Fluorides	3
Hydrogen selenide	286
Hydrogen sulfide	1
Nitrogen dioxide (NO_2)	3
Phosphorous oxychloride	167
Sulfur dioxide	3
Organic compounds	
Acetates, butyl and ethyl	3
Acetone	3
Acetophenone	3
Acrylate and methacrylate vapors	251
Benzene	3, 200
Benzine	3
Chloromethanes (CH_3Cl, CH_2Cl_2, $CHCl_3$, CCl_4)	3
Formaldehyde	64, 88
Menthol	3, 199
Organophosphates and other insecticides	229
Pentachlorophenol	3
Petroleum	2

Table 7 (*continued*)

Compounds, dusts, and processes	References
Solvent mixtures	220, 252
Trichloroethylene	3
Manufacturing processes	
Acids (organic and inorganic)	3, 200
Asphalt (oxidized)	3
Cement works	200
Cotton, knitting factory	200
Cutting oils (machining)	3
Flour, flour mill	200
Fragrances	3
Paint	3, 252
Paper, packing factory	200
Pavinol, a synthetic leather containing dibutyl phthalate	3
Peppermint	158
Spices, including paprika	3, 200
Tobacco	3, 200
Varnishes	3
Wastewater	3

treating a wide variety of taste disorders (114). Additional research is necessary before effective pharmacologic treatments for chemosensory disorders are found.

Addition of flavors to foods for persons with hyposmia is effective in counteracting modest olfactory losses. Schiffman (228) and Schiffman & Warwick (247) reported increased preference for flavor-amplified food in the elderly. The flavors used in these experiments were mixtures of odorous molecules selected by gas chromatographic analysis of natural products. For example, mashed potatoes amplified with simulated potato flavor was preferred to unenhanced mashed potatoes. This amplification of flavor not only increased the hedonic value of foods to which it was added, but also increased intake of nutrient-dense food in sick older persons (247). It should be noted, however, that flavor amplification was not always effective. For elderly persons who are totally anosmic (such as many Alzheimer's patients), additional flavors cannot be detected.

Literature Cited

1. Ahlborg, G. 1951. Hydrogen sulfide poisoning in shale oil industry. *Arch. Indust. Hyg.* 3:247–66
2. Ahlstrom, R., Berglund, B., Berglund, U., Lindvall, T., Wennberg, A. 1986. Impaired odor perception in tank cleaners. *Scand. J. Work. Environ. Health* 12:574–81
3. Amoore, J. E. 1986. Effects of chemical exposure on olfaction in humans. In *Toxicology of the Nasal Passages,* ed. C. S. Barrow, pp. 155–90. Washington, DC: Hemisphere
4. Amsterdam, J. D., Settle, R. G., Doty, R. L., Abelman, E., Winokor, A. 1987. Taste and smell perception in

depression. *Biol. Psychiatr.* 22:1481–85

5. Anand, M. P. 1964. Accidents in the home. In *Current Achievements in Geriatrics,* ed. W. F. Anderson, B. Isaacs, pp. 239–45. London: Cassell

6. Andria, G., Ballabio, A., Parenti, G. 1987. X-linked ichthyosis due to steroid sulfatase deficiency associated with hypogonadism and anosmia [letter]. *Ann. Neurol.* 22:98–99

7. Ansari, K. A., Johnson, A. 1975. Olfactory function in patients with Parkinson's disease. *J. Chron. Dis.* 28:493–97

8. Arey, L. B., Tremaine, M. J., Monzingo, F. L. 1935. The numerical and topographical relations of taste buds to human circumvallate papillae throughout the life span. *Anat. Rec.* 64:9–25

9. Arvidson, K. 1979. Location and variation in number of taste buds in human fungiform papillae. *Scand. J. Dental Res.* 87:435–42

10. Averback, P. 1983. Two new lesions in Alzheimer's disease. *Lancet* 2:1203

11. Axelrod, F. B., Branom, N., Becker, M., Nachtigall, R., Dancis, J. 1972. Treatment of familial dysautonomia with bethanecol (Urecholine). *J. Pediatr.* 81:573–78

12. Bakay, L. 1984. Olfactory meningiomas: The missed diagnosis. *J. Am. Med. Assoc.* 251:53–55

13. Ball, M. J. 1977. Neuronal loss, neurofibrillary tangles and granulovacuolar degeneration in the hippocampus with ageing and dementia: A quantitative study. *Acta Neuropathol.* 37:111–18

14. Barton, R. P. E. 1974. Olfaction in leprosy. *J. Laryngol. Otol.* 88:355–61

15. Beidler, L. M., Smallman, R. L. 1965. Renewal of cells within taste buds. *J. Cell Biol.* 27:263–72

16. Berger, B., Escourolle, R., Moyne, M. A. 1976. Axones catecholaminergiques du cortex cerebral humain. *Rev. Neurol.* 312:183–94

17. Berman, J. L. 1985. Dysosmia, dysgeusia, and diltiazem [letter]. *Ann. Intern. Med.* 102:717

18. Body, S. C. 1986. A taste of allicin? *Anaesth. Intensive Care* 14:94

19. Bourliere, F., Cendron, H., Rapaport, A. 1959. Action de l'acide acetylsalicylique sur la sensibilite au gout amer chez l'homme. *Rev. Fr. Études Clin. Biol.* 4:380–82

20. Bouvet, J. F., Delaleu, J. C., Holley, A. 1988. The activity of olfactory receptor cells is affected by acetylcholine and substance P. *Neurosci. Res.* 5:214–23

21. Bradley, R. M. 1973. Electrophysiological investigations of intravascular taste using perfused rat tongue. *Am. J. Physiol.* 224:300–4

22. Brenner, B. E., Simon, R. R. 1984. Glossitit and dysgeusia. *Am. J. Emerg. Med.* 2:147

23. Bressler, B. 1980. An unusal side-effect of lithium. *Psychosomatics* 21:688–89

24. Brittebo, E. B., Hogman, P. G., Brandt, I. 1987. Epithelial binding of hexachlorocyclohexanes in the respiratory and upper alimentary tracts: a comparison between the alpha-, beta- and gamma-isomers in mice. *Food Chem. Toxicol.* 25:773–80

25. Brizzee, K. R., Klara, P., Johnson, J. E. 1975. Changes in microanatomy, neurocytology, and fine structure with aging. *Adv. Behav. Biol.* 16:425–61

26. Brody, D., Serby, M., Etienne, N., Kalkestein, D. S. 1991. Olfactory identification deficits in HIV infection. *Am. J. Psychiatry* 148(2):248–50

27. Brun, A., Gustafson, L. 1976. Distribution of cerebral degeneration in Alzheimer's disease. A clinicopathological study. *Arch. Psychiatr. Nervenkr.* 223:15–33

28. Burch, R. E.., Sacklin, D. A., Ursick, J. A. Jetton, M. M., Sullivan, J. F. 1978. Decreased taste and smell acuity in cirrhosis. *Arch. Intern. Med.* 138:743–46

29. Byrd, E., Gertman, S. 1959. Taste sensitivity in aging persons. *Geriatrics* 14:381–84

30. Carmichael, K. A., Jennings, A. S., Doty, R. L. 1984. Reversible anosmia after pituitary irradiation. *Ann. Intern. Med.* 100:532–33

31. Catalanotto, F. A., Dore-Duffy, P., Donaldson, J. O., Testa, M., Peterson, M., et al. 1984. Quality-specific taste changes in multiple sclerosis. *Ann. Neurol.* 16:611–15

32. Chalke, H. D., Dewhurst, J. R., Ward, C. W. 1958. Loss of sense of smell in old people. *Public Health* 72:223–30

33. Chalke, H. D., Dewhurst, J. R. 1957. Accidental coal-gas poisoning: Loss of sense of smell as a possible contributory factory with old people. *Br. Med. J.* 2:915–17

34. Cherington, M. 1976. Guanidine and germine in Eaton-Lambert syndrome. *Neurology* 26:944–46

35. Chuah, M. I., Hui, B. S. 1986. Effect of amitriptyline on laminar differentiation of neonatal rat olfactory bulb. *Neurosci. Lett.* 70:28–33

36. Church, J. A., Bauer, H., Bellanti, J. A., Satterly, R. A., Henkin, R. I. 1978. Hyposmia associated atopy. *Ann. Allergy* 400:105–9
37. Ciechanover, M., Peresecenschi, G., Aviram, A., Steiner, J. E. 1980. Malrecognition of taste in uremia. *Nephron* 26:20–22
38. Cohen, I. K., Schechter, P. J., Henkin, R. I. 1973. Hypogeusia, anorexia, and altered zinc metabolism following thermal burn. *J. Am. Med. Assoc.* 223:914–16
39. Cohen, L. 1964. Disturbance of taste as a symptom of multiple sclerosis. *Br. J. Oral Surg.* 2:184–85
40. Conger, A. D. 1973. Loss and recovery of taste acuity in patients irradiated to the oral cavity. *Radiat. Res.* 53:338–47
41. Cooper, R. M., Bilash, I., Zubek, J. P. 1959. The effect of age on taste sensitivity. *J. Gerontol.* 14:56–58
42. Cowart, B. J. 1983. Direct scaling of the intensity of basic tastes: A life span study. *Assoc. Chemoreception Sci., Sarasota, Fla.*
43. Crosley, C. J., Dhamoon, S. 1983. Migrainous olfactory aura in a family [letter]. *Arch. Neurol.* 39:459
44. Currie, S., Heathfield, K. W. G., Henson, R. A., Scott, D. F. 1971. Clinical course and prognosis of temporal lobe epilepsy. A survey of 666 patients. *Brain* 94:173–90
45. Dahl, H., Norskov, K., Peitersen, E., Hilden, J. 1984. Zinc therapy of acetazolamide-induced side-effects. *Acta Ophthalmol.* 62:739–45
46. Das, S. K., Munro, I. R. 1979. Anosmia in Crouzon's syndrome and its recovery following cranio-facial reconstruction. *Br. J. Plast. Surg.* 32:55–56
47. Davies, P., Maloney, A. J. F. 1976. Selective loss of central cholinergic neurons in Alzheimer's disease [letter]. *Lancet* 2:1403
48. Delaney, P., Henkin, R. I., Manz, H., Satterly, R. A., Bauer, H. 1977. Olfactory sarcoidosis. *Arch. Otolaryngol.* 103:717–24
49. DeLorenzo, A. J. D. 1970. The olfactory neuron and the blood-brain barrier. In *Taste and Smell in Vertebrates*, ed. G. E. W. Wolstenholme, J. Knight, pp. 151–76. London: Churchill Ciba Found. Symp.
50. DeSimone, J. A., Heck, G. L., Bartoshuk, L. M. 1980. Surface active taste modifiers: A comparison of the physical and psychophysical properties of gymnemic acid and sodium lauryl sulfate. *Chem Senses* 5:317–30
51. Desor, J. A., Maller, O. 1975. Taste correlates of disease states: Cystic fibrosis. *J. Pediatr.* 87:93–96
52. DeWys, W. D., Walters, K. 1975. Abnormalities of taste sensation in cancer patients. *Cancer* 36:1888–96
53. Dodson, H. C., Bannister, L. H. 1980. Structural aspects of aging in the olfactory and vomeronasal epithelia in mice. In *Olfaction and Taste* ed. H. van der Starre, 7:151–54. London: IRL Press
54. Doty, R. L., Deems, D. A., Frye, R. E., Pelberg, R., Shapiro, A. 1988. Olfactory sensitivity, nasal resistance, and autonomic function in patients with multiple chemical sensitivities. *Arch. Otolaryngol. Head Neck Surg.* 114:1422–27
55. Doty, R. L., Deems, D. A., Stellar, S. 1988. Olfactory dysfunction in Parkinsonism: A general deficit unrelated to neurologic signs, disease stage, or disease duration. *Neurology* 38:1237–44
56. Doty, R. L., Reyes, P. F., Gregor, T. 1987. Presence of both odor identification and detection deficits in Alzheimer's disease. *Brain Res. Bull.* 18:597–600
57. Doty, R. L., Shaman, P., Applebaum, S. L., Gilberson, R., Siksorski, L., et al. 1984. Smell identification ability: Changes with age. *Science* 226:1441–43
58. Doty, R. L., Shaman, P., Dann, M. 1984. Development of the University of Pennsylvania Smell Identification Test: A standardized microencapsulated test of olfactory function. *Physiol. Behav.* 32:489–502
59. Duffield, J. E. 1973. Side effects of lithium carbonate. *Br. Med. J.* 1:491
60. Duhra, P., Foulds, I. S. 1988. Methotrexate-induced impairment of taste acuity. *Clin. Exp. Dermatol.* 13:126–27
61. Eichenbaum, H., Morton, T. H., Potter, H., Corkin, S. 1983. Selective olfactory deficits in case H.M. *Brain* 106:459–72
62. Ekstrand, T. 1979. Bell's palsy: Prognostic accuracy of case history, sialometry and taste impairment. *Clin. Otolarynogol.* 4:183–96
63. ElDeiry, A. 1990. Temporal lobe tumor manifested by localized dysgeusia. *Ann. Otolaryngol. Rhinol. Laryngol.* 99:586–87
64. Emmet, E. A. 1976. Parosmia and hyposmia induced by solvent exposure. *Br. J. Indust. Med.* 33:196–98
65. Erickson, R. P. 1963. Sensory neural patterns and gustation. In *Olfaction*

and Taste, ed. Y. Zotterman, pp. 205–13. Oxford: Pergamon

66. Erikssen, J., Seegaard, E., Naess, K. 1975. Side-effect of thiocarbamides. Lancet 1:231–32

67. Esiri, M. M., Tomlinson, A. H. 1984. Herpes simplex encephalitis: Immunohistochemical demonstration of spread of virus via olfactory and trigeminal pathways after infection of facial skin in mice. J. Neurol. Sci. 64:213–17

68. Esiri, M. M., Wilcock, G. K. 1984. The olfactory bulbs in Alzeimer's disease. J. Neurol. Neurosurg. Psychiatry 47:56–60

69. Ewing, R. C., Janda, S. M., Henann, N. E. 1989. Ageusia associated with transdermal nitroglycerin. Clin. Pharm. 8:146–47

70. Fallis, N., Lasagna, L., Tetreault, L. 1962. Gustatory thresholds in patients with hypertension. Nature 196:74–75

71. Farbman, A. I., Gonzales, F., Chuah, M. I. 1988. The effect of amitriptyline on growth of olfactory and cerebral neurons in vitro. Brain Res. 457:281–86

72. Fehm-Wolfsdorf, G., Scheible, E., Zenz, H., Born, J., Fehm, H. L. 1989. Taste thresholds in man are differentially influenced by hydrocortisone and dexamethasone. Psychoneuroendocrinology 14:433–40

73. Fein, B. T., Kamin, P. B., Fein, N. N. 1966. The loss of sense of smell in nasal allergy. Ann. Allergy 24:278–83

74. Ferguson, A. W., de la Harpe, P. L., Farquar, J. W. 1961. Dimethyldiguanide in the treatment of diabetic children. Lancet 1:1367–69

75. Fischer, R., Griffin, F., Archer, R. C., Zinsmeister, S. C., Jastram, P. S. 1965. Weber ratio in gustatory chemoreception: An indicator of systemic (drug) reactivity. Nature 207:1049–53

76. Fischer, R., Griffin, F., Rockey, M. A. 1966. Gustatory chemoreception in man: Multidisciplinary aspects and perspectives. Perspect. Biol. Med. 9:549–77

77. Fisher, C. M. 1971. Raeder's benign paratrigeminal syndrome with dysgeusia. Trans. Am. Neurol. Assoc. 96:234–36

78. Fogan, L. 1971. Griseofulvin and dysgeusia: implications? Ann. Intern. Med. 74:795

79. Forno, L. S. 1978. The locus coeruleus in Alzheimer's disease. J. Neuropathol. Exp. Neurol. 37:614

80. Frankel, D. H., Mostofi, R. S., Lorincz, A. L. 1985. Oral Crohn's disease: Report of two cases in brothers with metallic dysgeusia and review of the literature. J. Am. Acad. Dermatol. 12:260–68

81. Furstenberg, A. C., Crosby, E., Farrior, B. 1943. Neurologic lesions which influence the sense of smell. Arch. Otolaryngol. 38:529–30

82. Gallagher, P., Tweedle, D. E. 1983. Taste threshold and acceptability of commercial diets in cancer patients. J. Parenter. Enter. Nutr. 7:361–63

83. Garrett-Laster, M., Russell, R. M., Jacques, P. G. 1984. Impairment of taste and olfaction in patients with cirrhosis; the role of vitamin A. Hum. Nutr: Clin. Nutr. C 38:203–14

84. Ghorbanian, S. N., Paradise, J. L., Doty, R. L. 1978. Odor perception in children in relation to nasal obstruction. Pediatr. Res. 12:371

85. Gifford, R. W. 1970. Ethacrynic acid alone and in combination with methyldopa in management of mild hypertension: A report of 23 patients. Int. Z. Klin. Pharmakol. Ther. Toxikol. 3:255–60

86. Glanville, E. V., Kaplan, A. R., Fischer, R. 1964. Age, sex, and taste sensitivity. J. Gerontol. 19:474–78

87. Goetzl, F. R., Stone, F. 1948. The influence of amphetamine sulfate upon olfactory acuity and appetite. Gastroenterology 10:708–13

88. Gorman, W. 1964. The sense of smell. A clinical review. Eye Ear Nose Throat Mon. 43:54–58

89. Gottfries, C. G., Roos, B. E., Winblad, B. 1976. Monoamine and monoamine metabolites in the human brain post mortem in senile dementia. Aktuel. Gerontol. 6:429–35

90. Goy, J. J., Finci, L., Sigwart, U. 1985. Dysgeusia after high dose dipyridamole treatment [Short communication]. Arzneimittelforschung 35:854

91. Graber, M., Kellener, S. 1988. Side effects of acetazolamide: the champagne blues [letter]. Am. J. Med. 84:979–80

92. Green, R. F. 1971. Subclinical pellagra and idiopathic hypogeusia. J. Am. Med. Assoc. 218:1303

93. Greenamyre, J. T., Penney, J. B., Young, A. B., D'Amato, C. J., Hicks, S. P., et al. 1985. Alterations in L-glutamate binding in Alzheimer's and Huntington's diseases. Science 227:1496–98

94. Grossman, S. 1953. Loss of taste and smell due to propylthiouracil therapy. NY J. Med. 53:1236

95. Grzegorczyk, P. B., Jones, S. W., Mistretta, C. M. 1979. Age-related

differences in salt taste acuity. *J. Gerontol.* 34:834–40

96. Guthrie, D., Way, S. 1974. Treatment of advanced carcinoma of the cervix with adriamycin and methogrexate combined. *Obstet. Gynecol.* 44:586–89

97. Halbreich, U. 1974. Tegretol dependency and diversion of the sense of taste. *Isr. Ann. Psychiatry* 12:328–32

98. Hallman, B. L., Hurst, J. W. 1953. Loss of taste as toxic effect of methimazole (Tapazole) therapy. *J. Am. Med. Assoc.* 152:322

99. Halter, J., Kulkosky, P., Woods, S., Makous, W., Chen, M., et al. 1975. Afferent receptors, taste perception, and pancreatic endocrine function in man. *Diabetes* 24:414

100. Hardy, J. A., Adolfsson, R., Alafuzoff, I., Bucht, G., Marcusson, J., et al. 1985. Transmitter deficits in Alzheimer's disease. *Neurochem. Int.* 7:545–63

101. Hardy, J. A., Mann, D. M., Wester, P., Winblad, B. 1986. An integrative hypothesis concerning the pathogenesis and progression of Alzheimer's disease. *Neurobiol. Aging* 7:489–502

102. Hellekant, G., Gopal, V. 1975. Depression of taste responses by local or intravascular administration of salicylates in the rat. *Acta Physiol.* 95:286–92

103. Henkin, R. I. 1967. Abnormalities of taste and olfaction in patients with chromatin negative gonadal dysgenesis. *J. Clin. Endocrinol. Metab.* 27:1436–40

104. Henkin, R. I. 1968. Impairment of olfaction and of the tastes of sour and bitter in pseudohypoparathyroidism. *J. Clin. Endocrinol. Metab.* 28:624–28

105. Henkin, R. I. 1971. Griseofulvin and dysgeusia: implications? *Ann. Intern. Med.* 74:795–96

106. Henkin, R. I. 1974. Salt taste in patients with essential hypertension and with hypertension due to primary hyperaldosteronism. *J. Chron. Dis.* 27:235–44

107. Henkin, R. I. 1975. The role of adrenal corticosteroids in sensory processes. In *Handbook of Physiology. Endocrinology,* ed. H. Blaschko, A. D. Smith, G. Sayers, pp. 209–30. Baltimore: Williams & Wilkins

108. Henkin, R. I., Christiansen, R. L., Bosma, J. F. 1966. Impairment of recognition of oral sensation and familial hyposmia in patients with facial hypoplasia and growth retardation: A new syndrome. *Clin. Res.* 14:236

109. Henkin, R. I., Hoye, R. C., Ketcham, A. S., Gould, W. J. 1968. Hyposmia

following laryngectomy. *Lancet* 2:479–81

110. Henkin, R. I., Kopin, I. J. 1964. Abnormalities of taste and smell thresholds in familial dysautonomia: improvement with methacholine. *Life Sci.* 3: 1319–25

111. Henkin, R. I., Larson, A. L. 1972. On the mechanism of hyposmia following laryngectomy in man. *Laryngoscope* 82:836–43

112. Henkin, R. I., Larson, A. L., Powell, R. D. 1975. Hypogeusia, dysgeusia, hyposmia, and dysosmia following influenza-like infection. *Ann. Otolaryngol.* 84:672–82

113. Henkin, R. I., Powell, G. F. 1962. Increased sensitivity of taste and smell in cystic fibrosis. *Science* 138:1107–8

114. Henkin, R. I., Schechter, P. J., Friedewald, W. T., Demets, D. L., Raff, M. 1976. A double blind study of the effects of zinc sulfate on taste and smell dysfunction. *Am. J. Med. Sci.* 272:285–99

115. Henkin, R. I., Smith, F. R. 1971. Hyposmia in acute viral hepatitis. *Lancet* 1:823–26

116. Henkin, R. I., Talal, N., Larson, A. L., Mattern, C. F. T. 1972. Abnormalities of taste and smell in Sjogren's Syndrome. *Ann. Intern. Med.* 76:375–83

117. Hermel, J., Schonwetter, S., Samueloff, S. 1970. Taste sensation and age in man. *J. Oral Med.* 25:39–42

118. Hertz, J., Cain, W. W., Bartoschuk, L. M., Dolan, T. F. 1975. Olfactory and taste sensitivity in children and cystic fibrosis. *Physiol. Behav.* 14:89–94

119. Herzog, A. G., Kemper, T. L. 1980. Amygdaloid changes in aging and dementia. *Arch. Neurol.* 37:625–29

120. Hinds, J. W., McNelly, N. A. 1977. Aging of the rat olfactory bulb: Growth and atrophy of constituent layers and changes in size and number of mitral cells. *J. Comp. Neurol.* 171:345–68

121. Hinds, J. W., McNelly, N. A. 1978. Dispersion of cisternae of rough endoplasmic reticulum in aging CNS neurons: A strictly linear trend. *Am. J. Anat.* 152:433–39

122. Hinds, J. W., McNelly, N. A. 1979. Aging in the rat olfactory bulb: Quantitative changes in mitral cell organelles and somatodendritic synapses. *J. Comp. Neurol.* 184:811–20

123. Hinds, J. W., McNelly, N. A. 1981. Aging in the rat olfactory system: Correlation of changes in the olfactory

epithelium and olfactory bulb. *J. Comp. Neurol.* 203:441–53

124. Hinds, J. W., McNelly, N. A. 1982. Capillaries in aging rat olfactory bulb: A quantitative light and eletron microscopic analysis. *Neurobiol. Aging* 3: 197–207

125. Hodgson, T. G. 1981. Bad taste from cefamandole letter. *Drug Intell. Clin. Pharm.* 15:136

126. Hotchkiss, W. T. 1956. Influence of prednisone on nasal polyposis with anosmia. *Arch. Otolaryngol.* 64:478–79

127. Hoye, R. C., Ketcham, A. S., Henkin, R. I. 1970. Hyposmia after paranasal sinus exenteration or laryngectomy. *Am. J. Surg.* 120:485–91

128. Huff, F. J., Boller, F., Lucchelli, F., Querriera, R., Beyer, J., et al. 1987. The neurologic examination in patients with probable Alzheimer's disease. *Arch. Neurol.* 44:929–32

129. Hughes, G. 1969. Changes in taste sensitivity with advancing age. *Gerontol. Clin.* 11:224–30

130. Huskisson, E. C., Jaffe, I. A., Scott, J., Dieppe, P. A. 1980. 5-Thiopyridoxine in rheumatoid arthritis: Clinical and experimental studies. *Arthritis Rheum.* 23:106–10

131. Hyman, B. T., Van Hoesen, G. W., Damasio, A. R., Barnes, C. L. 1984. Alzheimer's disease: Cell-specific pathology isolates the hippocampal formation. *Science* 225:1168–70

132. Ishii, T. 1966. Distribution of Alzheimer's neurofibrillary changes in the brain stem and the hypothalamus of senile dementia. *Acta Neuropathol.* 6:181–87

133. Jackson, R. T., Tigges, J., Arnold, W. 1979. Subarachnoid space of the CNS, nasal mucosa, and lymphatic system. *Arch. Otolaryngol.* 105:180–84

134. Jaffe, I. A. 1970. Ampicillin rashes. *Lancet* 1:245

135. Jarus, G. D., Feldon, S. E. 1982. Clinical and computed tomographic findings in the Foster Kennedy syndrome. *Am. J. Ophthalmol.* 93:317–22

136. Jeppsson, P. H., Hallen, O. 1971. The taste after operation for otosclerosis. *Pract. Oto-Rhino-Laryngol.* 33:215–21

137. Johansson, B., Stenman, E., Bergman, M. 1984. Clinical study of patients referred for investigation regarding so-called galvanism. *Scand. J. Dental Res.* 92:469–75

138. Jones, B. P., Moskowitz, H. R., Butters, N. 1975. Olfactory discrimination in alcoholic Korsakoff's patients. *Neuropsychologia* 13:173–79

139. Jones, P. B. P., McCloskey, E. V.,

Kanis, J. A. 1987. Transient taste-loss during treatment with etidronate [letter]. *Lancet* 2:637

140. Jorgensen, M. B., Buch, N. H. 1961. Studies on sense of smell and taste in diabetics. *Acta Otolarngol.* 53:539–45

141. Kahn, J., Anderton, B. H., Miller, C. C., Wood, J. N., Esiri, M. M. 1987. Staining with monoclonal antibodies to neurofilaments distinguishes between subpopulations of neurofibrillary tangles, between groups of axons and between groups of dendrites. *J. Neurol.* 234:241–46

142. Kallmann, F. J., Schoenfeld, W. A., Barrera, S. E. 1944. The genetic aspects of primary eunuchoidism. *Am. J. Ment. Defic.* 48:203–36

143. Kalmus, H., Farnsworth, D. 1959. Impairment and recovery of taste following irradiation of the oropharynx. *J. Laryngol. Otol.* 73:180–82

144. Kalmus, H., Trotter, W. R. 1962. Direct assessment of the effect of age on P. T. C. sensitivity. *Ann. Hum. Genet.* 26:145–49

145. Kashima, H. K., Kalinowski, B. 1979. Taste impairment following laryngectomy. *Ear Nose Throat J.* 58:62–71

146. Kassirer, M. R., Such, R. V. 1989. Persistent high-altitude headache and agusia without anosmia. *Arch. Neurol.* 46:340–41

147. Keiser, H. R., Henkin, R. I., Bartter, F. C., Sjoerdsma, A. 1968. Loss of taste during therapy with penicillamine. *J. Am. Med. Assoc.* 203:381–83

148. Kesslak, J. P., Cotman, C. W., Chui, H. C., van den Noort, S., Fang, H., et al. 1988. Olfactory tests as possible probes for detecting and monitoring Alzheimer's disease. *Neurobiol. Aging* 9:399–403

149. Kimbrell, G. M., Furchtgott, E. 1963. The effect of aging on olfactory threshold. *J. Gerontol.* 18:364–65

150. Kimmelman, C. P. 1991. Medical imaging of smell and taste disorders. See Ref. 270, pp. 471–79

151. Knupfer, L., Spiegal, R. 1986. Differences in olfactory test performance between normal aged, Alzheimer and vascular type dementia individuals. *Int. J. Geriatr. Psychiatry* 1:3–14

152. Koss, E., Weiffenbach, J. M., Haxby, J. V., Friedland, R. P. 1987. Olfactory detection and recognition in Alzheimer's disease. *Lancet* 1:622

153. Koss, E., Weiffenbach, J. M., Haxby, J. V., Friedland, R. P. 1988. Olfactory detection and identification performance are dissociated in early Alzheimer's disease. *Neurology* 38:1228–32

154. Lahon, H. F. J., Mann, R. D. 1973. Glipizide: Results of a multicentre clinical trial. *J. Int. Med. Res.* 1:608–15
155. Landfield, P. W., Pitler, T. A. 1984. Prolonged Ca^{2+}-dependent after hyperpolarizations in hippocampal neurons in aged rats. *Science* 226:1089–92
156. Landfield, P. W., Waymire, J. C., Lynch, G. 1978. Hippocampal aging and adrenocorticoids: Quantitative correlations. *Science* 202:1098–102
157. Lang, N. P., Catalanotto, F. A., Knopfli, R. U., Antczak, A. A. 1988. Quality-specific taste impairment following the application of chlorhexidine digluconate mouthrinses. *J. Clin. Periodontol.* 15:43–48
158. Lehnhardt, E., Rollin, H. 1969. Berufsbedingte Riechstorungen. *HNO* 17:104–6
159. Leigh, A. D. 1943. Defects of smell after head injury. *Lancet* 1:38–40
160. Leopold, D. A., Preti, G., Mozell, M. M., Youngentob, S. L., Wright, H. N. 1990. Fish-odor syndrome presenting dysosmia. *Arch. Otolaryngol.* 116(3):354–55
161. Levin, H. S., High, W. M., Eisenberg, H. M. 1985. Impairment of olfactory recognition after closed head injury. *Brain* 108:579–91
162. Levinson, J. L., Kennedy, K. 1985. Dysosmia, dysgeusia, and nifedipine [letter]. *Ann. Intern. Med.* 102:135–36
163. Liss, L., Gomez, F. 1958. The nature of senile changes of the human olfactory bulb and tract. *Arch. Otolaryngol.* 67: 167–71
164. Little, A. C., Brinner, L. 1984. Taste responses to saltiness of experimentally prepared tomato juice samples. *J. Am. Dietetic Assoc.* 21:1022–27
165. Machado-Salas, J., Scheibel, M. E., Scheibel, A. B. 1977. Morphologic changes in the hypothalamus of old mouse. *Exp. Neurol.* 57:102–11
166. Macht, D. I., Macht, M. B. 1940. Comparison of effect of cobra venom and opiates on olfactory sense. *Am. J. Physiol.* 129:411–12
167. MacIntyre, I. 1971. Prolonged anosmia. *Br. Med. J.* 2:709
168. Magnasco, L. D., Magnasco, A. J. 1985. Metallic taste associated with tetracycline therapy. *Clin. Pharm.* 4: 455–56
169. Mahajan, S. K., Prasad, A. S., Lambujon, J., Abbasi, A. A., Briggs, W. A. 1980. Improvement of uremic hypogeusia by zinc: a double-blind study. *Am. J. Clin. Nutr.* 33:1517–21
170. Mair, R. G., Doty, R. L., Kelly, K.

M., Wilson, C. S., Langlais, P. J., et al. 1986. Multimodal sensory discrimination deficits in Korsakoff's psychosis. *Neuropsychologia* 24:831–39
171. Males, J. L., Townsend, J. L., Schneider, R. A. 1973. Hypogonadotrophic hypogonadism with anosmia-Kallman's syndrome. A disorder of olfactory and hypothalamic function. *Arch. Intern. Med.* 131:501–7
172. Mann, D. M. A., Yates, P. O., Marcyniuk, B. 1984. Alzheimer's presenile dementia, senile dementia of Alzheimer type and Down's syndrome in middle age form an age-related continuum of pathological changes. *Neuropathol. Appl. Neuobiol.* 10:185–207
173. Mann, D. M. A., Yates, P. O., Marcyniuk, B. 1985. Some morphometric observations on the cerebral cortex and hippocampus in presenile Alzheimer's disease, senile dementia of Alzheimer type and Down's syndrome in middle age. *J. Neurol. Sci.* 69:139–59
174. Mann, D. M. A., Yates, P. O., Marcyniuk, B. 1986. Dopaminergic neurotransmitter systems in Alzheimer's disease and in Down's syndrome at middle age. *J. Neurol. Neurosurg. Psychiatry* 50:341–44
175. Marshall, J. R., Henkin, R. I. 1971. Olfactory acuity, menstrual abnormalities, and oocyte status. *Ann. Int. Med.* 75:207–11
176. Mata, R. 1963. Effect of dextro-amphetamine on bitter taste threshold. *J. Neuropsychiatry* 4:315–20
177. Mattes, R. D., Christensen, C. M., Engelman, K. 1990. Effects of hydrochlorothiazide and amiloride on salt taste and excretion (intake). *Am. J. Hypertens.* 3:436–43
178. McConnell, R. J., Menendez, C. E., Smith, F. R., Henkin, R. I., Rivlin, R. S. 1975. Defects of taste and smell in patients with hypothyroidism. *Am. J. Med.* 59:354–64
179. McCurdy, P. R. 1964. Parenteral iron therapy. II. A new iron-sorbitol citric acid complex for intramuscular injection. *Ann. Int. Med.* 61:1053–64
180. McFate-Smith, W., Davies, R. O., Gabriel, M. A., Kramsch, D. M., Moncloa, F., et al. 1984. Tolerance and safety of enalapril. *Br. J. Clin. Pharmacol.* 18(Suppl. 2):249s–55s
181. McNeil, J. J., Anderson, A., Christophidis, N., Jarrott, B., Louis, W. J. 1979. Taste loss associated with oral captopril treatment. *Br. Med. J.* 2:1555–56

182. Meats, P. 1988. Olfactory hallucinations [letter]. *Br. Med. J.* 296:645
183. Megighian, D. 1958. Variazioni della soglia olfattiva nell'ets senile. *Minerva Otorinolaringol.* 9:331–37
184. Moberg, P. J., Pearlson, G. D., Speedie, L. J., Lipsey, J. R., Strauss, M. E., et al. 1987. Olfactory recognition: Differential impairments in early and late Huntington's and Alzheimer's diseases. *J. Clin. Exp. Neuropsychol.* 9:650–64
185. Mochizuki, Y. 1937. An observation on the numerical and topographical relations of the taste buds to circumvallate papillae of Japanese. *Okajimas Folia Ana. Jpn.* 15:595–608
186. Mochizuki, Y. 1939. Studies on the papillae foliata of Japanese. II. The number of taste buds. *Okajimas Folia Ana. Jpn.* 18:355–69
187. Monath, T. P., Cropp, C. B., Harrison, A. K. 1983. Mode of entry of a neurotropic arbovirus into the central nervous system: Reinvestigation of an old controversy. *Lab. Invest.* 48:399–410
188. Moore, L. M., Neilson, C. R., Mistretta, C. M. 1982. Sucrose taste thresholds: Age-related differences. *J. Gerontol.* 37:64–69
189. Moran, D. T., Jafek, B. W., Rowley, J. C., Eller, P. M. 1985. Electron microscopy of olfactory epithelia in two patients with anosmia. *Arch. Otolaryngol.* 111:122–26
190. Moses, S. W., Rotem, Y., Jagoda, N., Talmor, N., Eichhorn, F., et al. 1967. A clinical, genetic and biochemical study of familial dysautonomia in Israel. *Isr. J. Med. Sci.* 3:358–71
191. Moulton, D. G. 1974. Dynamics of cell populations in the olfactory epithelium. *Ann. NY Acad. Sci.* 237:52–61
192. Murphy, C. 1979. The effect of age on taste sensitivity. In *Special Senses in Aging: A Current Biological Assessment*, ed. S. S. Han, D. H. Coons, pp. 21–33. Ann Arbor: Univ. Mich. Inst. Gerontol.
193. Murphy, C. 1983. Age-related effects on the threshold, psychophysical function, and pleasantness of methol. *J. Gerontol.* 38:217–22
194. Murphy, C. 1985. Cognitive and chemosensory influences on age-related changes in the ability to indentify blended foods. *J. Gerontol.* 40:47–52
195. Murphy, C., Lasker, B. R., Salmon, D. P. 1987. Olfactory dysfunction and odor memory in Alzheimer's disease, Huntington's disease and normal aging.

196. Naessen, R. 1971. An inquiry on the morphological characteristics and possible changes with age in the olfactory region of man. *Acta Otolaryngol.* 71:49–62
197. Nakajima, Y., Utsumi, H., Takahashi, H. 1983. Ipsilateral disturbance of taste due to pontine hemorrhage. *J. Neurol.* 229:133–36
198. National Institute of Neurological and Communicative Disorders and Stroke. US Department of Health, Education, and Welfare, National Institutes of Health. 1979. Report of the Panel on Communicative Disorders to the National Advisory Neurological and Communicative Disorders and Stroke Council, June 1. *NIH Publ. No. 79-1914*, pp. 319. Washington, DC: Natl. Inst. Health
199. Naus, A. 1968. Alterations of the smell acuity caused by menthol. *J. Laryngol.* 82:1009–11
200. Naus, A. 1976. *Olphactoric Properties of Industrial Matters*, pp. 55–65. Prague: Charles Univ.
201. *Nutr. Rev.* 1978. Zinc deficiency, taste acuity and growth failure. 36:213–14
202. Ohm, T. G., Braak, H. 1987. Olfactory bulb changes in Alzheimer's disease. *Acta Neuropathol.* 73:365–69
203. Olsen, K. D., DeSanto, L. W. 1983. Olfactory neuroblastoma. *Arch. Otolaryngol.* 109:797–82
204. Peabody, C. A., Tinklenberg, J. R. 1985. Olfactory deficits and primary degenerative dementia. *Am. J. Psychiatry* 142:524–25
205. Pearson, R. C., Esiri, M. M., Hiorns, R. W., Wilcock, G. K., Powell, T. P. 1985. Anatomical correlates of the distribution of the pathological changes in the neocortex in Alzheimer disease. *Proc. Natl. Acad. Sci. USA* 82:4531–34
206. Perry, J. D., Frisch, S., Jafek, B., Jafek, M. 1980. Olfactory detection thresholds using pyridine, thiophene, and phenethyl alcohol. *Otolaryngol. Head Neck Surg.* 88:778–82
207. Pinching, A. J. 1977. Clinical testing of olfaction reassessed. *Brain* 100:377–88
208. Plath, P., Otten, E. 1969. Untersuchungen uber die Wirksamkeit von Hexetidine bei akuten Erkrankungen des Rachens und der Mundhohle sowie nach Tonsillektomie. *Therapiewocke* 19:1565–66
209. Prata, A. 1969. Clinical evaluation of niridazole in *Schistosoma mansoni* in-

fections. *Ann. NY Acad. Sci.* 160:660–69

210. Rabe, R. 1970. Isolierte ageusie: Ein neues Symptom als Nebenwirkung von Medikamenten. *Nervenarzt* 41:23–27

211. Reyes, E. S., Talley, R. W., O'Bryan, R. M., Gastesi, R. A. 1973. Clinical evaluation of 1,3-Bis(2-chloroethyl)-1-nitrosourea (BCNU; NSC-409962) with fluoxymesterone (NSC-12165) in the treatment of solid tumors. *Cancer Chemother. Rep.* 57:225–30

212. Reyes, P. F., Golden, G. T., Fagel, P. L., Fariello, R. G., Katz, L., et al. 1987. The prepiriform cortex in dementia of the Alzheimer type. *Arch. Neurol.* 44:644–45

213. Rezek, D. L. 1987. Olfactory deficits as a neurologic sign on dementia of the Alzheimer type. *Arch. Neurol.* 44:1030–32

214. Roberts, E. 1986. Alzheimer's disease may begin in the nose and may be caused by aluminosilicates. *Neurobiol. Aging* 7:561–67

215. Roberts, G. W., Crow, T. J., Polak, J. M. 1985. Location of neuronal tangles in somatostatin neurons in Alzheimer's disease. *Nature* 314:92–94

216. Rollin, H. 1978. Drug-related gustatory disorders. *Ann. Otol. Rhinol. Laryngol.* 87:37–42

217. Rossor, M. N., Emson, P. C., Mountjoy, C. Q., Roth, M., Iversen, L. L. 1980. Reduced amounts of immunoreactive somatostatin in the temporal cortex in senile dementia of Alzheimer type. *Neurosci. Lett.* 20:373–77

218. Rundles, R. W. 1946. Prognosis in the neurologic manifestations of pernicious anemia. *Blood* 1:209–19

219. Runge, L. A., Pinals, R. S., Lourie, S. H., Tomar, R. H. 1977. Treatment of rheumatoid arthritis with levamisole. *Arthritis Rheum.* 20:1445–48

220. Ryan, C. M., Morrow, L. A., Hodgson, M. 1988. Cacosmia and neurobehavioral dysfunction associated with occupational exposure to mixtures of organic solvents. *Am. J. Psychiatry* 145:1442–45

221. Ryan, R. E. Sr., Ryan, R. E. Jr. 1974. Acute nasal sinusitis. *Postgrad. Med.* 56:159–62

222. Schaupp, H., Seilz, J. 1969. Geruch und geschmack bei endokrinen. Erkrankungen. *Arch. Klin. Exp. Ohren. Nasen. Kehlkopfheilkd.* 195:179–91

223. Schechter, P. J., Henkin, R. I. 1974. Abnormalities of taste and smell after head trauma. *J. Neurol. Neurosurg. Psychiatry* 37:802–10

224. Scheibel, M. E., Scheibel, A. B. 1975. Structural changes in the aging brain. In *Aging: Clinical, Morphological, and Neurochemical Aspects in the Aging Central Nervous System,* ed. H. Brody, D. Harman, J. M. Ordy, 1:11–37. New York: Raven

225. Schellinger, D., Henkin, R. T., Smirniotopoulos, J. G. 1983. CT of the brain in taste and smell dysfunction. *Am. J. Neuroradiogr.* 4:752–54

226. Schemper, T., Voss, S., Cain, W. S. 1981. Odor identification in young and elderly persons: Sensory and cognitive limitations. *J. Gerontol.* 36:446–52

227. Schiffman, S. S. 1977. Food recognition by the elderly. *J. Gerontol.* 32:586–92

228. Schiffman, S. S. 1979. Changes in taste and smell with age: psychophysical aspects. In *Sensory Systems and Communication in the Elderly, Aging,* ed. J. M. Ordy, K. Brizzee, 10:227–46. New York: Raven

229. Schiffman, S. S. 1983. Taste and smell in disease. *N. Engl. J. Med.* 308:1275–79, 1337–43

230. Schiffman, S. S. 1987. Smell. In *Encyclopedia of Aging,* ed. G. L. Maddox, pp. 618–19. New York: Springer

231. Schiffman, S. S. 1991. Taste and smell perception in elderly persons. In *Nutrition Research: Future Directions and Applications,* ed. J. E. Fielding, H. I. Frier, pp. 61–73. New York: Raven

232. Schiffman, S. S. 1992. Olfaction in aging and medical disorders. In *Science of Olfaction,* ed. M. J. Serby, K. L. Chobor, pp. 500–25. New York: Springer-Verlag

233. Schiffman, S. S., Clark, C. M., Warwick, Z. S. 1990. Gustatory and olfactory dysfunction in dementia: Not specific to Alzheimer's disease. *Neurobiol. Aging* 11:597–600

234. Schiffman, S. S., Clark, T. B. 1980. Magnitude estimates of amino acids for young and elderly subjects. *Neurobiol. Aging* 1:81–91

235. Schiffman, S. S., Crumbliss, A. L., Warwick, Z. S., Graham, B. G. 1990. Thresholds for sodium salts in young and elderly subjects: correlation with molar conductivity of anion. *Chem. Senses* 15:671–78

236. Schiffman, S. S., Frey, A. E., Luboski, J. A., Foster, M. A., Erickson, R. P. 1991. Taste of glutmate salts in young and elderly subjects: role of inosine 5'-monophosphate and ions. *Physiol. Behav.* 49:843–54

237. Schiffman, S. S., Frey, A. E., Suggs, M. S., Cragoe, E. J. Jr., Erickson,

R. P. 1990. The effect of amiloride analogs on taste responses in gerbil. *Physiol. Behav.* 47:435–41

238. Schiffman, S. S., Hornack, K., Reilly, D. 1979. Increased taste thresholds of amino acids with age. *Am. J. Clin. Nutr.* 32:1622–27

239. Schiffman, S. S., Leffingwell, J. C. 1981. Perception of odors of simple pyrazines by young and elderly subjects: A multidimensional analysis. *Pharmacol. Biochem. Behav.* 14:787–98

240. Schiffman, S. S., Lindley, M. G., Clark, T. B., Makino, C. 1981. Molecular mechanism of sweet taste: relationship of hydrogen bonding to taste sensitivity for both young and elderly. *Neurobiol. Aging* 2:173–85

241. Schiffman, S. S., Lockhead, E., Maes, F. W. 1983. Amiloride reduces the taste intensity of Na^+ and Li^+ salts and sweeteners. *Proc. Natl. Acad. Sci. USA* 80:6136–40

242. Schiffman, S. S., Moss, J., Erickson, R. P. 1976. Thresholds of food odors in the elderly. *Exp. Aging Res.* 2:389–98

243. Schiffman, S. S., Nagle, H. T. 1992. Effect of environmental pollutants on taste and smell. *Otolaryngol. Head and Neck Surg.* 106:693–700

244. Schiffman, S. S., Nash, M. L., Dackis, C. 1978. Reduced olfactory discrimination in patients on chronic hemodialysis. *Physiol. Behav.* 21:239–42

245. Schiffman, S. S., Orlandi, M., Erickson, R. P. 1979. Changes in taste and smell with age: biological aspects. See Ref. 228, pp. 247–68

246. Schiffman, S. S., Pasternak, M. 1979. Decreased discrimination of food odors in the elderly. *J. Gerontol.* 34:73–79

247. Schiffman, S. S., Warwick, Z. S. 1988. Flavor enhancement of foods for the elderly can reverse anorexia. *Neurobiol. Aging* 9:24–26

248. Schiffman, S. S., Warwick, Z. S. 1991. Changes in taste and smell over the life span: Their effect on appetite and nutrition in the elderly. In *Chemical Senses, Appetite and Nutrition,* M. I. Friedman, M. G. Tordoff, M. R. Kare, 4:341–65. New York: Dekker

249. Schiffman, S. S., Warwick, Z. S. 1992. The biology of taste and food intake. In *Pennington Center Nutrition Series,* G. A. Bray, D. H. Ryan, 2:293–312. Baton Rouge: Louisiana State Univ. Press

250. Schneeberg, N. G. 1952. Loss of sense of taste due to methylthiouracil therapy. *J. Am. Med. Assoc.* 149:1091–93

251. Schwartz, B. S., Doty, R. L., Monroe, C., Frye, R., Barker, S. 1989. Olfactory function in chemical workers exposed to acrylate and methacrylate vapors. *Am. J. Public Health* 79:613–18

252. Schwartz, B. S., Ford, D. P., Bolla, K. I., Agnew, J., Rothman, N., et al. 1990. Solvent-associated decrements in olfactory function in paint manufacturing workers. *Am. J. Indust. Med.* 18:697–706

253. Scott, P. J. 1960. Glossitis with complete loss of taste sensation during Dindevon treatment: Report of a case. *NZ Med. J.* 59:296

254. Serby, M. 1986. Olfaction and Alzheimer's disease. *Prog. Neuropsychopharmacol. Biol. Psychiatry* 10:579–86

255. Serby, M. 1987. Olfactory deficits in Alzheimer's disease. *J. Neural Transm. Suppl.* 24:69–77

256. Serby, M., Corwin, J., Conrad, P., Rotrosen, J. 1985. Olfactory dysfunction in Alzheimer's disease and Parkinson's disease. *Am. J. Psychiatry* 142:781–82

257. Serby, M., Corwin, J., Novatt, A., Conrad, P., Rotrosen, J. 1985. Olfaction in dementia. *J. Neurol. Neurosurg. Psychiatry* 48:848–49

258. Seydell, E. M., McKnight, W. P. 1948. Disturbances of olfaction resulting from intranasal use of tyrothricin. *Arch. Otolaryngol.* 47:465–70

259. Shepard, T. H., Gartler, S. M. 1960. Increased incidence of nontasters of phenylthiocarbamide among congenital athyreotic cretins. *Science* 131:929

260. Shipley, M. T. 1985. Transport of molecules from nose to brain: Transneuronal anterograde and retrograde labeling in the rat olfactory system by wheat germ agglutinin–horseradish peroxidase applied to the nasal epithelium. *Brain Res. Bull.* 15:129–42

261. Siegfried, J., Zumstein, H. 1971. Changes in taste under L-DOPA therapy. *Z. Neurol.* 200:345–48

262. Simpson, J. R. 1975. Idoxuridine in the treatment of herpes zoster. *Practitioner* 215:226–29

263. Simpson, J., Yates, C. M., Gordon, A., St. Clair, D. M. 1984. Olfactory tubercle choline acetyltransferase activity in Alzheimer-type dementia, Down's syndrome and Huntington's chorea. *J. Neurol. Neurosurg. Psychiatry* 47:1138–39

264. Singh, N., Grewal, M. S., Austin, J. H. 1970. Familial anosmia. *Arch. Neurol.* 22:40–44

265. Skouby, A. P., Zilstorff-Pedersen, K.

1954. The influence of acetylcholine-like substances, menthol and strychnine, on olfactory receptors in man. *Acta Physiol.* 32:252–58

266. Smith, C. G. 1942. Age incidence of atrophy of olfactory nerves in man. *J. Comp. Neurol.* 77:589–95

267. Smith, F. R., Henkin, R. I., Dell, R. B. 1976. Disordered gustatory acuity in liver disease. *Gastroenterology* 70:568–71

268. Snow, J. B. Jr. 1991. Differential diagnosis of transport and sensorineural chemosensory disorders. See Ref. 270, pp. 469–70

269. Snow, J. B. Jr., Doty, R. L., Bartoshuk, L. M. 1991. Clinical evaluation of olfactory and gustatory disorders. See Ref. 270, pp. 463–67

270. Snow, J. B. Jr., Doty, R. L., Bartoshuk, L. M., Gethchell, T. V. 1991. Categorization of chemosensory disorders. In *Smell and Taste in Health and Disease*, ed. T. V. Getchell, R. L. Doty, L. M. Bartoshuk, J. B. Snow Jr., pp. 445–47. New York: Raven

271. Soni, N. K., Chatterji, P. 1976. Abnormalities of taste. *Br. Med. J.* 2:198

272. Soni, N. K., Chatterji, P. 1985. Disturbance of taste in leprosy. *J. Laryngol. Otol.* 95:717–20

273. Soni, N. K., Chatterji, P. 1985. Gustotoxicity of bleomycin. *J. Otol. Rhino. Laryngol. Relat. Spec.* 47:101–4

274. Soria, E. D., Candaras, M. M., Truax, B. T. 1990. Impairment of taste in the Guillain-Barre syndrome. *Clin. Neurol. Neurosurg.* 92(1):75–79

275. State, F. A., Hamed, M. S., Bonok, A. A. 1977. Effect of vincristine on the histological structure of taste buds. *Acta Anat.* 99:445–49

276. St. Clair, D. M., Simpson, J., Yates, C. M., Gordon, A. 1985. Olfaction in dementia: a response. *J. Neurol. Neurosurg. Psychiatry* 48:849

277. Steinlieb, I., Scheinberg, I. H. 1964. Penicillamine therapy for hepatolenticular degeneration. *J. Am. Med. Assoc.* 189:748–54

278. Stevens, D. A., Lawless, H. T. 1981. Age-related changes in flavor perception. *Appetite* 2:127–36

279. Stevens, J. C., Bartoshuk, L. M., Cain, W. S. 1984. Chemical senses and aging: Taste versus smell. *Chem. Senses* 9:167–79

280. Stevens, J. C., Cain, W. S. 1985. Age-related deficiency in the perceived strength of six odorants. *Chem. Senses* 10:517–29

281. Stevens, J. C., Plantinga, A., Cain, W. S. 1982. Reduction of odor and nasal pungency associated with aging. *Neurobiol. Aging* 3:125–32

282. Strandbygard, E. 1954. Treatment of ozena and rhinopharyngitis chronica sicca with vitamin A. *Arch. Otolaryngol.* 59:485–90

283. Strassman, H. D., Adams, B., Pearson, A. W. 1970. Metronidazole effect on social drinkers. *Q. J. Stud. Alcohol* 31:394–98

284. Sumner, D. 1964. Post-traumatic anosmia. *Brain* 87:107–20

285. Sunohara, N., Sakuragawa, N., Satoyoshi, E., Tanue, A., Shapiro, L. J. 1986. A new syndrome of anosmia, ichthyosis, hypogonadism, and various neurological manifestations with deficiency of steroid sulfatase andarylsulfatase C. *Ann. Neurol.* 19:98–99

286. Symanski, H. 1950. Ein Fall von Selenwasserstoffvergiftung. *Dtsch. Med. Wochenschr.* 75:1730

287. Talamo, B. R., Rudel, J. S. R., Kosik, K. S., Lee, V. M., Neff, S., et al. 1989. Pathological changes in olfactory neurons in patients with Alzheimer's disease. *Nature* 337:736–39

288. Thumfart, W., Plattig, K. H., Schlict, N. 1980. Smell and taste thresholds in older people. *Z. Gerontol.* 13:158–88

289. Tomlinson, B. E., Henderson, G. 1976. Some quantitative cerebral findings in normal and demented old people. In *Neurobiology of Aging*, ed. R. D. Terry, S. Gershon, 3:183–204. New York: Raven

290. Turner, P. 1965. Some observations on centrally-acting drugs in man. *Proc. R. Soc. Med.* 58:913–14

291. Ujike, H., Yamamoto, M., Hara, I. 1987. Taste loss as an initial symptom of primary amyloidosis [letter]. *J. Neurol. Neurosurg. Psychiatry* 50:111–12

292. Venstrom, D., Amoore, J. E. 1968. Olfactory threshold in relation to age, sex, or smoking. *J. Food Sci.* 33:264–65

293. Viskoper, R. J., Lugassy, G. 1979. Elevated taste threshold for salt in hypertensive subjects. *Kidney Int.* 15:582

294. Vlasses, P. H., Ferguson, R. K. 1979. Temporary ageusia related to captopril. *Lancet* 2:526

295. von Skramlik, E. 1963. The fundamental substrates of taste. See Ref. 65, pp. 125–32

296. Waldton, S. 1974. Clinical observations of impaired cranial nerve function in senile dementia. *Acta Psychiatry* 50:539–47

297. Ward, C. D., Hess, W. A., Caine, D. B. 1983. Olfactory impairment in

Parkinson's disease. *Neurology* 33: 943–46

298. Warner, M. D., Peabody, C. A., Berger, P. A. 1988. Olfactory deficits and Down's syndrome. *Biol. Psychiatry* 23:836–39

299. Warner, M. D., Peabody, C. A., Flattery, J. J., Tinklenberg, J. R. 1986. Olfactory deficits and Alzheimer's disease. *Biol. Psychiatry* 21:116–18

300. Weiffenbach, J. M., Baum, B. J., Burghauser, R. 1982. Taste thresholds: Quality specific variation with human aging. *J. Gerontol.* 37:372–77

301. Weinstock, R. S., Wright, H. N., Spiegel, A. M., Levine, M. A., Moses, A. M. 1986. Olfactory dysfunction in humans with deficient guanine nucleotide-binding protein. *Nature* 322:635–36

302. Whitehouse, P. J., Price, D. L., Clark, A. W., Coylee, J. T., DeLong, M. R. 1981. Alzheimer disease: evidence for selective loss of cholinergic neurons in the nucleus basalis. *Ann. Neurol.* 10:122–26

303. Whittington, J., Raftery, E. B. 1980. A controlled comparison of oxyfedrine, isosorbide dinitrate and placebo in the treatment of patients suffering attacks of angina pectoris. *Br. J. Clin. Pharmacol.* 10:211–15

304. Winblad, B., Adolfsson, R., Carlsson, A., Gottfries, C. G. 1982. Biogenic amines in brains of patients with Alzheimer's disease. In *Alzheimer's Disease: A Report of Progress. Aging.* ed. S. Corkin, 19:25–33. New York: Raven

305. Wolberg, F. L., Ziegler, D. K. 1986. Olfactory hallucination in migraine. *Arch. Neurol.* 39:382

306. Yamada, Y., Tomita, H. 1989. Influences on taste in the area of chorda tympani nerve after transtympanic injection of local anesthetic (4% lidocaine). *Auris. Nasus. Larynx 16 Suppl.* 1:s41–46

307. Zilstorff, K. 1965. Sense of smell alterations by cocaine and tetracaine. *Arch. Otolaryngol.* 82:53–55

308. Zilstorff, K., Herbild, O. 1979. Parosmia. *Acta Otolaryngol. Suppl.* 360: 40–41

Annu. Rev. Nutr. 1993. 13:437–61

EFFECTS OF EXOGENOUS BOVINE SOMATOTROPIN ON LACTATION

Dale E. Bauman

Department of Animal Science, Cornell University, Ithaca, New York 14853

Richard G. Vernon

Hannah Research Institute, Ayr, Scotland KA6 5HL

KEY WORDS: mammary gland, adipose tissue, homeorhesis, dairy cow

CONTENTS

INTRODUCTION 437
BACKGROUND 438
PRODUCTION RESPONSES 439
    Milk and Milk Components 439
    Bioenergetics, Nutrition, and Animal Well-Being 441
MECHANISMS OF ACTION 442
    Whole Body Metabolism 443
    Adipose Tissue 445
    Hepatocytes 449
    Mammary Gland 449
INTEGRATION 452
CONCLUSIONS 454

INTRODUCTION

Over 60 years ago scientists first demonstrated the presence of a substance from the anterior pituitary that increased growth of rats (54, 55). Using pair-fed rats treated with extract from bovine pituitaries, Lee & Schaffer (86) further documented that effects of treatment included a shift in composition of the gain so that muscle was increased and fat was reduced. This extract factor was named "somatotropin" from the Greek derivation meaning "tissue

437

0199-9885/93/0715-0437$02.00

growth." Somatotropin (ST) is also referred to as "growth hormone" in scientific and lay articles. About the same time, other scientists demonstrated that administration of an extract from the anterior pituitary also affected lactation in laboratory animals (133) and increased milk yield of lactating goats (6). In 1937, Russian scientists treated over 500 lactating dairy cows with subcutaneous injections of a crude extract from ox anterior pituitaries and observed a substantial increase in milk yield (7).

Major advances in our understanding of somatotropin occurred during World War II when food shortages caused British scientists to examine the possibility of using ST to increase milk supply. They established that ST was the galactopoietic factor in crude pituitary extracts and evaluated several dimensions of the milk response in dairy cows. However, results indicated that the amount of bovine somatotropin (bST) that would be available from pituitary tissue of slaughtered cattle would not be sufficient to have a substantial impact on their nation's milk supply [see review by Young (156)].

Over the next 40 years there was continued interest in bST. Particularly noteworthy were studies by Brumby & Hancock (29) and Machlin (92) that noted over 40% increases in milk yield of dairy cows over a 10- to 12-week treatment period. More recently, breakthroughs in biotechnology have made possible the production of proteins by recombinant DNA technology. The first study treating lactating cows with recombinantly derived bST was reported in 1982 (12), and the first long-term study in 1985 (16). Because treatment with bST results in unprecedented gains in productive efficiency, several companies have produced recombinant bST and this has led to an exponential increase in investigations to explore the potential for commercial use and to examine the role of ST in the biology of lactation. In some areas the research has been extensive and has led to a clear consensus. This is particularly true for many aspects of the production responses, and in these instances we will predominately cite reviews. However, in other aspects investigations have been less extensive. This is particularly true for the mechanisms of action where understanding is sometimes confused by apparently conflicting results and ideas. Finally, in the last section, we develop integrative concepts.

BACKGROUND

Somatotropin is a protein hormone synthesized by the anterior pituitary gland. Secretion from the pituitary gland is regulated by two peptides: growth hormone-releasing factor, which stimulates release, and somatostatin, which inhibits release. The amino acid sequence for somatotropin is known for many species (146). Bovine ST produced by the pituitary can have either a 191 or 190 amino acid sequence with either a leucine or valine at position 127 (153;

numbering based on the 191 amino acid variant). These represent the four major variants of bST that are produced naturally. Differences in the cleavage of the signal peptide cause the N-terminus to be an alanine (191 amino acid sequence) or a phenylalanine (190 amino acid sequence). Variation between valine or leucine at position 127 is due to differences in gene alleles, and the frequency of these alleles varies for the major dairy breeds (89). Recombinantly derived forms of bST that have been used experimentally can differ slightly from the bST produced by the pituitary gland. Depending on the manufacturing process, from 0 to 8 extra amino acids are attached to the N-terminus of the bST molecule (72). However, when the same purification techniques are used, recombinantly derived and pituitary-derived bST have similar potencies in various biological test systems (82, 153).

The discovery in the 1950s that some types of human dwarfism were due to inadequate pituitary production of ST stimulated interest in utilizing bST to treat this malady. However, clinical studies uniformly demonstrated that bST, as well as ST from other nonprimates, was not biologically active in humans. This led to the concept that ST was "species specific." Subsequent work demonstrated that the homology between hST and bST was only about 65% and that bST was not able to effectively bind to the ST receptor from human tissues (see reviews 72, 81). In contrast, the amino acid sequence for bovine and ovine ST only differs at a single position, and bST is biologically active in sheep (71).

The ST receptor has been isolated and characterized from several species and is a single peptide of about 620 amino acids consisting of an extracellular domain (about 250 amino acids, which is very similar to the ST-binding protein of plasma), a short trans-membrane domain (about 25 amino acids), and an intracellular domain (about 350 amino acids) (149). The receptor appears to belong to a novel family of receptors that includes the prolactin receptor (which has many similarities to the ST receptor) and a number of interleukin (cytokine) receptors (73, 94). A single ST molecule can bind to two receptor molecules, each binding to a different region of ST (46). The ST receptor may be internalized following binding of the ligand, but the role of internalization in signal transduction, if any, is unknown (126).

PRODUCTION RESPONSES

Milk and Milk Components

Milk-yield responses to bST have been reported in all dairy breeds. Milk yield gradually increases over the first few days of bST treatment and reaches a maximum during the first week. If treatment is terminated, milk yield gradually returns to pretreatment levels over a similar time period. However, when treatment is continued, the increased milk yield is maintained. Thus, bST results in a greater peak milk yield and an increased persistency in yield over the lactation cycle (see reviews 71, 111, 114).

Milk-yield increases after bST treatment are observed in cows of all parities, but the magnitude of the increase in milk yield varies according to stage of lactation (31, 95, 111, 114). In general, response has been small or negligible when bST is administered in early lactation prior to peak yield. Therefore, possible commercial use would probably be over the last two thirds or three fourths of the lactation cycle.

The gross composition of milk (fat, protein, and lactose) is not altered by treatment with bST (9, 21, 30, 84, 91, 95, 114, 135). A variety of factors affect the fat and protein content of milk, including breed, stage of lactation, diet composition, nutritional status, environment, and season; these factors have the same effects on the milk composition of bST-treated cows. For example, certain breeds have a higher milk fat content, and an increase in milk fat typically occurs in late lactation for all breeds; treatment with bST does not alter these relationships. Likewise, the increase in milk fat content that occurs when the cow is in negative energy balance and the decrease in milk protein content that occurs when the cow has an inadequate protein intake are also observed in bST-treated cows. Overall, results demonstrate that the same factors that typically affect milk composition also affect the milk composition of bST-treated cows, and the variation in milk content of fat and protein is not altered (9, 11, 30, 91).

Milk from bST-treated cows does not differ in vitamin content or in concentrations of nutritionally important mineral elements (11, 21, 135). In addition, proportions of total milk protein represented by whey proteins and the different casein fractions are not substantially altered, and factors that affect the fatty acid composition of milk fat have the same effects in bST-treated cows. In addition to a lack of effects on milk composition, bST has no impact on the manufacturing characteristics of milk (9, 21, 84, 91, 135).

Lactational response to exogenous bST is a function of the daily dose represented by a hyperbolic dose-response curve with a pattern of diminishing marginal returns to increasing bST dose (17, 101, 111). The daily dose needed to optimize milk yield response results in blood concentrations of ST that are within the range typically observed during episodic release of endogenous hormone, but average daily concentrations are several-fold higher than before treatment. As in the case of other species, endogenous release of ST in dairy cows normally occurs as irregular, episodic bursts with a half-life of about 15–30 min. Studies have demonstrated that a similar milk response occurs regardless of whether the daily dose of bST is administered as a single bolus, a constant infusion, or as equal episodic pulses at 4-hr intervals (see review

17). Typically, bST has been administered by daily injection. However, several prolonged-release formulations have been recently developed in which a small volume is injected at intervals ranging from 2 to 4 weeks (31, 66, 101, 111).

Bioenergetics, Nutrition, and Animal Well-Being

Milk production responses to bST are not dependent on special diets or unique feed ingredients. Substantial increases in milk yield have been observed on diets ranging from pasture only to typical concentrate:forage mixtures (11, 30, 31, 41). Treatment does not alter digestibilities of organic components of the diet. Thus, the biological effects of bST are predominantly associated with the use of absorbed nutrients. Bioenergetic studies have demonstrated that bST treatment does not alter the energy expenditure for maintenance or the partial efficiency of milk synthesis, so that nutrient requirements for maintenance and per unit of milk are not altered (77, 127, 134). Overall, daily nutrient requirements are increased by an amount equal to the increase in milk yield, and productive efficiency (milk per unit of feed) is improved because a greater proportion of the nutrient intake is used for milk synthesis.

Most studies have involved bST treatment for a few weeks or for a single lactation. However, several dozen multilactational studies have been conducted and treatment has been continued for as long as eight successive lactations (see review 111). Responses in multilactational studies are of interest because cows typically utilize body fat reserves during the early phase of the lactation cycle and then replenish these reserves during latter phases of the lactation cycle. Over the course of the first few weeks of bST treatment, cows adjust their voluntary intake in a predictable manner related to the extra nutrients required for the increased production of milk (11, 30, 31, 41). In general, similar lactational responses have been observed when bST has been administered for two or more consecutive lactations, provided that management practices allow for an adequate replenishment of body energy reserves over the latter portion of the lactation cycle. However, in cases where cows were not adequately fed to allow for an adjustment of voluntary intake and replenishment of body energy reserves, milk yield response to bST was reduced or even absent in the next lactation cycle (11, 41).

The impact of bST treatment on animal health and well-being has also been of interest. Some investigators anticipated that administration of bST to modern high-producing dairy cows might result in metabolic disorders such as ketosis, fatty liver, and chronic wasting. These "postulated" catastrophic effects were based on the nutrient needs associated with a rapid, substantial increase in milk yield and on ideas, which originated in the 1940s, that ST had acute lipolytic and hyperglycemic (diabetogenic) effects. Such effects would likely occur during the first few days of bST treatment (milk yield would have increased but voluntary intake would not yet have increased). Suffice it to say, these catastrophic effects have never been observed with bST treatment, even in animals with exceptionally large increases in milk yield (>10 kg/day) or animals that received exceptionally large doses of bST (dose equivalent to 4 yr of treatment given over a 2-week period), and the perceived mechanisms that were postulated to lead to such catastrophic effects are now known to be erroneous (11, 21, 30, 41, 85, 110, 118, 144).

Quality of management is the major factor affecting the magnitude of milk response to bST (11, 41, 113), and this comprises the nutritional program, milking procedures, herd health program, and environmental conditions. Several long-term studies have involved inadequate management conditions, and milk yield response to bST treatment was essentially zero. Adverse effects were not observed in any of these studies; cows simply had negligible milk yield response to bST (see reviews 11, 41, 111). Several reports have also summarized studies that encompass a range of environmental and management conditions in an effort to evaluate subtle health effects (1, 21, 38, 40, 56, 96, 109, 110, 118, 151). Variables have included physical examinations, blood chemistry, metabolic disorders, incidence of disease, mastitis and mammary health, and reproduction-related parameters of the treated cows, as well as the health and growth of their offspring. Results demonstrate that values for bST-treated cows are similar to controls and consistent with literature values for cows of comparable milk production. As a result of differences in management practices, substantial herd effects were apparent for many of these variables (e.g. mastitis or reproduction-related variables), but herd effects were the same for control and bST treatment groups. Analyses for subtle effects will be even more extensive as data accumulates and is used by regulatory agencies in their evaluation.

MECHANISMS OF ACTION

Somatotropin is a homeorhetic control that regulates utilization of absorbed nutrients. The dramatic increase in milk production that occurs in bST-treated cows requires the orchestration of diverse physiological processes in a number of tissues and must involve the metabolism of all nutrient classes. These adaptations involve both direct effects on some tissues and indirect effects that are probably mediated by somatotropin-dependent somatomedins (insulin-like growth factors, IGF-I and IGF-II) for other tissues. Two cell types that are well-established as major direct targets of ST are the adipocyte and the hepatocyte. In contrast, effects on mammary tissue are thought to be indirect. In this section we discuss the state of knowledge for whole body metabolism and these particular tissues.

Whole Body Metabolism

Physiological processes that are altered with bST treatment are summarized in Table 1. Adaptations in metabolism are major and of critical importance during the initial period of bST treatment, when milk yield has increased but intake has not. Overall, mammary uptake of all milk precursors increases

Table 1   Effect of bovine somatotropin on specific tissues and physiological processes in lactating cows[a]

Tissue	Process affected during first few days and weeks of treatment
Mammary	↑ Synthesis of milk with normal composition
	↑ Uptake of all nutrients used for milk synthesis
	↑ Activity per secretory cell
	↑ Number and/or maintenance of secretory cells
	↑ Blood flow consistent with increase in milk yield
Liver	↑ Basal rates of gluconeogenesis
	↓ Ability of insulin to inhibit gluconeogenesis
	φ Glucagon effects on gluconeogenesis and/or or glycogenolysis
Adipose	↓ Basal lipogenesis if in positive energy balance
	↑ Basal lipolysis if in negative energy balance
	↓ Ability of insulin to stimulate lipogenesis
	↓ Ability of adenosine to inhibit lipolysis
	↑ Ability of catecholamines to stimulate lipolysis
Muscle	↓ Uptake of glucose
Pancreas	φ Basal or glucose-stimulated secretion of insulin
	φ Basal or insulin/glucose-stimulated secretion of glucagon
Kidney[b]	↑ Production of 1,25-vitamin D_3
Intestine[b]	↑ Absorption of Ca, P, and other minerals required for milk
	↑ Ability of 1,25-vitamin D_3 to stimulate Ca-binding protein
	↑ Ca-binding protein
Whole body	↓ Oxidation of glucose
	↑ NEFA oxidation if in negative energy balance
	φ Insulin and glucagon clearance rates
	φ Energy expenditure for maintenance
	↑ Energy expenditure consistent with increase in milk yield (i.e. heat per unit of milk not changed)
	↑ Cardiac output consistent with increases in milk yield
	↑ Productive efficiency (milk per unit of energy intake)

[a] Adapted from Bauman et al (13). Changes (↑ = increased, ↓ = decreased, φ = no change) that occur in initial period of bovine somatotropin supplement when metabolic adjustments match the increased use of nutrients for milk synthesis. With longer-term treatment, voluntary intake increases to match nutrient requirements.
[b] Demonstrated in nonlactating animals and consistent with observed performance in lactating cows.

while metabolism of other body tissues is altered simultaneously so that a greater proportion of nutrients are used for milk synthesis.

In a high-producing dairy cow, glucose is derived predominately via hepatic gluconeogenesis. Glucose turnover is over 3 kg/day with 60–85% used for milk synthesis (15). Thus, adaptations in glucose metabolism are of particular importance. When bST treatment is initiated, glucose turnover increases and oxidation decreases (18); accordingly, hepatic production of glucose increases (37) and hindlimb use of glucose is reduced (98) (Table 1). Therefore, adaptations in glucose oxidation and production occur in bST-treated cows before the increase in voluntary feed intake, and the adjustments are quantitatively equal to the extra glucose required to support the increased milk synthesis (18).

Changes in lipid metabolism play an integral role in the response to ST treatment and vary according to the animal's energy balance (Table 1). When cows are near zero or in negative energy balance, bST treatment increases mobilization of body fat reserves as evidenced by chronic elevation in circulating concentrations of nonesterified fatty acids (NEFA), decreased body fat content, and an increased milk fat content with the pattern of these extra fatty acids reflecting body fat stores (22, 28, 31, 51, 128). Under such conditions, an increase in NEFA irreversible loss rate (ILR) is observed and the magnitude of the increase is related to the extent of the negative energy balance and quantitatively equal to the increase in whole body oxidation of NEFA and the increased secretion of milk fat (18). Rates of lipid synthesis in adipose tissue would already be low and relatively impervious to further attenuation by ST. This situation is most likely to occur when bST treatment is initiated in early- to mid-lactation and the increased reliance on NEFA as metabolic fuel facilitates the previously discussed reduction in glucose oxidation.

In contrast, when animals are in positive energy balance at the time bST-treatment is initiated (i.e. when some lipid synthesis and storage is occurring in adipose tissue), the major effect of ST is to inhibit lipid synthesis with little or no change in lipolysis or milk fat percent and fatty acid composition (51, 83, 114, 127). This situation is most likely to occur when bST is initiated in mid- or late-lactation and the decrease in nutrient utilization for body fat stores enables nutrients to be redirected to other tissues to support the increased milk synthesis. With prolonged ST treatment, voluntary food intake increases and animals can eventually return to a positive energy balance allowing the replenishment of body reserves (Table 1) despite continuing high circulating concentrations of ST.

The kinetics of amino acid metabolism have not been examined in bST-treated dairy cows. Abomasal infusions of casein or amino acids gave no increase in milk protein yield over that observed for the basal diet in bST-treated cows (3, 90, 115). However, the characteristic reduction in milk protein content that occurs when dietary protein is inadequate is also observed in bST-treated cows. Therefore, standard NRC protein requirements and dietary recommendations are also applicable to bST-treated cows (30, 41, 102).

Partitioning of minerals is altered by bST as indicated by the fact that the increased secretion of milk has a normal composition of nutritionally important minerals. Mechanisms have not been investigated in lactating cows, but changes in flux are coordinated with the increased milk secretion because blood concentrations of these minerals are not altered (13, 21, 51, 135). Recent studies with nonlactating animals (26) have demonstrated an altered tissue response to signals that maintain mineral homeostasis and, in the long term, increased absorption as shown for Ca and P (Table 1).

Adipose Tissue

The adipocyte is a major target of ST action. The hormone acts chronically to facilitate lipolysis and decrease lipid synthesis, in part by altering the ability of the tissue to respond to acute endocrine and other signals, but in addition ST may have some seemingly conflicting actions. In laboratory species and under rather unusual conditions (lack of prior exposure to ST for several hours, acute surgical stress), ST can exert an acute, transient, "insulin-like" effect (61, 141). The physiological significance of this is unclear, as the conditions required are unlikely to occur in vivo except perhaps in the young male rat with its highly erratic ST secretion (70). ST also promotes differentiation in several cell-lines (e.g. 3T3 F-442 cells) that can develop into adipocyte-like cells (26, 141); neither this, nor the acute "insulin-like" effect are thought to have any role in the chronic effect of ST on milk production. Some reports suggest ST can have an acute lipolytic effect; in many of the early studies the ST preparations were most probably contaminated with other peptides, but even the availability of pure recombinant ST has not completely resolved the controversy. For ruminants and pigs, ST apparently has no acute lipolytic effect (see reviews 26, 53, 141). Thus, much of the literature on effects of ST on adipocyte function has little relevance to the lactating animal treated chronically with ST.

Chronic treatment of lactating cows (97, 129) or growing steers (117) with ST dramatically increases the lipolytic response to in vivo challenges with catecholamines (Table 1). Sechen et al (128) further demonstrated that maximum response, but not sensitivity, was altered. In contrast, when responses to catecholamines are measured with in vitro incubations of subcutaneous adipose tissue obtained from cattle receiving ST, the differences between these responses and those of controls are much smaller or absent (83, 117). The reason for this apparent discrepancy between in vivo and in vitro measurements is not clear. The subcutaneous adipose tissue depot sampled for in vitro studies may not be representative of other depots. For example, in humans exercise has a greater effect on lipolysis in abdominal than in gluteal subcutaneous adipose tissue (5), whereas in sheep lactation has a greater effect on β-receptor number in omental adipose tissues than in carcass adipose tissues (25, 74). Alternatively, the adaptation may not be sufficiently robust to survive in vitro manipulations or ST may exert its effects by limiting inhibition by an antilipolytic factor. Adenosine is a possible candidate; an autocrine/paracrine factor, adenosine exerts an acute antilipolytic effect via its own receptor, which couples via Gi (an inhibitory GTP-binding protein) to adenylate cyclase (140). Chronic treatment with ST decreased response to adenosine in lactating rats (139) and cows (83) (Table 1). Diminished response to adenosine is also found after chronic exposure to ST in vitro (140). The mechanism has not been resolved but does not appear to involve changes in adenosine receptor number (150), which suggests that ST may be altering either the amount or activity of Gi. A decrease in the ability of adenosine to inhibit lipolysis would allow for an increased response to catecholamines and thereby provide a possible explanation for the enhanced in vivo response to catecholamines. Curiously, in rats and sheep, response to adenosine is increased during lactation (140) and perhaps acts as a brake to check lipolysis; treatment with ST may thus reduce the effectiveness of this putative brake.

Other mechanisms may also be operating. Culture of sheep subcutaneous adipose tissue with ST increased both responsiveness and sensitivity to catecholamines and also increased ligand binding to the β-adrenergic receptor (150). Curtailing lactation in rats either by litter removal (139) or by endocrine manipulation (10) causes a marked decrease in lipolytic response to catecholamines, which is prevented by treatment with ST. In these animals ST altered several components of the adrenergic signal transduction system, thereby increasing the number of β-receptors and hormone-sensitive lipase activity and decreasing cyclic AMP phosphodiesterase activity. The greatest effect of ST, however, was on the association of hormone-sensitive lipase with the lipid droplet following catecholamine stimulation (142).

In vivo treatment with ST decreases the rates of lipogenesis and activities of key enzymes involved in lipid synthesis (see reviews 26, 53, 141). Similar adaptations occur in untreated animals during the initial stages of lactation when concentrations of endogenous ST are high (15, 136). Evidence that effects are due to ST acting directly on adipose tissue comes from in vitro studies in which chronic exposure to ST decreases the rate of lipogenesis (see reviews 53, 141). Indeed it is possible by varying the concentration of insulin and ST in tissue culture to mimic the changes in lipogenesis seen in adipose tissue during the lactation cycle (138).

Most studies have focused on the control of lipogenesis and the key lipogenic enzyme acetyl CoA carboxylase (ACC), which exists in both active and inactive states within the cell. In ruminant animals in which acetate rather than glucose is the major precursor for fatty acid synthesis, ACC is a major control of flux and "total activity" is thought to reflect the amount of this enzyme (136). Tissue culture studies show that effects of ST on lipogenesis over the first 48 hr are due to a decrease in ACC in the active state with no change in total activity (137), which is consistent with the relatively long half-life (about 48 hr) for this enzyme (145). Exposure to ST for six days or more results in a decrease in total ACC activity; this has been observed with sheep adipose tissue in culture (137) or with in vivo ST treatment of lactating cows (83) and goats (R. G. Vernon, unpublished observation), or growing pigs (65, 88). The changes in activity were probably due to a decrease in enzyme synthesis, as Liu et al (88) demonstrated a decrease in ACC protein and message. The close relationship between total ACC activity and the rate of lipogenesis suggests that with prolonged ST treatment, a fall in the amount of ACC is responsible for the decreased rate of lipogenesis.

While ST reduces the effects of insulin on lipogenesis, it does not prevent an acute stimulation of lipogenesis by insulin in pigs in vivo (49) or in vitro (147). However, in vivo treatment of growing pigs with ST decreases sensitivity to insulin as measured by in vitro rates of glucose incorporation into adipose tissue lipid (147) or by in vivo rates of whole body glucose utilization (154). Similarly, treatment of lactating cows reduces glucose response to an insulin challenge (128). Thus, physiological concentrations of insulin would be less effective in increasing the rate of lipogenesis (Table 1). That ST does not completely abrogate the effect of insulin on lipogenesis in vivo can also be inferred from the recovery of adipose tissue reserves during the latter stages of lactation in bST-treated animals, despite high levels of ST.

The mechanism whereby ST inhibits the effects of insulin on lipogenesis is not known. ST treatment has no apparent effect either on the ability of adipocytes to bind insulin in pigs (93) or sheep (148), or on the ability of insulin to stimulate insulin-receptor tyrosine kinase activity (93) or down-regulate its receptor (148). Therefore, the site of action is at a postreceptor level, which is not surprising as ST does not inhibit all effects of insulin. For example, the antilipolytic effect of insulin (128) and insulin stimulation of protein synthesis (137) in cow and sheep adipose tissue, respectively, are not altered by ST. ST inhibits the activation of a phosphatidylinositol-specific phospholipase C by insulin in mouse adipocytes (32), possibly by interfering with the action of a putative Gi-like protein (125). This observation is of interest because lactation in rats results in a decreased ability of insulin to stimulate lipogenesis and activate lipogenic enzymes of adipocytes because of a postreceptor impairment at the level of the plasma membrane (76). In sheep, onset of lactation also results in the loss of ability by insulin to increase the rate of lipogenesis in vitro (138), apparently owing to the loss of a putative protein required for activation of acetyl CoA carboxylase by insulin (137). Production of this mediating protein can be restored by prolonged incubation with insulin in vitro and is prevented by ST (137). While most work has focused on ST as an insulin antagonist, ST can also act chronically to decrease the rate of lipogenesis in the absence of insulin (24, 131).

Effects of ST on adipocytes are thought to be mediated by ST itself, for although ST stimulates IGF-I mRNA production (39, 155) and IGF-I secretion (J. Beattie and R. G. Vernon, unpublished observations) by adipocytes, the adipocytes themselves lack IGF-I receptors (141). The function of this locally produced IGF-I in the tissue is uncertain, but may have a role in angiogenesis. IGF-I also failed to mimic chronic effects of ST on lipogenesis and lipolysis during lactation (10; D. P. D. Lanna and D. E. Bauman, unpublished observations). IGF-I can mimic effects of insulin on adipose tissue but concentrations required were high, which suggests that they were mediated via the insulin receptor (52, 138, 147). One very provocative study suggested that IGF-I and IGF-II mediated acute lipolytic effects of ST on adipocytes in sheep (87), but attempts to confirm this have proved unsuccessful (68; R. G. Vernon, unpublished observations).

Adipocytes have been a major target of studies on the ST signal transduction system, but the paradoxical actions of ST have slowed progress in this area. The structure of the ST receptor suggests that it is unlikely to be associated with GTP-binding proteins (a common mediator of signal transduction) and that it is unlikely to be a protein kinase. However, ST binding apparently causes phosphorylation of its own receptor by sequestration of a cytosolic protein kinase (132). Studies with differentiating pre-adipocyte cell-lines suggest that ST, presumably through the sequestered kinase, causes tyrosine phosphorylation of a number of proteins including mitogen-activated protein kinase (MAP kinase) (4). Some effects of ST in these cell lines also appear to be mediated by protein kinase C (48), thus suggesting that the hormone activates a protein kinase cascade. Less is known about mechanisms involved in the chronic effect of ST on mature adipocytes. Protein kinase C may have a minor role (142), and it is not known if MAP kinase is involved. The chronic inhibitory effects of ST on lipogenesis are blocked by actinomycin D and appear to involve some relatively short-lived (half-life less than 3 hr) product of gene transcription (24); ornithine decarboxylase is an obvious candidate for this product because its half-life is less than 30 min and its activity is enhanced by ST in the liver (69). However, although polyamines are required for inhibition of lipogenesis by ST, they probably have a permissive rather than a mediatory role (R. G. Vernon, unpublished observations).

Hepatocytes

Hepatic rates of gluconeogenesis are increased with ST treatment of dairy cows as demonstrated by in vivo (37) and in vitro studies (78, 119) (Table 1). Evidence that this is a direct effect comes from studies with sheep hepatocytes maintained in culture (50). Mechanisms have not been resolved but include a decreased ability of insulin to inhibit gluconeogenesis (23, 62) (Table 1). In contrast, ST treatment had no effect on liver glycogen concentration in lactating cattle in positive energy balance (119), although such treatment did induce a small decrease in cows in negative energy balance (78). This lack of an effect of ST is not surprising, as hepatic glycogen reserves are not sufficient to sustain increased glucose output by the liver for long.

Effects of ST on hepatic lipid metabolism appear to be slight. In vivo treatment of lactating cows with ST increased fatty acid oxidation to CO_2 in liver slices (119), which was consistent with the increased rates of gluconeogenesis. Chronic treatment of cows with ST in vivo (119) and culture of sheep hepatocytes with ST (50) had no effect on the ketogenic capacity (i.e. rate in vitro with a saturating concentration of fatty acid). Consequently, any effects of ST on ketogenesis are indirect, via changes in plasma NEFA concentrations. Treatment with ST, in vivo (112) and in vitro (50), decreased rates of fatty acid esterification and lipoprotein secretion by sheep liver. If such changes occur in lactating cows, they must be highly coupled because hepatic concentration of triacylglycerol is not altered (119). The overall effect of ST on hepatic lipid metabolism thus appears to be a small increase in fatty acid oxidation (to support gluconeogenesis) at the expense of esterification.

Mammary Gland

The dramatic increase in milk yield is a clear demonstration that mammary uptake and utilization of nutrients is increased in bST-treated cows (Table 1). The change in the lactation curve suggests an increased rate of milk synthesis per cell and, in the long-term, an increased number of mammary epithelial cells. Clarification of these postulates and of the mechanisms responsible for them has proved difficult. This is not unexpected as biochemical changes in vivo are likely to be relatively small and mammary tissue from lactating animals is difficult to maintain in vitro because of its high metabolic rate. In addition, assessing the role of somatomedins is complicated by the presence of specific binding proteins.

Baldwin (8) demonstrated that bST-treated cows had increased RNA per gland, and therefore increased protein synthetic capacity; he also reported increased activities of several enzymes but the key enzymes controlling metabolic flux were not measured. Other studies of lactating cows (80) and goats (79) observed similar trends in enzyme activity after ST treatment, but effects were not significant possibly owing to smaller increases in the milk yield response. Clear-cut evidence for an effect on activity and message level of mammary enzymes comes from studies of rats in which investigators treated animals with ST after blocking prolactin secretion with bromocriptine and neutralizing endogenous ST with an antiserum (10). The mammary gland is not metabolically homogeneous, so changes in synthetic capacity could result from an increased synthetic activity of active cells and/or the activation of resting differentiated cells (108). Treatment of cows with ST for a period during mid-lactation had no effect on total mammary DNA content (8), but in a longer-term study in which goats were treated with ST for 22 weeks, the decline in mammary cell number that normally occurs during lactation was prevented (79). No effect was observed on DNA synthesis (79), but the increase might have been too small to detect. The low milk levels of plasmin, a serine-protease associated with mammary gland involution, that are maintained during bST treatment (120) are also consistent with the proposed changes in maintenance and/or number of mammary cells.

Changes in mammary synthetic activity in response to ST are complemented by increased nutrient availability induced by the homeorhetic effect of ST and also by an increase in mammary blood flow (42, 57). However, merely increasing nutrient availability by itself does not mimic the effect of ST on milk yield (see review 114). Mepham et al (107) suggested that ST affects the mammary gland largely through an increase in blood flow, but it is now thought that the increased blood flow is the result rather than the cause of the increased mammary metabolism.

The mechanism whereby ST increases mammary gland function is still uncertain but appears to be indirect. Addition of bST to bovine mammary cells in culture had no effect on rates of synthesis of casein, fat, or α-lactalbumin (59). An attempt to demonstrate a direct effect of ST on the mammary gland using a close arterial infusion technique was unsuccessful (99); however, because of the half-life of ST and mammary blood flow rates, this approach would not allow for an adequate evaluation. Attempts to detect ST receptors in mammary tissue have been unsuccessful (2, 58, 75). Furthermore, concentrations of ST in milk are very low and not appreciably altered by bST treatment (72). Recent studies have reported the presence of mRNA for ST receptor in mammary tissue from pregnant (150 d), nonlactating heifers (67) and lactating cows (60), but in both cases the message level in mammary tissue was only a small fraction of that in liver. Therefore, although the message for bST receptors is present, either it is not translated or the number of receptors produced is too low to be detected by conventional techniques. As a result, the current view is that ST does not act directly on mammary epithelial cells, and efforts have focused on the role of the somatomedins as possible mediators.

Administration of exogenous bST to lactating cows causes an increase in concentrations of IGF-I in blood (36, 43, 124) and milk (72). Another candidate is IGF-II, although effects of ST on IGF-II are not consistent (106). Receptors for somatomedins are present in ruminant mammary tissue, and the number of available receptors increases during lactogenesis (45, 47, 63). When lactating cows are treated with bST, circulating concentrations of IGF-I begin to increase about 6–12 hr after the initial bST injection and reach maximum concentrations in approximately 48 hr (36). The response in milk yield is apparent about 24 hr after the first bST injection, and maximum production response occurs four to six days after start of treatment. In addition, IGF-I is present in milk, and concentrations increase with bST treatment (72). Therefore, the temporal pattern of changes in IGF-I is consistent with its possible role in mediating the effects of ST on milk production. Likewise, IGF-I stimulated casein synthesis in cultured mammary cells from lactating cows (64) and increased both casein synthesis and glucose transport in mammary explants from mid-pregnant mice (122). IGF-I also increased protein synthesis in mammary explants from pregnant rats (A. M. Gilhespy, C. J. Wilde, and R. G. Vernon, unpublished observations). On the other hand, IGF-I had no effect on fatty acid synthesis or α-lactalbumin secretion in mammary explants from lactating cows (130), but the medium also contained insulin (50 ng/mL), which may have masked effects of IGF-I. IGF-I also stimulates DNA synthesis in mammary tissue cultures (19, 116, 130, 152) and thus may play a role in maintaining cell number during long-term ST treatment.

Attempts to demonstrate an effect of IGF-I on milk secretion in vivo have had mixed success. While ST treatment increased milk secretion in goats, a three-day jugular infusion of IGF-I had no effect on milk yield even though blood concentrations of IGF-I were elevated to levels comparable to those of the ST-group (44). IGF-I injections also failed to mimic the effect of ST on mammary metabolism in rats treated with an antiserum to endogenous ST (10). In contrast, infusion of IGF-I into the pudendal artery of lactating goats for 6 hr increased milk production by about 30% (121). Differences in response to IGF-I in vivo could arise from problems relating to IGF-binding proteins.

The majority of somatomedins in physiological fluids are bound to soluble, high affinity binding proteins. There are six specific IGF-binding proteins (IGFBP) and their functions are not well established. Their postulated roles include serving as circulatory transport vehicles, retarding somatomedin degradation, facilitating transvascular movement, providing an extravascular pool, and/or modulating directly the actions of somatomedins at specific target cells either by enhancing or blocking their activity (20, 33, 123). The in vivo regulation of the two major IGFBP in bovine serum has been described more fully (35). As in the case of humans (33), ST treatment of lactating cows results in a threefold elevation of circulating IGFBP-3 and a decrease of about two thirds in circulating concentrations of IGFBP-2 (35, 105, 143), so it is not surprising that IGF-I infusions or injections have not mimicked the effects of ST. Somatomedins themselves stimulate mammary cells to produce both IGFBP-2 and IGFBP-3 (100). Thus, local production of somatomedins and their binding proteins may also play a role in control of mammary tissue.

INTEGRATION

Although many details have yet to be clarified, we now know that exogenous ST enhances milk production in dairy cows by coordinating a complex series of adaptations within the body. In essence, bST both increases the rate of milk production within the mammary gland and provides the necessary nutrients in support of this enhanced rate of milk synthesis (Figure 1). Direct actions of ST appear to be primarily concerned with nutrient availability as illustrated by the aforementioned alterations in the metabolism of adipose tissue and liver. On the other hand, the indirect effects of ST appear to be primarily associated with the mammary gland and the actions of the IGF complex. We do not have a clear understanding of how the IGF complex is

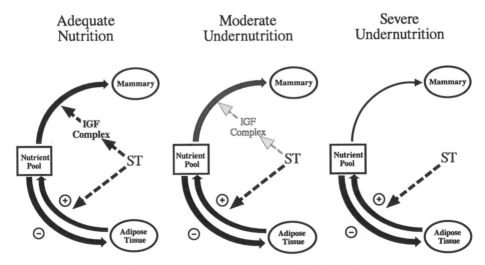

Figure 1   Conceptual model of the effects of somatotropin (ST). Direct effects include alterations in activities of key enzymes and tissue response to homeostatic signals as represented by plus and minus symbols on adipose tissue rates of lipolysis and lipogenesis, respectively. Indirect effects apparently involve the IGF complex (insulin-like growth factors and their binding proteins), and these are modulated by nutritional status as indicated. Model (developed by M. A. McGuire and D. E. Bauman, unpublished information) adapted from Bauman et al (14).

able to mediate mammary function, nor do we fully understand the interplay between the endocrine, autocrine, and/or paracrine aspects of the IGF complex. It is apparent, however, that changes in circulating concentrations of IGF-I and some of the IGFBP are closely tracking the biological events and the magnitude of milk responses that occur with bST treatment of dairy cows, indicating that the IGF complex has an important role in ST biology.

Nutritional status plays a key role in the regulation of somatomedins and their binding proteins (34, 106). In the lactating dairy cow, moderate undernutrition has no effect on basal concentrations of circulating IGF-I, but administration of bST results in a less dramatic increase in circulating IGF-I than when animals have an adequate nutritional status (104). When nutritional status is severely compromised by a short-term fast, basal concentrations of IGF-I are lower and the ability of bST to increase IGF-I is abolished (103; Figure 1). A similar impact of nutritional status on the somatotropin/somatomedin axis is observed in growing cattle (27) and other species including humans (34). Although not as extensively investigated, basal and bST-stimulated levels of IGFBP also appear to be modulated by nutritional status (103, 106).

The relationship between nutritional status and the somatotropin/somatomedin axis also provides a framework to consider variations in milk response to bST, which were discussed in the section on production responses. Moderate undernutrition attenuates both the increase in circulating IGF-I and milk yield response to bST (104). In addition, the small increases in milk yield that occur with bST treatment in the early portion of lactation are consistent with the representation in Figure 1. Cows in early lactation are typically in substantial negative energy balance, and the use of body fat reserves over the first 30 days of lactation can be energetically equivalent to one third of the milk produced (15). During this period, animals have high circulating levels of endogenous ST but low basal levels of IGF-I. Vicini et al (143) demonstrated that short-term bST treatment during early lactation resulted in lower responses in circulating IGF-I and milk yield than were found in cows during later lactation. Thus, the direct actions of ST on tissues such as adipose occur in early lactation to maximize nutrient supply to the mammary gland, but the somatotropin/somatomedin axis is attenuated by nutritional status.

Long-term studies with bST treatment have demonstrated that the magnitude and maintenance of the milk response is related to the quality of management (see section on production responses). As a major component of the management program, this would largely reflect the impact of nutritional status on the somatotropin/somatomedin axis. Thus, production studies in which bST was administered to cows with inadequate nutrient supply and/or to cows that had inadequate body reserves observed no adverse effects.

However, as would be predicted from the preceding discussion, the milk response to bST was negligible (see section on production responses). The situation in fasted or chronically underfed animals is an interesting comparison in other regards. At first it seems paradoxical that exogenous ST can increase milk production while one of the most dramatic ways to increase endogenous levels of circulating ST and decrease milk yield is to fast or severely underfeed an animal. In this case, the direct effects of ST are to partition nutrients away from storage toward utilization in an inadequately nourished cow, but effects on the IGF complex are uncoupled so that use by the mammary gland is not stimulated (Figure 1). Therefore, these adaptations provide nutrients for the animal's survival and minimize any use of nutrients for milk production.

CONCLUSIONS

Somatotropin treatment of dairy cows results in a remarkable increase in milk yield and an unprecedented gain in productive efficiency (milk per unit of feed). Aspects of the production responses including effects on milk components, bioenergetics, and animal well-being have been extensively examined with consistent results over a wide range of management and environmental conditions. Overall, somatotropin is a homeorhetic control that increases rates of milk synthesis by the mammary gland and coordinates a series of physiological adaptations in a variety of tissues to support nutrient needs for milk synthesis. These tissue adaptations include changes in activities of key enzymes and alterations in tissue response to homeostatic signals. In addition, nutritional status of the animal plays a major role in determining the extent to which milk yield is altered. As a result of the nutritional effects on the somatotropin/somatomedin axis, somatomedins and their binding proteins appear to be key links between nutritional state and cellular growth and developmental processes.

ACKNOWLEDGMENTS

We express our appreciation to Mark McGuire, Dottie Ceurter, Debra Dwyer, David Flint, Colin Wilde, Karen Houseknecht, Dante Lanna, Diane Harris, and Mikko Griinari for assistance, stimulating discussions, and constructive suggestions.

Literature Cited

1. Aguilar, A. A., Green, H. B., Basson, R. P., Overpeck-Alvey, M. J. 1991. Effect of somidobove on reproductive performance in lactating dairy cows. *J. Dairy Sci.* 74(Suppl. 1):192 (Abstr.)
2. Akers, R. M. 1985. Lactogenic hor-
mones: binding sites, mammary growth, secretory cell differentiation, and milk biosynthesis in ruminants. *J. Dairy Sci.* 68:501–19
3. Aldrich, J. M., Muller, L. D., Varga, G. A. 1990. Duodenal infusion of

methionine and lysine with bovine somatotropin for lactating dairy cows. *J. Dairy Sci.* 73(Suppl. 1):171 (Abstr.)

4. Anderson, N. G. 1992. Growth hormone activates mitogen-activated protein kinase and S6 kinase and promotes intracellular tyrosine phosphorylation in 3T3-F442A preadipocytes. *Biochem. J.* 284:649–52

5. Arner, P., Kriegholm, E., Engfeldt, P., Bolinder, J. 1990. Adrenergic regulation of lipolysis in situ at rest and during exercise. *J. Clin. Invest.* 85:893–98

6. Asdell, S. A. 1932. The effect of the injection of hypophyseal extract in advanced lactation. *Am. J. Physiol.* 100: 137–40

7. Asimov, G. J., Krouze, N. K. 1937. The lactogenic preparations from the anterior pituitary and the increase of milk yield in cows. *J. Dairy Sci.* 20:289–306

8. Baldwin, R. L. 1990. Overview of rbST development and use. In *NIH Technology Assessment Conference on Bovine Somatotropin,* pp. 29–34. Bethesda: Natl. Inst. Health

9. Barbano, D. M., Lynch, J. M., Bauman, D. E., Hartnell, G. F., Hintz, R. L., et al. 1992. Effect of a prolonged-release formulation of n-methionyl bovine somatotropin (sometribove) on milk composition. *J. Dairy Sci.* 75:1775–93

10. Barber, M. C., Clegg, R. A., Finley, E., Vernon, R. G., Flint, D. J. 1992. The role of growth hormone, prolactin and insulin-like growth factors in the regulation of rat mammary gland and adipose tissue metabolism during lactation. *J. Endocrinol.* 135:195–202

11. Bauman, D. E. 1992. Bovine somatotropin: review of an emerging animal technology. *J. Dairy Sci.* 75: 3432–51

12. Bauman, D. E., DeGeeter, M. J., Peel, C. J., Lanza, G. M., Gorewit, R. C., et al. 1982. Effect of recombinantly derived bovine growth hormone (bGH) on lactational performance of high yielding dairy cows. *J. Dairy Sci.* 65(Suppl. 1):121 (Abstr.)

13. Bauman, D. E., Dunshea, F. R., Boisclair, Y. R., McGuire, M. A., Harris, D. M., et al. 1989. Regulation of nutrient partitioning: homeostasis, homeorhesis and exogenous somatotropin. In *Proceedings of the Seventh International Conference on Production Disease in Farm Animals,* ed. F. A. Kallfelz, pp. 306–23. Ithaca, NY: Cornell Univ.

14. Bauman, D. E., Eisemann, J. H., Currie, W. B. 1982. Hormonal effects on partitioning of nutrients for tissue growth: role of growth hormone and prolactin. *Fed. Proc.* 41:2538–44

15. Bauman, D. E., Elliot, J. M. 1983. Control of nutrient partitioning in lactating ruminants. In *Biochemistry of Lactation,* ed. T. B. Mepham, pp. 437–68. Amsterdam: Elsevier Sci.

16. Bauman, D. E., Eppard, P. J., DeGeeter, M. J., Lanza, G. M. 1985. Responses of high-producing dairy cows to long-term treatment with pituitary somatotropin and recombinant somatotropin. *J. Dairy Sci.* 68:1352–62

17. Bauman, D. E., McCutcheon, S. N. 1986. The effects of growth hormone and prolactin on metabolism. In *Control of Digestion and Metabolism in Ruminants,* ed. L. P. Milligan, W. L. Grovum, A. Dobson, pp. 436–55. Englewood Cliffs, NJ: Prentice-Hall

18. Bauman, D. E., Peel, C. J., Steinhour, W. D., Reynolds, P. J., Tyrrell, H. F., et al. 1988. Effect of bovine somatotropin on metabolism of lactating dairy cows: influence on rates of irreversible loss and oxidation of glucose and nonesterified fatty acids. *J. Nutr.* 118:1031–40

19. Baumrucker, C. R., Stemberger, B. H. 1989. Insulin and insulin-like growth factor-I stimulate DNA synthesis in bovine mammary tissue in vitro. *J. Anim. Sci.* 67:3503–14

20. Baxter, R. C. 1988. The insulin-like growth factors and their binding proteins. *Comp. Biochem. Physiol. B* 91: 229–35

21. Benzi, G. 1990. *Biomedical Problems on Bovine Somatotropin Use in Milk Production,* pp. 1–110. Paris: John Libbey Eurotext

22. Bitman, J., Wood, D. L., Tyrrell, H. F., Bauman, D. E., Peel, C. J., et al. 1984. Blood and milk lipid responses induced by growth hormone administration in lactating cows. *J. Dairy Sci.* 67:2873–80

23. Boisclair, Y. R., Dunshea, F. R., Bell, A. W., Bauman, D. E., Harkins, M. 1989. Effect of bovine somatotropin on glucose metabolism in steers. *FASEB J.* 3:A938 (Abstr.)

24. Borland, C. A., Travers, M. T., Barber, M. C., Vernon, R. G. 1992. Studies on the mechanism of the inhibition of lipogenesis by growth hormone in sheep adipose tissue. *Biochem. Soc. Trans.* 20:268S (Abstr.)

25. Bowen, W. P., Flint, D. J., Vernon, R. G. 1992. Regional and interspecific

differences in the ligand binding properties of β-adrenergic receptors of individual white adipose tissue depots in the sheep and rat. *Biochem. Pharmacol.* 44:681–86

26. Boyd, R. D., Bauman, D. E. 1989. Mechanisms of action for somatotropin in growth. In *Current Concepts of Animal Growth Regulation,* ed. D. R. Campion, G. J. Hausman, R. J. Martin, pp. 257–93. New York: Plenum

27. Breier, B. H., Gluckman, P. D. 1991. The regulation of postnatal growth: nutritional influences on endocrine pathways and function of the somatotrophic axis. *Livest. Prod. Sci.* 27:77–94

28. Brown, D. L., Taylor, S. J., De Peters, E. J., Baldwin, R. L. 1989. Influence of sometribove, USAN (recombinant methionyl bovine somatotropin) on the body composition of lactating cattle. *J. Nutr.* 119:633–38

29. Brumby, P. J., Hancock, J. 1955. The galactopoetic role of growth hormone in dairy cattle. *NZ J. Sci. Technol.* 36A:417–36

30. Chalupa, W., Galligan, D. T. 1989. Nutritional implications of somatotropin for lactating cows. *J. Dairy Sci.* 72: 2510–24

31. Chilliard, Y. 1989. Long-term effects of recombinant bovine somatotropin (rBST) on dairy cow performances: a review. See Ref. 129a, pp. 61–87

32. Chou, S. Y., Kostyo, J. L., Adamafio, N. A. 1990. Growth hormone inhibits activation of phosphatidylinositol phospholipase C by insulin in ob/ob mouse adipose tissue. *Endocrinology* 126:62–66

33. Clemmons, D. R. 1990. Insulinlike growth factor binding proteins. *Trends Endocrinol. Metab.* 1:412–17

34. Clemmons, D. R., Underwood, L. E. 1991. Nutritional regulation of IGF-1 and IGF binding proteins. *Annu. Rev. Nutr.* 11:393–412

35. Cohick, W. S., McGuire, M. A., Clemmons, D. R., Bauman, D. E. 1992. Regulation of insulin-like growth factor-binding proteins in serum and lymph of lactating cows by somatotropin. *Endocrinology* 130:1508–14

36. Cohick, W. S., Plaut, K., Sechen, S. J., Bauman, D. E. 1989. Temporal pattern of insulin-like growth factor-I response to exogenous bovine somatotropin in lactating cows. *Domest. Anim. Endocrinol.* 6:263–74

37. Cohick, W. S., Slepetis, R., Harkins, M., Bauman, D. E. 1989. Effects of exogenous bovine somatotropin (bST) on net flux rates of glucose and insulin

across splanchnic tissues of lactating cows. *FASEB J.* 3:A938 (Abstr.)

38. Cole, W. J., Madsen, K. S., Hintz, R. L., Collier, R. J. 1991. Effect of recombinantly-derived bovine somatotropin on reproductive performance of dairy cattle. *Theriogenology* 36:573–95

39. Coleman, M. E., Russell, L., Etherton, T. D. 1992. Effects of porcine somatotropin (pST) on mRNA levels for GLUT4, IGF-I and IGFBP-3 in adipose tissue of growing pigs. *J. Anim. Sci.* 70(Suppl. 1):200 (Abstr.)

40. Craven, N. 1991. Milk production and mastitis susceptibility: genetic relationships and influence of bovine somatotropin treatment. See Ref. 51a, pp. 55–59

41. Crooker, B. A., Otterby, D. E. 1991. Management of the dairy herd treated with bovine somatotropin. *Vet. Clin. North Am., Food Anim. Pract.* 7:417–36

42. Davis, S. R., Collier, R. J., McNamara, J. P., Head, H. H., Sussman, W. 1988. Effects of thyroxine and growth hormone treatment of dairy cows on milk yield, cardiac output and mammary blood flow. *J. Anim. Sci.* 66:70–79

43. Davis, S. R., Gluckman, P. D., Hart, I. C., Henderson, H. V. 1987. Effects of injecting growth hormone or thyroxine on milk production and blood plasma concentrations of insulin-like growth factors I and II in dairy cows. *J. Endocrinol.* 114:17–24

44. Davis, S. R., Gluckman, P. D., Hodgkinson, S. C., Farr, V. C., Breier, B. H., et al. 1989. Comparison of the effects of administration of recombinant bovine growth hormone or N-Met insulin-like growth factor-I to lactating goats. *J. Endocrinol.* 123:33–39

45. Dehoff, M. H., Elgin, R. G., Collier, R. J., Clemmons, D. R. 1988. Both type I and II insulin-like growth factor receptor binding increase during lactogenesis in bovine mammary tissue. *Endocrinology* 122:2412–17

46. de Vos, A. M., Ultsch, M., Kossiakoff, A. A. 1992. Human growth hormone and extracellular domain of its receptor: crystal structure of the complex. *Science* 255:306–12

47. Disenhaus, C., Belair, L., Djiane, J. 1988. Caractérisation et évolution physiologique des récepteurs pour les "insulin-like growth factors" I et II (IGFs) dans la glande mammaire de brebis. *Reprod. Nutr. Dév.* 28:241–52

48. Doglio, A., Dani, C., Grimaldi, P., Ailhaud, G. 1989. Growth hormone

stimulates c-jos gene expression by means of protein kinase C without increasing inositol lipid turnover. *Proc. Natl. Acad. Sci. USA* 86:1148–52

49. Dunshea, F. R., Harris, D. M., Bauman, D. E., Boyd, R. D., Bell, A. W. 1992. Effect of porcine somatotropin on in vivo glucose kinetics and lipogenesis in growing pigs. *J. Anim. Sci.* 70:141–51

50. Emmison, N., Agius, L., Zammit, V. A. 1991. Regulation of fatty acid metabolism and gluconeogenesis by growth hormone and insulin in sheep hepatocyte cultures: effects of lactation and pregnancy. *Biochem. J.* 274:21–26

51. Eppard, P. J., Bauman, D. E., Bitman, J., Wood, D. L., Akers, R. M., et al. 1985. Effect of dose of bovine growth hormone on milk composition:α-lactalbumin, fatty acids, and mineral elements. *J. Dairy Sci.* 68:3047–54

51a. Espinasse, J., ed. 1991. *Mammites des Vaches Laitières*. Toulouse: Soc. Fr. Buiatrie

52. Etherton, T. D., Evock, C. M. 1986. Stimulation of lipogenesis in bovine adipose tissue by insulin and insulin-like growth factor. *J. Anim. Sci.* 62:357–62

53. Etherton, T. D., Smith, S. B. 1991. Somatotropin and β-adrenergic agonists: their efficacy and mechanisms of action. *J. Anim. Sci.* 69(Suppl. 2):2–26

54. Evans, H. M., Long, J. A. 1921. Characteristic effects upon growth, oestrus and ovulation induced by the intraperitoneal administration of fresh anterior hypophyseal substance. *Proc. Natl. Acad. Sci. USA* 8:38–39

55. Evans, H. M., Simpson, M. E. 1931. Hormones of the anterior hypophysis. *Am. J. Physiol.* 98:511–46

56. Ferguson, J. D. 1990. Bovine somatotropin—reproduction and health. See Ref. 8, pp. 65–81

57. Fullerton, F. M., Fleet, I. R., Heap, R. B., Hart, I. C., Mepham, T. B. 1989. Cardiovascular responses and mammary substrate uptake in Jersey cows treated with pituitary-derived growth hormone during late lactation. *J. Dairy Res.* 56:27–35

58. Gertler, A., Ashkenazi, A., Madar, Z. 1984. Binding sites of human growth hormone and ovine and bovine prolactins in the mammary gland and liver of lactating dairy cow. *Mol. Cell. Endocrinol.* 34:51–57

59. Gertler, A., Cohen, N., Maoz, A. 1983. Human growth hormone but not ovine or bovine growth hormones ex-hibits galactopoietic prolactin-like activity in organ culture from bovine lactating mammary gland. *Mol. Cell. Endocrinol.* 33:169–82

60. Glimm, D. R., Baracos, V. E., Kennelly, J. J. 1990. Molecular evidence for the presence of growth hormone receptors in the bovine mammary gland. *J. Endocrinol.* 126:R5–R8

61. Goodman, H. M., Coiro, V., Frick, G. P., Gorin, E., Grichting, G., et al. 1987. Effects of growth hormone on the rat adipocyte: a model for studying direct actions of growth hormone. *Endocrinol. Jpn.* 34(Suppl. 1):59–72

62. Gopinath, R., Etherton, T. D. 1989. Effects of porcine growth hormone on glucose metabolism of pigs: II. Glucose tolerance, peripheral tissue insulin sensitivity and glucose kinetics. *J. Anim. Sci.* 67:689–97

63. Hadsell, D. L., Campbell, P. G., Baumrucker, C. R. 1990. Characterization of the change in type I and II insulin-like growth factor receptors of bovine mammary tissue during the pre- and postpartum periods. *Endocrinology* 126:637–43

63a. Hallberg, M. C., ed. 1992. *Bovine Somatotropin and Emerging Issues: An Assessment*. Boulder: Westview

64. Hanigan, M. D., Choi, J., Calvert, C. C., Baldwin, R. L. 1992. Effects of IGF-I on rates of growth and milk protein production by bovine mammary secretory cells. *FASEB J.* 6:A1116 (Abstr.)

65. Harris, D. M., Dunshea, F. R., Bauman, D. E., Boyd, R. D. 1990. Effect of in vivo porcine somatotropin (pST) treatment on in vitro lipogenesis of porcine adipose tissue. *FASEB J.* 4:A505 (Abstr.)

66. Hartnell, G. F., Franson, S. E., Bauman, D. E., Head, H. H., Huber, J. T., et al. 1991. Evaluation of sometribove in prolonged-release system in lactating dairy cows—production responses. *J. Dairy Sci.* 74:2645–63

67. Hauser, S. D., McGrath, M. F., Collier, R. J., Krivi, G. G. 1990. Cloning and in vivo expression of bovine growth hormone receptor mRNA. *Mol. Cell. Endocrinol.* 72:187–200

68. Houseknecht, K. L., Beausoleil, A. R., Dwyer, D. A., Bauman, D. E., Byatt, J. C., et al. 1992. Somatotropin, prolactin, placental lactogen and insulin-like growth factors I and II are not acute effectors of lipolysis in growing ruminants. *J. Anim. Sci.* 70(Suppl. 1):213 (Abstr.)

69. Jänne, J., Pösö, H., Raina, A. 1978. Polyamines in rapid growth and cancer. *Biochim. Biophys. Acta* 473:241–93

70. Jansson, J. O., Eden, S., Isaksson, O. 1985. Sexual dimorphism in the control of growth hormone secretion. *Endocr. Rev.* 6:128–50

71. Johnsson, I. D., Hart, I. C. 1986. Manipulation of milk yield with growth hormone. In *Recent Advances in Animal Nutrition*, ed. W. Haresign, D. J. A. Cole, pp. 105–21. London: Butterworth

72. Juskevich, J. C., Guyer, C. G. 1990. Bovine growth hormone: human food safety evaluation. *Science* 249:875–84

73. Kelly, P. A., Djiane, J., Edery, M. 1992. Different forms of the prolactin receptor. Insights into the mechanism of prolactin action. *Trends Endocrinol. Metab.* 3:54–59

74. Kennedy, A. D., Vernon, R. G. 1990. Beta and alpha receptor binding characteristics in subcutaneous, omental and popliteal adipocyte membranes from lactating and non-lactating ewes. *J. Anim. Sci.* 68(Suppl. 1):283–84 (Abstr.)

75. Keys, J. E., Djiane, J. 1988. Prolactin and growth hormone binding in mammary and liver tissue of lactating cows. *J. Receptor Res.* 8:731–50

76. Kilgour, E., Vernon, R. G. 1988. Defect in signal transduction at the level of the plasma membrane accounts for inability of insulin to activate pyruvate dehydrogenase in white adipocytes of lactating rats. *Biochem. J.* 252:667–72

77. Kirchgessner, M., Windisch, W., Schwab, W., Müller, H. L. 1991. Energy metabolism of lactating dairy cows treated with prolonged-release bovine somatotropin or energy deficiency. *J. Dairy Sci.* 74(Suppl. 2):35–43

78. Knapp, J. R., Freetly, H. C., Reis, B. L., Calvert, C. C., Baldwin, R. L. 1992. Effects of somatotropin and substrates on patterns of liver metabolism in lactating dairy cattle. *J. Dairy Sci.* 75:1025–35

79. Knight, C. H., Fowler, P. A., Wilde, C. J. 1990. Galactopoietic and mammogenic effects of long-term treatment with bovine growth hormone and thrice daily milking in goats. *J. Endocrinol.* 127:129–38

80. Knight, C. H., Hillerton, J. E., Kerr, M. A., Teverson, R. M., Turvey, A., et al. 1992. Separate and additive stimulation of bovine milk yield by the local and systemic galactopoietic stimuli of frequent milking and growth hormone. *J. Dairy Res.* 59:243–52

81. Kostyo, J. L., Reagan, R. C. 1976. The biology of somatotropin. *Pharmacol. Theriogenol.* 2:591–604

82. Langley, K. E., Lai, P. -H., Wypych, J., Everett, R. R., Berg, T. F., et al. 1987. Recombinant-DNA-derived bovine growth hormone from *Escherichia coli* 2. Biochemical, biophysical, immunological and biological comparison with the pituitary hormone. *Eur. J. Biochem.* 163:323–30

83. Lanna, D. P. D., Houseknecht, K. L., Harris, D. M., Bauman, D. E. 1992. Effect of bovine somatotropin (bST) on lipolysis, lipogenesis and activities of some enzymes in adipose tissue of lactating cows. *J. Anim. Sci.* 70(Suppl. 1):193 (Abstr.)

84. Laurent, F., Vignon, B., Coomans, D., Wilkinson, J., Bonnel, A. 1992. Influence of bovine somatotropin on the composition and manufacturing properties of milk. *J. Dairy Sci.* 75: 2226–34

85. Lean, I. J., Troutt, H. F., Bruss, M. L., Baldwin, R. L. 1992. Bovine somatotropin. *Vet. Clin. North Am., Food Anim. Pract.* 8:147–63

86. Lee, M. O., Schaffer, N. K. 1933. Anterior pituitary growth hormone and the composition of growth. *J. Nutr.* 7:337–63

87. Lewis, K. J., Molan, P. C., Bass, J. J., Gluckman, P. D. 1988. The lipolytic activity of low concentrations of insulin-like growth factors in ovine adipose tissue. *Endocrinology* 122:2554–57

88. Liu, C. Y., Grant, A. L., Kim, K. -H., Mills, S. E. 1991. Effects of recombinant porcine somatotropin on acetyl-CoA carboxylase enzyme activity and gene expression in adipose tissue of pigs. *J. Anim. Sci.* 69(Suppl. 1):309 (Abstr.)

89. Lucy, M. C., Hauser, S. D., Eppard, P. J., Krivi, G. G., Collier, R. J. 1991. Genetic polymorphism within the bovine somatotropin (bST) gene detected by polymerase chain reaction and endonuclease digestion. *J. Dairy Sci.* 74(Suppl. 1):284 (Abstr.)

90. Lynch, G. L., Klusmeyer, T. H., Cameron, M. R., Clark, J. H. 1991. Effects of somatotropin and duodenal infusion of amino acids on nutrient passage to duodenum and performance of dairy cows. *J. Dairy Sci.* 74:3117–21

91. Lynch, J. M., Barbano, D. M., Bauman, D. E., Hartnell, G. F., Nemeth, M. A. 1992. Effect of a prolonged-release formulation of n-methionyl bovine somatotropin (sometribove) on milk fat. *J. Dairy Sci.* 75:1794–1809

92. Machlin, L. J. 1973. Effect of growth hormone on milk production and feed utilization in dairy cows. *J. Dairy Sci.* 56:575–80

93. Magri, K. A., Adamo, M., Leroith, D., Etherton, T. D. 1990. The inhibition of insulin action and glucose metabolism by porcine growth hormone in porcine adipocytes is not the result of any decrease in insulin binding or insulin receptor kinase activity. *Biochem. J.* 266:107–13

94. Mathews, L. S. 1991. Molecular biology of growth hormone receptors. *Trends Endocrinol. Metab.* 2:176–80

95. McBride, B. W., Burton, J. L., Burton, J. H. 1988. The influence of bovine growth hormone (somatotropin) on animals and their products. *Res. Dev. Agric.* 5:1–21

96. McClary, D. G., Green, H. B., Basson, R. P., Nickerson, S. C., Overpeck-Alvey, M. J., et al. 1991. Incidence and duration of clinical mastitis in lactating dairy cows receiving a sustained-release formulation of bST (somidobove). *J. Dairy Sci.* 74(Suppl. 1):205 (Abstr.)

97. McCutcheon, S. N., Bauman, D. E. 1986. Effect of chronic growth hormone treatment on responses to epinephrine and thyrotropin-releasing hormone in lactating cows. *J. Dairy Sci.* 69:44–51

98. McDowell, G. H., Gooden, J. M., Leenanuruksa, D., Jois, M., English, A. W. 1987. Effects of exogenous growth hormone on milk production and nutrient uptake by muscle and mammary tissues of dairy cows in mid-lactation. *Aust. J. Biol. Sci.* 40:295–306

99. McDowell, G. H., Hart, I. C., Kirby, A. C. 1987. Local intra-arterial infusion of growth hormone into the mammary glands of sheep and goats: effects on milk yield and composition, plasma hormones and metabolites. *Aust. J. Biol. Sci.* 40:181–89

100. McGrath, M. F., Collier, R. J., Clemmons, D. R., Busby, W. H., Sweeny, C. A., et al. 1991. The direct in vitro effect of insulin-like growth factors (IGFs) on normal bovine mammary cell proliferation and production of IGF binding proteins. *Endocrinology* 129:671–78

101. McGuffey, R. K., Basson, R. P., Snyder, D. L., Block, E., Harrison, J. H., et al. 1991. Effect of somidobove sustained release administration on the lactation performance of dairy cows. *J. Dairy Sci.* 74:1263–76

102. McGuffey, R. K., Wilkinson, J. I. D.

1991. Nutritional implications of bovine somatotropin for the lactating dairy cow. *J. Dairy Sci.* 74(Suppl. 2):63–71

103. McGuire, M. A., Bauman, D. E. 1992. Nutritional regulation of the somatotropin/somatomedin axis during lactation. *Int. Congr. on Nutrient Regulation during Pregnancy, Lactation and Infant Growth, Stockholm*, p. 31 (Abstr.)

104. McGuire, M. A., Bauman, D. E., Miller, M. A., Hartnell, G. F. 1992. Response of somatomedins (IGF-I and IGF-II) in lactating cows to variations in dietary energy and protein and treatment with recombinant n-methionyl bovine somatotropin. *J. Nutr.* 122:128–36

105. McGuire, M. A., Cohick, W. S., Clemmons, D. R., Bauman, D. E. 1991. Effects of protein and energy restriction on concentrations of IGFs and IGF binding protein-2 (IGFBP-2) in lactating cows treated with somatotropin (bST). *2nd Int. IGF Symp., San Francisco*, p. 148 (Abstr.)

106. McGuire, M. A., Vicini, J. L., Bauman, D. E., Veenhuizen, J. J. 1992. Insulin-like growth factors and binding proteins in ruminants and their nutritional regulation. *J. Anim. Sci.* 70:2901–10

107. Mepham, T. B., Lawrence, S. E., Peters, A. R., Hart, I. C. 1984. Effects of exogenous growth hormone on mammary function in lactating goats. *Horm. Metab. Res.* 16:248–53

108. Molenaar, A. J., Davis, S. R., Wilkins, R. J. 1992. Expression of α-lactalbumin, α-S1-casein, and lactoferrin genes is heterogeneous in sheep and cattle mammary tissue. *J. Histochem. Cytochem.* 40:611–18

109. Monsallier, G. 1991. Somatotropine bovine: impact sur la sante des mamelles. See Ref. 51a, pp. 60–67

110. Moore, D. A., Hutchinson, L. J. 1992. BST and animal health. See Ref. 63a, pp. 99–141

111. Muller, L. D. 1992. BST and dairy cow performance. See Ref. 63a, pp. 53–71

112. Niumsup, P., McDowell, G. H., Leenanuruksa, D., Gooden, J. M. 1985. Plasma triglyceride metabolism in lactating ewes and growing calves treated with growth hormone. *Proc. Nutr. Soc. Aust.* 10:154 (Abstr.)

113. Patton, R. A., Heald, C. W. 1992. Management of BST-supplemented cows. See Ref. 63a, pp. 73–98

114. Peel, C. J., Bauman, D. E. 1987. Somatotropin and lactation. *J. Dairy Sci.* 70:474–86

115. Peel, C. J., Fronk, T. J., Bauman, D. E., Gorewit, R. C. 1982. Lactational response to exogenous growth hormone and abomasal infusion of a glucose-sodium caseinate mixture in high-yielding dairy cows. *J. Nutr.* 112:1770–78

116. Peri, I., Shamay, A., McGrath, M. F., Collier, R. J., Gertler, A. 1992. Comparative mitogenic and galactopoietic effects of IGF-I, IGF-II and DES-3-IGF-I in bovine mammary gland in vitro. *Cell Biol. Int. Rep.* 16:359–68

117. Peters, J. P. 1986. Consequences of accelerated gain and growth hormone administration for lipid metabolism in growing beef steers. *J. Nutr.* 116:2490–2503

118. Phipps, R. H. 1989. A review of the influence of somatotropin on health, reproduction and welfare in lactating dairy cows. See Ref. 129a, pp. 88–119

119. Pocius, P. A., Herbein, J. H. 1986. Effects of in vivo administration of growth hormone on milk production and in vitro hepatic metabolism in dairy cattle. *J. Dairy Sci.* 69:713–20

120. Politis, I., Block, E., Turner, J. D. 1990. Effect of somatotropin on the plasminogen and plasmin system in the mammary gland: proposed mechanism of action for somatotropin on the mammary gland. *J. Dairy Sci.* 73:1494–99

121. Prosser, C. G., Fleet, I. R., Corps, A. N., Froesch, E. R., Heap, R. B. 1990. Increase in milk secretion and mammary blood flow by intra-arterial infusion of insulin-like growth factor-I into the mammary gland of the goat. *J. Endocrinol.* 126:437–43

122. Prosser, C. G., Sankaran, L., Hennighausen, L., Topper, Y. J. 1987. Comparison of the roles of insulin and insulin-like growth factor I in casein gene expression and in the development of α-lactalbumin and glucose transport activities in the mouse mammary epithelial cell. *Endocrinology* 120:1411–16

123. Rechler, M. M., Nissley, S. P. 1988. Insulin-like growth factors. In *Handbook of Experimental Pharmacology, Peptide Growth Factors and their Receptors,* ed. M. B. Sporn, A. B. Roberts, pp. 1–153. Heidelberg: Springer Verlag

124. Ronge, H., Blum, J. W. 1989. Insulinlike growthfactor I responses to growth hormone in dry and lactating dairy cows. *J. Anim. Physiol. Anim. Nutr.* 62:280–88

125. Roupas, P., Chou, S. Y., Towns, R. J., Kostyo, J. L. 1991. Growth hormone inhibits activation of phosphatidylinositol phospholipase C in adipose plasma membranes: evidence for a growth hormone-induced change in G protein function. *Proc. Natl. Acad. Sci. USA* 88:1691–95

126. Roupas, P., Herington, A. C. 1989. Cellular mechanisms in the processing of growth hormone and its receptors. *Mol. Cell. Endocrinol.* 61:1–12

127. Sechen, S. J., Bauman, D. E., Tyrrell, H. F., Reynolds, P. J. 1989. Effect of somatotropin on kinetics of nonesterified fatty acids and partition of energy, carbon, and nitrogen in lactating dairy cows. *J. Dairy Sci.* 72:59–67

128. Sechen, S. J., Dunshea, F. R., Bauman, D. E. 1990. Somatotropin in lactating cows: effect on response to epinephrine and insulin. *Am. J. Physiol.* 258:E582–88

129. Sechen, S. J., McCutcheon, S. N., Bauman, D. E. 1989. Response to metabolic challenges in early lactation dairy cows during treatment with bovine somatotropin. *Domest. Anim. Endocrinol.* 6:141–54

129a. Sejrsen, K., Vestergaard, M., Neimann-Sorensen, A., eds. 1989. *Use of Somatotropin in Livestock Production.* New York: Elsevier Appl. Sci.

130. Shamay, A., Cohen, N., Niwa, M., Gertler, A. 1988. Effect of insulin-like growth factor I on deoxyribonucleic acid synthesis and galactopoiesis in bovine undifferentiated and lactating mammary tissue in vitro. *Endocrinology* 123:804–9

131. Snoswell, A. M., Finley, E., Vernon, R. G. 1990. Novel effects of growth hormone on polyamine biosynthesis in sheep adipose tissue. *Horm. Metab. Res.* 22:650–51

132. Stred, S. S., Stubbart, J. R., Argetsinger, L. S., Smith, W. C., Shafer, J. A., et al. 1992. Stimulation by growth hormone (GH) of GH receptor-associated tyrosine kinase activity. *Endocrinology* 130:1626–36

133. Stricker, P., Grueter, F. 1928. Action du lobe antérieur de l'hypophyse sur la montée laiteuse. *Comptes Rendus* 99:1978–80

134. Tyrrell, H. F., Brown, A. C. G., Reynolds, P. J., Haaland, G. L., Bauman, D. E., et al. 1988. Effect of bovine somatotropin on metabolism of lactating dairy cows: energy and nitrogen utilization as determined by respiration calorimetry. *J. Nutr.* 118:1024–30

135. van den Berg, G. 1991. A review of quality and processing suitability of

milk from cows treated with bovine somatotropin. *J. Dairy Sci.* 74(Suppl. 2):2–11

136. Vernon, R. G. 1980. Lipid metabolism in the adipose tissue of ruminant animals. *Prog. Lipid Res.* 19:23–106

137. Vernon, R. G., Barber, M. C., Finley, E. 1991. Modulation of the activity of acetyl-CoAcarboxylase and other lipogenic enzymes by growth hormone, insulin and dexamethasone in sheep adipose tissue and relationship to adaptations to lactation. *Biochem. J.* 274: 543–48

138. Vernon, R. G., Finley, E. 1988. Roles of insulin and growth hormone in the adaptations of fatty acid synthesis in white adipose tissue during the lactation cycle in sheep. *Biochem. J.* 256:873–78

139. Vernon, R. G., Finley, E., Flint, D. J. 1987. Role of growth hormone in the adaptations of lipolysis in rat adipocytes during recovery from lactation. *Biochem. J.* 242:931–34

140. Vernon, R. G., Finley, E., Watt, P. W. 1991. Adenosine and the control of adrenergic regulation of adipose tissue lipolysis during lactation. *J. Dairy Sci.* 74:695–705

141. Vernon, R. G., Flint, D. J. 1989. Role of growth hormone in the regulation of adipocyte growth and function. In *Biotechnology in Growth Regulation,* ed. R. B. Heap, C. G. Prosser, G. E. Lamming, pp. 57–71. London: Butterworth

142. Vernon, R. G., Piperova, L., Watt, P. W., Finley, E., Lindsay-Watt, S. 1993. Mechanisms involved in the adaptations of the adipocyte adrenergic signal-transduction system and their modulation by growth hormone during the lactation cycle in the rat. *Biochem. J.* 289:845–51

143. Vicini, J. L., Buonomo, F. C., Veenhuizen, J. J., Miller, M. A., Clemmons, D. R., et al. 1991. Nutrient balance and stage of lactation affect responses of insulin, insulin-like growth factors I and II, and insulin-like growth factor-binding protein 2 to somatotropin administration in dairy cows. *J. Nutr.* 121:1656–64

144. Vicini, J. L., Hudson, S., Cole, W. J., Miller, M. A., Eppard, P. J., et al. 1990. Effect of acute challenge with an extreme dose of somatotropin in a prolonged-release formulation on

145. Volpe, J. J., Vagelos, P. R. 1976. Mechanisms and regulation of biosynthesis of saturated fatty acids. *Physiol. Rev.* 56:339–417

146. Wallis, M. 1975. The molecular evolution of pituitary hormones. *Biol. Rev.* 50:35–98

147. Walton, P. E., Etherton, T. D., Chung, C. S. 1987. Exogenous pituitary and recombinant growth hormones induce insulin and insulin-like growth factor 1 resistance in pig adipose tissue. *Domest. Anim. Endocrinol.* 4:183–89

148. Wastie, S., Buttery, P. J., Vernon, R. G. 1991. Regulation of insulin binding to sheep adipocyte membranes. *Proc. Nutr. Soc.* 50:210A (Abstr.)

149. Waters, M. J., Barnard, R. T., Lobie, P. E., Lim, L., Hamlin, G., et al. 1990. Growth hormone receptors—their structure, location and role. *Acta Paediatr. Scand. (Suppl.)* 366:60–72

150. Watt, P. W., Finley, E., Cork, S., Clegg, R. A., Vernon, R. G. 1991. Chronic control of the β- and α_2 -adrenergic systems of sheep adipose tissue by growth hormone and insulin. *Biochem. J.* 273:39–42

151. Wilkinson, J. I. D., Tarrant, M. E. 1991. Fertility of cows receiving somidobove in European studies. *J. Dairy Sci.* 74(Suppl. 1):192 (Abstr.)

152. Winder, S. J., Turvey, A., Forsyth, I. A. 1989. Stimulation of DNA synthesis in cultures of ovine mammary epithelial cells by insulin and insulin-like growth factors. *J. Endocrinol.* 123: 319–26

153. Wood, D. C., Salsgiver, W. J., Kasser, T. R., Lange, G. W., Rowold, E., et al. 1989. Purification and characterization of pituitary bovine somatotropin. *J. Biol. Chem.* 264:14741–47

154. Wray-Cahen, D., Bell, A. W., Dunshea, F. R., Harrell, R. J., Bauman, D. E., et al. 1990. Effect of somatotropin on glucose response to varying insulin doses in growing pigs. *J. Anim. Sci.* 68(Suppl. 1):278 (Abstr.)

155. Yang, S. -D., Novakofski, J. 1990. Regulation of rat white adipose tissue insulin-like growth factor-1 gene expression by growth hormone and nutrition. *FASEB J.* 4:A916 (Abstr.)

156. Young, F. G. 1947. Experimental stimulation (galactopoiesis) of lactation. *Br. Med. Bull.* 5:155–60

Annu. Rev. Nutr. 1993. 13:463–496

MAMMALIAN GLUCOKINASE

Richard L. Printz, Mark A. Magnuson, and Daryl K. Granner

Department of Molecular Physiology and Biophysics, Vanderbilt University School of Medicine, Nashville, Tennessee 37232-0615

KEY WORDS: hexokinase, liver, β cells, diabetes mellitus

CONTENTS

INTRODUCTION 463
   Discovery of Glucokinase 464
   The Glucokinase Reaction 466
   Regulation of Glucokinase Activity 468
GLUCOKINASE GENE, mRNA, AND PROTEIN 471
   Hepatic Glucokinase mRNA and Protein 471
   Rat Glucokinase Gene 472
   β-Cell Glucokinase mRNA and Protein 472
   Alternate Promoters in the Glucokinase Gene 473
   Multiple Glucokinase mRNAs 474
   Human Glucokinase 475
   Evolution of Glucokinase 476
FUNCTIONAL SIGNIFICANCE OF GLUCOKINASE 478
   Role of Glucokinase in the Hepatocyte 478
   Role of Glucokinase in the Pancreatic β Cell 481
CELL-SPECIFIC REGULATION OF GLUCOKINASE 482
   Regulation of Glucokinase in the Hepatocyte 483
   Regulation of Glucokinase in the Pancreatic β Cell 486
   Regulatory Elements in the Glucokinase Gene Promoter 487
ROLE OF THE GLUCOKINASE GENE IN DIABETES MELLITUS 488
CONCLUSIONS 490

INTRODUCTION

Glucose transport and phosphorylation are the initial events in glucose utilization by all tissues and cell types. The necessary first step in glucose utilization, the movement of the molecule across the plasma membrane, is accomplished by a family of glucose transporters, designated GLUT 1–5, that operate by facilitated diffusion to move glucose down a high to low concentration gradient (10, 78, 85). Glucose uptake occurs when the

0199-9885/93/0715-0463$02.00

concentration of extracellular glucose exceeds the intracellular concentration, thus favoring glucose entry. This is generally the case, a notable exception being hepatocytes that export glucose when they are actively engaged in glycogenolysis or gluconeogenesis, or intestinal and renal cells that are involved in the trans-epithelial movement of glucose. This downhill concentration gradient is maintained by the conversion of glucose to its phosphate ester, glucose-6-phosphate (G-6-P), which cannot exit the cell.

In mammalian cells the phosphorylation of glucose to G-6-P is catalyzed by a family of closely related enzymes, the hexokinases. Four mammalian hexokinases have been characterized (38, 55). These are designated hexokinase (HK) I, II, III, and IV, according to their relative mobility following starch gel electrophoresis, or, less commonly, A, B, C, and D, respectively, according to their order of elution from DEAE-cellulose (119). HK I–III have several properties in common, including a molecular weight of ~100 kd, the ability to phosphorylate several hexoses, and a relatively high affinity for glucose. In addition they are inhibited by physiologic concentrations of G-6-P, the product of the reaction when glucose is the substrate. Although generally similar, each of these hexokinases has a unique set of kinetic properties and a different pattern of tissue distribution (38, 55, 119). One family member, HK IV, more commonly known as glucokinase (GK), is structurally and functionally different from the others, and is the subject of this review. Some features that distinguish GK from HK I–III include a mass approximately half that of the other family members, a lower affinity for glucose, a much lower affinity for other hexoses, and the lack of significant feedback inhibition by physiologic levels of G-6-P [see Table 1 for comparison; and see (128)]. The significance of these differences in the function of GK in the hepatocyte and the β cell of pancreatic islets is a subject of this review, as are recent observations concerning the structure and regulation of the GK mRNAs in these cells. The structure of the GK gene, and the apparent role of this gene in some forms of noninsulin-dependent diabetes, are discussed. We have attempted to build upon the excellent review by Weinhouse (128) by emphasizing observations made in the past few years, and we apologize in advance for omissions of data and references that were caused by space limitations.

Discovery of Glucokinase

Glucose phosphorylating activity in mammalian cells was originally referred to as "hexokinase," but it soon became apparent that there were tissue differences not readily understandable on the basis of a single enzyme. For example, a complex situation was noted in liver. A hexokinase that had the typical low K_m for glucose, and that accepted several hexoses as substrates,

Table 1 A comparison of glucokinase with other hexokinases[a]

	GK	HK I-III
K_m glucose	5–12 mM[b]	0.02–0.13 mM
K_m ATP	~0.5 mM	0.2–0.5 mM
K_i G-6-P	60 mM	0.2–0.9 mM
Molecular weight	52 kd	~100 kd
Substrate preference		
Glucose	1[c]	1[c]
Mannose	0.8	1–1.2
2-Deoxyglucose	0.4	1–1.4
Fructose	0.2	1.1–1.3

[a] Several features of rat glucokinase are compared to rat hexokinases I-III (119, 128). Properties of the human isoforms are
similar to those of the rat counterparts.
[b] This is an approximate K_m of the purified enzyme. The exact
K_m cannot be determined because of the positive cooperativity
described in the text. The enzyme in homogenates of liver cells
has a higher K_m owing to the presence of the regulatory system
described in the text.
[c] The activity of glucose as a substrate is taken as 1. The other
numbers are expressed in relation to the activity of glucose as a
substrate.

was discovered first (103). A second hexokinase, which had a high K_m for
glucose oxidation to CO_2, was later identified in liver slices (13). This activity
was dependent upon insulin, since it was reduced in diabetic animals, and
was restored to normal with insulin treatment (105). Subsequent experiments
in liver homogenates confirmed the presence of a new hexokinase that had a
high K_m for glucose (10 mM) (100). This activity was named glucokinase
because it had a greater selectivity for glucose, and it was given a unique
number by the Enzyme Commission (EC 2.7.1.2). It is now generally accepted
that GK is a member of a family of enzymes that catalyze the same general
reaction; thus HK I–IV are collectively given the same designation (ATP:
D-hexose 6-phosphotransferase, EC 2.7.1.1), as discussed by Cornish-
Bowden (21). The names hexokinase IV and glucokinase can both be justified,
but for the purposes of this review we prefer to use glucokinase, the more
common designation.

An important feature of GK is its cell-specific distribution and regulation
(49, 65, 72, 92, 127). The enzyme is primarily found in hepatic parenchymal
cells and in the β cells of the pancreatic islets. The previously mentioned
kinetic and regulatory features that distinguish GK from HK I–III, and the
presence of the enzyme in the liver and the β cells of the pancreatic islets,

have physiologic importance. These tissues are fed by the portal vein, in which postprandial glucose concentrations reach high levels; therefore, GK is in position to play a key role in glucose homeostasis.

As mentioned above, at least five glucose transporters are involved in the movement of glucose across the plasma membrane of cells. A high K_m transporter (GLUT 2) is found in hepatocytes and β cells, which predominantly express GK, the high K_m hexokinase. The general association of a particular hexokinase with a specific glucose transporter has also been observed in the case of the lower K_m hexokinases. For instance, the lowest K_m transporter is generally associated with the lowest K_m hexokinase (GLUT 1 with HK I), and the intermediate K_m transporter with the corresponding intermediate K_m hexokinase (GLUT 4 with HK II). The reason(s) for these associations has not been completely established, but the combination of GLUT 4 and HK II appears to have a physiologic explanation. Both of these proteins are found in tissues in which insulin increases glucose uptake and utilization (10, 38, 55, 78, 85), and their coordinate regulation by insulin is probably of central importance to these processes. Similarly, the combination of GLUT 2 and GK (HK IV) is also involved in glucose homeostasis, as described below. GK is regulated by insulin in liver and by glucose in β cells (9), and GLUT 2, although not regulated by insulin, is at least indirectly involved in the secretion of insulin (74, 118).

The Glucokinase Reaction

Glucokinase catalyzes the reaction: Glucose + Mg•ATP → G-6-P + ADP. Attempts to purify GK began shortly after the discovery of the enzyme, but were complicated by the fact that the enzyme is not present in high concentration in either liver or β cells (and the latter are themselves not abundant), and it is more sensitive to denaturation and proteolysis than are the other hexokinases (86). Extensive purification with a yield suitable for peptide isolation and amino acid sequencing was accomplished only very recently (3). GK comprises about 0.005% of total protein in liver, so a 21,000-fold purification was required to obtain homogeneous enzyme (3). If GK is 20 times less abundant in β cells (49), a 400,000-fold purification would be required to obtain homogeneous enzyme from this source; needless to say, this has not been accomplished. The purified hepatic enzyme has a specific activity of ~180 U/mg [1 unit (U) of GK activity catalyzes the production of 1 μmol of G-6-P in 1 min at 32C], and it preferentially catalyzes hexose phosphorylation in the order: glucose>mannose>2-deoxyglucose> fructose [Table 1; (3, 119, 128)]. GK-activity is strongly inhibited by glucosamine and its derivatives, by mannoheptulose, and by alloxan (58, 128).

Glucokinase shows cooperative dependence (sigmoidal kinetics) with respect to the glucose concentration. This cooperativity increases with the Mg•ATP concentration, but the interaction of the latter with GK is itself not cooperative (108). A Hill coefficient of ~1.5 supports the observation that glucose binds to GK with positive cooperativity (108, 109). Cooperative interactions between subunits of an enzyme are frequently observed, but this kinetic behavior is unusual in monomeric enzymes such as GK (93). In the latter cases, this behavior is best explained on the basis of a "mnemonical" model in which the enzyme exhibits a "memory" phenomenon (109). According to this model, the enzyme exists in two conformations that are not in equilibrium with each other under steady-state conditions. Substrate (glucose) binds with differential affinity to the two enzyme forms, and an essential feature of the "mnemonical" model is that the enzyme relaxes relatively slowly after release or transformation of substrate. Enzymes like GK "remember" the high affinity conformation caused by their interaction with substrate, and in this state binding of the next substrate molecule proceeds more rapidly. The non-Michaelian or cooperative regulatory behavior is basically a consequence of the different affinity of two conformations of enzyme for substrate, e.g. glucokinase for glucose (89).

There is little GK activity below 2.5 mM glucose, and positive cooperativity is most apparent at glucose concentrations around 5 mM (108). Since transport is not thought to be rate-limiting, small elevations of the blood glucose above the normal fasting level of 5 mM result in rather large increases in GK activity and enhanced glucose phosphorylation. Glucose in the concentration range of 5–10 mM therefore has a greater effect on the activity of the enzyme than would occur in a system that operates on the basis of pure Michaelis-Menton kinetics. These observations regarding positive cooperativity apply to both the hepatic and β-cell enzyme (72).

The conformational changes predicted by the "mnemonical" model are supported by the X-ray crystal structures obtained for yeast hexokinase. This enzyme, like GK, is a 50-kd protein that is not subject to feedback inhibition by G-6-P (106). The structural similarities between yeast HK and GK make it likely that similar reaction mechanisms are employed by the two enzymes. Hexokinases contain two lobes separated by a deep cleft, and all undergo significant changes upon the binding of substrate into this cleft (1). Yeast hexokinase, with glucose bound, has a very different conformation from the enzyme without bound substrate (1, 12). Glucose binds to hexokinase in a deep cleft that closes to envelop the substrate and to orient catalytic groups and/or to exclude solvent. Glucose analogs with substitutions on the 2-carbon position are competitive inhibitors of glucose binding, but do not serve as substrates. These analogs prevent the lobes of the enzyme from approximating one another, so it is inferred that a glucose-induced conformational change is essential for catalysis.

In the case of yeast hexokinase, the carboxylate group of an aspartic acid residue (Asp^{211}) forms a hydrogen bond with the phosphoryl acceptor (the hydroxyl group on the 6-carbon position) and probably functions as a general base catalyst (1). Removal of solvent from this region of the enzyme is thought to enhance nucleophilicity and favor catalysis (1). The amino acids Ser^{158}, Asn^{210}, Asp^{211}, Glu^{269}, and Glu^{302} in yeast hexokinase are presumed to form hydrogen-bonds with the hydroxyl groups of glucose (75). These amino acids are conserved in GK as Ser^{151}, Asn^{204}, Asp^{205}, Glu^{256}, and Glu^{290}, respectively, so the binding of glucose to GK is probably by a mechanism similar to that employed by yeast HK (3). Asp^{205} in GK is certainly important for activity, as mutation of this residue to alanine results in an enzyme that has one five-hundreth the activity of the wild-type GK (57).

The residues involved in ATP binding have not been defined as precisely as those involved in glucose binding. A putative ATP-binding domain in mammalian hexokinase was identified based on the conservation of amino acid sequences between known hexokinases and the ATP-binding region found in protein kinases (3). A lysine located 11–14 residues from the putative core binding sequence, corresponding to Lys^{111} in yeast HK, appears to be involved. A role of Lys^{111} in ATP-binding in yeast HK was suggested by the observation that this residue covalently binds the ATP affinity label pyridoxyl 5'-diphospho-5'-adenosine (111). A 50 amino acid peptide from yeast HK, containing the predicted ATP-binding domain and some flanking sequence (Glu^{78} to Leu^{127}), also binds 2', (3')-0-(2,4,6-trinitrophenyl) adenosine-5'-triphosphate, an ATP analog that is a weak substrate for hexokinase. This provides further evidence that this domain is part of the catalytic site (6). Lys^{111} in yeast HK corresponds to Lys^{558} in mammalian HK I. Mutation of Lys^{558} to arginine results in a 30% decrease of the V_{max} of HK I, and mutation to methionine results in a 71% reduction (5). These mutations have no effect on the K_m for ATP (or glucose); thus Lys^{558} cannot be assigned a direct role in ATP-binding (5). No direct testing of the predicted ATP-binding site of GK, or the role of the invariant lysine, Lys^{102}, has been reported to date. More definitive information about the specific sites required for catalysis will be forthcoming as GK molecules with specific mutations are analyzed, and when the crystal structure of the protein is determined.

Regulation of Glucokinase Activity

Physiologic concentrations of G-6-P, the product of the glucokinase reaction, do not inhibit the enzyme, but more distal products of glucose and lipid metabolism can affect activity. G-6-P, in addition to being a substrate for glycogen synthesis, is also a substrate for fatty acid synthesis through the glycolytic and pentose phosphate pathways. Elevated levels of long-chain acyl-CoAs, such as palmitoyl CoA, reversibly inhibit GK from several species, and would therefore indirectly retard fatty acid synthesis by feedback inhibition of GK (116, 117). There is no indication that the micromolar concentrations of free, long-chain acyl-CoAs required for this inhibition of GK are ever achieved in cells; hence the physiologic relevance of this effect is questionable.

The short-term regulation of HK I–III activity is accomplished by G-6-P, and thus by the pathways that use this compound as a substrate. Glucose, through the "mnemonic" mechanism described above, provides short-term regulation of GK. Recent experiments reveal an additional complex and important mechanism for regulating GK activity (124). The original observation was that fructose increased the rate of glucose phosphorylation in isolated hepatocytes (18). The effect of fructose, which occurred at low, physiologic concentrations ($\sim$50 μM), was to decrease the K_m for glucose from the 15–20 mM range, typically seen in crude cell homogentates, to the 5–10 mM range seen when pure enzyme is assayed (18, 123). The effect of fructose was exerted within a few minutes and was lost if this hexose was removed from the incubation medium. The observation that this stimulatory effect was mimicked by sorbitol and D-glyceraldehyde, but not by glycerol or dihydroxy-acetone, led Van Schaftingen and Vandercammen to postulate that fructose-1-phosphate (F-1-P) was the mediator of this positive effect on GK (25, 123).

F-1-P did stimulate glucose phosphorylation in crude extracts of liver cells, but it was ineffective when tested against GK that had been partially purified by passage over an anion-exchange chromatography column. It should be noted, in this context, that GK elutes from such columns at a relatively high salt concentration. Aliquots of column fractions that eluted at a lower salt concentration directly inhibited purified GK and restored the ability of F-1-P to stimulate glucose phosphorylation. This observation led to the isolation of a regulatory protein which, upon further purification, also became ineffective. This was due to the removal of phosphoglucoisomerase, the enzyme that catalyzes the interconversion of G-6-P and fructose-6-phosphate (F-6-P). The requirement of the regulatory protein for F-6-P was formulated on the basis of this experiment, since G-6-P has no effect on GK (122).

This regulatory system therefore consists of F-1-P, F-6-P, and a protein of $\sim$62 kd (Figure 1). F-6-P is half-maximally effective at a concentration of $\sim$10 μM, and it interacts competitively with F-1-P. In the presence of F-6-P the regulatory protein (which has no enzymatic activity itself) forms a reversible, heterodimeric complex with GK [Figure 1; (120)]. This interaction results in competitive inhibition of GK with respect to glucose. Complex formation, and the inhibition of GK activity, is competitively prevented by F-1-P (Figure 1). The regulatory protein and palmitoyl CoA, another competitive inhibitor of glucose binding to GK, apparently bind to the same site. These compounds do not have additive effects, but both are synergistic

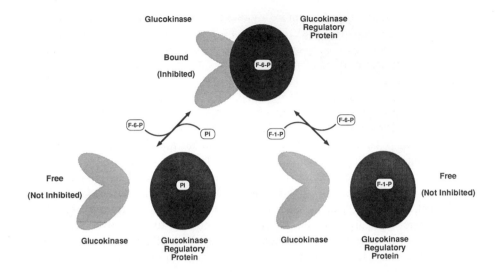

Figure 1 Proposed model for the regulation of glucokinase activity. The affinity of GK for glucose is changed by its interaction with the regulatory protein. The regulatory protein binds to GK allosterically and inhibits GK by decreasing the apparent affinity of the enzyme for glucose. The regulatory protein with fructose-6-phosphate (F-6-P) bound is in a conformation capable of interacting with, and inhibiting, GK. Fructose-1-phosphate (F-1-P) or inorganic phosphate (P$_i$) competes with F-6-P for binding to the regulatory protein. Regulatory protein with F-1-P or P$_i$ bound is in a conformation that is not capable of interacting with GK, thus GK is not inhibited.

with competitive inhibitors, such as *N*-acetyl-glucosamine, that bind to the catalytic site. It is therefore presumed that the regulatory protein binds to an allosteric site and that this interaction alters the affinity of the catalytic site for glucose.

Sorbitol-6-P, a F-6-P analog, inhibits GK by binding to the regulatory protein (27). This interaction is probably not of physiologic relevance, but it emphasizes the important role of F-6-P. Several compounds normally found in hepatocytes serve as activators, but of these only inorganic phosphate (P$_i$) is effective at concentrations achieved in the hepatocyte (27, 121). P$_i$, like F-1-P, is thought to prevent the interaction of the regulatory protein with GK (Figure 1).

The discovery of the regulatory protein provides an explanation for the previously enigmatic observations that (*a*) the apparent K_m of GK for glucose is higher in intact hepatocytes than it is with the pure enzyme, and (*b*) dietary fructose increases glucose utilization. The latter observation merits additional observation. Since there is no fructose in the portal vein during the post-absorptive state, there is no fructose in the hepatocyte, and no F-1-P. F-6-P levels in the hepatocyte are, however, in the 10–50 μM range, which is sufficient to bind to the regulatory protein. Under these circumstances the regulatory protein will bind to GK and raise the K_m for glucose of the enzyme. The ingestion of fructose, a constituent of most foods of vegetal origin, results in increased F-1-P levels in the hepatocyte, a decreased ability of the regulatory protein to bind to GK, and a decreased K_m (higher affinity) for glucose. In a direct test, fructose administration did increase glucokinase flux; thus this hexose could be a dietary signal for increased hepatic glucose uptake (123).

In summary, a regulatory protein binds F-6-P and this complex binds to, and inhibits, GK (see Figure 1). Although the regulatory protein is present in amounts sufficient to inhibit all GK activity in an hepatic cell, this inhibition is incomplete ($\sim 70\%$), presumably because P_i interferes with the interaction. F-1-P also interferes with the binding of F-6-P to the regulatory protein, and thus with the interaction of the latter with GK. F-1-P therefore causes a reduction of the K_m for glucose of GK in an intact cell or cell homogenate. The regulatory protein inhibits GK from many species, but has no effect on mammalian HK I–III, on yeast HK, or on bacterial GK (121). The regulatory protein is also found in the β cell, but the role of this protein in the regulation of GK in this cell type has not been established (68).

GLUCOKINASE GENE, mRNA, AND PROTEIN

In the past five years the techniques of molecular biology have been applied, with remarkable success, to the study of GK. The isolation of a cDNA for hepatic GK directly led to the isolation of the GK gene and of the islet cell GK cDNA. The initial studies were accomplished using rat tissues, but the human cDNAs and gene were quickly obtained. These observations played a key role in the discovery that mutations in the GK gene are associated with a form of noninsulin dependent diabetes mellitus (discussed below).

Hepatic Glucokinase mRNA and Protein

The independent cloning of hepatic GK cDNAs by two groups was the first step in the molecular genetic analysis of GK. A liver cDNA library was the obvious choice for the cloning of GK cDNA. The concentration of the enzyme in liver is greater than in β cells, the liver has a much larger mass, and the abundance of hepatic GK mRNA can be induced by dietary manipulation, hence there are more copies of GK cDNA in a library made from an hepatic source. Iynedjian et al utilized a GK antibody to screen an hepatic cDNA expression library. The cDNA isolated was used to show the expected regulation of hepatic GK mRNA by a variety of nutritional and hormonal stimuli. Based on these observations, and hybrid-selected translation of the mRNA, Iynedjian et al inferred that this was an authentic GK cDNA (51).

Andreone et al used a different approach (3). They purified hepatic GK to homogeneity, obtained amino acid sequence information for about half the protein, and then used this sequence to design oligonucleotide probes that were employed to isolate several hepatic GK cDNAs (3). Andreone et al deduced the complete sequence of hepatic GK from the cDNA sequence information and found it to be a 465 amino acid polypeptide with a mass of 51,924 daltons and a pI of 4.85 (3). All of the peptides sequenced from the purified GK were found in the sequence deduced from the cDNA, thus providing direct evidence of the authenticity of this GK cDNA. Putative glucose and ATP-binding domains (see above) were identified in the protein based on their similarity to domains found in yeast HK and mammalian HK I (3). The enzyme is very similar to the other known HK family members. The amino acid sequence of GK is 33% identical to yeast HK, 53% identical to the carboxy-terminal portion of the rat HK I, and 55% identical to the carboxy-terminal portion of rat HK II.

Rat Glucokinase Gene

The availability of the hepatic GK cDNA directly led to the isolation of the GK gene. A Southern blot analysis of rat genomic DNA was consistent with the presence of a single GK gene. Magnuson et al used the hepatic GK cDNA clone to isolate overlapping bacteriophage DNAs that contained all the exons encoding the hepatic GK mRNA (66). Ten exons (Figure 2A), spanning 15.5 kilobases (kb), were identified and the transcription initiation site was identified, as discussed below.

β-Cell Glucokinase mRNA and Protein

The availability of the hepatic GK cDNA also led to the isolation of GK cDNAs from libraries derived from cells of pancreatic β-cell origin. The analysis of these cDNAs led to some unexpected conclusions. Two groups found that the GK mRNAs in islet and insulinoma tissues are approximately 200 nucleotides (nt) longer than the liver mRNA (~2600 nt versus ~2400 nt) (50, 67). A comparison of the hepatic and insulinoma GK cDNAs revealed that the variation in the length is due to a difference at the 5' end of the mRNAs (67). The length of the open reading frame is the same in mRNAs produced in both tissues, but 11 of the first 15 amino acids encoded are different. The sequence of the remainder of the enzyme is identical (46, 66). These changes have a very small effect on the mass and pI of the enzyme, and the kinetic and physical characteristics of GK in the liver and pancreatic β cells are virtually indistinguishable (49, 72). This is probably why the existence of different isoforms was not suspected by biochemical and immunologic techniques.

A. Alternate Transcription Units

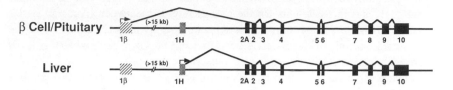

B. Alternate Splicing Variants

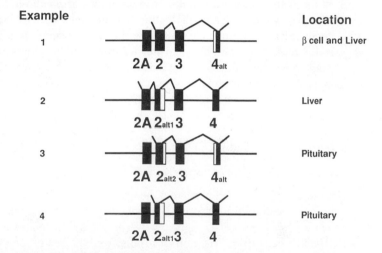

Figure 2 A schematic structure of the glucokinase gene showing alternate transcription units and splicing variants. Multiple glucokinase mRNAs are produced from a single gene through the use of alternate promoters and alternate RNA processing. Panel *A* shows how the different transcription units are formed in liver and β cell or pituitary cells. Panel *B* shows how four variant mRNAs are formed. These are described in detail in the text.

Alternate Promoters in the Glucokinase Gene

The hepatic and β-cell GK cDNA sequences diverge from each other at a point that coincides with the splice junction between the first and second exons in the hepatic transcription unit. This observation suggested that different first exons are used in the liver and β-cell transcription units (64, 66). An additional genomic DNA fragment was used to establish this point. An alternate first exon (1β), located upstream from the first exon utilized in liver (1H), encodes the sequence at the 5′ end of the β-cell GK mRNA (67). The cell-specific use of these alternate first exons explains why the N-terminal amino acid sequence of GK is different in liver and β cells. The hepatic GK transcription unit consists of 10 exons (1H and 2–10) that span a total of 15.5 kb (66). The β-cell transcription unit also has 10 exons (1β and 2–10), but 1β is longer than 1H, and this accounts for the size differences between liver and β-cell mRNA (Figure 2). At least 15 kb separate the 1β and 1H exons; thus the transcription unit of the β-cell gene is at least 30 kb in length. Exons 2–10 are identical in the liver and β-cell transcription units.

The presence of different first exons in the GK transcription units implies that different promoters are used in each cell (see Figure 2A). Transcription initiates from a downstream promoter in liver and from an upstream promoter in the pancreatic β cell. A comparison of the sequences immediately upstream from the transcription initiation sites in the liver and β cell did not reveal any similarities, which supports the notion that the gene is regulated differently in these cells. In the liver, transcription initiation occurs within a 4–5 base pair (bp) region located 127-bp upstream from the translation start codon; this appears to be under the control of a TATA box (66). Multiple start sites were mapped ~400-bp upstream from the translation initiation codon in rat insulinoma; these span a 60–65-bp region, and nothing resembling a TATA box is present in this region (67). This use of different promoters is in keeping with the different regulation required to provide the distinct physiologic functions of liver and β-cell GK (64).

Multiple Glucokinase mRNAs

GK mRNAs that are different from the major forms found in liver and β cells have been identified. These mRNAs are the products of specific, alternate splicing events. The first example of a variant GK mRNA was found in rat insulinoma cells (67). This mRNA results from the use of an alternate splice acceptor site in the fourth exon of the gene (example 1, Figure 2B). This alternate splicing event removes a 51-nucleotide fragment from the open reading frame, and this results in an in-frame loss of 17 amino acids. This mRNA variant comprises a very small fraction of the total GK mRNA in islets and liver (59), which may explain why the variant was not detected when 15 different rat islet cDNA clones were examined by another group (46). A more complex variant accounts for about 5% of hepatic GK mRNA (42). In this case use of a splice donor site in exon 2 results in the deletion of 52 nt from the reading frame (example 2, Figure 2B). In addition, an alternate exon (2A), located between exons 1H and 2 in the gene (see Figure 2A), is inserted and this adds 151 nt to the mRNA. The combined insertion and deletion events cause a double frameshift and a net addition of amino acids, giving a protein of 498 amino acids rather than the normal 465. Both of these GK variants have been expressed in prokaryotic cells, and neither is capable of phosphorylating glucose (59, 91).

Two different GK cDNA variants have been isolated from the pituitary gland. One variant (example 3 in Figure 2*B*) results from the use of two alternate splice sites (59). One of these alternate splice sites is in the fourth exon (the one that results in the minor variant shown as example 1). The second is an alternate splice donor site in the second exon that results in the deletion of 25 nt, a frame shift, and premature termination after amino acid 68 (59). A fourth variant, found in pituitary (example 4 in Figure 2*B*), is the same as example 2 except that the 2A cassette exon is not inserted (42, 46). An inactive, 58 amino acid peptide would result from the translation of this variant mRNA. Thus, although the pituitary has GK mRNA (46, 59), the use of alternate RNA splice sites results in mRNAs that, if translated, would encode short peptides that are enzymatically inactive.

In summary, a remarkable diversity of alternate splicing events occurs with this gene product. There are alternate first exons, alternate splice donor and acceptor sites, and a cassette exon is used. Some of these alternate splicing events occur in a cell-specific manner. The regulation of these alternate splicing events needs to be studied further, as this may be an important means of regulating the production of GK in specific cells.

Human Glucokinase

The elucidation of the structure of the rat liver and islet GK cDNAs, and of the rat gene (3, 66, 67), led to the identification and characterization of the human GK cDNAs and gene (56, 81, 107, 112, 113). The deduced amino acid sequences of the rat and human liver GK proteins are 97% identical (3, 112), and the genes have the same general exon/intron structure [Figure 3; and (66, 67, 107, 113)]. Two human liver GK mRNAs, produced by alternate

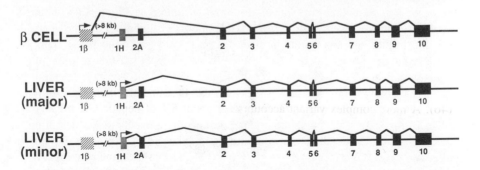

Figure 3   Human glucokinase gene and its transcription units. The overall structure of the human glucokinase gene is similar to that of rat (see Figure 2). Alternate promoters are utilized in the liver and pancreatic β cell. In addition, a cassette exon (2A) is utilized in a minor form of the mRNA found in human liver. The size and location of exon 2A differs from the corresponding exon found in the rat.

RNA processing, involve a 124-bp cassette exon 2A (see Figure 3). The insertion of exon 2A affects the amino-terminal residues of the enzyme and leads to a slightly larger protein of 467 residues. The enzyme produced without exon 2A is 465 residues long. Both are enzymatically active. The human GK gene is located on the short arm of chromosome 7, in band p13 (71, 81). Three microsatellite DNA polymorphisms (long stretches of di-, tri-, and tetra-nucleotide repeat sequences that can vary in length between individuals) are present within or near the gene (71, 81, 113). The identification of these polymorphisms was crucial to the studies that led to the linkage of the GK gene to certain types of noninsulin-dependent diabetes (see below).

Evolution of Glucokinase

The hypothesis that mammalian hexokinases evolved from a common precursor was advanced over twenty years ago (19, 28, 29, 119). According to this view, GK was thought to have evolved from a yeast-like precursor (see Figure 4; model 1). Yeast HK, like GK, has a molecular weight of ~50

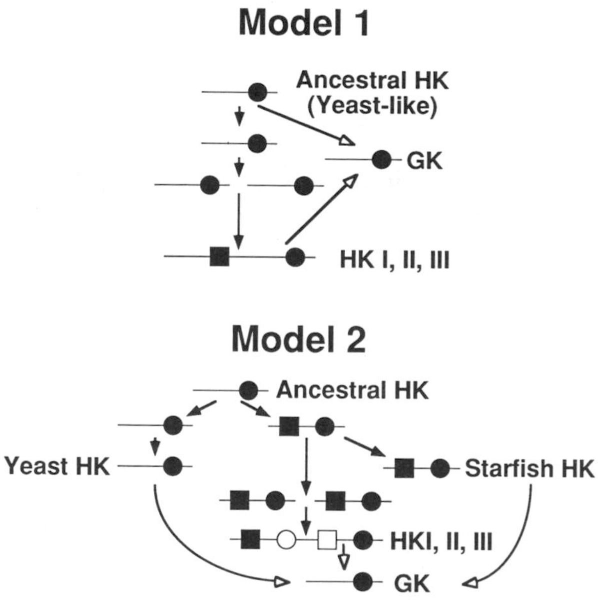

Figure 4   Two models of the evolution of the mammalian hexokinase gene family. In Model 1, a yeast-like HK is presumed to be the precursor, whereas in Model 2 a starfish-like precursor is hypothesized. The symbols are as follows: *solid circle* = the catalytic domain; *solid square* = the G-6-P binding regulatory domain; *open square* = a masked catalytic domain; *open circle* = a masked regulatory domain. The *open arrows* denote the possible routes of GK gene evolution.

kd and it is not inhibited by physiologic concentrations of G-6-P. The mammalian low K_m hexokinases (HK I–III) were thought to have arisen from a yeast-like precursor HK by gene duplication, with tandem ligation of the two products (19, 28, 29, 119). The catalytic site (*solid circle*) in one half of this fusion molecule was presumed to have evolved into a G-6-P binding, regulatory site (*solid square*). According to model 1, the C-terminal half of the HK molecule contains the catalytic site (glucose and ATP binding) and the N-terminal half contains the regulatory site (G-6-P binding). Indeed, the 100-kd HK I binds glucose and ATP, with high affinity, to single sites in the C-terminal half of the molecule, and G-6-P to a single site in the N-terminal half (129).

Representatives of all of the mammalian HKs have been cloned in the past three years. Deduced amino acid sequences obtained as a result of cDNA cloning show that these HKs are indeed closely related members of the same gene family (3, 97–99, 114). Amino acid and coding region nucleotide sequence identity between the family members is 50–70%, and the interspecies sequence identity of a specific family member is at least 85%, and is as high as 97%, as is the case with rat and human GK (see above) (3, 4, 80, 97, 98, 112). Thus there is an extraordinary degree of evolutionary conservation of these genes and proteins. A comparison of the amino acid sequences of the N- and C-terminal halves of HK I with each other, with GK, and with yeast HK, provides support for the gene duplication hypothesis (3, 80, 98).

The availability of cDNA clones led to more direct testing of the location of the functional domains in the 100-kd HKs, and the results obtained from these experiments challenge the hypothesis of HK evolution stated above. For example, the exclusive location of the regulatory site in the N-terminal half of HK I has become debatable (8, 63, 130), since the C-terminal half of HK I, expressed in *Escherichia coli,* has catalytic activity and shows inhibition by hexose 6-phosphates (63). The K_m for ATP, and the K_i for various hexose 6-phosphates of these half molecules, are similar to those of the purified, intact 100-kd enzyme. The amino acids presumed to be involved in the binding of glucose are conserved in both the N-terminal and C-terminal halves of HK I, but site-directed mutations of these residues result in the loss of catalytic activity only when those residing in the C-terminal half are mutated (5, 8). Also, the mutation of one of these residues in the N-terminal half fails to prevent G-6-P inhibition; thus the amino acids thought to be involved in the binding of glucose to the catalytic site in the C-terminal half, although conserved in the N-terminal half, are probably not involved in the binding of G-6-P (8). In view of these observations, it is difficult to imagine how HK I (and other family members) could have simply evolved from a yeast-like HK.

An alternate model has mammalian HKs evolving from a starfish-like HK, which is a 50-kd enzyme that is inhibited by G-6-P [(130); see model 2 in Figure 4]. Gene duplication and fusion, starting with a starfish-like precursor, would result in a 100-kd protein. According to this model, and in keeping with the glucose, ATP and G-6-P binding data cited above, one would predict a masking of the regulatory site in the C-terminal half (*open square*) and of the catalytic site in the N-terminal half (*open circle*), perhaps as a consequence of the folding of the 100-kd molecule (8, 130). If a starfish-like HK is the precursor of the mammalian HK family, yeast HK may have evolved along a separate path, perhaps from a more primitive precursor. GK still could have evolved from a yeast-like HK; this is unlikely, however, because the exon structures of the GK and HK II genes are very similar. In fact, a comparison of the exon sizes of the GK and HK II genes gives a remarkable clue as to how the latter may have evolved (90). With the exception of exons 1 and 3, the exon sizes in each half of HK II are identical in size to the corresponding exons in GK (90). GK therefore could have arisen from a starfish-like HK as a precursor to the 100-kd HKs, it could have evolved in parallel with the 100-kd HKs, or it could have evolved as a result of a gene splitting from the 100-kd forms, with a decrease in affinity of binding glucose, and a loss of the G-6-P regulatory site. It is apparent that major questions about the evolution of the mammalian hexokinases remain unanswered, but the reagents available should lead to rapid progress in this area.

FUNCTIONAL SIGNIFICANCE OF GLUCOKINASE

The cell-specific regulation of GK discussed later is related to the different functional roles that high K_m glucose phosphorylation catalyzed by GK plays in the molecular physiology of liver and pancreatic β cells. We discuss glucose utilization in the liver and β cell separately.

Role of Glucokinase in the Hepatocyte

The liver plays a central role in maintaining glucose homeostasis [for review, see (35, 43, 87)]. When the plasma glucose is elevated, as occurs after a meal, the liver takes up glucose, replenishes depleted glycogen stores, and then synthesizes fatty acids as another energy storage form. During a fast the liver produces and exports glucose from its glycogen stores, and from gluconeogenic precursors, and thereby provides a continuous energy supply to the brain and red blood cells. These adaptive mechanisms involve several regulatable substrate cycles (35, 87). GK is involved in one of these, the glucose/glucose-6-phosphate cycle. The enzymes that drive these cycles, including GK, are not distributed evenly throughout all hepatocytes, nor are the metabolic processes equally active in all hepatocytes. Instead, there is a "metabolic zonation" in the liver (53).

HEPATIC SUBSTRATE CYCLES   Hepatic glucose metabolism involves two major, reversible metabolic pathways. These interrelated pathways control the processes of glycolysis/gluconeogenesis and of glycogen synthesis/degradation. The rate-controlling steps in glycolysis/gluconeogenesis are organized in three cycles through which substrates move in opposing directions under the control of rate-limiting enzymes. These three cycles, named for the substrates involved, are the glucose/glucose-6-phosphate (G/G-6-P) cycle, the fructose-6-phosphate/fructose 1,6-bisphosphate (F-6-P/F-1,6-P$_2$) cycle, and the phosphoenolpyruvate/pyruvate (PEP/P) cycle [see (35, 87) for detailed reviews]. Within each cycle the product of one enzyme is the substrate of the counteracting enzyme. This would lead to futile cycling were it not for the fact that these cycles are subject to strict regulation by hormonal, neural, and allosteric mechanisms that shift flux in a coordinated manner (35, 87).

The F-6-P/F-1,6-P$_2$ and PEP/P cycles are most important in controlling the rates of glycolysis and gluconeognesis, as the substrates in these cycles are committed to one or the other of these pathways. The G/G-6-P cycle is involved in glucose entry or exit from the cell and is of additional interest because G-6-P is an uncommitted substrate that can enter the glycogen synthesis, glycolytic, or pentose phosphate shunt pathways. Flux through the G/G-6-P cycle is controlled by the relative activities of glucokinase and glucose-6-phosphatase (G-6-Pase). Hepatic glucose uptake is controlled by the action of GK, and most of glucose output from the liver occurs as a result of the hydrolysis of G-6-P by G-6-Pase (43).

In the basal state, at physiologic concentrations of glucose, the activities of GK and G-6-Pase are nearly balanced, so there is little, if any, net flux through this cycle (17). It has been calculated that each enzyme converts about 0.9 μmol of substrate/min per gram wet weight in liver (43). In isolated hepatocytes, which have lower enzyme activities and rates of flux than liver, net flux may be 0.03 μmol/min per gram wet weight in the direction of G-6-P (indicating a slightly greater activity of GK over G-6-Pase) (17).

As in the other hepatic substrate cycles, there is short-term (seconds to minutes) and long-term (minutes to hours) control of the G/G-6-P cycle. Neither GK nor G-6-Pase are affected by posttranslational modifications (e.g. phosphorylation) that modify the activity of the protein. Acute changes in flux through these enzymes are accomplished by changes in substrate concentration in the case of G-6-Pase and by changes in substrate concentration and the regulatory protein system in the case of GK. The K_m of G-6-Pase for G-6-P is about 2 mM, which is ~10 times greater than the normal intracellular concentration of the substrate, so this reaction proceeds by first-order kinetics under usual circumstances. Thus, when G-6-P levels are high, as in active gluconeogenesis and/or glycogenolysis, flux will be from G-6-P to glucose, and the latter is exported from the hepatocyte. The primary hormonal signals that result in an acute elevation of G-6-P are an elevated plasma glucagon (cAMP) and a decreased plasma insulin level. These signals, over the long term, result in the induction of G-6-Pase and the repression of GK [see below and Ref. (17)]. The absolute increase of G-6-Pase, coupled with its relative increase over GK, promotes increased flux from G-6-P toward glucose, and export of the latter. For example, a 2-h treatment of isolated hepatocytes with glucagon results in a net flux from G-6-P to glucose of 0.22 μmol/min per gram wet weight. In contrast, the acute elevation of portal vein glucose (or of glucose in an incubation medium) causes glucose to enter the cell through the GLUT 2 transporter and activate GK. This pushes flux in the direction of G-6-P. As long as glycogen synthesis occurs, the G-6-P level is low (as is the level of F-6-P through action of phosphoglucoisomerase) and glucose uptake continues. An increased portal vein glucose also stimulates the release of insulin, and this increases the rate of transcription of the GK gene, which results in increased GK mRNA and GK protein. At the same time, G-6-Pase synthesis is decreased by insulin. The long-term adaptation by insulin therefore involves reciprocal changes in the amount of GK and G-6-P. In isolated hepatocytes such effects result in a net flux toward G-6-P of 0.21 mmol/min per gram wet weight, a 7-fold increase over the basal rate (17).

METABOLIC ZONATION AND GLUCOKINASE   Virtually all hepatic functions show zonation, or variation of function in different anatomic regions of the organ (39, 53, 54) For example, gluconeogenesis is most prominent in the periportal area. The gluconeogenic enzymes phosphoenolpyruvate carboxykinase (PEPCK) and G-6-Pase are most abundant in those cells. Glucose uptake for glycogen synthesis, and glycolysis coupled to lipolysis, are most active in the perivenous/pericentral zone. The enzymes pyruvate kinase and GK are found in this zone. The amounts and activities of the enzymes are not constitutive in these zones, nor are the rates of the various metabolic processes. Apparently, these zones are established by gradients of oxygen, substrates and products of metabolic reactions, hormones and other mediators, and by the types and densities of various nerves (39, 53, 54). Of these multiple factors, oxygen and glucagon/insulin gradients are thought to be the most important in establishing the hepatic zonation for carbohydrate metabolism. The periportal to pericentral gradient of oxygen can be about twofold. A 2–4-fold gradient exists for hormones and substrates and can be greater in absorptive and post-absorptive states (53).

The hepatic distribution of GK and GK mRNA has been studied by a variety of techniques, including direct enzyme assays, immunohistochemical localization, and in situ mRNA hybridization. Very low levels of glucokinase mRNA are detected in the rat liver on neonatal day 1.5, but the pericentral to perivenous gradient is already apparent (77). GK activity is also very low at this time. There is little change until weaning, about postnatal day 15. The response to the ingestion of carbohydrate at this time is instructive. In the fasted animal there is little GK mRNA and no discernable gradient. Four hours after a glucose meal there is a definite pericentral to periportal gradient, and by six hours the mRNA is seen in all cells (77). Changes of GK activity occur more slowly owing to the different turnover times of the protein and mRNA. This experiment indicates that the borders of a zone are not fixed and that they depend upon the metabolic (hormonal) state of the animal. This zonal change is thought to reflect a true induction of GK, presumably by insulin (see below). The nutritional and hormonal conditions that result in the zonal display of GK also cause the disappearance of the periportal zonation of PEPCK. These zonal patterns are thought to reflect metabolic flux. In the example just cited, glucose uptake and glycolysis are increased in the perivenous/pericentral zone as gluconeogenesis is decreased in the periportal zone.

Role of Glucokinase in the Pancreatic β Cell

Pancreatic islet β cells secrete insulin in a glucose-dependent manner. The mechanisms involved have been intensively studied, and several proteins play crucial roles in the process. A key feature underlying the response of the β cell is that the glucose-induced insulin secretory response relies upon changes in the rate of glucose metabolism by these cells (70). Alterations in the rate of glucose utilization are, in turn, tightly linked to changes in the rate of insulin secretion. This coupling is hypothesized to occur as follows. The β cell is electrically active and has a resting membrane potential of about −45 mV [reviewed in (76)]. Increased glucose metabolism results in an increase in the ATP/ADP ratio, which results in decreased conductivity of an adenine nucleotide-sensitive K^+ channel. This leads to depolarization of the β cell (7, 20). The resultant rise in membrane potential opens voltage-dependent calcium channels, thereby allowing the rapid influx of extracellular Ca^{2+} (94, 95) This increase of the intracellular Ca^{2+} concentration is the event that triggers insulin secretion by exocytosis (131). The conductance of adenine nucleotide-sensitive K^+ channels and voltage-sensitive Ca^{2+} channels can be modulated by various hormones and drugs that also affect insulin secretion, but glucose metabolism is required for these effects (76).

The ability of the β cell to respond to glucose involves both glucose transport and phosphorylation, the initial steps in glucose metabolism. Glucose enters the β cell through the high K_m GLUT 2 transporter (83, 115), a process that is not normally rate-limiting, since transport capacity greatly exceeds metabolic flux (110). Low and high K_m hexokinases exist in the β cell (70, 73), but at physiologic glucose concentrations, GK, with its higher K_m for glucose, accounts for most glycolytic flux (74). Two specific kinetic properties of the enzyme are of paramount importance when the physiologic response of the islet is considered: a K_m that is within the physiologic range of portal vein glucose excursions, and the lack of significant feedback inhibition by G-6-P. The large difference in the capacity for transport versus phosphorylation in the β cell is important in at least two regards. First, the high transport capacity assures a rapid equilibration between extracellular and intracellular glucose. Secondly, the rate of glucose utilization by the β cell is determined by GK.

The rate-controlling effect of GK on glucose utilization by the β cell led Matschinsky and co-workers to suggest that GK is the pancreatic β-cell "glucose sensor" (69, 70, 73). Two recent developments provide additional support for the concept (30, 32, 126). First, mutations of the glucokinase gene are associated with noninsulin-dependent diabetes mellitus (32, 126), as is dicussed below. Second, the constitutive expression of a yeast HK gene in transgenic mice causes increased insulin secretion and hypoglycemia (30). These observations offer new evidence in support of a critical role for GK in determining glucose phosphorylation and insulin secretion rate in the β cell.

CELL-SPECIFIC REGULATION OF GLUCOKINASE

Animal studies provide evidence in support of the differential regulation of GK in hepatocytes and β cells. In animals implanted with insulinomas, the high plasma insulin increases hepatic GK activity and islet cell glucokinase activity is low in the face of a low plasma glucose level (9). The decline of the plasma insulin and the increase of the plasma glucose that occurs upon removal of the insulinoma results in a decrease of hepatic GK activity and an increase in islet GK activity (a V_{max} effect, not to be confused with the K_m effects of the "mnemonic" model discussed above). In other studies a GK cDNA was used to demonstrate that hepatic GK mRNA is decreased in fasted animals and increased in refed animals, but islet GK mRNA is unchanged (50). The differential regulation of glucokinase by insulin in the liver, and by glucose in the β cell, constitutes a potential feedback loop that may be fundamentally involved in the maintenance of euglycemia (9, 67). The structural differences in the transcripts of the hepatocytes and β cell, and the use of alternate promoter/regulatory regions in the gene, provide a structural basis for the differential regulation in these two cell types. The various mechanisms and factors employed to accomplish this differential regulation of GK in the liver and β cell are discussed in detail below.

Regulation of Glucokinase in the Hepatocyte

Nutritional studies provide the foundation for many of the current analyses of hepatic GK gene regulation. GK levels are very low in fasted rats or in animals fed a diet high in fat or protein, and it is difficult to detect the pericentral to periportal gradient of GK expression in such animals. In contrast, rats fed a carbohydrate-rich diet have abundant GK, and the zonal gradient described above is readily visualized. Insulin and glucagon were surmised to be the major regulators of hepatic GK, since the insulin/glucagon ratio is high after a carbohydrate meal and is low after a protein-rich or lipid-rich meal or during fasting. Accordingly, it was expected that insulin would stimulate, and glucagon would repress, GK synthesis. Nutritional studies also helped to define the roles thyroid hormone, glucocorticoids, and biotin have in controlling hepatic GK expression. These effects are discussed in the following sections.

INSULIN AND GLUCAGON   The dietary studies cited above suggested that insulin was a major stimulus of GK synthesis. In fact, there is little hepatic GK expression in rats with streptozotocin-induced diabetes, but the administration of insulin returns the enzyme to the normal level (104). It was first shown that these changes in GK activity were accompanied by proportionate changes in the rate of synthesis of the enzyme and that such changes were, in turn, related to changes in the amount of GK mRNA (104). The mechanism of action of insulin on GK gene expression has been studied using both animal models and primary hepatocyte systems. In diabetic rats, in which GK gene transcription is suppressed to a nondetectable level, insulin administration leads to a 20-fold increase in transcription within 45 min (47, 66). It is interesting to note that transcription of the PEPCK gene is reciprocally regulated. As GK gene transcription is increased by insulin, the transcription of the PEPCK gene is shut off (47, 66). Insulin therefore exerts a positive effect on one gene (GK) and a negative effect on another (PEPCK) in the same cell type. The net physiologic result is enhanced hepatic utilization of glucose, since uptake is enhanced and production is decreased. As noted below, glucagon, acting through cAMP, has exactly the opposite effect. This is an example of the coordinate regulation of the enzymes involved in the hepatic substrate cycles, a subject that has been extensively discussed in several recent reviews (35, 43, 87).

The action of insulin on the GK gene appears to be mediated through the insulin receptor. Insulin-like growth factors I and II are effective, but at the high concentrations characteristic of their binding to the insulin receptor rather than to their own receptors (2, 40, 41, 47). The rapid inductive action of insulin on GK gene transcription has led to the suggestion that the effect is direct and involves preexisting cellular proteins (e.g. transcription factors). Glucose does not affect GK gene transcription in primary hepatocytes, and there is no apparent requirement for glucose in the insulin effect (48). This is in marked contrast to the regulation, by insulin, of genes distal to GK in the glycolytic pathway. Glucose, or a metabolite, is required for the insulin effect on transcription of the bifunctional enzyme and pyruvate kinase genes (87). Possibly, these effects represent an indirect effect of insulin, in that they require glucose metabolism initiated by the primary induction of GK by insulin.

Glucagon decreases the rate of transcription of the GK gene by increasing intracellular levels of cAMP (48). Cyclic AMP has a direct inhibitory effect on GK gene transcription in isolated hepatocytes, and a concentration of insulin that results in a maximal induction of GK gene transcription is overridden by glucagon at a low concentration (6×10^{-10} M). This observation, that an inhibitory effect on transcription is dominant over a stimulatory action, is in keeping with the pattern noted for all enzymes in the three hepatic substrate cycles (35). The inhibitory effect appears to be dominant in all cases studied to date.

In summary, expression of the GK gene requires that glucagon (or other agents that induce hepatic cAMP) levels are low and insulin levels are high. This combination of events occurs after a meal, when dietary carbohydrate needs to be stored and/or utilized by the liver. Thus, nutritional cues are translated into alterations of the rate of transcription of specific genes, and the relative rates of transcription help govern glucose utilization and production.

THYROID HORMONE   Thyroid hormones exert a strong effect on lipogenesis through the induction of enzymes that promote the conversion of carbohydrate to triglycerides (45). GK promotes glucose phosphorylation, which leads to an increase in the production of the glycolytic and pentose shunt intermediates that are used in lipogenesis. Because of this chain of events, GK has been considered a lipogenic enzyme. It is therefore not surprising that triiodothyronine (T3), a lipogenic hormone, is also involved in the regulation of the GK gene. Nutrition experiments again provided the framework for subsequent studies of GK gene regulation by T3, and it soon became apparent that T3 and insulin interact in the regulation of the GK gene. One indication of this came from studies in which there was little induction of GK activity in hypothyroid rats that were fasted for 48 h and then were re-fed a high carbohydrate diet (102). In contrast, a very large increase was observed in euthyroid rats treated in the same manner. An analysis of the dietary and hormonal regulation of GK mRNA and GK gene transcription was possible when cDNA probes became available. Basal GK mRNA levels were about the same in euthyroid and hypothyroid starved rats (44). Hypothyroid rats that were fasted for 48 h and then re-fed a carbohydrate diet for 4 h showed a sluggish and modest increase of GK mRNA. There was no change at 1 h and only a 2-fold increase of GK mRNA at 4 h, but by 24 h this mRNA had returned to the normal value. These changes were accompanied by a 3-fold increase in the rate of GK gene transcription. In contrast, the response in euthyroid rats subjected to the same dietary manipulations was brisk and large. A 14-fold increase in GK gene transcription occurred, with a change noted as early as 30 min. By 1 h there was a 5-fold increase of GK mRNA and by 4 h this had increased 8-fold (44). The inference is that the carbohydrate-induced increase of insulin is the primary effector and that T3 plays an important permissive role (44). Alternatively, it is possible that the effect of glucagon or cAMP (high in fasted animals) is dominant and capable of blocking the effect of T3. The action of T3 is most pronounced in cultured neonatal rat hepatocytes in which it produces an increase in GK gene expression comparable to that seen with insulin alone (79). In these cells the combination of T3 and insulin is greater than the additive responses of T3 and insulin (79). A direct effect of T3 on the GK gene is evident, as GK mRNA is directly increased by T3 in primary hepatocytes isolated from neonatal rat liver.

GLUCOCORTICOIDS   Although glucocorticoids and insulin are generally thought to have opposing actions on metabolic processes, both promote glycogen deposition. Glucocorticoids apparently do not have a direct effect on GK gene transcription, but they seem to enhance the response of this gene to insulin. A greater effect of insulin is obtained in the presence of glucocorticoids and is concentration dependent (79). This may be one of the many examples in which glucocorticoids play a permissive role in a metabolic process (36).

BIOTIN   GK activity is low in biotin-deficient rats. Insulin normally does not induce GK in such animals, but biotin administration returns the activity of the enzyme to normal (22, 23). Biotin also induces a 3- to 4-fold increase of GK activity in starved rats, and, like insulin, it induces GK precociously in suckling rats (14, 24, 62). Biotin induces an extremely rapid and large increase of GK mRNA in rats fasted for 24 h. Within an hour after addition, GK mRNA increases ~20-fold. This effect is transient, as the GK mRNA quickly declines after 1 h. The kinetics of this response are very unusual, given the fact that GK gene transcription increases by 6–7 fold during this time (14), and the turnover time of GK mRNA is ~30 min (48). Since ~5 turnover times are required for the movement from one steady state to a new one, biotin may alter the turnover time of the mRNA. Some observations suggest that insulin and biotin act by similar mechanisms. For example, the combined effect of fasting and biotin deficiency on GK expression was not much different than the effect of either alone (62). Also, the combination of glucose, insulin, and biotin treatment of fasted-biotin deficient rats was only slightly more effective than simple biotin treatment (62). However, since the kinetics of the responses to insulin and biotin are very different, these two inducers must be doing something different.

DEVELOPMENTAL REGULATION   Hepatic GK is not appreciably expressed in the fetal or neonatal rat. Significant amounts of GK mRNA and protein first appear about day 15, at the suckling-weaning transition (34). Prior to this time, the suckling rat consumes a high fat milk diet that promotes high plasma glucagon and low plasma insulin levels. The key event associated with the initial expression of GK appears to be the decline of glucagon and the increase of insulin that occurs with the consumption of carbohydrates. Studies using primary cultures of hepatocytes isolated from neonatal rat liver before the physiologic onset of GK expression indicate that T3 and glucocorticoids are required in addition to a low glucagon and high insulin level (79). These findings may explain earlier observations which showed that GK could not be induced in very young neonatal rats by insulin alone (128). Plasma glucocorticoids and thyroid hormones begin to increase about 8–10 days after birth, which is about the earliest point that GK expression can be induced, and gradually rise to a peak near the end of weaning. These changes, combined with the diet-induced effects on insulin and glucagon noted above, stimulate the initial expression of GK. The initial (primary) induction of GK expression in neonatal hepatocytes appears to require de novo protein synthesis, possibly of one or more key transcription factors, since there is an 8–12-h lag between the addition of hormones and an increase of GK mRNA (79). The maximal induction occurs at ∼24 h under these conditions. In contrast, significant induction can be noted within 4 h, and the maximum level is achieved by 8 h, after a repeated (secondary) stimulation of GK mRNA (79). The chromatin events, transcription factors, and DNA elements involved in the control of GK regulation throughout development are not known.

Regulation of Glucokinase in the Pancreatic β Cell

GLUCOSE   Glucose appears to be the major regulator of the expression of pancreatic β-cell GK. Liang et al compared insulin secretion from freshly isolated islets with that from islets maintained in organ culture for 7 days at low and high glucose concentrations (60). Organ cultures of islets in 3 mM glucose showed a 50% reduction in GK activity, whereas those kept in 30 mM glucose showed a 236% increase in GK activity (as compared to GK activity of freshly isolated islets). This 4–5-fold increase was not due to an indirect induction by insulin released as a result of the high glucose concentration in the medium, since the addition of insulin at 350 ng/ml had no effect on GK activity in islets maintained in medium supplemented with 3 mM glucose. The GK activity in islets cultured at these two extremes of glucose concentration is highly correlated with both glucose-stimulated insulin secretion and glucose usage in the cultured islets, thus further strengthening the concept that GK is a key determinant of this coupled response (61). The mechanism whereby glucose regulates β-cell GK has not been extensively analyzed, but existing studies point to modulation at a posttranscriptional level. In the studies cited above, organ culture for 7 days in either 3 or 30 mM glucose had no effect on GK mRNA, but proportionate 5-fold increases of both GK protein and GK activity were observed (61). Glucose may therefore affect either the translation of GK mRNA or the stability of the protein in the β cell. These studies do not provide support for an effect of glucose on the transcription of the GK gene, through the upstream promoter, but this possibility should be excluded by direct experimentation.

HETEROGENEOUS EXPRESSION   Isolated pancreatic β cells differ in their individual responses to glucose (88). For example, insulin secretion, pro-insulin content, and membrane potential differ between individual β cells (26, 96). The metabolic responses of β cells differ; some cells have a greater insulin secretory response to glucose than do others. The basis for the metabolic variability of β cells has not been determined, but recently GK was observed to be heterogeneously expressed in β cells (52). While most β cells exhibit low levels of GK immunoreactivity, some β cells stain much more intensely for the enzyme (52). GK appears to be expressed in a random pattern, since no specific gradient of immunostaining, such as that noted in liver, has been observed (52). This observation remains to be fully explored, because it could explain, at least in part, the functional heterogeneity of individual β cells (88). The effect of glucose on β-cell GK heterogeneity has not been studied, but it could be involved in the recruitment of individual β cells into a more metabolically responsive state.

Regulatory Elements in the Glucokinase Gene Promoter

CIS-REGULATORY ELEMENTS IN THE HEPATIC PROMOTER   Little is known about the regulatory elements in the hepatic GK gene promoter. A major problem in studying this promoter arises from the fact that there is no permanently established, liver-derived cell line in which the GK gene is expressed or regulated. The lack of this fundamentally important resource has prompted studies in other model systems. For instance, transfection experiments utilizing hepatic promoter fragments containing up to 5.5 kb of 5′

flanking DNA ligated to a reporter gene have been performed in cultured primary hepatocytes (82). Unfortunately no hormonal regulation was observed, although weak reporter gene activity was detected. Detailed studies of the regulatory elements and *trans*- acting factors involved in the hepatocyte-specific expression of the gene, and its multihormonal regulation, await either analysis using transgenic animals or a conceptual or technological advance.

CIS-REGULATORY ELEMENTS IN THE β-CELL /PITUITARY PROMOTER   β-Cell-derived cell lines that secrete insulin have been used to define the elements responsible for directing GK gene expression. Shelton et al used both fusion gene and protein-DNA binding experiments to locate two different regulatory elements in the promoter (101). A series of 5′ deletion mutations of the promoter were used to identify a 294-bp segment that was sufficient for efficient transcription of a reporter gene in the HIT M2.2.2 hamster insulinoma cell line. This small region of DNA contains several components that appear to be involved in regulating GK gene transcription. One such element has the sequence TGGTCACCA and is found twice in the 294-bp proximal segment of the upstream GK promoter. This element consists of two inverted repeat segments separated by a single base pair. Mutation of either of these elements, designated Pal-1 or Pal-2, decreases transcription of a reporter gene in insulinoma cells. A second set of sequences, termed the upstream promoter elements (UPE), may also play a role in transcription of the GK gene in the β cell. The three UPEs (UPE-1, -2, and -3) have a similar sequence, CAT(T/C)A(C/G). Mutation of UPE-3 has the most deleterious effect on expression of the reporter gene expression; mutations of UPE-1 or UPE-2 are less detrimental (101). The UPEs bind a nuclear factor that appears to be β-cell specific, but further studies are needed to characterize the factors that bind to the UPE and the Pal elements in the upstream GK promoter, and the role these elements/factors play in β-cell GK gene regulation. Although more progress has been made in analyzing the β-cell promoter than is the case for the hepatic promoter, much remains to be accomplished.

ROLE OF THE GLUCOKINASE GENE IN DIABETES MELLITUS

Undoubtedly, a genetic basis exists for noninsulin-dependent diabetes mellitus (37). Many genes have been considered, and excluded, as candidates [see (37) for review]. The central role of GK in glucose utilization by both the liver and β cell led to the hypothesis that this gene might be involved in diabetes. Meglasson and Matschinsky postulated that small reductions of β-cell GK activity might elevate the glucose set point for insulin secretion, thus producing a clinical situation in which a higher than normal glucose concentration was required to elicit a given response of insulin secretion (69, 73). This concept was interesting in view of other observations which showed that faulty secretion of insulin is a characteristic pathophysiologic feature of noninsulin dependent diabetes mellitus (NIDDM). If β-cell GK is the glucose sensor for insulin secretion, a defect in the abundance or function of GK could result in an impairment of insulin secretion. The link between certain types of NIDDM, abnormal insulin secretion, and GK gene mutations now appears to have been made.

Froguel et al, using a DNA polymorphism located about 8 kilobases downstream from the 3' end of the human GK gene (see above), showed linkage between the GK gene and an uncommon type of NIDDM called "maturity onset diabetes of the young," or MODY (32, 71). MODY is inherited as an autosomal dominant trait, and many well-studied pedigrees are available. The first association between the GK gene and MODY was made by analyzing several French pedigrees, and a LOD score of 11.6 was recorded (32). This score indicated that the chance of random association of the GK gene to MODY was less than 1 in $\sim 10^{12}$. In a subsequent analysis of this group of patients, a mutation in exon 7 of the GK gene was detected in one family (126). In short order, several other mutations of the GK gene were detected in other kindreds. In fact, 18 of the 32 MODY families examined have mutations in the GK gene (P. Froguel et al, submitted for publication). At least 16 unique mutations have been identified. These involve missense, nonsense, and frameshift mutations that are scattered through the nine exons of the GK gene that are shared by both the liver and the β-cell enzyme (P. Froguel et al, submitted for publication). The majority are in exons 5, 7, and 8. These mutations have been sorted into two groups. One group appears to affect the active site cleft and/or surface loops that lead into the cleft (exons 7 and 8 are thought to form the surface of the cleft). These mutations cause large reductions of enzyme activity, which is of interest in light of the discussion of enzyme structure presented above. A second group includes residues located far from the active site in a region thought to undergo a conformational change upon glucose binding. These mutations have smaller V_{max} and K_m effects (33). At least one other mutation involves a stop codon at residue Glu[279], which results in the production of inactive enzyme.

Although the exact impact of all of these mutations on the function of GK in the patients has not yet been established, at least three kindreds so affected have been shown to have abnormal insulin secretion in response to a glucose challenge (125). This is interesting in view of the fact that one GK allele must be normal in such persons (because it is an autosomal dominant disorder); thus they must have at least 50% of the normal GK activity of unaffected individuals. On the basis of a variety of experiments, Meglasson &

Matschinsky suggested that a 15–30% reduction of β-cell GK activity could increase the threshold of insulin secretion by glucose from 5 mM to 6 mM (73). Whether a similar reduction in the activity of hepatic GK would have an effect of glucose uptake by the liver remains to be established. Linkage with a locus on chromosome 20, near the adenosine deaminase gene, has also been identified in one large MODY kindred (11). Whether this indicates that genes other than GK account for this disease, which is known to present as a variety of different phenotypes (31), or whether the chromosome 20 locus has something to do with regulating expression of the GK gene, or function of the protein (see section above for the discussion of the regulatory protein), remains to be established.

It has not yet been possible to fully assess the association of the GK gene mutations with more typical NIDDM. The belief that this association may be more significant than as a cause of some cases of MODY, which accounts for considerably fewer than 1% of the cases of diabetes in the United States, is supported by the observation of linkage of the GK gene to diabetes in Mauritian Creoles (15), who have a 12% incidence of the disease in adults, and in American blacks (16), who also have a high incidence of the disease. The association of GK with diabetes has received a great deal of attention in the past year. Interested readers are directed to several recent papers (33, 84), and many more can be expected in ensuing years.

CONCLUSIONS

The study of glucokinase is a paradigm of contemporary biomedical investigation. Numerous investigators have made remarkable progress in understanding how this enzyme works, how it evolved, how its activity and expression are regulated, and how it is involved in certain types of diabetes mellitus. This understanding would not have been possible without the interdigitation of information acquired through the disciplines of nutrition, physiology, biochemistry, molecular biology, and human genetics.

A similar, concerted approach is necessary to take the understanding of this critical enzyme to the next level. Every topic discussed in this review is the subject for further study. Such studies will shed light on how gene families evolve, how cell-specific gene expression is accomplished, how *cis/trans* regulation of transcription works, how hormones can stimulate the transcription of one gene in a cell while inhibiting transcription of another, how glucose metabolism is coupled to insulin secretion, how the heterogeneity of gene expression in organs affects their function, and how dietary cues are translated into altered metabolic fluxes. The role of glucokinase in certain forms of adult onset diabetes will be explored for obvious reasons, but mutations that affect the expression of this gene, or the function of its protein product, will provide information about the nature of these basic mechanisms. The advent of molecular genetics had a major impact on this field, but it is obvious that much remains to be done. As in the past, multiple aspects of glucokinase can be studied by investigators with a spectrum of interests.

ACKNOWLEDGMENTS

The authors thank D. Caplenor for typing the manuscript and P. Lucas and R. O'Brien for thoughtful comments. These studies were supported in part by HHS grants DK35107 (DKG), DK42612 (MAM), DK42502 (DKG and MAM), and DK20593 (the Vanderbilt Diabetes Research and Training Center) and by a gift from the Sandoz Research Institute.

Literature Cited

1. Anderson, C. M., Zucker, F. H., Steitz, T. A. 1979. Space-filling models of kinase clefts and conformation changes. *Science* 204:375–80
2. Andreone, T. L., Beale, E. G., Bar, R. S., Granner, D. K. 1982. Insulin decreases phosphoenolpyruvate carboxykinase (GTP) mRNA activity by a receptor-mediated process. *J. Biol. Chem.* 257:35–38
3. Andreone, T. L., Printz, R. L., Pilkis, S. J., Magnuson, M. A., Granner, D. K. 1989. The amino acid sequence of rat liver glucokinase deduced from cloned cDNA. *J. Biol. Chem.* 264:363–69
4. Arora, K. K., Fanciulli, M., Pedersen, P. L. 1990. Glucose phosphorylation in tumor cells. Cloning, sequencing, and overexpression in active form of a full-length cDNA encoding a mitochondrial bindable form of hexokinase. *J. Biol. Chem.* 265:6481–88
5. Arora, K. K., Filburn, C. R., Pedersen, P. L. 1991. Glucose phosphorylation. Site-directed mutations which impair the catalytic function of hexokinase. *J. Biol. Chem.* 266:5359–62
6. Arora, K. K., Shenbagamurthi, P., Fanciulli, M., Pedersen, P. L. 1990. Glucose phosphorylation. Interaction of a 50-amino acid peptide of yeast hexokinase with trinitrophenyl ATP. *J. Biol. Chem.* 265:5324–28
7. Ashcroft, F. M., Harrison, D. E., Ashcroft, S. J. H. 1984. Glucose induces closure of single potassium channels in isolated rat pancreatic beta-cells. *Nature* 312:446–48
8. Baijal, M., Wilson, J. E. 1992. Functional consequences of mutation of highly conserved serine residues, found at equivalent positions in the N- and C-terminal domains of mammalian hexokinases. *Arch. Biochem. Biophys.* 298:271–78
9. Bedoya, F. J., Matschinsky, F. M., Shimizu, T., O'Neil, J. J., Appel, M. C. 1986. Differential regulation of glucokinase activity in pancreatic islets and liver of the rat. *J. Biol. Chem.* 261:10760–64
10. Bell, G. I., Kayano, T., Buse, J. B., Burant, C. F., Takeda, J., et al. 1990. Molecular biology of mammalian glucose transporters. *Diabetes Care* 13: 198–208
11. Bell, G. I., Xiang, K. S., Newman, M. V., Wu, S. H., Wright, L. G., et al. 1991. Gene for non-insulin-dependent diabetes mellitus (maturity-onset diabetes of the young subtype) is linked to DNA polymorphism on human chromosome 20q. *Proc. Natl. Acad. Sci. USA* 88:1484–88
12. Bennett, W. S. Jr., Steitz, T. A. 1978. Glucose-induced conformational change in yeast hexokinase. *Proc. Natl. Acad. Sci. USA* 75:4848–52
13. Cahill, G. F. Jr., Hastings, A. B., Ashmore, J., Zottu, S. 1958. Studies on carbohydrate metabolism in rat liver slices. X. Factors in the regulation of pathways of glucose metabolism. *J. Biol. Chem.* 230:125–35
14. Chauhan, J., Dakshinamurti, K. 1991. Transcriptional regulation of the glucokinase gene by biotin in starved rats. *J. Biol. Chem.* 266:10035–38
15. Chiu, K. C., Province, M. A., Dowse, G. K., Zimmet, P. Z., Wagner, G., et al. 1992. A genetic marker at the glucokinase gene locus for type 2 (non-insulin-dependent) diabetes mellitus in

492   PRINTZ, MAGNUSON & GRANNER

Mauritian Creoles. *Diabetologia* 35: 632–38
16. Chiu, K. C., Province, M. A., Permutt, M. A. 1992. Glucokinase gene is genetic marker for NIDDM in American blacks. *Diabetes* 41:843–49
17. Christ, B., Probst, I., Jungermann, K. 1986. Antagonistic regulation of the glucose/glucose 6-phosphate cycle by insulin and glucagon in cultured hepatocytes. *Biochem. J.* 238:185–91
18. Clark, D. G., Filsell, O. H., Topping, D. L. 1979. Effects of fructose concentration on carbohydrate metabolism, heat production and substrate cycling in isolated rat hepatocytes. *Biochem. J.* 184:501–7
19. Colowick, S. P. 1973. The Hexokinases. In *The Enzymes*, ed. P. D. Boyer, 9:1–48. New York: Academic
20. Cook, D. L., Satin, L. S., Ashford, M. L. J., Hales, C. N. 1988. ATP-sensitive K+ channels in pancreatic beta-cells. *Diabetes* 37:495–98
21. Cornish-Bowden, A., Cárdenas, M. L. 1991. Hexokinase and 'glucokinase' in liver metabolism. *Trends Biochem. Sci.* 16:281–82
22. Dakshinamurti, K., Cheah, T. C. 1968. Biotin-mediated synthesis of hepatic glucokinase in the rat. *Arch. Biochem. Biophys.* 127:17–21
23. Dakshinamurti, K., Cheah, T. C. 1968. Liver glucokinase of the biotin deficient rat. *Can. J. Biochem.* 46:75–80
24. Dakshinamurti, K., Tarrago, L. L., Hong, H. C. 1970. Biotin and glucose metabolism. *Can. J. Biochem.* 48:493–500
25. Davies, D. R., Detheux, M., Van Schaftingen, E. 1990. Fructose 1-phosphate and the regulation of glucokinase activity in isolated hepatocytes. *Eur. J. Biochem.* 192:283–89
26. Dean, P. M., Matthews, E. K. 1970. Glucose-induced electrical activity in pancreatic islet cells. *J. Physiol.* 210:255–64
27. Detheux, M., Vandercammen, A., Van Schaftingen, E. 1991. Effectors of the regulatory protein acting on liver glucokinase: a kinetic investigation. *Eur. J. Biochem.* 200:553–61
28. Easterby, J. S. 1971. The polypetide chain molecular weight of a mammalian hexokinase. *FEBS Lett.* 18:23–26
29. Easterby, J. S., O'Brien, M. J. 1973. Purification and properties of pig-heart hexokinase. *Eur. J. Biochem.* 38:201–11
30. Epstein, P. N., Boschero, A. C., Atwater, I., Cai, X. E., Overbeek, P. A.

1993. Expression of yeast hexokinase in pancreatic beta-cells of transgenic mice reduces blood glucose, enhances insulin secretion, and decreases diabetes. *Proc. Natl. Acad. Sci. USA* 89:12038-42
31. Fajans, S. S. 1990. Scope and heterogeneous nature of MODY. *Diabetes Care* 13:49–64
32. Froguel, P., Vaxillaire, M., Sun, F., Velho, G., Zouali, H., et al. 1992. Close linkage of glucokinase locus on chromosome 7p to early-onset non-insulin-dependent diabetes mellitus. *Nature* 356:162–64
33. Gidh-Jain, M., Takeda, J., Xu, L. Z., Lange, A. J., Vionnet, N., et al. 1993. Glucokinase mutations associated with non-insulin-dependent (type 2) diabetes mellitus have decreased enzymatic activity: implications for structure/function relationships. *Proc. Natl. Acad. Sci. USA.* 90:1932–36
34. Girard, J., Decaux, J. F., Bossard, P. 1992. Regulation of the initial expression of hepatic phosphoenolpyruvate carboxykinase and glucokinase genes during development. *Diabete Metab.* 18:74–80
35. Granner, D., Pilkis, S. 1990. The genes of hepatic glucose metabolism. *J. Biol. Chem.* 265:10173–76
36. Granner, D. K. 1979. The role of glucocorticoid hormones as biological amplifiers. In *Glucocorticoid Hormone Action*, ed. J. D. Bacter, G. Rousseau, 12:593–609. Heidelberg: Springer-Verlag
37. Granner, D. K., O'Brien, R. M. 1992. Molecular physiology and genetics of NIDDM. Importance of metabolic staging. *Diabetes Care* 15:369–95
38. Grossbard, L., Schimke, R. T. 1966. Multiple hexokinases of rat tissues. Purification and comparison of soluble forms. *J. Biol. Chem.* 241:3546–60
39. Gumucio, J. J. 1989. Hepatocyte heterogeneity: the coming of age from the description of a biological curiosity to a partial understanding of its physiological meaning and regulation. *Hepatology* 9:154–60
40. Hartmann, H., Meyer, A. A., Braulke, T. 1992. Metabolic actions of insulin-like growth factor II in cultured adult rat hepatocytes are not mediated through the insulin-like growth factor II receptor. *Diabetologia* 35:216–23
41. Hartmann, H., Schmitz, F., Christ, B., Jungermann, K., Creutzfeldt, W. 1990. Metabolic actions of insulin-like growth factor-I in cultured hepatocytes from adult rats. *Hepatology* 12:1139–43

42. Hayzer, D. J., Iynedjian, P. B. 1990. Alternative splicing of glucokinase mRNA in rat liver. *Biochem. J.* 270: 261–63

43. Hers, H. G. 1990. Mechanisms of blood glucose homeostasis. *J. Inherit. Metab. Dis.* 13:395–410

44. Höppner, W., Seitz, H. J. 1989. Effect of thyroid hormones on glucokinase gene transcription in rat liver. *J. Biol. Chem.* 264:20643–47

45. Höppner, W., Seitz, H. J. 1990. Role of thyroid hormones in the regulation of hepatic glucokinase and phosphoenolpyruvate-carboxykinase gene expression during the starvation-refeeding transition. *Biochem. Soc. Trans.* 18: 845–47

46. Hughes, S. D., Quaade, C., Milburn, J. L., Cassidy, L., Newgard, C. B. 1991. Expression of normal and novel glucokinase mRNAs in anterior pituitary and islet cells. *J. Biol. Chem.* 266:4521–30

47. Iynedjian, P. B., Gjinovci, A., Renold, A. E. 1988. Stimulation by insulin of glucokinase gene transcription in liver of diabetic rats. *J. Biol. Chem.* 263: 740–44

48. Iynedjian, P. B., Jotterand, D., Nouspikel, T., Asfari, M., Pilot, P. R. 1989. Transcriptional induction of glucokinase gene by insulin in cultured liver cells and its repression by the glucagon-cAMP system. *J. Biol. Chem.* 264:21824–29

49. Iynedjian, P. B., Möbius, G., Seitz, H. J., Wollheim, C. B., Renold, A. E. 1986. Tissue-specific expression of glucokinase: identification of the gene product in liver and pancreatic islets. *Proc. Natl. Acad. Sci. USA* 83:1998–2001

50. Iynedjian, P. B., Pilot, P. R., Nouspikel, T., Milburn, J. L., Quaade, C., et al. 1989. Differential expression and regulation of the glucokinase gene in liver and islets of Langerhans. *Proc. Natl. Acad. Sci. USA* 86:7838–42

51. Iynedjian, P. B., Ucla, C., Mach, B. 1987. Molecular cloning of glucokinase cDNA. Developmental and dietary regulation of glucokinase mRNA in rat liver. *J. Biol. Chem.* 262:6032–38

52. Jetton, T. L., Magnuson, M. A. 1992. Heterogeneous expression of glucokinase among pancreatic beta cells. *Proc. Natl. Acad. Sci. USA* 89:2619–23

53. Jungermann, K. 1992. Role of intralobular compartmentation in hepatic metabolism. *Diabete Metab.* 18:81–86

54. Jungermann, K., Norbert, K. 1989. Functional specialization of different hepatocyte populations. *Physiol. Rev.* 69:708–64

55. Katzen, H. M., Schimke, R. T. 1965. Multiple forms of hexokinase in the rat: tissue distribution, age dependency, and properties. *Proc. Natl. Acad. Sci. USA* 54:1218–25

56. Koranyi, L. I., Tanizawa, Y., Welling, C. M., Rabin, D. U., Permutt, M. A. 1992. Human islet glucokinase gene. Isolation and sequence analysis of full-length cDNA. *Diabetes* 41:807–11

57. Lange, A. J., Xu, L. Z., Van Poelwijk, F., Lin, K., Granner, D. K., et al. 1991. Expression and site-directed mutagenesis of hepatic glucokinase. *Biochem. J.* 277:159–63

58. Lenzen, S., Panten, U. 1988. Alloxan: history and mechanism of action. *Diabetologia* 31:337–42

59. Liang, Y., Jetton, T. L., Zimmerman, E. C., Najafi, H., Matschinsky, F. M., et al. 1991. Effects of alternate RNA splicing on glucokinase isoform activities in the pancreatic islet, liver, and pituitary. *J. Biol. Chem.* 266:6999–7007

60. Liang, Y., Najafi, H., Matschinsky, F. M. 1990. Glucose regulates glucokinase activity in cultured islets from rat pancreas. *J. Biol. Chem.* 265: 16863–66

61. Liang, Y., Najafi, H., Smith, R. M., Zimmerman, E. C., Magnuson, M. A., et al. 1992. Concordant glucose induction of glucokinase, glucose usage, and glucose-stimulated insulin release in pancreatic islets maintained in organ culture. *Diabetes* 41:792–806

62. Li Hsieh, Y. T., Mistry, S. P. 1992. Effect of biotin on the regulation of glucokinase in the intact rat. *Nutr. Res.* 12:787–99

63. Magnani, M., Bianchi, M., Casabianca, A., Stocchi, V., Daniele, A., et al. 1992. A recombinant human 'mini'-hexokinase is catalytically active and regulated by hexose 6-phosphates. *Biochem. J.* 285:193–99

64. Magnuson, M. A. 1990. Glucokinase gene structure. Functional implications of molecular genetic studies. *Diabetes* 39:523–27

65. Magnuson, M. A. 1992. Tissue-specific regulation of glucokinase gene expression. *J. Cell. Biochem.* 48:115–21

66. Magnuson, M. A., Andreone, T. L., Printz, R. L., Koch, S., Granner, D. K. 1989. Rat glucokinase gene: structure and regulation by insulin. *Proc. Natl. Acad. Sci. USA* 86:4838–42

67. Magnuson, M. A., Shelton, K. D.

1989. An alternate promoter in the glucokinase gene is active in the pancreatic beta cell. *J. Biol. Chem.* 264: 15936–42

68. Malaisse, W. J., Malaisse, L. F., Davies, D. R., Vandercammen, A., Van Schaftingen, E. 1990. Regulation of glucokinase by a fructose-1-phosphate-sensitive protein in pancreatic islets. *Eur. J. Biochem.* 190:539–45

69. Matschinsky, F. M. 1990. Glucokinase as glucose sensor and metabolic signal generator in pancreatic beta-cells and hepatocytes. *Diabetes* 39:647–52

70. Matschinsky, F. M., Ellerman, J. E. 1968. Metabolism of glucose in the islets of Langerhans. *J. Biol. Chem.* 243:2730–36

71. Matsutani, A., Janssen, R., Donis, K. H., Permutt, M. A. 1992. A polymorphic (CA)n repeat element maps the human glucokinase gene (GCK) to chromosome 7p. *Genomics* 12:319–25

72. Meglasson, M. D., Burch, P. T., Berner, D. K., Najafi, H., Vogin, A. P., et al. 1983. Chromatographic resolution and kinetic characterization of glucokinase from islets of Langerhans. *Proc. Natl. Acad. Sci. USA* 80:85–89

73. Meglasson, M. D., Matschinsky, F. M. 1984. New perspectives on pancreatic islet glucokinase. *Am. J. Physiol.* 13:E1-E13

74. Meglasson, M. D., Matschinsky, F. M. 1986. Pancreatic islet glucose metabolism and regulation of insulin secretion. *Diabetes Metab. Rev.* 2: 163–214

75. Middleton, R. J. 1990. Hexokinases and glucokinases. *Biochem. Soc. Trans.* 18:180–83

76. Misler, S., Barnett, D. W., Gillis, K. D., Pressel, D. M. 1992. Electrophysiology of stimulus-secretion coupling in human beta-cells. *Diabetes* 41:1221–28

77. Moorman, A. F. M., de Boer, P. A. J., Charles, R., Lamers, W. H. 1991. Pericentral expression pattern of glucokinase mRNA in the rat liver lobulus. *FEBS Lett.* 287:47–52

78. Mueckler, M. 1990. Family of glucose-transporter genes. Implications for glucose homeostasis and diabetes. *Diabetes* 39:6–11

79. Narkewicz, M. R., Iynedjian, P. B., Ferre, P., Girard, J. 1990. Insulin and tri-iodothyronine induce glucokinase mRNA in primary cultures of neonatal rat hepatocytes. *Biochem. J.* 271:585–89

80. Nishi, S., Seino, S., Bell, G. I. 1988. Human hexokinase: sequences of amino- and carboxyl-terminal halves are homologous. *Biochem. Biophys. Res. Commun.* 157:937–43

81. Nishi, S., Stoffel, M., Xiang, K., Shows, T. B., Bell, G. I., et al. 1992. Human pancreatic beta-cell glucokinase: cDNA sequence and localization of the polymorphic gene to chromosome 7, band p 13. *Diabetologia* 35:743–47

82. Noguchi, T., Takenaka, M., Yamada, K., Matsuda, T., Hashimoto, M., et al. 1989. Characterization of the 5' flanking region of rat glucokinase gene. *Biochem. Biophys. Res. Commun.* 164: 1247–52

83. Orci, L., Thorens, B., Ravazzola, M., Lodish, H. F. 1989. Localization of the pancreatic beta cell glucose transporter to specific plasma membrane domains. *Science* 245:295–97

84. Permutt, M. A., Chiu, K. C., Tanizawa, Y. 1992. Glucokinase and NIDDM. A candidate gene that paid off. *Diabetes* 41:1367–72

85. Pessin, J. E., Bell, G. I. 1992. Mammalian facilitative glucose transporter family: structure and molecular regulation. *Annu. Rev. Physiol.* 54:911–30

86. Pilkis, S. J. 1972. Rat hepatic glucokinase: improved purification and some properties. *Arch. Biochem. Biophys.* 149:349–60

87. Pilkis, S. J., Granner, D. K. 1992. Molecular physiology of the regulation of hepatic gluconeogenesis and glycolysis. *Annu. Rev. Physiol.* 54:885–909

88. Pipeleers, D. G. 1992. Heterogeneity in pancreatic beta-cell population.*Diabetes* 41:777–81

89. Pollard, K. D., Cornish, B. A. 1982. Mechanism of liver glucokinase. *Mol. Cell. Biochem.* 44:71–80

90. Printz, R. L., Koch, S., Potter, L. R., O'Doherty, R. M., Tiesinga, J. J., et al. 1993. Hexokinase II mRNA and gene structure, regulation by insulin, and evolution. *J. Biol. Chem.* 268:5209–19

91. Quaade, C., Hughes, S. D., Coates, W. S., Sestak, A. L., Iynedjian, P. B., et al. 1991. Analysis of the protein products encoded by variant glucokinase transcripts via expression in bacteria. *FEBS Lett.* 280:47–52

92. Reyes, A., Cárdenas, M. L. 1984. All hexokinase isoenzymes coexist in rat hepatocytes. *Biochem. J.* 221:303–9

93. Ricard, J., Meunier, J. -C., Buc, J. 1974. Regulatory behavior of monomeric enzymes. 1. The mnemonical enzyme concept. *Eur. J. Biochem.* 49: 195–208

94. Rorsman, P., Trube, G. 1986. Calcium and delayed potassium currents in mouse pancreatic beta-cells under voltage-clamp conditions. *J. Physiol.* 374: 531–50

95. Satin, L. S., Cook, D. L. 1985. Voltage-gated inward current in pancreatic islet beta-cells. *Pfluegers Arch. Eur. J. Physiol.* 404:385–87

96. Schuit, F. C., In't Veld, P. A., Pipeleers, D. G. 1988. Glucose stimulates proinsulin biosynthesis by a dose-dependent recruitment of pancreatic beta cell. *Proc. Natl. Acad. Sci. USA* 85:3865–69

97. Schwab, D. A., Wilson, J. E. 1988. The complete amino acid sequence of the catalytic domain of rat brain hexokinase, deduced from the cloned cDNA. *J. Biol. Chem.* 263:3220–24

98. Schwab, D. A., Wilson, J. E. 1989. Complete amino acid sequence of rat brain hexokinase, deduced from the cloned cDNA, and proposed structure of a mammalian hexokinase. *Proc. Natl. Acad. Sci. USA* 86:2563–67

99. Schwab, D. A., Wilson, J. E. 1991. Complete amino acid sequence of the type III isozyme of rat hexokinase, deduced from the cloned cDNA. *Arch. Biochem. Biophys.* 285:365–70

100. Sharma, C., Manjeshwar, R., Weinhouse, S. 1963. Effects of diet and insulin on glucose-adenosine triphosphate phosphotransferases of rat liver. *J. Biol. Chem.* 238:3840–45

101. Shelton, K. D., Franklin, A., Khoor, A., Beechem, J., Magnuson, M. A. 1992. Multiple elements in the upstream glucokinase promoter are necessary for transcription in insulinoma cells. *Mol. Cell. Biol.* 12:4578–89

102. Sibrowski, W., Mller, M. J., Seitz, H. J. 1981. Effect of different thyroid states on rat liver glucokinase synthesis and degradation in vivo. *J. Biol. Chem.* 256:9490–94

103. Sols, A., Crane, R. K. 1954. Substrate specificity of brain hexokinase. *J. Biol. Chem.* 210:581–95

104. Spence, J. T. 1983. Levels of translatable mRNA coding for rat liver glucokinase. *J. Biol. Chem.* 258:9143–46

105. Spiro, R. G., Ashmore, J., Hastings, A. B. 1958. Studies on carbohydrate metabolism in rat liver slices. XII. Sequence of metabolic events following acute insulin deprivation. *J. Biol. Chem.* 230:761–71

106. Steitz, T. A., Anderson, W. F., Fletterick, R. J., Anderson, C. M. 1977. High resolution crystal structures of yeast hexokinase complexes with substrates, activators, and inhibitors. Evidence for an allosteric control site. *J. Biol. Chem.* 252:4494–500

107. Stoffel, M., Froguel, P., Takeda, J., Zouali, H., Vionnet, N., et al. 1992. Human glucokinase gene: isolation, characterization, and identification of two missense mutations linked to early-onset non-insulin-dependent (type 2) diabetes mellitus. *Proc. Natl. Acad. Sci. USA* 89:7698–702

108. Storer, A. C., Cornish, B. A. 1976. Kinetics of rat liver glucokinase. Cooperative interactions with glucose at physiologically significant concentrations. *Biochem. J.* 159:7–14

109. Storer, A. C., Cornish, B. A. 1977. Kinetic evidence for a 'mnemonical' mechanism for rat liver glucokinase. *Biochem. J.* 165:61–69

110. Tal, M., Liang, Y., Najafi, H., Lodish, H. F., Matschinsky, F. M. 1992. Expression and function of GLUT-1 and GLUT-2 glucose transporter isoforms in cells of cultured rat pancreatic islets. *J. Biol. Chem.* 267:17241–47

111. Tamura, J. K., LaDine, J. R., Cross, R. L. 1988. The adenine nucleotide binding site on yeast hexokinase PII. Affinity labeling of Lys-111 by pyridoxal 5′-diphospho-5′-adenosine. *J. Biol. Chem.* 263:7907–12

112. Tanizawa, Y., Koranyi, L. I., Welling, C. M., Permutt, M. A. 1991. Human liver glucokinase gene: cloning and sequence determination of two alternatively spliced cDNAs. *Proc. Natl. Acad. Sci. USA* 88:7294–97

113. Tanizawa, Y., Matsutani, A., Chiu, K. C., Permutt, M. A. 1992. Human glucokinase gene: isolation, structural characterization, and identification of a microsatellite repeat polymorphism. *Mol. Endocrinol.* 6:1070–81

114. Thelen, A. P., Wilson, J. E. 1991. Complete amino acid sequence of the type II isozyme of rat hexokinase, deduced from the cloned cDNA: comparison with a hexokinase from novikoff ascites tumor. *Arch. Biochem. Biophys.* 286:645–51

115. Thorens, B., Sarkar, H. K., Kaback, H. R., Lodish, H. F. 1988. Cloning and functional expression in bacteria of a novel glucose transporter present in liver, intestine, kidney, and beta-pancreatic islet cells. *Cell* 55:281–90

116. Tippett, P. S., Neet, K. E. 1982. An allosteric model for the inhibition of glucokinase by long chain acyl coenzyme A. *J. Biol. Chem.* 257:12846–52

117. Tippett, P. S., Neet, K. E. 1982.

Specific inhibition of glucokinase by long chain acyl coenzymes A below the critical micelle concentration. *J. Biol. Chem.* 257:12839–45

118. Unger, R. H. 1991. Diabetic hyperglycemia: link to impaired glucose transport in pancreatic beta cells. *Science* 251:1200–5

119. Ureta, T. 1982. The comparative isozymology of vertebrate hexokinases. *Comp. Biochem. Physiol. B Comp. Biochem.* 71:549–55

120. Vandercammen, A., Van Schaftingen, E. 1990. The mechanism by which rat liver glucokinase is inhibited by the regulatory protein. *Eur. J. Biochem.* 191:483–89

121. Vandercammen, A., Van Schaftingen, E. 1991. Competitive inhibition of liver glucokinase by its regulatory protein. *Eur. J. Biochem.* 200:545–51

122. Van Schaftingen, E. 1989. A protein from rat liver confers to glucokinase the property of being antagonistically regulated by fructose 6-phosphate and fructose 1-phosphate. *Eur. J. Biochem.* 179:179–84

123. Van Schaftingen, E., Vandercammen, A. 1989. Stimulation of glucose phosphorylation by fructose in isolated rat hepatocytes. *Eur. J. Biochem.* 179:173–77

124. Van Schaftingen, E., Vandercammen, A., Detheux, M., Davies, D. R. 1992. The regulatory protein of liver glucokinase. *Adv. Enzyme Regul.* 32:133–48

125. Velho, G., Froguel, P., Clement, K., Pueyo, M. E., Rakotoambinina, B., et al. 1992. Primary pancreatic beta-cell secretory defect caused by mutations in glucokinase gene in kindreds of maturity onset diabetes of the young. *Lancet* 340:444–48

126. Vionnet, N., Stoffel, M., Takeda, J., Yasuda, K., Bell, G. I., et al. 1992. Nonsense mutation in the glucokinase gene causes early-onset non-insulin-dependent diabetes mellitus. *Nature* 356:721–22

127. Watford, M. 1990. Tissue-specific regulation of glucokinase. *Trends Biochem. Sci.* 15:1–2

128. Weinhouse, S. 1976. Regulation of glucokinase in liver. *Curr. Top. Cell. Regul.* 11:1–50

129. White, T. K., Wilson, J. E. 1987. Rat brain hexokinase: location of the allosteric regulatory site in a structural domain at the N-terminus of the enzyme. *Arch. Biochem. Biophys.* 259:402–11

130. White, T. K., Wilson, J. E. 1989. Isolation and characterization of the discrete N- and C-terminal halves of rat brain hexokinase: retention of full catalytic activity in the isolated C-terminal half. *Arch. Biochem. Biophys.* 274:375–93

131. Wollheim, C. B., Sharp, W. G. 1981. Regulation of insulin secretion by calcium. *Physiol. Rev.* 61:914–73

Annu. Rev. Nutr. 1993. 13:497–520

REGULATION OF THE PYRUVATE DEHYDROGENASE MULTIENZYME COMPLEX

R. H. Behal, D. B. Buxton, J. G. Robertson, and M. S. Olson

Department of Biochemistry, University of Texas Health Science Center at San Antonio, San Antonio, Texas 78284-7760

KEY WORDS: pyruvate metabolism, α-keto acid dehydrogenase, enzymes, carbohydrate metabolism, tricarboxylic acid cycle

CONTENTS

INTRODUCTION   497
PYRUVATE DEHYDROGENASE CATALYTIC AND MOLECULAR PROPERTIES   498
REGULATION OF THE PYRUVATE DEHYDROGENASE COMPLEX   501
   Regulation of Pyruvate Dehydrogenase in Specific Tissues   505
   Regulation of Pyruvate Dehydrogenase by Hormones   509
   Pyruvate Dehydrogenase Deficiency States   512

INTRODUCTION

To maximize catalytic efficiency in metabolic pathways of both prokaryotic and eukaryotic cells, enzymatic components are occasionally clustered or complexed physically. Organization of multiple catalytic functions into a single enzyme complex can be accomplished in two ways. First, multifunctional enzymes utilize a single polypeptide chain to catalyze more than one enzymatic function; an example of a multifunctional enzyme is the mammalian fatty acid synthase. A more common means for clustering enzymatic functions is the assembly of multiple catalytic components into complexes held together by noncovalent bonds. The most prominent examples of multienzyme complexes are the α-keto acid dehydrogenase multienzyme complexes that catalyze the oxidative decarboxylation of pyruvate, α-keto-

497

0199-9885/93/0715-0497$02.00

glutarate, and branched chain α-keto acids (see Ref. 105 for several recent reviews). In this review article we discuss briefly several catalytic and molecular features of the pyruvate dehydrogenase multienzyme complex. We then describe selectively some of the characteristics of the regulatory mechanisms that modulate the activity of this enzyme complex in its normal metabolic function in the energy-generating pathways of aerobic cells/tissues.

PYRUVATE DEHYDROGENASE CATALYTIC AND MOLECULAR PROPERTIES

In the pyruvate dehydrogenase reaction, pyruvate is oxidatively decarboxylated to acetyl-CoA, CO_2, and NADH by a series of sequential reactions catalyzed by the three component enzymes of the pyruvate dehydrogenase complex: pyruvate dehydrogenase (E1), EC 1.2.4.1; dihydrolipoamide transacetylase (E2), EC 2.3.1.12; and dihydrolipoamide dehydrogenase (E3), EC 1.8.1.4. E1 catalyzes the decarboxylation of pyruvate and the subsequent reductive acetylation of the lipoyl moiety of E2. E2, in turn, catalyzes the transfer of the acetyl group to free CoA. The reduced lipoyl moiety of E2 is reoxidized by E3, with NAD^+ as the final electron acceptor (Figure 1).

Pyruvate dehydrogenase complex has been purified from numerous plant, microbial, and mammalian sources. Pyruvate dehydrogenase complexes from prokaryotes and eukaryotes have molecular weights in the millions; the subunit composition of bovine kidney PDC is shown in Table 1. The complex is organized around a central core composed of multiple copies of the E2 subunit; in *Escherichia coli* and other gram-negative bacteria, the core consists of 24

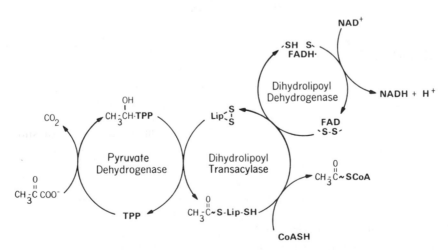

Figure 1   Catalytic mechanism for the pyruvate dehydrogenase reaction.

Table 1 Subunit composition of mammalian pyruvate dehydrogenase complex

Subunit	M_r	Subunits No.	Subunits M_r	Subunits per molecule of complex
Native complex	8,500,000			
E1 tetramer	154,000			30
E1α		2	41,000	
E1β		2	36,000	
E2 core	3,100,000		52,000	60
E3 dimer	110,000			6
E3		2	55,000	
X			50,000	6
Kinase	~100,000	1	48,000	
		1	45,000	
Phosphatase	~150,000	1	97,000	
		1	50,000	

copies of E2, arranged as a hollow cube of 8 trimers (75); in eukaryotes, such as yeast and mammalian systems, the core consists of 60 copies of E2 arranged in an icosahedral dodecahedron with 532 symmetry (99).

E1, pyruvate dehydrogenase, differs in structure between prokaryotic and eukaryotic systems: In *E. coli*, E1 exists as a single polypeptide of $M_r \approx$ 100,000 (39), whereas in yeast and mammalian systems, functional E1 consists of an $\alpha_2\beta_2$ tetramer composed of two copies each of E1α and E1β (1). In the yeast and mammalian pyruvate dehydrogenase complexes, 30 E1 tetramers are arrayed about the surface of the E2 core (98).

E3, dihydrolipoamide dehydrogenase, is representative of a class of ubiquitous flavin-containing dehydrogenases (9). In PDC (pyruvate dehydrogenase complex), E3 exists as a dimer of M_r 110,000, six of which are bound to the surface of the E2 core (98).

Recently, a fourth polypeptide, known as protein X, has been found in yeast and mammalian complexes (21, 132). Approximately six copies of protein X are associated tightly with the E2 core, and evidence indicates that protein X is involved in binding of E3 to the complex (35, 66).

Two other proteins are associated with the mammalian forms of pyruvate dehydrogenase. Pyruvate dehydrogenase kinase catalyzes the phosphorylation of three serine residues on the E1α subunit, causing inactivation of the complex (144). The kinase is a heterodimer consisting of an α subunit, of M_r 48,000, which is thought to possess the catalytic activity, and a β subunit, of M_r 45,000 (124). The kinase is present in very small quantities and is bound tightly to the complex (61). Pyruvate dehydrogenase phosphatase catalyzes the dephosphorylation of E1α, with the concomitant activation of the complex (61). The phosphatase is bound rather loosely to the complex and is a heterodimer of M_r 140,000–150,000; the subunits have M_r of 97,000 and 50,000 (129).

Human pyruvate dehydrogenase complex has been the subject of intense scrutiny because of clinical manifestations of several genetic deficiencies. The genes encoding both pyruvate dehydrogenase subunits (E1α and E1β), dihydrolipoamide transacetylase (E2), and dihydrolipoamide dehydrogenase (E3) have been cloned and sequenced; some of these genes have been isolated as distinct tissue- or growth stage-dependent isotypes.

cDNAs encoding human E1α have been cloned and sequenced by several different laboratories (20, 23, 48, 60). Differential expression of testis-specific versus somatic isoforms of the E1α gene has been reported (127); the testis-specific form has been localized to chromosome 4, while the X chromosome contains the somatic E1α gene (5, 19, 126). Evidence has been presented for the existence of a 5'-upstream enhancer region common to several enzymes involved in mitochondrial energy production, including E1α (74, 131). The gene encoding human E1β has been isolated and sequenced (13, 47, 51, 60) and has been localized to chromosome 3 (13).

Pyruvate dehydrogenase (E1) catalyzes the oxidative decarboxylation of pyruvate, and the reaction is the rate-limiting step in the overall reaction catalyzed by the pyruvate dehydrogenase complex. The reaction is completely dependent upon the cofactor, thiamin pyrophosphate; titrations with the transition state analog thiamine thiazoline pyrophosphate, which irreversibly inhibits pyruvate dehydrogenase, indicate that there are two thiamin pyrophosphate binding sites per tetramer (40). The enzymatic reaction also requires Mg^{2+}, which presumably complexes with the pyrophosphate linkage of thiamin pyrophosphate to facilitate binding (133).

Thiamin pyrophosphate contains an acidic proton that dissociates and results in the carbanion of thiamin pyrophosphate. This species then attacks the carbonyl carbon of pyruvate and forms CO_2 and enzyme-bound 2-α-hydroxy-ethylthiamin pyrophosphate, which then reacts with oxidized lipoic acid, in the presence of the other cofactors, to generate S-acetylhydrolipoate and free thiamin pyrophosphate.

The gene encoding dihydrolipoamide transacetylase (E2) has been cloned and sequenced from several sources, including human liver (130), human heart (79), and human placenta (30). Some differences exist among the deduced amino acid sequences; tissue-specific isoforms of E2 may occur (79).

E2 functions both as a structural and as a catalytic element; in addition to forming the core about which the other component elements of PDC are arranged, E2 catalyzes the transfer of acetyl groups from S-acetylhydrolipoate to CoA (8). Gene sequencing and genetic engineering have elucidated the multidomain structure of E2 (67, 130). The N-terminal portion of the protein consists of two identical copies of a lipoyl-bearing region (107). Each copy is capable of being lipoylated and acetylated (87), and each is adjacent to a conformationally flexible amino acid segment that is required for proper function of the complex (78); this "tether" links the lipoyl domains to the next domain, the putative E1 binding site. The C-terminal portion of E2 comprises the catalytic region. All dihydrolipoamide transacetylases contain the sequence His-Xaa-Xaa-Xaa-Asp-Gly near the C-terminus; this highly conserved sequence is present in chloramphenicol acetyltransferase (CAT) and is thought to be involved in the catalytic mechanism (38). Asp-431 to Asn, Ala, or Glu substitutions in the yeast E2 lead to substantial decreases in kcat; however, His-427 to Asn or Ala substitutions have no significant effect on E2 activity (80). Replacement of a conserved serine residue in *E. coli* E2, analogous to a conserved serine in CAT, supports the active-site hypothesis (109); an Arg-416 to Asp mutation in *Azotobacter vinelandii* E2, again a residue thought to be involved in the active site by analogy to CAT, had no effect on the catalytic activity of E2 (114).

Dihydrolipoamide dehydrogenase (E3) has been cloned and sequenced from human liver (95) and human small cell carcinoma (H378) (85) and has been localized to chromosome 7 (86). E3 catalyzes the oxidation of dihydrolipoic acid to lipoic acid, with the subsequent reduction of NAD^+ to NADH. Each molecule of the E3 homodimer contains single FAD and NAD^+ binding sites, as well as a highly conserved active-site residue (His-452) in the C-terminal interface region (9).

REGULATION OF THE PYRUVATE DEHYDROGENASE COMPLEX

The location of the various α-keto acid multienzyme complexes in the energy-generating pathways of most aerobic tissues/cells is illustrated in Figure 2. The mammalian pyruvate dehydrogenase complex is associated with the mitochondrial inner membrane and is a key enzyme in cellular metabolism; it irreversibly commits three-carbon intermediates derived from the catabolism of carbohydrate (i.e. glucose) or certain amino acids to conversion to acetyl-CoA. Subsequently, acetyl-CoA is oxidized in the tricarboxylic acid cycle or incorporated into long-chain fatty acids. Because of its location at a significant branch-point in the metabolic pathways channeling intermediates into the tricarboxylic acid cycle, the pyruvate dehydrogenase complex is an ideal candidate as a regulatory enzyme. For example, in liver the activity of pyruvate dehydrogenase must be suppressed under gluconeogenic conditions when pyruvate is needed to synthesize oxaloacetate for the pyruvate carboxylase reaction. During lipogenesis, increased pyruvate dehydrogenase

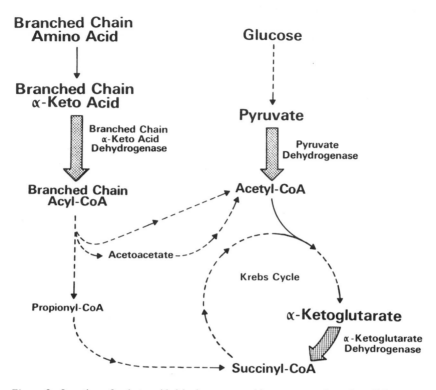

Figure 2 Location of α-keto acid dehydrogenase multienzyme complexes in cellular energy metabolism.

activity is required to supply acetyl-CoA for fatty acid or sterol biosynthesis. Also, pyruvate dehydrogenase in cardiac tissue needs to be able to react rapidly to increased work load by increasing its activity. In the presence of alternative substrates such as fatty acids or ketone bodies, suppression of pyruvate dehydrogenase activity is necessary to allow "sparing" of carbohydrate for other tissues (such as the brain) that are dependent upon glucose for essential energy metabolism. Thus, the regulatory systems for pyruvate dehydrogenase need to be sensitive both to the bioenergetic and biosynthetic requirements of various tissues of diverse function.

Two separate types of regulatory mechanisms have been characterized in order to accommodate the complexities of tissue- specific metabolic requirements in which pyruvate dehydrogenase is involved in higher organisms. The first mechanism, which is also the simplest, is merely end-product inhibition of the catalytically active pyruvate dehydrogenase complex. The second mechanism involves covalent modification of the complex by a phosphorylation/dephosphorylation mechanism, mediated by a specific protein kinase that is tightly bound to the enzyme complex and by a specific phosphoprotein phosphatase that is much less tightly associated with the pyruvate dehydrogenase complex.

For many years, investigators have observed experimentally that, in the presence of an alternative substrate such as fatty acid or ketone bodies, carbohydrate utilization by tissues such as heart is inhibited (31, 120, 143). A severe inhibition of pyruvate oxidation is responsible for this "carbohydrate-sparing" effect, and early attempts to elucidate the mechanism responsible for this type of inhibitory action on pyruvate dehydrogenase centered on end-product inhibition of the enzyme complex by NADH and acetyl-CoA. Studies using a partially purified preparation of pig heart pyruvate dehydrogenase demonstrated that the enzyme complex is inhibited by the end products of the pyruvate dehydrogenase reaction, NADH and acetyl-CoA (32, 55). Similar feedback inhibition of pyruvate dehydrogenase has been demonstrated using pyruvate dehydrogenase from a wide variety of cell and tissues. Values for the inhibition constant (K_i) from several mammalian systems for NADH (approximately 50 μM) and acetyl-CoA (5–10 μM) are similar to the K_m values for NAD$^+$ (approximately 60 μM) and CoASH (approximately 5 μM). Thus, under metabolic conditions causing elevated NADH$^+$/NAD$^+$ or acetyl-CoA/CoASH, the pyruvate dehydrogenase reaction should be inhibited.

The regulation of pyruvate dehydrogenase by a phosphorylation/dephosphorylation mechanism was first demonstrated in 1969 in the laboratory of Reed (70), using purified bovine kidney pyruvate dehyrogenase complex. The kinase and phosphatase reactions have since been demonstrated in a wide range of eukaryotic tissues (53, 69, 122, 128, 136). Pyruvate dehydrogenase is phosphorylated and inactivated by its specific, intrinsic, cAMP-independent protein kinase, using MgATP as substrate (14, 49). Reactivation of the enzyme complex is accomplished by a Mg^{2+}- and Ca^{2+}-dependent phosphoprotein phosphatase, which removes the phosphoryl groups from the phosphorylated enzyme.

The pyruvate dehydrogenase kinase/phosphatase system is regulated by a number of effectors, which are summarized in the cartoon depicted in Figure 3. Pyruvate dehydrogenase kinase is inhibited competitively with respect to ATP by ADP (69, 122, 138), and noncompetitively by pyruvate (14). ADP inhibition of the pyruvate dehydrogenase kinase is increased by the presence of K$^+$ or NH$_4$$^+$ because of lowering of the apparent K_i for ADP (106). On the other hand Robertson et al (102) demonstrated that monovalent cations stimulate pyruvate dehydrogenase kinase from bovine heart. The pyruvate dehydrogenase kinase is inhibited by NAD$^+$ and CoASH, and stimulated by NADH and acetyl-CoA (2, 3, 15, 93). Calcium also inhibits phosphorylation; half-maximal inhibition occurs at 0.5 mM (137). The coenzyme thiamin

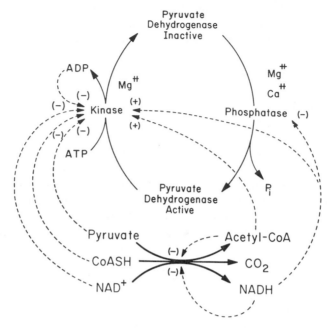

Figure 3 Regulatory mechanisms for pyruvate dehydrogenase by feedback inhibition and covalent modification via the protein kinase/phosphophoprotein phosphatase mechanism.

pyrophosphate inhibits phosphorylation, apparently by binding at the catalytic site of E1 to promote a conformational change, which in turn causes one of the serine hydroxyl groups on the α subunit of the pyruvate dehydrogenase to become less accessible to the pyruvate dehydrogenase kinase (7).

Regulation of the pyruvate dehydrogenase phosphatase appears to be less complicated than the regulation of the kinase. The phosphatase reaction requires Mg^{2+}, exhibiting a K_m of about 2 mM (121). Ca^{2+} stimulates the phosphatase reaction indirectly by facilitating binding of the phosphatase to the transacetylase core, thus enhancing dephosphorylation (94). NADH inhibits phosphatase activity and the inhibition is reversed by NAD^+ (93).

Another mechanism that has been proposed for the regulation of pyruvate dehydrogenase involves acetylation and/or acylation of the enzyme complex. Stimulation of the pyruvate dehydrogenase kinase activity by acetyl-CoA and NADH is thought to be due to acetylation and reduction, respectively, of the transacetylase lipoyl moieties (56, 104). Acetylation of dihydrolipoyl moieties of the pyruvate dehydrogenase complex has been demonstrated using [3-^{14}C]pyruvate and [1-^{14}C]acetyl-S-CoA (10, 11); the acetylated enzyme displays enhanced kinase activity, which is stable to gel filtration (10), and the extent of acetylation correlates with the degree of protein kinase activation (11). Reed's laboratory, using purified protein kinase and tryptic peptide substrates from the E1 dehydrogenase subunit, provided evidence, however, that NADH and acetyl-CoA have direct stimulatory effects on the pyruvate dehydrogenase kinase and that pyruvate has a direct inhibitory effect on the kinase (100).

Jackson & Singer (52) demonstrated that pyruvate dehydrogenase could be inactivated by incubation with α-ketoisovalerate and suggested that the formation of isobutyrylated lipoate residues was responsible. Further, they suggested that inactivation of pyruvate dehydrogenase by α-keto-isovalerate may contribute to the toxicity of elevated branched chain α-keto acids, as seen in maple syrup urine disease. Studies from this laboratory using rat liver mitochondria and the bovine heart complex (101) demonstrated directly the acylation of the E2 transacetylase by α-ketoisovalerate. Acylation of pyruvate dehydrogenase led to enhanced inactivation of the enzyme by kinase-mediated phosphorylation of the E1 component.

Pettit et al (92) demonstrated that pyruvate dehydrogenase kinase activity could be regulated by exchange of protein thiols and disulfides. These results suggested that thiol groups were responsible for maintaining the protein kinase in an active conformation; inhibition of the kinase by disulfides was specific and was reversed by thiols. Pettit et al suggested that naturally occurring disulfides may play an important role in the regulation of this protein kinase.

Regulation of Pyruvate Dehydrogenase in Specific Tissues

The discovery that a specific kinase and phosphatase interconvert purified pyruvate dehydrogenase complex between an active and inactive form immediately indicated that the enzyme must be phosphorylated to a greater or lesser extent in vivo and that the phosphorylation state in vivo must control the relative activity of the enzyme. Incubations of beef heart mitochondria in the presence of $[\gamma\text{-}^{32}P]ATP$ and SDS gel analysis of mitochondrial extracts demonstrated that the γ-phosphate of labelled ATP could be detected in the α subunit of pyruvate dehydrogenase, and thereby provided direct support in an intact metabolic system for pyruvate dehydrogenase inactivation by phosphorylation (118).

Estimates of the relative pyruvate dehydrogenase activity state in vivo using measurements of enzymatic activity in extracts of freeze-clamped tissue both before and after incubation with purified phosphatase have been made (140). In this method, the first assay measures the amount of "active" enzyme, whereas the second assay measures the amount of "total" enzyme, or the amount expressed only after complete activation by dephosphorylation. The active/total ratio reflects the percent activity in vivo. Measurement of the percent activity has been used extensively by many investigators to demonstrate pyruvate dehydrogenase regulation in vivo under a variety of conditions.

Heart and kidney tissue in fed rats normally contain about 70% active pyruvate dehydrogenase (140). However, fasting or induction of experimental diabetes decreases active enzyme to about 15% (140). In human skeletal muscle after a 12-hr fast, the enzyme is only about 20% active (123). Similar effects occur in heart muscle of normal and obese hyperglycemic mice (71). These effects can be reversed by insulin administration or refeeding. Brain tissue also contains about 70% active enzyme, but starvation has no effect on the activation state of the enzyme in brain (122). In contrast, liver and adipose tissue normally contain only about 20% active enzyme, and starvation or diabetes has no effect on the activation state in these tissues (137). Also, age appears to affect both the activation state and regulation of the enzyme. For example, the fetal rat liver enzyme exists in the fully activated state, in contrast to the normal liver (135), and the adipose tissue enzyme decreases as the rat matures (54). The metabolic factors responsible for the observed in vivo percent active enzyme are complex. Under some selected experimental conditions, such as in isolated mitochondria in the presence of various uncouplers and inhibitors, separate effects on the kinase and phosphatase can be estimated, whereas under steady-state conditions, such as in isolated mitochondria or in perfused organs, only the overall regulatory effects of certain parameters can be measured. In the case of the heart enzyme, originally it was suggested that pyruvate dehydrogenase exists naturally in its inactive form, and that activation occurs as Mg^{2+} becomes available to initiate dephosphorylation by the phosphatase (117, 139). Studies in rabbit heart mitochondria subsequently indicated that this may not be the case and that the enzyme most likely exists in the active form under most metabolic conditions, even in the presence of high ATP concentrations, in agreement with the observed percent active enzyme found in heart tissue from normally fed rats (116). In contrast to the idea that Mg^{2+} stimulates the phosphatase in vivo, decreased pyruvate oxidation in intact heart mitochondria, and hence pyruvate dehydrogenase inactivation, depends on increased Mg^{2+} and occurs at various ATP concentrations (115, 116). In the presence of ATP, metabolic conditions resulting in the release of Mg^{2+}, for example, uncoupler plus ADP (62), lead to an inhibition of pyruvate oxidation, presumably through the kinase/phosphatase interconversion system (116). Only during prolonged incubation in the absence of substrate or ATP does Mg^{2+} cause an activation of pyruvate dehydrogenase by phosphatase stimulation, and hence these conditions usually suffice for determining "total" enzyme only as an experimental tool.

Studies of the steady-state activity of pyruvate dehydrogenase in rat heart mitochondria, where both kinase and phosphatase are active, and under conditions where the effects of each effector couple can be segregated from the others, indicate that the CoA/acetyl-CoA, NAD^+/NADH, and ADP/ATP ratios all contribute to the steady-state activity (3, 42). At a fixed ratio of two effector couples, for example, shifting the third couple up or down increases or decreases the steady-state activity of pyruvate dehydrogenase. At a fixed ADP/ATP ratio of 3.5, which might plausibly represent the ratio during state 3 respiration, shifting either the CoA/acetyl-CoA or NAD^+/NADH ratio results in a 2-fold change in steady-state activity, but shifting both ratios at the same time produces an additive effect of more than a 4-fold change in steady-state activity. At a lower ADP/ATP ratio, shifting the CoA/acetyl-CoA ratio only affects the steady-state activity under highly oxidized conditions, such as NAD^+/NADH = 11.

In the perfused rat heart, the percent active enzyme complex depends on the perfusate pyruvate concentration (25). At low pyruvate concentrations the enzyme is almost 100% active. As the pyruvate concentration increases to 1 mM, the percent active enzyme steadily decreases to about 50% active. Then, as pyruvate continues to increase from 1 mM to 10 mM, the percent of active enzyme returns to almost 100% active. The decrease in the percent of active enzyme is consistent with decreases in the CoA/acetyl-CoA and NAD^+/NADH ratios measured in the same hearts, but the return to 100% active enzyme at high pyruvate concentrations cannot be explained by changes in these ratios. The reactivation is more consistent with kinase inhibition by pyruvate (25). Moreover, pyruvate concentrations have a major role in determining the activation state during flow-induced ischemia in the heart (90).

Regulation of the activation state by changing the concentration of infused pyruvate also involves regulation of pyruvate entry into the mitochondria via the monocarboxylate transporter. In the perfused rat heart, transport inhibition by α-cyanocinnamate and α-cyano-4-hydroxycinnamate suggests that pyruvate enters the mitochondria at low concentrations primarily via the transport system, whereas at high pyruvate concentrations a degree of passive diffusion occurs that cannot be blocked by either transport inhibitor (134). At low to intermediate pyruvate concentrations (0.2–1 mM), addition of transport inhibitor to the perfused heart decreases the flux of pyruvate through the enzyme complex and simultaneously converts the enzyme to 100% active form (134). This data further supports the idea that lowering the pyruvate concentration regulates interconversion, and suggests the possibility that factors influencing exchange rates on the translocator, for example, changes in concentrations of counter ions leaving the mitochondria, might make pyruvate entry rate limiting and thus link pyruvate dehydrogenase activity to metabolic processes producing counter ions (134).

Increases in fatty acid concentrations provide heart tissue with its preferred fuel source and cause major metabolic changes in the tissue. Studies conducted during the 1960s showed that the availability of fatty acids, ketones, acetate, or long-chain acylcarnitine derivatives substantially decreases pyruvate oxidation in rat heart (28, 97). Subsequently, many similar experiments have confirmed these effects and characterized them in terms of feedback inhibition and interconversion between the active and inactive forms of pyruvate dehydrogenase. In rat heart mitochondria, for example, palmitoylcarnitine oxidation in the presence of 50 μM pyruvate inhibits pyruvate dehydrogenase activity 61%, whereas there is little or no inhibition as the pyruvate concentration increases to 500 μM (43). Although the CoA/acetyl-CoA ratio clearly plays a major regulatory role under these conditions, the relative importance of feedback inhibition of the overall enzyme complex versus direct effects on the kinase is difficult to measure (3, 44). Moreover, not only may the CoA/acetyl-CoA ratio be important but so too may be the absolute concentration of acetyl-CoA (84).

In the perfused rat heart, substrates such as acetoacetate, β-hydroxybutyrate, and octanoate rapidly inhibit as much as 90% of the flux of [$^{14}CO_2$] production from labelled pyruvate (83). However, the percent of active enzyme decreases only by about 50%, which suggests that more than one regulatory effect governs overall flux through the enzyme under these conditions. Direct feedback inhibition by measured increases in acetyl-CoA concentrations in these hearts more than likely accounts for the additional inhibition of flux beyond the decrease in the percent active enzyme. Similarly, in the presence of dichloroacetate to inhibit kinase activity, acetate inhibits the flux of pyruvate through the enzyme complex. Even at 10 mM dichloroacetate, when the enzyme is 100% active, acetate causes a 35% decrease in flux through the enzyme complex. Moreover, in the presence of 10 mM pyruvate, when the enzyme again is 100% active, acetate and octanoate respectively inhibit 27% and 64% of flux through the enzyme complex but change only 2% and 6% of the percent of active enzyme. These experiments demonstrated that both regulatory systems, feedback inhibition and interconversion, operate in the perfused heart.

The regulatory effects of fatty acids and ketone bodies on the pyruvate dehydrogenase complex in the isolated perfused rat liver have been studied extensively in our laboratory. We observed that infusion of fatty acids into livers at a low, physiological concentration (0.05 mM) of pyruvate actually stimulated the decarboxylation of [1-^{14}C]pyruvate. However, at higher pyruvate concentrations, the often observed inhibition of the pyruvate dehydrogenase reaction occurred (24, 89, 113, 145). On the basis of these experimental results, we proposed that fatty acids or any other precursor of acetoacetate (i.e. α-ketoisocaproate, acetate, or β-hydroxybutyrate) stimulate pyruvate dehydrogenase in the liver by an exchange transport mechanism via the monocarboxylate translocator. This suggestion is illustrated schematically in Figure 4, which indicates that when ketogenesis (intramitochondrial acetoacetate synthesis) is stimulated at low cytosolic pyruvate levels, pyruvate-acetoacetate exchange on the translocator is stimulated. The increase in mitochondrial pyruvate inhibits the pyruvate dehydrogenase kinase, thereby activating the pyruvate dehydrogenase complex (88).

Under normal physiological conditions, glycolysis and the pyruvate dehydrogenase complex play a very important role in brain energy metabolism (63). In contrast to the enzyme in other tissues, pyruvate dehydrogenase activity in brain is not reduced by starvation (122), and remains about 70% active (4, 122). The insensitivity of brain pyruvate dehydrogenase to starvation is thought to be due to the ability of pyruvate to protect the enzyme from inactivation (4); the ability of brain mitochondria to accumulate a high concentration of pyruvate (64) might then maintain the enzyme in an active form and ensure a continuous supply of acetyl-CoA to the citric acid cycle.

Schaffer & Olson (112) demonstrated a rapid increase in $[1-^{14}C]$ pyruvate decarboxylation and in the active proportion of pyruvate dehydrogenase following synaptosomal membrane depolarization. Alternative substrates such as octanoate, acetate, and 3-hydroxybutyrate had no effect on the activation state of the enzyme, in contrast to other tissues (112). Studies using hippocampus slices have demonstrated that pyruvate dehydrogenase becomes phosphorylated during high frequency synaptic stimulation (6). Further studies have suggested a link between activity of brain pyruvate dehydrogenase and calcium uptake by brain mitochondria. Conditions favoring dephosphorylation of brain pyruvate dehydrogenase also increase pyruvate-supported calcium uptake (6).

Regulation of Pyruvate Dehydrogenase by Hormones

Several hormones influence regulatory mechanisms that control the activity of the pyruvate dehydrogenase complex in several tissues. For example, insulin stimulates pyruvate dehydrogenase activity several-fold in adipose tissue. While this response has been studied extensively, one cannot account for pyruvate dehydrogenase activation simply on the basis of changes in Ca^{2+} or changes in other known regulatory molecules within the mitochondria (16, 53, 135). In liver insulin appears to have only a very minor effect on enzyme activity (91). An indirect effect of insulin is to lower plasma free fatty acids in the whole rat and thereby cause enzyme activation by changing the substrates and metabolites in the liver. In the perfused rat heart, conflicting results have been reported. In diabetic rats, nicotinic acid alone lowers the concentration of free fatty acids but does not increase the percent active enzyme, whereas nicotinic acid plus insulin increases the percent active enzyme threefold in these hearts (81). Nevertheless, pyruvate dehydrogenase

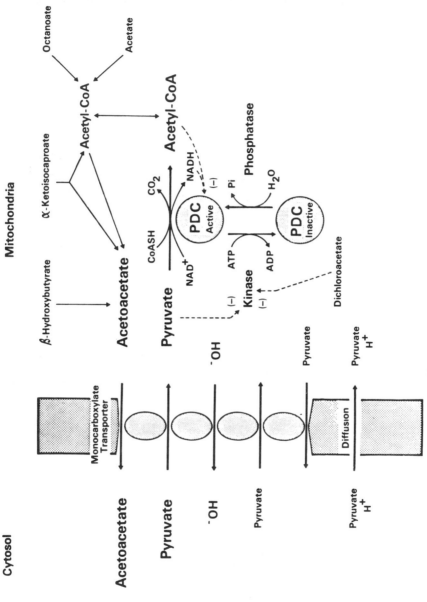

Figure 4 Regulation of the pyruvate dehydrogenase complex by pyruvate/acetoacetate exchange transport on the mitochondrial monocarboxylate transporter.

activation by insulin in diabetic hearts has not been confirmed by others (56). A separate report indicates that in beating mouse heart cells, in culture, insulin stimulates pyruvate oxidation, thereby suggesting enzyme activation in this system (119). Insulin has an activating effect on pyruvate dehydrogenase in lymphocytes (17). Cell-free preparations, from lymphocytes previously treated with insulin, are capable of stimulating pyruvate dehydrogenase activity (17, 18).

The precise signaling mechanism, from the insulin receptor on the cell surface to the pyruvate dehydrogenase complex located on the mitochondrial inner membrane, remains unresolved. Several mechanisms for the pyruvate dehydrogenase response to insulin have been proposed. Alteration of the phosphorylation state of intracellular proteins is a classical mode of insulin signal transduction. However, cell lines harboring mutant insulin receptors that are defective in tyrosine kinase activity are capable of insulin-stimulated pyruvate dehydrogenase activation (36). Several second messengers, activated by insulin binding to its receptor on the cell surface, have been proposed, including H_2O_2, Ca^{2+}, G proteins, and phosphatidylinositol metabolites (142).

One proposal for insulin signal transduction involving pyruvate dehydrogenase phosphatase activation depends upon the production of a small mediator molecule on the outside of the plasma membrane, which then interacts with yet another receptor on the cell surface. Several putative mediators of insulin responses have been characterized (37, 57, 65, 72, 111). One such mediator is derived from the glycophospholipid anchor of a membrane protein (65). Two extracellular enzymes, a *p*- aminobenzamidine-sensitive protease and phospholipase C, catalyze the release of the mediator into the extracellular space (65), where it could be available for both autocrine and paracrine regulation of pyruvate dehydrogenase. This mediator has a molecular weight of ~1000–1500, as judged by gel filtration; it contains D-chiro-inositol, galactosamine, and mannose; evidence suggests that the mediator contains ethanolamine, organic phosphorus, and possibly amino acids (65). Purified mediator can stimulate pyruvate dehydrogenase phosphatase in solution (65) by decreasing the divalent cation requirement of the phosphatase (68). A recently discovered, nonmetal ion-dependent, pyruvate dehydrogenase phosphatase from bovine heart mitochondria is also stimulated roughly threefold by this mediator (68).

A second type of small molecule mediator has been characterized (72, 110, 111); this substance is derived from treatment of an insulin-sensitive glycophospholipid with a phosphatidylinositol-specific phospholipase C (PI-PLC) (37). The polar head group resulting from this treatment was purified by gel filtration chromatography, and its activating effect in whole-cell assays was comparable to that of insulin, although the effect of the mediator declined after 10 min, as opposed to the longer-lasting effect of insulin (37). This mediator contains inositol, phosphate, glucosamine, and other monosaccharides (110).

Anti-inositol-glycan antibodies can selectively block a portion of the insulin-derived stimulation of pyruvate dehydrogenase (108); PI-PLC or a commercial nonspecific PLC can mimic the activating effect of insulin, but this activation is significantly less than that observed in insulin stimulation (73). Either or both of these small mediators may be responsible, in part, for insulin-triggered activation of pyruvate dehydrogenase.

Mediation of pyruvate dehydrogenase phosphatase by low-molecular-weight species that are generated at the cell surface would require the presence of transport mechanism(s) across the plasma membrane and the inner mitochondrial membrane. The long-term potentiation of pyruvate dehydrogenase phosphatase by insulin cannot be accounted for by these small mediators, especially in light of the observation that toluene-permeabilized mitochondria, isolated after insulin stimulation, maintain the active phosphatase under conditions in which the mediator could freely diffuse out of the mitochondria (26). Perhaps the existence, in the inner mitochondrial membrane, of a large molecular weight regulator that could be activated by the small mediator and then, in turn, cause activation of the pyruvate dehydrogenase phosphatase could account for the insulin effect.

In contrast to insulin, β-adenergic agonists and glucagon stimulate pyruvate oxidation to only a small extent in the perfused rat heart at intermediate to low pyruvate concentrations (46, 76). However, the effect can be demonstrated more clearly in the presence of fatty acids. For example, at 0.5 mM pyruvate, β-hydroxybutyrate decreases pyruvate dehydrogenase activity from about 50% to 28% and simultaneously decreases pyruvate oxidation. Under these inhibitory conditions, addition of isoproterenol increases the level of enzyme activity to about 72% and increases pyruvate oxidation approximately 3-fold (46). Addition of the β-receptor blocker propranolol prevents the β-agonist effect. Morever, the fact that both verapamil and A23187 prevent the β-agonist effect strongly suggests that Ca^{2+} movements are involved in the activation effect of β agonists in the perfused heart (46). Experiments with ruthenium red in the perfused rat heart also demonstrated a similar dependence on Ca^{2+} for enzyme activation (77).

Pyruvate Dehydrogenase Deficiency States

The pyruvate dehydrogenase complex is involved in several pathological conditions. Defects in one or more of the component enzymes of the complex are a major cause of primary lactic acidosis in infants and young children. Brain tissue, with its absolute requirement for aerobic glucose oxidation, appears to be a primary site for these metabolic lesions, with concomitant neurological symptoms. E1α is the major site of disruption, and mutations in the coding region of the gene account for the majority of the lesions reported (12, 22, 27, 41); one of these mutations involves a 21-base pair insertion of a tandem repeat which alters a serine phosphorylation site (22) that may be related to defective dephosphorylation of this subunit (58). The location of the E1α gene on the X chromosome may expose it to greater chance of damage (82). A mutant form of E1β, containing three frame shifts and an unusual 3' noncoding region, has been sequenced (51). Rapid proteolysis of uncomplexed E1α or E1β seems to indicate that a defect in one of the genes, which causes either low levels of expression of the subunit or production of a defective subunit, may lead to deficiencies of both pyruvate dehydrogenase subunits (50, 59). Although not as prevalent as E1 deficiencies, abnormalities in E2 and protein X (103) and E3 (45) have been reported.

Primary biliary cirrhosis is an autoimmune disease characterized by the production of antibodies against components of the pyruvate dehydrogenase complex (for recent review, see 33). The major autoantigen appears to be the E2 subunit, and the primary epitope is the inner lipoic acid binding domain. This site is conserved in protein X, thus making it another target of the autoimmune response (125). A third target is E1α; autoantibodies appear to be targeted against one of the functional sites of the protein (29).

Defects in TPP-containing enzymes, including pyruvate dehydrogenase, have been reported in brain and peripheral tissues from patients suffering from Alzheimer's disease (34).

ACKNOWLEDGMENTS

One of the authors (MSO) has been supported by NIH grant HL-24654.

Literature Cited

1. Barerra, C. R., Namihira, G., Hamilton, L., Munk, P., Eley, M. H., et al. 1972. α-Keto acid dehydrogenase complexes. XVI. Studies on the subunit structure of the pyruvate dehydrogenase complexes from bovine kidney and heart. *Arch. Biochem. Biophys.* 148: 343–58
2. Batenburg, J. J., Olson, M. S. 1975. Inactivation of pyruvate dehydrogenase by fatty acids in isolated rat liver mitochondria. *Biochem. Biophys. Res. Commun.* 66:533–40
3. Batenburg, J. J., Olson, M. S. 1976. Regulation of pyruvate dehydrogenase by fatty acid in isolated rat liver mitochondria. *J. Biol. Chem.* 241:1364–70
4. Booth, R. F. G., Clark, J. B. 1978.

The control of pyruvate dehydrogenase in isolated brain mitochondria. *J. Neurochem.* 30:1003–8
5. Brown, R. M., Dahl, H. H., Brown, G. K. 1989. X-chromosome localization of the functional gene for the E1 alpha subunit of the human pyruvate dehydrogenase complex. *Genomics* 4: 174–81
6. Browning, M., Baudry, M., Bennett, W. E., Lynch, G. 1981. Phosphorylation-mediated changes in pyruvate dehydrogenase activity influence pyruvate-supported calcium accumulation by brain mitochondria. *J. Neurochem.* 36:1932–40
7. Butler, J. R., Pettit, F. H., Davis, P. F., Reed, L. J. 1977. Binding of TPP to mammalian pyruvate dehydrogenase

and its effects on kinase and phosphatase activity. *Biochem. Biophys. Res. Commun.* 74:1667–74

8. Butterworth, P. J., Tsai, C. S., Eley, M. H., Roche, T. E., Reed, L. J. 1975. A kinetic study of dihydrolipoyl transacetylase from bovine kidney. *J. Biol. Chem.* 250:1921–25

9. Carothers, D. J., Pons, G., Patel, M. S. 1989. Dihydrolipoamide dehydrogenase: functional similarities and divergent evolution of the pyridine nucleo-tide-disulfide oxidoreductases. *Arch. Biochem. Biophys.* 268:409–25

10. Cate, R. L., Roche, T. E. 1978. A unifying mechanism for stimulation of pyruvate dehydrogenase kinase by NADH, dihydrolipoamide, acetyl CoA and pyruvate. *J. Biol. Chem.* 253:496–503

11. Cate, R. L., Roche, T. E. 1979. Function and regulation of mammalian pyruvate dehydrogenase complex. *J. Biol. Chem.* 254:1659–65

12. Chun, K., Mackay, N., Petrova-Benedict R., Robinson, B. H. 1991. Pyruvate dehydrogenase deficiency due to a 20-bp deletion in exon II of the pyruvate dehydrogenase (PDH) E1 alpha gene. *Am. J. Hum. Gen.* 49:414–20

13. Chun, K., Mackay, N., Willard, H. F., Robinson B. H. 1990. Isolation, characterization and chromosomal localization of clones for the E1 beta subunit of the pyruvate dehydrogenase complex. *Eur. J. Biochem.* 194:587–92

14. Cooper, R. H., Randle, P. J., Denton, R. M. 1974. Regulation of heart muscle pyruvate dehydrogenase kinase. *Biochem. J.* 143:625–41

15. Cooper, R. H., Randle, P. J., Denton, R. M. 1975. Stimulation of phosphorylation and inactivation of pyruvate dehydrogenase by inhibitors of the pyruvate dehydrogenase reaction. *Nature* 257:808–9

16. Coore, H. G., Denton, R. M., Martin, B. R., Randle, P. J. 1971. Regulation of adipose tissue pyruvate dehydrogenase by insulin and other hormones.*Biochem. J.* 125:115–27

17. Curto, M., Piccinini, M., Bruno, R., Mostert, M., Rinaudo, M. T. 1988. Insulin modulation of pyruvate dehydrogenase in human circulating lymphocytes. *Int. J. Biochem.* 20:1211–17

18. Curto, M., Piccinini, M., Marino, C., Mostert, M., Bruno, R., Rinaudo, M. T. 1990. Pyruvate dehydrogenase activation by insulin in human circulating lymphocytes and the possible pathway involved. *Int. J. Biochem.* 22:99–106

19. Dahl, H. H., Brown, R. M., Hutchison, W. M., Maragos, C., Brown, G. K. 1990. A testis-specific form of the human pyruvate dehydrogenase E1 alpha subunit is coded for by an intronless gene on chromosome 4. *Genomics* 8:225–32

20. Dahl, H. H., Hunt, S. M., Hutchison, W. M., Brown, G. K. 1987. The human pyruvate dehydrogenase complex isolation of cDNA clones for the E1 alpha subunit, sequence analysis and characterization of the mRNA. *J. Biol. Chem.* 262:7398–402

21. DeMarcucci, O., Lindsay, J. L. 1985. Component X. An immunologically distinct polypeptide associated with mammalian pyruvate dehydrogenase multienzyme complex. *Eur. J. Biochem.* 262:7398–403

22. De Meirleir, L., Lissens, W., Vamos, E., Liebaers, I. 1992. Pyruvate dehydrogenase (PDH) deficiency caused by a 21-base pair insertion mutation in the E1 alpha subunit. *Hum. Genet.* 88:649–52

23. De Meirleir, L., Mackay, N., Wah, A. M. L. H., Robinson, B. 1988. Isolation of a full-length complementary DNA coding for human E1 alpha subunit of the pyruvate dehydrogenase complex. *J. Biol. Chem.* 263:1991–95

24. Dennis, S. C., DeBuysere, M., Scholz, R., Olson, M. S. 1978. Studies on the relationship between ketogenesis and pyruvate oxidation in isolated rat liver mitochondria. *J. Biol. Chem.* 253:2229–37

25. Dennis, S. C., Padma, A., DeBuysere, M. S., Olson, M. S. 1979. Studies on the regulation of pyruvate dehydrogenase in the isolated perfused rat heart. *J. Biol. Chem.* 254:1252–58

26. Denton, R. M., Midgley, J. W. P., Rutter, G. A., Thomas, A. P., McCormack, J. G. 1989. Studies into the mechanism whereby insulin activates pyruvate. *Ann. NY Acad. Sci.* 573:274

27. Endo, H., Miyabayaski, S., Tada, K., Narisawa, K. 1991. A four-nucleotide insertion of the E1 alpha gene in a patient with pyruvate dehydrogenase deficiency. *J. Inherit. Metab. Dis.* 14:793–99

28. Evans, J. R., Opie, L. H., Renold, A. E. 1963. Pyruvate metabolism in the perfused rat heart. *Am. J. Physiol.* 205:971–76

29. Fregeau, D. R., Roche, T. E., Davis, P. A., Coppel, R., Gershwin, M. E. 1990. Primary biliary cirrhosis: inhibition of pyruvate dehydrogenase complex activity by autoantibodies specific

for E1, a non-lipoic acid containing mitochondrial enzyme. *J. Immunol.* 144:1671–76

30. Fussey, S. P. M., Guest, J. R., James, O. F. J., Bassendine M. F., Yeaman, S. J. 1988. Identification and analysis of the major M2 autoantigens in primary biliary cirrhosis. *Proc. Natl. Acad. Sci. USA* 85:8654–58

31. Garland, P. B., Newsholme, E. A., Randle, P. J. 1964. Effects of fatty acids and ketone bodies and of alloxan diabetes and starvation on pyruvate metabolism. *Biochem. J.* 93:665–78

32. Garland, P. B., Randle, P. J. 1964. Control of pyruvate dehydrogenase in the perfused heart by the intracellular concentration of acetyl-CoA. *Biochem. J.* 91:6–7

33. Gershwin, M. E., Mackay, I. R. 1991. Primary biliary cirrhosis: paradigm or paradox for auto immunity. *Gastroenterology* 100:822–33

34. Gibson, G. E., Sheu, K. G., Blass, J. P., Baker, A., Carlson, K. C., et al. 1988. Reduced activities of thiamine-dependent enzymes in the brains and peripheral tissues of patients with Alzheimer's disease.*Arch. Neurol.* 45:836–40

35. Gopalakrishnan, S., Rahmatullah, M., Radke, G. A., Powers-Greenwood, S. L., Roche, T. E. 1989. Role of protein X in the function of the mammalian pyruvate dehydrogenase complex. *Biochem. Biophys. Res. Commun.* 160:715–21

36. Gottschalk, W. K. 1991. The pathway mediating insulin's effects on pyruvate dehydrogenase bypasses the insulin receptor tyrosine kinase. *J. Biol. Chem.* 266:8814–19

37. Gottschalk, W. K., Jarett, L. 1988. The insulinomimetic effects of the polar head group of an insulin-sensitive glycophospholipid on pyruvate dehydrogenase in both subcellular and whole cell assays. *Arch. Biochem. Biophys.* 261:175–78

38. Guest, J. R. 1987. Functional implications of structural homologies between chloramphenicol acetyltransferase and dihydrolipoamide acetyl transferase. *FEMS Microbiol. Lett.* 44:417–22

39. Guest, J. R., Darlison, M. G., Spencer, M. E., Stephens, P. E. 1984. Cloning and sequence analysis of the private and 2-oxoglutarate dehydrogenase complex genes of *E. coli*. *Biochem. Soc. Trans.* 12:220–23

40. Gutowski, J. A., Lienhard, G. E.

1976. Transition state analogs for thiamin pyrophosphate-dependent enzymes. *J. Biol. Chem.* 251:2863–66

41. Hansen, L. L., Brown, G. K., Kirby, D. M., Dahl, H. H. 1991. Characterization of the mutations in three patients with pyruvate dehydrogenase E1 alpha deficiency. *J. Inherit. Metab. Dis.* 14:140–51

42. Hansford, R. G. 1976. Studies on the effects of coenzyme A-SH:acetyl coenzyme A, nicotinamide adenine dinucleotide, reduced nicotinamide adenine dinucleotide, and adenosine diphosphate: adenosine triphosphate ratios on the interconversion of active and inactive pyruvate dehydrogenase in isolated rat heart mitochondria. *J. Biol. Chem.* 251:5483–89

43. Hansford, R. G. 1977. Studies on inactivation of pyruvate dehydrogenase by palmitoylcarnitine oxidation in isolated rat heart mitochondria. *J. Biol. Chem.* 252:1552–60

44. Hansford, R. G., Cohen, L. 1978. Relative importance of pyruvate dehydrogenase interconversion and feedback inhibition in the effect of fatty acids on pyruvate oxidation by rat heart mitochondria. *Arch. Biochem. Biophys.* 191:65–81

45. Hinman, L. M., Sheu, K. F., Baker, A. C., Kim, Y. T., Blass, J. P. 1989. Deficiency of pyruvate dehydrogenase complex (PDHC) in Leigh's disease fibroblasts: an abnormality in lipoamide dehydrogenase affecting PDHC activation. *Neurology* 39:70–75

46. Hiraoka, T., DeBuysere, M. S., Olson, M. S. 1980. Studies of the effects of β-adrenergic agonists on the regulation of pyruvate dehydrogenase in the perfused rat heart. *J. Biol. Chem.* 255:7604–9

47. Ho, L., Javed, A. A., Pepin, R. A., Thekkumkara, T. J., Raefsky, C., et al. 1988. Identification of a cDNA clone for the beta-subunit of the pyruvate dehydrogenase component of human pyruvate dehydrogenase complex. *Biochem. Biophys. Res. Commun.* 150:904–8

48. Ho, L., Wexler, I. D., Liu, T. C., Thekkumkara, T. J., Patel, M. S. 1989. Characterization of cDNA's encoding human pyruvate dehydrogenase alpha subunit. *Proc. Natl. Acad. Sci. USA* 86:5330–34

49. Hucho, F., Randle, D. D., Roche, T. E., Burgett, M. W., Pelley, J. W., Reed, L. J. 1972. Kinetic and regulatory properties of pyruvate dehydrogenase kinase and phosphatase from

bovine kidney and heart. *Arch. Biochem. Biophys.* 151:328–40

50. Huh, A. H., Ito, M., Naito, E., Saijo, T., Takeda, E., Kuroda, Y. 1991. Demonstration of an unstable variant of pyruvate dehydrogenase protein (e1) in cultured fibroblasts from a patient with congenital lactic acidemia. *Pediatr. Res.* 30:11–14

51. Huh, T. L., Cassazza, J. P., Huh, J. W., Chi, Y. T., Song, B. J. 1990. Characterization of two cDNA clones for pyruvate dehydrogenase E1 beta subunit and its regulation in tricarboxylic acid cycle-deficient fibroblast. *J. Biol. Chem.* 265:13320–26

52. Jackson, R. H., Singer, T. P. 1983. Inactivation of the α-ketoglutarate and pyruvate dehydrogenase complexes of beef heart by branched chain keto acids. *J. Biol. Chem.* 258:1857–65

53. Jungas, R. L. 1971. Hormonal regulation of pyruvate dehydrogenase. *Metabolism* 20:43–53

54. Kankel, K.-F., Reinauer, H. 1976. Activity of the pyruvate dehydrogenase complex in the mammary gland of normal and diabetic rats. *Diabetologia* 12:149–54

55. Kanzaki, T., Hayakawa, T., Hamada, M., Fukuyoski, Y., Koike, M. 1969. Mammalian α-keto acid dehydrogenase complexes: substrate specificities of the pig heart pyruvate dehydrogenase and α-ketoglutarate dehydrogenase complexes. *J. Biol. Chem.* 244:1183–87

56. Kerbey, A. L., Randle, P. J., Cooper, R. H., Whitehouse, S., Pask, H. T., Denton, R. M. 1976. Regulation of pyruvate dehydrogenase in rat heart-mechanism of regulation of proportions of dephosphorylated and phosphorylated enzyme by oxidation of fatty acids and ketone bodies and of effects of diabetes: role of coenzyme A, acetyl-coenzyme A and reduced and oxidized nicotinamide-adenine dinucleotide. *Biochem. J.* 154:327–48

57. Kilgour, E., Vernon, R. G. 1991. Insulin promotes the release from rat mammary gland plasma membranes of a factor which activates mitochondrial pyruvate dehydrogenase. *Horm. Metab. Res.* 23:349–50

58. Kitano, A., Endo, F., Matsuda, I. 1990. Immunochemical analysis of pyruvate dehydrogenase complex in 2 boys with primary lactic acidemia. *Neurology* 40:1312–14

59. Kitano, A., Endo, F., Matsuda, I., Miyabayaski, S., Dahl, H. H. 1989. Mutation of the E1 alpha subunit of the pyruvate dehydrogenase complex, in relation to heterogeneity. *J. Inherit. Metab. Dis.* 12:97–107

60. Koike, K., Ohta, S., Urata, Y., Kagawa, Y., Koike, M. 1988. Cloning and sequence of cDNa's encoding alpha & beta subunits of human pyruvate dehydrogenase. *Proc. Natl. Acad. Sci. USA* 85:41–45

61. Koike, M., Shah, P. C., Reed, L. J. 1960. α-Keto acid dehydrogenation complexes. III. purification and properties of dihydrolipoyl dehydrogenase of *Escherichia coli*. *J. Biol. Chem.* 235:1939–43

62. Kun, E., Kearney, E. B., Wiedemann, I., Lee, N. M. 1969. Regulation of mitochondrial metabolism by specific cellular substances. II. The nature of stimulation of mitochondrial glutamate metabolism by a cytoplasmic component. *Biochemistry* 8:4443–49

63. Land, J. M., Booth, R. F. G., Berger, R., Clark, J. B. 1977. Development of mitochondrial energy metabolism in the rat brain. *Biochem. J.* 164:339–48

64. Land, J. M., Moubray, J., Clark, J. B. 1976. Control of pyruvate and β-hydroxybutyrate utilization in rat brain mitochondria and its relevance to phenylketonuria and MSUD. *J. Neurochem.* 26:823–30

65. Larner, J., Huang, C., Suzuki, S., Tang, G., Zhang, C., et al. 1989. Insulin mediators and the control of pyruvate dehydrogenase complex. *Ann. NY Acad. Sci.* 573:279

66. Lawson, J. E., Behal, R. H., Reed, L. J. 1991. Disruption and mutagenesis of the *Saccharomyces cerevisiae* PDX1 gene encoding the protein X component of the pyruvate dehydrogenase complex. *Biochemistry* 30:2834–39

67. Lawson, J. E., Niu, X. D., Reed, L. J. 1991. Functional analysis of the domains of dihydrolipoamide acetyltransferase from *Saccharomyces cerevisiae*. *Biochemistry* 30:11249–54

68. Lilley, K., Zhang, C., Villar-Palasi, C., Larner, J., Huang, L. 1992. Insulin mediator stimulation of pyruvate dehydrogenase phosphatases. *Arch. Biochem. Biophys.* 296:170–74

69. Linn, T. C., Pettit, F. H., Hucho, F., Reed, L. J. 1969. Comparative studies of regulatory properties of the pyruvate dehydrogenase complexes from kidney, heart and liver mitochondria. *Proc. Natl. Acad. Sci. USA* 64:227–34

70. Linn, T. C., Pettit, F. H., Reed, L. J. 1969. Regulation of the activity of the pyruvate dehydrogenase complex from beef kidney mitochondria by phos-

phorylation and dephosphorylation. *Proc. Natl. Acad. Sci. USA* 62:234–41

71. Lombardo, Y. B., Menahan, L. A. 1978. Pyruvate dehydrogenase activity in several tissues of genetically obese hyperglycemic mice. *Life Sci.* 22:1033–42

72. Macaulay, S. L., Larkins, R. G. 1990. Isolation of insulin-sensitive phosphatidylinositol-glycan from rat adipocytes. Its impaired breakdown in the streptozotocin-diabetic rat. *Biochem. J.* 271: 427–35

73. Macaulay, S. L., Larkins, R. G. 1990. Phospholipase C mimics insulin action on pyruvate dehydrogenase and insulin mediator generation but not glycose transport or utilization. *Cell. Signal.* 2:9–19

74. Maragos, C., Hutchison, W. M., Hayasaka, K., Brown, G. K., Dahl, H. H. 1989. Structural organization of the gene for the E1 alpha subunit of the human pyruvate dehydrogenase complex. *J. Biol. Chem.* 264:12294–98

75. Mattevi, A., Obmolova, G., Schulze, E., Kalk, K. H., Westpal, A. H., de Kok, A., Hol, W. G. 1992. Atomic structure of the cubic core of the pyruvate dehydrogenase multienzyme complex. *Science* 255:1544–50

76. McCormack, J. G., Denton, R. M. 1981. The activation of pyruvate dehydrogenase in the perfused rat heart by adrenaline and other inotropic agents. *Biochem. J.* 194:639–43

77. McCormack, J. G., England, P. J. 1983. Ruthenium red inhibits the activation of pyruvate dehydrogenase caused by positive inotropic agents in the perfused rat heart. *Biochem. J.* 214:581–85

78. Miles, J. S., Guest, J. R., Radford, S. W., Perham, R. N. 1988. Investigation of the mechanism of active site coupling in the pyruvate dehydrogenase multienzyme complex of *Escherichia coli* by protein engineering. *J. Mol. Biol.* 202:97–106

79. Moehario, L. H., Smooker, P. M., Devenish, R. J., Mackay, I. R., Gershwin, M. E., Marzuki, S. 1990. Nucleotide sequence of a cDNA encoding the lipoate acetyl transferase (E2) of human heart pyruvate dehydrogenase complex differs from that of human placenta. *Biochem. Int.* 20:417–22

80. Niu, X. D., Stoops, J. K., Reed, L. J. 1990. Overexpression and mutagenesis of the catalytic domain of dihydrolipoamide acetyltransferase from *Saccharomyces cerevisiae. Biochemistry* 29:8614–19

81. Ohlen, J., Seiss, E. A., Löffler, G., Wieland, O. H. 1978. The effect of insulin on pyruvate dehydrogenase interconversion in heart muscle of alloxan-diabetic rats. *Diabetologia* 14: 135–39

82. Old, S. E., De Vivo, D. S. 1989. Pyruvate dehydrogenase complex deficiency: biochemical and immunoblot analysis of cultured skin fibroblasts.*Ann. Neurol.* 26:746–51

83. Olson, M. S., Dennis, S. C., DeBuysere, M. S., Padma, A. 1978. The regulation of pyruvate dehydrogenase in the isolated perfused rat heart. *J. Biol. Chem.* 253:7369–75

84. Olson, M. S., Dennis, S. C., Routh, C. A., DeBuysere, M. S. 1978. The regulation of pyruvate dehydrogenase by fatty acids in isolated rabbit heart mitochondria. *Arch. Biochem. Biophys.* 187:121–31

85. Otulakowski, G., Robinson, B. H. 1987. Isolation and sequence determination of cDNA clones for porcine and human lipoamide dehydrogenase. Homology to other disulfide oxido reductases. *J. Biol. Chem.* 262:17313–18

86. Otulakowski, G., Robinson, B. H., Willard, H. F. 1988. Gene for lipoamide dehydrogenase maps to human chromosome 7. *Somat. Cell Mol. Genet.* 14:411–14

87. Packman, L. C., Green, B., Perham, R. N. 1991. Lipoylation of the E2 components of the 2-oxo acid dehydrogenase multienzyme complexes of *Escherichia coli. Biochem. J.* 277:153–58

88. Patel, T. B., Barron, L. L., Olson, M. S. 1984. The stimulation of hepatic gluconeogenesis by acetoacetate precursors: a role for the monocarboxylate translocator. *J. Biol. Chem.* 259:7525–31

89. Patel, T. B., DeBuysere, M. S., Scholz, R., Olson, M. S. 1982. Regulation of the pyruvate dehydrogenase complex in the perfused rat liver: a role for the monocarboxylate translocator. *Arch. Biochem. Biophys.* 213: 573–84

90. Patel, T. B., Olson, M. S. 1984. Regulation of pyruvate dehydrogenase complex in ischemic rat heart. *Am. J. Physiol.* 246:H858–64

91. Patzelt, C., Loffler, G., Wieland, O. H. 1973. Interconversion of pyruvate dehydrogenase in the isolated perfused rat liver. *Eur. J. Biochem.* 33:117–22

92. Pettit, F. H., Humphreys, J., Reed, L. J. 1982. Regulation of pyruvate dehydrogenase kinase activity by pro-

518   BEHAL ET AL

tein thiol-disulfide exchange. *Proc. Natl. Acad. Sci. USA* 79:3945–48

93. Pettit, F. H., Pelley, J. W., Reed, L. J. 1975. Regulation of pyruvate dehydrogenase kinase and phosphatase by acetyl CoA/CoA and NADH/NAD⁺ ratios. *Biochem. Biophys. Res. Commun.* 65:575–81

94. Pettit, F. H., Roche, T. E., Reed, L. J. 1972. Function of calcium ions in pyruvate dehydrogenase phosphatase activity. *Biochem. Biophys. Res. Commun.* 49:563–71

95. Pons, G., Raefsny-Estrin, C., Carothers, D. J., Pepin, R. A., Javed, A. A., et al. 1988. Cloning and cDNA sequence of the dihydrolipoamide dehydrogenase component of human alpha-ketoacid dehydrogenase complexes. *Proc. Natl. Acad. Sci. USA* 85:1422–26

96. Pratt, M. L., Maher, J. F., Roche, T. E. 1982. Purification of bovine kidney and heart pyruvate dehydrogenase b phosphatase on sepharose derivatized with the pyruvate dehydrogenase complex. *Eur. J. Biochem.* 125:349–55

97. Randle, P. J., Denton, R. M. 1970. Control of the tricarboxylate cycle and its interactions with glycolysis during acetate utilization in rat heart. *Biochem. J.* 117:677–95

98. Reed, L. J. 1974. Multienzyme complexes. *Acc. Chem. Res.* 7:40–46

99. Reed, L. J., Oliver, R. M. 1968. The multienzyme alpha-keto acid dehydrogenase complexes. *Brookhaven Symp. Biol.* 21:397–411

100. Reed, L. J., Pettit, F. H., Yeaman, S. J., Teague, W. M., Bleile, D. M. 1980. Structure, function and regulation of the mammalian pyruvate dehydrogenase complex. In *Enzyme Regulation and Mechanism of Action*, ed. P. Mildnar, B. Ries, pp. 47–56. Oxford: Pergamon

101. Robertson, J. G., Barron, L. L., Olson, M. S. 1986. Effects of α-ketoisovalerate on bovine heart pyruvate dehydrogenase and pyruvate dehydrogenase kinase. *J. Biol. Chem.* 261:76–81

102. Robertson, J. G., Barron, L. L., Olson, M. S. 1989. Bovine heart pyruvate dehydrogenase kinase stimulation by monovalent ions. *J. Biol. Chem.* 264 11626–31

103. Robinson, B. H., MacKay, N., Petrova-Benedict, R., Ozalp, I., Coskun, T., Stacpoole, P. W. 1990. Defects in the E2 lipoyl transacetylase and the X-lipoyl containing component of the pyruvate dehydrogenase complex

in patients with lactic acidemia. *J. Clin. Invest.* 85:1821–24

104. Roche, T. E., Cate, R. L. 1976. Evidence for lipoic acid-mediated NADH and acetyl CoA stimulation of liver and kidney pyruvate dehydrogenase kinase. *Biochem. Biophys. Res. Commun.* 72:1375–83

105. Roche, T. E., Patel, M. S., eds. 1989. α-Keto acid dehydrogenase complexes: organization, regulation and biomedical ramifications. *Ann. NY Acad. Sci.* 573: 1–473

106. Roche, T. E., Reed, L. J. 1974. Monovalent cation requirements for ADP inhibitors of pyruvate dehydrogenase kinase. *Biochem. Biophys. Res. Commun.* 59:1341–48

107. Roche, T. E., Rahmatullah, M., Powers-Greenwood, S. L., Radke, G. A., Gopalakrishnan, S., Chang, C. L. 1989. The lipoyl-containing components of the mammalian pyruvate dehydrogenase complex: structural comparison and subdomain roles. *Ann. NY Acad. Sci.* 573:66–75

108. Romero, G., Gamez, G., Huang, L. C., Lilley, K., Luttrell, L. 1990. Anti-inositolglycan antibodies selectively block some of the actions of insulin in intact BC3H1 cells. *Proc. Natl. Acad. USA* 87:1476–80

109. Russell, G. C., Guest, J. R. 1991. Site-directed mutagenesis of the lipoate acetyltransferase of *Escherichia coli*. *Proc. R. Soc. London Ser. B* 243:155–60

110. Saltiel, A. R. 1987. Insulin generates an enzyme modulator from hepatic plasma membranes: regulation of adenosine 3′,5′-monophosphate phosphodiesterase, pyruvate dehydrogenase, and adenyalte cyclase. *Endocrinology* 120: 967–72

111. Saltiel, A. R., Fox, J. A., Sherline, P., Cuatrecasas, P. 1986. Insulin-stimulated hydrolysis of a novel glycolipid generates modulators of camp-phosphodiesterase. *Science* 233:967–72

112. Schaffer, W. T., Olson, M. S. 1980. The regulation of pyruvate oxidation during membrane depolarization of rat brain synaptosomes. *Biochem. J.* 192: 741–51

113. Scholz, R., Olson, M. S., Schwab, A., Schwabe, U., Noell, C., Braun, W. 1978. The effect of fatty acids on the regulation of pyruvate dehydrogenase in perfused rat liver. *Eur. J. Biochem.* 86:519–30

114. Schulze, E., Westphal, A. H., Boumans, H., de Kok, A. 1991. Site-directed mutagenesis of the dihydro-

lipoyl transacetylase component (E2p) of the pyruvate dehydrogenase complex from *AzotobacterVinelandii*. Binding of the peripheral components E1p and E3. *Eur. J. Biochem.* 202:841–48

115. Schuster, S. M., Olson, M. S. 1972. Effect of magnesium chelators on the regulation of pyruvate oxidation by rabbit heart mitochondria. *Biochemistry* 22:4166–72

116. Schuster, S. M., Olson, M. S. 1972. Regulation of pyruvate oxidation in isolated rabbit heart mitochondria. *J. Biol. Chem.* 247:5088–94

117. Schuster, S. M., Olson, M. S. 1974. The regulation of pyruvate dehydrogenase in isolated beef heart mitochondria: the role of calcium, magnesium and permeant anions. *J. Biol. Chem.* 249:7159–65

118. Schuster, S. M., Olson, M. S., Routh, C. A. 1975. Studies on the regulation of pyruvate dehydrogenase in isolated beef heart mitochondria. *Arch. Biochem. Biophys.* 171:745–52

119. Shaw, W. N., Boder, G. B. 1972. Effect of insulin on pyruvate and glucose metabolism of beating mouse heart cells. *J. Mol. Cell. Cardiol.* 4:485–93

120. Shipp, J. C., Opie, L. H., Challoner, D. R. 1961. Fatty acid and glucose metabolism in the perfused heart. *Nature* 189:1018–19

121. Siess, E. A., Wieland, O. H. 1972. Purification and characterization of pyruvate dehydrogenase phosphatase from pig heart muscle. *Eur. J. Biochem.* 26:96–105

122. Siess, E. A., Wittman, J., Wieland, O. H. 1971. Interconversion and kinetic properties of pyruvate dehydrogenase from brain. *Hoppe-Seylers Z. Physiol. Chem.* 352:447–52

123. Stansbie, D. 1976. Regulation of the human pyruvate dehydrogenase complex. *Clin. Sci. Mol. Med.* 51:445–52

124. Stepp, L. R., Pettit, F. H., Yeaman, S. J., Reed, L. J. 1983. Purification and properties of pyruvate dehydrogenase kinase from bovine kidney. *J. Biol. Chem.* 258:9454–548

125. Surh, C. D., Roche, T. E., Danner, D. J., Ansari, A., Coppel, R. L., et al. 1989. Antimitochondrial autoantibodies in primary biliary cirrhosis recognize cross-reactive epitope(s) on protein X and dihydrolipoamide acetyltransferase of pyruvate dehydrogenase complex. *Hepatology* 10:127–33

126. Szabo, P., Sheu, K. F., Robinson, R. M., Grzeschik, K. H., Blass, J. P. 1990. The gene for the alpha polypeptide of pyruvate dehydrogenase is X-linked in humans. *Am. J. Hum. Genet.* 46:874–78

127. Takakubo, F., Dahl, H. H. 1992. The expression pattern of the pyruvate dehydrogenase E1 alpha subunit genes during spermatogenesis in adult mouse. *Exp. Cell Res.* 199:39–49

128. Taylor, W. M., Halperin, M. L. 1973. Regulation of pyruvate dehydrogenase in muscle. *J. Biol. Chem.* 248:6080–83

129. Teague, W. W., Pettit, F. H., Wu, T.-L., Silberman, S. R., Reed, L. J. 1982. Purification and properties of pyruvate dehydrogenase phosphatase from bovine heart and kidney. *Biochemistry* 21:5585–92

130. Thekkumkara, T. J., Ho, L., Wexler, I. D., Pons, G., Liu, T. C., Patel, M. S. 1988. Nucleotide sequence of a cDNA for the dihydrolipoamide acetyltransferase component of human pyruvate dehydrogenase complex. *FEBS Lett.* 240:45–48

131. Tomura, H., Endo, H., Kagawa, Y., Ohta, S. 1990. Novel regulatory enhancer in the nuclear gene of the human mitochondrial ATP synthase beta-subunit. *J. Biol. Chem.* 265:6525–27

132. Uhlinger, D. J., Yan, C. Y., Reed, L. J. 1986. Phosphorylation-dephosphorylation of pyruvate dehydrogenase from bakers yeast. *Biochemistry* 25:5673–77

133. Walsh, D. A., Cooper, R. H., Denton, R. M., Bridges, B. J., Randle, P. J. 1976. The elementary reactions of the pig heart pyruvate dehydrogenase complex. *Biochem. J.* 157:41–67

134. Waymack, P. P., DeBuysere, M. S., Olson, M. S. 1979. The effect of pyruvate transport inhibitors on the regulation of pyruvate dehydrogenase in the perfused rat heart. *Arch. Biochem. Biophys.* 194:258–64

135. Weiss, L., Kreisel, K., Haslbeck, M., Wieland, O. H. 1975. Activity in adipose tissue and liver of pyruvate dehydrogenase and atp-citrate lyase. *Diabetologia* 11:383–89

136. Weiss, L., Löffler, G., Schirmann, A., Wieland, O. H. 1971. Control of pyruvate dehydrogenase interconversion of adipose tissue by insulin. *FEBS Lett.* 15:229–31

137. Wieland, O. H. 1983. The mammalian pyruvate dehydrogenase complex: structure and regulation. *Rev. Physiol. Biochem. Pharmacol.* 96:123–70

138. Wieland, O. H., Jagow-Westermann, B. 1969. ADP-dependent inactivation of heart muscle and inactivation by Mg^{+2}. *FEBS Lett.* 3:271–74

139. Wieland, O. H., Siess, E. 1970. In-

terconversion of phospho- and dephos-pho-forms of pig heart pyruvate dehy-drogenase. *Proc. Natl. Acad. Sci. USA* 65:947–54

140. Wieland, O. H., Siess, E., Schulze-Wethmar, F. H., Funcke, H. J. v., Winton, B. 1971. Active and inactive forms of pyruvate dehydrogenase in rat heart and kidney: effect of diabetes, fasting, and refeeding on pyruvate de-hydrogenase interconversion. *Arch. Biochem. Biophys.* 143:593–601

141. Wieland, O. H., Siess, E. A., Weiss, L., Löffler, G., Patzalt, C., et al. 1973. Regulation of the mammalian pyruvate dehydrogenase complex by covalent modification. *Symp. Soc. Exp. Biol.* 27:371–400

142. Wieland, O. H., Urumow, T., Drexler, P. 1989. Insulin, phospholipase, and the activation of the pyruvate dehydro-genase complex: an enigma. *Ann. NY Acad. Sci.* 573:274–84

143. Williamson, J. R., Krebs, H. A. 1961. Acetate as a fuel of respiration in the perfused rat heart. *Biochem. J.* 80:540–47

144. Yeaman, S. J., Hutcheson, E. T., Roche, T. E., Pettit, F. H., Brown, J. R., et al. 1978. Sites of phosphor-ylation on pyruvate dehydrogenase from bovine kidney and heart. *Biochemistry* 17:2364–70

145. Zwiebel, F. M., Schwabe, U., Scholz, R., Olson, M. S. 1982. The relationship between pyruvate oxidation and keto-genesis. The possible role of pyruvate transport in the regulation of pyruvate dehydrogenase in the perfused rat liver. *Biochemistry* 21:346–53

Annu. Rev. Nutr. 1993. 13:521–37

IRON DEFICIENCY AND COGNITIVE FUNCTION

Ernesto Pollitt

Department of Pediatrics, School of Medicine and Program of International
Nutrition, University of California, Davis 95616

KEY WORDS: anemia, malnutrition, iron deficiency, behavior, cognition

CONTENTS

DEFINITION OF PREDICTOR AND OUTCOME VARIABLES   522
   Iron Deficiency   522
   Cognitive Variables   523
ASSOCIATIONS BETWEEN DEFICIENCY AND BEHAVIORAL ALTERATIONS   524
   Infancy and Early Childhood (0–24 months)   524
   Preschool and School Children (≥24 months)   526
IRON DEFICIENCY AS A CAUSE OF ALTERATIONS IN COGNITION   528
   Infancy and Early Childhood (0–24 months)   528
   Preschool and School-Age Children (≥24 months)   530
ON THE NATURE OF THE EFFECT   532

The intent of this review is to determine whether iron deficiency (ID) is a developmental risk factor as defined by an increment in the probabilities of a deviation from a normal developmental trajectory. The data available from published reports have been used selectively, as most studies that are cited had an experimental or quasi-experimental research design with a focus on causality. A broader view, including discussion of methods and research designs and descriptions of particular studies, is available elsewhere (8, 31, 33, 48).

Among the many different pathways through which iron deficiency can affect cognition (see Table 1) are two that have been most frequently discussed. Briefly, one proposes that even at the very early stages of iron deficiency, a decrement in iron-dependent dopamine D2 receptors in the cortex alters dopamine neurotransmission, which, in turn, impairs cognitive function (16, 45, 48–50). The alternative hypothesis is less explicit and refers to more advanced stages of iron deficiency when hemoglobin concentration is com-

521

0199-9885/93/0715-0521$02.00

Table 1   Areas of possible impact of iron deficiency on the central nervous system[a]

General biochemical	Specific sites	Impact
Heme synthesis	1. Porphyrin synthesis (general $\downarrow$; $\uparrow$ FEP)	Toxic or intracellular deficiency
	2. Mitochondrial cytochromes (c, oxidase)	Respiration, oxidative phosphorylation
	3. Microsomal cytochromes (P_{450}, b_5)	Toxic
Krebs cycle	Succinate dehydrogenase (Fe-S flavoprotein), aconitase (Fe cofactor)	Respiration
Fe-S flavoproteins	NADH-ubiquinone reductase, α-GP dehydrogenase	Respiration, oxidative phosphorylation
Nucleic acids	DNA synthesis, mitosis	Brain growth
Catecholamines	Phenylalanine hydroxylase, tyrosine hydroxylase, monoamine oxidase	Neurotransmitter levels
Serotonin	Tryptophan pyrrolase, tryptophan hydroxylase, aldehyde oxidase	Neurotransmitter levels
Folic acid/B_{12}	Formimino transferase, THF methyl-transferase	

[a] Source: Reference 17.

promised. It postulates that in the presence of anemia there may be systemic effects that interfere with cognition (16). Neither hypothesis has been validated; however, most research in this area has focused on dopamine neurotransmission.

The following review is divided into four sections. First I discuss some issues of definition regarding both predictor (i.e. iron deficiency) and outcome (i.e. cognition) variables. Next, I discuss the associations that have been reported for iron deficiency anemia (IDA) without addressing the issue of causality, which is covered in the third section. The review ends with an attempt to make explicit the nature of the cognitive alterations found among children with IDA.

DEFINITION OF PREDICTOR AND OUTCOME VARIABLES

Iron Deficiency

The requirement for use of multiple indicators (e.g. ferritin, erythrocyte protoporphyrin, hemoglobin) in the definition of iron deficiency is no longer an issue among investigators concerned with the functional effects of ID. Presently, there is no valid substitute for such an approach, because none of the indicators can monitor the entire spectrum of iron deficiency. Multiple indicators increase the sensitivity of the diagnosis and reduce the risk of sample heterogeneity in studies on functional effects (3, 10, 17, 35, 47).

The studies cited in the following review included no less than two iron indicators to establish iron class and generally relied on the standard cut-off points to define deficiency. In some instances the sensitivity and specificity of the criteria for IDA were tested by a comparison of the class criteria with the hemoglobin response to iron therapy (14, 22). In all cases the dose in iron therapy was adjusted according to the age and weight of the children.

A main concern of investigators today is to define the course of the deficiency from its onset to the time when it is first identified. Its duration and changes in severity, in addition to its timing (i.e. developmental period when present), are likely to play the role of effect modifiers (20, 34). At present, however, no exact methodologies and ethically acceptable research designs are available to directly measure duration and timing. Based on the pathophysiology of iron deficiency, an estimate of its duration is indirectly derived from its severity. A promising option to estimate duration is the use of prospective research protocols that identify new cases in the same cohorts of children within pre-established time periods.

Cognitive Variables

Investigators agree on the need to establish the effect of ID on "mental development" or cognition, broadly defined. Because the most complex postnatal neural changes that take place in the human brain occur during the first two years of postnatal life, the infant's development is thought to be particularly vulnerable to ID (5, 6, 9, 15, 50). This assumption is partly supported by experimental work with protein and calorie restrictions of laboratory animals during the lactation period that resulted in permanent structural changes in the central nervous system (9). ID in rodent pups results in a deficit in the availability of iron in the brain, which persists following the saturation of iron stores (5, 6).

Investigators working with infants prefer to use the Bayley Scales of Mental and Motor Development (BSMMD[1]), while those working with preschoolers

---

[1]The Bayley Scales of Mental and Motor Development are standardized instruments that sample different categories of behaviors in infants from 2 to 30 months. The Mental scale yields an aggregate score, the Mental Development Index (MDI) with a mean of 100 and a standard deviation of 16 MDI points. This scale characterizes the behavioral development of infants with samples of different mental functions such as memory, learning, and vocabulary. The Motor scale yields the Psychomotor Development Index (PDI), with the same mean and standard deviation as the MDI, This scale samples gross and fine motor skills.

The Infant Behavior Record is the third component of the Bayley Scales. This rating scale assesses different emotional and motivational expressions of the child during testing.

and school-age children have chosen IQ tests [e.g. Wechsler Intelligence Scale for Children (WISC), Raven's Progressive Matrices[2]], learning tasks (e.g. discrimination and oddity learning), and school achievement measures. Presumably, the psychological construct that lies behind these outcomes from studies with different age groups remains constant from infancy to late childhood. However, such an assumption is supported neither by theory nor by empirical data.

While the names of these tests used in studies on infants and older children might suggest otherwise, the scales of mental (e.g. BSMD) development used among children during the first two years of life and the intelligence and cognitive tests used among preschool and school age children tap different constructs. On one hand, the BSMD (2) intends to characterize the behavioral repertoire of an infant at a particular age, with a disclaimer that this characterization is a reflection of intelligence or mental competence. On the other hand, the intelligence tests (e.g. WISC) and the learning tasks used with older children intend (with different degrees of success) to scale children within a spectrum of mental ability (2, 30). This difference in the nature of the tests is discussed below in more detail, as it is pertinent to our understanding of the nature of the effects that have been reported. If such differences in the very nature of the tests used do exist, why is there such remarkable consistency in the findings across studies with different age groups? A valid answer to this query, in my view, will place us very close to an understanding of the functional effect of iron deficiency.

ASSOCIATIONS BETWEEN DEFICIENCY AND BEHAVIORAL ALTERATIONS

Studies on infants, preschoolers, and school children report a remarkable consistency in their findings. With a few exceptions, most such studies show that IDA, on average, is associated with poor performance in infant developmental scales, IQ and learning tasks in preschool children, and educational achievement among school-age children.

Infancy and Early Childhood (0–24 months)

An illustration of the consistency of the findings across different studies is found in the case of infants and young children with moderate IDA (Hb 100 g/liter). Without exceptions, the differences in the scores [mental development index (MDI)] on the Bayley scales of mental development among

---

[2]The Raven Progressive Matrices is an alleged cultural-free test that assesses nonverbal intelligence and has been widely used in clinical as well as in developmental research.

infants with sufficient iron stores and with moderate IDA have ranged from one-half to one and one-half a standard deviation. This developmental test score pattern has been reported in studies of infants in industrialized (e.g. United States, Great Britain) and developing countries (e.g. Guatemala, Thailand, Indonesia) (12, 21, 22, 27, 32, 41, 42). Few areas in developmental pediatrics observe such distinct patterns. For example, the well-researched area of behavioral alterations and elevated blood lead levels has observed neither the consistency nor the strength of the associations that characterize IDA test score patterns (7, 25).

There are some disagreements between findings in the case of milder IDA. Not all studies have reported a comparatively poor performance of infants with mild IDA (22). Those disagreements can be explained by the positive covariation that has been observed between Hb level and mental scores on the Bayley Scale (1, 22, 41). In some instances the effect of IDA on the MDI might remain undetected because of a weakness in the research design that did not include a sample with enough subjects. However, in a recent study the MDIs of infants with mild and moderate degrees of anemia did not differ from each other, and both scores were lower than those of infants without ID (14).

Within the range of IDA that has been studied, duration and not severity per se may account for a low level of test performance. As these two properties of IDA are confounded with each other, there is a risk of attributing the effect to one (e.g. severity) and not to the other (e.g. duration). A valid discrimination of effects between such attributes could only be achieved with accurate quantitative data on the course of the deficiency.

The large difference (e.g. one-half to one standard deviation) between the developmental test performance of infants with and without IDA should *not* be interpreted as an indication of a severe developmental delay in the infant with IDA. In most instances, the mean MDI of infants with moderate IDA has been within the range of the performance expected in healthy, average infants in the United States. For instance, the mean MDI of infants with a Hb 105 g/liter was 94.6 in Costa Rica (22) as compared to the average MDI of 100 for the standardized population of the Bayley Scale (standard deviation = 16). Briefly, a large and statistically significant difference between the MDI of infants with IDA and infants with replete iron stores is not necessarily a sign that the IDA infants are developmentally delayed as compared to the reference population (11).

It is still not possible to draw conclusive inferences regarding the association between ID without anemia and infant development even though most studies that have assessed such a theoretically reasonable association have found no statistical evidence to support it. A low-level association might remain undetected because of a lack of power in the research designs. The sample size that may be required is possibly larger than that previously used. Some support for the argument that even in the absence of anemia ID could affect test performance is found in the improvement observed in the MDI of nonanemic iron-deficient infants following iron therapy (26). Moreover, a study in Thailand with school children that included, up to the time of its publication, the largest sample ever used with any age group did find a statistical association between ID without anemia and poor performance in school achievement tests (32).

Infants with IDA are also delayed in motor maturation as reflected by comparatively poorer scores on the Bayley Scale of Motor Development (14, 22, 41); few studies (42) that test this relationship failed to see the developmental delay observed in most other studies (14, 22, 41). However, in contrast to the positive association observed between severity of anemia and magnitude of delay in the MDI, those studies that reported an association between moderate and mild IDA and poor motor development scores have failed to see a correspondence between level of motor delays and the severity of the anemia.

Whether or not IDA is associated with delays in the timetable of critical motor milestones such as creeping, standing, or walking is not yet known. In one study, IDA in infancy was associated with delays in motor balance and coordination four years later (23).

Of particular importance to our present concern is that infants with IDA also show behaviors characterized by a disengagement from the task at hand during developmental testing. In agreement with what is observed in clinical exams, IDA infants have been described as unhappy, tense, fearful, or withdrawn as well as less responsive to testers and less goal directed (24). Briefly, they seem to be less active than expected for their age. Infants that show some of these behaviors are generally those that obtain the poorer scores on the developmental scales (24). Following therapy, however, the atypical affective state changed and the infants' responsiveness to the social environment became equivalent to that of iron-replete infants (26, 30). This change has been observed in a few instances a week or two after the iron intervention (26).

Preschool and School Children (≥24 months)

While maintaining socioeconomic status (SES) constant, studies show that the performance of IDA children from the ages of two to about five years has been poorer than that of iron-sufficient children in tests of intelligence and of particular cognitive processes (e.g. discrimination learning) (34, 39). For instance, the number of trials it takes a child with IDA to learn how to discriminate between almost but not completely identical visual stimuli on the basis of particular cues is larger than among controls (39). One explanation for these differences is a diminished ability to attend selectively to available environmental information. Another explanation that does not exclude the attention hypothesis is that children with IDA maintain a dysphoric state and have reduced motivation that interferes with test performance. Observations of test behavior similar to those that have been made among infants are needed, particularly because, as previously noted, research with infants has shown changes in affect after iron therapy.

With exceptions (32), IDA among school children ($\geq$ 6 yr old) has been associated with poor performance on intelligence tests such as the WISC. The magnitude of the IQ differences between subjects with IDA and subjects that are iron replete has been about one-half of a standard deviation.[3] IDA has also been associated with comparatively poor performance on tests of specific cognitive processes such as short-term memory and attention (37, 38) and with comparatively low scores in school achievement measures (32, 38). For example, in rural Thailand the scores in a school language test of 8- to 11-yr-old iron-deficient children with and without anemia lagged behind that of iron-sufficient children (32).

Iron deficiency anemia among infants also predicts performance in cognitive tests at a later developmental period. In Costa Rica 5-yr-old children with histories of chronic and moderately severe IDA (Hb 100 g/liter) during early childhood scored lower in a wide range of tests of cognition (e.g. quantitative concepts, visual matching, nonverbal IQ) than a group without IDA in their nutritional history (23). At age five there was no evidence of IDA in any of the groups of children that were compared. Similar differences in test performance between the previously anemic and controls were observed in tests of fine and gross motor proficiency.

The cognitive test performance of the Costa Rican children with a history of mild IDA in infancy did not differ from that of well-nourished controls. An exception were children, mildly anemic in infancy (Hb 101 to 110 g/liter), who had not corrected their iron deficiency following 3 months of iron therapy. In follow-up testing, their performance did not differ from that of the moderately anemic children; however, it was poorer than that of the controls (23).

In sum, despite the differences in the nature of the psychological tests that were administered to infants with IDA and older children, there is strong agreement in the findings across age groups. Independent of age, the subjects with IDA perform, on average, less well than those whose iron stores are

---

[3]Most intelligence scales such as the Wechsler Scale for Children have a mean of 100 with a deviation of 16 IQ points and a standard error of 6 points (43).

replete, in so-called mental tests. Among infants up to 2 years of age, the poor developmental test performance is more likely to be observed among those whose Hb 105 g/liter. Among preschool and school age children, the relationship between psychological test performance and severity of anemia has not been explored sufficiently well to warrant an inference.

IRON DEFICIENCY AS A CAUSE OF ALTERATIONS IN COGNITION

Association, time order, and direction of effects, are the three main criteria for establishing causality (20, 40). Among these, the only one that must be met through appropriate experimental design is the direction of effects. Unlike any other design, double-blind, randomized clinical trials can determine whether a change in outcome is a consequence of a change in an antecedent variable. Accordingly, the present focus is on data from studies that meet the requirements for causal inference because of their research format. Only those studies that assigned subjects to iron and placebo conditions within iron status class are included. Data from quasi-experimental studies with designs that provided iron treatment for subjects that differed in iron status are included as backup.

Infancy and Early Childhood (0–24 months)

The trials that tested the developmental effects of IDA during the first two years of life are classified into two categories according to the interim time between the pre- and post-treatment evaluation. One group includes trials that assessed effects of either intramuscular or oral iron interventions for 7 to 10 days (21, 22, 26, 27, 41, 42). As noted, the studies in this first group intended to test the hypothesis that ID results in the cerebral depletion of cellular iron, which, in turn, affects cognition. The other set of published studies assessed the same effects after 8 to 16 weeks of oral iron therapy, but did not discriminate among mechanisms (1, 14). The hemoglobin of infants originally diagnosed with IDA generally falls within the normal limits after 8 weeks of iron intervention at a dosage that accounts for age and body weight. Therapeutic trials to correct IDA generally include 3 to 6 mg of elemental iron per kilogram of body weight daily.

Among infants with IDA, the effects on the BSMMD, observed 7 to 10 days after the administration of oral or intramuscular iron, have not differed from those observed after the administration of a placebo. This statement is valid for most studies. One exception is a study conducted in the United States (26). Seven days after the intramuscular administration of iron calculated to provide sufficient iron to raise the Hb to 120 g/liter, infants with IDA experienced a significant improvement (14 MDI points) in their performance on the Bayley Scale of Mental Development. Conversely, the upward change (6 points) of the subjects exposed to placebo was not statistically significant. However, the difference between the two groups in the size of the MDI changes (8 points) was also not statistically significant.

In a trial that excluded a placebo condition, large developmental improvement was observed 11 days after the administration of intramuscular iron (48). The MDI increase among nonanemic iron-deficient infants was 22 points, while the change in the iron-depleted and iron-sufficient infants did not exceed 6 MDI points.

Two double-blind, randomized clinical trials that tested the long-term developmental effects of iron therapy on infants with IDA found evidence consistent with a causal hypothesis (1, 14). In the most recent study (14), 12- to 18-month-old infants with IDA who were exposed to a 4-month iron oral intervention (3 mg per day of elemental iron per kilogram of body weight) had, on average, a 20-point incremental change in their Bayley MDI from a pre- to a post-treatment evaluation. Conversely, the MDI increment in the infants with IDA who received placebo was negligible.

The iron-dependent change in the psychomotor development index (PDI) (24 points) was even larger than the change in the MDI. In addition, the MDI and PDI responses of the iron-sufficient and nonanemic iron-deficient cases to the iron and placebo interventions were inconsequential (14).

A previous study that used the Denver Developmental Screening Test[4] included an interim time of 8 to 9 weeks from the pre- to the post-treatment developmental evaluation (1). IDA infants with a modest Hb response to the iron therapy (20 mg per day of ferrous sulfate) showed a nonsignificant developmental change on the Denver Scale. Significant changes in test performance were observed among those whose Hb response to the intervention was equal or larger than 20 g/liter. The probabilities of improvement on the developmental scale were also positively related to the success of the treatment.

The differences in the developmental response of the infants with IDA in the two studies (1, 14) reviewed above are likely to depend, in part, on how successful a recovery followed the interventions. As noted, iron therapy lasted four months in one study (14), and all children who received this treatment fully recovered from the IDA. In the previous study, the treatment was restricted to two months and IDA was not fully reversed in all cases.

These two double-blind, randomized, clinical trials point to a causal relation between IDA and developmental behavioral alterations in infancy. They also

---

[4]The Denver Developmental Screening Test was devised to identify infants and young children at risk in four main areas: gross motor, language, fine motor adaptive, and personal social. It does not attempt to characterize mental and motor development.

show that, at least within the age range and degree of severity in the IDA that were studied, these alterations are reversed following the repletion of iron stores.

The findings reviewed above are at odds with those of most studies that tested the effects of oral and intramuscular iron over 7 to 14 days. Briefly, while the 2 clinical trials showed effects 2 to 4 months after baseline, 4 of the 5 trials that tested for effects over 7 to 14 days did not observe any such changes. This discrepancy suggests that, among infants and young children with IDA up to about 24 months, a sudden increase in cerebral iron following iron intervention does not produce a similar upward change in performance in developmental tests.

A pattern that emerges from the findings of quasi-experimental studies is that in some cases iron therapy for 12 weeks was not sufficient to improve the MDI of IDA infants although it did improve the PDI (1, 22, 41). This pattern was particularly clear among cases of moderate anemia (Hb $\leq$ 100 g/liter) that failed to show full reversal of the nutrient deficiency, and it coincides with a part of the findings of the Denver Developmental Screening Test previously reviewed.

Preschool and School-Age Children ($\geq$ 24 months)

Recently published studies on the performance of IDA preschool and school children in cognitive and school achievement tests have used double-blind testing and random assignment to either iron therapy or placebo condition within iron class (32, 34, 37–39). Accordingly, there is a data base that allows for testing causality.

Preschool children with IDA that were exposed to iron therapy have shown improvements in performance in some cognitive tests that were not observed among those that received placebo. Illustrative are studies in India and Indonesia where the interim time between the first and second test was about 8 weeks. In India, the pre- to post-treatment changes in the Verbal and Performance IQ (WISC) of IDA (Hb 105 g/liter) subjects that received iron were greater than 10 points respectively (37), while those of subjects on placebo was less than 6 points. These differences between groups were particularly striking in the Performance Scale of the WISC. The IQ of those on placebo improved from 98 to 104, while the IQ of those on iron changed from 100 to 117. This 17-point change in IQ is reminiscent of the 20-point change in MDI observed in IDA infants treated with iron.

In the study of preschool children in Indonesia (39), the size of the improvement in a battery of learning tests was not as striking as that observed in India (35). However, the differential change in 2 of the 3 cognitive tasks (i.e. discriminant and oddity learning) that were administered among IDA (Hb 110 g/liter) preschoolers with and without exposure to a dose-appropriate

8-week iron intervention was consonant with the causal hypothesis. For instance, the size of the decrement in the number of errors in discriminant learning tasks among the IDA subjects treated with iron was larger than that occurring in the placebo group. However, the changes in performance were not as large as had been expected. This finding may also be associated with the duration of the intervention (8 weeks) and with its moderate success in replenishing iron stores.

The results of 4 of the 5 clinical trials on school children are similar to those observed among preschoolers (32, 37, 38). School children with IDA who were exposed to a dose-appropriate iron intervention showed a significant improvement in their performance on tests of particular cognitive processes (e.g. attention, visual-perceptual organization, short-term recall) that was not observed among IDA children of the same age who received a placebo. The effects of IDA are obviously relevant to educational concerns and policy.

The battery of psychological tests used in 2 of the 5 studies with school children included school achievement measures (32, 38). The respective results, however, are in conflict. In one of these trials (38) 9- to 11-year-old Javanese children with IDA in grades 3 to 5 performed less well in standardized educational achievement tests than did iron-replete children. After 12 weeks of iron treatment the anemic children showed a marked improvement in their test scores, whereas the test performance of the anemic children that received a placebo remained stable from the first to the second testing. Note that the post-treatment score of the IDA children treated with iron still lagged behind that of the children who were replete at the beginning of the study.

In contrast to the results in Java, a study in Thailand failed to show the expected improvement in educational test scores among IDA school children treated with iron (32). The Thai study included 16 schools and a total of 2,268 children aged 9 to 11. These children were randomly assigned to an iron and placebo intervention for 14 weeks. After the code for randomization was broken, 1,358 children met 1 of 3 iron status criteria (i.e. IDA was defined by a Hb 120 g/liter plus two of the three following criteria: serum ferritin 10 μ/liter, transferrin saturation 16%, and free erythrocyte protoporphyrin 700 μg/liter RBC. Iron depleted was defined by the same criteria except for a Hb ≥ 120 g/liter). At base line the IQ (Raven Progressive Matrices) and the mean scores in a Thai language test of the children with IDA and ID were significantly lower than those of the iron-replete group. However, these differences remained unchanged following the experimental intervention.

In sum, the results from clinical trials on preschool and school-age children with IDA show a distinct pattern. In general, among IDA subjects, dose-appropriate iron interventions that lasted for two months or more resulted in major improvements in IQ or in one or more tests that tapped particular cognitive processes such as attention. In contrast, the changes in test performance observed among IDA subjects that received placebo were inconsequential. In conclusion, iron deficiency anemia causes an alteration in cognitive function among preschool and school age children that is reversible following the repletion of iron stores.

ON THE NATURE OF THE EFFECT

Having established that IDA increases the probabilities of a deviation on the developmental trajectory of a child, I now turn to the question, What is the specific nature of the psychological effect? This discussion is presented with the admonition that on this particular issue the evidence is insufficient to draw conclusions. At best, only inferences are warranted.

Ideally this discussion should begin with a definition of the locus of the biological system that is altered by iron deficiency which results in the behavioral changes that have been observed among children with IDA. However, this ideal must defer to a future date because, in my view, the information currently available is insufficient to define the genesis of the behavioral problem. Despite claims to the contrary (46, 47, 50), we are not yet able to determine whether the underlying problem is a reduction of nonheme iron in the brain or other systemic changes in the organism associated with the reduction in the transport of oxygen. While there is no reason to assume that these two explanations are mutually exclusive, the arguments that address causality focus almost exclusively on the role of iron in the brain (8, 31, 33). Moreover, the compensatory mechanisms activated by the organism in the presence of mild to moderate anemia suggest that the root of the problem is not found in the reduction of hemoglobin (16).

The data and arguments in favor of a neurochemical explanation are found in recent publications (8, 31, 49) and are the subjects of controversy (4, 13, 18, 19, 46, 48–50). This review focuses on an analysis of the psychological test data, particularly on some of the conclusions presented in the previous sections: (a) the consistently poor psychological test performance of IDA subjects across ages, (b) behavioral descriptions on affect and motivation, and (c) magnitude of the effects in test performance.

As previously discussed, numerous psychological tests have discriminated between infants, preschoolers, and school-age children with and without IDA. How do we explain the striking agreement of the results obtained if, as already noted, the tests that have been administered to young and older children do not tap the same psychological constructs? In my view, the following considerations regarding the constructs behind the tests are useful in discussing this issue. One possibility is that IDA has a uniform effect across age groups on a particular cognitive function that is tapped by all tests that have been administered across age groups.

If this were the case then the similarity in the findings among infants and older children is not surprising. A second possibility is that IDA affects multiple functions independent of age and that the different tests that have been used tapped at least some of those multiple functions. Finally, the possibility exists that the functional effects in infants and young children are different from those observed among older preschoolers and school children and that the tests administered at these respective ages (e.g. BSMMD up to 24 months) are sensitive to those particular age effects. The following discussion focuses on these three possibilities.

The interpretation that the tests tap the same cognitive construct and function must be rejected on theoretical and statistical grounds. Analytical comparisons of the objectives of the tests that have been used (e.g. Bayley Scales, Oddity Learning, and Raven Progressive Matrices) point to a wide variability in the constructs they tap. Moreover, psychometric data uncover discriminant functions. For example, statistics on predictive validity show either a zero or a low-level correlation between the MDI of the Bayley Scale (used in the infancy studies) administered at 12 months of age and an IQ obtained at 5 years (11, 29). These correlational data do not address the reliability or the validity of either test, but they do show a lack of convergence between tests.

To test the possibility that a wide spectrum of psychological functions are affected by IDA or that the functions that are affected differ by age would have required systematic, focal assessments of different functions and of different age groups. What is available is far removed from meeting these two criteria; there are few instances where attempts were made to assess particular functions (e.g. attention) that were assumed to be affected by iron deficiency among particular age groups (23, 39). There are also posthoc data-driven analyses of the items in the BSMMD that were most likely to discriminate between infants with IDA and controls. In any event, these available data show that with the possible exceptions of attentional processes (across ages) and verbal items of the BSMMD (in infancy) that seem to be sensitive to IDA, there are no consistent data that point to effects on multiple distinct functions.

When the focus of concern moves away from cognitive function, the picture is clearer. The pattern that emerges from the existing data with infants and older children is that IDA has an effect on affect and motivation that interferes with attentiveness (time on task). As noted, studies have shown that during testing infants with IDA are unhappy, tense, fearful, or withdrawn (20, 24), and that therapy reverses the dysphoric behavior. Studies among older children, on the other hand, have reported alterations in attention and in the reception of environmental information. Conjointly, these observations may explain the poor performance on observed discriminant and oddity learning tasks among preschoolers. Briefly, it does seem likely that a relatively narrow effect on affect and motivation and reduction of motor activity precludes good test performance among infants and preschool and school-age children. Thus, there may not be a direct effect on cognition but an indirect effect through affective states and motivation.

Changes in test performance of about one standard deviation over a period of 2 to 4 months can also be explained by a narrow effect on affect and motivation. Decrements in tension and fear, with increments in sociability and positive affect, lead to increased engagement with tasks and therefore to better test performance. On the other hand, the large increments in test scores clash with the assumption of multiple functional effects, as one would expect that rates of recovery in different cognitive process would vary widely.

Narrow effects on affect and motivation could have broad developmental implications. First, these effects would explain the poor performance of infants in motor and mental development scales, and of preschool and school age children in IQ tests, learning tasks, or school performance. Accordingly, the comparatively poor scores in such a large array of psychological and educational tasks would have no relation to the particular psychological constructs that are purported to be assessed by the tests that have been used. The poor scores would be the result of an organismic state that is largely incompatible with doing well on a test—any test.

A dominant effect on affect and motivation is not likely to involve the neural and chemical basis for complex cognitive processes. In fact, the effect could be a restricted alteration in the first step of the process through which the organism changes signals into responses. In particular, I am referring to alterations in arousal (i.e. alerting effect of sensory signals) and activation (i.e. motor disposition to respond) that are critical and distinct components of attention (36). Decrements in these two processes in infants and children would have the distinct effect of altering the responses to different kinds of tests and would, therefore, explain why the test performance of IDA is consistent across age groups.

In conclusion, iron deficiency anemia is a risk factor that increases the probabilities of deviation in the development of infants and children from a normal developmental trajectory. At this time, however, this conclusion cannot be securely tied to a particular set of mechanisms related to the role of cerebral iron or to possible systemic changes associated to anemia.

In particular, neither the data on developmental test performance nor the existing information on the consequences of altered dopamine neurotransmission are sufficiently detailed to validate the hypothesis that the decrements in iron-dependent dopamine D2 receptors in the cortex explain the observed behavioral alterations associated with iron deficiency anemia. In my opinion, the most suggestive data from studies in humans that could be tentatively used in favor of such a mechanism lie in the area of motor activity. As previously suggested in this review, perhaps the clearest evidence of a causal effect of iron deficiency on behavior is in the area of psychomotor development. On the one hand, while the particular motor functions altered by iron deficiency are not yet clearly defined, we now know that infants and young children with IDA score poorly in motor development tests and that this performance has been shown to improve significantly with iron therapeutic trials in experimental and quasi-experimental studies. In addition, it has been observed that infants with IDA display less motor activity and maintain closer physical proximity to their mothers than infants with replete iron stores (20). This type of motor display has also been shown in laboratory studies of experimentally induced iron deficiency among rodents (43, 48, 49). On the other hand, we also know that dopamine antagonists produce states of hypo-motility and reduced ambulatory activity and that these effects are dose related. However, note that other drugs such as GABA agonists also produce significant decrements in motor activity (28).

The gaps in knowledge, however, should not affect program implementation. The data presented represent a strong justification for interventions to prevent and remedy iron deficiency wherever needed.

Literature Cited

1. Aukett, M. A., Parks, Y. A., Scott, P. H., Wharton, B. A. 1986. Treatment with iron increases weight gain and psychomotor development. *Arch. Dis. Child.* 61:849–57
2. Bayley, N. 1969. *Manual for Development.* New York: Am. Psychol. Assoc. 178 pp
3. Beaton, G. H., Corey, P., Steele, C. 1989. Conceptual and methodological issues regarding the epidemiology of iron deficiency and their implications for studies of the functional consequences of iron deficiency. *Am. J. Clin. Nutr.* 50(Suppl.):575–88
4. Dallman, P. R. 1990. Commentary. See Ref. 8, pp. 101–3
5. Dallman, P. R., Siimes, M. A., Manies, E. C. 1975. Brain iron: persistent deficiency following short-term iron deprivation in the young rat. *Br. J. Haematol.* 31:209–15
6. Dallman, P. R., Spirito, R. A. 1977. Brain iron in the rat: extremely slow turnover in normal rats may explain the long-lasting effects of early iron deficiency. *J. Nutr.* 107:1075–81
7. Davis, J. M. 1990. Risk assessment of the developmental neurotoxicity of lead. *Neurotoxicology* 11:285–92
8. Dobbing, J., ed. 1990. *Brain, Behaviour, and Iron in the Infant Diet.* London: Springer-Verlag. 195 pp
9. Dobbing, J. 1990. Vulnerable periods in developing brain. See Ref. 8, pp. 1–25
10. Fairchild, M. W., Haas, J. D., Habicht, J.-P. 1989. Iron deficiency and behavior: criteria for testing causality. *Am. J. Clin. Nutr.* 50(Suppl.):566–74
11. Goodman, J. F. 1989. Infant intelligence: do we, can we, should we assess it? In *Handbook of Psychological and Educational Assessment,* ed. C. R. Reynolds, R. Kamphaus, 1:183–208. New York: Guilford
12. Grindulis, H., Scott, P. H., Belton, N. R., Wharton, B. A. 1986. Combined deficiency of iron and vitamin D in Asian toddlers. *Arch. Dis. Child.* 61:843–48
13. Hill, J. M. 1989. Comments. *Am. J. Clin. Nutr.* 50(Suppl.):616–17
14. Idjradinata, P., Pollitt, E. 1993. Reversal of developmental delays among

iron deficient anemic infants treated with iron. *Lancet.* 341:1–4

15. Larkin, E. C., Rao, G. A. 1990. Importance of fetal and neonatal iron: adequacy for normal development of central nervous system. See Ref. 8, pp. 43–61

16. Leibel, R., Greenfield, D. B., Pollitt, E. 1979. Iron deficiency: behavior and brain biochemistry. In *Nutrition, Pre- and Postnatal Development,* ed. M. Winick, 1:383–439. New York: Plenum. 496 pp

17. Leibel, R., Pollitt, E., Kim, I., Viteri, F. 1982. Studies regarding the impact of micronutrient status on behavior in man: iron deficiency as a model. *Am. J. Clin. Nutr.* 35(Suppl.):1211–21

18. Lozoff, B. 1990. Commentary. See Ref. 8, pp. 103–5

19. Lozoff, B. 1990. Commentary. See Ref. 8, pp. 77–79

20. Lozoff, B. 1990. Has iron deficiency been shown to cause altered behavior in infants? See Ref. 8, pp. 107–31

21. Lozoff, B., Brittenham, G. M., Viteri, F. E., Wolf, A. W., Urrutia, J. J. 1982. The effects of short-term oral iron therapy on developmental deficits in iron-deficient anemic infants. *J. Pediatr.* 100:351–57

22. Lozoff, B., Brittenham, G. M., Wolf, A. W., McClish, D. K., Kuhnert, P. M., et al. 1987. Iron deficiency anemia and iron therapy effects on infant developmental test performance. *Pediatrics* 79:981–95

23. Lozoff, B., Jimenez, E., Wolf, A. W. 1991. Long-term developmental outcome of infants with iron deficiency. *N. Engl. J. Med.* 325:687–94

24. Lozoff, B., Wolf, A. W., Urrutia, J. J., Viteri, F. E. 1985. Abnormal behavior and low developmental test scores in iron-deficient anemic infants. *Dev. Behav. Pediatr.* 6:69–75

25. Mushak, P., Davis, J. M., Crocetti, A. F., Grant, L. D. 1989. Prenatal and postnatal effects of low-level lead exposure: integrated summary of a report to the U.S. Congress on childhood lead poisoning. *Environ. Res.* 50:11–36

26. Oski, F. A., Honig, A. S. 1978. The effects of therapy on the developmental scores of iron-deficient infants. *J. Pediatr.* 92:21–25

27. Oski, F. A., Honig, A. S., Helu, B., Howanitz, P. 1983. Effect of iron therapy on behavior performance in nonanemic, iron-deficient infants. *Pediatrics* 71:877–80

28. Paredes, R. G., Agmo, A. 1992.

GABA and behavior: The role of receptor subtypes. *Neurosci. Biobehav. Rev.* 16:145–70

29. Pollitt, E. 1989. Comments. *Am. J. Clin. Nutr.* 50(Suppl.):662–64

30. Pollitt, E., Greenfield, D., Saco-Pollitt, C., Joos, S. 1984. A validation of attention-retention tests in studies on malnutrition and behavior in two cultures. In *Malnutrition and Behavior: Critical Assessment of Key Issues,* ed. J. Brozek, B. Schurch, pp. 186–202. Lausanne, Switzerland: Nestle Found. 201 pp

31. Pollitt, E., Haas, J., Levitsky, D. 1989. Functional effects of iron deficiency on cognition. *Food Nutr. Bull.* 11:57–58

32. Pollitt, E., Hathirat, P., Kotchabhakdi, N. J., Missell, L., Valyasevi, A. 1989. Iron deficiency and educational achievement in Thailand. *Am. J. Clin. Nutr.* 50(Suppl.):687–97

33. Pollitt, E., Leibel, R. 1982. *Iron Deficiency: Brain Biochemistry and Behavior.* New York: Raven. 214 pp

34. Pollitt, E., Metallinos-Katsaras, E. 1990. Iron deficiency and behavior: constructs, methods and validity of the findings. In *Nutrition and the Brain,* ed. R. J. Wurtman, J. J. Wurtman, 8:101–46. New York: Raven. 203 pp

35. Pollitt, E., Saco-Pollitt, C., Leibel, R. L., Viteri, F. E. 1986. Iron deficiency and behavioral development in infants and preschool children. *Am. J. Clin. Nutr.* 43:555–65

36. Pribram, K. H., McGuines, D. 1975. Arousal, activation and effort in the control of attention. *Psychol. Rev.* 82:116–49

37. Seshadri, S., Gopaldas, T. 1989. Impact of iron supplementation on cognitive functions in preschool and school-aged children: the Indian experience. *Am. J. Clin. Nutr.* 50(Suppl.): 675–86

38. Soemantri, A. G. 1989. Preliminary findings on iron supplementation and learning achievement of rural Indonesian children. *Am. J. Clin. Nutr.* 50(Suppl.):698–702

39. Soewondo, S., Husaini, M., Pollitt, E. 1989. Effects of iron deficiency on attention and learning processes in preschool children: Bandung, Indonesia. *Am. J. Clin. Nutr.* 50(Suppl.):667–74

40. Susser, M. 1991. What is a cause and how do we know one? A grammar for pragmatic epidemiology. *Am. J. Epidemiol.* 133:635–48

41. Walter, T. 1989. Infancy: mental and motor development. *Am. J. Clin. Nutr.* 50(Suppl.):655–64

42. Walter, T., Kovalskys, J., Stekel, A. 1983. Effect of mild iron deficiency on infant mental development scores. *J. Pediatr.* 102:519–22

43. Wechsler, D. 1949. *Wechsler Intelligence Scale for Children: Manual. New York: Psychol. Corp.*

44. Weinberg, J. 1982. Behavioral and physiological effects of early iron deficiency in the rat. See Ref. 28, pp. 93–123

45. Wrigglesworth, J. M., Baum, H. 1988. Iron-dependent enzymes in the brain. See Ref. 46, pp. 25–66

46. Yehuda, S., Youdim, M. B. H. 1989. Brain iron: a lesson from animal models. *Am. J. Clin. Nutr.* 50(Suppl.):618–29

47. Yip, R. 1990. The epidemiology of childhood iron deficiency: evidence for improving iron nutrition among U.S. children. See Ref. 8, pp. 27–42

48. Youdim, M. B. H., ed. 1988. *Brain Iron: Neurochemical and Behavioural Aspects,* Vol. 2. London: Taylor & Francis. 148 pp.

49. Youdim, M. B. H. 1990. Neuropharmacological and neurobiochemical aspects of iron deficiency. See Ref. 8, pp. 83–106

50. Youdim, M. B. H., Ben-Shachar, D., Yehuda, S. 1989. Putative biological mechanisms of the effect of iron deficiency on brain biochemistry and behavior. *Am. J. Clin. Nutr.* 50(Suppl.): 607–15

Annu. Rev. Nutr. 1993. 13:539–59

LIPID MODULATION OF CELL FUNCTION

Alfred H. Merrill, Jr. and Joseph J. Schroeder

Department of Biochemistry, Rollins Research Center, Emory University School of Medicine, Atlanta, Georgia 30322-3050

KEY WORDS: lipid second messengers, protein kinases, fatty acids, diacylglycerols, glycerolipids, sphingolipids

CONTENTS

INTRODUCTION 539
PROPERTIES OF LIPIDS RELEVANT TO THEIR PARTICIPATION IN CELL
    REGULATION 541
    Physiochemical Properties 541
    Interactions With Proteins, Membranes, and Other Structures 542
PROTEIN KINASE C AS A MODEL FOR LIPID REGULATION OF CELL
    FUNCTION 543
    The Protein Kinase C Family 544
    Lipid Modulators of Protein Kinase C 545
PERSPECTIVES FOR CELL REGULATION BY LIPIDS 550
    Dietary Lipids and Protein Kinase C 550
    Implications for Nutritional Toxicology 552
    Perspectives for the Function of Other Bioactive Lipids 553

INTRODUCTION

Lipids constitute the most structurally diverse class of nutrients. The major lipid classes (glycerolipids, sphingolipids, steroids, waxes, fat-soluble vitamins, etc) are composed of subgroupings within each class (the different phospholipids, for example), and within each subgrouping there is great structural heterogeneity (such as the compositional and positional variations in the fatty acids of phospholipids). It has been estimated that there are more than 1,000 distinct molecular species of lipids in eukaryotic membranes (100), and this is probably a conservative estimate. Does this imply that the exact structures are not important, or that they are so important that even subtle changes have biological consequences?

0199-9885/93/0715-0539$02.00

To answer this question it is helpful to envision lipids as they actually appear in biological membranes. Figure 1 depicts tracings of the space-filling models of the major lipids in rat liver plasma membranes. They are shown in the approximate amounts and distribution across the bilayer. When one looks closely at the difference in the shapes of the molecules, it is clear that they have different ways of interacting with each other and with membrane proteins. Despite the complexity of this diagram, it is an oversimplification because most lipids can assume a large number of conformations. Dipalmitoylphosphatidylcholine, for example, has been estimated to have 436,755 rotational isomeric configurations (94). Most membrane lipids also have a high degree of lateral mobility; in-plane exchange rates for phospholipids are on the order of 10^7 per second (33), although some lipids exist in separate, less fluid domains. Transbilayer movement is generally slow; however, this is not as true for the lipid hydrolysis products that are utilized as second messengers. Even phosphatidic acid crosses bilayers rather rapidly (with a half-time of 4.1 min) in the neutral (protonated) form (35). Despite

EXAMPLES OF LIPIDS AS MODULATORS OF CELL FUNCTION

Figure 1 Diagrammatic representation of tracings of the space-filling models of proteins and the major lipids in rat liver plasma membranes shown in their approximate amounts and distribution across the bilayer (2, 39, 46, 52, 72, 76, 125–127, 144). The highlighted lipids illustrate (from left to right): (*a*) noncovalent binding of lipids to cellular proteins to alter their behavior, as exemplified by the down-regulation of the EGF receptor by ganglioside G_{M3}; (*b*) covalent binding of lipids to proteins, as seen in attachment of some proteins to membranes via phosphatidylinositol glycan linkages; (*c*) dynamic interactions of lipids with enzymes to modulate their activities as part of signal transduction cascades, as in the activation of protein kinase C by diacylgylcerol and phosphatidylserine(s); (*d*) noncovalent interactions between cellular lipids and extracellular proteins, as exemplified by interactions between glycolipids and cytoskeletal proteins such as fibronectin; and, (*e*) association of some lipids with other lipids, as reflected in the apparent interaction of cholesterol and sphingomyelin.

these caveats, this model is a reasonable starting point to consider how lipids modulate cell behavior, particularly by affecting signal transduction.

PROPERTIES OF LIPIDS RELEVANT TO THEIR PARTICIPATION IN CELL REGULATION

Physiochemical Properties

Over a century ago, J. L. W. Thudichum (119) said, "The physical properties of lipids are, viewed from a teleological point of standing, eminently adapted to their functions." He was referring to the amphipathic nature of phospholipids: One domain is hydrophobic and tends to aggregate away from water, while another is hydrophilic and provides a more stable boundary at the water interface. These features allow lipids to form membrane bilayers, lipoproteins, pulmonary surfactant, and other biological structures, which Robert M. Bell has referred to as the "ordinary" functions of lipids. In comparison, Bell has termed the roles of lipids as second messengers and other bioactive compounds as the "extraordinary" functions of lipids.

One way that lipids modulate cell behavior is through subtle alterations in membrane "fluidity" (110). Lipid mobility allows vesicles to form and fuse with other membranes, enables cells to change shape during cell division and other processes, and provides a spontaneous mechanism that facilitates "self-sealing" when membranes are mechanically or biochemically disrupted. It also permits membrane-associated receptors, transporters, electron-transport enzymes, and other proteins to move as needed to perform their functions. Nonetheless, many changes in cell lipid composition and behavior do not correlate with fluidity changes (see Ref. 128), perhaps because cells tend to adjust their lipid composition to maintain a relatively constant overall fluidity. Many of the physiological changes attributed to alteration of the fatty acid composition of membrane lipids are probably due to alterations in discrete membrane domains or, as will be discussed later, to lipid-mediated signal transduction systems.

There are many different types of membrane domains. For example, simple neutral glycosphingolipids (such as glucosylceramide) tend to form patches of around 100 molecules. This causes the local concentration to become very high (1 to 2 M), which may facilitate binding by proteins (118). Another "cluster" is formed by lipids that tend to form nonbilayer structures (inverted micelles termed H_{II} micelles) (30). Lipids that form inverted micelles generally possess alkyl chains that occupy a relatively large area compared with that of the headgroup, such as dioleoylphosphatidylethanolamine. Some lipids can convert between bilayer and inverted micelle structures when there is a change in the effective area occupied by the headgroup; for example, when the carboxyl group of phosphatidylserine is protonated or is chelated by a divalent cation (31, 74). Nonbilayer structures may facilitate transbilayer movement of lipids as well as membrane fusion.

Another type of domain can exist when there are preferred interactions between two different lipids, such as the interaction between cholesterol and sphingomyelin. This apparent association affects the interaction of cholesterol with cholesterol acyltransferase, the cholesterol side-chain cleavage enzyme, and other enzymes and influences cholesterol transport and metabolism in vivo (51, 86, 112). Cholesterol feeding alters sphingomyelin metabolism, as well (86). Even when lipids are in fluid membranes, the van der Waals attraction energies can be quite large and transient interactions that are analogous to the "flickering clusters" that occur between water molecules can take place. Van der Waals attraction energies have been calculated to be $\sim$27 kcal/mol for a phospholipid with two saturated alkyl chains of 10-carbon atoms separated by a distance of 5 Å (108).

Interactions With Proteins, Membranes, and Other Structures

Many enzymes require lipids for activity and, while this requirement can sometimes be met by any hydrophobic environment, some proteins are highly specific for particular lipid classes (141). The mitochondrial enzymes cytochrome c oxidase (140) and the cholesterol side-chain cleavage enzyme, cytochrome P450scc (96), are stimulated by cardiolipin, the major phospholipid in mitochondria. In addition, some phospholipases not only utilize lipids as substrates but also require phospholipids as activators (32).

Another mode in which lipids can interact with proteins is as allosteric regulators. Ganglioside G_{M3} binds the epidermal growth factor receptor, resulting in down regulation of the protein kinase activity of the receptor (53). This has been proposed as a mechanism for cells to modulate their responsiveness to growth factors. Cell surface sphingolipid-protein interactions are also exemplified by the binding of cytoskeletal proteins to lipids on the external leaflet of cells (for example, fibronectin has binding sites for sulfatides), by the recognition of cell surface antigens by antibodies (some glycolipids are blood group antigens), and by microbial toxins (such as the binding of cholera toxin to ganglioside G_{M1}) (78).

Other lipid-protein interactions are covalent, such as the modification of proteins by fatty acids (47), more complex phospholipids (as in the phosphatidylinositol-glycan linked proteins)(41, 73), long-chain, thioether-linked isoprenyl groups (45, 106), and ceramides (41). The covalently attached lipid can be critical for binding of the protein to membranes (63), where they can become associated with other components of cellular signal transduction systems (115).

PROTEIN KINASE C AS A MODEL FOR LIPID REGULATION OF CELL FUNCTION

A recurring theme among lipid second messengers has been that the bioactive species are generally formed after cleavage of phospholipids by phospholipases (32, 43). These include the eicosanoids, platelet-activating factor, diacylclycerols, and diverse other lipid mediators. This review focuses primarily on one system, protein kinase C, as a prototype for a lipid-mediated signal transduction pathway that interacts with many different lipids that serve as activators and inhibitors (12). The major activators of protein kinase C and the pertinent phospholipases are shown in Figure 2, which is drawn from the perspective of protein kinase C as it approaches the membrane. Nearly all of the possible products of phospholipid cleavage (i.e. phospholipid headgroups, lysophospholipids, diacylglycerols, phosphatidic acid, fatty acids) have been implicated in the activation of protein kinase C. The reasons for the existence of multiple activators of protein kinase C are not entirely clear; they may provide synergistic activation of protein kinase C as is seen with diacylglycerol

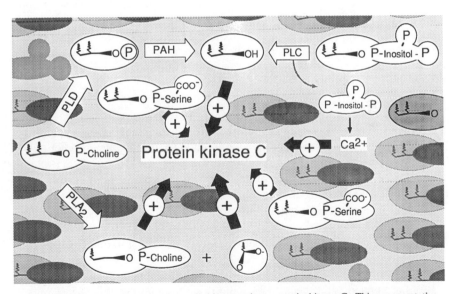

Figure 2   The turnover of membrane lipids to activate protein kinase C. This representation shows the hydrolysis of phosphatidylinositol 4,5-diphosphate by phospholipase C (PLC) to diacylglycerol and inositol triphosphate (IP₃, which stimulates release of calcium from intracellular stores), hydrolysis of phosphatidylcholine to phosphatidic acid by phospholipase D (PLD) (followed by the action of phosphatidic acid phosphohydrolase, PAH), and hydrolysis of phosphatidylcholine by phospholipase A₂ (PLA₂) to produce lysophosphatidylcholine and fatty acid. Also shown is the activation of protein kinase C by phosphatidylserine.

and fatty acids (87, 111). As shown in Figure 2, diacylglycerols can be derived from multiple phospholipids via different paths (i.e. cleavage by phospholipase C or by phospholipase D and phosphatidic acid phosphohydrolase). This seeming redundancy is thought to allow multi-phase or sustained activation (87); these two processes may be interrelated, because agonists can trigger the rapid release of diacylglycerol from phospholipids via phospholipase C to activate protein kinase C, which stimulates phospholipase D to generate more diacylglycerol (87, 124). Another consequence of utilization of different types of phospholipids is that the cleavage products can have different alkyl-chain compositions and can include both 1,2-diacylglycerols and 1-alkyl,2-acyl glycerols (from alkyl-ether lipids and plasmalogens) (104). Furthermore, utilization of phosphatidylinositol diphosphate in the first burst of diacylglycerol yields signals for both protein kinase C and other calcium activated systems, whereas the later mobilization of diacylglycerol from phosphatidylcholine will not necessarily involve intracellular calcium pools but may be dependent on extracellular calcium (6). These examples illustrate the extensive communication or "cross-talk" that occurs between different types of signalling systems (60).

Although it is not evident in the figure, multiple intracellular sites can be involved in these processes. For example, phospholipase C cleavage of inositol phospholipids in the plasma membrane generates the water-soluble second messenger inositol triphosphate, which triggers Ca^{2+} release from the endoplasmic reticulum. Ca^{2+}, in turn, facilitates the binding of some isozymes of protein kinase C to the plasma membrane.

The Protein Kinase C Family

Protein kinase C was initially characterized as a phospholipid-dependent and diacylglycerol-activated protein kinase, and most subsequent studies have implicated lipids as important regulators of the activity in vivo (87). Protein kinase C is actually a family of enzymes (4, 12, 87, 136) with different characteristics and tissue distribution, some of which are summarized in Table 1. The common features of these isozymes are that they each have a regulatory domain and a catalytic domain; variations in these regions determine the lipid activators, protein substrates, requirement for calcium, and other characteristics of the individual isozymes. In addition to the features shown in Table 1, recent analyses of protein kinase C have revealed that approximately four zinc atoms are bound per molecule (99).

A large number of polypeptides are phosphorylated by this kinase in vitro and in intact cells. Acidic proteins in the molecular weight range of 65–87 kDa have been identified as major and specific substrates for protein kinase C in several cell types (21). Many of these proteins are alanine rich and myristoylated at the amino terminus, and one of note is referred to as the

Table 1   Characteristics of protein kinase C isozymes[a]

Subspecies	Known lipid activators	Tissues		Structural domains
Alpha (α)	PS,Ca^{2+},DG,FFA,LysoPC	Universal		V1 V2 V3 V4 V5
Beta (βI/βII)	PS,Ca^{2+},DG,FFA,LysoPC	Some tissues	cPKC	
Gamma (γ)	PS,Ca^{2+},DG,FFA,LysoPC	Many tissues		C1 C2 C3 C4
Delta (δ)	PS,DG	Brain only		
Epsilon (ε)	PS,DG,FFA	Universal		
Eta (η)	?	Brain & others	nPKC	
Theta (θ)	?	Lung, skin & heart		
Zeta (ζ)	PS,FFA	Universal		
Lambda (λ)	?	Ovary, testis etc.	aPKC	
				Regulatory Kinase
				domain domain

[a]Shown are the known isozymes of protein kinase C and current information about their lipid activators and tissue localization. The overall structures of the three main groupings of the isozymes (cPKC, nPKC, and aPKC) are given diagrammatically with the variable domains (V1\–5) in solid and the conserved domains (C1\–4) in open (for the ATP-binding region) and partially filled blocks. Also indicated are the polypeptides that have the major regulatory (lipid-binding) domains and the protein kinase domains. Modified from Y. Nishizuka, 1992. Intracellular hydrolysis of phospholipids and activation of protein kinase C. Science 258:607-14.

MARCKS protein (myristoylated alanine-rich C-kinase substrate) (107). Selectivity for different protein substrates can be used to distinguish new isozymes (66).

Lipid Modulators of Protein Kinase C

The regulation of protein kinase C activation is generally thought to involve three lipid-mediated processes: association of the enzyme with membranes, activation of the enzyme by diacylglycerol and/or other lipids, and termination of the activation by removal of the lipids and/or proteolysis of protein kinase C to split the regulatory and kinase domains. Mindful of the inherent risks of oversimplification, one can summarize these events as follows.

MEMBRANE BINDING   An early event in the activation of many of the isozymes of protein kinase C is association of the enzyme with membranes through its binding to phosphatidylserine and (for some isozymes) calcium (9, 113). The Ca^{2+}-binding site(s) for the calcium-requiring isozymes are thought to be generated at the interface between protein kinase C and the membrane (9), because this divalent cation complexes phosphatidylserine (83, 117). The binding of protein kinase C to membranes induces an increase in surface pressure (113) that can be interpreted as a reorientation of the phospholipids and/or as possible insertion of a protein domain into the membrane.

There is little specificity toward the glycerol backbone of the phospholipid; 1,3-diacylphosphatidylserine activates protein kinase C despite considerable deviation from the usual 1,2-diacyl configuration (12, 69). Phosphatidyl-serines with unsaturated fatty acids are somewhat better activators than are the saturated phospholipids. However, this greater activation appears to be due to spacing of the anionic headgroups rather than to a specific interaction with the unsaturated fatty acid, because activation can be achieved with saturated phosphatidylserines when other phospholipids with unsaturated fatty acids are present or when cholesterol is added as a spacing group (17).

The nature of the phospholipid headgroup is more critical; the L-serine headgroup yields greater activity than do most other naturally occurring phospholipids or synthetic phospholipids made from serine analogs (12, 69). Activation can also be achieved by other acidic lipids (12, 70, 71). In some cases, such as with phosphatidylinositol 4,5-bisphosphate, phospholipids can reduce the concentration of phosphatidylserine required for activation (70). Whether the remainder of the phospholipid is phosphatidylethanolamine or phosphatidylcholine also influences the activation of protein kinase C (11, 23).

The exact stoichiometry of the interaction between protein kinase C and phosphatidylserine is not known; however, based on our understanding of the cooperativity of activation, at least four phosphatidylserines appear to be involved (56, 84). It has been suggested that electrostatic interactions with phospholipids promote the binding of protein kinase C to membranes, but cooperative interactions with phosphatidylserine provide the driving force for activation of the enzyme (93).

The requirement of a fairly large number of phosphatidylserines (and/or other acidic lipids) for activation has a number of structural implications. The ionization state of the carboxyl group of phosphatidylserine, and of many other ionizable groups in this environment [such as fatty acids (114) and phosphatidic acid (35)], is several units lower than the bulk pH (74); therefore, large proportions of negatively charged lipids will still be found on model membranes and plasma membranes in vivo. As a result, these membranes have a significant electrostatic potential that might affect second messenger systems (67, 77). Studies with annexin VI (annexins refer to the family of proteins, including protein kinase C, that bind to membranes in a calcium-dependent manner) have suggested that binding induces a clustering of the acidic phospholipids (10), and that the rate of clustering is slower with phos-phatidylethanolamine than with phosphatidylcholine.

After binding phosphatidylserine (and calcium, for the relevant isozymes), protein kinase C is thought to bind diacylglycerol (or phorbol esters) to become fully active (8). Phosphatidylserine alters the specificity of protein kinase C such that substrate phosphorylation is favored over autophosphorylation (85), presumably through reorientation of amino acid groups coupled to the catalytic site of the enzyme.

Depending on the conditions, lysophospholipids are able to both activate and inhibit protein kinase C (3, 90).

ACTIVATION BY DIACYLGLYCEROLS AND OTHER LIPIDS   Protein kinase C is affected by numerous phospholipase cleavage products, which sometimes interact synergistically. The lipid-activated domain of protein kinase C is located in the amino terminal region, and binding of the lipid activator(s) is generally thought to induce a conformation change that displaces a pseudo-substrate polypeptide from the active site of the enzyme (87).

Activation by diacylglycerols requires fatty acids at positions 1 and 2 of sn-1,2-diacylglycerols (1,3- and 2,3- isomers are not active) and a free hydroxyl group at position 3. The nature of the alkyl chains is less important, and shorter- chain diacylglycerols will activate if they are sufficiently hydrophobic to be membrane bound (44). Alkyl-acyl diglycerides, as are found in plasmalogens, are also activators of protein kinase C (42). Studies of the structures of diacylglycerols, phorbol esters, and other modulators of the activity of protein kinase C have revealed functional groups that overlay well and probably define the structural requirements for activation (82, 102, 134). By reducing the alkyl chain length of phorbol esters (to phorbol dibutyrate), one can measure binding to protein kinase C directly, and K_d on the nanomolar order are typically obtained. A similar strategy led to the development of short-chain analogs of diacylglycerols (1-oleoyl,2-acetyl-glycerol and, the more useful, 1,2-dioctanoylglycerol) as more water-soluble activators of protein kinase C (44).

Unsaturated fatty acids (oleic, linoleic, linolenic, and docosahexanoic acids) are activators of some protein kinase C isozymes, both individually (36, 105) and in combination with diacylglycerols (142). This suggests that the receptor-mediated activation of multiple phospholipases (A$_2$, C, and D) leads to second messengers that can act in concert to activate protein kinase C. CoA-thioesters of long-chain fatty acids and ciprofibrate (a peroxisome proliferator) apparently can potentiate diacylglycerol-activated protein kinase C by decreasing the phosphatidylserine requirement (92).

Protein kinase C occurs in multiple intracellular sites so that the intracellular location of the lipid modulators is an important factor in the biological responses. Since the intracellular movement of lipids is very difficult to follow, this aspect of protein kinase C activation has not been evaluated thoroughly. Diacylglycerols are thought to be formed in the same membranes as protein kinase C because they move very slowly between membranes; however, they could be generated on either leaflet because their rates of transbilayer movement appear to be fast ($t_{1/2}$ of ~10 ms) (54). Lysophospholipids and fatty acids can move more rapidly through the aqueous phase, and unsaturated fatty acids (36) and perhaps other lipids (19) may interact with cytosolic protein kinase C.

The location of the phorbol ester binding site in the regulatory domain of protein kinase C has been confirmed using deletion and truncation mutants expressed in the baculovirus-insect cell expression system (22). Mutation of the two cysteine-rich regions of the first conserved sequence (C1) revealed that each contains high-affinity binding sites for phorbol dibutyrate. Phorbol ester binding has been regarded as a marker for protein kinase C; however, one isozyme (zeta) does not appear to bind phorbol esters, although it is induced to translocate by phorbols (75). Protein kinase C eta binds phorbol esters, but it does not translocate to membranes in human neutrophils (75).

For many years protein kinase C was thought to be the only protein that binds phorbol esters tightly. n-Chimaerin, a neuron-specific protein, has considerable sequence homology with protein kinase C and binds phorbol dibutyrate with a nanomolar dissociation constant (1). These findings underscore the need to be cautious in using phorbol ester binding or translocation as proof (or disproof) that protein kinase C is involved in a cellular process. An additional word of warning: Biological responses to diacylglycerols do not necessarily mean that protein kinase C is involved. Diacylglycerols are thought to stimulate the respiratory burst of human neutrophils by both protein kinase C-dependent and -independent pathways (121); to increase actin polymerization by formation of actin polymerization sites (109); and to modulate the activity of the CTP:choline-phosphate cytidylyltransferase (123).

TRANSCRIPTIONAL ACTIVATION   Treatment of HL-60 cells with 1-alpha,25-dihydroxyvitamin D3 increases expression of the beta isozyme of protein kinase C by two- to threefold (89), primarily because of transcriptional activation. Phorbol esters also induce expression of this isozyme through transcriptional regulation of a promoter in the −111 to +43 region of the gene (88). Regulation of protein kinase C at this level may account for many instances in which increases in both the cytosolic and particulate activities are observed, rather than simply translocation of the enzyme.

INACTIVATION OF PROTEIN KINASE C   Protein kinase C is inhibited by a number of compounds, but sphingosine, the long-chain base backbone of sphingolipids, is of particular interest. Initially, sphingosine and other long-chain bases were shown to inhibit protein kinase C in vitro (57) and cellular responses to protein kinase C activators in platelets (57), neutrophils

(137), and HL-60 cells (80). Unlike most other inhibitors, which act as substrate analogs, sphingosine is competitive with diacylglycerol, phorbol dibutyrate (PDB), and Ca^{2+}; sphingosine also blocks protein kinase C activation by unsaturated fatty acids and other lipids (90, 137). Sphingosine has now been shown to inhibit protein kinase C-dependent processes in over one hundred different cell types (13, 55, 116). Therefore, cells may utilize the backbones of glycerolipids (diacylglycerols, lysophospholipids, and fatty acids) as activators of protein kinase C and the backbones of sphingolipids (sphingosine and related long-chain bases) as inhibitors. The mechanism of protein kinase C inhibition by sphingosine is not known; however, since acidic lipids (e.g. phosphatidylserine) are required for maximal activity of protein kinase C, positively charged long-chain bases may localize in the same region of the membrane and block binding and/or activity (7, 57, 79, 101). Care must be taken in the handling of these and other inhibitors of protein kinase C because it is easy to introduce artifacts and/or overinterpret the specificity of the inhibitor. These factors have been analyzed recently (64).

In contrast to fatty acids, which activate protein kinase C, the CoA thioesters can either increase (by substituting for phosphatidylserine) (92) or inhibit (9, 75, 123) activity. The inhibition appears to be selective for only some protein kinase C isozymes (in neutrophils, nPKA is inhibited by micromolar fatty acyl-CoA but beta-PKC is not) (75). The chemotactic peptide formyl-methionyl-leucyl-phenylalanine triggers a transient doubling of the amounts of fatty acyl-CoA's in neutrophils; therefore, this inhibition may play a role in the regulation of nPKC during the activation sequence for these cells. Fatty acyl-CoA's play a central role in diverse metabolic pathways (129), and we believe that this facet of protein kinase C regulation warrants further investigation.

Alpha-tocopherol reportedly (19) stimulates phorbol dibutyrate binding by smooth muscle cells and inhibits the translocation, activation, and phorbol ester-induced down-regulation of protein kinase C. Alpha-tocopherol may interact with the cytosolic form of protein kinase C, and this may account for some of the effects of vitamin E on cell proliferation.

There are also protein inhibitors for protein kinase C. Pearson et al (95) have characterized a 13,390 dalton polypeptide that inhibits protein kinase C. The polypeptide has been detected in bovine, murine, avian, and human tissues. In the cow, the inhibitor is most concentrated in secretory tissues and striated muscle and is lowest in smooth muscle. Another protein kinase C inhibitor with a molecular mass of 41 kDa has been isolated from human neutrophils (5). A protein activator of protein kinase C has also been isolated (48); therefore, polypeptides may play a more important role in the regulation of protein kinase C than has heretofore been suspected.

OTHER CONSIDERATIONS   Some discrepancies in the abilities of diacylglycerols liberated from various phosphoglycerolipids to activate protein kinase
C may reflect intracellular compartmentation (68). One should keep in mind
that there is both intracellular compartmentation and extensive movement of
lipids (59). Furthermore, the asymmetry of phosphatidylserine in plasma
membranes appears to be maintained by ATP-dependent "aminophospholipid
translocase(s)" (33). These issues are especially pertinent to protein kinase C
because many of the biological processes regulated by this enzyme involve
some form of membrane movement and remodelling.

PERSPECTIVES FOR CELL REGULATION BY LIPIDS

Dietary Lipids and Protein Kinase C

The involvement of protein kinase C in diverse aspects of cell growth,
differentiation, and function and its implication as a causal or contributing
factor for numerous diseases makes it a major target for the development of
new strategies to prevent and treat disease. This is of particular interest to the
field of nutrition, given the roles of lipids in the regulation of protein kinase
C and the many associations of dietary fat with chronic disease.

Perhaps the most obvious way that diet might alter the activity of protein
kinase C would be through release of activators (and/or inhibitors) in the
intestine during digestion and absorption of fat. This has been explored
primarily in the colon because activation of protein kinase C would be
suspected to stimulate cell proliferation, thereby promoting tumor formation
(62). Craven & DeRubertis (27) found that intracolonic instillation of
arachidonic, linoleic, or oleic acids (but not palmitic) induced the translocation
of protein kinase C to membranes and increased the incorporation of
[3H]thymidine into DNA, which suggests that luminal fatty acids may serve
as tumor promotors via activation of protein kinase C. Diacylglycerols,
apparently formed by intestinal microflora, have been found in human feces
(81) and may be able to activate protein kinase C in colonic epithelial cells.
Bile acids additionally affect protein kinase C activity in the colon (29).
Protein kinase C activity is altered in colonic cells that are in a preneoplastic
state (20) and in colon cancers (28, 49, 130); the particulate activity is elevated
in colonic mucosa in ulcerative colitis (103), a disease that is similar in some
respects to cancer because it is believed to begin with mucosal hyperprolifera-
tion and subsequent inflammation. Therefore, modulation of the activity of
this enzyme may not only be involved in the occurrence of cancer but also
may provide a target for chemotherapy.

Diet may affect protein kinase C in other parts of the body as well (14).
High fat diets have been shown to increase the level of diacylglycerol and

the amount of membrane-associated protein kinase C activity in epidermal cells (14, 15, 24, 34), a model often utilized for two-stage tumorigenesis. Additionally, protein kinase C may be involved in lipotroph-deficient diet-induced hepatocarcinogenesis (16).

As inhibitors of protein kinase C, sphingosine and other long-chain bases have potential as antitumor agents (57), especially since sphingolipids are widespread in nature (although rarely found in prokaryotes). Sphingosine blocked the induction of ornithine decarboxylase by phorbol esters in mouse skin (38, 50), one biochemical marker of tumor promotion; however, it did not reduce the number of tumors in a longer term study (37). In a cell culture model of transformation (mouse C3H10T1/2 cells) (18), sphingosine and sphinganine reduced cell transformation in response to gamma irradiation and phorbol esters. In addition, a recent carcinogenesis study using mice treated with N,N-dimethylhydrazine (DMH) to induce colon tumors (D. L. Dillehay et al, unpublished observations) showed that including milk sphingomyelin in the diet reduced the number of aberrant colonic crypts in short-term studies and decreased the tumor incidence by approximately one third. Apparently, the effects of sphingosine depend on the cell type because low concentrations of long-chain bases are mitogenic for Swiss 3T3 cells (143).

Diacylglycerol levels can be affected by other factors, such as increasing the concentration of glucose (25, 26, 40, 98, 131, 138, 139), and the implications for these changes with respect to activation of protein kinase C have been explored. Studies with isolated glomeruli (26) observed that increasing the glucose concentration from 5 to 30 mM increased the mass of diacylglycerol within 5 to 15 min and activated protein kinase C as assessed by translocation of the activity from the soluble to particulate fraction. The authors suggest that this may be a stimulus for kidney growth in diabetes and may mediate glomerular hypertrophy in this disorder (26). Glucose also increased de novo synthesis of diacylglycerol in rat skin, which resulted in marked increases in vascular clearance of albumin and blood flow (139). These changes appear to be mediated via protein kinase C because they could be mimicked by phorbol esters and were attenuated by a protein kinase C inhibitor. Hepatocytes treated with insulin show both increased synthesis of diacylglycerol and higher cytosolic and particulate protein kinase C activities (25). A number of factors can affect the diacylglycerol levels of liver (120). Cytosolic protein kinase C activity is decreased in the epithelial cells from the small intestine of rats with streptozotocin-induced diabetes, but the particulate activity was unchanged despite an elevated diacylglycerol mass (131). Administration of insulin increased the levels of diacylglycerol further, and cytosolic protein kinase C returned to normal levels. These findings illustrate the complex nature of protein kinase C regulation.

Various leukocytes (neutrophils, monocytes, macrophages, etc) and platelets are regularly exposed to unsaturated fatty acids and other activators of protein kinase C, for example, during the release of fatty acids from circulating lipoproteins by lipoprotein lipase. While much is known about the utilization of endogenous lipids as second messengers in the activation of these cells (97, 135), there is less information about the effects of plasma lipids on the behavior of these cells. Uhlinger et al (122) have observed that neutrophils isolated from subjects who had consumed a lipid-rich meal exhibit character- istics of "priming"—that is, the cells are not yet activated but have progressed to a state that is more readily activated. Such priming can occur when neutrophils are treated with low concentrations of protein kinase C activators. Consumption of dietary fat (58) and phospholipids (61) also affects the behavior of platelets and neutrophils. These findings have been interpreted as a reflection of changes in eicosanoid metabolism, although the results could be attributable to effects of unsaturated fatty acids on protein kinase C.

Implications for Nutritional Toxicology

If one considers the role of protein kinase C in the activation of leukocytes, there may be instances in which dietary fat causes inflammation of the gastrointestinal tract by activating local neutrophils or macrophages. This may account for the elevated particulate protein kinase C activity in colonic mucosa in ulcerative colitis (103). Activation of leukocytes results in the generation of superoxide anions, hydroxyl radicals, and other reactive oxygen species as well as the secretion of proteases and other bacteriostatic enzymes. These toxic species have been implicated in atherosclerosis, cancer, and inflam- matory diseases.

At the other end of the spectrum, recent studies have discovered a marked elevation in the amounts of two inhibitors of protein kinase C, sphinganine and sphingosine, when animals were fed fumonisins (133), mycotoxins produced by *Fusarium moniliforme* and related molds (for additional infor- mation, consult the chapter in this volume by Riley, Norred & Bacon). These long-chain bases accumulate because fumonisins are potent inhibitors of ceramide synthase (132). Consumption of feed contaminated with *F. moni- liforme,* the prevalent mold on corn worldwide, is known to result in several agricultural diseases (such as equine leukoencephalomalacia and porcine pulmonary syndrome) and has been correlated with human esophageal cancer (see chapter in this volume by Riley, Norred & Bacon). The mechanisms whereby accumulation of sphinganine and sphingosine produces these diseases are not known; however, these compounds are toxic to cells at high concentrations, seemingly because of inhibition of protein kinase C (79).

As more is learned about the pathways of cell regulation by lipids, a better understanding of some of the health effects of many other dietary constituents will emerge.

Perspectives for the Function of Other Bioactive Lipids

That so many new compounds—and new functions for old compounds—are still being discovered today is somewhat astonishing. In part, this is due to the development of better methods for analyzing lipids that are present in small amounts as second messengers. However, it is probably equally attributable to the general acceptance of a new paradigm that lipids function in diverse ways as modulators of cell function.

Our current knowledge about protein kinase C and other bioactive lipids (the eicosanoids, steroid hormones, etc) gives a glimpse of the complexity of these systems. Much is known about how phospholipases act on glycerolipids to activate protein kinase C, but we have probably only uncovered a few of the factors that regulate this system. Studies are just beginning to explore how the metabolism of an even more diverse class of lipids, the sphingolipids, participates in cell regulation. The hydrolysis of sphingomyelin to ceramides has already been implicated in some of the cellular responses to 1-alpha,25-dihydroxyvitamin D_3, tumor necrosis factor, and gamma-interferon (55, 65, 91). Other hydrolysis products of sphingolipids (e.g. sphingosine and some lysosphingolipids) are potent inhibitors of protein kinase C, as described above, and also have been found to inhibit a number of other regulatory enzymes (including the Na^+,K^+-ATPase and phosphatidic acid phospho-hydrolase) and to activate the epidermal growth factor receptor (78). When one considers the iterative fine-tuning that nucleic acids and proteins have undergone over the course of evolution, one should not be surprised by the evolution of sophisticated properties in lipids.

ACKNOWLEDGMENTS

We thank Elizabeth R. Smith for helpful comments concerning this manuscript. Most of the work by the authors described in this review was supported by NIH grants GM33369 and GM46368, USDA grant 91-37204-6684, and an NIH postdoctoral fellowship to J. J. Schroeder (GM14733).

Literature Cited

1. Ahmed, S., Kozma, R., Monfries, C., Hall, C., Lim, H. H., et al. 1990. Human brain n-chimaerin cDNA encodes a novel phorbol ester receptor. *Biochem. J.* 272:767–73
2. Alberts, B., Bray, D., Lewis, J., Raff, M., Roberts, K., et al., eds. 1983. *Molecular Biology of the Cell.* New York: Garland. 260 pp.
3. Asaoka, Y., Oka, M., Yoshida, K., Sasaki, Y., Nishizuka, Y. 1992. Role of lysophosphatidylcholine in T-lymphocyte activation: involvement of phospholipase A_2 in signal transduction through protein kinase C. *Proc. Natl. Acad. Sci. USA* 89:6447–51
4. Azzi, A., Boscoboinik, D., Hansey, C. 1992. The protein kinase C family. *Eur. J. Biochem.* 208:547–57
5. Balazovich, K. J., McEwen, E. L., Lutzke, M. L., Boxer, L. A., White, T. 1992. Purification of PKC-I, an endogenous protein kinase C inhibitor, and types II and III protein kinase C

isoenzymes from human neutrophils. *Biochem. J.* 284:399–405

6. Baldassare, J. J., Henderson, P. A., Burns, D., Loomis, C., Fisher, G. J. 1992. Translocation of protein kinase C isozymes in thrombin-stimulated human platelets. Correlation with 1,2-diacylglycerol levels. *J. Biol. Chem.* 267:15585–90

7. Bazzi, M. D., Nelsestuen, G. L. 1987. Mechanism of protein kinase C inhibition by sphingosine. *Biochem. Biophys. Res. Commun.* 146:203–7

8. Bazzi, M. D., Nelsestuen, G. L. 1989. Properties of the protein kinase C-phorbol ester interaction. *Biochemistry* 28:3577–85

9. Bazzi, M. D., Nelsestuen, G. L. 1990. Protein kinase C interaction with calcium: a phospholipid-dependent process. *Biochemistry* 29:7624–30

10. Bazzi, M. D., Nelsestuen, G. L. 1992. Interaction of annexin VI with membranes: highly restricted dissipation of clustered phospholipids in membranes containing phosphatidylethanolamine. *Biochemistry* 31:10406–13

11. Bazzi, M. D., Youakim, M. A., Nelsestuen, G. L. 1992. Importance of phosphatidylethanolamine for association of protein kinase C and other cytoplasmic proteins with membranes. *Biochemistry* 31:1125–34

12. Bell, R. M., Burns, D. J. 1991. Lipid activation of protein kinase C. *J. Biol. Chem.* 266:4661–64

13. Bell, R. M., Loomis, C. R., Hannun, Y. A. 1988. Protein kinase C regulation by sphingosine/lysosphingolipids. *Cold Spring Harbor Symp. Quant. Biol.* 53:103–10

14. Birt, D. F. 1990. The influence of dietary fat on carcinogenesis: lessons from experimental models. *Nutr. Rev.* 48:1–5

15. Birt, D. F., Kris, E. S., Choe, M., Pelling, J. C. 1992. Dietary energy and fat effects on tumor promotion. *Cancer Res.* 52:2035s–39s

16. Blusztajn, J. K., Zeisel, S. H. 1989. 1,2-sn-diacylglycerol accumulates in choline-deficient liver. A possible mechanism of hepatic carcinogenesis via alteration in protein kinase C activity? *FEBS Lett.* 243:267–70

17. Bolen, E. J., Sando, J. J. 1992. Effect of phospholipid unsaturation on protein kinase C activation. *Biochemistry* 31:5945–51

18. Borek, C., Ong, A., Stevens, V. L., Wang, E., Merrill, A. H. 1991. Long-chain (sphingoid) bases inhibit multistage carcinogenesis in mouse C3H10T1/2 cells treated with radiation and phorbol 12-myristate 13-acetate. *Proc. Natl. Acad. Sci. USA* 88:1953–57

19. Boscoboinik, D., Szewezyk, A., Hensey, C., Azzi, A. 1991. Inhibition of cell proliferation by alpha-tocopherol. Role of protein kinase C. *J. Biol. Chem.* 266:6188–94

20. Braun, C. L., Wali, R. K., Sitrin, M. D., Bolt, M. J. G., Brasitus, T. A. 1990. 1,2-Dimethylhydrazine-induced alterations in protein kinase C activity in the rat preneoplastic colon. *Cancer Res.* 50:3915–20

21. Brooks, S. F., Herget, T., Broad, S., Rozengurt, E. 1992. The expression of 80K/MARCKS, a major substrate of protein kinase C (PKC), is down-regulated through both PKC-dependent and -independent pathways. *J. Biol. Chem.* 267:14212–18

22. Burns, D. J., Bell, R. M. 1991. Protein kinase C contains two phorbol ester binding domains. *J. Biol. Chem.* 266:18330–38

23. Chen, S. G., Kulju, D., Halt, S., Murakami, K. 1992. Phosphatidylcholine-dependent protein kinase C activation. *Biochem. J.* 284:221–26

24. Choe, M., Kris, E. S., Luthra, R., Copenhaver, J., Pelling, J. C., et al. 1993. Activation of protein kinase C and elevation of diacylglycerol in epidermal cells from Sencar mice fed high-fat diets. *J. Nutr.* In press

25. Cooper, D. R., Hernandez, H., Kuo, J. Y., Farese, R. V. 1990. Insulin increases the synthesis of phospholipid and diacylglycerol and protein kinase C activity in rat hepatocytes. *Arch. Biochem. Biophys.* 276:486–94

26. Craven, P. A., Davidson, C. M., DeRubertis, F. R. 1990. Increase in diacylglycerol mass in isolated glomeruli by glucose from de novo synthesis of glycerolipids. *Diabetes* 39:667–74

27. Craven, P. A., DeRubertis, F. R. 1988. Role of activation of protein kinase C in the stimulation of colonic epithelial proliferation by unsaturated fatty acids. *Gastroenterology* 95:676–85

28. Craven, P. A., DeRubertis, F. R. 1992. Alterations in protein kinase C in 1,2-dimethylhydrazine induced colon carcinogenesis. *Cancer Res.* 15:2216–21

29. Craven, P. A., Pfanstiel, J., DeRubertis, F. R. 1987. Role of activation of protein kinase C in the stimulation of colonic epithelial proliferation and reactive oxygen formation by bile acids. *J. Clin. Invest.* 79:532–41

30. Cullis, P. R., Hope, M. J. 1991. Physical and functional roles of lipids in membranes. In *Biochemistry of Lipids, Lipoproteins and Membranes,* ed. D. E. Vance, J. Vance, pp. 1–41. Amsterdam: Elsevier Sci.

31. Dekroom, A. I. P. M., Timmermans, J. W., Killian, J. A., Dekruijff, B. 1990. The pH dependence of headgroup and acyl chain structure and dynamics of phosphatidylserine, studied by ^{2}H-NMR. *Chem. Phys. Lipids* 54:33–42

32. Dennis, E. A., Rhee, S. G., Billah, M. M., Hannun, Y. A. 1991. Role of phospholipases in generating lipid second messengers in signal transduction. *FASEB J.* 5:2068–77

33. Devaux, P. F. 1991. Static and dynamic lipid asymmetry in cell membranes. *Biochemistry* 30:1163–73

34. Donnelly, T. E. Jr., Birt, D. F., Sittler, R., Anderson, C. L., Choe, M., et al. 1987. Dietary fat regulation of the association of protein kinase C activity with epidermal cell membranes. *Carcinogenesis* 8:1867–70

35. Eastman, S. J., Hope, M. J., Cullis, P. R. 1991. Transbilayer transport of phosphatidic acid in response to transmembrane pH gradients. *Biochemistry* 30:1740–45

36. El Touny, S., Khan, W., Hannun, Y. 1990. Regulation of platelet protein kinase C by oleic acid. Kinetic analysis of allosteric regulation and effects on autophosphorylation, phorbol ester binding, and susceptibility to inhibition. *J. Biol. Chem.* 265:16437–43

37. Enkvetchakul, B., Barnett, T., Liotta, D. C., Geisler, V., Menaldino, D., et al. 1992. Influences of sphingosine on two-stage skin tumorigenesis in Sencar mice. *Cancer Lett.* 62:35–42

38. Enkvetchakul, B., Merrill, A. H. Jr., Birt, D. F. 1989. Inhibition of the induction of ornithine decarboxylase activity by 12-o-tetradecanoylphorbol-13-acetate in mouse skin by sphingosine sulfate. *Carcinogenesis* 10:379–81

39. Evans, W. H. 1980. A biochemical dissection of the functional polarity of the plasma membrane of the hepatocyte. *Biochim. Biophys. Acta* 604:27–64

40. Farese, R. V., Cooper, D. R., Konda, T. S., Nair, G., Standaert, M. L., et al. 1988. Mechanisms whereby insulin increases diacylglycerol in BC3H-1 myocytes. *Biochem. J.* 256:175–84

41. Fergerson, M. A. J. 1991. Lipid anchors on membrane proteins. *Curr. Opin. Struct. Biol.* 1:522–29

42. Ford, D. A., Gross, R. W. 1990. Activation of myocardial protein kinase

C by plasmalogenic diglycerides. *Am. J. Physiol.* 258:C30–36

43. Ganong, B. R. 1991. Roles of lipid turnover in transmembrane signal transduction. *Am. J. Med. Sci.* 302:304–12

44. Ganong, B. R., Loomis, C. R., Hannun, Y. A., Bell, R. M. 1986. Specificity and mechanism of protein kinase C activation by *sn*-1,2-diacylglycerols. *Proc. Natl. Acad. Sci. USA* 83:1184–88

45. Glomset, J. A., Gelb, M. H., Farnsworth, C. C. 1990. Prenyl proteins in eukaryotic cells: a new type of membrane anchor. *Trends. Biochem. Sci.* 15:139–42

46. Goodsell, D. S. 1992. A look inside the living cell. *Am. Scientist* 80:457–65

47. Gordon, J. I., Duronio, R. J., Rudnick, D. A., Adams, S. P., Gokel, G. W. 1991. Protein N-myristoylation. *J. Biol. Chem.* 266:8647–50

48. Goueli, S. A. 1991. Isolation and identification of a novel cellular protein that potently activates Ca^{2+}/phospholipid-dependent protein kinase (protein kinase C). *Biochem. J.* 279:695–98

49. Guillem, J. G., O'Brien, C. A., Fitzer, C. J., Forde, K. A., LoGerfo, P., et al. 1987. Altered levels of protein kinase C and Ca^{++}-dependent protein kinases in human colon carcinomas. *Cancer Res.* 47:2036–37

50. Gupta, A. K., Fischer, G. J., Elder, J. T., Nickoloff, B. J., Voorhees, J. J. 1988. Sphingosine inhibits phorbol ester-induced inflammation, ornithine decarboxylase activity, and activation of protein kinase C in mouse skin. *J. Invest. Dermatol.* 91:486–91

51. Gupta, A. K., Rudney, H. 1991. Plasma membrane sphingomyelin and the regulation of HMG-CoA reductase activity and cholesterol biosynthesis in cell cultures. *J. Lipid. Res.* 32:125–36

52. Hakomori, S. -I. 1983. Chemistry of glycosphingolipids. In *Handbook of Lipid Research,* ed. D. Hanahan, 3:1–166. New York: Plenum

53. Hakomori, S. -I. 1990. Bifunctional roles of glycosphingolipids. Modulators for transmembrane signalling and mediators for cellular interactions. *J. Biol. Chem.* 265:18713–16

54. Hamilton, J. A., Bhamidipati, S. P., Kodali, D. R., Small, D. M. 1991. The interfacial conformation and transbilayer movement of diacylglycerols in phospholipid bilayers. *J. Biol. Chem.* 266:1177–86

55. Hannun, Y. A., Bell, R. M. 1989. Functions of sphingolipids and

sphingolipid breakdown products in cellular regulation. *Science* 243:500–7

56. Hannun, Y. A., Loomis, C. R., Bell, R. M. 1986. Protein kinase C activation in mixed micelles. *J. Biol. Chem.* 261:7184–90

57. Hannun, Y. A., Loomis, C. R., Merrill, A., Bell, R. M. 1986. Sphingosine inhibition of protein kinase C activity and of phorbol dibutyrate binding in vitro and in human platelets. *J. Biol. Chem.* 261:12604–9

58. Heemskerk, J. W. M., Feijge, M. A. H., Kester, A., Hornstra, G. 1991. Dietary fat modifies thromboxane A_2-induced stimulation of rat platelets. *Biochem. J.* 278:399–404

59. Hjelmstad, R. H., Bell, R. M. 1991. Molecular insights into enzymes of membrane bilayer assembly. *Biochemistry* 30:1731–39

60. Houslay, M. D. 1991. "Crosstalk": a pivotal role for protein kinase C in modulating relationships between signal transduction pathways. *Eur. J. Biochem.* 195:9–27

61. Jannace, P. W., Lerman, R. H., Santos, J. I., Vitale, J. J. 1992. Effects of oral soy phosphatidylcholine on phagocytosis, arachidonate concentrations, and killing by human polymorphonuclear leukocytes. *Am. J. Clin. Nutr.* 56:599–603

62. Johnson, M. D., Housey, G. M., O'Brian, C. A., Kirschmeier, P. T., Weinstein, I. B. 1987. Role of protein kinase C in gene expression and relevance to tumor promotion. *Environ. Health Perspect.* 76:89–95

63. Kato, K., Cox, A. D., Hisaka, M. M., Graham, S. M., Buss, J. E., et al. 1992. Isoprenoid addition to Ras protein is the critical modification for its membrane association and transforming activity. *Proc. Natl. Acad. Sci. USA* 89:6403–7

64. Khan, W. A., Mascarella, S. W., Lewin, A. H., Wyrick, C. D., Carroll, F. I., et al. 1991. Use of D-erythrosphingosine as a pharmacological inhibitor of protein kinase C in human platelets. *Biochem. J.* 278:387–92

65. Kim, M. -Y., Linardic, C., Obeid, L., Hannun, Y. 1991. Identification of sphingomyelin turnover as an effector mechanism for the activation of tumor necrosis factor-alpha and gamma-interferon. Specific role in cell differentiation. *J. Biol. Chem.* 266:484–89

66. Koide, H., Ogita, K., Kikkawa, U., Nishizuka, Y. 1992. Isolation and characterization of the epsilon subspecies

of protein kinase C from rat brain. *Proc. Natl. Acad. Sci. USA* 89:1149–53

67. Langner, M., Cafiso, D., Marcelja, S., McLaughlin, S. 1990. Electrostatics of phosphoinositide bilayer membranes. Theoretical and experimental results. *Biophys. J.* 57:335–49

68. Leach, K. L., Ruff, V. A., Wright, T. M., Pessin, M. S., Raben, D. M. 1991. Dissociation of protein kinase C activation and sn-1,2-diacylglycerol formation. Comparison of phosphatidylinositol- and phosphatidylcholine-derived diglycerides in alpha-thrombin-stimulated fibroblasts. *J. Biol. Chem.* 266:3215–21

69. Lee, M. -H., Bell, R. M. 1989. Phospholipid functional groups involved in protein kinase C activation, phorbol ester binding, and binding to mixed micelles. *J. Biol. Chem.* 264:14797–805

70. Lee, M. -H., Bell, R. M. 1991. Mechanism of protein kinase C activation by phosphatidylinositol 4,5-bisphosphate. *Biochemistry* 30:1041–49

71. Lee, M. -H., Bell, R. M. 1992. Supplementation of the phosphadityl-L-serine requirement of protein kinase C with nonactivating phospholipids. *Biochemistry* 31:5176–82

72. Lehninger, A. L. 1975. *Biochemistry*. New York: Worth. 2nd ed.

73. Low, M. G. 1989. Glycosyl-phosphatidylinositol: a versatile anchor for cell surface proteins. *FASEB J.* 3:1600–8

74. MacDonald, R. C., Simon, S. A., Baer, E. 1976. Ionic influences on the phase transition of dipalmitoylphosphatidylserine. *Biochemistry* 15:885–91

75. Majumdar, S., Rossi, M. W., Fujiki, T., Phillips, W. A., Disa, S., et al. 1991. Protein kinase C isotypes and signalling in neutrophils. *J. Biol. Chem.* 266:9285–94

76. Matyas, G. R., Morre, D. J. 1987. Subcellular distribution and biosynthesis of rat liver gangliosides. *Biochim. Biophys. Acta* 921:599–614

77. McLaughlin, S. 1989. The electrostatic properties of membranes. *Annu. Rev. Biophys. Biophys. Chem.* 18:113–36

78. Merrill, A. H. Jr. 1991. Cell regulation by sphingosine and more complex sphingolipids. *J. Bioenerget. Biomembr.* 23:83–104

79. Merrill, A. H. Jr., Nimkar, S., Menaldino, D., Hannun, Y. A., Loomis, C., et al. 1989. Structural requirements for long-chain (sphingoid) base inhibition of protein kinase C in vitro and for the cellular effects of

these compounds. *Biochemistry* 28: 3138–45

80. Merrill, A. H. Jr., Sereni, A. M., Stevens, V. L., Hannun, Y. A., Bell, R. M., et al. 1986. Inhibition of phorbol ester-dependent differentiation of human promelocytic leukemic (HL-60) cells by sphingosine and other long-chain bases. *J. Biol. Chem.* 261:12610–15

81. Morotomi, M., Guillem, J. G., LoFerfo, P., Weinstein, I. B. 1990. Production of diacylglycerol, an activator of protein kinase C, by human intestinal microflora. *Cancer Res.* 50: 3595–99

82. Nakamura, H., Kishi, Y., Pajares, M. A., Rando, R. R. 1989. Structural basis of protein kinase C activation by tumor promoters. *Proc. Natl. Acad. Sci. USA* 86:9672–76

83. Nelsestuen, G. L., Lim, T. K. 1977. Equilibria involved in prothrombin and blood-clotting factor X-membrane binding. *Biochemistry* 16:4164–71

84. Newton, A. C., Koshland, D. E. 1989. High cooperativity, specificity, and multiplicity in the protein kinase C-lipid interaction. *J. Biol. Chem.* 264:14909–15

85. Newton, A. C., Koshland, D. E. 1990. Phosphatidylserine affects specificity of protein kinase C substrate phosphorylation and autophosphorylation. *Biochemistry* 29:6656–61

86. Nikolova-Karakashian, M. N., Petkova, H., Koumanov, K. S. 1992. Influence of cholesterol on sphingomyelin metabolism and hemileaflet fluidity of rat liver plasma membranes. *Biochemie* 74:153–59

87. Nishizuka, Y. 1992. Intracellular signaling by hydrolysis of phospholipids and activation of protein kinase C. *Science* 258:607–14

88. Obeid, L. M., Blobe, G. C., Karolak, L. A., Hannun, Y. A. 1992. Cloning and characterization of the major promoter of the human protein kinase C beta gene. *J. Biol. Chem.* 267:20804–10

89. Obeid, L. M., Okazaki, T., Karolak, L. A., Hannun, Y. A. 1990. Transcriptional regulation of protein kinase C by 1,25-dihydroxyvitamin D_3 in HL-60 cells. *J. Biol. Chem.* 265:2370–74

90. Oishi, K., Raynor, R. L., Charp, P. A., Kuo, J. -F. 1988. Regulation of protein kinase C by lysophospholipds. Potential role in signal transduction. *J. Biol. Chem.* 263:6865–71

91. Okazaki, T., Bielawska, A., Bell, R. M., Hannun, Y. A. 1990. Role of ceramide as a lipid mediator of 1-alpha,25-dihydroxyvitamin D_3-induced HL-60 cell differentiation. *J. Biol. Chem.* 265:15823–31

92. Orellana, A., Hidalgo, P. C., Morales, M. N., Mezzane, D., Broneman, M. 1990. Palmitoyl-CoA and the acyl-CoA thioester of the carcinogenic peroxisome-proliferator ciprofibrate potentiate diacylglycerol-activated protein kinase C by decreasing the phosphatidylserine requirement of the enzyme. *Eur. J. Biochem.* 190:57–61

93. Orr, J. W., Newton, A. C. 1992. Interaction of protein kinase C with phosphatidylserine. 2. Specificity and regulation. *Biochemistry* 31:4667–73

94. Pastor, R. W., Venable, R. M., Karplus, M. 1991. Model for the structure of the lipid bilayer. *Proc. Natl. Acad. Sci. USA* 88:892–96

95. Pearson, J. D., DeWald, D. B., Mathews, W. R., Mozier, N. M., Zurcher-Neely, H. A., et al. 1990. Amino acid sequence and characterization of a protein inhibitor of protein kinase C. *J. Biol. Chem.* 265:4583–91

96. Pember, S. O., Powell, G. L., Lambeth, J. D. 1983. Cytochrome P-450scc-phospholipid interactions: evidence for a cardiolipin binding site and thermodynamics of enzyme interactions with cardiolipin, cholesterol, and adrenodoxin. *J. Biol. Chem.* 258: 3198–206

97. Perry, D. K., Hand, W. L., Edmondson, D. E., Lambeth, J. D. 1992. Role of phospholipase D-derived diradylglycerol in the activation of the human neutrophil respiratory burst oxidase. Inhibition by phosphatidic acid phosphohydrolase inhibitors. *J. Immunol.* 149:2749–58

98. Peter-Riesch, B., Fahti, M., Schlegel, W., Wollheim, C. B. 1988. Glucose and carbacol generate 1,2-diacylglycerol by different mechanisms in pancreatic islets. *J. Clin. Invest.* 81: 1154–61

99. Quest, A. F. G., Bloomenthal, J., Bardes, E. S. G., Bell, R. M. 1992. The regulatory domain of protein kinase C coordinates four atoms of zinc. *J. Biol. Chem.* 267:10193–97

100. Raetz, C. R. H. 1986. Molecular genetics of membrane phospholipid synthesis. *Annu. Rev. Genet.* 20:253–95

101. Rando, R. R. 1988. Regulation of protein kinase C activity by lipids. *FASEB J.* 2:2348–55

102. Rando, R. R., Kishi, Y. 1992. Structural basis of protein kinase C activation

by diacylglycerols and tumor promoters. *Biochemistry* 31:2211–18

103. Sakanoue, Y., Hatada, T., Horai, T., Shoji, Y., Kusunoki, M., et al. 1992. Protein kinase C activity of colonic mucosa in ulcerative colitis. *Scand. J. Gastroenterol.* 27:275–80

104. Sebladt, R. J., Adams, D. O., Uhing, R. J. 1992. Quantitation of contributions of phospholipid precursors to diradylglycerols in stimulated mononuclear phagocytes. *Biochem. J.* 284:367–75

105. Seifert, R., Schachtele, C., Rosenthal, W., Schultz, G. 1988. Activation of protein kinase C by cis- and trans-fatty acids and its potentiation by diacylglycerol. *Biochem. Biophys. Res. Commun.* 154:20–26

106. Sepp-Lorenzino, L., Rao, S., Coleman, P. S. 1991. Cell-cycle-dependent, differential prenylation of proteins. *Eur. J. Biochem.* 200:579–90

107. Seykora, J. T., Ravetch, J. V., Aderem, A. 1991. Cloning and molecular characterization of the murine macrophage "68-kDa" protein kinase C substrate and its regulation by bacterial lipopolysaccharide. *Proc. Natl. Acad. Sci. USA* 88:2505–9

108. Shapiro, E., Ohki, S. 1974. The interaction energy between hydrocarbon chains. *J. Cell. Int. Sci.* 47:38–99

109. Shariff, A., Luna, E. J. 1992. Diacylglycerol-stimulated formation of actin nucleation sites at plasma membranes. *Science* 256:245–47

110. Shinitzky, M. 1984. Membrane fluidity and cellular function. In *Physiology of Membrane Fluidity,* ed. M. Shinitzky, 1:1–51. Boca Raton, Fla: CRC Press

111. Shinomura, T., Asaoka, Y., Oka, M., Yoshida, K., Nishizuka, Y. 1991. Synergistic action of diacylglycerol and unsaturated fatty acid for protein kinase C activation: its possible implication. *Proc. Natl. Acad. Sci. USA* 88:5149–53

112. Slotte, J., Tenhumen, J., Porn, I. 1990. Effect of sphingomyelin degradation on cholesterol mobilization and efflux of high density lipoprotein in cultured fibroblasts. *Biochim. Biophys. Acta* 1025:152–56

113. Souvignet, C., Pelosin, J., Daniel, S., Chambaz, E. M., Ransac, S., et al. 1991. Activation of protein kinase C in lipid monolayers. *J. Biol. Chem.* 266:40–44

114. Spooner, P. J. R., Clark, S. B., Gantz, D. L., Hamilton, J. A., Small, D. M. 1988. The ionization and distribution behavior of oleic acid in chylomicrons

and chylomicron-like emulsion particles and the influence of serum albumin. *J. Biol. Chem.* 263:1444–55

115. Stefanova, I., Horejsi, V., Ansotegui, I. J., Knapp, W., Stockinger, H. 1991. GPI-anchored cell-surface molecules complexed to protein tyrosine kinases. *Science* 254:1016–19

116. Stevens, V. L., Winton, E. F., Smith, E. E., Owens, N. E., Kinkade, J. M. Jr., et al. 1989. Differential effects of long-chain (sphingoid) bases on the monocytic differentiation of human leukemic (HL-60) cells induced by phorbol esters, 1-alpha,25-dihydroxyvitamin D_3, or ganglioside GM_3. *Cancer Res.* 49:3229–34

117. Swanson, J. E., Feigenson, G. W. 1990. Thermodynamics of mixing of phosphatidylserine/phosphatidylcholine from measurements of high-affinity calcium binding. *Biochemistry* 29:8291–97

118. Thompson, T. E., Tillack, T. W. 1985. Organization of glycosphingolipids in bilayers and plasma membranes of mammalian cells. *Annu. Rev. Biophys. Biophys. Chem.* 14:361–86

119. Thudichum, J. L. W. 1884. *A Treatise on the Chemical Constitution of the Brain.* London: Bailliere, Tindall & Cox

120. Turinsky, J., Bayly, B. P., O'Sullivan, D. M. 1991. 1,2-Diacylglycerol and ceramide levels in rat liver and skeletal muscle in vivo. *Am. J. Physiol.* 261:E620–27

121. Uhlinger, D. J., Burnham, D. N., Lambeth, J. D. 1991. Nucleoside triphosphate requirements for superoxide generation and phosphorylation in a cell-free system from human neutrophils. dodium dodecyl sulfate and diacylglycerol activate independently of protein kinase C. *J. Biol. Chem.* 266:20990–97

122. Uhlinger, D. J., Burnham, D. N., Mullins, R. E., Kalmar, J. R., Cutler, C. W., et al. 1991. Functional differences in human neutrophils isolated pre- and post-prandially. *FEBS Lett.* 286:28–32

123. Utal, A. K., Jamil, H., Vance, D. E. 1991. Diacylglycerol signals the translocation of CTP:choline-phosphate cytidyltransferase in HeLa cells treated with 12-O-tetradecanoylphorbol-13-acetate. *J. Biol. Chem.* 266:24084–91

124. van Blitterswijk, W. J., Hilkmann, H., Widt, J., van der Bend, R. L. 1991. Phospholipid metabolism in bradykinin-stimulated human fibroblasts. II. Phosphatidylcholine breakdown by

phospholipases C and D; Involvement of protein kinase C. *J. Biol. Chem.* 266:10344–50

125. van Hoeven, R. P., Emmelot, P. 1972. Studies on plasma membranes. XVIII. Lipid class composition of plasma membranes isloated from rat and mouse liver and hepatomas. *J. Membr. Biol.* 9:105–26

126. Vance, D. E. 1983. See Ref. 144, pp. 471–503

127. Vance, D. E. 1983. See Ref. 144, pp. 504–43

128. Wahnon, R., Cogan, U., Mokady, S. 1992. Dietary fish oil modulates the alkaline phosphatase activity and not the fluidity of rat intestinal microvillus membrane. *J. Nutr.* 122:1077–84

129. Waku, K. 1992. Origins and fates of fatty acyl-CoA esters. *Biochim. Biophys. Acta* 1124:101–11

130. Wali, R. K., Baum, C. L., Bolt, M. J. G., Dudeja, P. K., Sitrin, M. D., Brasitus, T. A. 1991. Down regulation of protein kinase C activity in 1,2-dimethylhydrazine-induced rat colonic tumors. *Biochim. Biophys. Acta* 1092: 119–23

131. Wali, R. K., Dudeja, P. K., Bolt, M. J. G., Sitrin, M. D., Brasitus, T. A. 1990. Correction of abnormal small intestinal cytosolic protein kinase C activity in streptozotocin-induced diabetes by insulin therapy. *Biochem. J.* 272:653–58

132. Wang, E., Norred, W. P., Bacon, C. W., Riley, R. T., Merrill, A. H. Jr. 1991. Inhibition of sphingolipid biosynthesis by fumonisins. *J. Biol. Chem.* 266:14486–90

133. Wang, E., Ross, F., Wilson, T. M., Riley, R. T., Merrill, A. H. Jr. 1992. Increases in serum sphingosine and sphinganine and decreases in complex sphingolipids in ponies given feed containing fumonisins, mycotoxins produced by Fusarium moniliforme. *J. Nutr.* 122:1706–16

134. Wender, P. A., Koehler, K. F., Sharkley, N. A., Dell'Aquilla, M. L., Blumberg, P. 1986. Analysis of the phorbol ester pharmacophore on protein kinase C as a guide to the rational design of new classes of analogs. *Proc. Natl. Acad. Sci. USA* 83:4214–18

135. Werner, M. H., Senzel, L., Bielawska, A., Khan, W., Hannun, Y. A. 1991. Diacylglycerol overcomes aspirin inhibition of platelets: evidence for a necessary role for diacylglycerol accumulation in platelet activation. *Mol. Pharmacol.* 39:547–56

136. Wetsel, W. C., Khan, W. A., Merchenthaler, I., Rivera, H., Halpern, A. E., et al. 1992. Tissue and cellular distribution of the extended family of protein kinase C isozymes. *J. Cell Biol.* 117:121–33

137. Wilson, E., Olcott, M. C., Bell, R. M., Merrill, A. H. Jr., Lambeth, J. D. 1986. Inhibition of the oxidative burst in human neutrophils by sphingoid long-chain bases. Role of protein kinase C in activation of the burst. *J. Biol. Chem.* 261:12616–23

138. Wold, B. A., Easom, R. A., McDaniel, M. L., Turk, J. 1990. Diacylglycerol synthesis de novo from glucose by pancreatic islets isolated from rats and humans. *J. Clin. Invest.* 85:482–90

139. Wolf, B. A., Williamson, J. R., Easom, R. A., Chang, K., Sherman, W. R., et al. 1991. Diacylglycerol accumulation and microvascular abnormalities induced by elevated glucose levels. *J. Clin. Invest.* 87:31–38

140. Yamaoka-Doseki, S., Urade, R., Kito, M. 1991. Cardiolipids from rats fed different dietary lipids affect bovine heart cytochrome c oxidase activity. *J. Nutr.* 121:956–58

141. Yeagle, P. L. 1989. Lipid regulation of cell membrane structure and function. *FASEB J.* 3:1833–42

142. Yoshida, K., Asaoka, Y., Nishizuka, Y. 1992. Platelet activation by simultaneous actions of diacylglycerol and unsaturated fatty acids. *Proc. Natl. Acad. Sci. USA* 89:6443–46

143. Zhang, H., Buckley, N. E., Gibson, K., Spiegel, S. 1990. Sphingosine stimulates cellular proliferation via a protein kinase C-independent pathway. *J. Biol. Chem.* 265:76–81

144. Zubay, G. 1983. *Biochemistry*. Reading, Mass: Addison-Wesley

Annu. Rev. Nutr. 1993. 13:561–87

ACTIONS OF CAROTENOIDS IN BIOLOGICAL SYSTEMS

Norman I. Krinsky

Department of Biochemistry, Tufts University School of Medicine, Boston, MA
02111-1837

KEY WORDS: antioxidant, anticarcinogen, β-carotene, dietary supplements, protective agents

CONTENTS

INTRODUCTION 561
CAROTENOID FUNCTIONS 564
CAROTENOID ACTIONS 564
   In vitro Antioxidant Actions 564
   In vivo Antioxidant Actions 571
   Antimutagenesis 573
   Protection Against Genotoxicity and Malignant Transformation 573
   Anticarcinogenesis 575
CAROTENOID ASSOCIATIONS 580
FUTURE CONSIDERATIONS 580

INTRODUCTION

Carotenoids have attracted a variety of investigators since they were first isolated from carrots by Wackenroder in 1831. However, it was not until the appearance in 1952 of Trevor Goodwin's excellent book, *The Comparative Biochemistry of the Carotenoids* (32), that one could say that carotenoid biochemistry had become a legitimate field of endeavor. Goodwin's book was followed by a second edition that appeared as two volumes in 1980 (33) and 1984 (34). During the interim, Otto Isler edited a multi-author compendium, entitled *Carotenoids,* that focused primarily on carotenoid chemistry, although it did include a section devoted to carotenoid function (51). Carotenoid biochemistry is an extremely broad field: It attracts chemists intent on unraveling the structures of natural carotenoids through structural analysis and

561

0199-9885/93/0715-0561$02.00

synthesis, taxonomists using carotenoid distribution to help deduce classification of organisms, botanists interested in the distribution of carotenoids among plants, plant physiologists studying the role of carotenoids in photosynthesis and photomovement, photobiologists studying effects of light on carotenoids, biochemists studying the metabolism of carotenoids, both with respect to interconversions and conversion to retinoids, nutritionists learning about the relative biopotency of provitamin A carotenoids and their availability from different foodstuffs, and chromatographers eager to test their skill in separating the vast panoply of carotenoids found in nature, of which there are almost 600 by the latest count (97). Members of these various specialties have interacted at triennial International Carotenoid Symposia, first held in Trondheim, Norway in 1966, and meeting again in Trondheim in 1993. During this 27-year period, representatives of all of the above groups have spoken about their fields, lobbied for attention to their discoveries, and stimulated each other to achieve more and more interesting results.

This broad circle of investigators has recently been expanded by the inclusion of clinicians. Clinical studies with carotenoids date back to two important publications. In 1970, Micheline Mathews-Roth and her associates first demonstrated that the principle of carotenoid protection against photosensitized damage in bacteria, algae, and plants (50) could be applied to humans suffering from the light-sensitive disease, erythropoietic protoporphyria (77). Since that publication, hundreds of such patients have been successfully treated, thus enabling investigators to conclude that oral β-carotene, at doses up to 180 mg/day, is a safe, nontoxic supplement for humans (7).

The second article that brought carotenoids to the attention of clinicians appeared in 1981 and raised the question, can β-carotene act as a dietary anticarcinogen (96)? The appearance of that article has led to a virtual explosion of interest in carotenoid action, in both in vitro studies and animal models, and the potential health benefits of carotenoids in humans. Over a dozen dietary intervention studies now underway will try to determine the efficacy of supplemental β-carotene in decreasing cancer mortality. In the last few years, another clinical area involving carotenoids has developed, namely, whether a causal relationship exists between carotenoid ingestion, or plasma levels, and coronary heart disease (28, 61). Investigations in this area are likely to grow as rapidly as the number of studies attempting to relate carotenoids to cancer.

Because of space limitations, this review only evaluates current work on the biological activities of carotenoids. Although it has been customary to write about and discuss the functions of carotenoids, J. A. Olson has suggested that we should differentiate between biological activities of carotenoids with respect to their functions, actions, and associations (87). The various biological effects of carotenoids can be grouped into these three categories as follows:

1. Functions: accessory pigments in photosynthesis, via singlet excited carotenoid; protection against photosensitization, via triplet excited carotenoid; provitamin A, via central and excentric cleavage.
2. Actions: antioxidant; immunoenhancement; inhibition of mutagenesis and transformation; inhibition of premalignant lesions; screening pigment in primate fovea.
3. Associations: decreased risk of macular degeneration and cataracts; decreased risk of some cancers; decreased risk of some cardiovascular events; nonphotochemical fluorescence quenching.

Figure 1 illustrates the structures of the carotenoids that are discussed below.

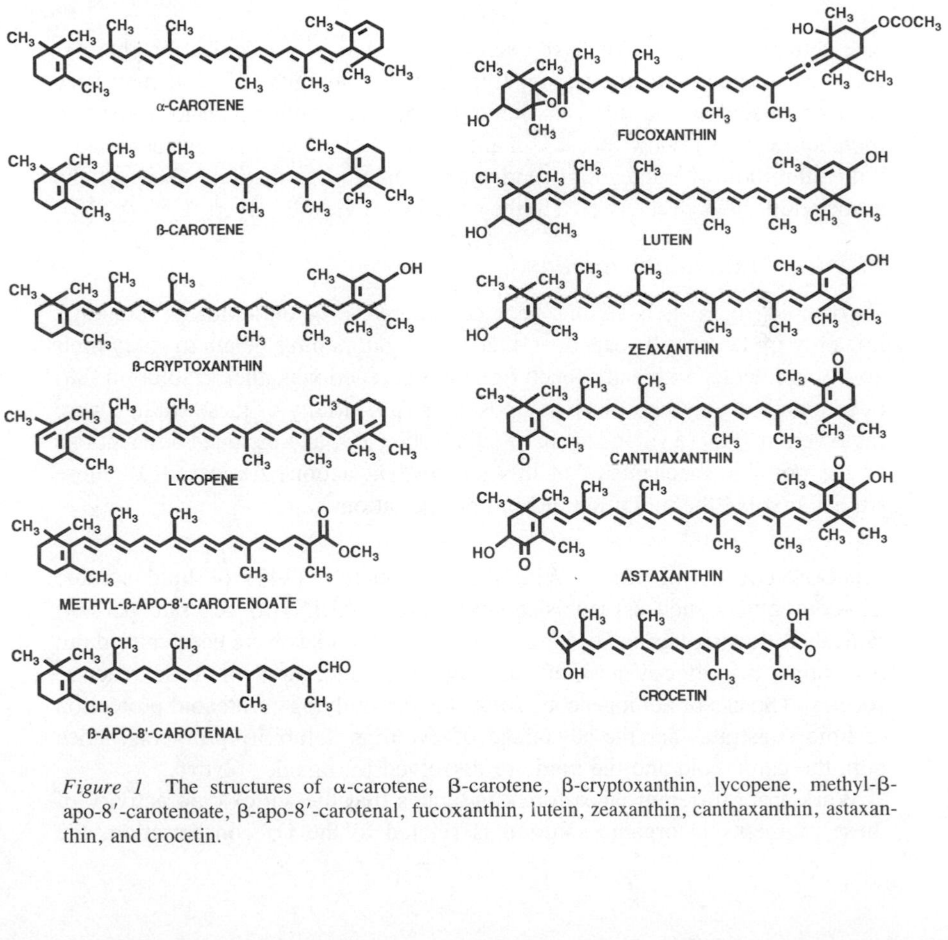

Figure 1 The structures of α-carotene, β-carotene, β-cryptoxanthin, lycopene, methyl-β-apo-8′-carotenoate, β-apo-8′-carotenal, fucoxanthin, lutein, zeaxanthin, canthaxanthin, astaxanthin, and crocetin.

CAROTENOID FUNCTIONS

Carotenoid functions are essential to the normal well-being of the organism in question. Because of their importance they are well documented and reviewed frequently. Carotenoid function as accessory pigments in photosynthetic organisms has been reviewed by Cogdell & Frank (16). Protection against light sensitization has been reviewed by Mathews-Roth (74) and by Will & Scovel (139). In the case of animals on vitamin A-deficient diets, the metabolism of the provitamin A carotenoids to retinol and retinoic acid is viewed as a function. Although we are no longer discovering new provitamin A carotenoids in nature, new information is available about the conversion of carotenoids to retinoids. A comparison of central and excentric cleavage of β-carotene has appeared recently (60)

CAROTENOID ACTIONS

The actions of carotenoids have been described as physiological or pharmacological responses to the administration of carotenoids (87) and may very well be related to the intact carotenoid molecule, rather than to a specific metabolite. This review focuses on antioxidant effects and actions associated with inhibition of mutagenesis and malignant transformation. Many of the associations have been covered in the excellent review by Byers & Perry (12).

In vitro Antioxidant Actions

Carotenoid pigments have long been considered to be antioxidants, although it is only in the last 10 years or so that investigators have begun to study their ability to interact with and quench free radical reactions either in solution (88) or in membrane systems such as liposomes (59). Many of these studies were reviewed in 1989 (53), and again in 1992 (90, 105), and included descriptions of the possible mechanisms of this antioxidant action. Almost all of these studies involve the inhibition of lipid peroxidation.

HOMOGENEOUS SOLUTIONS   With the introduction (142) of lipid soluble azo-compounds such as azobisisobutyl nitrile (AIBN) to generate peroxyl radicals following thermal decomposition, many studies have been carried out evaluating the effectiveness of carotenoids as inhibitors of these reactive species. The use of homogeneous solutions for studying carotenoid protection of lipid substrates has the advantage of avoiding solubility problems, since both the carotenoid and the lipid are dissolved in organic solvents.

Work from different laboratories indicates that the antioxidant activity of these pigments in organic solution is related to the O_2 concentration, the chemical structures of carotenoids, and the concomitant presence of other antioxidants. These three aspects are discussed below.

Oxygen Pressure Burton (10) recently reported on the effects of varying the partial pressure of O_2 (15–760 torr) and the concentration of β-carotene (0.05–5 mM) on the AIBN-induced oxidation of methyl linoleate. At low O_2 tensions (15 torr), β-carotene is an effective antioxidant, but at higher O_2 tensions (760 torr), the initial antioxidant activity is followed by an action of β-carotene that has been described as pro-oxidant (11).

Stocker et al (124) have also presented evidence supporting the increased effectiveness of β-carotene at low O_2 pressures. They compared the effect of both 20% (150 torr) and 2% (15 torr) O_2 on the antioxidant properties of β-carotene and α-tocopherol. From their data one can calculate that β-carotene was about 6% as effective as α-tocopherol at 20% O_2, but increased about 3-fold to 18% effectiveness at 2% O_2. Another example of increased antioxidant activity of β-carotene at low oxygen tensions has been reported by Vile & Winterbourn in adriamycin-treated rat liver microsomes (132). In the presence of increasing concentrations of either α-tocopherol or β-carotene (1 to 100 nmoles/mg protein), β-carotene was a better antioxidant at low pO_2 (4 mm Hg) than was α-tocopherol in terms of inhibiting malondialdehyde (MDA) formation. At a pO_2 of 8 mm Hg and above, α-tocopherol became the more effective antioxidant. Kennedy & Liebler (47) have also studied the antioxidant effectiveness of β-carotene as a function of the oxygen tension, and they conclude that it is quite effective at a physiological oxygen tension of 15 torr.

Palozza & Krinsky (89) have obtained similar results using a hexane solution of lipids isolated from rat liver microsomal membranes. Using either MDA or conjugated diene production to quantitate lipid peroxidation after AIBN treatment at 37C, they found that α-tocopherol is about 40–50 times better than β-carotene as an antioxidant in air (150 torr). However, when the pO_2 is reduced to under 20 torr, the difference in effectiveness decreases by about 40%, confirming the enhanced antioxidant activity of β-carotene at lower oxygen tensions. Since the O_2 pressures found in mammalian tissues are usually below 20 torr, these observations suggest an important role for β-carotene as an antioxidant in such environments.

Chemical structure When Krinsky & Deneke (59) first studied the antioxidant properties of β-carotene and its diketo-derivative, canthaxanthin, they did not attempt to quantitate any possible differences between these two compounds. Terao (128) was the first to report on the role of carotenoid structure in determining antioxidant activity; he compared β-carotene, canthaxanthin, astaxanthin, and zeaxanthin with respect to their ability to inhibit the formation of hydroperoxides of methyl linoleate in a radical-initiated system. The antioxidant activities of the two keto-carotenoids, canthaxanthin and astaxanthin, were better and lasted longer than the antioxidant activites of either β-carotene or zeaxanthin. Miki (79) also observed the increased effectiveness of conjugated keto-groups in a study of β-carotene, lutein, zeaxanthin, astaxanthin, tunaxanthin, and canthaxanthin, in comparison with α-tocopherol. Using a heme-protein-Fe^{2+} as a free radical generator and measuring MDA production, he found that astaxanthin is the most efficient scavenger, with an ED_{50} of 0.2 μM, followed by zeaxanthin, canthaxanthin, lutein, tunaxanthin, and β-carotene respectively, showing an ED_{50} in the range of 0.4–1.0 μM. In contrast, the ED_{50} of α-tocopherol in this system was about 3 μM. Other studies of keto-carotenoid effectiveness in membrane systems are reported below in the section on liposomes and biological membranes.

Carotenoid-tocopherol interactions   Just as the presence of δ-tocopherol enhances the protective effect of β-carotene on $^{1}O_{2}$-initiated photo-oxidation of methyl linoleate (129), so does β-carotene delay markedly the AIBN-induced loss of endogenous microsomal tocopherols (89). However, a synergistic interaction is seen in microsomes supplemented with both β-carotene and α-tocopherol, and will be discussed in the section on biological membranes (92).

LIPOSOMES   Krinsky & Deneke (59) introduced the use of liposomes to study β-carotene and canthaxanthin inhibition of radical-initiated lipid peroxidation, and there are now many studies using this model membrane. Liposome preparations are amenable to manipulation of lipid composition, pH, temperature, and they avoid some of the complications associated with the introduction of carotenoids into biological membranes.

Cabrini et al (13) reported that β-carotene could inhibit liposomal autoxidation, but when 0.3 mM $FeCl_3$ was added, the protection was lost. These observations were in contrast to their findings that ubiquinone could inhibit both types of lipid oxidation. The work of Stocker et al (124) on β-carotene protection at two different oxygen tensions has already been discussed.

In agreement with the data obtained in homogeneous solutions, Kennedy & Liebler (47) reported that in liposomes, the antioxidant activity of β-carotene varies with the O_2 tension and is more effective at 15 torr than at 760 torr. They suggest that this difference could be due to the rapid formation of autoxidation products of β-carotene at high oxygen tensions, but this difference may be an example similar to the pro-oxidant effect reported at high pO_2 (11). In addition, Kennedy & Liebler suggest that α-tocopherol, by decreasing the extent of β-carotene autoxidation, might increase the effectiveness of β-carotene as an antioxidant (47).

Terao and his associates (66) have now reported that astaxanthin, zeaxanthin, and canthaxanthin are better than β-carotene in protecting liposomes from peroxyl radical attack. A recent, preliminary publication (131) suggests that in dioleylpalmitoylcholine liposomes treated with azobis(2,4-dimethylvaleronitrile) (AMVN), β-carotene is considerably more effective than α-tocopherol in preventing a loss in the fluorescence of *cis*-parinaric acid, a method used to determine antioxidant activity.

Other workers have addressed the antioxidant properties of carotenoids in micelles. Pryor et al (100) compared the antioxidant effectiveness of various isomers of α-tocopherol in aqueous sodium dodecyl sulfate micelle solutions. Using an aqueous radical initiator, they reported that the effect of β-carotene was too small to measure. If this type of experiment was duplicated with lipid-soluble radical initiators, it would be interesting to see if the observation could be explained by the strict compartmentalization imposed on the system by the formation of micelles. In addition, Canfield et al (14) demonstrated that micellar solutions of β-carotene could inhibit soybean lipoxygenase-induced formation of conjugated dienes from linoleic acid, as well as decrease the formation of linoleic acid hydroperoxides.

LIPOPROTEINS   Two factors make lipoproteins an interesting in vitro system for the elucidation of the antioxidant activities of carotenoids: the fact that the initiation of atherosclerosis has now been related to oxidative modifications of low-density lipoproteins (LDL) (119) and the well-established observation that LDL is the major carrier of β-carotene in humans (58).

Much of the work on the antioxidant role of carotenoids in LDL comes from Esterbauer's group, and this subject has been reviewed very recently (25). Human LDL, treated with Cu^{2+} as a pro-oxidant, is oxidized and the level of oxidation is highly related to the endogenous level of antioxidants. The presence of the antioxidants prolongs the lag phase that precedes the rapid oxidation of LDL, and the antioxidants are consumed in the following sequence: α-tocopherol, γ-tocopherol, lycopene, phytofluene, and β-carotene (27). Although an initial study reported a correlation between the content of endogenous tocopherols and resistance to oxidative stress in pig LDL (49), they now report that some human LDL preparations, with practically equal amounts of tocopherols, have very different lag phases (24), which indicates that factors other than the tocopherols must play a role in protecting LDL. One of these factors might be ubiquinol-10, even though it is present in much smaller amounts than the α-tocopherol. For example, Stocker et al (123) claim that ascorbate-free LDL preparations exposed to azobis-2-amidinopropane (AAPH) are first protected by ubiquinol-10, and upon destruction of this antioxidant, lipid peroxidation begins, even though 80% of the original carotenoids and 95% of the original tocopherols are still present.

The actual role of β-carotene as an antioxidant in LDL remains controversial. Morel et al (81) reported that the addition of β-carotene to an LDL dialysate did not protect the survival of cultured human skin fibroblasts, unlike the protection offered by α-tocopherol or butylated hydroxytoluene. However, the conditions of this experiment are not clear. They claim that they used a 1.9-mM solution of β-carotene in ethanol as their stock solution and that it was added to the saline dialysate, which would have led to the precipitation of the β-carotene. In an attempt to answer directly the question of β-carotene involvement in protecting LDL against oxidation, Jialal et al (45) added β-carotene directly to LDL and initiated lipid oxidation by treatment with $CuSO_4$. Under these conditions, they report that the β-carotene was 20-fold better than an equivalent amount of added α-tocopherol in preventing lipid peroxidation. A cellular approach was used by Navab et al (84), who measured the effect of co-incubation of LDL with human aortic wall cells and measured monocyte transmigration. When the LDL was pre-treated with either β-carotene or α-tocopherol, no effect on migration was noted, but when the aortic cells were pre-treated with these two antioxidants, there was a very marked inhibition of monocyte transmigration. These findings suggest that the normal LDL oxidation brought about by the aortic cells is inhibited when the cells contain the antioxidants, in contrast to the LDL containing the antioxidants.

BIOLOGICAL MEMBRANES   Studies on membrane lipid peroxidation in the presence of carotenoids are summarized in Table 1 and are briefly discussed below. Although working with membranes should represent a more physiological approach to the study of the antioxidant activity of carotenoids, the use of this model is complicated by the fact that the membranes are isolated as aqueous suspensions and the carotenoids are virtually insoluble in this medium. This fact, in addition to the limited solubility of carotenoids in organic solvents such as alcohols, may explain the very large discrepancies reported in Table 1.

Dixit et al studied the effect of β-carotene in epidermal microsomes undergoing NADPH-dependent lipid peroxidation (22). They reported that at concentrations of 5–10 μM, β-carotene inhibited MDA formation more effectively than similar concentrations of α-tocopherol. However, they would have had to have a stock solution of β-carotene in ethanol of 0.3 mM, which exceeds the solubility of the pigment in this solvent (19).

Searle & Willson (117) reported a weak inhibition of MDA formation in rat liver microsomes exposed to $FeSO_4$ and cysteine when a suspension of β-carotene, estimated to be 1–10 mM, was added. They suggested that the

Table 1 Summary of the studies on membrane lipid peroxidation in the presence of carotenoids

Membrane	Pro-oxidant	Carotenoid	MDA inhibition (% of control)	Reference
Rat skin microsomes	1 mM NADPH	5 μM β-carotene	58%	22
		10 μM β-carotene	69%	
Rat liver microsomes	5 μM FeSO$_4$ +	1 mM β-carotene	7%	117
	500 μM cysteine	10 mM β-carotene	13%	
Bovine seminal vesicles	cyclooxygenase or	20 μM β-carotene	34%[a]	37
	lipoxygenase	40 μM β-carotene	56%[a]	
Rat liver microsomes	100 μM NADPH +	25 μM β-carotene	40%	132
	1.0 μM FeCl$_3$ +		70%[b]	
	30 μM adriamycin			
Rat liver microsomes	0.1 mM NADPH +	100 μM β-carotene, or	20%	48
	0.1 mM FeCl$_3$ +	100 μM α-carotene, or	37%	
	1.7 mM ADP	100 μM lycopene, or	42%	
		100 μM lutein	33%	
Rat liver microsomes	0.2 mM paraquat +	100 μM β-carotene, or	18%	48
	0.5 mM NADPH	100 μM α-carotene, or	30%	
		100 μM lycopene or lutein	33%	
Rat liver mitochondria	100 μM Fe^{2+}	4.2 μM astaxanthin	100%	63
Rat liver mitochondria	? FeSO$_4$	0.1 μM astaxanthin	100%	79
Rat liver microsomes	25 mM AAPH /AMVN	50 nmol β-car/mg protein	Modest	93
	0.4 μM NADPH +	10 nmol β-car/mg protein	11%	
	0.05 mM FeCl$_3$ +			
	1.7 mM ADP			
Rat liver microsomes	NADPH/ADP/Fe^{2+}	10 nmol β-car/mg protein	7%	92
Rat liver microsomes	AAPH	10 nmol β-car/mg protein	4%	
Rat liver microsomes	AAPH	10 nmol astax/mg protein	30%	91
Rat liver microsomes	AAPH	10 nmol canth/mg protein	30%	
Rat liver microsomes	NADPH/ADP/Fe^{2+}	10 nmol astax/mg protein	25%	

[a] Inhibition of prostanoid products.
[b] Incubation at 4 mm Hg O$_2$.

weak effect was due to the difficulty of dissolving the β-carotene suspension in the microsomes.

Halevy & Sklan (37) used a very different approach in assaying the antioxidant effect of β-carotene. They measured the conversion of arachidonic acid to either PGE_2 or to HETE, thus measuring either cyclooxygenase or lipoxygenase activities, and they reported that an aqueous dispersion of β-carotene at 100 μM was a more effective inhibitor than a 1-mM solution of α-tocopherol. Reports such as this one are always interesting in view of the fact that α-tocopherol is still considered to be the major lipid-soluble antioxidant in membranes (10).

As reported above, Vile & Winterbourn (132) found that β-carotene was a better antioxidant than α-tocopherol at low oxygen tensions in adriamycin-treated rat liver microsomes. The β-carotene was added to the microsomes as a concentrated chloroform solution, but it was not clear whether any attempt was made to eliminate the chloroform from the preparation.

Kim (48) has also looked at rat liver microsomal peroxidations, induced by either Fe^{+3}-ADP/NADPH or paraquat/NADPH, in the presence of several carotenoids, including α-carotene, β-carotene, lutein and lycopene, and α-tocopherol. She found that lycopene, lutein, and α-carotene were better antioxidants than β-carotene or α-tocopherol. Although the results are suggestive, it is difficult to understand how she dissolved her hydrocarbon carotenoids at 0.1 mM in absolute ethanol (19).

Recently, several publications have appeared indicating that astaxanthin is a very powerful lipid antioxidant, either equivalent to, or considerably stronger than α-tocopherol. Kurashige et al (63) reported astaxanthin protection of liver mitochondria from vitamin E-deficient rats, exposed to Fe^{2+} to initiate lipid peroxidation. The inhibitory effect of astaxanthin, dissolved in dimethylsulfoxide at concentrations ranging from 0.13 nM to 1.3 mM, on mitochondrial MDA formation was reported to be 100–500 times stronger than that of α-tocopherol. Miki (79) has reported similar results in homogenates of rat liver mitochondria exposed to Fe^{2+} and suggests that the strong antioxidant activity of astaxanthin could be related to the high affinity of this molecule for mitochondrial membranes, because of the chemical structure of this pigment. We have recently investigated the efficacy of two keto-carotenoids, astaxanthin and canthaxanthin, in inhibiting radical-initiated lipid peroxidation in rat liver microsomal membranes (91). Both of these carotenoids were found to be as effective as α-tocopherol, which is in sharp contrast to the very weak antioxidant action of β-carotene when added alone to this system (93).

A synergistic interaction of β-carotene and α-tocopherol has now been demonstrated in microsomal membranes by Palozza & Krinsky (92). These observations support earlier evidence of a synergistic effect in vivo (65) and could very well represent the inhibition, by α-tocopherol, of any pro-oxidant effects of the β-carotene peroxyl radical (β-car-OO•), assumed to be formed during the antioxidant action of β-carotene (53). Previously, we had demonstrated that α-tocopherol protects β-carotene from autoxidation (38), although Kagan et al were not able to see this type of protection in liposomes supplemented with both α-tocopherol and β-carotene and exposed to ultraviolet (UV) light (46).

CELLS   There have been very few demonstrations of carotenoids functioning as antioxidants in isolated cells. Endothelial cells of isolated, perfused rabbit cornea, treated with either β-carotene (1 μg/ml) or α-tocopherol (10 μg/ml), demonstrated extended survival times over control cells or in cells treated with either water-soluble antioxidants or the enzymes SOD or catalase (68). A good example of antioxidant behavior in cells comes from the laboratory of Bertram and his associates (144). This group added various carotenoids, as well as α-tocopherol, to C3H 10T1/2 cells and then monitored MDA production as a measure of lipid peroxidation. Under these conditions, they report that the order of effectiveness of the antioxidants is α-tocopherol > canthaxanthin = lutein = methyl bixin > β-carotene = lycopene > α-carotene. Interestingly, they do not find a relationship between the antioxidant effectiveness and the ability to enhance gap junctional communication.

In vivo Antioxidant Actions

As in the case of the in vitro studies reported on above, much of the evidence for carotenoid antioxidant effects in vivo is evaluated by the inhibition of lipid peroxidation in the presence of carotenoids. Increasing evidence that carotenoids can function as antioxidants in vivo has been reported recently in animal models in which the pigments have been injected in the animals or added directly to the diet.

Two aspects of the antioxidant activity of carotenoids seem to be particularly important in vivo. The first is the efficiency that these molecules display in directly decreasing lipid peroxidation. The second is the ability of these molecules to modulate endogenous levels of other antioxidants.

Many workers have demonstrated the antioxidant activity of carotenoid molecules in animal models. For example, Tappel and his associates reported (62) that an injection of β-carotene in mineral oil significantly blocks the increased expiration of ethane and pentane observed in ascorbate-deficient guinea pigs. They also put rats on a Se-deficient diet, and found that β-carotene, at 30 mg/day, was as effective as either supplemental Se or α-tocopherol in preventing liver damage (143). Most recently, Tappel's laboratory has demonstrated that tissue slices from animals fed various antioxidants and then treated with t-butylhydroperoxide can be used to measure antioxidant effectiveness in vivo (65). Of particular interest was the finding that rats fed β-carotene showed very little protection in the tissues treated with *t*-butylhydroperoxide, but when the β-carotene was added to tissues containing either α-tocopherol, Se, or ubiquinone, it displayed a synergistic protective action.

Tan & Chu (126) have fed various palm carotenoids to rats and have measured cytochrome P450-mediated metabolism of benzo[*a*]pyrene (BP). In their system, they claim that β-carotene is much more potent than α-tocopherol in inhibiting the formation of both the 9,10-diol and the 3-OH-metabolite of the benzo[*a*]pyrene.

Another report (95) indicates that the dopaminergic neurotoxic effects of *N*-methyl-4-phenyl-1,2,3,6-tetrahydropyridine can be prevented by subcutaneous injections of either β-carotene or α-tocopherol, as well as aqueous ascorbate and *N*-acetylcysteine, suggesting that the neurotoxin works by means of an oxidative mechanism.

A study in humans (80) who were maintained on a carotenoid-free diet for two weeks and then repleted with β-carotene demonstrated a decrease in serum lipid peroxide values, without affecting neutrophil superoxide production. This effect of β-carotene appeared to be independent of the repletion concentration, as similar effects were seen with either 15 or 120 mg/day. This study is the only example of an antioxidant effect of carotenoids in humans.

In a very preliminary report, Clausen (15) has observed a decrease in luminol-enhanced chemiluminescence from polymorphonuclear leukocytes (PMN) isolated from smokers after a 10-day treatment with various antioxidants. He reports that effectiveness is as follows: Se $>>$ β-carotene $>>$ ascorbic acid $>$ α-tocopherol; ubiquinone is much less effective.

In some cases, the addition of carotenoids has not led to any enhanced antioxidant effect, and, in fact, the added carotenoid has been reported to function as a pro-oxidant. Lomnitski et al (67) reported that rats maintained on a diet deficient in α-tocopherol and supplemented with oxidized soy bean oil develop increased levels of MDA in the testes, along with increased amounts of 15-lipoxygenase activity. An additional supplementation with β-carotene at 500 mg/g resulted in increased testes MDA and 15-lipoxygenase activity. They concluded that the additional β-carotene added to an α-tocopherol deficient diet behaved like a pro-oxidant. Another example of a failure of supplemental β-carotene to prevent oxidative damage has been reported by Witt et al (140) who fed human volunteers 533 mg α-tocopherol, 1 g ascorbic acid, and 10 mg β-carotene for 1 month. These individuals were tested for exercise capacity and excretion of the oxidized RNA base, 8-hydroxyguanosine, and no difference in either parameter was detected after supplementation.

In agreement with the in vitro experiments demonstrating the antioxidant activity of astaxanthin (63, 66, 79, 91, 128), this activity has been confirmed in vivo. For example, the uncoupling of mitochondrial respiration observed in rats deficient in α-tocopherol can be prevented by feeding the rats 1 mg/100 g astaxanthin (63). Similarly, the ability of the radical-generating system, xanthine oxidase and xanthine, to induce lysis of erythrocyte ghosts from α-tocopherol-deficient rats was also protected by the addition of astaxanthin at a level of 1 g/kg (79).

INTERACTIONS WITH OTHER ANTIOXIDANTS   The work cited above indicates that carotenoid pigments can provide antioxidant activity in vivo, but it is possible that the effect is not direct. An alternative mechanism is suggested by Mayne & Parker (78), who reported that the addition of dietary canthaxanthin to chicks deficient in vitamin E and selenium increased the resistance to lipid peroxidation, primarily by increasing membrane α-tocopherol levels, and only secondarily by providing weak direct antioxidant activity.

Other interactions between antioxidants in vivo have been confirmed by Blakely and associates (9). They reported that β-carotene modulates the increase of SOD induced by peroxyl radicals produced by a high fat diet. Another interesting observation on interactions was reported by Jialal & Grundy (44), who found that added ascorbate was able to protect the endogenous tocopherols and β-carotene in human LDL oxidized with Cu^{2+}, but added probucol was without effect. In addition, Leibovitz et al (65) have reported on a clear synergistic action between β-carotene and other antioxidants in the protection of different rat organs from both spontaneous and induced lipid peroxidation.

One of the possible explanations for the lack of antioxidant activity in some of these experiments may be the poor storage of β-carotene in rat tissues or, in accord with the hypothesis of Burton & Ingold (11), the possibility that, under certain circumstances (concentration of β-carotene, oxygen tensions in the tissues, modality of administration), the action of β-carotene represents the balance between anti- and pro-oxidant properties.

Antimutagenesis

The ability of carotenoids to prevent bacterial mutagenesis has been reviewed recently (57). In summary, several investigators have clearly demonstrated antimutagenic activity in *Salmonella typhimurium* for carotenoids such as β-carotene, canthaxanthin, cryptoxanthin, β-apo-8'-carotenal, and methyl-β-apo-8'-carotenoate. A single negative study (130) has also been reported.

Protection Against Genotoxicity and Malignant Transformation

Many attempts have been made to evaluate the protection afforded cell or organ culture by the addition of carotenoids. However, to compare one experiment with another is very difficult because of the variability in methodology used by different investigators adding carotenoids to their systems. Since most carotenoids are insoluble in aqueous environments, or poorly soluble in many polar organic solvents, a variety of techniques have been used to try to incorporate these compounds into cells. Therefore, although carotenoid concentrations are frequently reported, it is probably best not to put too much stock in the actual values. In addition, because of their hydrophobic nature, carotenoids will associate with membranes and hydrophobic portions of cells.

When this topic was first reviewed (52), only a handful of papers had demonstrated the cellular effects of carotenoids. The number of investigations has grown considerably, and Table 2 lists most of the studies that have tested carotenoids in cellular systems as protective agents. As this material has been reviewed several times recently (54, 55, 57), I only discuss some of the newer observations.

Hazuka et al (39) have added β-carotene and other antioxidants to cultures of mouse B-16 melanoma cells and have observed morphological differentiation in these cells, along with inhibition of growth and decreased survival. In addition, this treatment decreases both basal and melanocyte hormone-stimulated adenyl cyclase activity. They used β-carotene in a 1:10 mixture of DMSO:ethanol at concentrations up to 37.2 μM. Because the solvent was never above 0.4% in these cultures, their starting solutions of β-carotene were 9.3 mM in the DMSO:ethanol solution. Similar effects on growth inhibition were observed with α-carotene, retinol, and butylated hydroxyanisole, but the latter was not able to modulate the adenyl cyclase activity.

Watson and his associates have added β-carotene to either human PMN or to peripheral blood mononuclear cells (PBMC). In the former case, they report (1) secretion of a cytokine that is cytotoxic in 4 out of 6 human tumor cells lines studied and that had only low level toxicity to a normal diploid fibroblast line. Maximum secretion occurred at $0.1-1 \times 10^{-9}$ M β-carotene. In the case of the PBMC, β-carotene treatment resulted in an increase in the expression of various markers, including the interleukin-2 receptor, as well as an increase in the number of natural killer (NK) cells. Very recently, this group has used canthaxanthin added to cells, and they claim that 0.1 mM canthaxanthin inhibits 3 tumor cell lines, but stimulates the growth of 3T3 cells. The canthaxanthin is dissolved in either ethanol or DMSO as the vehicle, and since the solvent is never used above 0.1%, their original vehicle solution must have been 100 mM, i.e. it must have contained 56 mg/ml of canthaxanthin. This value is much too high for solubility in either of the organic solvents. Furthermore, they claim that the vehicle is subsequently added to their medium to yield a stock solution of 1 mM. This concentration of canthaxanthin in an aqueous medium is suspect.

Schwartz and his associates have also provided evidence that carotenoids can specifically inhibit the growth of tumor cells in culture. The addition of β-carotene or canthaxanthin at 70 μM in liposomes inhibited the proliferation of cultured human squamous cells (SK-MES lung carcinoma or SCC-25 oral carcinoma), but there was no effect on the growth of normal human keratinocytes (115). In addition, these workers report that β-carotene, at concentrations up to 100 μM in PBS/0.1% DMSO, is toxic to SCC-25 cells in culture (116). Again, the ability to achieve such concentrations of β-carotene in an aqueous medium is difficult to accept and would certainly be accompanied by the precipitation of a large amount of this material. An additional publication (112) claims that 70 μM β-carotene or canthaxanthin is selectively toxic to 7 malignant tumor cell lines and is without effect in normal keratinocytes.

Some of the most interesting cellular effects of carotenoids have been reported by Bertram and his associates. In an early publication (101), both β-carotene and canthaxanthin, in the form of water-dispersible beadlets provided by Hoffmann-La Roche, when added to C3H/10T1/2 cells, decreased the extent of malignant transformation induced either by methylcholanthrene or by X-ray treatment. These observations have been extended to other carotenoids, for α-carotene and lycopene were also effective in inhibiting MCA-induced malignant transformation (8). In these experiments, the carotenoids were dissolved in 99.5% tetrahydrofuran to give 2-mM solutions, which are achievable in this solvent (19), and then diluted directly into the culture medium to yield solutions as high as 10^{-5} M. Although lutein was inhibitory at 10 μM, it actually increased the number of transformants at lower concentrations. α-Tocopherol also inhibited malignant transformation, but was only about 10% as active as lycopene. Recently, Bertram et al reported that these carotenoids inhibit gap junctional communication in the C3H/10T1/2 cells (144) and that apparently there is no relationship between the ability of these carotenoids to inhibit this process and their antioxidant capacity, as measured by TBARS production. Furthermore, this group has now found evidence that β-carotene, canthaxanthin, and lycopene can up-regulate the expression of the connexin43 gene, the gene responsible for the production of one of the important components of the gap junction (145). This process was not related to the antioxidant capacities of these carotenoids, and added α-tocopherol had no effect.

The above discussion would seem to indicate that distinct effects on cells have been observed when carotenoids are added, but much work needs to be carried out to see if the effects are due to the intact carotenoids to or to an enzymatic or chemical breakdown product.

Anticarcinogenesis

The preliminary reports of carotenoids inhibiting tumor formation in animals supplemented with β-carotene (70, 107) served as one of the foundations for the hypothesis that β-carotene might function as a dietary anticarcinogen in humans (96). Work of this nature has continued with animals, although with

Table 2 The effects of carotenoids on cells and cellular systems[a]

Carotenoid	Cells	Action measured	Initiated by	Observed effect	Reference
β-Carotene	Mammary; mouse	Alveolar lesions	DMBA	Inhibition	118
β-Carotene	Mammary; mouse	SCE	DMBA/MNU/DENA	Inhibition	69
β-Carotene	CHO	SCE	PMNL OR HX/XO	Reduces SCE	138
β-Carotene	Hamster bone marrow	Chromosome breaks	MMS/thiotepa/busulfan	Protection	103, 104
β-Carotene	Bone marrow; mouse	Chromosome breaks	B[a]P; mitomycin C	Protective	102
β-Carotene	CHO	SCE	MMS; 4-NQO	Protection	121
β-Carotene/α-car	Human lymphocytes	Mitogenesis; E-rosettes	Concanavalin A	Inhibits proliferation	82
β-Carotene	HCPC-1	Growth	DMBA	Inhibition	114
β-Carotene	Human PBMC	HLA-DR antigen expression	Opsonized zymosan	Prevents decrease	36
β-Carotene/canth	C3H/10T1/2	Transformation	X-rays; MCA	Canth > β-carotene	101
β-Carotene	Human PBMC	↓ Phagocytic activity	UV-B exposure	Prevention	111
α-Car/β-carotene	Neuroblastoma GOTO	Growth	Spontaneous	Inhibits; α-car > β-car	85
β-Carotene	V79	SCE	MNNG	Increases SCE	20
α-Car/β-carotene	Neuroblastoma GOTO	Growth; N-myc mRNA	Spontaneous	Inhibits/suppresses	83
β-Carotene	Human PMNL	Cytotoxic cytokine	β-Carotene	Induces secretion	1
β-Carotene/canth	Human PBMC	Expression of markers	Spontaneous	Increased expression	99
β-Carotene	Human PBMC	Expression of markers	Spontaneous	↑ NK cells/IL-2 receptor	98
β-Carotene	Human PMNL	Chemiluminescence	FMLP or luminol	↓ Chemiluminescence	5
β-Carotene/canth	Transformed C127	Chromosome instability	BPV transformation	Inhibits	122
β-Carotene	Melanoma: Mouse	Differentiation	Spontaneous	Increases	122
β-Carotene	Mouse	Adenylate cyclase	MSH, NaF	Reduces	39

Carotenoid	Cell/system	Endpoint	Inducer	Effect	Ref.
β-Carotene/canth	Human squamous	Growth	Spontaneous	Inhibited	115
	Normal keratinocytes	Growth	Spontaneous	No Effect	
Fucoxanthin	Neuroblastoma: GOTO	Growth	Spontaneous	Inhibited	86
Crocetin	C3H/10T1/2	Cytotoxicity; DNA adducts	Aflatoxin B1	Decreased	134, 136, 137
β-Carotene	Squamous carcinoma	Archidonic acid metabolism to PG	Spontaneous	Increased	23
Canthaxanthin	Squamous carcinoma		Spontaneous	Decreased	
β-Carotene/α-car canth/lycopene	C3H/10T1/2	Transformation	MCA	Decreased	8
β-Carotene/α-car lycopene/lutein/canth	C3H/10T1/2	Gap junctional communication	Spontaneous	Increased	144
β-Carotene/lycopene canthaxanthin	C3H/10T1/2	Connexin43 expression	Spontaneous	Up-regulated	145
Canthaxanthin	NIH-3T3	Growth	Spontaneous	Stimulates	41
	Tumor lines (JB/MS, B16F10, PYB6)		Spontaneous	Inhibits	
β-Carotene/canth	7 Tumor lines	Proliferation	Spontaneous	Inhibition; ↑70 kD protein	112
	Normal keratinocytes			No effect	
β-Carotene/canth	SCC-25 carcinoma line	Growth, SOD, GSH-transferase	Spontaneous	Inhibition	116
	Normal keratinocytes	Growth	Spontaneous	No effect	

somewhat mixed results. A major problem has been that most of the animals tested are extremely poor absorbers of carotenoids, and therefore investigators have frequently used pharmacological doses in order to see effects. This, in turn, raises questions about the purity of the compounds used and what accompanying material might be administered at the same time as the carotenoids. The purity of the starting material is particularly important when one considers that the autoxidation of β-carotene produces breakdown products, such as retinoic acid, that have powerful biological activities (38).

ANIMAL STUDIES   The anticarcinogenic properties of carotenoids have been reviewed recently by Rousseau et al (105), and in somewhat greater detail by Krinsky (55, 56). UV light (73, 75), or a combination of UV light and carcinogens such as benzo[a]pyrene (108, 109), dimethylbenzanthracene (DMBA) (71), or 8-methoxypsoralen (106) have been used to induce tumors in rats and mice, and carotenoids have been shown to be protective in all of the above studies. More recently, investigators have demonstrated that canthaxanthin, at 10 g/kg, can reduce the UV-induced tumor burden in mice without influencing the tumor incidence (29), and the effect is even more striking when a combination of canthaxanthin and retinyl palmitate (120 IU/g) is added to the diet.

Carotenoids have also been shown to be protective when environmental carcinogens are administered to experimental animals; positive effects have been reported against DMBA (2–4), dimethylhydrazine (DMH) (6, 127), or N'N-methylnitro-nitrosoguanidine (MNNG) (110). Even topical administration of β-carotene inhibited (125) or reversed (114) squamous cell carcinoma produced in the hamster buccal pouch by treatment with topical DMBA. Either β-carotene, canthaxanthin, or an algal extract containing carotenoids was reported to be effective in this assay (113). This work has now been confirmed and extended. Topically applied β-carotene not only prevents DMBA-induced cheek tumors in hamsters, but it also prevents the accompanying stomach tumors (31). In addition, these β-carotene-treated animals retained a normal SDS-polyacrylamide electrophoretic pattern of cheek pouch keratin, whereas keratin from DMBA-treated hamsters had an abnormal pattern. A similar decrease in tumor incidence in DMBA-treated hamsters, as well as a decrease in polyamine levels in erythrocytes and urine in the β-carotene-treated animals, have also been reported recently (40).

Another method for demonstrating the anticarcinogenic activity of β-carotene has been to provide combined treatment with the carcinogen DMBA as well as with the tumor promoter phorbol myristyl acetate (PMA). When Skh or Sencar mice are treated with DMBA/PMA and supplemented with 3% β-carotene in their diets, either in the form of beadlets (containing 10% β-carotene) or by adding the crystalline pigment directly to the chow, skin tumors develop; both preparations protect Skh mice, but they do not protect the Sencar strain (64). These experiments point out the difficulty of comparing experimental results from different laboratories, for the strain differences reported above would be greatly exaggerated when one compares experiments in different species. For example, a similar protocol using DMBA/PMA-induction of skin tumors in Skh mice reported a significant decrease in the number of skin papillomas with administration of β-carotene at 2.4 mg/kg, but no effect on the ultimate development of malignant tumors (120). Based on these observations, these authors concluded that β-carotene was working during the PMA-induced promotional phase of tumor formation.

When canthaxanthin, at 1.1–3.4 mg (2–6 mmoles)/kg was fed to rats for 3 weeks prior to treatment with DMBA, a 65% decrease in the incidence of mammary tumors was observed (35).

Following an earlier report of a modest effect of crocetin in animals (72), this 20-carbon dicarboxylate carotenoid (Figure 1), along with β-carotene and lycopene, was administered by intraperitoneal injection and found to inhibit the growth of C-6 glial cells in rats (133, 135). In C3H/10T1/2 cells exposed to aflatoxin B_1 (AFB), 100 mM crocetin results in an elevation in the concentration of cytosolic GSH and an increase in the activity of GSH S-transferase and GSH peroxidase (137). These effects might explain the action of crocetin in altering the activity of microsome-activated AFB, and the resultant decrease in cytotoxicity and the decrease in AFB-DNA adducts (136).

Murakoshi et al (83) have reported that α-carotene is more effective than β-carotene in preventing spontaneous liver cancer in C3H/He male mice, and is more effective in preventing both 4-nitroquinoline-1-oxide-induced and glycerol-promoted lung cancer and DMBA-induced and PMA-promoted skin cancer in mice. The α-carotene had been prepared from palm oil carotenoids, and they also indicated that minor carotenoids of this preparation, such as γ-carotene and lycopene, may also have activity in preventing carcinogenesis.

Certainly, not all of the studies of carotenoids and cancer in animals have resulted in support for the anticarcinogenic hypothesis. As noted above, supplementation with 3% β-carotene did not significantly protect Sencar mice from DMBA/PMA-induced tumors (64), whereas SKH mice were protected. When DMH and methylnitrosourea were administered sequentially in F344 rats, β-carotene (0.2%) had only weak, organ-specific effects in preventing tumor formation (42). In addition, two reports have appeared on the effects of carotenoids on induced N-butyl-N-(4-hydroxybutyl)-nitrosamine (OH-BBN) bladder cancer. In one case, β-carotene fed to rats at 1.6 g/kg for 42 weeks colored the organs but did not protect against tumor formation (94). In another report, β-carotene or canthaxanthin was fed at 1 g/kg for 5 weeks before and 26 weeks after treatment with OH-BBN, and only the mice receiving the β-carotene supplement showed significant protection against the development of bladder cancer (76). The different results reported in these papers may be a result of species differences in response to either the carotenoid or the carcinogen. In addition, Colacchio et al (17, 18) have not been able to demonstrate carotenoid protection of DMH-induced colorectal cancers in rats.

Although the evidence of an association between carotenoid intake and anticarcinogenesis is not always positive and many workers have used systems unique to their laboratories, the data seem to suggest a clear anticarcinogenic role of carotenoids in animal models. However, there is still no direct evidence that any of these effects can be attributed to an antioxidant action of these carotenoids.

HUMAN STUDIES   In recent years, the possibility that carotenoid pigments may exert a preventive role in some diseases in which free radicals seem to be involved has attracted increasing interest. The rationale for this interest came primarily from human epidemiological data showing that carotenoids may reduce the risk of cancer or other diseases (12). In most cases, reviews of these studies (21, 26, 30, 43) frequently attribute the effects to the antioxidant activity of these pigments. Nevertheless, we cannot as yet claim that carotenoids function as antioxidants in disease prevention in humans. In fact, consideration should be given to the single, recent report of a significant reduction in plasma α-tocopherol levels in volunteers receiving as little as 15 mg β-carotene/day for 9 months (141).

CAROTENOID ASSOCIATIONS

Many biological effects have been attributed to carotenoids, but we still lack evidence that these are anything more than associations, which may or may not be causally related. Unfortunately, with many of these associations, we are still at a very early stage in trying to understand the relationship between the structure of the carotenoid pigments, the species studied, and the observed effects. Nevertheless, the potential significance of these associations, particularly with respect to human health issues, is of such importance that it underlines the need for continued support of investigators working in this field.

FUTURE CONSIDERATIONS

Several areas of investigation require more work if we are to have a clearer understanding of carotenoid actions in biological systems. For example, better animal models should be used to test various hypotheses about possible carotenoid action. Rats and mice are notoriously poor absorbers of carotenoids, and animals such as the ferret, which can absorb β-carotene, might yield more informative results. In particular, what is needed are clear-cut studies indicating whether or not carotenoids behave as antioxidants in vivo. We also have to pay attention to the other carotenoids in the foods that have been implicated as preventing disease. Finally, are the reported effects due to the intact carotenoid molecule or to enzymatic or nonenzymatic breakdown products? This question applies not only to β-carotene but also to the other carotenoids commonly found in the body, such as α-carotene, cryptoxanthin, lycopene, lutein, and zeaxanthin.

ACKNOWLEDGMENTS

The work in the author's laboratory has been supported by the National Cancer Institute, grant number CA 51506.

Literature Cited

1. Abril, E. R., Rybski, J. A., Scuderi, P., Watson, R. R. 1989. Beta-carotene stimulates human leukocytes to secrete a novel cytokine. *J. Leuk. Biol.* 45:255–61

2. Alam, B. S., Alam, S. Q. 1987. The effect of different levels of dietary β-carotene on DMBA-induced salivary gland tumors. *Nutr. Cancer* 9:93–101

3. Alam, B. S., Alam, S. Q., Weir, J. C. Jr. 1988. Effects of excess vitamin A and canthaxanthin on salivary gland tumors. *Nutr. Cancer* 11:233–41

4. Alam, B. S., Alam, S. Q., Weir, J. C. Jr., Gibson, W. A. 1984. Chemopreventive effects of β-carotene and 13-*cis*-retinoic acid on salivary gland tumors. *Nutr. Cancer* 6:4–12

5. Anderson, R., Theron, A. J. 1990. Physiological potential of ascorbate, β-carotene and α-tocopherol individually and in combination in the prevention of tissue damage, carcinogenesis and immune dysfunction mediated by phagocyte-derived reactive oxidants. *World Rev. Nutr. Diet* 62:27–58

6. Basu, T. K., Temple, N. J., Hodgson, A. M. 1988. Vitamin A, beta-carotene and cancer. In *Nutrition, Growth, and Cancer,* ed. G. P. Tryfiades, K. N. Prasad, pp. 217–28. New York: Liss

7. Bendich, A. 1988. The safety of β-carotene. *Nutr. Cancer* 11:207–14

8. Bertram, J. S., Pung, A., Churley, M., Kappock, T. J. IV, Wilkins, L. R., et al. 1991. Diverse carotenoids protect against chemically induced neoplastic transformation. *Carcinogenesis* 12:671–78

9. Blakely, S. R., Slaughter, L., Adkins, J., Knight, E. V. 1988. Effects of β-carotene and retinyl palmitate on corn oil-induced superoxide dismutase and catalase in rats. *J. Nutr.* 118:152–58

10. Burton, G. W. 1989. Antioxidant action of carotenoids. *J. Nutr.* 119:109–11

11. Burton, G. W., Ingold, K. U. 1984. β-Carotene: an unusual type of lipid antioxidant. *Science* 224:569–73

12. Byers, T., Perry, G. 1992. Dietary carotenes, vitamin C, and vitamin E as protective antioxidants in human cancers. *Annu. Rev. Nutr.* 12:139–59

13. Cabrini, L., Pasquali, P., Tadolini, B., Sechi, A. M., Landi, L. 1986. Antioxidant behaviour of ubiquinone and β-carotene incorporated in model membranes. *Free Radic. Res. Commun.* 2:85–92

14. Canfield, L. M., Forage, J. W., Valenzuela, J. G. 1992. Carotenoids as cellular antioxidants. *Proc. Soc. Exp. Biol. Med.* 200:260–65

15. Clausen, J. 1992. The influence of antioxidants on the enhanced respiratory burst reaction in smokers. *Ann. NY Acad. Sci.* 669:337–41

16. Cogdell, R. J., Frank, H. A. 1987. How carotenoids function in photosynthetic bacteria. *Biochim. Biophys. Acta* 895:63–79

17. Colacchio, T. A., Memoli, V. A. 1986. Chemoprevention of colorectal neoplasms. Ascorbic acid and β-carotene. *Arch. Surg.* 121:1421–24

18. Colacchio, T. A., Memoli, V. A., Hildebrandt, L. 1989. Antioxidants vs carotenoids. Inhibitors or promoters of experimental colorectal cancers. *Arch. Surg.* 124:217–21

19. Craft, N. E., Soares, J. H. Jr. 1992. Relative ʹsolubility, stability, and absorptivity of lutein and β-carotene in organic solvents. *J. Agric. Food Chem.* 40:431–34

20. Deng, D. J., Hu, G. G., Luo, X. M. 1988. Effect of beta-carotene on sister chromatid exchanges induced by MNNG and aflatoxin B1 in V79 cells. *Chung-Hua Chung Liu Tsa Chih.* 10: 89–91

21. Diplock, A. T. 1991. Antioxidant nutrients and disease prevention: an overview. *Am. J. Clin. Nutr.* 53:189S–93S

22. Dixit, R., Mukhtar, H., Bickers, D. R. 1983. Studies on the role of reactive oxygen species in mediating lipid peroxide formation in epidermal microsomes of rat skin. *J. Invest. Dermatol.* 81:369–75

23. ElAttar, T. M. A., Lin, H. S. 1991. Effect of retinoids and carotenoids on prostaglandin formation by oral squamous carcinoma cells. *Prostaglandins, Leukotrienes, Essent. Fatty Acids* 43: 175–78

24. Esterbauer, H., Dieber-Rotheneder, M., Striegl, G., Waeg, G. 1991. Role of vitamin E in preventing the oxidation of low-density lipoprotein. *Am. J. Clin. Nutr.* 53:314S–21S

25. Esterbauer, H., Gebicki, J., Puhl, H., Jürgens, G. 1992. The role of lipid peroxidation and antioxidants in oxidative modification of LDL. *Free Radic. Biol. Med.* 13:341–90

26. Esterbauer, H., Gey, F. K., Fuchs, J., Clemens, M. R., Sies, H. 1990. Antioxidative vitamine und degenerative erkrankungen. *Dtsch. Artzebl.* 87: B2620–24

27. Esterbauer, H., Striegl, G., Puhl, H., Rotheneder, M. 1989. Continuous monitoring of in vitro oxidation of human low density lipoprotein. *Free Radic. Res. Commun.* 6:67–75

28. Gaziano, J. M., Manson, J. E., Buring, J. E., Hennekens, C. H. 1992. Dietary antioxidants and cardiovascular disease. *Ann. NY Acad. Sci.* 669:249–59

29. Gensler, H. L., Aickin, M., Peng, Y. M. 1990. Cumulative reduction of primary skin tumor growth in UV-irradiated mice by the combination of retinyl palmitate and canthaxanthin. *Cancer Lett.* 53:27–31

30. Gey, K. F. 1990. The antioxidant hypothesis of cardiovascular disease: epidemiology and mechanism. *Biochem. Soc. Trans.* 18:1041–45

31. Gijare, P. S., Rao, K. V. K., Bhide, S. V. 1990. Modulatory effects of snuff, retinoic acid, and β-carotene on DMBA-induced hamster cheek pouch carcinogenesis in relation to keratin expression. *Nutr. Cancer* 14:253–59

32. Goodwin, T. W. 1952. *The Comparative Biochemistry of the Carotenoids,* pp. 1–356. London: Chapman & Hall

33. Goodwin, T. W. 1980. *The Biochemistry of the Carotenoids,* Vol. 1, *Plants,* pp. 1–377. London: Chapman & Hall. 2nd ed.

34. Goodwin, T. W. 1984. *The Biochemistry of the Carotenoids,* Vol. 2, *Animals,* pp. 1–224. London: Chapman & Hall. 2nd ed.

35. Grubbs, C. J., Eto, I., Juliana, M. M., Whitaker, L. M. 1991. Effect of canthaxanthin on chemically induced mammary carcinogenesis. *Oncology* 48: 239–45

36. Gruner, S., Volk, H., Falck, P., Von Baehr, R. 1986. The influence of phagocytic stimuli on the expression of HLA-DR antigens; role of reactive oxygen intermediates. *Eur. J. Immunol.* 16:212–15

37. Halevy, O., Sklan, D. 1987. Inhibition of arachidonic acid oxidation by β-carotene, retinol and α-tocopherol. *Biochim. Biophys. Acta* 918:304–7

38. Handelman, G. J., van Kuijk, F. J. G. M., Chatterjee, A., Krinsky, N. I. 1991. Characterization of products formed during the autoxidation of β-carotene. *Free Radic. Biol. Med.* 10: 427–37

39. Hazuka, M. B., Edwards-Prasad, J., Newman, F., Kinzie, J. J., Prasad, K. N. 1990. β-Carotene induces morphological differentiation and decreases adenylate cyclase activity in melanoma cells in culture. *J. Am. Coll. Nutr.* 9:143–49

40. Hibino, T., Shimpo, K., Kawai, K., Chihara, T., Maruta, K., et al. 1990. Polyamine levels of urine and erythrocytes on inhibition of DMBA-induced oral carcinogenesis by topical beta-carotene. *Biogenic Amines* 7:209–16

41. Huang, D. S., Odeleye, O. E., Watson, R. R. 1992. Inhibitory effects of canthaxanthin on in vitro growth of murine tumor cells. *Cancer Lett.* 65:209–13

42. Imaida, K., Hirose, M., Yamaguchi,

S., Takahashi, S., Ito, N. 1990. Effects of naturally occurring antioxidants on combined 1,2-dimethylhydrazine- and 1-methyl-1-nitrosourea-initiated carcinogenesis in F344 male rats. *Cancer Lett.* 55:53–59

43. Jacques, P. F., Chylack, L. T. Jr. 1991. Epidemiologic evidence of a role for the antioxidant vitamins and carotenoids in cataract prevention. *Am. J. Clin. Nutr.* 53:352S-55S

44. Jialal, I., Grundy, S. M. 1991. Preservation of the endogenous antioxidants in low density lipoprotein by ascorbate but not probucol during oxidative modification. *J. Clin. Invest.* 87:597–601

45. Jialal, I., Norkus, E. P., Cristol, L., Grundy, S. M. 1991. β-Carotene inhibits the oxidative modification of low-density lipoprotein. *Biochim. Biophys. Acta* 1086:134–38

46. Kagan, V., Witt, E., Goldman, R., Scita, G., Packer, L. 1992. Ultraviolet light-induced generation of vitamin E radicals and their recycling. A possible photosensitizing effect of vitamin E in the skin. *Free Radic. Res. Commun.* 16:51–64

47. Kennedy, T. A., Liebler, D. C. 1992. Peroxyl radical scavenging by β-carotene in lipid bilayers. Effect of oxygen partial pressure. *J. Biol. Chem.* 267:4658–63

48. Kim(Jun), H. 1990. Comparison of antioxidant activity of α-, β-carotene, lutein and lycopene by high pressure liquid chromatography. *Korean J. Nutr.* 23:434–42

49. Knipping, G., Rotheneder, M., Striegl, G., Esterbauer, H. 1990. Antioxidants and resistance against oxidation of porcine LDL subfractions. *J. Lipid Res.* 31:1965–72

50. Krinsky, N. I. 1968. The protective function of carotenoid pigments. In *Photophysiology*, ed. A. C. Giese, 2:123–95. New York: Academic

51. Krinsky, N. I. 1971. Function of carotenoids. In *Carotenoids*, ed. O. Isler, pp. 669–716. Basel/Stuttgart: Birkhäuser

52. Krinsky, N. I. 1988. The evidence for the role of carotenes in preventive health. *Clin. Nutr.* 7:107–14

53. Krinsky, N. I. 1989. Antioxidant functions of carotenoids. *Free Radic. Biol. Med.* 7:617–35

54. Krinsky, N. I. 1991. Effects of carotenoids in cellular and animal systems. *Am. J. Clin. Nutr.* 53:238S-46S

55. Krinsky, N. I. 1992. Anticarcinogenic activities of carotenoids in animals and cellular systems. In *Free Radicals and Aging*, ed. I. Emerit, B. Chance, pp. 227–34. Basel: Birkhäuser

56. Krinsky, N. I. 1993. Actions of carotenoids in cells and animals. In *Vitamins and Cancer Prevention*, ed. G. A. Bray, D. H. Ryan, pp. 260–70. Baton Rouge: Louisiana State Univ.

57. Krinsky, N. I. 1993. Micronutrients and their influence on mutagenicity and malignant transformation. *Ann. NY Acad. Sci.* 686:229–42

58. Krinsky, N. I., Cornwell, D. G., Oncley, J. L. 1958. The transport of vitamin A and carotenoids in human plasma. *Arch. Biochem. Biophys.* 73:233–46

59. Krinsky, N. I., Deneke, S. M. 1982. The interaction of oxygen and oxyradicals with carotenoids. *JNCI* 69:205–10

60. Krinsky, N. I., Wang, X.-D., Tang, G., Russell, R. M. 1993. Conversion of carotenoids to retinoids. In *Retinoids: Progress in Research and Clinical Applications*, ed. M. A. Livrea, L. Packer, pp. 1–16. New York: Marcel Dekker

61. Kritchevsky, D. 1992. Antioxidant vitamins in the prevention of cardiovascular disease. *Nutr. Today* 27:30–33

62. Kunert, K.-J., Tappel, A. L. 1983. The effect of vitamin C on in vivo lipid peroxidation in guinea pigs as measured by pentane and ethane production. *Lipids* 18:271–74

63. Kurashige, M., Okimasu, E., Inoue, M., Utsumi, K. 1990. Inhibition of oxidative injury of biological membranes by astaxanthin. *Physiol. Chem. Phys. Med. NMR* 22:27–38

64. Lambert, L. A., Koch, W. H., Wamer, W. G., Kornhauser, A. 1990. Antitumor activity in skin of SKH and Sencar mice by two dietary β-carotene formulations. *Nutr. Cancer* 13:213–21

65. Leibovitz, B., Hu, M.-L., Tappel, A. L. 1990. Dietary supplements of vitamin E, β-carotene, coenzyme Q10 and selenium protect tissues against lipid peroxidation in rat tissue slices. *J. Nutr.* 120:97–104

66. Lim, B. P., Nagao, A., Terao, J., Tanaka, K., Suzuki, T., et al. 1992. Antioxidant activity of xanthophylls on peroxyl radical-mediated phospholipid peroxidation. *Biochim. Biophys. Acta* 1126:178–84

67. Lomnitski, L., Bergman, M., Schön, I., Grossman, S. 1991. The effect of dietary vitamin E and β-carotene on oxidation processes in the rat testis. *Biochim. Biophys. Acta* 1082:101–7

68. Lux-Neuwirth, O., Millar, T. J. 1990. Lipid-soluble antioxidants preserve rab-

bit corneal cell function. *Current Eye Res.* 9:103–9

69. Manoharan, K., Banerjee, M. R. 1985. β-Carotene reduces sister chromatid exchanges induced by chemical carcinogens in mouse mammary cells in organ culture. *Cell. Biol. Int. Rep.* 9:783–89

70. Mathews-Roth, M. M. 1980. Carotenoid pigments as antitumor agents. In *Current Chemotherapy and Infectious Diseases*, ed. J. D. Nelson, C. Grassi, pp. 1503–5. Washington, DC: Am. Soc. Microbiol.

71. Mathews-Roth, M. M. 1982. Antitumor activity of β-carotene, canthaxanthin and phytoene. *Oncology* 39:33–37

72. Mathews-Roth, M. M. 1982. Effect of crocetin on experimental skin tumors in hairless mice. *Oncology* 39:362–64

73. Mathews-Roth, M. M. 1983. Carotenoid pigment administration and delay in development of UV-B-induced tumors. *Photochem. Photobiol.* 37:509–11

74. Mathews-Roth, M. M. 1987. Photoprotection by carotenoids. *Fed. Proc.* 46:1890–93

75. Mathews-Roth, M. M., Krinsky, N. I. 1987. Carotenoids affect development of UV-B induced skin cancer. *Photochem. Photobiol.* 46:507–9

76. Mathews-Roth, M. M., Lausen, N., Drouin, G., Richter, A., Krinsky, N. I. 1991. Effects of carotenoid administration on bladder cancer prevention. *Oncology* 48:177–79

77. Mathews-Roth, M. M., Pathak, M. A., Fitzpatrick, T. B., Harber, L. C., Kass, E. H. 1970. Beta-carotene as a photoprotective agent in erythropoietic protoporphyria. *N. Engl. J. Med.* 282:1231–34

78. Mayne, S. T., Parker, R. S. 1989. Antioxidant activity of dietary canthaxanthin. *Nutr. Cancer* 12:225–36

79. Miki, W. 1991. Biological functions and activities of animal carotenoids. *Pure Appl. Chem.* 63:141–46

80. Mobarhan, S., Bowen, P., Anderson, B., Evans, M., Stacewicz-Sapuntzakis, M., et al. 1990. Effects of β-carotene repletion on β-carotene absorption, lipid peroxidation, and neutrophil superoxide formation in young men. *Nutr. Cancer* 14:195–206

81. Morel, D. W., Hessler, J. R., Chisolm, G. M. 1983. Low density lipoprotein cytotoxicity induced by free radical peroxidation of lipid. *J. Lipid Res.* 24:1070–76

82. Moriguchi, S., Jackson, J. C., Watson, R. R. 1985. Effects of retinoids on human lymphocyte functions in vitro. *Human Toxicol.* 4:365–78

83. Murakoshi, M., Takayasu, J., Kimura, O., Kohmura, E., Nishino, H., et al. 1989. Inhibitory effects of α-carotene on proliferation of the human neuroblastoma cell line GOTO. *J. Natl. Cancer Inst.* 81:1649–52

84. Navab, M., Imes, S. S., Hama, S. Y., Hough, G. P., Ross, L. A., et al. 1991. Monocyte transmigration induced by modification of low density lipoprotein in cocultures of human aortic wall cells is due to induction of monocyte chemotactic protein 1 synthesis and is abolished by high density lipoprotein. *J. Clin. Invest.* 88:2039–46

85. Nishino, H., Takayasu, J., Hasegawa, T., Kimura, O., Kohmura, E., et al. 1988. Inhibitory effect of natural carotenes on the growth of human malignant cells. *J. Kyoto Pref. Univ. Med.* 97:1097–102

86. Okuzumi, J., Nishino, H., Murakoshi, M., Iwashima, A., Tanaka, Y., et al. 1990. Inhibitory effects of fucoxanthin, a natural carotenoid, on N-myc expression and cell cycle progression in human malignant tumor cells. *Cancer Lett.* 55:75–81

87. Olson, J. A. 1989. Biological actions of carotenoids. *J. Nutr.* 119:94–95

88. Packer, J. E., Mahood, J. S., Mora-Arellano, V. O., Slater, T. F., Willson, R. L., et al. 1981. Free radicals and singlet oxygen scavengers: reaction of a peroxy-radical with β-carotene diphenyl furan and 1,4-diazobicyclo (2,2,2)-octane. *Biochem. Biophys. Res. Commun.* 98:901–6

89. Palozza, P., Krinsky, N. I. 1991. The inhibition of radical-initiated peroxidation of microsomal lipids by both α-tocopherol and β-carotene. *Free Radic. Biol. Med.* 11:407–14

90. Palozza, P., Krinsky, N. I. 1992. Antioxidant effects of carotenoids in vitro and in vivo: an overview. *Methods Enzymol.* 213:403–20

91. Palozza, P., Krinsky, N. I. 1992. Astaxanthin and canthaxanthin are potent antioxidants in a membrane model. *Arch. Biochem. Biophys.* 297:291–95

92. Palozza, P., Krinsky, N. I. 1992. β-Carotene and α-tocopherol are synergistic antioxidants. *Arch. Biochem. Biophys.* 297:184–87

93. Palozza, P., Moualla, S., Krinsky, N. I. 1992. Effects of β-carotene and α-tocopherol on radical-initiated peroxidation of microsomes. *Free Radic. Biol. Med.* 13:127–36

94. Pedrick, M. S., Turton, J. A., Hicks, R. M. 1990. The incidence of bladder cancer in carcinogen-treated rats is not substantially reduced by dietary B-carotene (BC). *Int. J. Vit. Nutr. Res.* 60:189–90

95. Perry, T. L., Yong, V. W., Clavier, R. M., Jones, K., Wright, J. M., et al. 1985. Partial protection from the dopaminergic neurotoxin N-methyl-4-phenyl-1,2,3,6-tetrahydropyridine by four different antioxidants in the mouse. *Neurosci. Lett.* 60:109–14

96. Peto, R., Doll, R. J., Buckley, J. D., Sporn, M. B. 1981. Can dietary β-carotene materially reduce human cancer rates? *Nature* 290:201–8

97. Pfander, H., ed. 1987. *Key to Carotenoids*, pp. 1–296. Basel: Birkhäuser. 2nd ed.

98. Prabhala, R. H., Garewal, H. S., Meyskens, F. L. Jr., Watson, R. R. 1990. Immunomodulation in humans caused by beta-carotene and vitamin A. *Nutr. Res.* 10:1473–86

99. Prabhala, R. H., Maxey, V., Hicks, M. J., Watson, R. R. 1989. Enhancement of the expression of activation markers on human peripheral blood mononuclear cells by in vitro culture with retinoids and carotenoids. *J. Leukocyte Biol.* 45:249–54

100. Pryor, W. A., Strickland, T., Church, D. F. 1988. Comparison of the efficiencies of several natural and synthetic antioxidants in aqueous sodium dodecyl sulfate micelle solutions. *J. Am. Chem. Soc.* 110:2224–29

101. Pung, A. O., Rundhaug, J. E., Yoshizawa, C. N., Bertram, J. S. 1988. β-Carotene and canthaxanthin inhibit chemically- and physically-induced neoplastic transformation in 10T1/2 cells. *Carcinogenesis* 9:1533–39

102. Raj, A. S., Katz, M. 1985. β-Carotene as an inhibitor of benzo(a)pyrene and mitomycin C induced chromosomal breaks in the bone marrow of mice. *Can. J. Genet. Cytol.* 27:598–602

103. Renner, H. W. 1985. Anticlastogenic effect of β-carotene in Chinese hamsters. Time and dose response studies with different mutagens. *Mutat. Res.* 144:251–56

104. Renner, H. W. 1990. In vivo effects of single or combined dietary antimutagens on mutagen-induced chromosomal aberrations. *Mutat. Res.* 244: 185–88

105. Rousseau, E. J., Davison, A. J., Dunn, B. 1992. Protection by β-carotene and related compounds against oxygen mediated cytotoxicity and genotoxicity. *Free Radic. Biol. Med.* 13:407–33

106. Santamaria, L., Bianchi, A., Andreoni, L., Santagati, G., Arnaboldi, A., et al. 1984. 8-Methoxypsoralen photocarcinogenesis and its prevention by dietary carotenoids. Preliminary results. *Med. Biol. Environ.* 12:533–37

107. Santamaria, L., Bianchi, A., Arnaboldi, A., Adreoni, L. 1980. Prevention of the benzo[a]pyrene photocarcinogenic effect by β-carotene and canthaxanthine. Preliminary study. *Boll. Chim. Farm.* 119:745–48

108. Santamaria, L., Bianchi, A., Arnaboldi, A., Andreoni, L. 1981. Prevention of the benzo[a]pyrene photocarcinogenic effect by β-carotene and canthaxanthin. *Med. Biol. Environ.* 9: 113–20

109. Santamaria, L., Bianchi, A., Arnaboldi, A., Andreoni, L., Bermond, P. 1983. Benzo[a]pyrene carcinogenicity and its prevention by carotenoids. Relevance in social medicine. In *Modulation and Mediation of Cancer by Vitamins*, ed. F. L. Meyskens, K. N. Prasad, pp. 81–88. Basel: Karger

110. Santamaria, L., Bianchi, A., Ravetto, C., Arnaboldi, A., Santagati, G., et al. 1985. Supplemental carotenoids prevent MNNG induced cancer in rats. *Med. Biol. Environ.* 13:745–50

111. Schoen, D. J., Watson, R. R. 1988. Prevention of UV irradiation induced suppression of monocyte functions by retinoids and carotenoids in vitro. *Photochem. Photobiol.* 48:659–63

112. Schwartz, J., Shklar, G. 1992. The selective cytotoxic effect of carotenoids and atocopherol on human cancer cell lines in vitro. *J. Oral Maxillofac. Surg.* 50:367–73

113. Schwartz, J., Shklar, G., Reid, S., Trickler, D. 1988. Prevention of experimental oral cancer by extracts of Spirulina-Dunaliella algae. *Nutr. Cancer* 11:127–34

114. Schwartz, J., Suda, D., Light, G. 1986. Beta carotene is associated with the regression of hamster buccal pouch carcinoma and the induction of tumor necrosis factor in macrophages. *Biochem. Biophys. Res. Commun.* 136: 1130–35

115. Schwartz, J. L., Singh, R. P., Teicher, B., Wright, J. E., Trites, D. H., et al. 1990. Induction of a 70-kd protein associated with the selective cytotoxicity of beta-carotene in human epidermal carcinoma. *Biochem. Biophys. Res. Commun.* 169:941–46

116. Schwartz, J. L., Tanaka, J.,

Khandekar, V., Herman, T. S., Teicher, B. A. 1992. β-Carotene and/or vitamin E as modulators of alkylating agents in SCC-25 human squamous carcinoma cells. *Cancer Chemother. Pharmacol.* 29:207–13

117. Searle, A. J. F., Willson, R. L. 1983. Stimulation of microsomal lipid peroxidation by iron and cysteine. *Biochem. J.* 212:549–54

118. Som, S., Chatterjee, M., Banerjee, M. R. 1984. b-Carotene inhibition of 7, 12-dimethylbenz[a]anthracene - induced transformation of murine mammary cells in vitro. *Carcinogenesis* 5:937–40

119. Steinberg, D. 1991. Antioxidants and atherosclerosis. A current assessment. *Circulation* 84:1420–25

120. Steinel, H. H., Baker, R. S. U. 1990. Effects of β-carotene on chemically-induced skin tumors in HRA/SKH hairless mice. *Cancer Lett.* 51:163–68

121. Stich, H. F., Dunn, B. P. 1986. Relationship between cellular levels of beta-carotene and sensitivity to genotoxic agents. *Int. J. Cancer* 38:713–17

122. Stich, H. F., Tsang, S. S., Palcic, B. 1990. The effect of retinoids, carotenoids and phenolics on chromosomal instability of bovine papillomavirus DNA-carrying cells. *Mutat. Res.* 241:387–93

123. Stocker, R., Bowry, V. W., Frei, B. 1991. Ubiquinol-10 protects human low density lipoprotein more efficiently against lipid peroxidation than does α-tocopherol. *Proc. Natl. Acad. Sci. USA* 88:1646–50

124. Stocker, R., Yamamoto, Y., McDonagh, A. F., Glazer, A. N., Ames, B. N. 1987. Bilirubin is an antioxidant of possible physiological importance. *Science* 235:1043–46

125. Suda, D., Schwartz, J., Shklar, G. 1986. Inhibition of experimental oral carcinogenesis by topical beta-carotene. *Carcinogenesis* 7:711–15

126. Tan, B., Chu, F. L. 1991. Effects of palm carotenoids in rat hepatic cytochrome P450-mediated benzo(a)pyrene metabolism. *Am. J. Clin. Nutr.* 53: 1071s-75s

127. Temple, N. J., Basu, T. K. 1987. Protective effect of β-carotene against colon tumors in mice. *JNCI* 78:1211–14

128. Terao, J. 1989. Antioxidant activity of β-carotene-related carotenoids in solution. *Lipids* 24:659–61

129. Terao, J., Yamauchi, R., Murakami, H., Matsushita, S. 1980. Inhibitory effects of tocopherols and β-carotene on singlet oxygen-initiated photoxidation of methyl linoleate and soybean oil. *J. Food Proc. Preserv.* 4:79–93

130. Terwell, L., van der Hoeven, J. C. M. 1985. Antimutagenic activity of some naturally occurring compounds towards cigarette-smoke condensate and benzo[a]pyrene in the Salmonella/microsome assay. *Mutat. Res.* 152:1–4

131. Tsuchiya, M., Scita, G., Freisleben, H.-J., Kagan, V. E., Packer, L. 1992. Antioxidant radical-scavenging activity of carotenoids and retinoids compared to α-tocopherol. *Methods Enzymol.* 213:460–72

132. Vile, G. F., Winterbourn, C. C. 1988. Inhibition of adriamycin-promoted microsomal lipid peroxidation by β-carotene, α-tocopherol and retinal at high and low oxygen partial pressures. *FEBS Lett.* 238:353–56

133. Wang, C.-J., Chou, M.-Y., Lin, J.-K. 1989. Inhibition of growth and development of the transplantable C-6 glioma cells inoculated in rats by retinoids and carotenoids. *Cancer Lett.* 48:135–42

134. Wang, C.-J., Hsu, J.-D., Lin, J.-K. 1991. Suppression of aflatoxin B1-induced hepatotoxic lesions by crocetin (a natural carotenoid). *Carcinogenesis* 12:1807–10

135. Wang, C.-J., Lin, J.-K. 1989. Inhibitory effects of carotenoids and retinoids on the in vitro growth of rat C-6 glioma cells. *Proc. Natl. Sci. Council B ROC* 13:176–83

136. Wang, C.-J., Shiah, H.-S., Lin, J.-K. 1991. Modulatory effect of crocetin on aflatoxin B1 cytotoxicity and DNA adduct formation in C3H10T1/2 fibroblast cells. *Cancer Lett.* 56:1–10

137. Wang, C.-J., Shiow, S.-J., Lin, J.-K. 1991. Effects of crocetin on the hepatotoxicity and hepatic DNA binding of aflatoxin B1 in rats. *Carcinogenesis* 12:459–62

138. Weitzman, S. A., Weitberg, A. B., Clark, E. P., Stossel, T. P. 1985. Phagocytes as carcinogens: malignant transformation produced by human neutrophils. *Science* 227:1231–33

139. Will, O. H. III, Scovel, C. A. 1989. Photoprotective functions of carotenoids. In *Carotenoids: Chemistry and Biology,* ed. N. I. Krinsky, M. M. Mathews-Roth, R. F. Taylor, pp. 229–36. New York/London: Plenum

140. Witt, E. H., Reznick, A. Z., Viguie, C. A., Starke-Reed, P., Packer, L. 1992. Exercise, oxidative damage and effects of antioxidant manipulation. *J. Nutr.* 122:766–73

141. Xu, M. J., Plezia, P. M., Alberts, D.

S., Emerson, S. S., Peng, Y. M., et al. 1992. Reduction in plasma or skin alpha-tocopherol concentrations with long-term oral administration of beta-carotene in humans and mice. *J. Natl. Cancer Inst.* 84:1559–65

142. Yamamoto, Y., Haga, S., Niki, E., Kamiya, Y. 1984. Oxidation of lipids. V. Oxidation of methyl linoleate in aqueous dispersion. *Bull. Chem. Soc. Jpn.* 57:1260–64

143. Zamora, R., Hidalgo, F. J., Tappel, A. L. 1991. Comparative antioxidant effectiveness of dietary β-carotene, vitamin E, selenium and coenzyme Q10 in rat erythrocytes and plasma. *J. Nutr.* 121:50–56

144. Zhang, L.-X., Cooney, R. V., Bertram, J. S. 1991. Carotenoids enhance gap junctional communication and inhibit lipid peroxidation in C3H/10T1/2 cells: relationship to their cancer chemopreventive action. *Carcinogenesis* 12: 2109–14

145. Zhang, L.-X., Cooney, R. V., Bertram, J. S. 1992. Carotenoids up-regulate connexin43 gene expression independent of pro-vitamin A or antioxidant properties. *Cancer Res.* 52:5707–12

SUBJECT INDEX

A

A23187 calcium ionophore
  amino acid transport and, 153
  pyruvate dehydrogenase and,
    512
AAL toxins
  fumonisins and, 175-76
Abdominal symptoms
  cystic fibrosis and, 118
  glycogen storage diseases
    and, 104
ACC deaminase
  plant genetic engineering and,
    198, 206
ACC oxidase
  plant genetic engineering and,
    197-98, 206
ACC synthase
  plant genetic engineering and,
    206
Acetate
  short-chain fatty acids and,
    218, 222-23, 225-27
Acetazolamide
  taste disorders and, 412
Acetic acid
  bovine milk fat digestion and,
    219
Acetolactate synthase
  plant genetic engineering and,
    208
Acetylcholine
  chemosensory dysfunction
    and, 422-23
  tetrahydrobiopterin and, 280
Acetylcholine-like substances
  smell disorders and, 413
Acetyl-CoA
  cholesterol and, 356
  fatty acids and, 359, 370
  glycogen storage diseases
    and, 89
  pyruvate dehydrogenase and,
    498, 501-5, 507-10
Acetyl-CoA carboxylase
  bovine somatotropin and, 447-
    48
  covalent flavoproteins and,
    18
N-Acetylcysteine
  cystic fibrosis and, 124
N-Acetylserotonin
  tetrahydrobiopterin and, 267-
    68
Acetyl transferase
  plant genetic engineering and,
    208
Achlorhydria
  aluminum and, 49
Acid glucosidase deficiency
  dietary treatment and, 102
Acidosis
  glycogen storage diseases
    and, 85

Acquired immunodeficiency syn-
    drome (AIDS)
  neopterin and, 269
Across-fiber pattern theory
  smell disorders and, 420
Actinomycin D
  bovine somatotropin and, 448
Acyl-ACP thioesterase
  plant genetic engineering and,
    206
Acyl carrier protein
  covalent flavoproteins and, 18
  plant lipids and, 200-1
AcylCoA:cholesterol
    acyltransferase (ACAT)
  LDL-cholesterol levels and,
    374
N-Acyltransferases
  fumonisins and, 177-79
ADA exchanges
  glycogen storage diseases
    and, 96
Adaptive regulation
  intestinal brush border and,
    150-52
Adenoid hypertrophy
  smell disorders and, 416
Adenosine
  bovine somatotropin and, 446
  glycogen storage diseases
    and, 92
Adenosine diphosphate (ADP)
  glycogen storage diseases
    and, 93
  nitrogen fixation and, 330-31
  pyruvate dehydrogenase and,
    503-4, 507, 510
Adenosine triphosphate (ATP)
  aminophospholipid trans-
    locases and, 550
  covalent flavoproteins and, 22
  cystic fibrosis and, 120
  glycogen storage diseases
    and, 91-93
  nitrogen fixation and, 323-24,
    326
  pyruvate dehydrogenase and,
    503-7, 510
  selenoproteins and, 71
S-Adenosylmethionine
  genetically engineered toma-
    toes and, 197
Adenylate kinase 1 locus
  obesity and, 350
Adenyl cyclase
  aluminum and, 56
Adenyl ribonucleotides
  glycogen storage diseases
    and, 91
Adipocytes
  bovine somatotropin and,
    443, 445-48
  obesity and, 350
Adolescents
  blood pressure and, 250-51

calcium and, 297-99
cystic fibrosis and, 112, 114,
    118, 123, 126, 128, 130
glycogen storage diseases
    and, 101
Adoption studies
  obesity and, 338, 340-41, 346
Adrenal cortical insufficiency
  chemosensory dysfunction
    and, 415-16
β-Adrenergic agonists
  pyruvate dehydrogenase and,
    512
Adults
  calcium and, 297-99, 304-5
  cystic fibrosis and, 112, 118,
    123, 126, 128, 130-31
  dietary fiber and, 304-5
  glycogen storage diseases
    and, 88, 101-2, 104
  LDL-cholesterol levels and,
    368
  obesity and, 340-45, 348
  osteoporosis and, 288-99, 300-
    5, 307
  oxygen and, 397
  phosphorus and, 305
  vitamin D and, 307
Aflatoxins
  foods and, 168
Africa
  sub-Saharan
    malnutrition and, 2, 6
Ageusia
  classification of, 406
Aging
  aluminum and, 52-53
  chemosensory losses and,
    406, 408, 414-20
  cystic fibrosis and, 125, 127-
    28, 131
  glycogen storage diseases
    and, 98, 101
  osteoporosis and, 288, 291,
    299-302, 310
  oxygen radicals and, 398
β-Agonists
  cystic fibrosis and, 122
Agrobacterium tumefaciens-
    based vectors
  plant transformation and, 192-
    94
AIB
  amino acid transport and,
    143, 152-55, 157
AIDS
  see Acquired immunodefici-
    ency syndrome
Alanine
  amino acid transport and,
    145, 151
  bovine somatotropin and,
    439
  covalent flavoproteins and, 22-
    23

glycogen storage diseases
and, 103, 105
protein kinase C and, 544
Alanine aminotransferase
covalent flavoproteins and, 18
Albumin
aluminum and, 46, 54
cystic fibrosis and, 127
osteoporosis and, 310
Alcohol status
osteoporosis and, 290-91
Aldose reductase
tetrahydrobiopterin and, 267
Aldosterone
blood pressure and, 254
Alfalfa
nitrogen fixation and, 321
Alkaline phosphatase
bone formation and, 309
butyrate and, 229
Allergic rhinitis
smell disorders and, 416
Allicin
smell disorders and, 413
Alloantigens
neopterin and, 269-70
Allopurinol
glycogen storage diseases
and, 94
taste disorders and, 411
Altitude
high
reduced oxygen tension
and, 396
taste disorders and, 415
Aluminum
metabolism of
absorption, 46-52
distribution and excretion,
52-56
oral exposure to
diet and water as sources
of, 43-46
pharmaceutical products as
sources of, 46
requirement for, 56
toxicity of, 57
Alternaria alternata f. sp.
lycopersici
fumonisins and, 170, 175
Alternaria spp.
plant genetic engineering and,
209
Alzheimer's disease
aluminum and, 53, 57
pyruvate dehydrogenase and,
513
chemosensory dysfunction
and, 415-17
Amenorrhea
primary
smell disorders and, 416
Amiloride
taste disorders and, 412
D-Amino acid oxidase
covalent flavoproteins and, 18
Amino acids
bovine somatotropin and, 438-
39, 444
covalent flavoproteins and, 27
cystic fibrosis and, 112, 114
gastric lipase and, 220

glycogen storage diseases
and, 102-3, 105-6
nitrogen fixation and, 318
plant genetic engineering and,
205
selenium and, 66
taste disorders and, 416-17
transport systems and, 137-38
adaptive regulation in intestinal brush border, 150-
52
amino acid delivery to
fetus, 155-57
brain transporters, 147-49
cell cycle and regeneration,
155
cell proliferation and transport, 152-55
cytokines, 152-55
facilitated transport, 138-43
future research, 157-58
growth factors, 152-55
hepatic zonal heterogeneity,
149-50
metabolism, 149-52
regulatory subunits, 141-43
secondary active transporters, 143-47
System A, 143-45
System b$^{o,+}$, 139-40, 146-
47
System Gly, 145
System L, 138-39
System N, 145-46
System y$^+$, 140-41
transformation, 152-55
Aminoacyl-flavin bonds
flavoproteins and, 19
Aminobicyclo-(2,2,1)-heptane-2-
carboxylic acid (BCH)
amino acid tranport and, 138-
39, 146, 151
1-Aminocyclopropane-1-carbox-
ylic acid
genetically engineered tomatoes and, 197
Aminoglycosides
cystic fibrosis and, 124
resistance to
plant transformation and,
193
2-Amino-4-hydroxy-6-(1,2-
dihydroxypropyl) pteridine
Crithidia fasiculata and, 261-
62
Aminophospholipid translocases
cell function and, 550
Amitriptyline
smell disorders and, 413
Ammonia
fumonisins and, 182
glycogen storage diseases
and, 105
nitrogen fixation and, 321
Amphetamines
chemosensory dysfunction
and, 412-13
Amphiphile molecules
short-chain fatty acids and,
221
Amphotericin B
taste disorders and, 411

Ampicillin
taste disorders and, 411
α-Amylase
plant genetic engineering and,
204, 206
Amylo-1,6-glucosidase
glycogen storage diseases
and, 102
Amyloidosis
chemosensory dysfunction
and, 415-16
Amylopectin
plant genetic engineering and,
204
Amylose
plant genetic engineering and,
204
Amyotrophic lateral sclerosis
(ALS)
aluminum and, 53, 57
Anabaena azollae
nitrogen fixation and, 326,
328
Anaerobic diazotrophy
nitrogen fixation and, 326
Analgesics
buffered
aluminum and, 46
Anemia
aluminum and, 55
cystic fibrosis and, 124, 127
oxygen and, 396
Angina pectoris
oxygen and, 396
Angiotensin II
borage oil and, 246
Anions
inorganic
aluminum absorption and,
49, 51-52
Annexin VI
lipids and, 546
Anorexia
chemosensory dysfunction
and, 406
cystic fibrosis and, 116, 118,
121, 123, 127
Anosmia
classification of, 407
Antacids
aluminum and, 46, 56
Antibiotics
genes for resistance to, 193
Antibodies
monoclonal
fumonisins and, 181
neopterin and, 269
polyclonal
fumonisins and, 181
selenoproteins and, 75
Anti-caking agents
aluminum and, 45
Antifreeze proteins
genetically engineered plants
and, 198-99, 206
Antioxidants
carotenoids and, 564-73
Antisense DNA
plant genetic engineering and,
198
Antisense RNA
obesity and, 351

plant genetic engineering and, 195, 198-200, 204, 206, 208
Antivitamins
thiamin oxidase and, 30
Aorta
PUFAs and, 244, 246
Apoenzymes
covalent flavoproteins and, 18, 21, 23-24, 27-29
Apo-6-hydroxy-D-nicotine oxidase
covalent flavoproteins and, 21-23
Apples
aluminum and, 44
Applied nutrition research
nutrition malpractice and, 2-13
Arabidopsis spp.
desaturase and, 200
glycerol-3-phosphate acyltransferase and, 201
Arachidonate
hypertension and, 244
Arachidonic acid
cytochrome P450s and, 394
hypertension and, 246-47, 253
protein kinase C and, 550
Archaebacteria
nitrogen fixation and, 319, 325
Arginine
amino acid transport and, 139-40, 151
covalent flavoproteins and, 23
fumarate reductase and, 33
nitric oxide synthase and, 274-75
nitrogen fixation and, 331
Aromatic amino acid hydroxylases
tetrahydrobiopterin and, 262-64
Arthrobacter globiformis
covalent flavoproteins and, 20
Arthrobacter oxidans
covalent flavoproteins and, 20-21, 27-28, 33
Ascorbic acid
see Vitamin C
Ashkenazic Jews
cystic fibrosis and, 113
Asia
nitrogen fixation and, 326
protein and, 306
Asparagine
amino acid transport and, 145
gastric lipase and, 220
Asparagus
aluminum and, 44
Aspartate
amino acid transport and, 149, 151
Aspartic acid
taste disorders and, 417
Aspergillus flavus
foods and, 168
Astrocytes
smell disorders and, 420
tetrahydrobiopterin and, 269
ATCC 25589 soil bacterium
covalent flavoproteins and, 20

Atherosclerosis
dietary fiber and, 217, 226
fumonisins and, 174-75
LDL-cholesterol levels and, 355-56
oxygen radicals and, 396, 398
Atopy
smell disorders and, 416
Atrial muscle
fumonisins and, 180
Australia
cystic fibrosis and, 130-31
Azathioprine
taste disorders and, 411
Azoferredoxin
nitrogen fixation and, 322
Azolla sp.
nitrogen fixation and, 326
Azosporillum spp.
nitrogen fixation and, 319, 331-32
Azotobacter chroococcum
nitrogen fixation and, 319, 321
Azotobacters
nitrogen fixation and, 327
Azotobacter vinelandii
pyruvate dehydrogenase and, 501
Azotorrhea
cystic fibrosis and, 117

B

Baboons
fumonisins and, 172
short-chain fatty acids and, 220, 226
Bacillus lichenformis
α-amylase and, 204, 206
Bacillus subtilis
covalent flavoproteins and, 20, 27
Bacillus thuringiensis
plant genetic engineering and, 195, 209
Backfat
short-chain fatty acids and, 225
Baclofen
taste disorders and, 412
Bacteria
nitrogen fixation and, 318-20, 324-32
Bacterial infections
chemosensory losses and, 408
glycogen storage diseases and, 85
neopterin and, 269
Bacterium sp. W_3A_41
covalent flavoproteins and, 20
Bacteroides spp.
short-chain fatty acids and, 218
Bacteroids
nitrogen fixation and, 319
Baking
fumonisins and, 182
Baking powder
aluminum and, 44
Balanced-peptide formula
cystic fibrosis and, 130

Bamifylline hydrochloride
taste disorders and, 412
Bananas
aluminum and, 44
plant transformation and, 193
Bangladesh
nutrition programs and, 14
Barley
calcium and, 304
Basil
aluminum and, 44
Bay
plant genetic engineering and, 206
Beagles
tetrahydrobiopterin and, 266
Beans
dry
nitrogen fixation and, 320-21
green
aluminum and, 44
plant genetic engineering and, 208-9
Beer
aluminum and, 44
fumonisins and, 173, 183
Bell's palsy
taste disorders and, 415
Bentonite
aluminum and, 45
Benzocaine
taste disorders and, 411
N-Benzyl-tyrosyl-aminobenzoic acid
cystic fibrosis and, 126
Bethanechol
chemosensory dysfunction and, 423
Bicarbonate
cystic fibrosis and, 117
Bifidobacterium spp.
short-chain fatty acids and, 218
Bile
acids
cystic fibrosis and, 117
protein kinase C and, 550
short-chain fatty acids and, 223-26
aluminum and, 55-56
salts
cystic fibrosis and, 116-18
short-chain fatty acids and, 221
Biocytin
covalent flavoproteins and, 18
Biopterin
tetrahydrobiopterin and, 261-62, 265-66, 270
Biotechnology
foods and, 191-210
Biotin
free and bound forms of, 18
glucokinase and, 485-86
Biphosphonates
osteoporosis and, 303
Biscuits
aluminum and, 44
Black beans
nitrogen fixation and, 320

Blastocyst
    amino acid transport and, 146
Bleach
    fumonisins and, 182
Bleeding
    glycogen storage diseases
        and, 93
Bleomycin
    taste disorders and, 411
Blood
    aluminum and, 48, 50
    prostaglandins and, 246
    short-chain fatty acids and,
        222-23
    tetrahydrobiopterin and, 266
Blue-green algae
    nitrogen fixation and, 319,
        326, 328
B-lymphocytes
    amino acid transport and, 139
Body fat
    excess
        genetics of, 340-42
Body mass index (BMI)
    obesity and, 340-42, 346-48,
        350
Boiling
    fumonisins and, 182, 183
Bone
    aluminum and, 50, 52-53
    glycogen storage diseases
        and, 94
    osteoporosis and, 287-11
Bone Gla protein (BGP)
    vitamin K and, 309
Bone marrow
    selenoproteins and, 77
    tetrahydrobiopterin and, 266
Borage oil
    hypertension and, 246
Bovine growth hormone
    milk production and, 210
Bovine serum albumin (BSA)
    short-chain fatty acids and,
        221
Bovine somatotropin (bST)
    lactation and
        adipose tissue, 445-48
        background information on,
            437-39
        bioenergetics, nutrition,
            and animal well-being,
            441-42
        hepatocytes, 449
        homeorhesis, 442, 450, 454
        integration, 452-54
        mammary gland, 449-52
        mechanisms of action, 442-
            52
        milk and milk components,
            439-41
        production responses, 439-
            42
        whole body metabolism,
            443-45
Bowel obstruction
    cystic fibrosis and, 112, 115
Bradyrhizobium japonicum
    nitrogen fixation and, 324,
        328
Brain
    aluminum and, 50, 52-55

amino acid transport and,
    145, 147-49
equine leucoencephalomalacia
    and, 172
glycogen storage diseases
    and, 88, 104
iron deficiency and, 522
pyruvate dehydrogenase and,
    509, 512-13
tetrahydrobiopterin and, 269
Bran
    aluminum and, 44
    calcium and, 304-5
    short-chain fatty acids and,
        219, 223, 228-29
Branching enzyme
    glycogen storage diseases
        and, 104
Brassica rapa
    desaturase and, 200
    stearate and, 200
Brazil
    legumes and, 320
Brazil nut
    plant genetic engineering and,
        205-6
Bread
    aluminum and, 44
    calcium and, 304
    glycogen storage diseases
        and, 99-100
Britain
    calcium and, 298
Broad beans
    nitrogen fixation and, 320
Bromocriptine
    bovine somatotropin and, 450
Bromoxynil
    plant genetic engineering and,
        208
Bronchial asthma
    smell disorders and, 416
Bronchodilators
    inhaled
        cystic fibrosis and, 122
Brush border membrane
    intestinal
        amino acid transport and,
            147, 150-52
Butter
    cystic fibrosis and, 115
Butyrate
    absorption and metabolism of,
        222-23
    colon cancer and, 228-30
    microbial fermentation and,
        218
    trophic effects of on colonic
        mucosa, 227
Butyric acid
    bovine milk fat digestion and,
        219-20

C

C3H-10T1/2 cells
    amino acid transport and, 154
C18 series fatty acids
    plant genetic engineering and,
        200-1
Ca²⁺
    aluminum and, 54

cell function and, 544
pyruvate dehydrogenase and,
    503-4, 512
sphingolipids and, 180
Cabbage
    aluminum and, 44
Calcitonin
    extracellular fluid Ca² and,
        296
    osteoporosis and, 303
Calcitriol
    extracellular fluid Ca² and,
        296
    phosphorus and, 305
    vitamin D and, 308
Calcium
    aluminum and, 46, 48, 50-51,
        57
    bovine somatotropin and,
        445
    cystic fibrosis and, 119
    fumonisins and, 171, 180
    glycogen storage diseases
        and, 98
    osteoporosis and, 290-302
    pyruvate dehydrogenase and,
        509
    requirement for, 295-96
    smell disorders and, 420
Calgene Inc.
    plant genetic engineering and,
        207-9
Caloric intake
    amino acid transport and, 157
    cystic fibrosis and, 115, 119,
        122, 126, 128, 130
    genetics of obesity and, 348-
        49
    glycogen storage diseases
        and, 94, 96, 98, 102,
        105-6
Calves
    short-chain fatty acids and,
        220
CaMV 35S
    genetically engineered toma-
        toes and, 196
Canada
    cystic fibrosis and, 115, 130-
        32
    fumonisins and, 182
    genetics of obesity and, 341-
        43, 345-46, 348
    nutrition programs and, 3
Cancer
    aflatoxins and, 169
    butyrate and, 228-30
    carotenoids and, 573-75, 578-
        80
    chemosensory losses and, 408-
        9
    fumonisins and, 169, 173-74,
        179
    high-fat diet and, 320-21
    oxygen radicals and, 398
    pterins and, 269
    selenium and, 67
Canola oil
    hypertension and, 246
Caproate
    microbial fermentation and,
        218

Caproic acid
  bovine milk fat digestion and,
    219-20
Captopril
  taste disorders and, 409, 412,
    423
Carbamazepine
  taste disorders and, 412
Carbimazole
  chemosensory dysfunction
    and, 412-13
Carbohydrate
  cystic fibrosis and, 115
  glycogen storage diseases
    and, 87, 96-98, 100
  nitrogen fixation and, 326
  pyruvate dehydrogenase and,
    501-3
Carbonated beverages
  glycogen storage diseases
    and, 99-100
Carbon dioxide (CO$_2$)
  bovine somatotropin and, 449
  cystic fibrosis and, 119
  glycogen storage diseases
    and, 95
  microbial fermentation and,
    218
  plant genetic engineering and,
    201-2
  pyruvate dehydrogenase and,
    498, 500
Carbon tetrachloride
  amino acid transport and, 149
Carcinoembryonic antigen (CEA)
  short-chain fatty acids and,
    229
Cardiac failure
  glycogen storage diseases
    and, 85, 101
Cardiolipin
  cell function and, 542
Cardiomegaly
  glycogen storage diseases
    and, 103
Carmustine
  taste disorders and, 411
Carotenoids
  actions of, 563
    anticarcinogenesis, 575,
      578-80
    in vitro antioxidant actions,
      564-71
    in vivo antioxidant actions,
      571-73
    protection against
      genotoxicity and anti-
      malignant transforma-
      tion, 573-77
  animal studies and, 578-80
  associations with, 563, 580
  biological membranes and,
    568-71
  cells and, 571
  cystic fibrosis and, 126
  functions of, 563-64
  future research on, 580-81
  homogeneous solutions and,
    564-65
  human studies and, 580
  lipoproteins and, 567-68
  liposomes and, 566-67

  oxygen pressure and, 565
  structures of, 563, 565-66
  tocopherols and, 566
Casein
  bovine somatotropin and, 450-
    51
Cassava
  plant genetic engineering and,
    208
Castration
  chemosensory dysfunction
    and, 414
  osteoporosis and, 290, 300
Catabolism
  glycogen storage diseases
    and, 94, 106
Catecholamines
  bovine somatotropin and, 445-
    46
  hypertension and, 254
  iron deficiency and, 522
  tetrahydrobiopterin and, 280
Cations
  amino acid transport and, 139-
    40, 146
  covalent flavoproteins and, 18
Cats
  short-chain fatty acids and,
    220
Caucasians
  osteoporosis and, 295, 306
  protein and, 306
Cauliflower
  aluminum and, 44
Cecum
  short-chain fatty acids and,
    218, 224-27
Cefamandole
  taste disorders and, 411
Celery seed
  aluminum and, 44
Cell cycle
  amino acid transport and, 155
Cell function
  lipids and, 539-53
Cell-mediated immunity
  tetrahydrobiopterin and, 269-
    72
Cell proliferation
  amino acid transport and, 152-
    55
  fumonisins and, 179
  short-chain fatty acids and,
    227
  tetrahydrobiopterin and, 266-
    69
Cellular glutathione peroxidase
    (cGSH-Px)
  selenoproteins and, 67-68,
    70, 73-78
Cellulases
  short-chain fatty acids and,
    230
Cellulose
  short-chain fatty acids and,
    218-19, 223, 228
Central America
  legumes and, 320
Central nervous system (CNS)
  amino acid transport and,
    145, 148
  fumonisins and, 172

Ceramides
  cell function and, 541-42, 553
Ceramide synthases
  fumonisins and, 177
Cerebrum
  equine leucoencephalomalacia
    and, 172
Ceruloplasmin
  cystic fibrosis and, 124
CFTR gene
  cystic fibrosis and, 112-13,
    120
Cheeks
  taste and, 407
Cheese
  aluminum and, 44-45
Chemolithotrophic metabolism
  nitrogen fixation and, 326
Chemosensory dysfunction
  aging and, 406, 415-20
  Alzheimer's disease and, 408,
    410, 421-22
  classification of, 406-7
  clinical evaluation of
    medical imaging, 410
    patient history, 409
    physical examination, 409-
      10
    psychophysical testing, 410
  diseases and, 408, 414-16
  drugs and, 408-14
  environmental pollution and,
    408, 422-25
  treatment or compensation
    for, 423, 425
  types of, 408-9
Chickens
  fumonisins and, 173, 179
Chickpeas
  nitrogen fixation and, 320
Chicks
  aluminum absorption and, 52
  fumonisins and, 173
Children
  blood pressure and, 251
  calcium and, 296-98, 303
  cystic fibrosis and, 112, 114-
    15, 119, 124-32
  food distribution problems
    and, 9-10
  glycogen storage diseases
    and, 85, 89-90, 94-97,
    99-104
  iron deficiency and, 523-34
  nutrition programs and, 3
  obesity and, 340-45, 348, 350
  PUFAs and, 251
  pyruvate dehydrogenase and,
    512
  worm loads and, 10
Chile
  direct nutrition programs and,
    2
n-Chimaerin
  protein kinase C and, 548
Chimpanzees
  calcium and, 299
Chinese hamster ovary (CHO)
    cells
  amino acid transport and,
    138
  tetrahydrobiopterin and, 269

Chitinases
    plant genetic engineering and,
        209
Chloramphenicol acetyl transfer-
        ase (CAT)
    winter flounder antifreeze pro-
        tein and, 199
Chlorhexidine digluconate
        mouth rinses
    taste disorders and, 412
Chloride
    blood pressure and, 245
    channels
        CFTR and, 113, 120
Chlormezanone
    taste disorders and, 412
Chlorobium spp.
    flavocytochromes c and, 37
Chlorobium thiosulfatophilum
    covalent flavoproteins and, 20
Chlorocarbonylcyanide
        phenylhydrazone (CCCP)
    nitrogen fixation and, 331
Chlorpheniramine maleate
    taste disorders and, 411
Chorda tympani
    damage to
        taste disorders and, 415
Clostridium pasterianum
    nitrogen fixation and, 319,
        322
Cholestasis
    cystic fibrosis and, 125
Cholesterol
    cell function and, 540, 542
    glycogen storage diseases
        and, 87, 89, 98
    low-density lipoprotein and,
        355-77
    propionate and, 223-27
Cholesterol oxidase
    covalent flavoproteins and,
        20, 31
Cholesteryl esters
    hepatic
        low-density lipoprotein
            and, 356, 362, 368-
            70, 372-73
Choline oxidase
    covalent flavoproteins and,
        20, 27, 35-36
Chromatin
    butyrate and, 229
Chromatium spp.
    covalent flavoproteins and, 20
    flavocytochromes c and, 37
Chronic lymphocytic leukemia
        (CLL)
    amino acid transport and, 139
Chymotrypsin
    cystic fibrosis and, 126
8-Cl-FAD
    covalent flavoproteins and,
        22
Cinnamon
    aluminum and, 44
Ciprofibrate
    protein kinase C and, 547
Cirrhosis
    cystic fibrosis and, 118
    glycogen storage diseases
        and, 85, 103-4

pyruvate dehydrogenase and,
        513
    smell disorders and, 416
13-cis-retinal
    free and bound forms of, 18
Citral
    smell disorders and, 418
Citrate
    aluminum and, 48-51, 54
    covalent flavoproteins and, 25
Citric acid
    aluminum and, 46, 49-51
    pyruvate dehydrogenase and,
        509
L-Citrulline
    nitric oxide synthase and, 274-
        76
Citrus fruits
    genetically engineered, 198,
        204
Cl⁻
    short-chain fatty acids and,
        222
Claudication
    intermittent
        oxygen and, 396
Clofibrate
    glycogen storage diseases
        and, 89-90
    taste disorders and, 411
Clostridium sticklandii
    glycine reductase complex
        and, 66
Clover
    nitrogen fixation and, 321
CLUSTAL program
    amino acid transport and,
        142
Coal
    chemical fixation of N₂ and,
        318
CoASH
    pyruvate dehydrogenase and,
        503
Cobalamin
    see Vitamin B₁₂
Cocaine hydrochloride
    smell disorders and, 413
Coconut oil
    hydrogenated
        cholesterol and, 367
Codeine
    smell disorders and, 413
Cod-liver oil
    hypertension and, 246, 253
Coenzyme A
    free and bound forms of, 18
    plant lipids and, 200
Coffee
    smell disorders and, 418
Cognitive function
    iron deficiency and, 521-35
Cola
    canned
        as aluminum source, 44
Colchicine
    short-chain fatty acids and,
        227
    taste disorders and, 411
Cold tolerance
    genetically engineered plants
        and, 198-99

Colipase
    cystic fibrosis and, 116-17
    short-chain fatty acids and,
        221
Collagen
    glycogen storage diseases
        and, 93
Colon
    cancer
        butyrate and, 228-30
        dietary fiber and, 217
        high-fat diet and, 321
    cystic fibrosis and, 118
    dietary fiber and, 304
    protein kinase C and, 550-51
    short-chain fatty acids and,
        221-22, 224, 226-28
Computed tomography (CT)
    chemosensory losses and, 410
Conconavalin A (ConA)
    tetrahydrobiopterin and, 270
Congenital adrenal hyperplasia
    taste disorders and, 415
Constipation
    cystic fibrosis and, 118
Copper
    aluminum and, 46
    cystic fibrosis and, 124
    osteoporosis and, 289-90, 310
Copy DNA (cDNA)
    cGSH-Px, 68
    dimethylglycine dehydroge-
        nase, 27
    gastric lipase, 220
    glucokinase, 472
    lipoprotein lipase, 219
    pyruvate dehydrogenase, 500
    selenoprotein, 67-69
    transporter protein, 138, 140
Copy RNA (cRNA)
    transporter protein, 140
Corn
    aluminum and, 44
    fumonisins and, 167-79, 181-
        83
    genetically engineered, 193,
        199, 206
    nitrogen fixation and, 321
Corn oil
    hypertension and, 253-54
Corn syrup
    glycogen storage diseases
        and, 99
Cornstarch
    glycogen storage diseases
        and, 95, 97, 99-100
Cortex
    taste signals and, 407
Corticosteroids
    obesity and, 351
    smell disorders and, 420
Corynebacterium sp. P-1
    sarcosine oxidase and, 36
Corynebacterium sp. U-96
    covalent flavoproteins and, 20
Costa Rica
    iron deficiency anemia and,
        525, 527
Cosuppression
    gene inactivation and, 195-96
Coughing
    cystic fibrosis and, 118, 123

Cowpeas
  nitrogen fixation and, 320
Cows
  aflatoxin B_1 and, 168
  osteoporosis and, 310
  short-chain fatty acids and,
    219-24
  somatotropin and lactation in,
    438-54
Crackers
  glycogen storage diseases
    and, 99-100
Cramping
  cystic fibrosis and, 118
  glycogen storage diseases
    and, 85, 104-5
Cranial nerves
  taste signals and, 407-8
Cream substitute
  powdered
    aluminum and, 44
Creatinine kinase
  glycogen storage diseases
    and, 103, 105
p-Cresol methylhydroxylase
  covalent flavoproteins and,
    20, 38-39
Cretinism
  taste disorders and, 415
Crithidia fasiculata
  tetrahydrobiopterin and, 261-
    62, 266, 280
Criticare HN
  glycogen storage diseases
    and, 96
Crohn's disease
  oral
    taste disorders and, 415
Crouzon's syndrome
  smell disorders and, 416
CTP:choline-phosphate
    cytidylyltransferase
  protein kinase C and, 548
Cucumbers
  aluminum and, 44
Cushing's syndrome
  chemosensory dysfunction
    and, 415-16
Cyanide
  aluminum and, 48
Cyanobacteria
  heterocysts and, 326, 328
  nitrogen fixation and, 319,
    326, 328
Cyclic adenosine monophos-
    phate (cAMP)
  amino acid transport and, 152
  CFTR and, 113, 120
  short-chain fatty acids and,
    228
Cyclic adenosine monophos-
    phate (cAMP) phos-
    phodiesterase
  bovine somatotropin and, 446
Cyclodextrin glycosyltransferase
  plant genetic engineering and,
    204, 206
Cycloheximide
  amino acid transport and, 143-
    44, 152, 154
Cyclooxygenase enzymes
  blood pressure and, 246-47

Cyclopiazonate oxidocyclase
  covalent flavoproteins and,
    20, 30
Cynomolgus monkeys
  cholesterol and, 361-62
Cysteine
  amino acid transport and, 145
  cystic fibrosis and, 124
  fumarate reductase and, 33
  gastric lipase and, 220
  plant genetic engineering and,
    205
  selenoproteins and, 66, 70-
    73, 77
Cysteinyl residues
  flavoproteins with flavin
    bound to, 37-38
Cystic fibrosis
  chemosensory dysfunction
    and, 415-16
  deficits of essential nutrients
    in, 124
    essential fatty acid defi-
      ciency, 124-25
    fat-soluble vitamins, 123-24
    trace metal deficiencies, 124
    water-soluble vitamins, 123
  gene for, 112-13, 119-20
  general features of, 112-14
  nutritional evaluation and ther-
    apy for
    age-related nutritional
      guidelines, 127-28
    biochemical parameters,
      126-27
    clinical parameters, 125-26
    nutritional intervention in
      long-term studies, 130-33
      short-term studies, 129-30
    overview of nutritional prob-
      lems in, 114-16
  pathogenesis of energy imbal-
    ance
    energy expenditure and me-
      tabolism, 119-22
    energy intake, 118-19
    energy losses, 116-18
    pathogenesis of an energy
      deficit, 122-23
Cytochalasin B
  amino acid transport and,
    154
Cytochrome b
  covalent flavoproteins and,
    18
Cytochrome c
  aluminum and, 56
  covalent flavoproteins and,
    18
Cytochrome c oxidase
  lipids and, 542
Cytochrome oxidases
  oxygen and, 392-93
Cytochrome P450
  lipids and, 542
  oxygen and, 393-95
Cytokines
  amino acid transport and, 152-
    55
  pterins and, 269, 270-72, 278
Cytosine
  tetrahydrobiopterin and, 262

D

D2/NAA sequence
  amino acid transport and, 142-
    43
Dairy products
  calcium and, 297, 299
  cystic fibrosis and, 115, 128
  dietary fiber and, 304
  glycogen storage diseases
    and, 98-102
  short-chain fatty acids and,
    219
Datura stramonium
  fumonisins and, 171
Daytime feedings
  glycogen storage diseases, 96-
    98, 104
Death
  early
    glycogen storage diseases
      and, 85, 101, 104
5-deaza-FAD
  covalent flavoproteins and,
    22
Debranching enzyme
  glycogen storage diseases
    and, 102
Dehydratase
  tetrahydrobiopterin and, 263,
    265
Denmark
  cystic fibrosis and, 113
Dental problems
  aluminum and, 56
  taste disorders and, 414
Depression
  chemosensory dysfunction
    and, 406
  cystic fibrosis and, 116, 118
Desaturases
  plant genetic engineering and,
    200-1, 206
Desferrioxamine
  aluminum and, 53
Desulfovibrio spp.
  nitrogen fixation and, 319
Developing countries
  malnutrition and, 2
Dexamethasone
  taste disorders and, 411
Diabetes mellitus
  chemosensory dysfunction
    and, 406, 415-16
  cystic fibrosis and, 116, 118
  dietary fiber and, 98
  glucokinase and, 488-90
Diacylglycerols
  cell function and, 540, 543-51
  short-chain fatty acids and,
    221
2,4-Diamino-6-hydroxypyrimid-
    ine (DAHP)
  tetrahydrobiopterin and, 274,
    278
Diazotrophs
  nitrogen fixation and, 326-27,
    329-30
Diazoxide
  taste disorders and, 412
Dicarboxylic acids
  covalent flavoproteins and, 25

5,10-Dideaza-5,6,7,8-
tetrahydrofolate
glycinamide ribonucleotide
transformylase and, 277
Diet
calcium and, 293-98
cholesterol and, 355-77
fatty acids and, 355-77
fiber and, 304
hypertension and, 243-56
phosphorus and, 305
protein and, 306
protein kinase C and, 550-52
sodium and, 306
Digestion
calcium and, 305
cystic fibrosis and, 113, 115-
118
fatty acids and, 218-21
Dihydrolipoyl transacetylase
covalent flavoproteins and,
18
Dihydropicolinate synthase
plant genetic engineering and,
205-6
Dihydropteridine reductase
(DHPR)
pterins and, 263-64, 267, 273
3,4-Dihydroxyphenylalanine
tetrahydrobiopterin and, 265
Diltiazem
chemosensory dysfunction
and, 412-13
Dimethylamine dehydrogenase
covalent flavoproteins and,
20, 38
Dimethylglycine dehydrogenase
covalent flavoproteins and, 20-
21, 27, 29, 36
1,2-Dimethylhydrazine (DMH)
colorectal cancer and, 228-29,
551
Dimethyl sulfoxide (DMSO)
tetrahydrobiopterin and, 268
Dinitrogenase
nitrogen fixation and, 322-27,
331
Dinitrogenase reductase
nitrogen fixation and, 322-25,
327, 330-32
Dinitrogenase reductase activating glycohydrolase (DRAG)
nitrogen fixation and, 331-32
Dinotrogenase reductase ADP-
ribosyl transferase (DRAT)
nitrogen fixation and, 331-32
Dinitrophenol
aluminum and, 48, 50-51
Dioleoylphosphatidylethanolamine
cell function and, 541
Dipalmitoylphosphatidylcholine
cell function and, 540
Diphenyl iodinium (DPI)
apo-6-hydroxy- apD ap-
nicotine oxidase and, 21
Dipyridamole
taste disorders and, 412
Diquat
selenoprotein P and, 69
Distal intestinal obstruction syndrome

cystic fibrosis and, 118, 124-
25
Dithiodinitrobenzoic acid
(DTNB)
covalent flavoproteins and, 23
DMPH4
indoleamine dioxygenase and,
272
Docosahexaenoic acid (DHA)
hypertension and, 244, 246,
248, 254
protein kinase C and, 547
Dogs
aluminum absorption and, 56
cholesterol and, 360
short-chain fatty acids and,
220
tetrahydrobiopterin and, 266
Dopamine
Alzheimer's disease and, 422
amino acid transport and, 147-
48
iron deficiency and, 534-35
tetrahydrobiopterin and, 263,
279-80
Down's syndrome
smell disorders and, 416
Doxorubicin
taste disorders and, 411
Drosophila melanogaster
biopterin and, 262
Drosophila spp.
aluminum absorption and, 53
Duckweed
fumonisins and, 171
Duodenum
aluminum and, 48-49
cystic fibrosis and, 117
Dysgeusia
classification of, 406
Dysosmia
classification of, 407

E

EcoRV morph 2
D-loop region
obesity and, 350
Edema
cystic fibrosis and, 127
Ef-Tu elongation factor
SELB elongation factor and,
71
Eggs
glycogen storage diseases
and, 98
Egypt
nutrition programs and, 14
Ehrlich cell
amino acid tranport and, 137-
38, 140, 143
Eicosanoids
cell function and, 543, 552-53
phGSH-Px and, 69
Eicosapentaenoic acid (EPA)
hypertension and, 244, 246-
48, 254
Eicosatrienoic acid
cystic fibrosis and, 124
Elderly
blood pressure and, 248, 250

chemosensory losses and,
406, 415-20
glycogen storage diseases
and, 94
osteoporosis and, 288-89, 301-
3, 306, 310
phosphate and, 305
protein and, 306
PUFAs and, 248, 250
vitamin D and, 307
Electrolytes
cystic fibrosis and, 127
Electron paramagnetic resonance
(EPR)
nitrogen fixation and, 322-23
Elemental formulas
glycogen storage diseases
and, 95-98, 104
Elongation factors
selenoproteins and, 71-72
Emden-Meyerhoff pathway
glycogen storage diseases
and, 91
Emphysema
oxygen and, 396
Emulsifying agents
aluminum and, 45
Enalapril
taste disorders and, 412
Endoplasmic reticulum (ER)
type I iodothyronine 5'-
deiodinase and, 69
Endothelial cells
amino acid transport and,
140, 146, 153
Energy needs
cystic fibrosis and, 116-23
glycogen storage diseases
and, 96
obesity and, 343-46, 349-50
short-chain fatty acids and,
230-31
Enteral nutrition
cystic fibrosis and, 129-31
glycogen storage diseases
and, 99, 102
Enterococcus spp.
short-chain fatty acids and,
218
Enterocytes
aluminum and, 48
amino acid transport and, 150-
52
Enteroglucagon
short-chain fatty acids and,
228
Environmental pollution
chemosensory losses and,
408, 422-25
Enzymes
covalently bound flavin and,
17-39
glycogen storage diseases
and, 85
oxygen-reacting, 391-95
Epidermal growth factor (EGF)
amino acid transport and,
152
dietary fiber and, 228
lipids and, 540, 542, 553
Epilepsy
smell disorders and, 416

Epinephrine
glycogen storage diseases
and, 93
Epithelial cells
amino acid transport and,
147, 150-51
cystic fibrosis and, 112
EPSP synthase
plant genetic engineering and,
208
Equine leucoencephalomalacia
(ELEM) syndrome
fumonisins and, 172, 178, 182
Erythroblasts
selenoproteins and, 77
Erythrocyte acid phosphatase
(locus 1) (2p25) phenotypes
obesity and, 350
Erythrocytes
glycogen storage diseases
and, 102
hemoglobin and, 390
tetrahydrobiopterin and, 266
Escherichia coli
covalent flavoproteins and, 20-
22, 25
plant genetic engineering and,
192-94, 203, 206
pyruvate dehydrogenase and,
498-99
selenoproteins and, 70
short-chain fatty acids and,
218
Esophageal cancer
fumonisins and, 173-74
high-fat diet and, 321
Esophagitis
cystic fibrosis and, 116, 118,
125
Essential fatty acids (EFAs)
cystic fibrosis and, 124-25
glycogen storage diseases
and, 90
hypertension and, 245
Estrogen
withdrawal of
osteoporosis and, 291, 300
Estrogen replacement therapy
(ERT)
osteoporosis and, 300-301,
303
Ethacrynic acid
taste disorders and, 412
Ethambutol hydrochloride
taste disorders and, 411
Ethylene
genetically engineered tomatoes and, 196-98
N-Ethylmaleimide (NEM)
amino acid transport and, 144-
45
Etidronate
taste disorders and, 412
Eubacteria
nitrogen fixation and, 325
Eukaryotes
covalent flavoproteins and, 27-
28
lipids and, 539
microbial fermentation and,
218
oxygen and, 383, 395

selenoprotein synthesis and,
71-74, 76-77
Europe
cystic fibrosis and, 112-13
fumonisins and, 182
vitamin D and, 307
Evening primrose oil
hypertension and, 245-46, 248
Evolution
nitrogenase systems and, 324-
27
Exercise
cystic fibrosis and, 126
glycogen storage diseases
and, 85, 105
obesity and, 345-46
osteoporosis and, 288, 291
Extracellular fluid
calcium and, 296
phosphate and, 306
Extracellular glutathione peroxidase (eGSH-Px)
selenoproteins and, 68, 70, 75
Extrahepatic biliary obstruction
cystic fibrosis and, 118

F

4F2 protein
amino acid transport and, 142-
43
F4N cells
tetrahydrobiopterin and, 268
Facial hypoplasia
taste disorders and, 415
FAD
covalent flavoproteins and,
18, 20-37, 39
free and bound forms of, 18
fad series genes
plant lipids and, 201
Failure to thrive
glycogen storage diseases
and, 104
Familial dysautonomia
taste disorders and, 415, 423
Family studies
obesity and, 338, 340-46, 350
Fao hepatoma cells
amino acid transport and, 140-
41, 146
Fasting
chemosensory dysfunction
and, 414
Fat
bovine somatotropin and,
443, 445-48, 450
cystic fibrosis and, 115-18,
125-27, 131
glycogen storage diseases
and, 96, 98, 100, 105
protein kinase C and, 550-52
Fatty acids
bovine somatotropin and,
444, 449, 451
cell function and, 539, 541-
43, 546-52
cGSH-Px and, 68
cytochrome P450s and, 394
glycogen storage diseases
and, 89-90, 105

LDL-cholesterol levels and,
355-77
n-3
hypertension and, 247-48,
253-56
n-6
hypertension and, 245-53,
255-56
phGSH-Px and, 68
plant lipids and, 199-01
pyruvate dehydrogenase and,
502-3, 507-9, 512
short-chain
absorption of, 221-23
biological effects of, 223-30
bovine milk fat digestion
and, 219-21
butyrate effect on colon cancer and, 228-30
digestive tract and, 218-21
energy requirements and,
230-31
introduction to, 217-18
metabolism of, 221-23
microbial fermentation and,
218-19
plant lipids and, 201
propionate and cholesterol
levels, 223-27
trophic effects of on colon
mucosa, 227-28
tetrahydrobiopterin and, 262
Fe²⁺
aluminum and, 54
Feces
aluminum and, 47, 55
cystic fibrosis and, 115-17,
125-27
diacylglycerol and, 550
short-chain fatty acids and,
218-19, 221, 223-24, 229
Feeding disorders
cystic fibrosis and, 116, 119,
127
FeMoco
nitrogen fixation and, 322,
324
Fermentation
nitrogen fixation and, 326
Ferredoxin
nitrogen fixation and, 322-23
Ferrets
carotenoids and, 581
Ferritin
cystic fibrosis and, 124, 127
osteoporosis and, 310
Fertilizers
nitrogen fixation and, 320
Fe-S flavoproteins
iron deficiency and, 522
Fetus
amino acid transport and, 155-
57
Fiber, dietary
glycogen storage diseases
and, 97-99
osteoporosis and, 303-5
short-chain fatty acids and,
217-19, 223-30
Fibroblasts
amino acid transport and,
140, 146, 153-54

cystic fibrosis and, 119
glycogen storage diseases
and, 102, 104
Fibronectin
lipids and, 540, 542
Fibrosis
hepatic
glycogen storage diseases
and, 103
Finland
osteoporosis and, 307
PUFAs and, 250-51
vitamin D and, 307
Fish oil
glycogen storage diseases
and, 89, 98, 100
hypertension and, 253
Flavanone glucosides
plant genetic engineering and,
204-5
Flavin adenine dinucleotide
(FAD)
nitric oxide synthase and, 275-
76
pyruvate dehydrogenase and,
501
Flavin mononucleotide (FMN)
covalent flavoproteins and, 18
indoleamine dioxygenase and,
273
nitric oxide synthase and, 275-
76
Flavinylation covalent flavoproteins
biosynthesis of covalent flavin-
protein bond
advantage of covalency, 26-
28
cleavage of covalent bond,
25-26
histidyl(N3)-8α-flavin linkage synthesis, 21-25
nutritional aspects, 28-29
specific features of covalent
flavoproteins, 25-29
covalent factor-apoenzyme attachment
aminoacyl-flavin bonds,
19
coenzyme attachment, 18
covalently bound coen-
zymes in flavopro-
teins, 18-21
flavoproteins with covalently
bound flavin cofactors
flavin bound to cysteinyl
residue and, 37-38
histidyl(N1)-8α-flavin linkage and, 29-32
histidyl(N3)-8α-flavin linkage and, 32-36
flavoprotein with tyrosyl(O)-
8α-flavin linkage, 38-39
introduction to, 17
Flavocytochromes c
covalent flavoproteins and,
20, 37
Flour
developing countries and, 10
Fluoride
aluminum and, 46, 50-51, 56-
57

osteoporosis and, 303
free and bound forms of, 18
fnr gene
nitrogen fixation and, 329
Folic acid
covalent flavoproteins and, 18
iron deficiency and, 522
Food additives
aluminum and, 43
Food and Drug Adeministration
(FDA)
aflatoxin B1 and, 168
plant genetic engineering and,
207
Total Diet Study by, 43, 45
Food colors and dyes
aluminum and, 45
Foods
aluminum and, 43-4657
calcium and, 290, 293-97, 304
developing countries and, 9-10
fungal toxins and, 167-83
plant genetic engineering and,
191-210
thermic effect of, 345
Foreign body reaction
glycogen storage diseases
and, 104
Formate
microbial fermentation and,
218
Formyl-methionyl-leucyl-phenylalanine
protein kinase C and, 549
Fossil fuels
chemical fixation of N2 and,
318
Fractures
osteoporosis and, 287-92,
302, 306-7, 309-11
Frankia spp.
nitrogen fixation and, 319
Free enthalpy
covalent flavoproteins and, 21
Freeze tolerance
plant genetic engineering and,
198-99
Fructose
glycogen storage diseases
and, 92, 98-99
plant genetic engineering and,
202-3
Fruits
aluminum and, 44
glycogen storage diseases
and, 98-99, 102
FTTa
glycogen storage diseases
and, 85
Fumarate
covalent flavoproteins and, 25
Fumarate reductase
covalent flavoproteins and,
20, 25, 27, 32-33
Functional hepatocyte heterogeneity
amino acid transport and, 149
Fungi
foods and, 167-83
gene inactivation and, 195
Fusarium moniliforme
biology of

control potentials, 171
fungus description and taxonomy, 169
occurrence and pathogenicity in plants, 169-70
plant toxicity, 170-71
diseases associated with
equine
leucoencephalomalacia,
172, 178, 182
esophageal cancer, 173-74
porcine pulmonary edema
syndrome, 172-73, 182
poultry toxicity, 173
studies with laboratory animals, 174-75
fumonisins and
alterations in free sphingoid
bases in vivo, 177-79
altered sphingolipid biosynthesis and animal dis-
eases, 179-80
chemistry of fumonisins
and related com-
pounds, 175-76
detection and occurrence of
fumonisins, 181-83
inhibition of sphingolipid
biosynthesis in vitro,
176-77
mode of action of
fumonisins, 176-80
other hypothesized modes
of action, 180
protein kinase C and, 552
introduction to, 167-69

G

Ga-67
aluminum absorption and, 53
apL ap-Galactonolactone oxidase
covalent flavoproteins and, 31
Galactose
glycogen storage diseases
and, 98-99
β-Galactosidase
covalent flavoproteins and, 22
Galvanic currents
weak
taste thresholds and, 416
Gambia
calcium and, 298
Gamma-aminobutyric acid
(GABA)
amino acid transport and,
147
Ganglioside GM3
cell function and, 540, 542
Gas chromatography-mass spectrometry (GC-MS)
fumonisins and, 181
Gastric acid
cystic fibrosis and, 117
Gastric lipase
short-chain fatty acids and,
220-21
Gastrointestinal symptoms
cystic fibrosis and, 112
glycogen storage diseases
and, 104

Germine monoacetate
taste disorders and, 412
Gibberella fujikuroi
fumonisins and, 169-70
Gi protein
bovine somatotropin and, 446-47
Glipizide
taste disorders and, 412
Global regulators
transcriptional control by
nitrogen fixation and, 329-30
Glomerulosclerosis
glycogen storage diseases
and, 94
Glossitis
taste disorders and, 415
Glucagon
amino acid transport and, 143-45, 152
glucokinase and, 483-84
glycogen storage diseases
and, 88, 92-94
pyruvate dehydrogenase and, 512
α-1,4-Glucan-6-glycosyl transferase
glycogen storage diseases
and, 104
Glucocorticoids
amino acid transport and, 145
glucokinase and, 485
obesity and, 351
Glucokinase
alternate promoters in
glucokinase gene and, 473-74
β-cells and, 472, 481-82, 486-90
biotin and, 485-86
cis-regulatory elements in hepatic promoter and, 487-88
cell-specific regulation of, 482-88
developmental regulation and, 486
diabetes mellitus and, 488-90
discovery of, 464-66
evolution of, 476-78
glucagon and, 483-84
glucocorticoids and, 485
glucokinase reaction and, 466-68
hepatocytes and, 471-72, 478-81, 483-86
heterogeneous expression
and, 487
human, 475-76
insulin and, 483-84
multiple glucokinase mRNAs
and, 474-75
rat glucokinase gene and, 472-73
regulation of activity of, 468-71
thyroid hormone and, 484-85
D-Gluconolactone oxidase (dehydrogenase)
covalent flavoproteins and, 20, 36

Glucose
aluminum and, 48
bovine somatotropin and, 444, 449, 451
diacylglycerol and, 551
glycogen storage diseases
and, 87-88, 92-93, 95-99, 101, 104-5
plant genetic engineering and, 202-3
pyruvate dehydrogenase and, 501-2
short-chain fatty acids and, 222
Glucose-6-phosphatase
glycogen storage diseases
and, 84, 86-88, 91-92
β-Glucuronidase
plant transformation and, 194
Gluphosinate
plant genetic engineering and, 208
Glutamate
amino acid transport and, 149, 151, 156
glycogen storage diseases
and, 90
nitrogen fixation and, 329
taste disorders and, 416-17
tetrahydrobiopterin and, 280
umami and, 408
Glutamic acid
Alzheimer's disease and, 422
nitrogen fixation and, 321
taste disorders and, 417
vitamin K and, 308
Glutamic-pyruvate transaminase
locus
obesity and, 350
Glutaminase
amino acid transport and, 149
Glutamine
amino acid transport and, 145-46, 150, 153, 156
glycogen storage diseases
and, 90-91
nitrogen fixation and, 321, 329
short-chain fatty acids and, 222
Glutamine pyrophosphate-ribose-phosphate amidotransferase
glycogen storage diseases
and, 91
Glutamine synthetase
amino acid transport and, 149
Glutathione
thyroid function and, 69
Glyceraldehyde 3-phosphate
covalent flavoproteins and, 22
Glycerate 3-phosphate
covalent flavoproteins and, 22
Glycerol 3-phosphate
covalent flavoproteins and, 22-23
glycogen storage diseases
and, 89
Glycerol 3-phosphate
acyltransferase
plant genetic engineering and, 201, 206

Glyceryl ethers
tetrahydrobiopterin and, 264
Glycine
amino acid transport and, 145, 147-48, 151-52, 156
covalent flavoproteins and, 27
glycogen storage diseases
and, 90
Glycine reductase complex
protein A of, 66
Glycocholate
cystic fibrosis and, 117
Glycogen storage diseases
classification of, 85
introduction to, 84-86
liver glycogen metabolism
and, 84
type I glycogen storage disease, 85-87
blood glucose changes and, 87-88
daytime feedings and, 97-98
growth impairment and, 94
hepatic adenoma and, 94
hyperlipidemia and, 89-90
hyperuricemia and, 90-92
hypophosphatemia and, 92-93
lactic acid changes and, 88-89
nocturnal nutrient infusion
and, 95-97
nutritional management of, 95-101
oxidative phosphorylation
and, 93
patient education and, 98-101
platelet dysfunction and, 93-94
prognosis for, 101
renal involvement and, 94-95
type II glycogen storage disease, 85, 101-2
type III glycogen storage disease, 85, 102-4
type IV glycogen storage disease, 85, 104
type V glycogen storage disease, 85, 104-6
type VI-X glycogen storage
diseases, 85, 106
Glycosuria
cystic fibrosis and, 118
Glyphosate
plant genetic engineering and, 208
Goats
short-chain fatty acids and, 219
somatotropin and, 447, 449-51
Goiter
developing countries and, 2
Gold
taste disorders and, 411
Gonadal dysgenesis
chemosensory dysfunction
and, 415-16

Gonadal hormones
    withdrawal of
        osteoporosis and, 288, 293,
            300
Gout
    glycogen storage diseases
        and, 90
Grains
    aluminum and, 44
    glycogen storage diseases
        and, 97-98, 100
Grapefruit juice
    plant genetic engineering and,
        204
GRAS List Survey–Phase II
    aluminum-containing food ad-
        ditives and, 45
Gray matter
    equine leucoencephalomalacia
        and, 172
Great Britain
    iron deficiency anemia and,
        525
Greece
    legumes and, 320
Griseofulvin
    taste disorders and, 411
Groundnut oil
    hypertension and, 249
Growth factors
    amino acid transport and, 152-
        55
Growth hormone (GH)
    glycogen storage diseases
        and, 94
Growth rate
    cystic fibrosis and, 114, 116,
        124-25, 129-30
    glycogen storage diseases
        and, 85, 94-95, 103-4
GTP-binding protein
    bovine somatotropin and, 446-
        48
GTP cyclohydrolase
    pterins and, 266-68, 270-71,
        273
Guam
    aluminum accumulation and,
        53, 57
Guanine:queuine tRNA trans-
        glycosylase
    tetrahydrobiopterin and, 268
Guanosine triphosphate (GTP)
    tetrahydrobiopterin and, 267
Guanyl ribonucleotides
    glycogen storage diseases
        and, 91
Guar gum
    glycogen storage diseases
        and, 98
    short-chain fatty acids and,
        224, 229
Guatemala
    iron deficiency anemia and,
        525
Guillain-Barre syndrome
    taste disorders and, 415
Guinea pigs
    amino acid transport and, 156-
        57
    carotenoids and, 571
    cholesterol and, 361

selenoproteins and, 76-77
    short-chain fatty acids and,
        220
    apL   ap-Gulonolactone   oxi-
        dase
        covalent flavoproteins and, 20-
            21, 32
Gum arabic
    short-chain fatty acids and,
        219
Gums
    short-chain fatty acids and,
        223, 228
Gus gene product
    plant transformation and, 194
Gustatory hallucination
    classification of, 406
Gut
    aluminum and, 48-50, 52, 55
    iron and, 55
Gyrase
    inhibitors
        nitrogen fixation and, 329

H

H+
    short-chain fatty acids and,
        229
H4-II-EC3 cells
    amino acid transport and, 146
H-35 cells
    amino acid transport and, 146
Haber-Bosch process
    chemical fixation of N₂ and,
        318
Hallucinations
    gustatory, 406
    olfactory, 407
Hamsters
    carotenoids and, 578
    cholesterol and, 360-62
    LDL-cholesterol levels and,
        365, 367-71, 375
HCO₃⁻
    short-chain fatty acids and,
        222
Head trauma
    chemosensory dysfunction
        and, 409, 413-16
Heart
    aluminum and, 52
    cystic fibrosis and, 119, 133
    glycogen storage diseases
        and, 103-4
    high-fat diet and, 320
    pyruvate dehydrogenase and,
        502-3, 505-9, 511-12
Heat
    summer
        cystic fibrosis and, 127
Heavy metals
    selenium complexed with, 67
HELIX MEM program
    amino acid transport and, 148
Heme
    free and bound forms of, 18
    synthesis
        iron deficiency and, 522
Hemicellulose
    microbial fermentation and,
        218

Hemoglobin
    iron deficiency and, 524-25,
        527-31
    oxygen and, 384, 390
Hemopoietic cells
    tetrahydrobiopterin and, 266,
        268
Hemorrhage
    glycogen storage diseases
        and, 93
Hemothorax
    oxygen and, 396
Hepatic adenomas
    glycogen storage diseases
        and, 87, 94, 101
Hepatic Aid II
    glycogen storage diseases
        and, 102
Hepatic carcinoma
    glycogen storage diseases
        and, 94
Hepatic decompensation
    cystic fibrosis and, 125
Hepatic zonal heterogeneity
    amino acid transport and, 149-
        50
Hepatitis
    acute viral
        smell disorders and, 416
Hepatobiliary disease
    cystic fibrosis and, 116, 126
Hepatocytes
    amino acid transport and,
        138, 140-41, 144-46,
        148-50, 152-55
    bovine somatotropin and, 449
    fumonisins and, 177
    glucokinase and, 478-81, 483-
        86
    LDL-cholesterol levels and,
        358, 369-70, 377
    short-chain fatty acids and,
        222, 225
Hepatoma cells
    amino acid transport and, 140-
        41, 145-46, 155
Hepatomegaly
    glycogen storage diseases
        and, 85, 103
Hepatosplenomegaly
    glycogen storage diseases
        and, 85, 104
HepG2 cells
    amino acid transport and, 146
Herbicides
    genes for resistance to, 193,
        208-9
Herbs
    aluminum and, 43-45
Heredity
    osteoporosis and, 288, 290-91
Heterocysts
    nitrogen fixation and, 326,
        328
Hexamethylene bisacetamide
    tetrahydrobiopterin and, 266-
        67
Hexetidine
    taste disorders and, 411
Hexokinases
    mammalian glucokinase and,
        464-91

Hexose monophosphate shunt
glycogen storage diseases
and, 91
Hexoses
plant genetic engineering and,
202
High-carbohydrate diet
cystic fibrosis and, 115
High-density lipoproteins
(HDLs)
reverse cholesterol transport
and, 357
High-fat diet
cancer and, 320-21
coronary heart disease and,
320
High-pressure liquid chromatography (HPLC)
fumonisins and, 182
High-protein diet
glycogen storage diseases
and, 102, 104-6
High-starch diet
glycogen storage diseases
and, 95, 97, 104
Hindgut
short-chain fatty acids and,
222, 227-28, 230
Hip
fracture of
nutrition and, 310-11
Hippocampus
pyruvate dehydrogenase and,
509
smell disorders and, 408,
420
Histidine
amino acid transport and,
138, 145-46, 150, 156
covalent flavoproteins and, 19-
25, 29-32, 32-36
Histones
butyrate and, 229
HIV
see Human immunodeficiency
virus
HLA system
class I loci of
obesity and, 350
HMG-CoA reductase
short-chain fatty acids and,
224-25
HMG-CoA synthase
short-chain fatty acids and,
224-25
Hogs
short-chain fatty acids and,
220
Homology targeted gene inactivation
plants and, 195
Homo sapiens
short-chain fatty acids and,
218
Hormones
amino acid transport and,
143, 145
glycogen storage diseases
and, 88
osteoporosis and, 291, 293
pyruvate dehydrogenase complex and, 509, 511-12

Horses
fumonisins and, 172, 177-78,
182
short-chain fatty acids and,
220
HTC cells
amino acid transport and,
145
Human immunodeficiency virus
(HIV)
smell disorders and, 416
Hunter-gatherers
contemporary
calcium and, 299
hup gene
nitrogen fixation and, 324
Hydrazine
nitrogen fixation and, 321
Hydrocortisone
taste disorders and, 411
Hydrogen (H_2)
chemical fixation of N_2 and,
318, 326
microbial fermentation and,
218
Hydrogen peroxide
cGSH-Px and, 68
Hydromorphone hydrochloride
smell disorders and, 413
Hydroperoxides
cGSH-Px and, 68
β-Hydroxybutyrate
pyruvate dehydrogenase and,
512
Hydroxylamine
nitrogen fixation and, 321
3-Hydroxy-3-methylglutaryl
CoA reductase
glycogen storage diseases
and, 89
Hydroxy nicotine oxidase
covalent flavoproteins and, 20-
23, 25, 27-28, 33-35
Hydroxyproline
phosphorus and, 305
vitamin K and, 309
5-Hydroxytryptophan
tetrahydrobiopterin and, 265
Hypergeusia
classification of, 406
Hyperglycemia
glycogen storage diseases
and, 99
Hyperketonemia
glycogen storage diseases
and, 85
Hyperlipidemia
glycogen storage diseases
and, 87, 89-90, 93, 95,
101
Hyperosmia
classification of, 407
Hyperphenylalaninemia
tetrahydrobiopterin and, 265-
66
Hyperphosphatemia
aluminum and, 51
Hypertension
background information on,
243-45
n-3 fatty acids and, 247-48,
253-56

n-6 fatty acids and, 245-53,
255-56
prostaglandins and, 245-56
taste disorders and, 406, 409,
412-13, 415, 423
Hyperuricemia
glycogen storage diseases
and, 87, 90-93, 95, 103,
105
Hyphomicrobium X
covalent flavoproteins and,
20
Hypoalbuminemia
cystic fibrosis and, 127
Hypogeusia
classification of, 406
Hypoglycemia
glycogen storage diseases
and, 85, 87-88, 91, 93,
98-99, 101, 103
taste disorders and, 412
Hypogonadotropic hypogonadism
smell disorders and, 416
Hypomagnesia
cystic fibrosis and, 124
Hypophosphatemia
glycogen storage diseases
and, 92-93
Hypophysectomy
chemosensory dysfunction
and, 414
Hyposmia
classification of, 407
Hypothalamus
chemosensory dysfunction
and, 407-8, 420
Hypothyroidism
chemosensory dysfunction
and, 415-16
Hypotonia
glycogen storage diseases
and, 85, 101, 104

I

Idoxuridine
taste disorders and, 412
IGF-binding proteins
bovine somatotropin and, 451-
54
Ileum
cystic fibrosis and, 118, 123
Immune function
cystic fibrosis and, 123
fumonisins and, 173
tetrahydrobiopterin and, 269-
72
vitamin D and, 308
India
direct nutrition programs and,
2, 10, 14
iodine deficiency and, 2
iron deficiency anemia and,
530
legumes and, 320
Indoleacetic acid
fumonisins and, 171
Indoleamine dioxygenase
tetrahydrobiopterin and, 272-
74
Indomethacin
hypertension and, 244, 247

Indonesia
  iron deficiency anemia and,
    525, 530
Infant formulas
  aluminum and, 46
  cystic fibrosis and, 128
  glycogen storage diseases
    and, 96-97
Infants
  cystic fibrosis and, 119-20,
    127-28, 131
  glycogen storage diseases
    and, 85, 95-97, 101, 103-
    4
  iron deficiency and, 523-26,
    528-30, 532-35
  LDL-cholesterol levels and,
    368
  oxygen and, 398
  pyruvate dehydrogenase and,
    512
  taste and, 407
Infection
  cystic fibrosis and, 124
  taste disorders and, 415
Infertility
  cystic fibrosis and, 112
Inflammation
  initiation of
    oxygen radicals and, 386,
      398
Influenza-like infections
  chemosensory dysfunction
    and, 415-16
Inosine
  glycogen storage diseases
    and, 91-92
Insulin
  bovine somatotropin and, 445-
    48, 451
  glucokinase and, 483-84
  glycogen storage diseases
    and, 88, 94, 98
  pyruvate dehydrogenase and,
    506, 509, 511-12
Insulin-like growth factor I (IGF-
  I)
  bovine somatotropin and,
    448, 451-54
Insulin-like growth factor II
  (IGF-II)
  bovine somatotropin and,
    448, 451-54
Interferon γ (IFNγ)
  pterins and, 269-74, 278
Interleukin 1 (IL-1)
  amino acid transport and, 152-
    53
Interleukin 2 (IL-2)
  pterins and, 270
Interleukin 6 (IL-6)
  amino acid transport and, 153
International nutrition policy
  efforts in, 2-15
Intestines
  aluminum and, 48-51
  amino acid transport and, 150-
    52
  bovine somatotropin and, 443
  cholesterol and, 356, 359, 361
  cystic fibrosis and, 112, 116-
    18, 124-25

dietary fiber and, 303-4
  indoleamine dioxygenase and,
    272-73
  LDL-cholesterol levels and,
    363-64
  protein kinase C and, 550
  short-chain fatty acids and,
    218-19, 224-26, 28, 230
Intrauterine growth retardation
  (IUGR)
  amino acid transport and, 157
Invertase
  plant genetic engineering and,
    202, 206
Iodacetamide
  covalent flavoproteins and,
    23, 38
Iodine
  deficiency
    developing countries and, 2-
      3
Iodothyronine 5'-deiodinase
  type I
    selenoproteins and, 69, 74,
      77
Ion channel proteins
  amino acid transport and, 148
Ionizing radiation
  chemosensory dysfunction
    and, 414
Ireland
  calcium and, 298
Iringa
  direct nutrition programs and,
    2, 10, 14
Iron
  aluminum and, 54-55, 57
  cystic fibrosis and, 127
  nitrogen fixation and, 322,
    324
  tetrahydrobiopterin and, 262
Iron deficiency anemia
  cognitive function and, 521-35
  cystic fibrosis and, 124
  developing countries and, 2
Iron sorbitex
  taste disorders and, 412
Iron-sulfur protein
  nitrogen fixation and, 327
Isobutyrate
  microbial fermentation and,
    218
Isocitrate
  covalent flavoproteins and, 25
Isoleucine
  glycogen storage diseases
    and, 105
Isovalerate
  microbial fermentation and,
    218
Israel
  cystic fibrosis and, 113
Italy
  PUFAs and, 250-51

J

Japan
  calcium and, 298
Java
  iron deficiency anemia and,
    531

Jejunum
  aluminum and, 48
  cystic fibrosis and, 117
  short-chain fatty acids and,
    228
Jimsonweed
  fumonisins and, 171
Juices
  glycogen storage diseases
    and, 98-100
  plant genetic engineering and,
    204

K

K+
  short-chain fatty acids and,
    222
Kale
  calcium and, 304
Kallman's syndrome
  smell disorders and, 416
Kanamycin
  resistance
    plant transformation and,
      193, 207-8
Kenya
  nutrition programs and, 14
α-Keto-acid dehydrogenase
  pyruvate dehydrogenase multi-
    enzyme complex and, 497
α-Ketobutyric acid
  genetically engineered toma-
    toes and, 198
Ketones
  bovine somatotropin and, 449
  glycogen storage diseases
    and, 85
  pyruvate dehydrogenase and,
    502-3, 508-9
  short-chain fatty acids and,
    222
Kidney beans
  nitrogen fixation and, 320
Kidney Gla protein
  vitamin K and, 309
Kidneys
  aluminum and, 51-55
  amino acid transport and,
    143, 150, 154
  blood pressure and, 245-47,
    251-52, 254
  bovine somatotropin and, 443
  calcitriol and, 305
  calcium and, 292, 303
  failure of
    smell disorders and, 416
  fumonisins and, 174, 178-80
  glycogen storage diseases
    and, 84, 86, 94-95, 101
  PUFAs and, 245-47, 251-52,
    254
  selenoproteins and, 68-69, 76-
    77
  vitamin D and, 307-8
Klebsiella pneumoniae
  nitrogen fixation and, 329
Klebsiella spp.
  cyclodextrin
    glycosyltransferase and,
      204, 206
  nitrogen fixation and, 319

Korsakoff's syndrome
  smell disorders and, 416
Kpn1 morph 2
  D-loop region
    obesity and, 350
Krebs cycle
  iron deficiency and, 522
Kynurenine
  indoleamine dioxygenase and,
    272
  nitric oxide synthase and, 274

L

α-Lactalbumin
  bovine somatotropin and, 450-
    51
Lactate
  aluminum and, 54
  glycogen storage diseases
    and, 87-90, 105
Lactation
  bovine somatotropin and, 437-
    54
Lactic acid
  aluminum and, 51
  glycogen storage diseases
    and, 87-89, 93-94, 97
  pyruvate dehydrogenase and,
    512
b-Lactoglobulin
  short-chain fatty acids and,
    221
Lactulose
  short-chain fatty acids and,
    225
Large intestine
  short-chain fatty acids and,
    218-19
Laryngectomy
  chemosensory dysfunction
    and, 415-16
Latin America
  government child-feeding pro-
    grams and, 9
Lead
  aluminum and, 51
Leavening agents
  aluminum and, 45
Leghemoglobin
  nitrogen fixation and, 326
Legumes
  aluminum and, 44
  nitrogen fixation and, 319-32
Lemna minor   L.
  fumonisins and, 171
Lemon juice
  aluminum and, 50
Lentils
  nitrogen fixation and, 320
Leprosy
  chemosensory dysfunction
    and, 415-16
Lettuce
  aluminum and, 44
Leucine
  amino acid transport and, 138-
    39, 148, 151-52
  bovine somatotropin and, 438-
    39
  covalent flavoproteins and, 27

glycogen storage diseases
    and, 105
Leucocytes
  glycogen storage diseases
    and, 91, 102
  protein kinase C and, 552
Leucyl-tRNA
  amino acid transport and, 138
Leukemia
  amino acid transport and, 139
Leukotrienes
  cytochrome P450s and, 394
Levamisole
  taste disorders and, 411
Levodopa
  taste disorders and, 412
Lidocaine
  taste disorders and, 411
Lime
  nitrogen fixation and, 320
Lime water
  fumonisins and, 183
Lincomycin
  taste disorders and, 411
Lingual lipase
  short-chain fatty acids and,
    220
Linoleic acid
  hypertension and, 244-45,
    247-54
  protein kinase C and, 547,
    550
  tetrahydrobiopterin and, 262
Linolenic acids
  hypertension and, 244, 246-
    49, 251, 254
  protein kinase C and, 547
Linseed oil
  hypertension and, 246, 248
Lipase
  cystic fibrosis and, 117
Lipemia
  glycogen storage diseases
    and, 85
Lipid peroxidation
  carotenoids and, 568-70
  phGSH-Px and, 69
  PUFAs and, 255
Lipids
  cell function and, 539-53
  cystic fibrosis and, 124
  flickering clusters and, 542
  glycogen storage diseases
    and, 87, 89-90, 93, 95,
    101
  physiochemical properties of,
    541-42
  plant genetic engineering and,
    199-201
  protein kinase C and, 543-50
  proteins and, 542
  second messengers and, 543,
    553
  selenoproteins and, 69
  Western diet and, 358-60
α-Lipoic acid
  free and bound forms of, 18
Lipopolysaccharide (LPS)
  pterins and, 270, 272, 278
Lipoprotein lipase
  bovine milk fat digestion and,
    219-20

Lipoproteins
  carotenoids and, 567-68
  glycogen storage diseases
    and, 90
Liposomes
  carotenoids and, 566-67
Liposyn
  hypertension and, 252
Lips
  taste and, 407
Liquid chromatography
  fumonisins and, 181
Lithium
  amino acid transport and, 146
  taste disorders and, 412
Liver
  aflatoxins and, 169
  aluminum and, 52-53
  amino acid transport and,
    138, 140-41, 143, 145-
    46, 148-56
  bovine somatotropin and, 443-
    44, 448-49, 452
  cancer
    protein kinase C and, 551
  cGSH-Px and, 68, 70, 76-77
  cholesterol and, 356-58, 360-
    62
  covalent flavoproteins and, 20-
    21, 28
  cystic fibrosis and, 112, 116,
    118, 123, 125, 127
  diacylglycerol and, 551
  disease
    smell disorders and, 416
  fumonisins and, 172-75, 177-
    80
  glucokinase and, 471-72, 478-
    81, 483-90
  glycogen storage diseases
    and, 84-87, 89-91, 94-
    95, 102-4
  indoleamine dioxygenase and,
    272
  lipids and, 540
  LDL-cholesterol levels and,
    362-64, 368-74, 376-77
  pyruvate dehydrogenase and,
    501, 505, 508-9, 513
  selenoproteins and, 69, 76-78
  short-chain fatty acids and,
    222-26
LLC-PK$_1$ cells
  amino acid transport and, 154
Lovastatin
  glycogen storage diseases
    and, 89
Low-density lipoproteins (LDLs)
  carotenoids and, 567-68
  cholesterol and, 355-77
  dietary fiber and, 223
Low-fat diet
  cystic fibrosis and, 115
  glycogen storage diseases
    and, 89-90
Lungs
  aluminum and, 52
  cancer of
    cytochrome P450s and, 394
    high-fat diet and, 321
  cystic fibrosis and, 112, 114,
    116, 118-25, 127-33

eGSH-Px and, 68
fumonisins and, 172-73, 178-79
indoleamine dioxygenase and, 272
tetrahydrobiopterin and, 266
Lupines
nitrogen fixation and, 320
Lymphocytes
tetrahydrobiopterin and, 270
Lysine
amino acid transport and, 140, 151
covalent flavoproteins and, 23
plant genetic engineering and, 205-6
Lysosomes
glycogen storage diseases and, 85, 101

M

Macaques
obesity and, 350
short-chain fatty acids and, 220
Magnesium
aluminum and, 57
cystic fibrosis and, 124
Magnetic resonance imaging (MRI)
chemosensory losses and, 410
glycogen storage diseases and, 106
Maize
genetically engineered, 193, 199, 206
nitrogen fixation and, 321
Malabsorption
cystic fibrosis and, 113, 115-16, 117-18, 123
Malnutrition
cystic fibrosis and, 112, 114-15, 121, 124, 126, 129-31
oxygen and, 395-97
Malondialdehyde (MDA)
carotenoids and, 565-66, 571
Malonyl-ACC
genetically engineered tomatoes and, 198
Malpractice
nutrition, 1-15
Mammary gland
lactating
bovine somatotropin and, 443, 449-52
short-chain fatty acids and, 219
Manganese
aluminum and, 54
osteoporosis and, 289-90, 310
MAP kinase
bovine somatotropin and, 448
Marine oil
hypertension and, 247-48, 252-55
MARCKS protein
protein kinase C and, 545
MaxEPA
hypertension and, 245, 247, 253-54

MDCK cells
amino acid transport and, 153-54
MeAIB
amino acid transport and, 143, 145, 151
Meal planning
glycogen storage diseases and, 99-100
Meats
aluminum and, 44
blood pressure and, 253
cystic fibrosis and, 115
glycogen storage diseases and, 96, 98, 100, 102
Meconium ileus
cystic fibrosis and, 112, 118, 123, 127
Mediterranean countries
cystic fibrosis and, 113
MEL cells
tetrahydrobiopterin and, 266-68
Men
blood pressure and, 248-55
aluminum consumption and, 43
cystic fibrosis and, 112, 114-15, 131
obesity and, 340-45, 348, 350
osteoporosis and, 289-90, 299-301
PUFAs and, 248-55
Menaquinone
hip fracture and, 309
Menhaden oil
hypertension and, 246
Menopause
osteoporosis and, 290-91, 293, 295, 299-302, 307, 310
vitamin D and, 307
Menstrual cycle
PUFAs and, 252
Mercaptoethanol
covalent flavoproteins and, 23
Mercury
selenium complexed with, 67
Messenger RNA (mRNA)
apo B, 371
bovine somatotropin, 450
CF gene, 112
cGSH-Px, 73, 75-78
glucokinase, 471-72, 474-75, 481-82
6-hydroxy- apD ap-nicotine oxidase, 33
IGF-I, 448
LDL-R, 372-73
phaseolin gene, 205
selenoprotein, 69-78
System y$^+$ transporter, 140
type I iodothyronine 5'-deiodinase, 74
Metabolic zonation
amino acid transport and, 149
glucokinase and, 480-81
Metabolism
aluminum, 43-57
amino acid transport and, 149-52
bone, 291

bovine somatotropin, 443-45
calcium, 294, 302
chemolithotrophic, 326
cystic fibrosis and, 116, 119-22
eicosanoid, 69
glutamine, 146
glycogen storage diseases and, 86-88, 94-95, 105
obesity and, 344-46
riboflavin, 26
selenium, 66-67
short-chain fatty acids and, 221-23
Methacholine
chemosensory dysfunction and, 423
Methane (CH$_4$)
microbial fermentation and, 218
Methimazole
chemosensory dysfunction and, 412-13
Methionine
amino acid transport and, 156
plant genetic engineering and, 205
selenoproteins and, 66
Methotrexate
chemosensory dysfunction and, 411, 414
tetrahydrobiopterin and, 267
Methylcellulose
short-chain fatty acids and, 224
Methylene blue
indoleamine dioxygenase and, 272-73
Methylthiouracil
chemosensory dysfunction and, 412-13
Metronidazole
taste disorders and, 411
Mevalonate
short-chain fatty acids and, 226
Mevalonic acid
short-chain fatty acids and, 225
Mexico
legumes and, 320
Mg^{2+}
aluminum and, 54
pyruvate dehydrogenase and, 503-4, 506
MgATP
nitrogen fixation and, 323-24
pyruvate dehydrogenase and, 503
Mice
aluminum absorption and, 53
carotenoids and, 576, 578-81
gene inactivation and, 195
indoleamine dioxygenase and, 272
obesity and, 351
pyruvate dehydrogenase and, 506
short-chain fatty acids and, 220
somatotropin and, 451
tetrahydrobiopterin and, 266

Microbial fermentation
  fatty acids and, 218-19
Microprojectiles
  DNA-coated
    plant transformation and,
      194
Microsomes
  covalent flavoproteins and, 20
Middle East
  cystic fibrosis and, 113
Migraine
  smell disorders and, 416
Milk
  aluminum and, 44, 46
  bovine growth hormone and,
    210
  bovine somatotropin and, 439-
    41
  calcium and, 297
  cystic fibrosis and, 128
  developing countries and, 10
  dietary fiber and, 304
  fat
    bovine digestion and, 219-
      21
  glycogen storage diseases
    and, 99-100
  LDL-cholesterol levels and,
    368
  sphingomyelin and, 551
  vitamin D and, 307
Minerals
  deficiency of
    chemosensory dysfunction
      and, 414
Mitochondria
  covalent flavoproteins and, 20-
    21, 27
  lipids and, 542
  oxygen and, 390-92, 396-97
  pyruvate dehydrogenase and,
    500-1, 505-12
  succinate dehydrogenase and,
    18
Mitochondrial DNA (mtDNA)
  obesity and, 350
Moducal
  glycogen storage diseases
    and, 99
Molybdenum
  nitrogen fixation and, 322,
    324-25, 327
Molybdoferredoxin
  nitrogen fixation and, 322
Monellin
  plant genetic engineering and,
    204, 206
Monkeys
  cholesterol and, 361-62
  fumonisins and, 174
  LDL-cholesterol levels and,
    371
Monoamine oxidase
  covalent flavoproteins and, 20-
    21, 27, 29, 37
Monocytes
  neopterin and, 269
N^G-Monomethylarginine
  nitric oxide synthase and,
    279
Monosaccharides
  cystic fibrosis and, 126

Morphine
  smell disorders and, 413
Mucus
  cystic fibrosis and, 118
Multiple sclerosis
  chemosensory dysfunction
    and, 415-16
Multiprotein complexes
  amino acid transport and, 148
Multivitamins
  glycogen storage diseases
    and, 98
Municipal water supplies
  aluminum and, 45
Muscle
  aluminum and, 52
  amino acid transport and, 146
  bovine somatotropin and, 443
  calcium and, 296
  cystic fibrosis and, 123-24,
    126
  glycogen storage diseases
    and, 85, 101-6
Muscular dystrophy
  glycogen storage diseases
    and, 85
Mycotoxins
  foods and, 167-83
Myocardial infarction
  oxygen and, 396
Myoglobin
  glycogen storage diseases
    and, 85, 105
  oxygen and, 384, 389, 396
Myopathy
  glycogen storage diseases
    and, 85, 102-5
Myophosphorylase
  glycogen storage diseases
    and, 104-5

N

N3-histidyl residue
  mechanism for covalent
    flavinylation of, 24
Na$^+$
  amino acid tranport and, 138-
    41, 143, 145-51, 153-
    54, 156, 158
  short-chain fatty acids and,
    222, 229
NAD
  nitrogen fixation and, 331
  tetrahydrobiopterin and, 262
NADH
  glycogen storage diseases
    and, 89, 92
  pyruvate dehydrogenase and,
    498, 501, 503-5, 507
  tetrahydrobiopterin and, 263
NADHQ-reductase
  covalent flavoproteins and, 18
NADPH
  cytochrome P450s and, 394
  glycogen storage diseases
    and, 89
  indoleamine dioxygenase and,
    273
  nitric oxide synthase and, 274-
    76
  tetrahydrobiopterin and, 274

Napin storage protein promoter
  plant lipids and, 200
Nasal tissue
  odorant response of
    cytochrome P450s and, 394
Natural gas
  chemical fixation of N$_2$ and,
    318
Navy beans
  nitrogen fixation and, 320
Negative energy balance
  obesity and, 349-50
Neohesperidin dihydrochalcone
  taste disorders and, 417
Neomycin phosphotransferase
  plant genetic engineering and,
    193, 208
Neopterin
  cell-mediated immunity and,
    269-71
Nephrocalcin
  vitamin K and, 309
Netherlands
  aluminum and, 43
  osteoporosis and, 292
  PUFAs and, 253
Neural losses
  chemosensory dysfunction
    and, 408-9
Neurofibrillary tangles
  aluminum and, 53
Neurolathyrism
  legume seeds and, 320
Neurological disorders
  aluminum and, 57
Neurosteroids
  brain
    cytochrome P450s and, 394
Neurotransmitters
  Alzheimer's disease and, 422
  iron deficiency and, 522, 534-
    35
  tetrahydrobiopterin and, 263,
    279-80
Neutropenia
  glycogen storage diseases
    and, 85-86
NHANES II
  phosphate and, 305
Niacin
  chemosensory dysfunction
    and, 414-15
  covalent flavoproteins and, 18
  glycogen storage diseases
    and, 89-90
  taste disorders and, 414-15
Nicotine
  bacterial degradation of, 34
  covalent flavoproteins and, 21
Nicotinic acid
  pyruvate dehydrogenase and,
    509
Nifedipine
  chemosensory dysfunction
    and, 412-13
nif genes
  cotranscription and coregula-
    tion of, 327-28
  evolution of nitrogenase sys-
    tems and, 324-26
  genome rearrangements in nif
    regions, 328

linkage of known, 327
transcriptional control and, 330
NifNE protein
nitrogen fixation and, 324
Niridazole
taste disorders and, 411
Nitric oxide synthase
tetrahydrobiopterin and, 274-79
Nitrilase
plant genetic engineering and, 208
Nitrogen (N₂)
amino acid transport and, 145, 156
cystic fibrosis and, 126, 130
Nitrogen (N₂) fixation
biological fixation of, 318-19
agents, 319
agronomic applications, 319
dinotrogenase and dinotrogenase reductase, 322
energetics and electron transfer, 322-24
key intermediate in, 321-22
mechanism for, 321-24
nutrition and, 320-21
chemical fixation of, 318
control of nitrogenase, 328-29
nif-specific transcriptional control, 330
posttranslational control of nitrogenase, 330-32
transcriptional control by global regulators, 329-30
evolution of nitrogenase systems
adaptation of nitrogenase to different organisms and environments, 326-27
similarity of nitrogenases from diverse sources, 324-26
introduction to, 318
organization of genes encoding nitrogenase systems
cotranscription and coregulation of nif genes, 327-28
genome rearrangements in nif regions, 328
linkage of known nif genes, 327
Nitroglycerin patch
taste disorders and, 412
Nocturnal enteral supplements
cystic fibrosis and, 121, 130
glycogen storage diseases and, 95-98, 104
Nonesterified fatty acids (NEFAs)
bovine somatotropin and, 444, 449
Nonsteroidal anti-inflammatory agents (NSAIDs)
PUFAs and, 244
Norepinephrine
Alzheimer's disease and, 422

amino acid transport and, 147-48
borage oil and, 246
tetrahydrobiopterin and, 263
North America
calcium and, 298
vitamin D and, 307
Northern blot analysis
amino acid transport and, 140-41, 145
Northern Europe
cystic fibrosis and, 112-13
Norway
genetics of obesity and, 341-42
PUFAs and, 253
Nosebleeds
glycogen storage diseases and, 93
Novocain
taste disorders and, 411
NtrC protein
nitrogen fixation and, 329
ntr gene
nitrogen fixation and, 329
Nuclear magnetic resonance (NMR)
fumonisins and, 176
histidyl-flavins and, 26
Nutrient partitioning
obesity and, 346
Nutritional diseases
oxygen and, 395-98
Nutrition engineers
need for, 12-13
Nutrition malpractice
sliding toward, 1-15
Nuts
nitrogen fixation and, 321

O

Oat bran
short-chain fatty acids and, 219, 223, 229
Obesity
genetics of
contribution of single genes, 350-51
energy and nutrient intake, 343-44
excess body fat, 340-42
genetic-environment interaction, 348-50
human genetic research strategies, 338-40
introduction to, 337-38
major gene effects, 346-48
metabolic rate and energy expenditure, 344-46
negative energy balance, 349-50
nutrient partitioning, 346
overfeeding, 348-49
physical activity level, 345-46
regional fat distribution, 342-43
resting metabolic rate, 344-46
temporal trends, 348
thermic effect of food, 345

glycogen storage diseases and, 98
O-cycle
proton-motive, 392
Oil crops
plant lipids and, 199-200
Oleic acid
cystic fibrosis and, 124
protein kinase C and, 547, 550
tetrahydrobiopterin and, 262
Oleyl-ACP
plant lipids and, 200
Olfactory hallucination
classification of, 407
Olive oil
hypertension and, 246, 253
Oncogenes
short-chain fatty acids and, 229
Open reading frames (ORFs)
selenoprotein P and, 69, 72, 75
Oral bentiromide test
cystic fibrosis and, 126
Oranges
aluminum and, 44
Oregano
aluminum and, 44
Organelles
cystic fibrosis and, 113
Organic acids
aluminum and, 46, 51
nitrogen fixation and, 326
Ornithine decarboxylase
bovine somatotropin and, 448
sphingosine and, 551
Orotic acid
tetrahydrobiopterin and, 262
Osteocalcin
vitamin D and, 308
vitamin K and, 309
Osteodystrophy
aluminum and, 57
Osteoporosis
bone mass/density and, 290
calcium and, 290-302
in treatment of established osteoporosis, 303
risk of fracture and, 302-3
conservation of acquired bone mass and, 299-302
dietary fiber and, 303-5
frailty and injury, 288
genetically programmed bone mass and, 296-99
glycogen storage diseases and, 94
hip fracture and, 310-11
intrinsic bony strength and fragility, 289
nutrient-nutrient interactions and, 303-6
overview of, 287-89
phosphorus and, 305-6
postmenopause and, 300-2
premenopause and, 299-300
protein and, 306
senescence and, 301-2
sodium and, 306
trace minerals and, 310
vitamin D and, 306-8
vitamin K and, 308-9

Ovalbumin
    short-chain fatty acids and,
        221
Overfeeding
    obesity and, 348-49
Oxalic acid
    aluminum and, 51
Oxidative cleavage
    tetrahydrobiopterin and, 264
Oxidative phosphorylation
    glycogen storage diseases
        and, 93
    iron deficiency and, 522
Oxyfedrine
    taste disorders and, 412
Oxygen (O_2)
    carotenoids and, 565-66
    cystic fibrosis and, 119-20
    glycogen storage diseases
        and, 95, 105
    nitrogen fixation and, 321,
        326-27, 329-31
    nutritional diseases and
        malnutrition or limitation
            of oxygen supplied to
            tissues, 395-97
        overnutrition or oversupply
            of oxygen to cells,
            397-98
    nutritional requirements and
        balance of oxygen uptake
        delivery of oxygen, 389-90
        meeting demand for oxy-
            gen, 390-91
        oxygen as gaseous nutrient,
            387-89
    oxygen paradox and, 398
    oxygen-reacting enzymes and,
        391-92
        cytochrome oxidase, 392-93
        cytochrome P450s, 393-95
    sources of, 384-86
    tetrahydrobiopterin and, 263
    uniqueness of, 386-87, 399
Oxythiamin
    thiamin oxidase and, 30
Oyster shell calcium
    aluminum and, 46
Ozena
    smell disorders and, 416

P

Packaging
    aluminum and, 43, 45-46
PAH-stimulating protein
    tetrahydrobiopterin and, 263
Pain
    cystic fibrosis and, 118
Palmitoleic acid
    cystic fibrosis and, 124
Palm oil
    hypertension and, 254
Pancreas
    bovine somatotropin and,
        443
    cystic fibrosis and, 112-14,
        116-18, 123-26, 128
    glucokinase and, 472, 481-
        82, 486-90
    short-chain fatty acids and,
        221

Pancreatic ribonuclease
    selenite and, 66
Panhypopituitarism
    taste disorders and, 415
4-P-Pantetheine
    free and bound forms of, 18
Pantothenic acid
    covalent flavoproteins and, 18
pAO1 plasmid
    6-hydroxy-D-nicotine oxidase
        and, 21
Papillae
    taste and, 407, 417-18
Paracoccus denitrificans
    cytochrome oxidase and, 393
Parageusia
    classification of, 406
Paranasal sinus exenteration
    smell disorders and, 416
Parathyroid glands
    aluminum and, 48
Parathyroid hormone (PTH)
    extracellular fluid Ca^2 and,
        296
    osteoporosis and, 303
    phosphorus and, 305
    vitamin D and, 307-8
    vitamin K and, 309
Parenteral nutrition
    cystic fibrosis and, 129
Pargyline
    covalent flavoproteins and, 37
Parkinson's dementia
    aluminum and, 53, 57
    drugs for treatment of
        chemosensory dysfunction
        and, 412, 416
Patient education
    glycogen storage diseases
        and, 98-101
PC-GENE
    amino acid transport and,
        142, 148
PCO_2
    short-chain fatty acids and,
        222
Peaches
    aluminum and, 44
Peanut butter
    aluminum and, 44
Peanut oil
    hypertension and, 249
Peanuts
    nitrogen fixation and, 320
Pea plants
    nitrogen fixation and, 319
Peas
    aluminum and, 44
    dry
        nitrogen fixation and, 320-
            21
Pectin
    glycogen storage diseases
        and, 98
    short-chain fatty acids and,
        219, 223, 226, 228
Penformin
    taste disorders and, 412
Penicillamine
    taste disorders and, 409, 411
Penicillium cyaneofulvum
    covalent flavoproteins and, 20

apD ap-erythorbic acid
    and, 36
Penicillium cyclopium
    covalent flavoproteins and, 20
    cyclopiazonate oxidocyclase
        and, 30
Pepper
    black
        as aluminum source, 44
Perimenopause
    osteoporosis and, 293
Peripheral blood monocytes
    indoleamine dioxygenase and,
        272
Peru
    fumonisins and, 183
Pests
    genes for resistance to, 208-9
pH
    aluminum and, 48-51
    cystic fibrosis and, 117
    gastric lipase and, 221
    nitrogen fixation and, 320
    short-chain fatty acids and,
        222
Phaseolin gene
    plant genetic engineering and,
        205
Phenazine methosulfate
    nitrogen fixation and, 331
Phenindione
    taste disorders and, 411
Phenmetrazine theoclate
    with fenbutrazate hydrochlo-
        ride
        smell disorders and, 413
Phenylalanine
    amino acid transport and,
        143, 151
    bovine somatotropin and, 439
    cystic fibrosis and, 112
    tetrahydrobiopterin and, 262-
        64
Phenylalanine hydroxylase
    (PAH)
    nitric oxide synthase and, 276-
        77
    tetrahydrobiopterin and, 263-
        66
Phenylbutazone
    taste disorders and, 411
Phenylhydrazine
    covalent flavoproteins and,
        37
    tetrahydrobiopterin and, 266
Phenylketonuria (PKU)
    tetrahydrobiopterin and, 264-
        66
Phenytoin
    taste disorders and, 412
Phorbol esters
    amino acid transport and,
        139, 153-54
    protein kinase C and, 546-49,
        551
Phosphate
    aluminum and, 46, 50
    glycogen storage diseases
        and, 91-93
    nitrogen fixation and, 320
Phosphatidic acid phosphatase
    sphingolipids and, 180

Phosphatidylcholine
  bovine milk fat digestion and,
    220
Phosphoenolpyruvate
  covalent flavoproteins and, 22
Phospholipase C
  phosphatidylinositol-specific
    bovine somatotropin and,
    447
  pyruvate dehydrogenase
    and, 512
Phospholipid hydroperoxide glutathione peroxidase (phSH-
  Px)
  selenoproteins and, 68-69
Phospholipids
  cell function and, 540-50,
    552-53
5-Phosphoribosyl-1-amine
  glycogen storage diseases
    and, 90-92
Phosphoribosylpyrophosphate
  (PRPP)
  glycogen storage diseases
    and, 90-92
Phosphorus
  aluminum and, 51, 57
  bovine somatotropin and, 445
  osteoporosis and, 288, 290,
    305-6
Phosphorylase
  covalent flavoproteins and, 18
  glycogen storage diseases
    and, 103
Phosphorylase kinase
  glycogen storage diseases
    and, 103
Photosynthesis
  nitrogen fixation and, 319,
    326-27, 330-31
  oxygen and, 385-86
Phylloquinone
  covalent flavoproteins and, 18
Physical inactivity
  osteoporosis and, 288
Phytates
  calcium and, 304
Phytohemmaglutinin (PHA)
  neopterin and, 269
Pickles
  aluminum and, 44
Pigeon peas
  nitrogen fixation and, 320
Pigeons
  amino acid transport and, 145
Pigs
  fumonisins and, 172-73, 178-
    79, 182
  pyruvate dehydrogenase and,
    503
  short-chain fatty acids and,
    224-26
  somatotropin and, 445, 447
Pipecolic acid
  amino acid transport and, 151
Placenta
  amino acid transport and,
    146, 156-57
Plant genetic engineering
  enhanced quality and
    cold and freeze tolerance,
      198-99

plant lipids, 199-201
    proteins, 205-6
    starch, 201-5
    storage ability of the fresh
      market tomato, 196-98
    sugars, 201-5
  introduction to, 191-92
  prospectives for, 210
  safety and public acceptance
    of, 207-10
  technologies of
    gene expression, 194-95
    gene inactivation, 195-96
    plant transformation, 192-94
Plants
  nitrogen fixation and, 318-20,
    332
Plasma
  aluminum and, 50, 53-54
  cystic fibrosis and, 124
  eGSH-Px and, 70
  glutathione peroxidase and, 68
  LDL-cholesterol levels and,
    355-77
  selenoproteins and, 69-70
Plasmin
  bovine somatotropin and, 450
Platelet-activating factor (PAF)
  cell function and, 543
Platelet-derived growth factor
  (PDGF)
  amino acid transport and, 153
Platelets
  glycogen storage diseases
    and, 87, 93-94
Poliomyelitis
  oxygen and, 396
Polycose
  glycogen storage diseases
    and, 99
Polycythemia
  cystic fibrosis and, 124
Polygalacturonase
  plant genetic engineering and,
    196-98, 206, 208
Polymerase chain reaction (PCR)
  amino acid transport and, 147
Polymorphonuclear leucocytes
  glycogen storage diseases
    and, 85
Polyposis
  smell disorders and, 416
Polysaccharides
  cystic fibrosis and, 128
  glycogen storage diseases
    and, 99
  microbial fermentation and,
    218
  short-chain fatty acids and,
    224
Polyunsaturated fats (PUFAs)
  blood pressure and, 243-56
  cytochrome P450s and, 394
  LDL-cholesterol levels and,
    376
  oxygen and, 387
Ponies
  fumonisins and, 177-78
  short-chain fatty acids and,
    230
Porcine pulmonary edema syndrome

fumonisins and, 172-73, 182
Postmenopause
  osteoporosis and, 291, 293,
    295, 299-301, 303, 307,
    310
  vitamin D and, 307
Posttraumatic neuronal necrosis
  oxygen radicals and, 397
Potassium
  cystic fibrosis and, 130-31
  hypertension and, 244, 249
  nitrogen fixation and, 320
Potatoes
  aluminum and, 44
  plant genetic engineering and,
    203-4, 208
Poultry
  glycogen storage diseases
    and, 98
  toxicity
    fumonisins and, 173
PPi gene
  plant genetic engineering and,
    203
Prader-Willi syndrome
  genetics of obesity and, 351
Pre-albumin
  cystic fibrosis and, 127
Pregastric esterase
  short-chain fatty acids and,
    220
Pregestimil
  glycogen storage diseases
    and, 96
Premenopause
  osteoporosis and, 299-300
Primary biliary cirrhosis
  pyruvate dehydrogenase and,
    513
Primates
  cholesterol and, 360
  LDL-cholesterol levels and,
    368
  obesity and, 350
Procaine hydrochloride
  taste disorders and, 411
Prokaryotes
  covalent flavoproteins and, 27-
    28
  microbial fermentation and,
    218
  nitrogen fixation and, 318-19
  selenoprotein synthesis and,
    70, 72-73, 77
Prolactin
  bovine somatotropin and, 450
Proline
  amino acid transport and, 147-
    48, 151, 156
Promoterless reporter genes
  plant transformation and, 193
Propionate
  absorption and metabolism of,
    222-23
  cholesterol levels and, 223-27
  microbial fermentation and,
    218
  trophic effects of on colonic
    mucosa, 227
Propionyl-CoA
  short-chain fatty acids and,
    224

Propranolol
  pyruvate dehydrogenase and,
    512
Propylthiouracil
  chemosensory dysfunction
    and, 412-13
Prosobee
  glycogen storage diseases
    and, 96
Prostaglandins
  cytochrome P450s and, 394
  glycogen storage diseases
    and, 90
  hypertension and, 245-56
  oxygen and, 384
Prostanoids
  hypertension and, 245
Protein
  bovine somatotropin and,
    445, 451
  calcium and, 297
  chemosensory dysfunction
    and, 414
  cystic fibrosis and, 113, 118,
    121, 126, 128, 131
  glycogen storage diseases
    and, 94, 96, 98, 100,
    102-6
  lipids and, 542
  osteoporosis and, 290, 297,
    306
  plant genetic engineering and,
    205-6
Protein kinase C (PKC)
  amino acid transport and, 153-
    54
  bovine somatotropin and, 448
  lipids and, 540, 543-50
  sphingolipids and, 180
Proteoliposomes
  amino acid transport and, 144
Protoplasts
  plant transformation and, 193-
    94
Pseudohypoparathyroidism
  chemosensory dysfunction
    and, 415-16
Pseudomonas putida
  covalent flavoproteins and,
    20
  p-cresol and, 38
Pseudomonas spp.
  ACC deaminase and, 198, 206
  covalent flavoproteins and,
    20, 39
  cystic fibrosis and, 112
  flavocytochromes c and, 37
Psilocybin
  taste disorders and, 412
Psychiatric disorders
  chemosensory dysfunction
    and, 415-16
Puberty
  cystic fibrosis and, 128
  glycogen storage diseases
    and, 89-90
Pulmonary disease
  chronic
    oxygen and, 396
Purines
  glycogen storage diseases
    and, 87, 90-92, 94

Puromycin
  amino acid transport and, 144
Pyridoxal-P
  free and bound forms of, 18
Pyridoxine
  covalent flavoproteins and, 18
Pyridoxyl 5-phosphate
  selenoproteins and, 71
Pyrithiamin
  thiamin oxidase and, 30
Pyrophosphatase
  plant genetic engineering and,
    203, 206
Pyrophosphorylase
  plant genetic engineering and,
    202-3, 206
Pyruvate
  glycogen storage diseases
    and, 92
Pyruvate dehydrogenase
  background information on,
    497-98
  catalytic properties of, 498-
    501
  covalent flavoproteins and, 18
  deficiency states and, 512-13
  hormones and, 509, 511-12
  molecular properties of, 498-
    501
  regulation of pyruvate dehy-
    drogenase complex, 501-
    13
  subunit composition of, 499
6-Pyruvoyltetrahydropterin
  tetrahydrobiopterin and, 267,
    271, 274

R

RA264 cells
  tetrahydrobiopterin and, 278
Rabbits
  aluminum absorption and, 52,
    54
  amino acid transport and,
    143, 145
  cholesterol and, 360-61
  LDL-cholesterol levels and,
    371
  PUFAs and, 244
  short-chain fatty acids and,
    220, 222, 230
Radiation therapy
  chemosensory losses and, 408-
    9, 413, 415
Raeder's paratrigeminal syn-
    drome
  taste disorders and, 415
Rapeseed
  plant genetic engineering and,
    200, 205
Rats
  aluminum and, 47-49, 50-51,
    53-56
  amino acid transport and, 140-
    41, 144-46, 150, 155,
    157
  calcium and, 296
  carotenoids and, 565, 569-73,
    578-79, 581
  cholesterol and, 361-62
  diacylglycerol and, 551

fumonisins and, 172, 174,
    177, 179-80, 182
  glucokinase and, 472-73
  LDL-cholesterol levels and,
    365
  lipids and, 540
  obesity and, 350
  osteoporosis and, 296, 310
  oxygen and, 397-98
  PUFAs and, 244-48, 255
  pyruvate dehydrogenase and,
    505-9, 512
  selenoproteins and, 67-70, 74-
    76
  short-chain fatty acids and,
    220, 222-24, 226-28
  somatotropin and, 437, 445-
    46, 450-51
  tetrahydrobiopterin and, 269,
    279-80
rBAT sequence
  amino acid transport and, 142-
    43
Rebaudioside
  taste disorders and, 417
Recommended daily allowance
    (RDA)
  calcium, 297-98, 300
  cystic fibrosis and, 118
  glycogen storage diseases
    and, 95, 98
Red blood cells (RBCs)
  glycogen storage diseases
    and, 85
  selenoproteins and, 76-77
  tetrahydrobiopterin and, 266
Red clover
  nitrogen fixation and, 321
Regeneration
  amino acid transport and, 155
Regurgitation
  reflux
    cystic fibrosis and, 116,
    118, 125
Renin
  hypertension and, 254
Replicases
  viral
    plant genetic engineering
    and, 209
Reproductive tract
  cystic fibrosis and, 112
Respiratory function
  cystic fibrosis and, 118, 131-
    32
  glycogen storage diseases
    and, 101
Resting energy expenditure
    (RER)
  cystic fibrosis and, 119-23,
    127
Resting metabolic rate (RMR)
  obesity and, 344-45
Reticulocytes
  selenoproteins and, 77
  tetrahydrobiopterin and, 266
Retinoids
  cytochrome P450s and, 394
Retinol
  covalent flavoproteins and,
    18
  cystic fibrosis and, 127

Retinol-binding protein
cystic fibrosis and, 124, 127
Retrolental fibrodysplasia
oxygen and, 398
Retroviruses
amino acid transport and,
140
Rheumatoid arthritis
neopterin and, 269
Rheumatoid diseases
oxygen radicals and, 398
Rhizobia
nitrogen fixation and, 319,
324, 328, 332
Rhizobium trifolii
nitrogen fixation and, 321
Rhizobium   spp.
plant genetic engineering and,
209
Rhodopsin
covalent flavoproteins and, 18
Rhodosporillum rubrum
nitrogen fixation and, 330-31
Riboflavin
covalent flavoproteins and, 18
deficiency
covalent attachment and,
28-29
metabolism of, 26
Ribose-5-phosphate
glycogen storage diseases
and, 91-92
Ribosomes
selenoproteins and, 73
Ribulose
plant genetic engineering and,
202
Rice
aluminum and, 44
cereal
glycogen storage diseases
and, 97
nitrogen fixation and, 326
Rickets
type II
vitamin D-dependent, 308
RNA polymerase
nitrogen fixation and, 330
Root nodules
nitrogen fixation and, 319-20,
326, 332
RpoN sigma factor
nitrogen fixation and, 329-30
Ruthenium red
aluminum and, 51
pyruvate dehydrogenase and,
512

S

Saccharomyces cerevisiae
covalent flavoproteins and, 33
Saccharose
covalent flavoproteins and, 22
Safflower oil
cholesterol and, 367
hypertension and, 246-47,
249, 252, 254
Sahel region
malnutrition and, 6
Salbutamol
cystic fibrosis and, 122

Salivary glands
cystic fibrosis and, 112
Salmon
aluminum and, 51
Salmonella mutagenicity assay
fumonisins and, 174
Salmonella typhimurium
carotenoids and, 573
Salt
aluminum and, 44
fortification
iodine deficiency and, 2
Sarcoidosis
chemosensory dysfunction
and, 415-16
Sarcoplasmic reticumum
calcium and, 296
Sarcosine dehydrogenase
covalent flavoproteins and, 20-
21, 29, 36
Sarcosine oxidase
covalent flavoproteins and,
20
Saturated fatty acids (SFAs)
LDL-cholesterol levels and,
356, 359-60, 369-70, 373
Schizophyllum commune
cholesterol oxidase and, 31
covalent flavoproteins and20,
40
Scotland
calcium and, 296-97
SECIS motifs
selenoproteins and, 73-74
Second messengers
sphingolipids and, 180
Seeds
nitrogen fixation and, 320
SELB elongation factor
selenoproteins and, 71
SELD enzyme
selenoproteins and, 71-72
Selectable marker genes
plant genetic engineering and,
193, 207-8
Selenium
anticarcinogenic properties of,
67
carotenoids and, 571-73
cystic fibrosis and, 124
deficiency, 67
selenoprotein regulation
and, 69-70, 78
selenoprotein synthesis and,
74-75
triiodothyronine and, 69
Selenocysteine synthase
selenoproteins and, 71-73
Selenoprotein P (Se-P)
plasma, 69-70, 73-76
Selenoproteins
factors influencing levels of,
76-77
forms of selenium in protein,
67
selenium-heavy metal com-
plexes, 67
selenocysteine, 66, 70-73,
77
selenomethionine, 66
selenotrisulfides, 66
importance of

cellular glutathione peroxidase, 67- 68
extracellular glutathione peroxidase, 68
phospholipid hydroperoxide
glutathione peroxi-
dase, 68-69
selenoprotein P, 69
type I iodothyronine 5'-
deiodinase, 69
introduction to, 65-66
regulation of, 69-70
selenium deficiency and
mRNA levels, 75-78
posttranslational effects, 74-
75
supply of selenium, 76
synthesis mechanisms of, 70-
74
Semi-elemental diet
cystic fibrosis and, 130-31
Semiquinones
covalent flavoproteins and,
26, 30
Senescence
osteoporosis and, 301-2
Sensorineural losses
chemosensory dysfunction
and, 408
Sensory losses
chemosensory dysfunction
and, 408-9
Sepiapterin
tetrahydrobiopterin and, 267-
68, 271, 278
Serine
amino acid transport and,
145, 156
covalent flavoproteins and, 22
fumarate reductase and, 33
selenoproteins and, 71-74
Serotonin
Alzheimer's disease and, 422
amino acid transport and, 147-
48
iron deficiency and, 522
tetrahydrobiopterin and, 263,
280
Sheep
fumonisins and, 172
hypertension and, 248
osteoporosis and, 310
short-chain fatty acids and,
219-20
somatotropin and, 446-49
Shethna protein
nitrogen fixation and, 327
SH-group blockers
covalent flavoproteins and, 23
Shohl's solution
aluminum and, 50
Shwachman syndrome
cystic fibrosis and, 117
Sigma factor
nitrogen fixation and, 329-30
Signal transduction
lipids and, 540-43, 553
Silicon
aluminum and, 51
Simian virus 40 (SV40)
amino acid transport and,
154

Sinusitis
  smell disorders and, 416
Site-directed mutagenesis
  covalent flavoproteins and, 22-23
Sjögren's syndrome
  chemosensory dysfunction
    and, 415-16
Skeletal disorders
  aluminum and, 52, 57
  glycogen storage diseases
    and, 85, 101, 104-5
Skeletal program
  genetically small
    osteoporosis and, 288
Small intestine
  aluminum and, 49
  amino acid transport and, 150-51
  chemosensory dysfunction
    and, 414
  cholesterol and, 356, 361-62
  glycogen storage diseases
    and, 86, 98
  indoleamine dioxygenase and,
    272
  LDL-cholesterol levels and,
    363-64
  short-chain fatty acids and,
    230
Smell
  anatomy of, 408
  disorders
    aging and, 406, 415-20
    Alzheimer's disease and,
      408, 410, 421-22
    causes of perceptual losses
      and, 420
    classification of, 406-7
    clinical evaluation of, 409-10
    discrimination tasks includ-
      ing multidimensional
      scaling techniques,
      419-20
    disease-related dysfunctions
      and, 408, 414-16
    drug-related dysfunctions
      and, 408-15
    environmental pollution
      and, 408, 422-25
    identification tasks and, 419
    magnitude estimation and,
      418
    suprathreshold losses and,
      418-20
    threshold losses and, 418
    treatment or compensation
      for, 423, 425
  neural losses and, 408-9
  physiology of, 408
  sensorineural losses and, 408
  sensory losses and, 408-9
  transport losses and, 408
Smell agnosia
  classification of, 407
Smoking
  osteoporosis and, 290-91
Sodium
  aluminum and, 48
  hypertension and, 244-45,
    247, 249, 251, 255

osteoporosis and, 306
salts
  taste disorders and, 411,
    416-17
Sodium lauryl sulfate
  taste disorders and, 412
Soft tissues
  aluminum and, 52
Soil
  ACC deaminase and, 198
  aluminum and, 43, 45
Solar energy
  biological fixation of N_2 and,
    318
Somatostatin
  Alzheimer's disease and, 422
Somatotropin
  bovine, 437-54
South Africa
  fumonisins and, 173-74, 182
South America
  fumonisins and, 182
  legumes and, 320
Soybean oil
  bovine milk fat digestion and,
    220
  hypertension and, 246, 249
Soybeans
  aluminum and, 46
  calcium and, 304
  nitrogen fixation and, 320-21,
    324
  plant lipids and, 200
Sphingoid bases
  free
    fumonisins and, 177-79
Sphingolipids
  cell function and, 539-42,
    548-49, 551-53
  fumonisins and, 176-77, 179-80
Spices
  aluminum and, 44
Spinach
  aluminum and, 44
Spleen
  aluminum and, 52
  glycogen storage diseases
    and, 85, 104
  tetrahydrobiopterin and, 266
Squash
  plant lipids and, 201
Squirrel monkeys
  cholesterol and, 362
Staphylococcal protein A
  winter flounder antifreeze pro-
    tein and, 199
Starch
  glycogen storage diseases
    and, 95, 97-100, 104
  plant genetic engineering and,
    201-5
  short-chain fatty acids and,
    218
Starvation
  chemosensory dysfunction
    and, 414
Stearate
  plant lipids and, 200
Stearoyl-ACP desaturase
  plant genetic engineering and,
    206

Stearoyl-acyl carrier protein
  plant lipids and, 200
Steatorrhea
  cystic fibrosis and, 116-17
Steatosis
  hepatic
    glycogen storage diseases
      and, 89
Stem-loop structures
  selenoproteins and, 71-73, 75
Steroids
  oxygen and, 384
Steroid sulfatase deficiency
  smell disorders and, 416
Sterols
  short-chain fatty acids and,
    225
Stomach
  cancer
    high-fat diet and, 321
    indoleamine dioxygenase and,
      272
  short-chain fatty acids and,
    226
Storage ability
  genetically engineered toma-
    toes and, 196-98
Storage proteins
  plant genetic engineering and,
    205-6
Strawberries
  aluminum and, 44
  genetically engineered, 198
Streptomycin
  smell disorders and, 413
Stress
  chemosensory dysfunction
    and, 406
Stresskin
  glycogen storage diseases
    and, 102
Stroke
  oxygen and, 396
Strychnine
  smell disorders and, 413
Substance P
  chemosensory dysfunction
    and, 423
Succinate
  covalent flavoproteins and, 25
Succinate dehydrogenase
  aluminum and, 56
  covalent flavoproteins and,
    18, 20-21, 25, 27-29, 32-33, 35
Sucrose
  glycogen storage diseases
    and, 99-100
  plant genetic engineering and,
    202-3, 206
Sudden-death victims
  human
    short-chain fatty acids and,
      223
Sugars
  plant genetic engineering and,
    201-5
Suicide inhibitors
  covalent flavoproteins and, 37-38
Sulfasalazine
  taste disorders and, 411

Sulfonylureas
plant genetic engineering and,
208
Sulfur
nitrogen fixation and, 327
plant genetic engineering and,
205-6
selenium and, 67
Sunflowers
plant lipids and, 200
Sunflowerseed oil
hypertension and, 245, 247-49
Supercoiling
nitrogen fixation and, 330
Sweat glands
cystic fibrosis and, 112
Switzerland
calcium and, 298
Symphomimetic amines
cystic fibrosis and, 122
Synthases
plant genetic engineering and,
204, 206
System A
amino acid transport and, 143-
45, 151, 153-56
System ASC
amino acid transport and, 151-
56
System β
amino acid transport and, 151
System B
amino acid transport and, 151-
52
System b$^{o,+}$
amino acid transport and, 139-
40, 146-47, 151-52
System Gly
amino acid transport and, 145
Systemic lupus erythematosus
(SLE)
neopterin and, 269
System IMINO
amino acid transport and, 151
System L
amino acid transport and, 138-
39, 151-53, 156
System N
amino acid transport and, 145-
46, 155
System X$^-_{AG}$
amino acid transport and, 151-
52, 156
System y$^+$
amino acid transport and, 140-
41, 151-52

T

Table sugar
glycogen storage diseases
and, 98
Taiwan
nutrition programs and, 14
Tallow
cholesterol and, 224
Tamil Nadu
direct nutrition programs and,
2, 10, 14
Tanzania
direct nutrition programs and,
2, 10, 14

Tartaric acid
aluminum and, 51
Taste
anatomy of, 407
disorders
aging and, 406, 415-20
Alzheimer's disease and,
408, 410, 421-22
causes of perceptual losses
and, 417-18
classification of, 406
clinical evaluation of, 409-
10
disease-related dysfunctions
and, 408, 414-16
drug-related dysfunctions
and, 408-15
environmental pollution
and, 408, 422-25
magnitude estimation and,
417
suprathreshold losses and,
417
threshold losses and, 416-17
treatment or compensation
for, 423, 425
neural losses and, 408
physiology of, 407-8
sensorineural losses and, 408
sensory losses and, 408-9
transport losses and, 408
Taste agnosia
classification of, 406
Taurine
cystic fibrosis and, 118
Taurocholate
cystic fibrosis and, 117
T-cells
neopterin and, 269-70
Tea
aluminum and, 43-45
Tempeh
nitrogen fixation and, 320
Testis
phGSH-Px and, 69
Tetracaine hydrochloride
smell disorders and, 413
Tetracyclines
taste disorders and, 411
Tetrahydrobiopterin (BH$_4$)
aromatic amino acid
hydroxylases and, 262-
64
background information on,
261-62
cell proliferation and, 266-
69
cell-mediated immunity and,
269-72
indoleamine dioxygenase
and, 272-74
nitric oxide synthase and,
274-79
as neurotransmitter-releasing
factor, 279-80
phenylketonuria and, 264-66
structure of, 263
Tetranorprostanedioic acid
hypertension and, 252
Tetrodotoxin
tetrahydrobiopterin and,
280

Thailand
iron deficiency anemia and,
525-27, 531
nutrition programs and, 2, 14
Thaumatin
plant genetic engineering and,
204, 206
taste disorders and, 417
Thermal burn
taste disorders and, 415
Thermic effect of food
obesity and, 345
Thiamin
covalent flavoproteins and, 18
Thiamin dehydrogenase
covalent flavoproteins and, 20
Thiamin oxidase
covalent flavoproteins and, 29-
30
Thiazide diuretics
hip fracture and, 302
Thin-layer chromatography
(TLC)
fumonisins and, 181
Thioesterase
acyl carrier protein and, 201
5-Thiopyridoxine
taste disorders and, 411
Thiouracil
taste disorders and, 412
Third World
short-chain fatty acids and,
231
Threonine
amino acid transport and, 151
Thrombocytes
cystic fibrosis and, 124
glycogen storage diseases
and, 85
Thromboxane A$_2$ (TXA$_2$)
PUFAs and, 245
Thromboxane B$_2$ (TXB$_2$)
PUFAs and, 245, 252-54
Thyme
aluminum and, 44
Thyroid
function
deiodinase enzymes and, 69
Thyroidectomy
chemosensory dysfunction
and, 414
Thyroid hormone
glucokinase and, 484-85
glycogen storage diseases
and, 94
Thyroxine
selenoproteins and, 69
Tibia
aluminum and, 50, 53
Tight junctions
aluminum and, 48, 51
Tobacco
genetically engineered, 199,
201, 203, 205
Tobacco mosaic virus
plant genetic engineering and,
209
α-Tocopherol
carotenoids and, 565-68, 570-
73
cystic fibrosis and, 127
protein kinase C and, 549

Tofu
  nitrogen fixation and, 320
Tolerex
  glycogen storage diseases
    and, 96
Tomatine
  toxicity of, 208
Tomatoes
  aluminum and, 44
  fumonisins and, 170-71, 175
  genetically engineered, 196-
    99, 203-4, 208-9
Tomato juice
  taste disorders and, 417
Tongue
  taste and, 407
Total daily energy expenditure
  (TDEE)
  cystic fibrosis and, 122
Total parenteral nutrition
  phosphate and, 305
Trace metals
  cystic fibrosis and, 124
Trace minerals
  osteoporosis and, 310
Transaminases
  glycogen storage diseases
    and, 103-4
Transfer RNA (tRNA)
  selenoprotein, 67, 71-72, 76
Transferrin
  aluminum and, 54-55
  cystic fibrosis and, 127
Transformation
  amino acid transport and, 152-
    55
  plant
    genetic engineering and,
      192-94
Transforming growth factor β
  (TGFβ)
  amino acid transport and, 153
Transkei region
  fumonisins and, 173-74, 182
Transmembrane segment 2
  amino acid transport and,
    148
Transport losses
  chemosensory dysfunction
    and, 408
Trans-stimulation
  amino acid transport and,
    152
Transverse-Aid HBC
  glycogen storage diseases
    and, 102
Travesorb Hepatic
  glycogen storage diseases
    and, 102
Tremulousness
  cystic fibrosis and, 124
Triacylglycerols
  bovine milk fat digestion and,
    219-21
  bovine somatotropin and, 449
  glycogen storage diseases
    and, 90
  HMG-CoA reductase and, 224
  LDL-cholesterol levels and,
    356-58, 360-64, 366-76
  trophic effects of on colonic
    mucosa, 228

Tributyrin
  bovine milk fat digestion and,
    220-21
Trifluoperazine
  taste disorders and, 412
Triglycerides
  cystic fibrosis and, 115, 128
  glycogen storage diseases
    and, 87, 89-90, 97-98
  plant lipids and, 199-201
6-Trihydroxypropylpterin
  Crithidia fasiculata and, 262
Triiodothyronine (T3)
  selenoproteins and, 69
Trimethylamine dehydrogenase
  covalent flavoproteins and,
    18, 20, 37-38
Trimethylaminuria
  smell disorders and, 416
Triose
  plant genetic engineering and,
    202
Trisulfides
  selenoproteins and, 66
Trousseau sign
  cystic fibrosis and, 124
Trypsin
  cystic fibrosis and, 126
Trypsinogen
  cystic fibrosis and, 126
Tryptophan
  indoleamine dioxygenase and,
    272
  tetrahydrobiopterin and, 263
Tryptophan hydroxylase
  tetrahydrobiopterin and, 265-
    66
Tumor DNA (T-DNA)
  plant transformation and, 192-
    94
Tumor necrosis factor α (TNFα)
  amino acid transport and, 153
  biopterin and, 271
  nitric oxide synthase and, 278-
    79
Tuna oil
  hypertension and, 248
Tunicamycin
  amino acid transport and, 144
Turkey
  legumes and, 320
Turner's syndrome
  chemosensory dysfunction
    and, 415-16
Twin studies
  calcium and, 297
  obesity and, 338, 340-45,
    348-49
Tyrosine
  covalent flavoproteins and,
    22
  fumarate reductase and, 33
  tetrahydrobiopterin and, 262-
    64, 266, 279
Tyrosine hydroxylase
  tetrahydrobiopterin and, 265-
    66, 279
Tyrosine kinase
  bovine somatotropin and,
    447
Tyrothricin
  smell disorders and, 413

U

UDPG-glucose
  plant genetic engineering and,
    202-3
uidA gene
  plant transformation and, 194
Ulcerative colitis
  protein kinase C and, 550
  short-chain fatty acids and,
    227
Umami
  taste sensations and, 408
United States
  aflatoxin B1 and, 168
  cystic fibrosis and, 115
  fumonisins and, 168, 182-83
  hypertension and, 250-51
  iron deficiency anemia and,
    525
  legumes and, 320-21
  mycotoxins and, 168-69
  nutrition problems in develop-
    ing countries and, 2
  phosphorus and, 305
Universities
  nutrition research and, 4, 6-14
Unsaturated fatty acids (UFAs)
  cell function and, 546-48,
    551-52
  LDL-cholesterol levels and,
    356, 359-60, 369-71, 376
  tetrahydrobiopterin and, 262
Uracil
  tetrahydrobiopterin and, 262
Urea cycle
  arginine and, 140
Uremia
  chemosensory dysfunction
    and, 414
Uric acid
  glycogen storage diseases
    and, 87, 90-93, 95, 97,
    103, 105
USSR
  former
    legumes and, 320
Utensils
  aluminum and, 43, 45-46

V

Valerate
  microbial fermentation and,
    218
Valine
  bovine somatotropin and, 438-
    39
  covalent flavoproteins and, 27
Vanadate
  aluminum and, 48
Vanadium
  nitrogen fixation and, 325
Vasorelaxation
  short-chain fatty acids and,
    228
Vegetable oil
  hypertension and, 253
Vegetables
  aluminum and, 43-44
  glycogen storage diseases
    and, 97, 100, 102

Venezuela
food and nutrition programs
in, 3
Verapamil
aluminum and, 48
pyruvate dehydrogenase and,
512
Vervet monkeys
fumonisins and, 174
Very-low-density lipoproteins
(VLDLs)
cholesterol and, 357-58, 362
Vetch
nitrogen fixation and, 320
Vincristine sulfate
taste disorders and, 411
Viral coat protein genes
plant genetic engineering and,
209
Viral infections
chemosensory dysfunction
and, 408, 414-15
neopterin and, 269
Vital HN
glycogen storage diseases
and, 96
Vitamin A
childhood mortality reduction
and, 2
cystic fibrosis and, 123-24,
126-27
deficiency
nutrition malpractice and, 5
osteoporosis and, 310
Vitamin B₂
see Riboflavin
Vitamin B₃
see Niacin
Vitamin B₁₂
covalent flavoproteins and, 18
cystic fibrosis and, 123
iron deficiency and, 522
smell disorders and, 416
Vitamin C
glycogen storage diseases
and, 98
indoleamine dioxygenase and,
272
osteoporosis and, 288, 290
taste disorders and, 412
Vitamin D
aluminum aborption and, 48,
57
cystic fibrosis and, 123
cytochrome P450s and, 394
osteoporosis and, 288-89, 302-
3, 306-8
protein kinase C and, 548, 553
Vitamin E
carotenoids and, 573
cystic fibrosis and, 123, 126-
27
protein kinase C and, 549
Vitamin K

cystic fibrosis and, 123
osteoporosis and, 288-90, 308-
9
Vitamins
bovine somatotropin and, 440
chemosensory dysfunction
and, 414
covalent flavoproteins and, 18
fat-soluble
cystic fibrosis and, 123-24,
126-27
glycogen storage diseases
and, 98
water-soluble
cystic fibrosis and, 123
Vivonex TEN
glycogen storage diseases
and, 96, 102
Volatile fatty acids (VFAs)
nonruminant mammals and,
217-31
Vomiting
cystic fibrosis and, 118, 123
von Gierke's disease
glucose-6-phosphatase and, 84

W

W1282X mutation
cystic fibrosis and, 113
Wasting
cystic fibrosis and, 123
glycogen storage diseases
and, 106
Water
aluminum and, 43-46, 49-50
Weakness
cystic fibrosis and, 105-6, 124
glycogen storage diseases
and, 85, 101-4
Weight
cystic fibrosis and, 114, 118-
19, 123, 125-26, 129-31
glycogen storage diseases
and, 95-96
Western diet
calcium and, 299
lipids and, 358-60
Wheat
aluminum and, 44
bran
calcium and, 304-5
short-chain fatty acids and,
219, 223, 228-29
glycogen storage diseases
and, 99
plant transformation and, 193
Winter flounder antifreeze protein
plant genetic engineering and,
199, 206
Wollinella succinogenes
covalent flavoproteins and,
33, 40

Women
blood pressure and, 248-55
calcium and, 297, 298
copper and, 310
cystic fibrosis and, 114-15,
128, 131
obesity and, 340-45, 350
osteoporosis and, 289-90,
293, 295, 297-303, 305-
7, 310
phosphate and, 305
protein and, 306
PUFAs and, 248-55
sodium and, 306
vitamin D and, 307
Worm loads
debilitating levels of
children and, 10
Wound healing
cystic fibrosis and, 124

X

Xanthine
glycogen storage diseases
and, 91-92
Xanthine oxidase
purine catabolism and, 397
Xanthomas
glycogen storage diseases
and, 89
Xenopus laevis
amino acid transport and, 143-
44, 146
Xerostomia
transport losses and, 408
X-linked ichthyosis
due to steroid sulfatase deficiency
smell disorders and, 416
Xylanases
short-chain fatty acids and,
230

Y

Yeast
covalent flavoproteins and, 20
plant genetic engineering and,
206

Z

Zinc
aluminum and, 51
chemosensory dysfunction
and, 414-15, 423
cystic fibrosis and, 124
osteoporosis and, 289-90, 310

CUMULATIVE INDEXES

CONTRIBUTING AUTHORS, VOLUMES 9–13

A

Ailhaud, G., 12:207–33
Anderson, K. E., 11:141–67
Argov, Z., 11:449–64
Arnaud, C. D., 10:397–414
Aw, T. Y., 9:229–51
Axley, M. J., 9:127–37

B

Bacon, C. W., 13:167–89
Baker, D. H., 11:239–63
Balena, R., 11:309–24
Ballew, M., 13:83–109
Bauman, D. E., 13:437–61
Baynes, R. D., 10:133–48
Beattie, J. H., 10:63–83
Behal, R. H., 13:497–520
Belongia, E. A., 12:235–56
Bensadoun, A., 11:217–37
Bentéjac, M., 13:217–41
Berg, A., 13:1–15
Berg, R. A., 12:369–90
Berk, P. D., 9:253–70
Beutler, E., 9:287–302
Blomhoff, R., 12:37–57
Bothwell, T. H., 10:133–48
Bouchard, C., 13:337–54
Bowman, B. B., 9:187–99
Brannon, P. M., 10:85–105
Bremner, I., 10:63–83
Brennan, M. F., 10:107–32
Broquist, H. P., 11:435–48
Bugaut, M., 13:217–41
Bunce, G. E., 10:233–54
Burger, A. G., 9:201–27
Burk, R. F., 13:65–81
Burris, R. H., 13:317–35
Burton, G. W., 10:357–82
Buxton, D. B., 13:497–520
Byers, T., 12:139–59

C

Chance, B., 11:449–64
Claus, T. H., 11:465–515
Clemmons, D. R., 11:393–412
Coates, P. M., 9:139–60
Coburn, J. W., 11:93–119
Comai, L., 13:191–215
Cortner, J. A., 9:139–60

Crapo, P. A., 11:21–39
Czarnecki-Maulden, G. L., 11:239–63

D

Danforth, E., 9:201–27
Decker, K. F., 13:17–41
Dietschy, J. M., 13:355–81
Dills, W. L., 9:161–86
DiPalma, J. R., 11:169–87
Dougherty, R. M., 13:243–60
Duine, J. A., 10:297–318
Dunn, J. T., 9:21–38
Durie, P. R., 13:111–36
Dwyer, J. T., 11:61–91

E

Eastwood, M. A., 12:19–35
Edens, N. K., 9:417–43
Elwyn, D. H., 9:445–73
Estabrook, R. W., 13:383–403

F

Farthing, M. J. G., 10:475–501
Ferris, A. M., 12:417–41
Fisher, E. A., 9:139–60
Fjeld, C. R., 11:355–73
Forster, R. E., 13:383–403
Fried, S. K., 9:417–43
Friedman, M., 12:119–37

G

Gahl, W. A., 9:39–61
Gaitan, E., 10:21–39
Ganapathy, V., 12:183–206
Gatlin, C. A., 13:405–36
Gershwin, M. E., 10:415–31
Glinsmann, W. H., 12:473–87
Goldstein, S. A., 9:445–73
Gopalan, C., 12:1–17
Granner, D. K., 13:463–96
Green, J. B., 10:41–61
Green, M. H., 10:41–61; 12:37–57
Greene, H. L., 13:83–109
Greenwood, M. R. C., 11:325–53
Greger, J. L., 13:43–63

Grimaldi, P., 12:207–33
Groen, B. W., 10:297–318
Grubbs, C. J., 12:161–81
Guo, B., 12:345–68

H

Hayes, K. C., 12:299–326
Heaney, R. P., 13:287–316
Henderson, G. B., 10:319–35
Henry, R. R., 11:21–39
Hetzel, B. S., 9:21–38
Hill, D. L., 12:161–81
Hill, K. E., 13:65–81
Hopkins, P. N., 9:303–45
Horton, E. S., 10:255–75
Horwitz, B. A., 11:325–53
Horwitz, J., 10:233–54
Howard, G. R., 9:63–86

I

Iacono, J. M., 13:243–60

J

Jensen, R. G., 12:417–41
Johnson, P. R., 11:325–53
Jones, D. P., 9:229–51; 12:327–43
Jukes, T. H., 10:1–20

K

Kang, S.-S., 12:279–98
Kappas, A., 11:141–67
Kassarjian, Z., 9:271–85
Kaufman, S., 13:261–86
Keen, C. L., 10:415–31
Kerr, J. S., 12:369–90
Keusch, G. T., 10:475–501
Kilberg, M. S., 13:137–65
Kinoshita, J., 10:233–54
Kirke, P. N., 10:277–95
Klahr, S., 9:87–108
Kleerekoper, M., 11:309–24
Klein, G. L., 11:93–119
Krinsky, N. I., 13:561–87
Kritchevsky, D., 12:391–416
Kritchevsky, S. B., 12:391–416

615

L

Lammi-Keefe, C. J., 12:417–41
Lands, W. E. M., 11:41–60
Lane, H. W., 12:257–78
Lei, K. Y., 11:265–83
Leibel, R. L., 9:417–43
Leibold, E. A., 12:345–68
Livingston, A., 12:299–326
Lonnerdal, B., 9:109–25

M

Magnuson, M. A., 13:463–96
Malinow, M. R., 12:279–98
Mauer, A. M., 11:375–91
Mayeno, A. N., 12:235–56
McCormick, D. B., 9:187–99
Merrill, A. H., 13:539–59
Metz, J., 12:59–79
Miller, C. C., 10:433–50
Moe, A. J., 12:183–206
Morley, J. E., 10:383–95
Morris, S. M., 12:81–101

N

Négrel, R., 12:207–33
Nestel, P. J., 10:149–67
Norred, W. P., 13:167–89
Norum, K. R., 12:37–57
Novak, D. A., 13:137–65

O

Olson, M. S., 13:497–520
Osterholm, M. T., 12:235–56

P

Palfrey, H. C., 9:347–76
Park, Y., 12:327–43
Parker, P. H., 13:83–109
Patel, S. C., 9:395–416
Pencharz, P. B., 13:111–36
Pentchev, P. G., 9:395–416

Perman, J. A., 9:475–502
Perry, G., 12:139–59
Pérusse, L., 13:337–54
Petkovich, M., 12:443–71
Pike, J. W., 11:189–216
Pilkis, S. J., 11:465–515
Pisters, P. W. T., 10:107–32
Poehlman, E. T., 10:255–75
Pollitt, E., 13:521–37
Potter, B. J., 9:253–70
Printz, R. L., 13:463–96
Pursel, V. G., 10:213–32

Q

Quig, D. W., 10:169–93

R

Rasmussen, K. M., 12:103–17
Riley, R. T., 13:167–89
Roberts, G. P., 13:317–35
Robertson, J. G., 13:497–520
Rosenberg, I. H., 9:187–99
Russell, R. M., 9:271–85

S

Saavedra, J. M., 9:475–502
Sanchez, S. D., 10:397–414
Schiffman, S. S., 13:405–36
Schoeller, D. A., 11:355–73
Schroeder, J. J., 13:539–59
Schulz, L. O., 12:257–78
Scott, J. M., 10:277–95
Shan, X., 12:327–43
Shinki, T., 10:195–211
Small, D. M., 11:413–34
Smith, C. H., 12:183–206
Snell, E. E., 9:1–19
Sommer, A., 9:63–86
Sorrentino, D., 9:253–70
Souba, W. W., 11:285–308
Spady, D. K., 13:355–81
Stadtman, T. C., 9:127–37
Stare, F. J., 11:1–20

Steele, N. C., 10:213–32
Stern, J. S., 11:325–53
Stevens, B. R., 13:137–65
Suda, T., 10:195–211
Sunde, R. A., 10:451–74
Suttle, N. F., 11:121–40

T

Takahashi, N., 10:195–211
Thayer, W. S., 11:169–87
Thorburn, A. W., 11:21–39
Traber, M. G., 10:357–82
Trautwein, E. A., 12:299–326

U

Underwood, L. E., 11:393–412

V

van der Meer, R. A., 10:297–318
Vance, D. E., 10:337–56
Vance, J. E., 10:337–56
Vanderveen, J. E., 12:473–87
Vernon, R. G., 13:437–61
Villereal, M. L., 9:347–76

W

Weir, D. G., 10:277–95
West, K. P., 9:63–86
Wharton, B. A., 9:377–94
Williams, R. R., 9:303–45
Wong, P. W. K., 12:279–98
Woollett, L. A., 13:355–81

Z

Ziboh, V. A., 10:433–50
Zilversmit, D. B., 10:169–93

CHAPTER TITLES, VOLUMES 9-13

PREFATORY ESSAYS

Nutrition Research with Lactic Acid Bacteria:
A Retrospective View   E. E. Snell   9:1-19

Nutrition Science from Vitamins to Molecular
Biology   T. H. Jukes   10:1-20

Nutrition Research from Respiration and
Vitamins to Cholesterol and Atherosclerosis   F. J. Stare   11:1-20

The Contribution of Nutrition Research to the
Control of Undernutrition: The Indian
Experience   C. Gopalan   12:1-17

Sliding Toward Nutrition Malpractice: Time to
Reconsider and Redeploy   A. Berg   13:1-15

ENERGY METABOLISM

Nutrient Supply and Mitochondrial Function   T. Y. Aw, D. P. Jones   9:229-51

The Effects of Injury and Sepsis on Fuel
Utilization   S. A. Goldstein, D. H. Elwyn   9:445-73

Regulation of Energy Expenditure in Aging
Humans   E. T. Poehlman, E. S. Horton   10:255-75

Human Energy Metabolism: What Have We
Learned from the Doubly Labeled Water
Method?   D. A. Schoeller, C. R. Fjeld   11:355-73

Phosphorus Magnetic Resonance Spectroscopy
in Nutritional Research   Z. Argov, B. Chance   11:449-64

Hepatic Gluconeogenesis/Glycolysis:
Regulation and Structure/ Function
Relationships of Substrate Cycle Enzymes   S. J. Pilkis, T. H. Claus   11:465-515

Coordinated Multisite Regulation of Cellular
Energy Metabolism   D. P. Jones, X. Shan, Y. Park   12:327-43

Genetics of Obesity   C. Bouchard, L. Pérusse   13:337-54

Is Oxygen an Essential Nutrient?   R. E. Forster, R. W. Estabrook   13:383-403

CARBOHYDRATES

Sugar Alcohols as Bulk Sweeteners   W. L. Dills, Jr.   9:161-86

Current Concepts in Lactose Malabsorption
and Intolerance   J. M. Saavedra, J. A. Perman   9:475-502

Current Issues in Fructose Metabolism   R. R. Henry, P. A. Crapo, A. W. Thorburn   11:21-39

Hepatic Gluconeogenesis/Glycolysis:
Regulation and Structure/ Function
Relationships of Substrate Cycle Enzymes   S. J. Pilkis, T. H. Claus   11:465-515

The Physiological Effect of Dietary Fiber: An
Update   M. A. Eastwood   12:19-35

Nutritional Management of Glycogen Storage
Disease   P. H. Parker, M. Ballew, H. L. Greene   13:83-109

LIPIDS

Mechanisms of Cellular Uptake of Free Fatty
Acids   B. J. Potter, D. Sorrentino, P. D. Berk   9:253-70

Genetic Defects of Lysosomal Function in
Animals   S. C. Patel, P. G. Pentchev   9:395-416

617

Effects of N-3 Fatty Acids on Lipid
  Metabolism   P. J. Nestel   10:149–67
Plasma Lipid Transfer Activities   D. W. Quig, D. B. Zilversmit   10:169–93
Lipoprotein Assembly and Secretion by
  Hepatocytes   J. E. Vance, D. E. Vance   10:337–56
Essential Fatty Acids and Polyunsaturated
  Fatty Acids: Significance in Cutaneous
  Biology   V. A. Ziboh, C. C. Miller   10:433–50
Biosynthesis of Prostaglandins   W. E. M. Lands   11:41–60
Lipoprotein Lipase   A. Bensadoun   11:217–37
Should There Be Intervention to Alter Serum
  Lipids in Children?   A. M. Mauer   11:375–91
The Effects of Glyceride Structure on
  Absorption and Metabolism   D. M. Small   11:413–34
Cellular and Molecular Aspects of Adipose
  Tissue Development   G. Ailhaud, P. Grimaldi, R. Negrél   12:207–33
Dietary Impact on Biliary Lipids and
  Gallstones   K. C. Hayes, A. Livingston, E. A.   12:299–326
                                              Trautwein
Serum Cholesterol and Cancer Risk: An
  Epidemiologic Perspective   S. B. Kritchevsky, D. Kritchevsky   12:391–416
Lipids in Human Milk and Infant Formulas   R. G. Jensen, A. M. Ferris, C. J.   12:417–41
                                              Lammi-Keefe
Biological Effects of Short-Chain Fatty Acids
  in Nonruminant Mammals   M. Bugaut, M. Bentéjac   13:217–41
Regulation of Plasma LDL-Cholesterol Levels
  by Dietary Cholesterol and Fatty Acids   D. K. Spady, L. A. Woollett, J. M.   13:355–81
                                              Dietschy
Lipid Modulation of Cell Function   A. H. Merrill, Jr., J. J. Schroeder   13:539–59

PROTEINS, PEPTIDES, AND AMINO ACIDS
Effects of Protein Intake on the Progression of
  Renal Disease   S. Klahr   9:87–108
Gene Polymorphisms and Variability of
  Human Apolipoproteins   E. A. Fisher, P. M. Coates, J. A.   9:139–60
                                              Cortner
Nutritional and Metabolic Aspects of
  Glutathione   E. Beutler   9:287–302
Adaptation of the Exocrine Pancreas to Diet P. M. Brannon   10:85–105
Amino Acid Metabolism in Human Cancer
  Cachexia   P. W. T. Pisters, M. F. Brennan   10:107–32
Molecular Biology of Selenoproteins   R. A. Sunde   10:451–74
Glutamine: A Key Substrate for the
  Splanchnic Bed   W. W. Souba   11:285–308
Lysine-Pipecolic Acid Metabolic Relationships
  in Microbes and Mammals   H. P. Broquist   11:435–48
Regulation of Enzymes of Urea and Arginine
  Synthesis   S. M. Morris, Jr.   12:81–101
The Eosinophilia-Myalgia Syndrome and
  Tryptophan   E. A. Belongia, A. N. Mayeno, M.   12:235–56
                                              T. Osterholm
Hyperhomocyst(e)inemia as a Risk Factor for
  Occlusive Vascular Disease   S.-S. Kang, P. W. K. Wong, M. R.   12:279–98
                                              Malinow
Nutritional Aspects of Collagen Metabolism   R. A. Berg, J. S. Kerr   12:369–90
Recent Advances in Mammalian Amino Acid
  Transport   M. S. Kilberg, B. R. Stevens, D.   13:137–65
                                              A. Novak

VITAMINS
Vitamin A and Infection: Public Health
  Implications   K. P. West, Jr., G. R. Howard, A.   9:63–86
                                              Sommer

Epithelial Transport of Water-Soluble Vitamins   B. B. Bowman, D. B. McCormick,   9:187–99
                                                  I. H. Rosenberg
The Role of Vitamin D in Bone and Intestinal
  Cell Differentiation   T. Suda, T. Shinki, N. Takahashi   10:195–211
The Cofactor Pyrroloquinoline Quinone   J. A. Duine, R. A. van der Meer,   10:297–318
                                                  B. W. Groen
Folate-Binding Proteins   G. B. Henderson   10:319–35
Vitamin E: Antioxidant Activity, Biokinetics,
  and Bioavailability   G. W. Burton, M. G. Traber   10:357–82
Use of Niacin as a Drug   J. R. DiPalma, W. S. Thayer   11:169–87
Vitamin D3 Receptors: Structure and Function
  in Transcription   J. W. Pike   11:189–216
Vitamin A: Physiological and Biochemical
  Processing   R. Blomhoff, K. R. Norum, M. H.   12:37–57
                                                  Green
Cobalamin Deficiency and the Pathogenesis of
  Nervous System Disease   J. Metz   12:59–79
Dietary Carotenes, Vitamin C, and Vitamin E
  as Protective Antioxidants in Human
  Cancers   T. Byers, G. Perry   12:139–59
Retinoids and Cancer Prevention   D. L. Hill, C. J. Grubbs   12:161–81
Regulation of Gene Expression by Vitamin A:
  The Role of Nuclear Retinoic Acid
  Receptors   M. Petkovich   12:443–71
Biosynthesis and Function of Enzymes With
  Covalently Bound Flavin   K. F. Decker   13:17–41
New Tetrahydrobiopterin-Dependent Systems   S. Kaufman   13:261–86
Actions of Carotenoids in Biological Systems   N. I. Krinsky   13:561–87

INORGANIC NUTRIENTS
The Iodine Deficiency Disorders: Their Nature
  and Prevention   B. S. Hetzel, J. T. Dunn   9:21–38
Trace Element Nutrition in Infants   B. Lonnerdal   9:109–25
Intracellular Calcium and Cell Function   M. L. Villereal, H. C. Palfrey   9:347–76
Goitrogens in Food and Water   E. Gaitan   10:21–39
Metallothionein and the Trace Minerals   I. Bremner, J. H. Beattie   10:63–83
Iron Deficiency   R. D. Baynes, T. H. Bothwell   10:133–48
The Role of Calcium in Osteoporosis   C. D. Arnaud, S. D. Sanchez   10:397–414
Zinc Deficiency and Immune Function   C. L. Keen, M. E. Gershwin   10:415–31
The Interactions Between Copper,
  Molybdenum, and Sulphur in Ruminant
  Nutrition   N. F. Suttle   11:121–40
Dietary Copper: Cholesterol and Lipoprotein
  Metabolism   K. Y. Lei   11:265–83
Fluorides and Osteoporosis   M. Kleerekoper, R. Balena   11:309–24
Iron-Dependent Regulation of Ferritin and
  Transferrin Receptor Expression by the
  Iron-Responsive Element Binding Protein   E. A. Leibold, B. Guo   12:345–68
Aluminum Metabolism   J. L. Greger   13:43–63
Regulation of Selenoproteins   R. F. Burk, K. E. Hill   13:65–81
Is Oxygen an Essential Nutrient?   R. E. Forster, R. W. Estabrook   13:383–403
Iron Deficiency and Cognitive Function   E. Pollitt   13:521–37

OTHER FOOD COMPONENTS
Fat Substitutes: A Regulatory Perspective   J. E. Vanderveen, W. H. Glinsmann   12:473–87
Impact of Plant Genetic Engineering on Foods
  and Nutrition   L. Comai   13:191–215
Biological Nitrogen Fixation   R. H. Burris, G. P. Roberts   13:317–35
Regulation of the Pyruvate Dehydrogenase
  Multienzyme Complex   R. H. Behal, D. B. Buxton, J. G.   13:497–520
                                                  Robertson, M. S. Olson
Actions of Carotenoids in Biological Systems   N. I. Krinsky   13:561–87

NUTRITION AND METABOLIC REGULATION
The Application of Compartmental Analysis to
  Research in Nutrition   M. H. Green, J. B. Green   10:41–61
Dietary Regulation of Cytochrome P450   K. E. Anderson, A. Kappas   11:141–67
Dietary Copper: Cholesterol and Lipoprotein
  Metabolism   K. Y. Lei   11:265–83
Animal Models of Obesity: Genetic Aspects   P. R. Johnson, M. R. C.   11:325–53
                                                 Greenwood, B. A. Horwitz, J. S.
                                                 Stern

Nutritional Regulation of IGF-I and IGF
  Binding Proteins   D. R. Clemmons, L. E. Underwood   11:393–412
Phosphorus Magnetic Resonance Spectroscopy
  in Nutritional Research   Z. Argov, B. Chance   11:449–64
Cellular and Molecular Aspects of Adipose
  Tissue Development   G. Ailhaud, P. Grimaldi, R. Negrél 12:207–33
New Tetrahydrobiopterin-Dependent Systems   S. Kaufman   13:261–86
Regulation of Plasma LDL-Cholesterol Levels
  by Dietary Cholesterol and Fatty Acids   D. K. Spady, L. A. Woollett, J. M. 13:355–81
                                                 Dietschy
Effects of Exogenous Bovine Somatotropin on
  Lactation   D. E. Bauman, R. G. Vernon   13:437–61
Regulation of the Pyruvate Dehydrogenase
  Multienzyme Complex   R. H. Behal, D. B. Buxton, J. G. 13:497–520
                                                 Robertson, M. S. Olson
Lipid Modulation of Cell Function   A. H. Merrill, Jr., J. J. Schroeder 13:539–59

GENETICS AND MOLECULAR BIOLOGY
Human Genetics and Coronary Heart Disease:
  A Public Health Perspective   P. N. Hopkins, R. R. Williams   9:303–45
Genetic Defects of Lysosomal Function in
  Animals   S. C. Patel, P. G. Pentchev   9:395–416
The Role of Vitamin D in Bone and Intestinal
  Cell Differentiation   T. Suda, T. Shinki, N. Takahashi 10:195–211
Nutrient Partitioning by Transgenic Animals   N. C. Steele, V. G. Pursel   10:213–32
Molecular Biology of Selenoproteins   R. A. Sunde   10:451–74
Vitamin D₃ Receptors: Structure and Function
  in Transcription   J. W. Pike   11:189–216
Animal Models of Obesity: Genetic Aspects   P. R. Johnson, M. R. C.   11:325–53
                                                 Greenwood, B. A. Horwitz, J. S.
                                                 Stern

Iron-Dependent Regulation of Ferritin and
  Transferrin Receptor Expression by the
  Iron-Responsive Element Binding Protein   E. A. Leibold, B. Guo   12:345–68
Regulation of Gene Expression by Vitamin A:
  The Role of Nuclear Retinoic Acid
  Receptors   M. Petkovich   12:443–71
Genetics of Obesity   C. Bouchard, L. Pérusse   13:337–54
Mammalian Glucokinase   R. L. Printz, M. A. Magnuson, D. 13:463–96
                                                 K. Granner

CLINICAL NUTRITION
Effects of Protein Intake on the Progression of
  Renal Disease   S. Klahr   9:87–108
The Impact of Nutrition on Thyroid Hormone
  Physiology and Action   E. Danforth, Jr., A. G. Burger   9:201–27
Hypochlorhydria: A Factor in Nutrition   Z. Kassarjian, R. M. Russell   9:271–85
Human Genetics and Coronary Heart Disease:
  A Public Health Perspective   P. N. Hopkins, R. R. Williams   9:303–45
Weaning and Child Health   B. A. Wharton   9:377–94
Physiologic Basis for the Control of Body Fat
  Distribution in Humans   R. L. Leibel, N. K. Edens, S. K. 9:417–43
                                                 Fried

Current Concepts in Lactose Malabsorption
and Intolerance   J. M. Saavedra, J. A. Perman   9:475–502
Amino Acid Metabolism in Human Cancer
Cachexia   P. W. T. Pisters, M. F. Brennan   10:107–32
Nutritional Factors in Cataract   G. E. Bunce, J. Kinoshita, J.   10:233–54
Horwitz
The Role of Nutrition in Neural Tube Defects   J. M. Scott, P. N. Kirke, D. G.   10:277–95
Weir
Appetite Regulation by Gut Peptides   J. E. Morley   10:383–95
The Role of Calcium in Osteoporosis   C. D. Arnaud, S. D. Sanchez   10:397–414
Nutritional Aspects of AIDS   G. T. Keusch, M. J. G. Farthing   10:475–501
Nutritional Consequences of Vegetarianism   J. T. Dwyer   11:61–91
Parenteral Nutrition: Effect on Bone and
Mineral Homeostasis   G. L. Klein, J. W. Coburn   11:93–119
Should There Be Intervention to Alter Serum
Lipids in Children?   A. M. Mauer   11:375–91
The Influence of Maternal Nutrition on
Lactation   K. M. Rasmussen   12:103–17
Dietary Carotenes, Vitamin C, and Vitamin E
as Protective Antioxidants in Human
Cancers   T. Byers, G. Perry   12:139–59
Retinoids and Cancer Prevention   D. L. Hill, C. J. Grubbs   12:161–81
Nutrient Transport Pathways Across the
Epithelium of the Placenta   C. H. Smith, A. J. Moe, V.   12:183–206
Ganapathy
Nutritional Questions Relevant to Space Flight   H. W. Lane, L. O. Schulz   12:257–78
Hyperhomocyst(e)inemia as a Risk Factor for
Occlusive Vascular Disease   S.-S. Kang, P. W. K. Wong, M. R.   12:279–98
Malinow
Serum Cholesterol and Cancer Risk: An
Epidemiologic Perspective   S. B. Kritchevsky, D. Kritchevsky   12:391–416
Nutritional Management of Glycogen Storage
Disease   P. H. Parker, M. Ballew, H. L.   13:83–109
Greene
Iron Deficiency and Cognitive Function   E. Pollitt   13:521–37

NUTRITIONAL PHARMACOLOGY AND TOXICOLOGY
Dietary Impact of Food Processing   M. Friedman   12:119–37

NUTRITIONAL MICROBIOLOGY
Selenium Metabolism and
Selenium-Dependent Enzymes in
Microorganisms   M. J. Axley, T. C. Stadtman   9:127–37

PUBLIC HEALTH NUTRITION
Nutritional Consequences of Vegetarianism   J. T. Dwyer   11:61–91
Should There Be Intervention to Alter Serum
Lipids in Children?   A. M. Mauer   11:375–91

COMPARATIVE NUTRITION
Comparative Nutrition of Cats and Dogs   D. H. Baker, G. L.   11:239–63
Czarnecki-Maulden

SPECIAL TOPICS
Lysosomal Membrane Transport in Cellular
Nutrition   W. A. Gahl   9:39–61

ANNUAL REVIEWS INC.

a nonprofit scientific publisher
4139 El Camino Way
P. O. Box 10139
Palo Alto, CA 94303-0897 • USA

Annual Reviews Inc. publications may be ordered directly from our office; through booksellers and subscription agents, worldwide; and through participating professional societies. **Prices are subject to change without notice.** California Corp. #161041 • ARI Federal I.D. #94-1156476

- **Individual Buyers:** Prepayment required on new accounts by check or money order (in U.S. dollars, check drawn on U.S. bank) or charge to MasterCard, VISA, or American Express.

- **Institutional Buyers:** Please include purchase order.

- **Students/Recent Graduates:** $10.00 discount from retail price, per volume. Discount does not apply to Special Publications, standing orders, or institutional buyers. **Requirements:** [1] be a degree candidate at, or a graduate within the past three years from, an accredited institution; [2] present proof of status (photocopy of your student I.D. or proof of date of graduation); [3] Order direct from Annual Reviews; [4] prepay.

- **Professional Society Members:** Societies that have a contractual arrangement with Annual Reviews offer our books to members at reduced rates. Check your society for information.

- **California orders** must add applicable sales tax.

- **Canadian orders** must add 7% General Sales Tax. GST Registration #R 121 449-029. Now you can also telephone orders Toll Free from anywhere in Canada (see below).

- **Telephone orders,** paid by credit card, welcomed. **Call Toll Free 1-800-523-8635** from anywhere in USA or Canada. From elsewhere call 415-493-4400, Ext. 1 (not toll free). Monday – Friday, 8:00 am – 4:00 pm, Pacific Time. Students or recent graduates ordering by telephone must supply (by FAX or mail) proof of status if current proof is not on file at Annual Reviews. Written confirmation required on purchase orders from universities before shipment.

- **FAX: 415-855-9815** – 24 hours a day.

- **Postage paid** by Annual Reviews (4th class bookrate). UPS ground service (within continental U.S.) available at $2.00 extra per book. UPS air service or Airmail also available at cost. UPS requires a street address. P.O. Box, APO, FPO, not acceptable.

- **Regular Orders:** Please list below the volumes you wish to order by volume number.

- **Standing Orders:** New volume in series is sent automatically each year upon publication. Please indicate volume number to begin the standing order. Each year you can save 10% by prepayment of standing-order invoices sent 90 days prior to the publication date. Cancellation may be made at any time.

- **Prepublication Orders:** Volumes not yet published will be shipped in month and year indicated

- **We do not ship on approval.**

ANNUAL REVIEWS SERIES *Volumes not listed are no longer in print*	Prices, postpaid, per volume. USA / other countries (incl. Canada)	Regular Order Please send Volume(s):	Standing Order Begin with Volume:
Annual Review of ANTHROPOLOGY			
Vols. 1-20 (1972-1991)............................ $41.00/$46.00			
Vol. 21 (1992).. $44.00/$49.00			
Vol. 22 (avail. Oct. 1993)................... $44.00/$49.00		Vol(s). _____	Vol._____
Annual Review of ASTRONOMY AND ASTROPHYSICS			
Vols. 1, 5-14 (1963, 1967-1976)			
16-29 (1978-1991)........................... $53.00/$58.00			
Vol. 30 (1992)..................................... $57.00/$62.00			
Vol. 31 (avail. Sept. 1993).................. $57.00/$62.00		Vol(s). _____	Vol._____
Annual Review of BIOCHEMISTRY			
Vols. 30-34, 36-60 (1961-1965, 1967-1991) .... $41.00/$47.00			
Vol. 61 (1992) .... $46.00/$52.00			
Vol. 62 (avail. July 1993) .... $46.00/$52.00		Vol(s). _____	Vol._____

ANNUAL REVIEWS SERIES *Volumes not listed are no longer in print*	Prices, postpaid, per volume. USA / other countries (incl. Canada)	Regular Order Please send Volume(s):	Standing Order Begin with Volume:
Annual Review of BIOPHYSICS AND BIOMOLECULAR STRUCTURE			
Vols. 1-20 (1972-1991)............................$55.00/$60.00			
Vol. 21 (1992)......................................$59.00/$64.00			
Vol. 22 (avail. June 1993)...................$59.00/$64.00	Vol(s). _____	Vol._____	
Annual Review of CELL BIOLOGY			
Vols. 1-7 (1985-1991)............................$41.00/$46.00			
Vol. 8 (1992)......................................$46.00/$51.00			
Vol. 9 (avail. Nov. 1993)...................$46.00/$51.00	Vol(s). _____	Vol._____	
Annual Review of COMPUTER SCIENCE			
Vols. 1-2 (1986-1987)............................$41.00/$46.00			
Vols. 3-4 (1998-1989/1990)....................$47.00/$52.00	Vol(s). _____	Vol._____	

Series suspended until further notice. Purchase the complete set for the special promotional price of $100.00 USA / $115.00 other countries, when all four volumes are ordered at the same time. Orders at the special price must be prepaid.

Annual Review of EARTH AND PLANETARY SCIENCES			
Vols. 1-19 (1973-1991)............................$55.00/$60.00			
Vol. 20 (1992)......................................$59.00/$64.00			
Vol. 21 (avail. May 1993)...................$59.00/$64.00	Vol(s). _____	Vol._____	
Annual Review of ECOLOGY AND SYSTEMATICS			
Vols. 2-12, 14-22 (1971-1981, 1983-1991).........$40.00/$45.00			
Vol. 23 (1992)......................................$44.00/$49.00			
Vol. 24 (avail. Nov. 1993)...................$44.00/$49.00	Vol(s). _____	Vol._____	
Annual Review of ENERGY AND THE ENVIRONMENT			
Vols. 1-16 (1976-1991)............................$64.00/$69.00			
Vol. 17 (1992)......................................$68.00/$73.00			
Vol. 18 (avail. Oct. 1993)...................$68.00/$73.00	Vol(s). _____	Vol._____	
Annual Review of ENTOMOLOGY			
Vols. 10-16, 18 (1965-1971, 1973)			
20-36 (1975-1991)............................$40.00/$45.00			
Vol. 37 (1992) ....$44.00/$49.00			
Vol. 38 (avail. Jan. 1993) ....$44.00/$49.00	Vol(s). _____	Vol._____	
Annual Review of FLUID MECHANICS			
Vols. 2-4, 7, 9-11 (1970-1972, 1975, 1977-1979)			
14-23 (1982-1991) ....$40.00/$45.00			
Vol. 24 (1992) ....$44.00/$49.00			
Vol. 25 (avail. Jan. 1993) ....$44.00/$49.00	Vol(s). _____	Vol._____	
Annual Review of GENETICS			
Vols. 1-12, 14-25 (1967-1978, 1980-1991) ....$40.00/$45.00			
Vol. 26 (1992)......................................$44.00/$49.00			
Vol. 27 (avail. Dec. 1993)...................$44.00/$49.00	Vol(s). _____	Vol._____	
Annual Review of IMMUNOLOGY			
Vols. 1-9 (1983-1991) ....$41.00/$46.00			
Vol. 10 (1992) ....$45.00/$50.00			
Vol. 11 (avail. April 1993) ....$45.00/$50.00	Vol(s). _____	Vol._____	
Annual Review of MATERIALS SCIENCE			
Vols. 1, 3-19 (1971, 1973-1989)...................$68.00/$73.00			
Vols. 20-22 (1990-1992) ....$72.00/$77.00			
Vol. 23 (avail. Aug. 1993) ....$72.00/$77.00	Vol(s). _____	Vol._____	

From:

Name _____

Address _____

_____

Zip Code _____

ANNUAL REVIEWS INC.
4139 EL CAMINO WAY
P. O. BOX 10139
PALO ALTO CA 94303-0897

<table>
<tr><td>ANNUAL REVIEWS SERIES

Volumes not listed are no longer in print</td><td>Prices, postpaid, per volume.
USA / other countries
(incl. Canada)</td><td>Regular Order
Please send Volume(s):</td><td>Standing Order
Begin with Volume:</td></tr>
</table>

Annual Review of **PUBLIC HEALTH**
Vols. 1-12   (1980-1991) .... $45.00/$50.00
Vol.   13   (1992) .... $49.00/$54.00
Vol.   14   (avail. May 1993) .... $49.00/$54.00   Vol(s). _____   Vol._____

Annual Review of **SOCIOLOGY**
Vols. 1-17   (1975-1991) .... $45.00/$50.00
Vol.   18   (1992) .... $49.00/$54.00
Vol.   19   (avail. Aug. 1993) .... $49.00/$54.00   Vol(s). _____   Vol._____

NEW! Comprehensive Multiyear Index to Annual Review publications on computer disks. Available in the fall of 1992. Price to be announced.
❏ Please send complete information when available.   ❏ DOS   ❏ MAC

<table>
<tr><td>SPECIAL PUBLICATIONS</td><td>Prices, postpaid, per volume.
USA / other countries
(incl. Canada)</td><td>Regular Order
Please send:</td></tr>
</table>

The Excitement and Fascination of Science
Volume 1   (1965 softcover) .... $25.00/$29.00   _____ Copy(ies).
Volume 2   (1978 softcover)...................... $25.00/$29.00   _____ Copy(ies).
Volume 3   (1990 hardcover).................... $90.00/$95.00   _____ Copy(ies).
(Volume 3 is published in two parts with complete indexes for Volume 1, 2, and both parts of Volume 3. **Sold as a two-part set only.**)

Intelligence and Affectivity:
Their Relationship During Child Development
                 (1981 hardcover).................... $8.00/$9.00   _____ Copy(ies).

Send To: **ANNUAL REVIEWS INC., a nonprofit scientific publisher**
               4139 El Camino Way • P. O. Box 10139
               Palo Alto, CA 94303-0897   USA

❏ Please enter my order for publications indicated above. Prices are subject to change without notice.

Date of Order _____

Institutional Purchase Order No. _____

Individuals: Prepayment is required in U.S. funds or charge to bank card listed below.

❏ Amount of remittance enclosed: _____

Or charge my   ❏ VISA

❏ MasterCard   ❏ American Express

❏ Proof of student status enclosed

❏ California order, must add applicable sales tax

❏ Canadian order must add 7% GST.

❏ Optional UPS shipping (domestic ground service except to AK or HI), add $2.00 per volume. UPS requires a street address. No P.O. Box, APO or FPO.

Account Number _____ Exp. Date ____ / ____

Signature_____

Name _____
         please print
Address _____
         please print
_____ Zip Code _____

_____ Send free copy of current *Prospectus* ❏

Area(s) of interest   Calif. Corp. No. 161041   ARI Federal I.D. No. 94-1156476